W9-BRG-646

general physiology

general physiology

a molecular approach

ROBERT M. DOWBEN

Division of Biological and Medical Sciences
Brown University

HARPER & ROW, PUBLISHERS
New York, Evanston, and London

Cover micrograph: Canine skeletal muscle. Magnification 46,000.

GENERAL PHYSIOLOGY: A Molecular Approach

Copyright © 1969 by Robert M. Dowben

Printed in the United States of America. All rights reserved. No part of this book may be used or reproduced in any manner whatsoever without written permission except in the case of brief quotations embodied in critical articles and reviews. For information address Harper & Row, Publishers, Incorporated, 49 East 33rd Street, New York, N.Y. 10016.

LIBRARY OF CONGRESS CATALOG CARD NUMBER: 69-17109

To Carla especially, and
to Peter, Jonathan, and Susan,
with whom I shared the experience
of writing a book.

contents

3. molecular constituents of biological systems 81

4. physical chemical principles 165

5. energetics and regulation of metabolic processes 235

6. protein synthesis and its regulation 308

7. cell membranes 351

8. biophysics of transport 427

9. contractility 483

10. cell division 541

preface

The biological sciences have undergone a period of much development during the past three decades. The great strides that have been made have prompted a general revision of the biology courses in many institutions. New physiology courses have been developed, with a view toward setting out the important fundamentals and orienting students toward the areas where the exciting advances may be expected. Often two basic physiology courses are given: a course in general physiology approached from the molecular level and a course in systems physiology with an integrative orientation.

This book was prepared as a text for the first course. It should be useful not only to biology majors and graduate students but also to medical students and physicians, particularly those whose careers are in teaching and research, and to scientists in other fields who become interested in biological problems. The diversity of living forms and the sheer mass of biological observations is sometimes overwhelming. A broad view is presented in this book, and an attempt is made to organize unifying concepts in a coherent manner to provide a framework upon which particular pieces of information can be added later. As a result, the content is neither encyclopedic nor exhaustive. Numerous review articles and monographs on specialized subjects are available which present individual topics in more detail. Many of them are cited in the references, and the reader may turn to them for more information about subjects of particular interest.

Freshman undergraduates arrive at the university much better prepared today than they did a decade ago. Often they already have had elementary organic chemistry, elementary calculus, and advanced courses in physics and biology; as a result, they start at and maintain a higher level of achievement in the university. The new courses in biology take into account this new level of achievement. By the time students take physiology as upperclassmen, they have had still more mathematics and chemistry. Organic chemistry, physical chemistry, and biochemistry seem to be logical prerequisites for a course in physiology. Thus biology students today are generally capable of handling more exciting and more difficult material than they were a decade or two ago.

The question of what is difficult subject matter bears some scrutiny. The instructor must be careful to distinguish between what is difficult for the student and what he finds difficult himself. Most of us did not learn in the same manner as students are taught today. In many cases we even have had to unlearn old concepts to make way for the new. Sometimes we had to learn new background material in addition. What may be difficult material for us as instructors may not necessarily be difficult for a well-prepared student who sees it for the first time.

In spirit and general organization, this volume has been indelibly influenced by Bayliss's *General Physiology* and its revised version by Hugh Davson, and by Rudolph Höber's *Physical Chemistry of Cells and Tissues*. We all owe a debt of gratitude to these classics. Even more than these earlier volumes, this book stresses the analysis of biological processes. Instead of mere descriptions, the mechanism of the processes are emphasized—in quantitative terms where possible. As knowledge in this field develops, I hope that a more theoretical treatment can be substituted for sections that now are mainly descriptive.

As a result, this book is more mathematical than physiology texts have been in the past. It is curious that biology was a mathematical science in the nineteenth century and that physiologists made outstanding contributions to physics and chemistry. J. Bronowski[1] calls attention to the influence of biology on modern physical thought. The ideas of evolution and natural selection had a profound influence on the pioneers of statistical mechanics, and Ludwig Boltzmann, for example, frequently refers to Darwin as a source of inspiration in his essays. A considerable amount of physical chemistry is included in this volume, not as a substitute for a course in that subject, but rather to set out the formalisms in terms that are particularly meaningful and useful for biologists.

I hasten, however, to reassure the reader who is not versed in mathematics not to be frightened. Just as many tourists find their journeys to foreign countries greatly rewarding even though their knowledge of the language is rudimentary, the reader who finds the mathematical expressions a bit difficult will still find much of value in this volume.

The kind and thoughtful suggestions of David F. Waugh, with whom I shared teaching responsibilities for a number of years, are deeply appreciated. Thomas P. Ashford made a number of electron micrographs especially for this volume. Karl Kornacker read and keenly analyzed some of the theoretical sections of the manuscript and graciously restated fuzzy passages with clarity and precision. I am also indebted to a number of colleagues for reading and criticizing portions of the text: Renato Baserga, G. Craig Bolon, S. Roy Kaplan, Kent M. Chapman, Peter Noël Dilly, Sidney W. Fox, John Gergely, Hyman Hartman, Terrill L. Hill, Robert Middlebrook, Keith R. Porter,

[1]Bronowski, J. "*The Philosophy of Biology*." Lecture to the Federation of American Societies for Experimental Biology, April, 1964.

John P. Reeves, Duane L. Rohlfing, Babette T. Stewart, Peter A. Stewart, and Patrick D. Wall. In spite of all this help there may very well be errors of commission or omission for which I shoulder the responsibility myself. I hope that readers will call these, together with constructive suggestions, to my attention.

I should like to thank H. Bloomquist and his staff of the Countway Medical Library of Harvard University, and J. M. Dagnese and his staff at the Science Library of the Massachusetts Institute of Technology, for their help. I am indebted to Mrs. Wilma McCord not only for numerous typescripts of the manuscript but also for gathering bibliographic references, editing, and numerous other tasks which were required in the preparation of the manuscript. Mr. Andrew D. Sinauer and his staff at Harper & Row dealt with the problems of production with resourcefulness and skill.

ROBERT M. DOWBEN

symbols

Å	Ångstrom
A	Helmholtz free energy, affinity of reaction
a	activity, distance of closest approach
$\mathfrak{A}$	area
B	affinity of phase transition
C	specific heat capacity, concentration-dependent source
c	local molar concentration
D	diffusion coefficient, dipole moment
d	derivative
$đ$	inexact differential
∂	differential
E	electric potential
e	local electric potential
Eq	equivalent
F	force
f	function, frictional coefficient
$\mathbf{f}$	fugacity
$\mathfrak{F}$	Faraday, charge
G	Gibbs free energy

G^0	standard free energy of formation
g	local free energy density, conductance
H	enthalpy
ΔH^0	standard enthalpy of formation
h	local enthalpy density
$\mathbf{h}$	Planck's constant
I	electric current
i	van't Hoff's factor, local electric current density
$\mathfrak{J}$	flow
K	equilibrium constant
$\mathbf{k}$	Boltzmann's constant
L	phenomenological coupling coefficient
l	length
M	molar
M	mass, molecular weight, molarity
m	stoichiometric coefficient, molality
n	refractive index, mole number
$\mathbf{N}$	Avogadro's number
$\mathcal{N}$	advancement of phase transition
P	pressure
Q	heat
q	local heat density
$\mathbf{q}$	unit electronic charge
R	gas constant
r	radius
$\mathfrak{R}$	resistive phenomenological coefficient
$\mathbf{r}$	resistance
S	entropy
S_T^0	absolute entropy content
s	local entropy density
T	temperature
t	time, transference number
U	energy
u	local energy density, ionic mobility
$\mathbf{u}$	ionic strength
V	volume
$\mathbf{v}$	velocity
W	work
$\mathbf{W}$	charge density
X	intensive thermodynamic variable
$\mathbf{X}$	thermodynamic force
Y	extensive thermodynamic variable
Z	valence
α	polarizability, dissociation coefficient
β	electrosmotic coefficient
Γ	surface tension
γ	activity coefficient
Δ	increment or difference
δ	interval of distance
ε	dielectric constant

ζ	electrokinetic potential
η	viscosity
Θ	total free energy
θ	local total free energy density
κ	Debye-Hückel coefficient, electrical conductance
Λ	critical distance of approach
λ	local phenomenological coupling coefficient
μ	dipole moment, chemical potential
ν	ionization potential, stoichiometric coefficient, local advancement of phase transition
Ξ	advancement of reaction
ξ	local advancement of reaction
Π	osmotic pressure
π	3.14159, surface pressure
ρ	density, charge density
σ	reflection coefficient, excess surface concentration
τ	interval of time
Φ	dissipation function
φ	osmotic coefficient, volume fraction
Ψ	potential difference
ψ	local electric potential
ω	solute permeability coefficient, mobility
∇	vector gradient operator
ϑ	tortuosity coefficient
ln	natural logarithm
log	logarithm to the base 10
lim	limit
grad	gradient operator
div	divergence operator

general physiology

chapter 1
introduction

the domain of physiology

Physiology is a branch of biology concerned with the mechanism of functional operation and the coordination of function of living organisms in both the plant and animal kingdoms. Implicit in physiology is the idea that the collective results of studies of partial phenomena dissected apart in living organisms will lead to an understanding of life processes. It is like the astronomer who proposes to understand the universe by patient observation of the motions of the stars. Physiology emphasizes the integrative aspects of organ function and cellular function and, in this sense, is one side of a coin, the other side being embyrology, which emphasizes differentiation. The function of organs and cells depends upon *processes*; the analysis of these processes is the domain of physiology.

Excepting the lowest forms of life, organisms are composed of organs among which there is a division of labor. The philosophers of antiquity discerned this division of labor and reflected on the relationship of function to structure. These structure-function relationships are, in essence, the problem of physiology, and in modern times they have been studied in microscopic and, very recently, in molecular terms. In considering such cause-and-effect relationships, one must guard against invoking teleological reasoning, that is, the doctrine that asserts that all things were produced for, and can be explained by, the end which they fulfill.[1] It is not always possible to discern the details of the mechanism of a biological process from its end result, and it may be misleading to examine structure primarily in terms of its apparent function. On the other hand, the pressures of evolution have resulted in the application of Occam's razor[2] to most biological functions, with the result that there are exceedingly few organs and processes that are useless.

In recent years, several areas of interest to physiologists have developed to the point where they operate as separate disciplines. Microbiology and genetics, of course, developed independently. However, biochemistry, or physiological chemistry as it was called until recently, grew out of the mainstream of physiological investigation. Within the last two or three decades, organ-oriented physiological investigation has moved largely into the hands of practicing physicians, as a result of the great increase in clinical research following World War II. This has resulted in dramatic advances in the understanding and treatment of disease processes. These trends have led to a reassessment of the direction of fundamental physiological investigation and thought. Contemporary physiology appears to be developing in two directions: (1) toward an appraisal of the function of organ systems, such as the nervous or the respiratory system, particularly as they are functionally integrated (this is called *systems physiology*); and (2) toward the study of function primarily on a cellular level as a consequence of molecular structure and in terms of chemical and physical principles; this study is called *general physiology*.

Of the two parts of physiological relationships, the details of structure have been more apparent and easier to analyze than the mechanisms of function. Yet the analysis of function usually offers greater rewards in increased understanding of biological processes. Physiological functions are carried out by biological engines whose modes of operation are open to analysis just as man-made machines can be analyzed. The analysis of an engine consists of three types of considerations: (1) a description of the external properties of the machine, such as its size, shape, number, location, etc.; (2) an analysis of the organization and order of a machine in terms of its structure and of the mechanics of its operation; and (3) an analysis of the transfers of matter and energy which the machine carries out during its operation. The analyses of biological machines, like the analyses of all machines, are often best done in terms of formalisms derived from first principles that are not readily deduced from an examination of the raw experimental data. Nevertheless, the formalisms so developed provide a framework into which experimental data can be satisfyingly fitted.

the beginnings of physiology

The origin of physiology probably lies in the desire of ancient physicians to develop explanations of disease which were rational as opposed to divine or magical. The

[1] To quote Iago Galdston, "Teleology discovers purpose and intention as permeant in the universe, perfusing the whole with a luminous rationality. The fish is for the fisherman, and the fisherman is for the glory of God!" (in Brooks, C. McC., and Cranefield, P. F., eds. *The Historical Development of Physiological Thought*. New York: Hafner, 1959, p. 293). To which one of my students added, "And ice is lighter than water so that the fish won't be killed during the winter."

[2] William of Occam (1300–1349) was a Franciscan monk who was an intellectual leader of the skeptical movement against the extravagant pretentions of papal authority. He taught in Oxford and sided with Emperor Louis of Bavaria in his contest with the papal curia. Occam's razor is his dictum, *Entia non sunt multiplicanda praeter necessitatem* (phenomena ought not to be multiplied except out of necessity), which is also known as the law of parsimony.

writings attributed to Hippocrates of Cos (460–375 B.C.) make a great impact, even today, because they were written in this vein, applying logic to observations and drawing conclusions with caution. In classical times it was believed that all matter was composed of four elements: *earth, air, fire,* and *water.* These were associated with four qualities: *heat, cold, dry,* and *wet.* Living things were thought to be composed of four humors: *blood, yellow bile* (cholera), *black bile* (melancholia), and *phlegm.* The relation of the elements, qualities, and humors to one another is shown diagrammatically in Fig. 1-1.

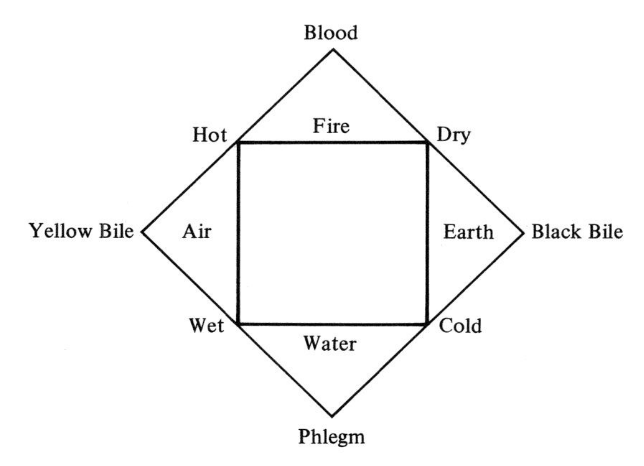

fig. 1-1. The relationship of the four elements, the four qualities, and the four humors of the ancients.

Heat was regarded to be the essential quality of life, but in order for equilibrium to be maintained, it was necessary that air permeate it. The left heart was supposed to be the seat of heat, and air reached the heart by way of the trachea; the mixture of heat and air was then distributed to all parts of the body through the arteries. Each of the humors was associated with a specific organ: blood with the liver, yellow bile with the gall bladder, black bile with the spleen, and phlegm with the lungs. Health resulted from the presence of the humors in the right proportions or *temperance.* These terms have persisted in modern language when we assess a man's temperament and speak of him as being sanguine, choleric, melancholy, or phlegmatic, and occasionally of his venting his spleen. The *Aphorisms* of Hippocrates on the diagnosis and prognosis of disease begins with the following penetrating observation:

> Life is short, and the art is long; the occasion fleeting; experience sometimes fallacious, and judgment difficult.

Aristotle (384–322 B.C.) had a strong interest in biology. His anatomical descriptions are remarkable for their detail and completeness. Aristotle observed and described *in extenso* the natural history of many animals. One of his projects was a systematic classification of animals in order of complexity, a system which anticipates our contemporary phylogenetic system of classification. Aristotle's *On the Parts of Animals* is probably the earliest textbook of physiology. In it, the parts of many different kinds of animals and their characteristic actions were described in terms of their structures. Complex phenomena, such as parthenogenesis, were described, as were a number of physiological experiments such as the examination of the stomach contents of various animals from which Aristotle drew deductions about digestion in ruminants.

Theophrastus (374–287 B.C.), who was guardian of Aristotle's children and succeeded him in the Lyceum, presiding over the Peripatetic School for the ensuing 35 years, made similar contributions to botany. He defined the parts of plants, using terms such as *pericarp* that are still current. Being a practical man, he described medicinal herbs and the preparation of drugs. Theophrastus denied that one kind of plant could be transmuted into another kind of plant, recognized male and female date palms, observed that shaking the dust of male flowers over the fruit of a female date tree prevented barrenness, and listed seven modes of reproduction in plants (from roots and cuttings, as well as from seeds). Yet Theophrastus and Aristotle and all biologists until the seventeenth century believed in spontaneous generation; that is, they believed that living plants and animals could arise without the intervention of parents, out of matter that could not be regarded as living.

After Aristotle and Theophrastus, there were few fundamental biological discoveries for sixteen centuries. Until the middle Renaissance, Scholasticism pervaded the universities. There was dependence upon the unfaithful copies by compilers of ancient works, whose books were a potpourri of correct and erroneous information. A quick wit in argument appeared to be more highly esteemed than careful observation. In fairness, it should be said that scholastic writings of medieval science, beginning as they did with arguments *against* the orthodox proposition to be proved, frequently provoked an interest in unorthodox views which, in turn, often led to innovation.

The beginning of a respect for firsthand observation, however, may well have begun in the fourteenth century at Bologna, where the teaching of medicine was carried on as part of the faculty of law. Dissection was revived there after a millenium of neglect, as a part of the process of legal investigation. There followed a period of avid and intense observation and description of living things, both animal and plant. The works of these Renaissance naturalists are sometimes scorned as "unsophisticated." They are accurate, however. These students of natural history tended their gardens with love and tenderness and observed and dissected their specimens with reverence. They had a feeling for living organisms which is often missing in this age of molecular biology.

The real start of systematic physiological inquiry came with the discovery of the circulation of the blood. From firsthand experience with wounds, even primitive people realized that blood flows, that the heartbeat is a vital sign, and that there is a relationship between the pulse and the heartbeat. Aristotle studied the developing chick embryo and observed its beating heart. It is truly amazing, however, that the relationship of heart action to blood flow proved to be so elusive. Erasistratus, an Alexandrian Greek who lived in the third century B.C., noted that three vessels, an artery, a vein, and a nerve, reached every organ. He observed empty arteries and full veins after death and concluded that the arteries carried the vital spirit, air, and the veins carried blood from the heart to the periphery of the animal. Erasistratus thought that the semilunar valves in the heart prevented the return of the vital spirits and blood. He named and described the function of the tricuspid valve.

Although Galen (130–200 A.D.) argued against the views of Erasistratus, he propounded a similar dogma which stated that some of the "nutritive spirits" passed from right to left through the septum of the heart and combined there with air coming from the lungs. The combination was then distributed to all parts of the body through a "boiling over" of the heart into the arteries. Galen also stated that some of the "vital spirits" penetrated the skull and were converted into "animal spirits" which were distributed to all parts of the body through the nerves and were necessary for contraction of the muscles. It might be mentioned parenthetically that human vivisection may have been practiced occasionally in the ancient world, probably on condemned prisoners. Certainly the Alexandrian physicians, Galen, and others, carried out vivisection on animals, and some Alexandrian vivisectionists realized that arteries as well as veins contained blood because they bled when cut. According to Erasistratus, the bleeding of arteries resulted from a flow of blood from the veins through a network of exceedingly fine communicating vessels. Were it not for his insistence upon the pneumatic theory, Erasistratus might have discovered the circulation of the blood.

Leonardo da Vinci (1452–1519) made some remarkable drawings of the heart and blood vessels which show the direction of blood flow through the heart valves and the movement of blood in the larger arteries, even showing eddies of turbulence. Yet, so powerful was the influence of tradition that he missed entirely the true interpretation of his observations. Andreas Vesalius (1514–1564) denied the existence of pores in the heart septum and disclaimed any communication between the right and left sides of the heart. Michael Servetus (1511–1553), a heretical and argumentative Spaniard who dissected with Vesalius, realized the function of the pulmonary circulation and described it in an obtuse book, *Restitution of Christianity*, which was burned with him at the stake at the instigation of John Calvin. The drawings of Girolamo Fabrizzi (1537–1619) show the valves in the veins, and he noted that they tend to close if blood flows in a peripheral direction. He also demonstrated that the veins swell up with blood if a tourniquet is applied tightly to a limb (Fig. 1-2). Yet, Fabrizzi's explanation

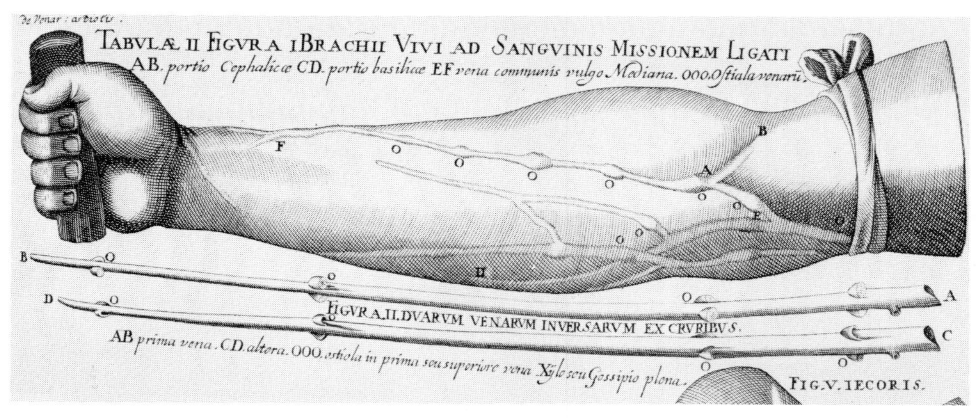

fig. 1-2. A drawing by G. Fabrizzi showing valves in the veins (*De Venarum Ostiolis,* Padua, 1603). (Courtesy of the Countway Library of Medicine.)

of the function of the valves was that they delayed and regulated the peripheral flow of blood through the veins and prevented the accumulation of blood in the feet or hands. Realdus Colombo (1516–1559) also reported the simultaneous contraction of the right and left sides of the heart, described the pulmonary circulation, and claimed that blood and air were mixed in the lungs. Andrea Cesalpino (1519–1603) demonstrated central flow of blood in the veins without impressing himself or his contemporaries with the importance of the discovery.

The great step made by William Harvey (1578–1657) was reported in a remarkably brief monograph, *Anatomica de Motu Cordis et Sanguinis* (1628). In it he describes his observations of the circulation in some forty species, including worms, arthropods, and fish, as well as higher vertebrates. Harvey summarized his concept thus:

> Briefly let me now sum up and propose generally my idea of the circulation of the blood.
>
> It has been shown by reason and experiment that blood by the beat of the ventricles flows through the lungs and heart and is pumped to the whole body. There it passes through pores in the flesh into the veins through which it returns from the periphery everywhere to the center, from the smaller veins into the larger ones, finally coming to the vena cava and right auricle. This occurs in such an amount, with such an outflow through the arteries, and such a reflux through the veins, that it cannot be supplied by the food consumed. It is also much more than is needed for nutrition. It must therefore be concluded that the blood in the animal body moves around in a circle continuously, and that the action or function of the heart is to accomplish this by pumping. This is the only reason for the motion and beat of the heart.[3]

It remained only for Marcello Malpighi (1628–1694) to demonstrate by microscopic observation the capillaries in frog lung, anastomoses between the arteries and veins whose existence Harvey could only surmise.

Harvey's monograph (see Fig. 1-3) was remarkable not only for describing the circulation of the blood but also because it established the most effective method of procedure for discovery and proof in biology and served as a model of physiological

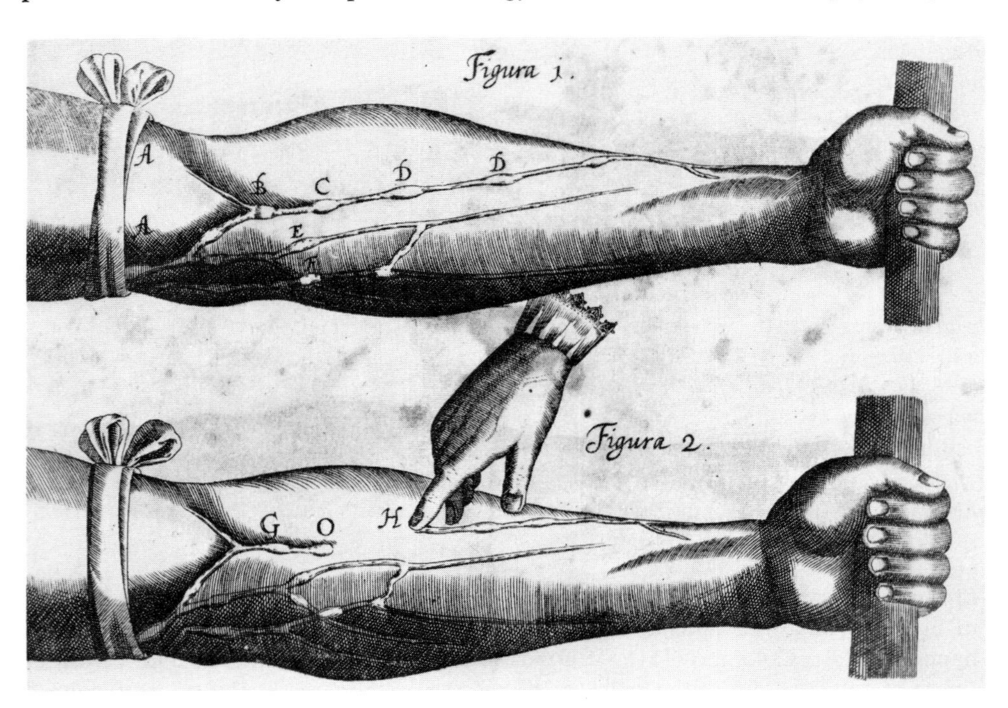

fig. 1-3. A drawing by William Harvey demonstrating the direction of blood flow in the veins (*De Motu Cordis,* Frankfurt, 1628). (Courtesy of the Countway Library of Medicine.)

[3] From Harvey, W., trans. by Leake, Chauncey D. *Anatomical Studies on the Motion of the Heart and Blood,* third ed. Springfield, Ill.: Charles C Thomas, 1941. Reprinted by permission.

investigation. The steps of procedure were:

1. Methodical and accurate observation of a phenomenon
2. Careful description of the observations, accompanied by illustrations where possible
3. Proposal of a tentative hypothesis to explain the observations
4. Controlled testing of the hypothesis by experiment
5. Conclusions consistent with all results of the experiments

the emergence of physiological chemistry

We owe the view that life processes are fundamentally chemical to a Swiss physician, Philippus Aureolus Theophrastus Bombastus von Hohenheim (1493–1541), commonly called Paracelsus because of his proclivity for using the prefix "para" in his writings. He attacked authoritarianism, invoking observation and experience as the arbiters of veracity. Paracelsus had an interest in alchemy, and, although many of his views were magical and fabulous, he introduced chemical concepts into biology and chemical procedures into investigation.

His pupil, Jan Baptista van Helmont (1577–1644), a Belgian physician, held similarly mystical and fantastic views. Van Helmont believed that the world was ruled by a hierarchy of invisible, supernatural forces. In his opinion, life processes (particularly digestion) were typified by fermentative processes and ruled by lesser forces, which he termed *blas*. The term was chosen because it sounded like the Greek *chaos*, with which the evanescent blas or gas liberated by fermentation had much in common. Van Helmont demonstrated the liberation of carbon dioxide upon the burning of wood and gunpowder, and during the fermentation of grapes and malt.

As much as anyone, Justus von Liebig (1803–1873) was the creator of modern physiological chemistry. Over the door to Liebig's laboratory was inscribed the dictum, "God has ordered all His creation by weight and measure." He carefully analyzed foods and excreta and discovered urea, hippuric acid, uric acid, and other organic compounds, and described the carbon and nitrogen cycles in plants and animals. Friedrich Wöhler, a colleague of Liebig's, synthesized urea in 1828, thereby ushering in synthetic organic chemistry. The chemistry of natural products was the major concern of organic chemistry for the remainder of the nineteenth century.

The recognition of enzymes grew out of the interest in fermentation and digestion. A. Payen and J. F. Persoz reported in 1833 that an alcohol precipitate of malt contained a heat-labile substance which rapidly converted starch into sugar. They called the material *diastase* (Gk. "to separate"). The term *enzyme* (Gk. from "yeast") was introduced by W. Kühne in 1878 because the activity of these substances resembled that of yeast cells. In 1897, Eduard Buchner ground yeast with fine sand to break up the cells. The juice which he obtained could catalyze the same fermentative reactions as the intact yeast cells. The detailed structural knowledge of organic compounds of biological interest led Emil Fischer (1852) to study the specificity of enzymes and to develop the idea of steric compatibility between enzyme and substrate. The purification of enzymes began with Richard Willstätter (1872–1945) and led to the preparation of urease in crystalline form by J. B. Sumner in 1926. With the development of enzymology, physiological chemistry was launched as an independent biological discipline.

vitalism versus mechanism

Progress in the biological sciences was hampered in the early 1800s by *vitalism*, a doctrine holding that life resulted from *vis vitalis*, vital forces of supernatural origin not open to experimental study. This theory had existed since classical times, although the idea that these forces were distributed through the arteries had long been abandoned. Even though Paracelsus, van Helmont, and Jacobus Sylvius (who held the chair in the College de France later occupied by Magendie and Claude Bernard) sought to understand the functions of living organisms in terms of chemical and physical phenomena, they still believed in vital forces. Johannes Müller, the inspiring teacher of physiology who devoted much time to inquiries concerning the function of the senses and who conveyed a spirit of skepticism to his many students, rebuked Johann Christian Reil for holding "that the phenomena of life are the result, manifestation, or property of a certain combination of elements." It should be said, however, that Müller, like his contemporaries, was a vitalist in the sense that he believed that when the explanation of biological phenomena in chemical and physical terms was pushed as far as possible, a large residue of phenomena would remain that could not be explained by any such analysis. The work of Müller and his pupils attests to the fact that, in spite of being a vitalist, he encouraged the approach to biological phenomena by the same experimental method and with the same spirit of inquiry as a chemist or physicist would approach his problems.

In the early part of the nineteenth century, the doctrine of vitalism was tenaciously held in France, where science has always been more parochial and views have been more passionately championed than in other countries. Not only were phenomena resulting from vital forces not open to experimental inquiry, but it was believed that living organisms in general could never be the subjects of exact experimentation. Marie F. X. Bichat (1771–1802) put forward the view that the life of a complex organism is the result of the combined and adjusted lives of its individual constituent tissues. As a consequence, he divided the vital forces among the various tissues and organs of complex organisms, attributing to each vital force a unique function. Bichat felt that the living state was the result of a conflict between the vital forces on the one side and the chemical-physical forces on the other side. The physical laws were obeyed entirely only after death, when the chemical and physical forces had full reign. Pasteur, whose meticulous experiments laid the notion of spontaneous generation to rest once and for all, believed that while some parts of the process of fermentation, such as the conversion of starch to sugar, could be carried out by ferments (enzymes) isolated from yeast extracts, complete fermentation of sugar into alcohol and carbon dioxide required the living yeast cell and, therefore, the intervention of a vital factor, which removed the process from the category of ordinary chemical reactions.

At this time, François Magendie (1783–1855) appeared on the scene, a constant and indefatigable experimenter, who took every physiological question to the laboratory. Sir Michael Foster[4] said of Magendie,

> Repelled by the sterile discussions in which the vitalists and other doctrinaires of the day spent their intellectual activity, he was driven towards the other extreme, and arrived almost at the position of substituting experiment for thinking. For his worship of the experimental method came very near to

[4] Foster, M. *Claude Bernard.* New York: McKay, 1899, p. 39.

> being idolatry. So far from regarding an experiment as a thing to be had recourse to as a test, by which to determine whether a view derived from observation and meditation were true or no, he rather thought, or seemed by his practice and indeed his teaching to think, that an experiment was the first step towards getting light.

In his furious experimentation, Magendie did much that was unimportant or misleading, but he also made many great contributions to physiology, including the proof of Charles Bell's conjecture that the anterior and posterior roots of the spinal nerves have essentially different functions. Magendie observed anaphylaxis, promoted the idea that pathology should be approached as abnormal physiology, demonstrated the nutritional requirement for proteins, and investigated the site and mechanism of action of many drugs, including strychnine, morphine, and veratrine. As a result, Magendie's influence was felt far and wide, and he was instrumental in discrediting vitalism.

the *milieu intérieur*

Magendie's experimental approach was carried on, albeit less tempestuously, by his many pupils. Among them are J. J. C. Legallois (1770–1814), who is known for localizing the respiratory center in the medulla and who also studied the influence of the vagus nerve on the heartbeat and respiration; J. M. P. Flourens (1794–1867), who studied the spinal reflexes and was the first to investigate the sensory projections in the cerebral cortex; François Longet (1811–1871), who is known for a variety of neuroanatomical studies, including some of the long tracts of the spinal cord; and J. L. M. Poiseuille (1799–1869), who made fundamental contributions to the study of flow of viscous fluids and to cardiovascular physiology. But Magendie's most distinguished pupil was Claude Bernard (1813–1878) (see Fig. 1-4).

Bernard's family owned a small vineyard in Beaujolais; for lack of financial support, he started his career as a pharmacist's apprentice. He soon became disenchanted with pharmacy, perhaps because of his master's lack of candor, and turned with some success to writing plays. In 1834, he moved to Paris and, on the advice of the noted critic Girardin, studied medicine in order that he might have a secure livelihood to support his efforts as a playwright. In 1839, while serving as an intern in the Hôtel Dieu, he was by chance assigned to Magendie, who was an attending physician there. Bernard proved to be an extraordinarily facile and capable experimentalist. Unlike Magendie, who called himself "a rag picker," experimenting in an unplanned fashion without a preconceived goal, Bernard's experiments were methodically planned, leavened with a vivid imagination, and reflected a vast knowledge of the experimental work of others. Bernard is known for his aphorism that, on entering the laboratory, one should divest oneself of the imagination as one does an overcoat, and that on emerging, one should don both the imagination and the overcoat.

A remarkable genius, Bernard made many important contributions to physiology. It was believed at that time that animals were not able to synthesize complex molecules but had to ingest them from plant sources. He discovered the gluconeogenic function of the liver, demonstrating the presence of sugar in the hepatic veins of dogs fed on protein or dogs that had been starved as well as those fed carbohydrates. This work culminated in the isolation of glycogen, the demonstration of its depletion in starvation, and the excessive gluconeogenesis in diabetes mellitus. Bernard also discovered and studied *in extenso* the digestive properties of pancreatic juice. Prior to his experiments, digestion had been thought to take place almost completely in the stomach. Bernard's

fig. 1-4. Claude Bernard (1813–1878).

doctoral thesis concerned the function of the *chorda tympani*, an interest that grew into extensive studies on the organization of the sympathetic nervous system and its function in the regulation of visceral blood flow, gastrointestinal motility, and secretion. He also investigated the action of curare, carbon monoxide, and other poisons.

The greatest of Claude Bernard's contributions was the concept of the *milieu intérieur*, the relatively constant internal environment[5] that bathes the cells of complex animals, an adaptive mechanism of monumental importance which enables the animal to survive in the face of the most adverse environment. It is strange that Bernard's contemporaries, and indeed the following few generations of biologists, failed to appreciate the significance of this discovery; it receives scant or no mention in Bernard's biographies, not even those by Sir Michael Foster and by Paul Bert, Bernard's pupil and successor. The idea was revived and expanded by Walter Cannon in the 1920s with a series of elegant experiments on *homeostasis*, the term Cannon coined for the control of the internal environment.

In the case of unicellular organisms, their food, minerals, oxygen, and water are contained in the immediate environment. Similarly, the one-celled animal discharges its waste products directly into the environment. The distances which food or waste traverse are small, less than the diameter of the cell. The need that cells of the less complex animals have to exchange materials readily with the environment limits these animals to a thickness of a few cells.

The most primitive adaptation to provide increased means of exchange was the development of a gastric cavity in animals like *Hydra*. In the flatworms, the gastric

[5] Bernard, C. *Lecons sur les phénomènes de la vie*. Paris: Baillière, 1878.

cavity becomes highly branched, and the terminal ramifications penetrate to all parts of the body. In this system, each cell still faces the external environment; but while exchange can occur, the limitations are obvious. In most higher animals, there is a closed circulatory system with ramifications of one sort or another so that each cell of the organism is in the vicinity of a vessel of the circulatory system (Fig. 1-5). The circulatory system operates as an intermediary, carrying food from the gastrointestinal tract and oxygen from the gills or lungs to each cell and, contrariwise, carrying the waste products and carbon dioxide from each cell to the kidney or other excretory organs. Because of the circulatory system, the location of cells is no longer constrained; it provides ready communication with the environment for even the most distant cells.

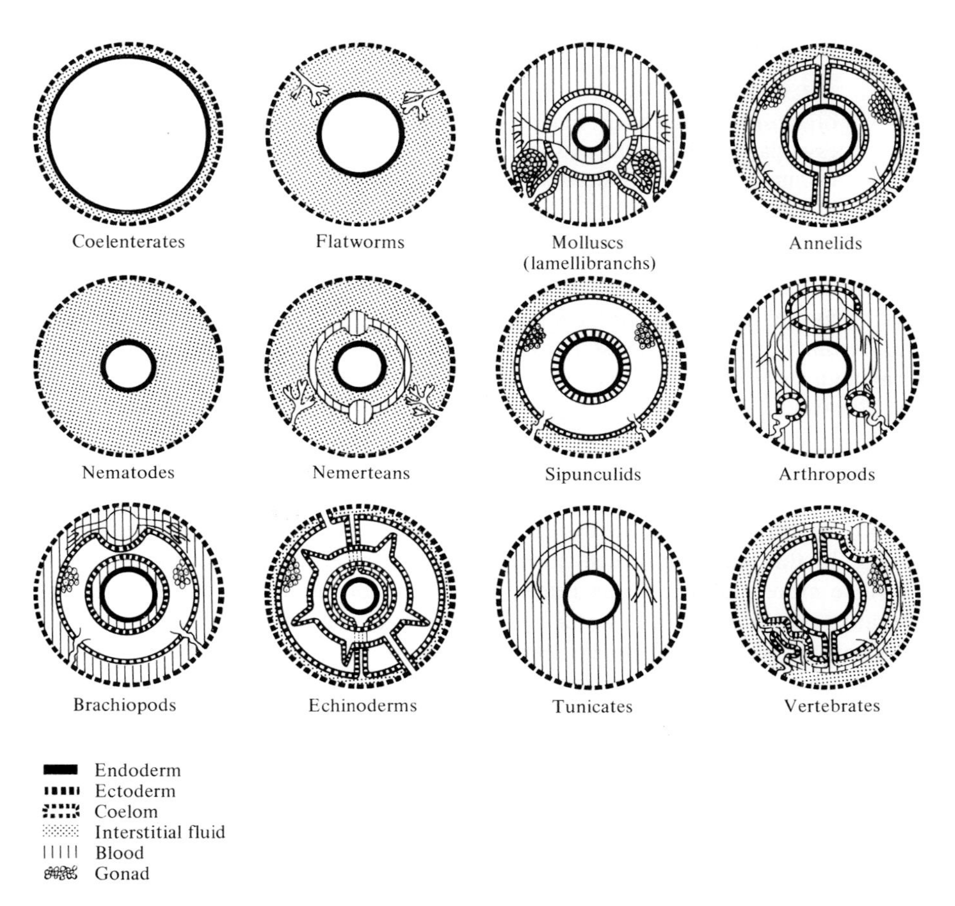

fig. 1-5. Cross-section diagrams of animals from twelve phyla showing the arrangement of body cavities. The complexity of the body compartments increases with greater complexity of the organism. (From Florey, E. *An Introduction to General and Comparative Animal Physiology.* Philadelphia: Saunders, 1966, p. 39.)

Over and above the function of transport, a circulatory system provides enormous advantages to the individual cells. Instead of facing the external environment directly, the individual cell now faces the intermediary internal environment. Complex animals have developed mechanisms for keeping the internal environment relatively constant in the face of great changes in the external environment. Thus, the *p*H, the osmolarity, the ionic composition, the glucose concentration, etc., of the blood and extracellular fluid are kept within narrow ranges, even though the external conditions change drastically. The individual cell, then, is presented with a much more constant environment than the whole animal, and by being one step removed from the external environment, each individual cell can function much more effectively.

the earth as a setting for the genesis of life

Many years ago, Lawrence J. Henderson proposed that a hospitable environment on the surface of the earth was a necessary condition for the emergence and evolution of living forms.[6] To quote Henderson,

> Darwinian fitness is compounded of a mutual relationship between the organism and the environment. Of this, fitness of the environment is quite as essential a component as the fitness which arises in the process of organic evolution; and in fundamental characteristics the actual environment is the fittest possible abode of life.

This theme has important implications. Of course, one cannot view this as the best of all possible worlds. In subsequent sections, a number of examples where the physical properties of matter are particularly suited to physiological processes will be considered in detail. Perhaps the most important attributes of the environment which make it particularly suitable for living organisms center around the physical properties of water. Because it has a high specific heat, a high heat of fusion, and a high heat of vaporization, water acts as a temperature buffer. That is, it tends to absorb heat or give off heat, and thereby it minimizes temperature fluctuations. A large amount of heat is removed from tropical regions because of the relatively greater amount of vaporization, and much of this heat is given up in the polar regions by condensation and freezing. In this way, water acts to make the temperature distribution over the earth's surface more uniform. In addition, the solvent properties of water are significant. Because ice is lighter than water and freezes over the surface of ponds, etc., it acts as an insulator of sorts and thus permits aquatic life to survive cold weather in the water beneath the ice. Water vapor in the upper atmosphere serves to reflect radiated heat (infrared) back to the surface of the earth.

Similarly, the properties of carbon which lend themselves to the formation of very complex molecules and the properties of phosphorus which enable it to form energy-rich esters are important. On the other hand, the physical properties of matter and the physical condition of the surface of the earth imposed constraints which, no doubt, limited the range of possibilities for developing living forms. The earth differs from its neighboring planets in several important respects, including the relative abundance of the elements, the abundance of water, and the temperature and range of temperature of the surfaces. It appears that the environment on the surface of the earth has more unique features than universal ones. It is difficult to imagine the development of living forms as we know them without environmental preconditions, which sometimes are taken for granted. With the thought in mind that the nature of the environment plays an integral role in the emergence and evolution of living forms, let us summarize the current thoughts about the ancient history of the earth.

---

[6] Henderson, L. J. *The Fitness of the Environment.* New York: Macmillan, 1913.

The solar system is thought to have formed from a common pool of cosmic material, a vast, diffuse cloud consisting of 90 percent gaseous hydrogen, while all the other elements, some in the form of chemical compounds, comprised the remaining 10 percent.[7] The cloud condensed into a dense, compact mass, liberating large quantities of heat and developing enormous pressures at the center of the mass. Upon contraction, a thermonuclear reaction began within the primitive sun, which, like other stars, has since undergone the usual sequence of stellar evolution with gradual increase in luminosity. In its very early, preplanetary stage, the sun may have emitted an intense flux of radiation. Present evidence indicates, however, that the temperature of the sun has been fairly stable for some time; it does not differ now by more than 10 percent from its temperature 5 billion years ago. On the other hand, the effective radius of the sun may have been somewhat greater then. Taken together, it seems safe to assume that the sun has been emitting ultraviolet, thermal, and ionizing radiation at approximately the same rate during the past 5 billion years.

It is believed that the earth was formed about 4½ to 5 billion years ago by a process of aggregation and accretion of cosmic material. Although in the past the earth was believed to have formed by a condensation of hot gases, at present the consensus seems to favor a cold origin. The gravitational field of the sun forced the outlying, more diffuse cosmic material into a flattened, disc-shaped mass, which broke up into fragments of various sizes, the protoplanets. In each protoplanet, including the earth, local condensation of cosmic material occurred.

The universe consists mainly of hydrogen and helium. It seems likely that the bulk of the earth's original atmosphere consisted of these light gases and that they have since been lost. The rate of loss from the earth's gravitational field would have been greater if the prevailing temperatures were higher at some antique time than they are now. Even if the earth had a cold origin, a transient high-temperature phase was possible; the required thermal energy could have come from the gravitational potential energy of accretion or from the decay of large quantities of short-lived radioisotopes.

A requirement for the origination of life is the presence of organic compounds. Recent fascinating observations indicate that the earth may have acquired large amounts of organic material of cosmic origin early in its history. Spectroscopic evidence indicates that the synthesis of organic compounds occurs in the atmospheres of carbon stars. Presumably, synthesis begins as soon as hydrogen, carbon, nitrogen, oxygen, phosphorus, sulfur, etc., leave the interior of the star and become part of a cool atmosphere. Analysis of the atmospheres of carbon stars indicates the presence of molecular spectra, mainly diatomic combinations of carbon with hydrogen, carbon with nitrogen, carbon with oxygen, and carbon with carbon. It is possible, then, that the planetary precursors of the earth already contained appreciable quantities of organic material. It is also possible that material once formed by other carbon stars was ejected into interstellar space and eventually found its way into the solar system. It has been suggested that pulsating carbon stars of type *N* eject about 5×10^{25} grams of particles consisting largely of carbon compounds into space each year.[8] While the possibility of contamination from extraneous sources is real, meteorites, particularly the carbonaceous chondrites, appear to contain abiogenic amino acids.[9]

After the loss of the original hydrogen and helium atmosphere, the earth acquired a second atmosphere which was strongly reducing in character. Some scientists believe

[7] Urey, H. C. *Geochim. Cosmochim. Acta*, *26*, 1 (1962).
[8] Hoyle, F., and Wickramasinghe, N. C. *Notices Roy. Astron. Soc.*, *124*, 417 (1962).
[9] Kaplan, I. R., Degens, E. T., and Reuter, J. H. *Geochim. Cosmochim. Acta*, *27*, 805 (1963).

that carbon monoxide and carbon dioxide arising from volcanoes and fumaroles, were the most abundant carbon compounds, and that these gases were major constituents of the secondary atmosphere. Other scientists conjecture that the primitive atmosphere formed in the following way: the lack of oxygen in the atmosphere, and hence ozone in the upper atmosphere, permitted a continual and intense influx of ultraviolet and other radiation from the sun. Ultraviolet light, acting on water, produced hydrogen and oxygen. Oxygen reacted rapidly with a variety of reducing substances, and this reaction led to the formation of, for example, the metal oxides. Meteorites containing iron and water, on striking the earth, would generate enough heat to cause the formation of iron oxide and hydrogen. Iron oxide and carbon reacted to form carbon monoxide and carbon dioxide. Carbon dioxide reacted with hydrogen to form methane and other hydrocarbons. Thus, carbon dioxide was converted to nonvolatile carbonates and, according to this theory, would have been lacking in the secondary atmosphere. Metal carbides, nitrides, and sulfides, upon reacting with water, yielded hydrocarbons, ammonia, and hydrogen sulfide.

It is believed, then, that the primitive atmosphere was composed primarily of methane, ammonia, hydrogen, and water. Supposedly, it also contained smaller amounts of hydrogen sulfide, higher hydrocarbons, carbon monoxide, and nitrogen. Clearly, it was a reducing atmosphere. Oxygen was essentially absent; as discussed below, the presence of oxygen leads to rapid decomposition of organic compounds and is detrimental to primordial model syntheses. These, then, are the major starting materials from which complex organic molecules, leading eventually to the emergence of living organisms, were formed.

Sources of energy necessary for the chemical conversions of these gases into more complex molecules were both varied and plentiful. As mentioned above, the lack of a protective ozone layer in the atmosphere permitted a continual bombardment of the earth with short-wavelength ultraviolet light and other types of radiation. Intense and prolonged periods of thunderstorm activity provided a plentiful supply of electrical energy. Localized hot areas resulted from volcanic activity. Bombardment by meteorites, which were very much more abundant when the earth was young, created intense pressures and temperatures. While these forces are not compatible with modern living organisms, they were of great importance for the synthesis of organic molecules.

the origins of life[10]

The manner in which life originated is a puzzle that has intrigued man for centuries. The earliest Greek philosophers believed that all life originated from sea slime by the action of heat, sun, and air. The Greeks, of course, believed that the entire universe was a living entity and that living matter could be neither created nor destroyed. Something in addition conferred the quality of intimate viability upon living things. For Anaxagoras (510–428 B.C.) tiny seeds, *spermata*, were brought down from the air by rain water to fructify the earth. For Aristotle, actively living things possessed a soul, an *entelechy*. With great prescience, Democritus (460–370 B.C.), who proposed an atomic theory of matter, thought that animals passed through a long process of evolution and development before acquiring the forms they have today. By and large, however, the Greeks believed in spontaneous generation, and Aristotle maintained that many

[10] The sections on the origins of life were written with the collaboration of Dr. Duane L. Rohlfing.

animals as well as plants could be observed to originate from the earth, particularly in association with decaying material. In the course of translating and recopying classical manuscripts during the Middle Ages, fabulous embellishments were added to the writings of Aristotle and others. Although Pasteur finally laid the idea of spontaneous generation to rest, showing that all living organisms originated from other living organisms, the problem of the genesis of the first living forms remained.

There are two general hypotheses to explain the emergence of the first living organisms currently in vogue. The *mechanistic theory* holds that an appropriate collection of nonliving molecules accumulated at a given time and place and integrated into a living form. This event occurred entirely by chance, even though the overall likelihood of its taking place was very improbable. Such an event probably occurred only once, but certainly not more than a few times, in the history of the earth. The mechanistic theory has given way in recent years to the *materialistic theory* of the origin of life, which was championed by the Russian biochemist A. I. Oparin and the late J. B. S. Haldane. The latter theory holds that organic molecules were formed abiogenically from inorganic materials, as a series of probable events, given the environment of the ancient earth. Gradually, the organic molecules increased in complexity and absolute quantity. Eventually a level of complexity and organization was achieved, together with a capacity for faithful reproduction of form, so that a living system evolved. According to this view, it is likely that life originated more than once in time and in more than one place. The development of true living forms was probably preceded by many almost successful events.

According to the materialistic hypothesis, the development of living forms occurred in a number of stages. In the first stage, organic compounds of low molecular weight were formed in a reducing atmosphere. In the second stage, these compounds accumulated in pools or lagoons, or on the surface of clays, and condensed into macromolecules, which possessed catalytic properties. In the third stage, the macromolecules

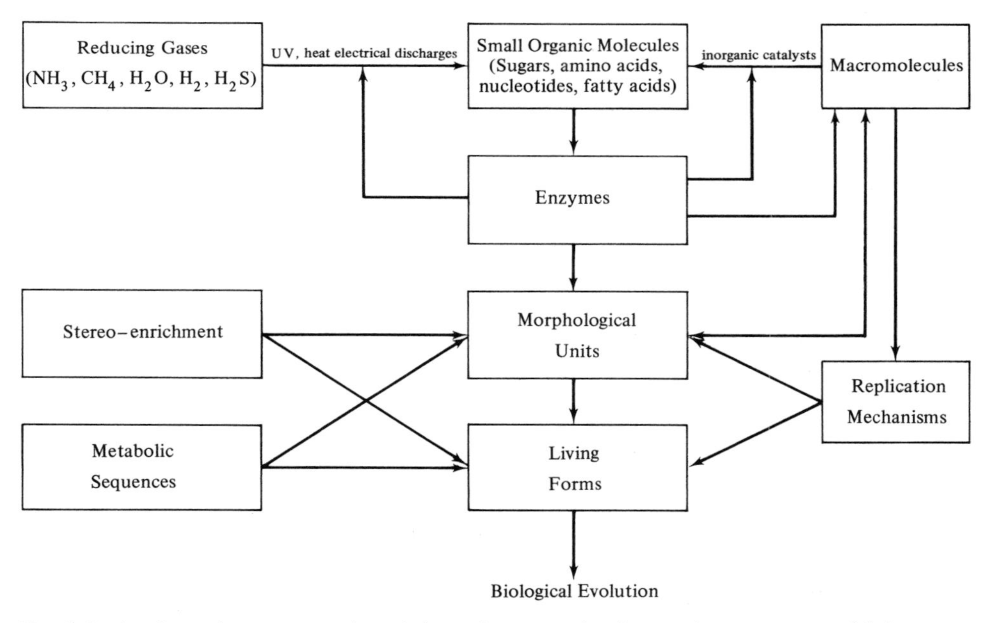

fig. 1-6. A schematic representation of the major stages leading to the emergence of living forms. (Courtesy of Dr. D. L. Rohlfing.)

and low-molecular-weight compounds were organized into living forms capable of autocatalytic reproduction. This entire process took place more than 4.0 billion years ago, at which time it is certain that living organisms must have been present. The oldest known fossil, a calcareous alga, is about 2.7 billion years old according to dating experiments. A general hypothetical scheme leading to the emergence of living forms is shown in Fig. 1-6. During the past fifteen years, there has been great interest in this area of inquiry, and many laboratories have provided experimental evidence bearing on the manner in which life originated. By and large, this evidence has come from investigations in which attempts were made to duplicate conditions on the primitive earth. Such evidence is necessarily indirect, and it is limited by the fact that the nature of the primitive environment of the earth is not known but can only be surmised.

abiogenic synthesis of low-molecular-weight organic compounds

In 1951, W. M. Garrison and his colleagues,[11] working in M. Calvin's laboratory, bombarded carbon dioxide and water with ionizing radiation from a cyclotron and obtained low yields of formic acid, acetic acid, oxalic acid, and formaldehyde. A few years later, Stanley Miller, then a graduate student of Harold Urey, undertook some experiments in which the environmental conditions of the primitive earth were more

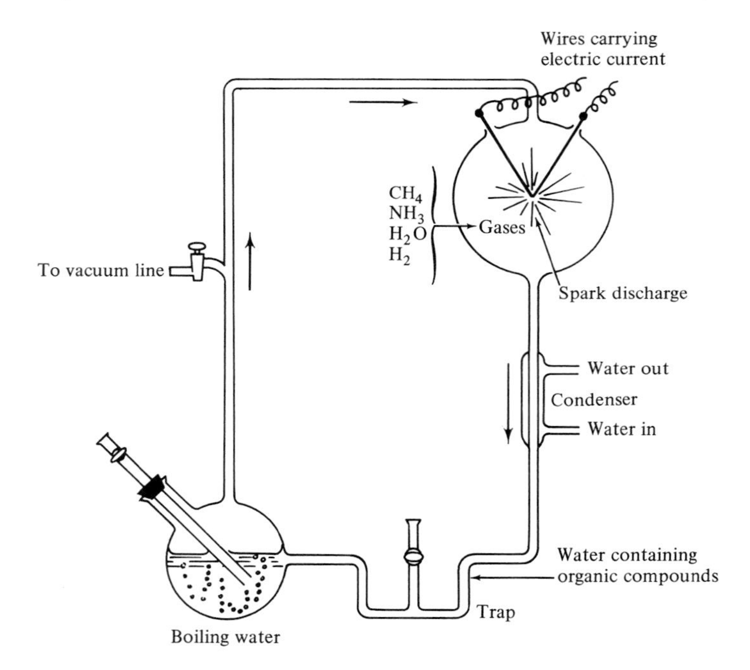

fig. 1-7. The apparatus used by Stanley Miller for the synthesis of amino acids and other biologically important compounds under conditions similar to those of the primitive earth. (Redrawn from Miller, S. L. *J. Am. Chem. Soc., 77,* 2352 [1955]. Copyright 1955 by the American Chemical Society; reprinted by permission.)

[11] Garrison, W. M., Morrison, D. C., Hamilton, J. G., Benson, A. A., and Calvin, M. *Science, 114,* 416 (1951).

faithfully mimicked. Miller[12] subjected mixtures of methane, ammonia, water, and hydrogen to an electrical spark discharge to simulate lightning, using the apparatus shown in Fig. 1-7. After a week, a number of organic compounds of biological importance were recovered as products. These included the amino acids glycine, alanine, sarcosine, β-alanine, α-aminobutyric acid, N-methylglycine, aspartic acid, and glutamic acid; several organic acids, including formic acid, acetic acid, propionic acid, glycolic acid, lactic acid, α-hydroxybutyric acid, and succinic acid; and urea, methylurea, and imino acids. Hydrogen cyanide and aldehydes were intermediates which disappeared as they were converted to more complex products (Fig. 1-8).

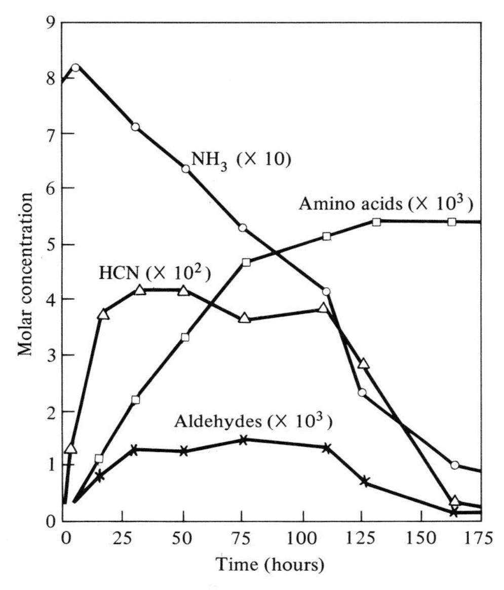

fig. 1-8. The formation of hydrogen cyanide and aldehydes from methane, ammonia, and water in Stanley Miller's spark reactor, and their subsequent conversion to more complex molecules. (From Miller, S. L. *Biochim. Biophys. Acta, 23*, 484 [1957].)

Carbon dioxide, carbon monoxide, and nitrogen were also formed, as were polymeric materials. Careful controls were used to guard against microbial contaminants.

Miller's findings were extended by other investigators. P. Abelson,[13] for example, tried other types of atmospheres. For example, carbon dioxide, carbon monoxide, formaldehyde, and several other simple carbon compounds were used in place of methane as a carbon source. Such experiments led to the synthesis of a wide variety of complex compounds *provided that a reducing atmosphere was maintained.* Little organic synthesis occurred in an oxidizing atmosphere. With hydrogen sulfide present in the reactants, sulfur-containing compounds, including thiourea, thioacetamide, and thiocyanate, were formed in addition. Deleting hydrogen from the reactants led to the formation of lysine as well as the amino acids found by Miller, provided that non-oxidizing conditions were used. Hydrogen would be the first gas to escape from the primitive atmosphere. Furthermore, the absence of hydrogen results in a more favorable

[12] Miller, S. *Science, 117*, 528 (1953); *J. Am. Chem. Soc., 77*, 2351 (1955); *Biochim. Biophys. Acta, 23* 480 (1957).
[13] Abelson, P. H. *Science, 124*, 935 (1956).

free energy of reaction for the formation of amino acids. Thus, abiogenic synthesis occurs in a wide variety of reducing atmospheres, and the exact composition of the primitive atmosphere is a relatively unimportant consideration.

A variety of energy sources other than spark discharge have been employed experimentally, including heat, visible and ultraviolet light, ionizing radiation, ultrasonic vibration, and ultrasonics. Harada and Fox[14] heated methane, ammonia, and water in a silica tube at 900 to 1000°C and obtained 18 naturally occurring amino acids. Amino acids, including basic and aromatic ones, were formed by exposing a mixture of paraformaldehyde, ferric chloride, and potassium nitrate or ammonia to strong sunlight.[15] J. Oró[16] prepared several amino acids, formic acid, glycolic acid, and lactic acid by heating solutions of formaldehyde and hydroxylamine or solutions of ammonia and hydrogen cyanide to between 70 and 100°. Sugars and unidentified polyhydroxyaldehydes were also found in these experiments. Oró synthesized the important sugar 2-deoxyribose by condensation of formaldehyde and acetaldehyde or acetaldehyde and glyceraldehyde in aqueous salt solution. Ribose and deoxyribose were synthesized by C. Ponnamperuma[17] by irradiating dilute solutions of formaldehyde with ultraviolet or gamma rays. Perhaps the best illustration of the large numbers of compounds which can be produced is afforded by Lowe et al.,[18] who heated hydrogen cyanide and aqueous ammonia and obtained 75 ninhydrin positive compounds (not all of which were amino acids) and at least 50 other compounds, as well as some polymeric materials.

Because the purines and pyrimidines play vital roles in living systems, their synthesis has received considerable experimental attention. Adenine was produced via the biologically important intermediates glycine and 5-aminoimidazole–4-carboximide, by heating a solution of ammonium cyanide. Uracil was formed by heating malic acid and urea. Ponnamperuma prepared adenine and guanine by irradiating hydrogen cyanide. Adenine was also formed by irradiating methane, ammonia, and water with a 5-Mev electron beam. Ponnamperuma also prepared adenosine and the adenine nucleotides by the use of the reactive ester, ethyl*meta*phosphate. Typical reactions, in which the yields are given in parentheses, are

REACTANTS	PRODUCTS
Adenine + ribose + ethyl*meta*phosphate	Adenosine (0.01 %)
	Adenosine monophosphate (0.08 %)
	Adenosine diphosphate (0.06 %)
	Adenosine triphosphate (0.05 %)
	Adenosine tetraphosphate (0.04 %)
Adenosine + ethyl*meta*phosphate	Adenosine monophosphate (0.5 %)
	Adenosine diphosphate (0.2 %)
	Adenosine triphosphate (0.1 %)
	Adenosine tetraphosphate (0.1 %)
Adenosine monophosphate + ethy*meta*phosphate	Adenosine diphosphate (3.0 %)
	Adenosine triphosphate (0.3 %)
	Adenosine tetraphosphate (0.1 %)

[14] Harada, K., and Fox, S. W. *Nature*, *201*, 335 (1964).
[15] Bahadur, K. *Nature*, *173*, 1141 (1954).
[16] Oró, J., in Fox, S. W., ed. *The Origins of Prebiological Systems*. New York: Academic Press, 1965, p. 137.
[17] Ponnamperuma, C., in Fox, S. W., ed. *The Origins of Prebiological Systems*. New York: Academic Press, 1965, p. 221.
[18] Lowe, C. U., Rees, M. W., and Markham, R. *Nature*, *199*, 219 (1963).

abiogenic synthesis of macromolecules

The examples set out above, although far from comprehensive, illustrate the large variety of biologically important low-molecular-weight organic compounds which have been formed in simulated prebiological environments. These experiments lend support to the idea that a wide range of such compounds existed on the primitive earth. The next stage of complexity involved the synthesis of biologically important macromolecules. These biopolymers are anhydropolymers (that is, formed with the concomitant loss of water) of amino acid, nucleotide, or sugar monomers. Such polymers can exhibit the essential properties of catalytic activity and "memory." A knowledge of how such biologically important polymers might have been formed abiogenically is of great importance in the overall understanding of the origin of life.

Schramm[19] reported the formation of polynucleotides upon heating nucleotides with ethyl*meta*phosphate. The polymers contained 60 to 200 nucleotide residues and were effective in coding for RNA, using the RNA polymerase system. A reservation to the use of ethyl*meta*phosphate is the fact that it is not clear whether this reactive ester could have existed in the primitive environment. Schwartz and Fox[20] prepared a polycytidylic acid by heating cytidine monophosphate and polyphosphoric acid. Although it is more likely that polyphosphoric acid was present on the ancient earth, the chain lengths of the polynucleotides were much smaller than those prepared by Schramm. The formation of polynucleotides on the primitive earth would have offered a potential means for effecting self-replicative or memory-type processes.

There has been some success in the preparation of models of protein under prebiotic conditions. For example, after the carboxyl groups of amino acids or of tripeptides have been activated by phosphate ester or amide formation, condensations have been observed in aqueous media. A different approach has been studied by Akabori,[21] who adsorbed polyglycine, which is formed in the amino-acid-containing soups described above, on clay. Side groups were then introduced into the polyglycine, forming serine, threonine, and other residues, by ultraviolet irradiation of reaction mixtures containing the appropriate aldehydes. The polyglycine adsorbs on the clay by an attachment involving three points of each glycine residue, which results in the same stereo configuration for the more complex amino acid residues formed by introduction of side chains.

A very fruitful method of forming polyamino acids is that of simply heating mixtures of dry amino acids, provided the acidic amino acids, glutamic acid and aspartic acid, are present in excess. Using this process, Fox[22] has been able to prepare polymers that contain each of the 18 amino acids generally found in present-day proteins. Such products, termed *proteinoids*, resemble proteins in many ways (see Fig. 1-9). The proteinoids synthesized thus far do not possess demonstrable antigenic properties, an important qualitative difference from proteins. One important property exhibited by proteinoids is catalytic activity. Like enzymes, they are able to catalyze the hydrolysis of several substances such as *p*-nitrophenyl acetate, oxaloacetic acid, acetoacetic acid, pyruvic acid, glucose, glucuronic acid, and adenosine triphosphate. At times, the

[19] Schramm, G., in Fox, S. W., ed. *The Origins of Prebiological Systems.* New York: Academic Press 1965, p. 299.
[20] Schwartz, A. W., Bradley, E., and Fox, S. W., in Fox, S. W., ed. *The Origins of Prebiological Systems.* New York: Academic Press, 1965, p. 317.
[21] Akabori, S., Okawa, K., and Sato, M. *Bull. Chem. Soc. Japan, 29*, 608 (1956).
[22] Fox, S. W. *Nature, 205*, 328 (1965).

fig. 1-9. Properties and interpretations associated with thermal polyamino acids and proteins. (From Fox, S. W. *Nature, 205,* 332 [1965].)

Composition, qualitative
Molecular-weight range
Color tests
Inclusion of non-amino-acid groups
Solubility ranges
Salting-in and salting-out properties
Precipitability by protein reagents
Composition, quantitative
Intramolecular bonds
  Peptide (imide)
    Biuret
    IR maxima (1550, 1650, 3080, 3300 cm^{-1})
      (1720, 1780 cm^{-1} for imide)
    Release of amino acids by HCl hydrolysis
    Proteolysability
  Disulphide
    By oxidizability to cysteic acid
Nonrandom arrangements of amino acid residues
  Terminal residues and total composition
  Sequences in fragments
Susceptibility to proteolytic enzymes
Nutritive quality
Catalytic activity
Morphogenicity

catalytic activity was largely lost when the polymers were heated in buffer, a phenomenon resembling denaturation. The synthetic polymers, however, are hundreds to thousands of times less active than the corresponding natural enzymes. Nevertheless, these results do show that primitive enzymes with weak activities may have been formed abiogenically.

The formation of primitive enzymes must have had a great bearing on the course of events. Chemical reactions could have occurred without the need for drastic conditions of intense heat, ultraviolet irradiation, etc. Relatively unstable compounds could form which would have been destroyed by these more intense sources of energy. In addition, reactions could be selective and controlled. The proper juxtaposition of enzymes with different specificities could have initiated series of reactions and, eventually, metabolic sequences.

formation of morphological units

The next level of complexity involves the formation of morphological units and, eventually, cell-like structures. It is difficult to visualize the sequences of unit processes carried on by living forms occurring without self-contained units in which the constituents can develop organization and orientation. At the turn of the century, there was considerable interest in artificial cell models which mimicked living cells in appearance and some functions.[23] There is a natural tendency for many mixtures of organic materials and salts to form condensed structures with phase boundaries. A. I. Oparin has argued that such *coacervates* played an important role in the development of living units. For example, when colloidal suspensions of gum arabic and gelatin are mixed under appropriate conditions, large numbers of coacervate droplets of microscopic size settle out of the mixture. Similar coacervate droplets are formed when a polynucleotide and a polypeptide are enzymatically synthesized in the same solution simultaneously. Coacervate droplets selectively imbibe materials from the surrounding medium, including dyes and enzymes. For example, coacervate droplets formed from gum arabic and histone solutions imbibe the enzymes phosphorylase and β-amylase. When such droplets are suspended in a medium containing glucose-1-phosphate, starch is formed within the droplets, and it is degraded in turn to maltose. The relative rates of these two processes can be controlled by the relative amounts of the enzymes which the droplets are permitted to take up; if there is more phosphorylase activity, for example, starch granules accumulate within the droplets. Many other experiments have been performed with coacervate droplets which illustrate their importance in localizing biologically important materials and carrying out sequences of metabolic reactions.

Another type of precellular model system, developed by S. W. Fox and his colleagues,[24] makes use of proteinoid, the thermally prepared polyamino acids described above. When a clear, concentrated, aqueous solution of proteinoid is cooled, microscopic globules called *microspheres* separate out of solution. These microspheres exhibit several features characteristic of living cells: (1) their size, which depends upon the conditions of preparation, usually is of the same order of magnitude as that of bacteria; (2) they stain either Gram-positive or Gram-negative, depending upon the composition of the proteinoid; (3) they swell in hypotonic solutions and shrink in hypertonic solutions; (4) when formed in the presence of zinc hydroxide, they catalyze the hydrolysis of adenosine triphosphate; and (5) their centers can be dissolved away, leaving a membranelike double wall, and, upon appropriate treatment, the microspheres undergo septate division, forming two spheres from one (see Figs. 1-10 and 1-11). From these experiments, it appears that simple systems are capable of carrying out many cellular functions, albeit much less effectively than living cells. These model systems lend credence to the theory of intermediate stages of organization in the development of living systems.

Many biologically important compounds are asymmetric; it is a characteristic of living systems that only one of the optically active enantiomorphs is present. Furthermore, the same enantiomorph is almost universally present in all forms of life. For example, almost all amino acids found in nature are of the L-form, almost all sugars are of the D-form, etc. This preference results from the fact that the enzymes of living systems are themselves asymmetric. The model syntheses discussed above generally lead to racemic mixtures, containing equal amounts of both optical isomers; this fact leaves the present proclivity for asymmetric molecules unexplained. A slight asymmetry in the natural forces, for example, a slight degree of circularly polarized or plane-polarized light as a result of reflection from the moon or the surface of oceans, might lead to accumulation of compounds enriched in one enantiomorph. Reactions of adsorbed materials on surfaces such as clays or quartz crystals could lead to the

---

[23] Herrera, A. L. *Arch. Plasmol. Gen.*, *1*, 55 (1912); Crile, G., Telkes, M., and Rowland, A. F. *Protoplasma*, *15*, 337 (1932).

[24] Fox, S. W., Harada, K., and Kendrick, J. *Science*, *129*, 1221 (1959).

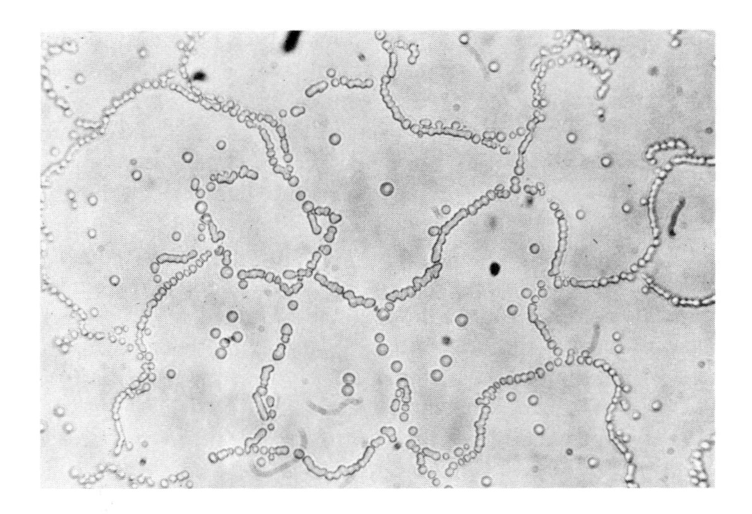

fig. 1-10. Rows of "budding" microspheres prepared from proteinoid synthesized by heating dry mixtures of amino acids. (Courtesy of Dr. Sidney W. Fox.)

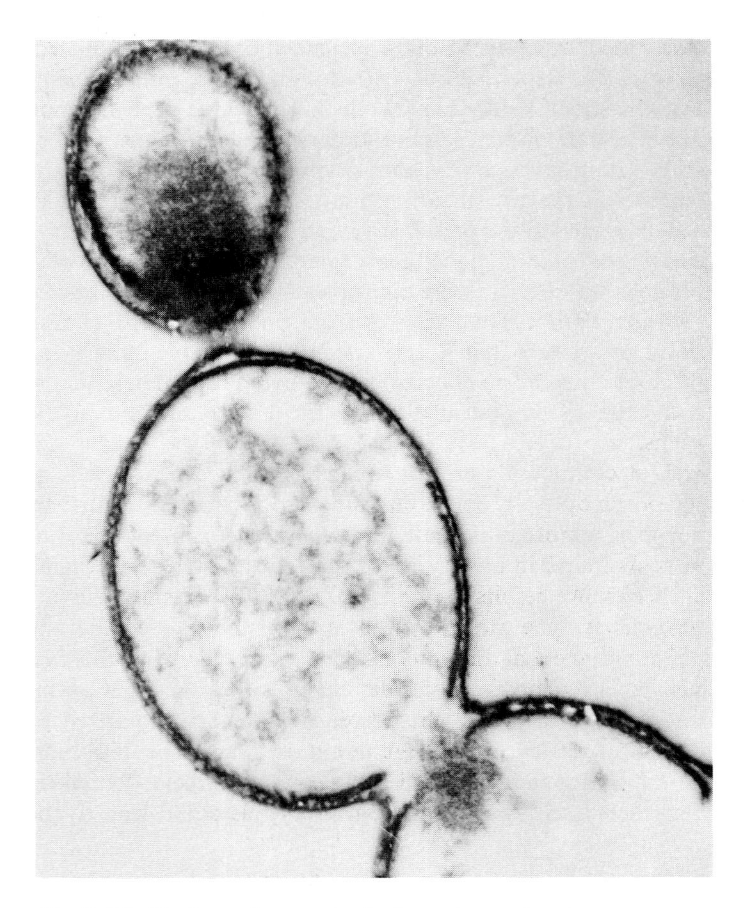

fig. 1-11. Electron micrograph of microspheres showing membranelike double wall. (Courtesy of Dr. Sidney W. Fox.)

synthesis of asymmetric compounds. An example mentioned previously is Akabori's synthesis of polyamino acids. Harada[25] has reported a nonenzymatic synthesis of L-alanine as well as the selective resolution of the optical isomers of a number of amino acids. Selective crystallizations of saturated solutions could leave deposits of crystals enriched in one enantiomorph, and coacervates often prefer one enantiomorph as a guest inclusion over the other. Of course, once living systems became well established, the optically active molecules preferred by those systems would become universally established.

At the present time, it is only possible to present this vague sketch concerning the origins of life, but with great current interest in this area, our information should fill in the gaps in the near future. More will be said about specific aspects in several later sections of this book, and the energetic aspects of the origins of living systems will be discussed in Chapter 4.

references

Bernard, C. *Leçons sur les phénomènes de la vie.* Paris: Baillière, 1878.

Blum, H. F. *Time's Arrow and Evolution.* New York: Harper & Row, 1962.

Dawes, B. *A Hundred Years of Biology.* New York: Macmillan, 1952.

Foster, M. *Claude Bernard.* New York: McKay, 1899.

Fox, S. W. *The Origins of Prebiological Systems.* New York: Academic Press, 1965.

Fulton, J. F. *Selected Readings in the History of Physiology*, 2nd ed. Springfield, Ill.: Charles C Thomas, 1966.

Keosian, J. *The Origin of Life.* New York: Reinhold, 1964.

Oparin, A. I. *Origin of Life.* New York: Dover, 1953.

Pledge, H. T. *Science Since 1500.* New York: Harper & Row, 1959.

Power, d'Arcy. *William Harvey.* London: G. Allen, 1897.

Singer, C. *A History of Biology*, 3rd ed. London: Abelard-Schuman, 1959.

[25] Harada, K. *Nature, 200*, 1201 (1963).

chapter 2

organization of cells

history of the cell doctrine

The modern concept of the cell, which is the keystone of general physiology, is a development of the last 300 years. The Latin word *cellula*, which the Romans used to describe the chambers of a honeycomb, means a small room. This word has survived in such English phrases as "a prison cell." Robert Hooke in his *Micrographia* (1665) noted the similarity of the structure of cork to that of a honeycomb and applied the term *cellulae* to the minute cavities he observed in cork. Although he was looking at the thickened walls of dead cells, he also perceived that the surface of living plants, when magnified, appeared to be divided into similar units which usually contained fluid. Nehemiah Grew, in his *Anatomy of Plants* (1682), and Marcello Malpighi (1628–1694) observed both animal and plant cells and recorded many new details.

Cells are very small objects in the main, and their study has required suitable instruments and techniques for magnifying living objects. The development of the cell doctrine and the development of the microscope are inexorably linked. The use of a combination of two lenses to make distant objects appear nearer or small objects appear larger, generally is believed to have begun in Holland at the beginning of the seventeenth century. The short-lived Accademia dei Lincei, founded in 1609 in Rome by

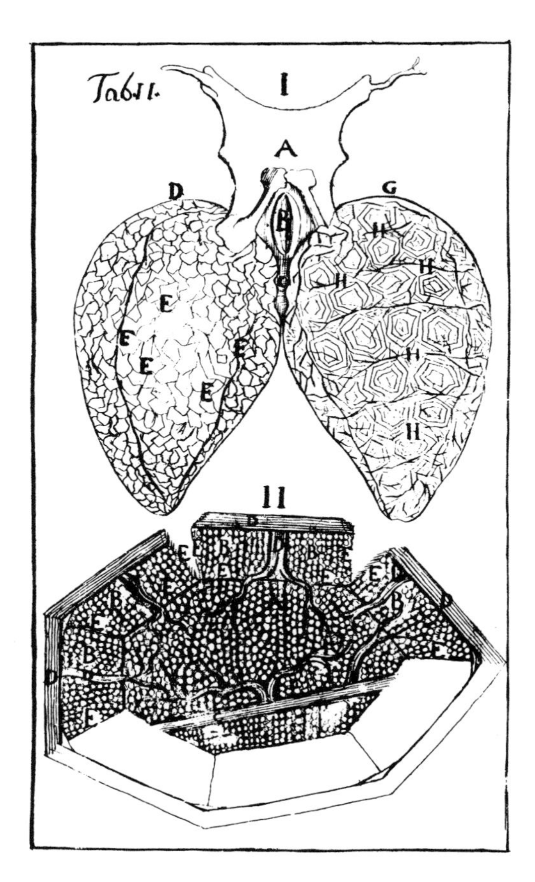

fig. 2-1. Diagram of the pulmonary circulation accompanying the description of the pulmonary capillaries observed with the microscope by Marcello Malpighi, *de Pulmonibus Observationes Anatomicae* (1683). (Courtesy of the Countway Library of Medicine.)

Duke Federigo Cesi, was the first association of microscopists who used microscopes imported from Holland. An important early microscopic discovery was Marcello Malpighi's observation of blood capillaries linking the arteries with the veins (Fig. 2-1).

Extensive and sustained use of the microscope is associated with the early history of the English Royal Society which appointed Robert Hooke as its first curator. Hooke and Grew, also a curator of the Royal Society, used compound microscopes which gave about 30 diameters magnification (Fig. 2-2). It is not surprising that there was also great interest in microscopy in Holland. Swammerdam in his *Biblia naturae* describes blood corpuscles in the circulatory channels of the louse and in frog's blood.

The errors of simple lenses are multiplied when they are used in series. The two main errors are spherical aberration, by which light rays passing through the lens at different distances from the axis are brought to a focus at slightly different depths, and chromatic aberration, which brings light of different wavelengths to slightly different foci and produces a minute color spectrum around each point in the image. With microscopes such as Hooke and Grew used, a tolerable image can be obtained only

fig. 2-2. Drawing of a microscope and associated instruments from Robert Hooke's *Micrographia* (1667). (Courtesy of the Countway Library of Medicine.)

when the aperture of the lenses is restricted to the central portion, a maneuver which seriously limits the light intensity.

A single lens, however, can be used at a much larger aperture. Antoni van Leeuwenhoek (1632–1723), a linen draper of Delft, remains a unique figure in the annals of biology. An amateur microscopist, he used simple lenses of very short focal length mounted between brass plates to obtain magnifications of several hundred diameters. Leeuwenhoek jealously kept the details of his methods secret; it is possible that he reduced the aberrations of simple lenses still further by grinding them to an aspherical surface. A patient and omnivorous observer, he described in a series of some 200 letters written over a period of 50 years to the Royal Society (to which he was ultimately elected a Fellow) microorganisms, spermatozoa, blood corpuscles, a variety of other cells with nuclei (Fig. 2-3), budding of hydra, and parthenogenesis in aphids.

fig. 2-3. A drawing of a leaf showing cells from Antoni van Leeuwenhoek's *Anatomia seu Interiora Rerum* (1687). (Courtesy of the Countway Library of Medicine.)

His reports contain a degree of morphological detail that was not to be equalled for over 100 years.[1]

Further progress was delayed until improved lenses were available. An achromatic refracting telescope was first made by Chester Moor Hall in 1733 by combining components made from different glasses in which the refractive index varied differently with the wavelength of light. The first successful achromatic microscope was made about 1791 by another Dutch amateur, Francois Beeldsnijder, an officer of the Amsterdam cavalry. At about the same time, Joseph Jackson Lister discovered that the degree of

[1] In the delightful book by C. Dobell (*Anthony van Leeuwenhoek and his "Little Animals."* New York: Dover, 1960), Dobell points out that Leeuwenhoek was completely unschooled in science and that he described his discoveries disarmingly in nontechnical (and frequently ungrammatical) Dutch, the only language he knew.

spherical aberration of an achromatic lens varies at different points along the axis and is at a minimum at two points called the aplanatic foci. He also realized that lenses could be combined in such a way as to minimize spherical aberration. In the 1830s, the microscopic observations of biological materials again became an active area of investigation. However, the performance of the achromatic microscopes of that period was no better than the best of Leeuwenhoek's single lenses. There followed a period of rapid improvement in microscope design, so that by 1870, a resolving power of less than half a micron was achieved, a level of performance which has not yet been substantially bettered by light microscopes. The resolving power of a microscope is limited by the wavelength of light. Recently, the use of ultraviolet light of very short wavelength has permitted slightly better resolution.

It was in the 1830s, the decade that saw the renaissance of microscopic observation, that Matthias Jacob Schleiden (1804–1881) and Theodor Schwann (1810–1882), the two men most frequently regarded as laying the foundations of the modern cell doctrine, formulated their ideas. Some prescient forecasts of the doctrine, of course, had appeared earlier. Lorenz Oken, who spent most of his active life in Jena, wrote in *Die Zeugung* (1805) that "all organic beings originate from and consist of vesicles or cells." He went on to say that complex species of organisms are made up of a union of various types of living cells. The botanist and physiologist René Dutrochet (1776–1847), who introduced the manometer into the study of osmotic pressure and established the similarity of respiration in plants to that in animals by showing that plant respiration was accompanied by the liberation of heat, stated,[2] "all organic tissues are actually globular cells of exceeding smallness, which appear to be united only by simple adhesive forces." Of Dutrochet's conclusion, Homer Smith[3] remarked, "it was at best an informed guess, but it had the supreme virtue of being right."

Although nuclei had been depicted in blood corpuscles by Leeuwenhoek and other eighteenth-century observers and an 1823 illustration by Franz Bauer bears the legend *nucleus*, Robert Brown (1831) was the first to realize that a nucleus was present in all plant cells and to introduce the term into common usage. Johannes Purkinje observed nuclei in many types of animal cells. Wilhelm Wagner and Gabriel Gustav Valentin described the nucleolus as a constant inclusion of nuclei in 1836. As an undergraduate student at Jena, Schleiden began to develop Brown's views and demonstrated that a nucleated cell is the only original constituent of the plant embryo (1837) and that all plant cells come from preexisting plant cells (1838), an idea opposed to the then-current doctrine of spontaneous generation. Unfortunately, Schleiden erroneously believed that a daughter cell (*cytoblast*, cell bud) was formed inside a parent cell and that the nuclear membrane was transformed into the wall of the new cell. Schleiden had a vivid and forceful personality and is responsible for inducing many younger men to undertake research in this field, among them Hofmeister and Nägeli, and for convincing Karl Zeiss to devote himself to optics. Jena thus became a center for work on microscopes and for cell biologists.

In 1837, Schleiden impressed Schwann with his belief in the importance of the role of the nucleus in the development of plant cells. This prompted Schwann to recall similar structures he had seen in the cells of the notochord, and he immediately realized their parallel significance (Fig. 2-4). Schwann extended Schleiden's cell theory to animal cells, a difficult task in view of the great diversity of animal cells. Schwann

[2] Dutrochet, R. J. H. *Recherches anatomiques et physiologiques sur la structure intime des animaux et des végétaux*. Paris: Baillière, 1824.

[3] Smith, H. *Circulation, 26*, 988 (1962).

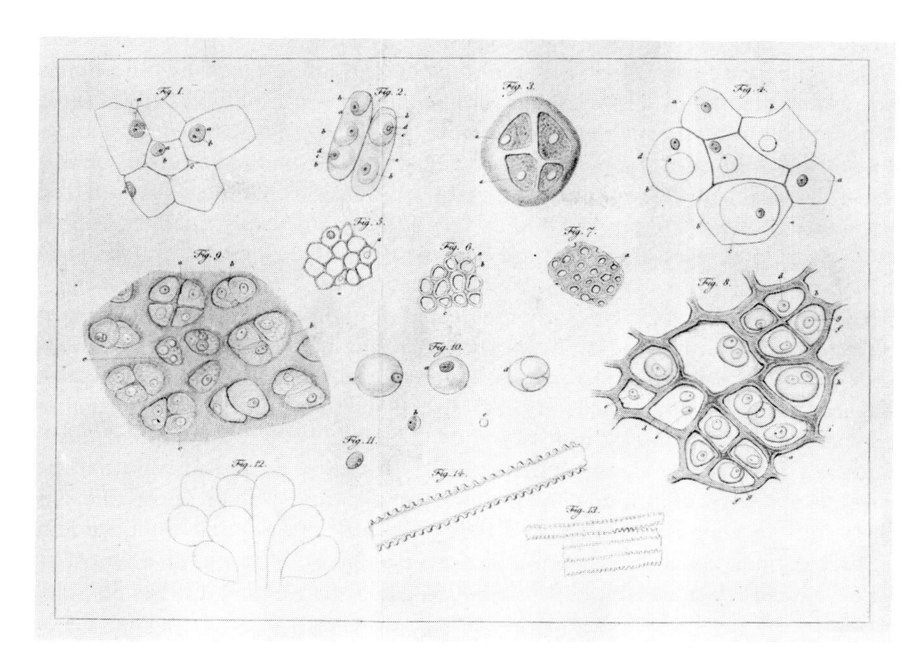

fig. 2-4. Plate 1 from Theodore Schwann's *Mikroskopische Untersuchungen* (1839) showing nucleated cells from the notochord. (Courtesy of the Countway Library of Medicine.)

concluded from his studies that (1) plant and animal organisms are composed entirely of cells or substances produced by cells, (2) the cells of which organisms are composed have a life that is to some extent their own, and (3) this life of individual cells is subject to the life of the organism as a whole. Schwann was a student of Johannes Müller (1801–1858), another remarkable teacher who had a number of illustrious students, among them Henle, Helmholtz, Du Bois-Reymond, Köllicker, and Virchow.

The biologists of this period began to concern themselves with the substance which filled the space between the nucleus and the cell wall. Because of the difficulties in observing living cells of complex organisms, the importance of the cytoplasm was appreciated first in unicellular *protozoa.* Schleiden (1842) referred to the contents of the plant cells as *Pflanzenschleim* (plant slime) and Nägeli called it the *Schleimschicht* (slimy layer), while Dujardin (1835) applied the term *sarcode* to the contents of animal cells. Hugo von Mohl (1846) equated the *Pflanzenschleim* of plant cells and the *sarcode* of animal cells, using for both the term *protoplasm.* The term protoplasm, which had been used in religious writing to denote primordial living matter, was used by the Bohemian physiologist Johannes Purkinje (1840) as a name for the granular, mucilaginous substance of the animal ovum. Nägeli was the first to show that the protoplasm contained nitrogenous substances and differed in composition from other cell structures, particularly from the cell wall and the stored starch.

The early biologists were aware that the number of cells in a complex organism increased as the organism grew, and they suggested numerous hypotheses about the origin of the new cells. It was difficult to observe the details of the process, particularly in mature organisms where cell division is not a frequent event. Although Schleiden stimulated many bright young men to study biology, his strong personality discouraged explanations that differed from his own. Schwann, who described cell division in embryos, never corrected Schleiden's erroneous theory that new cells arose from budding of nuclei. Robert Remak (1841) first realized the real manner in which new cells are formed, and described in detail the division of entire white blood corpuscles of chick embryos into two equal daughter cells. Albrecht Kölliker (1844) carried Schwann's observations of embryonic development further, regarding the ovum as a single cell and the process of development as repeated, complete cell division. Kölliker also realized the cellular nature of muscle fibers, striated and smooth, and demonstrated that nerve fibers are elongated processes of cells whose bodies are located in the central nervous system or in ganglia.

Rudolf Virchow (1821–1902), the father of cellular pathology, analyzed diseased tissue in terms of cell structure, seeking abnormalities characteristic of the disease, and attempted to explain the morbid processes in terms of altered cell function. Although Virchow regarded cell division as securely established for botany, zoology, and medicine, and said so with firm finality in his famous aphorism "*omnis cellula e cellula*" (every cell comes from a preexisting cell), free cell formation and even spontaneous generation at large were commonly held views for another two or three decades after Virchow had presented his beliefs. The idea of the cell as a partially independent individual, first enunciated by Schleiden and extended by Schwann and others, was expounded with great enthusiasm by Virchow. Virchow had rather liberal political views also and drew the inevitable analogy that "the body is a free state of equal individuals, a federation of cells, a democratic cell-state."[4] Cell division and related phenomena will be discussed in detail in a later chapter; the discussion at present concerns cellular structure and physiological processes of cells.

methods of studying cell structure

Prior to the 1870s, the biologist's tools consisted essentially of a microscope. The botanist made thin sections of plant material with a barber's razor. The scum on the surface of a freshwater pond was a favorite object of study because no special preparation of the material was required. Johann Moldenhawar (1812) introduced the technique of macerating tissues in water, which enabled him to isolate cells and fibers and examine them separately under the microscope. Such *teased* preparations were used with considerable success by the early cytologists. The study of living cells directly was no easy task until the recent development of the phase-contrast microscope, because the unstained structural components are distinguished mainly by virtue of differences in refractive index, which tend to be small. Teasing can produce serious distortions. The dramatic elucidation of cell structure at the close of the nineteenth century resulted from the introduction of techniques for preserving, staining, and sectioning tissues.

Preservation of cells began in the 1850s. Cells were killed and the protoplasm coagulated, or *fixed*, by the use of chromic acid or lead acetate; osmium tetroxide was first used for fixation in 1865 and later formalin and picric acid were introduced. Permanent preparations have advantages for study if they provide a reasonably faithful representation of the features of living cells and tissues. Fixed preparations are

[4] This analogy has been taken up by other authors from time to time and developed most fully in reciprocal fashion in an almost farcical essay by Morley Roberts (1938), for whom the army was a national ectoderm, the policeman a social phagocyte, and the social organism generally comparable not to a mammal but to a low-grade invertebrate (*Biopolitics*. London: Dent, 1938).

also much more permeable to stains than unfixed ones. Fixation usually is followed by dehydration in organic solvents, frequently in ethanol. In the *freeze-drying* method of fixation, the tissue is frozen rapidly by the use of liquid carbon dioxide and then dehydrated at low temperatures in a high vacuum. Freeze-drying does not render the intracellular proteins insoluble, and treatment with additional reagents is required if the specimens are to remain fixed in aqueous solutions.

After fixation, small blocks of tissue are infiltrated with molten paraffin (a technique introduced by Theodor Klebs in 1860) or with collodion or other plastic material which hardens upon cooling or aging. The microtome for cutting thin sections was introduced by Wilhelm His, Sr., in 1866. Sections also may be cut with a freezing microtome without the necessity of prior fixation or embedding.

Since 1862, aniline dyes have been used extensively for staining. Tissue stains fall into two main classes: acid dyes, of which eosin is the prototype, which combine with basic, or *eosinophilic*, macromolecular residues in the fixed cell; and basic dyes, of which hematoxylin is the prototype, which combine with acidic, or *basophilic*, substances. Thus, the commonest reaction in staining is salt formation. Usually an acidic and a basic dye are used together. The nucleic acids in the cell nucleus possess a net acidic reaction; they are basophilic and tend to stain purple with hematoxylin (Fig. 2-5). The cytoplasmic proteins, on the other hand, tend to be basic and stain with

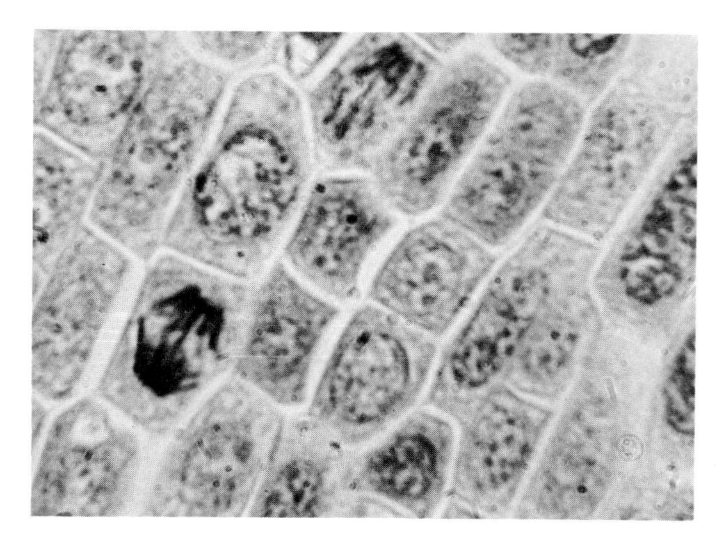

fig. 2-5. Phase contrast photomicrograph of cells in a radish root tip. Two dividing cells in the metaphase of mitosis are seen at the left. Magnification 650.

eosin, particularly when heavy metals, which combine with the acidic groups, are used in fixation. Other fixatives—formaldehyde, for example—tend to make proteins more basophilic by combining with the free amino groups. Cytoplasm contains ribonucleic acid, a basophilic material. This accounts for the basophilic (purple) speckling in a otherwise eosinophilic (pink) cytoplasm.

In addition, there are special stains: orcein, which stains elastic fibers orange against a pale background; nile blue sulfate, which stains fat orange against a pale blue background; periodate-Schiff stain for polysaccharides; and a type of silver impregnation, the Golgi stain, which makes visible entire nerve cells and their processes. Striking differences in appearance may result from the various techniques of fixation and staining used on a given tissue.

The study of living or surviving cells was revived after the discovery of *vital dyes*, which penetrate living cells and stain the intracellular structures selectively, often without serious alteration of cellular metabolism and function. Janus green B, for example, selectively stains mitochondria; and methylene blue often is taken up by the Golgi apparatus and stains nuclear chromatin. Neutral red and related dyes can often be used as cytoplasmic stains, although in some cells they accumulate in vacuoles. When trypan blue is injected into the bloodstream of an animal, it accumulates in the cells of the renal tubules, staining them. Brilliant cresyl blue and related dyes are used to stain selectively reticulocytes, which are immature red blood cells.

The phase contrast microscope, in which slight differences in the optical paths through adjacent structures are converted into light-intensity differences, has made it possible to observe intracellular structures in living cells without recourse to staining. Small differences in refractive index or thickness result in phase changes in the transmitted light, which appear as differences in intensity of light in the image plane (Fig. 2-6). The phase contrast microscope has been especially powerful for observing

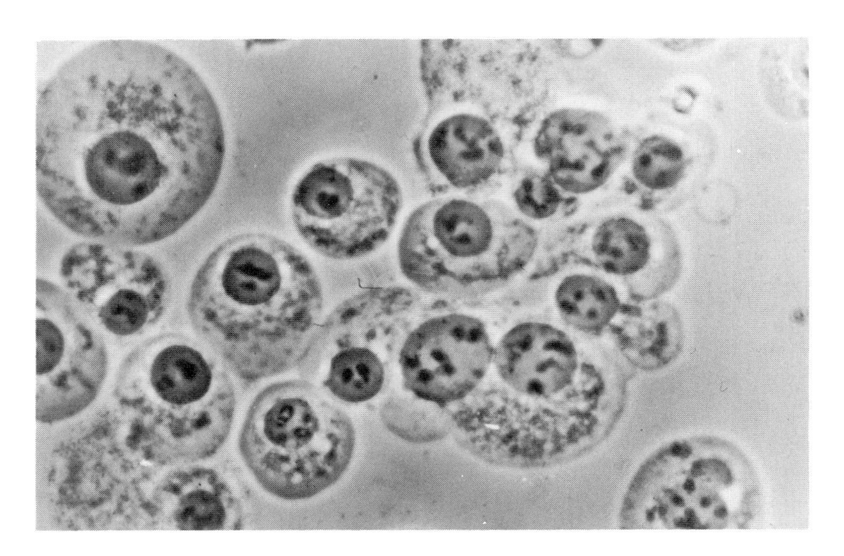

fig. 2-6. Phase contrast photomicrograph of tissue-cultured HeLa cells. Magnification 360. (Courtesy of Dr. Sheldon Penman.)

changes in the appearance of organelles which accompany physiological processes. For example, the complex series of changes that take place during mitosis, ingestion of substances, and secretion can be followed with ease. The phase contrast microscope has provided convincing evidence that the structures identified in fixed and stained preparations are real and not artifacts.

histochemical studies of cell constituents

Histochemical staining and *immunochemical staining* provide other approaches to the assignment of cellular locations to specific molecular constituents and serve as means of corroborating information obtained from different types of studies. Histochemical methods have a number of limitations, particularly with regard to specificity, sensitivity, and freedom from interference. The faithfulness of localization is frequently a problem. Drift of the reaction products of histochemical reactions from the points at which they are formed is the greatest source of uncertainty with these methods. In general, the techniques are only qualitative, but some types of determinations can be quantitative, particularly those involving a direct physical measurement, such as fluorescence photometry and x-ray absorption. The constituent under investigation is identified by means of a characteristic chemical reaction or a physical property.

Usually a method employed in macroscopic, chemical analysis is adapted for use in tissues. In the case of a chemical reaction, the aim is the deposition of a colored or opaque insoluble product in the same site. In the case of physical methods, resolution of microscopic dimensions is required. The substance being studied and the products of the chemical reactions should be immobilized at the original location. Fixation, using the methods mentioned above, will render the intracellular macromolecules insoluble. However, the immobilization of carbohydrate material, small organic molecules, and inorganic ions is very difficult. While fixation will immobilize proteins, most methods will also denature them, so that ordinary techniques of fixation are unsatisfactory when an enzyme is to be localized. Freeze-drying of tissue is commonly used in histochemical studies.

Nucleic acids can be localized by several histochemical methods. A direct method, which depends upon the specific absorption of the nucleotide bases at 260 mμ, has been exploited by Caspersson and others using a microspectrophotometer. Because of their strongly acidic character, the nucleic acids tend to stain with basic dyes. Among the basic dyes, azure blue B and methyl green show some specificity for nucleic acids and less interference from acidic polysaccharides and other substances. The Schiff reagent is a widely used cytochemical stain for aldehyde groups. This reagent is prepared by decolorizing basic fuchsin, tris-(aminophenyl)methane, with sulfurous acid, which converts it into the colorless bis-(N-aminosulfonic acid) derivative. In the presence of aldehydes, a colored product is formed again. The Schiff reagent can be used to stain for deoxyribonucleic acid (DNA) by use of the Feulgen stain. The tissue is first subjected to mild acid hydrolysis under carefully controlled conditions. This results (1) in the hydrolysis of most of the ribonucleic acid (RNA) but little or no hydrolysis of the DNA, and (2) in the hydrolysis of the purine-deoxyribose bond within the DNA, liberating the purine bases and exposing the aldehydic groups of the deoxyribose residues. The acid hydrolysis is followed by staining with the Schiff reagent (Fig. 2-7). The specificity of the staining procedure can be checked by comparison with a serial section pretreated with deoxyribonuclease, an enzyme which hydrolyzes the DNA.

The Schiff reagent can also be used to stain a number of polysaccharides, including starch, cellulose, pectins, mucoproteins and mucins, and hyaluronic acid, after pretreatment with periodic acid. The treatment with periodic acid results in the selective oxidation of the 1,2-hydroxyl groups, if they are not asymmetric, with rupture of the chain and formation of aldehyde groups. The Schiff reagent also stains glycogen (Fig. 2-8). A number of so-called metachromatic dyes, including toluidine blue and alcian blue, are fairly specific for polysaccharides.

Lipids stain fairly specifically with a number of dyes. Sudan red III and scarlet red are lipid-soluble dyes which accumulate in fat droplets. Sudan black B is also accumulated by steroid and phospholipid aggregates. The Schiff reagent also stains long-chain aliphatic aldehydes.

A large number of more or less specific histochemical reactions for the localization

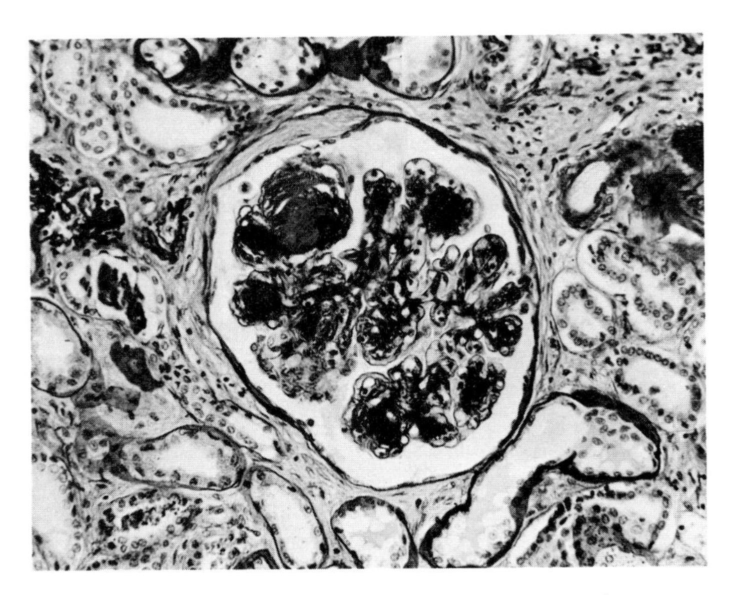

fig. 2-7. Periodic acid-Schiff stain of a section of kidney from a patient with intercapillary glomerulosclerosis showing the deposition of polysaccharide material in a glomerulus and some tubules. Magnification 320. (Courtesy of Dr. David G. Freiman.)

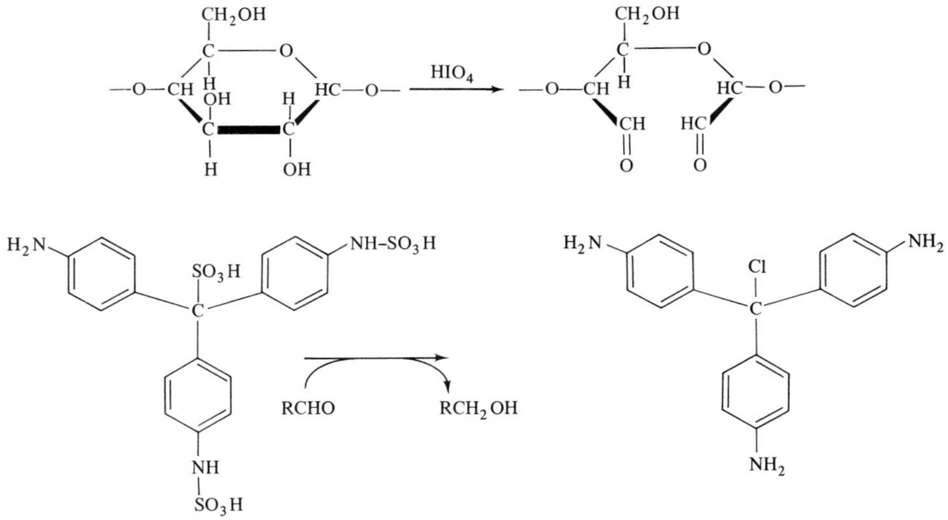

CH_2OH C O —O—CH H OH H HC—O— C C H OH $\xrightarrow{HIO_4}$ CH_2OH C O —O—CH H HC—O— CH HC O O

H_2N SO_3H C NH-SO_3H NH SO_3H RCHO → RCH_2OH H_2N Cl C NH_2 NH_2

fig. 2-8. The chemical reaction which takes place in the periodate-Schiff histochemical stain.

of enzymes have been developed. Cytochrome oxidase gives rise to a colored oxidation product when exposed to a mixture of α-naphthol and N,N-dimethylphenylenediamine (Fig. 2-9). The original Gomori reaction for alkaline phosphatase uses β-glycerylphosphate as the substrate in the presence of calcium ions (Fig. 2-10). The phosphate liberated by the enzyme forms insoluble calcium phosphate, which, in turn, can be

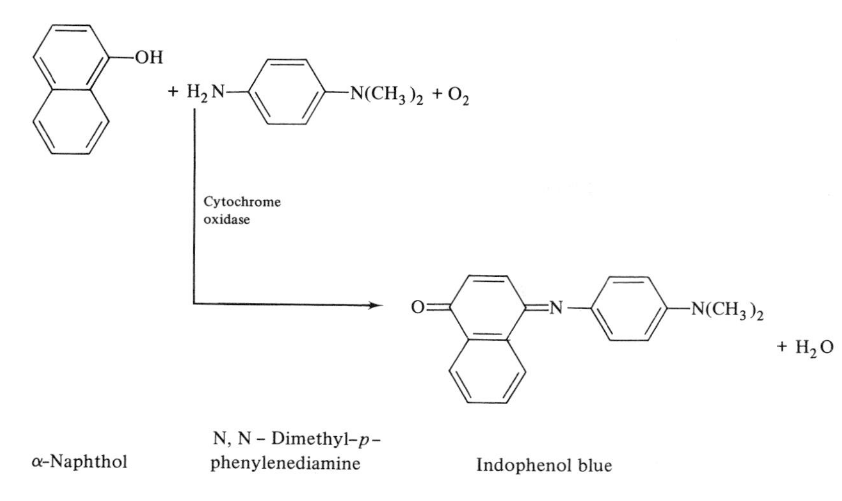

fig. 2-9. The chemical reaction which gives the Nadi stain for cytochrome oxidase.

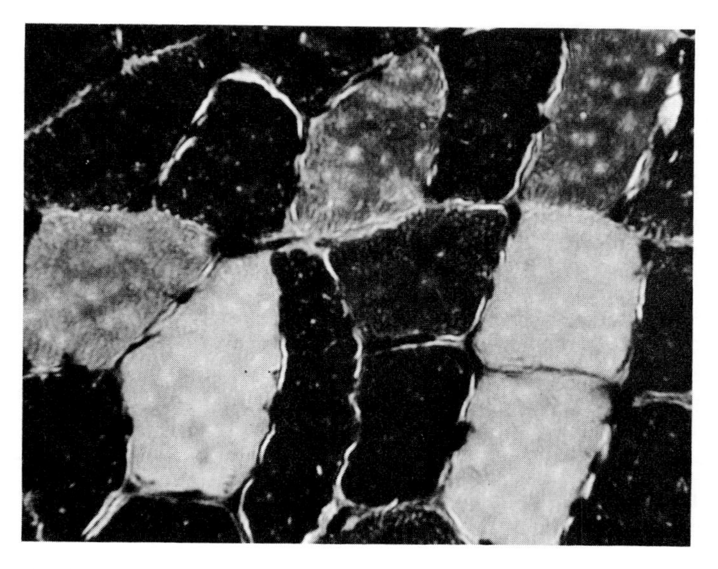

fig. 2-10. Histochemical stain for myosin ATPase activity; cross section of rat gastrocnemius muscle. Red muscle fibers stain more intensely than white muscle fibers. Magnification 330. (Courtesy of Dr. David G. Freiman.)

visualized by a number of methods. A newer method for alkaline phosphatase utilizes β-naphthol phosphate as the substrate in the presence of a stable diazonium salt. The β-naphthol liberated as a result of enzyme activity reacts with the diazonium salt to give a colored azo dye. Esterases can be detected by a similar method, which utilizes β-naphthol acetate as the substrate. Another technique uses β-naphthol glucuronide to localize β-glucuronidase (Fig. 2-11). Acid phosphatase can be localized by use of an alkaline phosphatase method at *p*H 4.5 instead of *p*H 8.6. Dehydrogenases such as

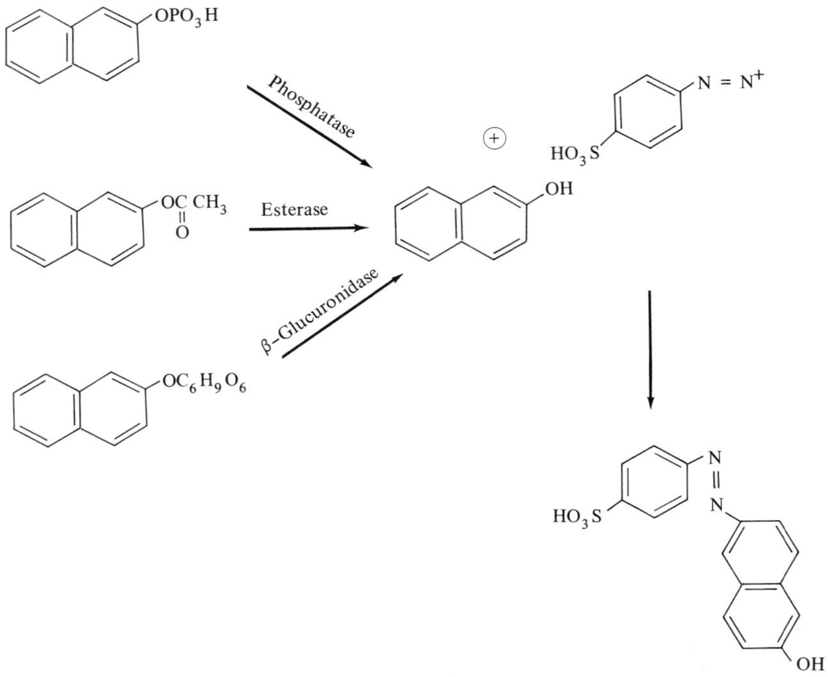

fig. 2-11. Histochemical reactions for phosphatase, esterase, or β-glucuronidase which lead to the formation of an azo dye.

lactate dehydrogenase, which converts lactate into pyruvate, can be detected in the combined presence of (1) the appropriate substrate, lactate in this case, (2) the proper cofactor, nicotinamide adenine dinucleotide (NAD) in this instance [or nicotinamide adenine trinucleotide (NADP), if required], and (3) a colorless, soluble tetrazolium salt. As the substrate is converted into product, the cofactor is reduced, and that in turn reduces the tetrazolium salt to an insoluble, colored formazan. This method can be used for alcohol dehydrogenase, malate dehydrogenase, isocitrate dehydrogenase, and other enzymes by use of the appropriate substrate and cofactor. Of course, the histochemical reactions must be carried out at the *p*H optimum for the enzyme, and the proper metal ions and cofactors must be present if they are required. If specific inhibitors are known, the specificity of the method can be evaluated and increased by comparison of serial sections, one with and one without the addition of the inhibitor.

electron microscopy

The electron microscope, which was developed in the 1930s, has proved a powerful tool for studying the ultrastructure of cells because it has much greater resolving power than light microscopes. It permits a degree of localization and definition of structural details not possible by light microscopy.

In the electron microscope, an electron beam passes through the specimen and is focused by electrostatic and/or magnetic "lenses." The image is viewed on a fluorescent screen or photographed. The increased resolution of the electron microscope is possible because the paths of electrons can be resolved to much smaller distances than light. In practice, a resolution of 10 to 15 Å is common, and greater resolution is possible with special techniques. The entire "optical" system of the electron microscope is enclosed in a high-vacuum chamber. The samples must be dry and nonvolatile. Furthermore, they must be cut into extraordinarily thin sections, because electrons lose energy in passing through the sample, which results in changes in their wavelength and in a kind of "chromatic aberration" that limits resolution. Thinner sections decrease the image overlap and allow clearer interpretation. A dividend of thin-section techniques developed for electron microscopy has been their use for fixed-stained tissue for examination by light microscopy, resulting in preparations of much greater clarity.

While image formation in the light microscope depends upon differences in light absorption, image formation in the electron microscope results mainly from differences in electron scattering. In general, the scattering of electrons depends on the thickness and mass packing of the object in their path, so that regions of high density, in which atoms of high atomic number are aggregated, will appear darker than regions of low density. Specimens are prepared for electron microscopy by use of *electron stains* containing elements of high atomic number, which react selectively with cellular structures; compounds containing uranium, osmium, and chromium are commonly used both for fixing specimens and for staining them. The specimens are mounted on a carbon film, or on a backing of formvar or collodion, which in turn is supported on a fine wire screen. The specimen is visualized through the holes of the screen.

Another method of preparing specimens consists of evaporating a heavy metal in a vacuum chamber at an angle to the specimen. The specimen becomes coated with heavy metal, depending on the height of the material, producing a *shadow cast* in the electron microscope. Alternatively, the specimen may be coated with a thin film of plastic which is stripped off when dried and shadowed with heavy metal to give a *shadowed replica*. These techniques are particularly useful for studying details of surfaces.

cell ultrastructure

Usually the cell is clearly a unit, bounded everywhere by a limiting *cell membrane*. The cell membrane is to be distinguished from the cell wall of plant cells and bacteria. The latter is really a secreted, extracellular structure and is not essential to cellular viability. Within the boundary of the cell membrane is a fluid substance, the *cytoplasm*, holding in suspension a variety of organelles, vesicles, inclusions, and granules. An idealized cell is depicted diagrammatically in Fig. 2-12. A rat liver cell, which illustrates cellular ultrastructure particularly well, is shown in Figs. 2-13 and 2-14. Intestinal epithelial cells are shown in Fig. 2-15; and Fig. 2-16 is an electron micrograph of a blood platelet, an example of an anucleate cell. While the existence of a limiting cell membrane as distinct from the cell wall could not be established with certainty by light microscopy, its presence was inferred from the osmotic behavior of intact cells and the loss of cytoplasm through tears. In most cells, the genetic material is condensed in a *nucleus*. These cells are *eukaryotic*. Bacteria, rickettsiae, viruses, and other organisms are *prokaryotic*; that is, the genetic material is not segregated in a nucleus but is suspended in the cytoplasm, not uniformly but with a tendency to aggregate in the central part of the cell. The physiology of bacteria, viruses, and other prokaryotic organisms is sufficiently unique to merit separate consideration; generally these organisms will not be discussed in this book.

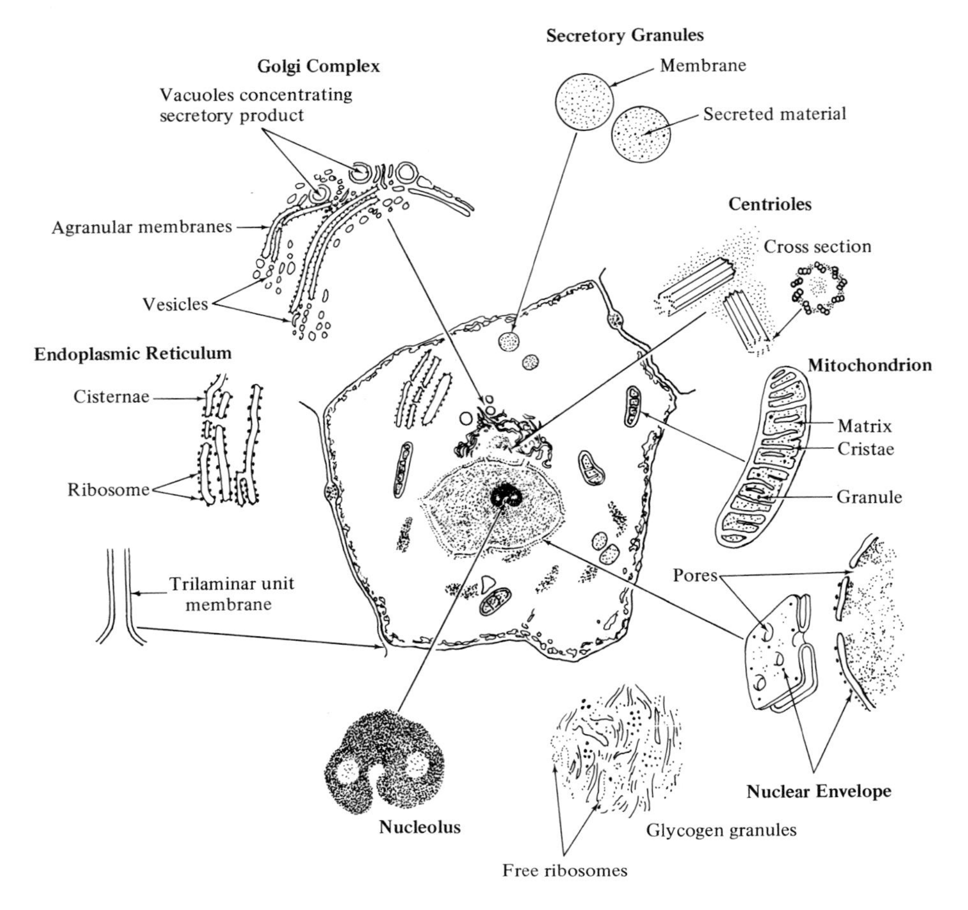

fig. 2-12. A diagram of an idealized cell emphasizing the details of its ultrastructure. The intracellular organelles and inclusions are drawn to emphasize the characteristic details of their structure.

Cells of higher organisms ordinarily contain a nucleus.[5] The few naturally occurring examples of anucleate cells, such as the mature mammalian erythrocyte, platelets, the cells making up the outer layers of the skin, and the cells in the lens of the eye, are not able to grow or divide and cannot synthesize protein. However, certain nucleated cells, such as mature neurons, divide rarely, if ever. Because of the abundance of nucleic acids, the nucleus stains with basic dyes, each cell type displaying an often-characteristic pattern of deeply staining granules, called *chromatin*. The chromatin is specifically stained by the Feulgen stain for deoxyribonucleic acid (DNA) and represents the genetic material of the cell. The nucleus has one or more spherical, usually deeply basophilic, eccentrically placed organelles, the *nucleoli* (Fig. 2-17). A nucleolus fails to stain with the Feulgen stain for DNA but has been shown to contain large quantities of RNA. The chromatin and nucleolus are dispersed in a matrix of finely granular material, called the *nuclear ground substance*, or *karyolymph* (Fig. 2-18). The nucleus is surrounded by a double unit membrane, the layers of which are connected to each other at intervals to form discontinuities, or *pores* (Fig. 2-19). At the sites of the pores, the nuclear ground substance tends to be less dense and to be devoid of chromatin.

[5] Wischnitzer, S. *Intern. Rev. Cytol., 10*, 137 (1960) reviews the ultrastructure of the nucleus.

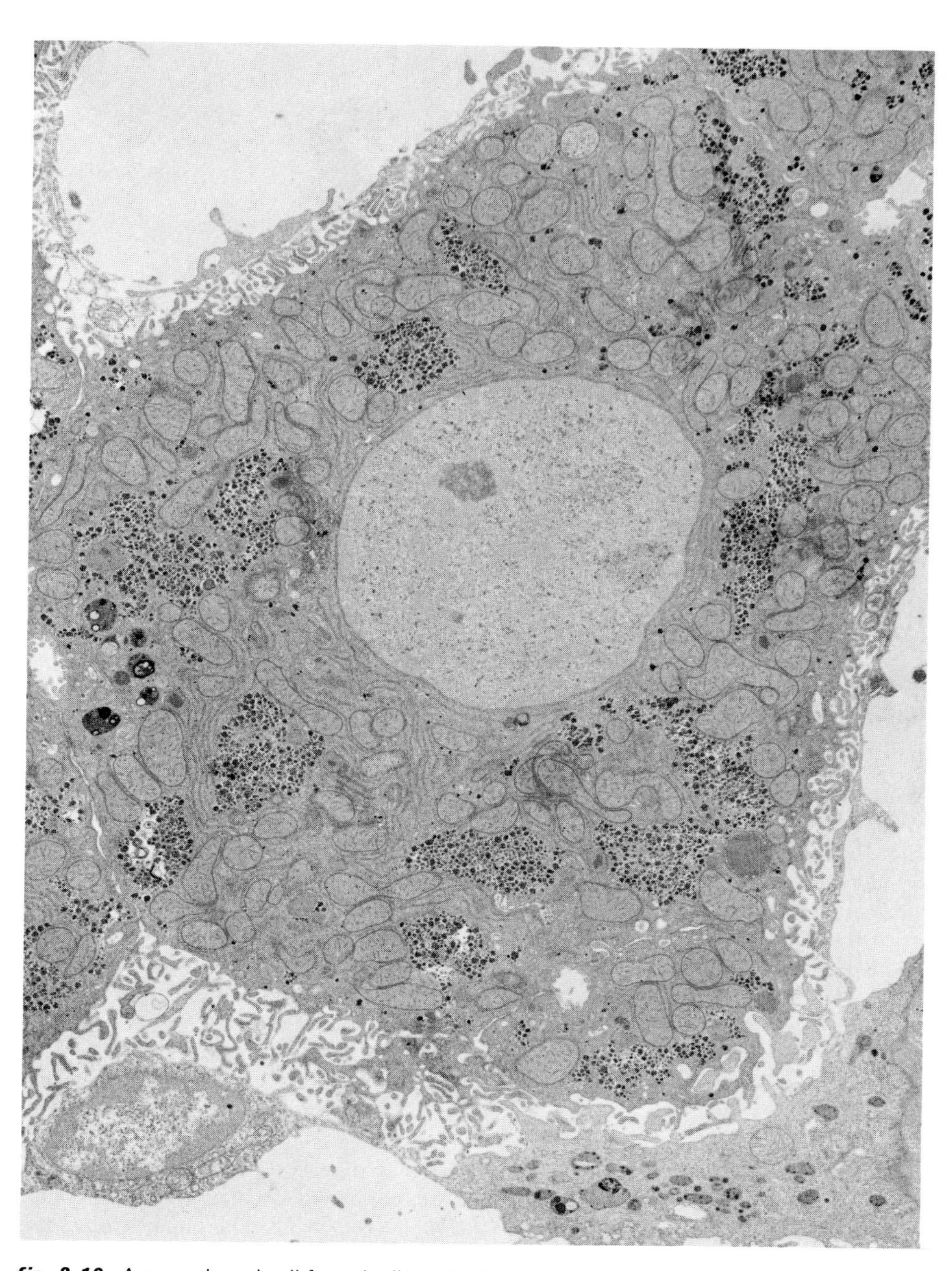

fig. 2-13. A parenchymal cell from the liver of a Sprague-Dawley rat. Magnification 6200. (Courtesy of Dr. Thomas P. Ashford.)

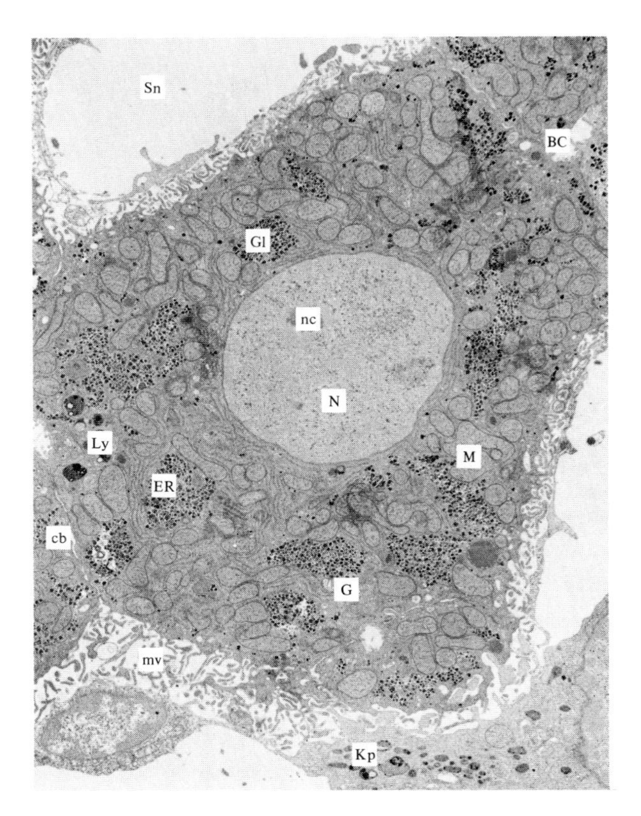

fig. 2-14. The same cell shown in Fig. 2-13, but with the visible structures labeled as follows: N, nucleus; nc, nucleolus; M, mitochondria; G, Golgi apparatus; ER, endoplasmic reticulum; Ly, lysosomes; Gl, glycogen granules; cb, intercellular space between two parenchymal cells; BC, bile canaliculus; Sn, sinusoid; mv, microvilli; and Kp, part of a Kupfer (reticuloendothelial) cell.

The *mitochondria* are granular or filamentous organelles found in the cytoplasm (Fig. 2-20). They were described by several nineteenth-century cytologists. After Altmann discovered a specific fuchsin stain and Michaelis discovered the specific supravital staining technique using Janus green, mitochondria were found in almost all types of cells. The mitochondria are the site of oxidative respiration and the coupling of this process to the production of energy-rich metabolic intermediates, particularly adenosine triphosphate. In tissue-cultured cells, mitochondria can be seen to undergo continuous changes in cellular location. There are continuous and often rhythmic changes in shape and volume, appearing as cycles of contraction and swelling which are related to the respiratory state. These cycles may be inhibited by drugs which uncouple oxidative phosphorylation. Mitochondrial movement is more active during interphase than during mitosis.

Mitochondria are usually roughly ovoid, but they may assume a filamentous shape or a vesicular form with a clear central zone.[6] Club and racket shapes are sometimes observed. Mitochondria are bounded by a double membrane. The inner layer of the

[6] Palade, G. *J. Histochem. Cytochem.*, *1*, 188 (1953); Hackenbrock, C. R. *J. Cell Biol.*, *30*, 269 (1966).

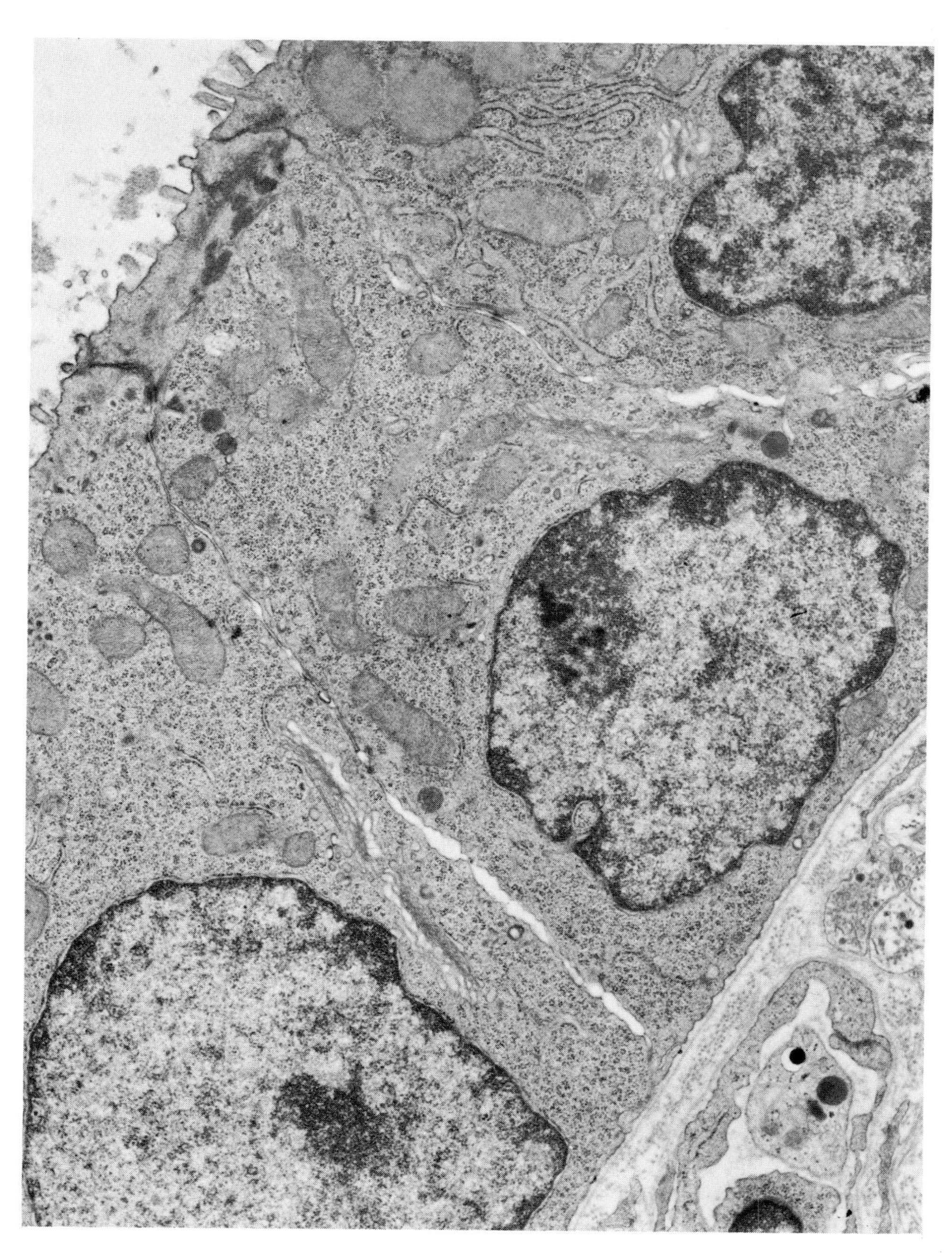

fig. 2-15. Three undifferentiated epithelial cells from the base of a crypt of the rat duodenum. The cell boundaries are clearly seen, as is the basement membrane beneath the epithelial cells. A small capillary is seen in the lower right-hand corner containing a platelet and a portion of a leucocyte. Magnification 13,000. (Courtesy of Dr. Thomas P. Ashford.)

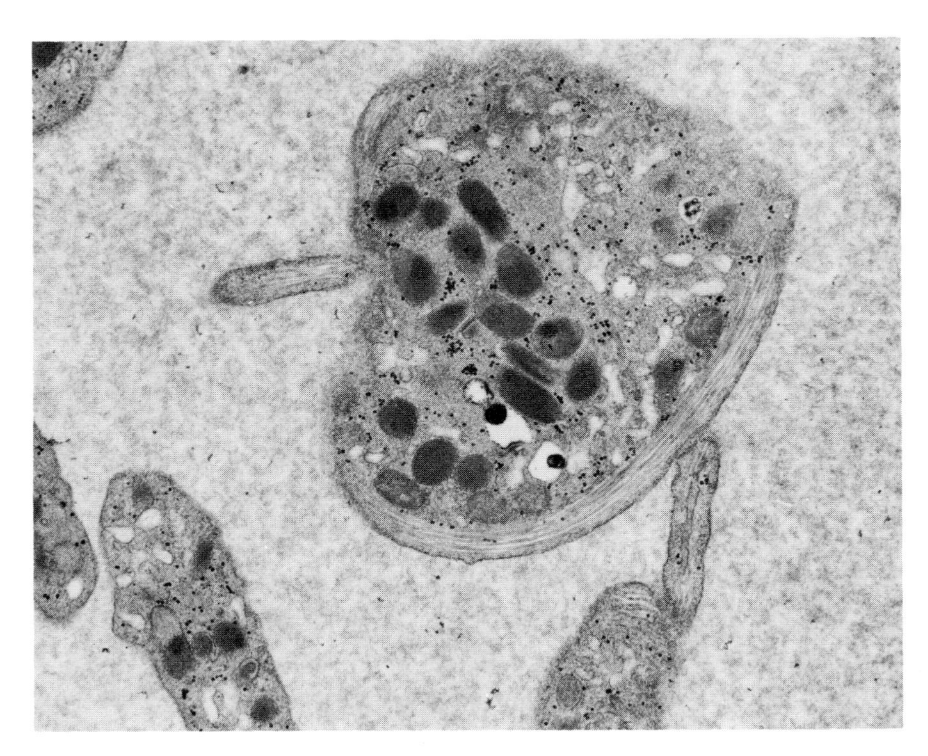

fig. 2-16. A blood platelet, an anucleate cell. Magnification 49,000. (Courtesy of Dr. Thomas P. Ashford.)

membrane usually has numerous parallel interdigitating invaginations, the mitochondrial *cristae*, which project from the walls into the interior (Fig. 2-21). A finely granular, homogeneous *matrix* fills the large cavity of the mitochondrion, which also usually contains some very *dense granules*. The dense granules may be the result of precipitation of insoluble salts of calcium and other ions accumulated by the mitochondria. Particles approximately 100 Å in diameter called *elementary particles* appear to cover the inner surface of the mitochondrial membrane and cristae in a regular geometrical array at about 200-Å intervals. Mitochondria are pleomorphic and undergo great changes in appearance with metabolic changes.

Mitochondria are frequently located adjacent to intracellular lipid droplets. Sometimes the lipid droplets appear to be fused to the mitochondria, particularly after a short period of starvation or in rapidly metabolizing tissue such as cardiac muscle. In cells actively engaged in absorption or excretion—the intestinal epithelium or renal tubular cells, for example—mitochondria tend to localize at the cell surface. Cells with greater rates of metabolism tend to have more mitochondria.

The cell membrane appears as a thin band approximately 100 Å thick. The band consists of two dark lines, each about 30 Å thick, on either side of a light zone, and this ubiquitous, trilaminar structure is commonly referred to as a *unit membrane*. Unit membranes occur not only at the cell boundary but also in the interior of cells as part of the *endoplasmic reticulum*. Sometimes the outer line is thicker and denser than the inner one, thereby presenting an asymmetric appearance. Unit membranes vary somewhat in total thickness. The cell membrane is thicker at free surfaces of cells than where it is in contact with other cells in tissue, and it is thicker than the unit membranes

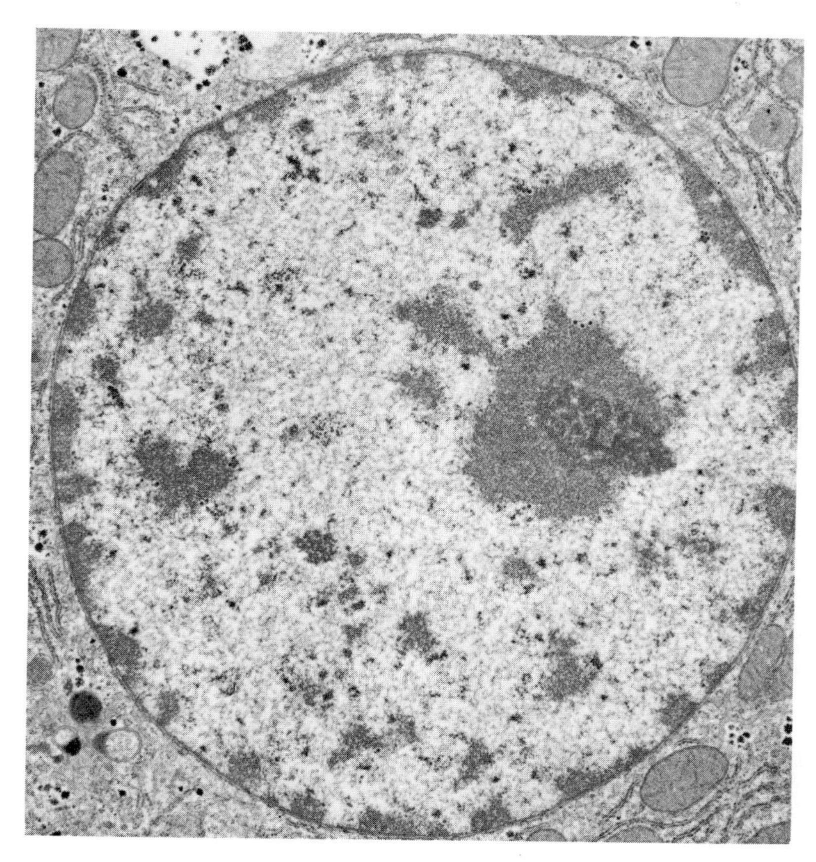

fig. 2-17. Nucleus from the liver cell of a Sprague-Dawley rat. The chromatin is dispersed; the dense, rounded body on the right side of the nucleus is the nucleolus. Magnification 10,000. (Courtesy of Dr. Thomas P. Ashford.)

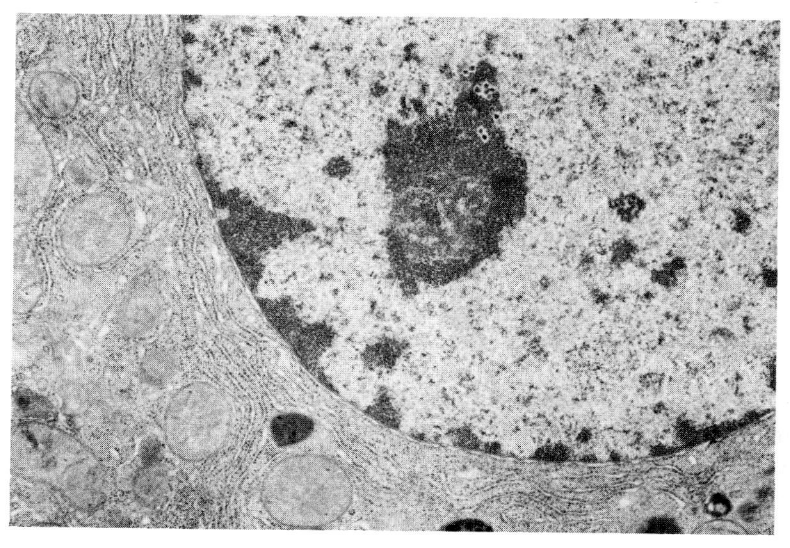

fig. 2-18. A portion of a rat liver cell showing the texture of the karyolymph. Magnification 11,000. (Courtesy of Dr. Thomas P. Ashford.)

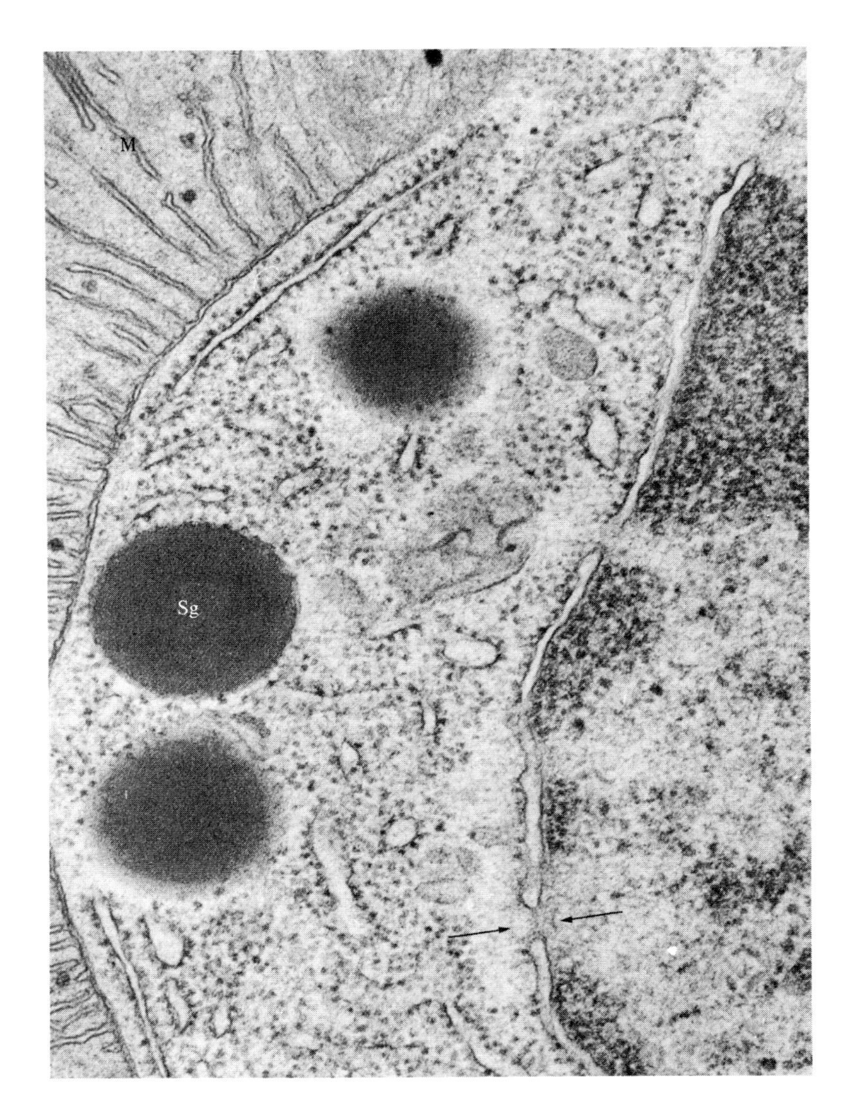

fig. 2-19. A portion of an acinar cell from the pancreas of a bat. A portion of the nucleus is at the right showing pores (one indicated by the arrows) in the nuclear envelope. A portion of a mitrochondrion (M) is at the left, and dark secretory granules (Sg) are seen. Magnification 55,000. (Courtesy of Dr. Keith R. Porter.)

of endoplasmic reticulum. Nuclei and mitochondria are also surrounded by unit membranes.

The endoplasmic reticulum[7] is an intracellular system of branching, intercommunicating tubules bounded by unit membranes. The outer surfaces of these membranous systems are often covered with dense granules. These granules and similar granules found free in the cytoplasm are *ribosomes*, structures intimately involved in protein

[7] Porter, K. R. *J. Exptl. Med.*, *97*, 727 (1953); Palade, G. E., and Porter, K. R. *J. Exptl. Med.*, *100*, 641 (1954); Palade, G. E. *J. Biophys. Biochem. Cytol.*, *1*, 59 (1955).

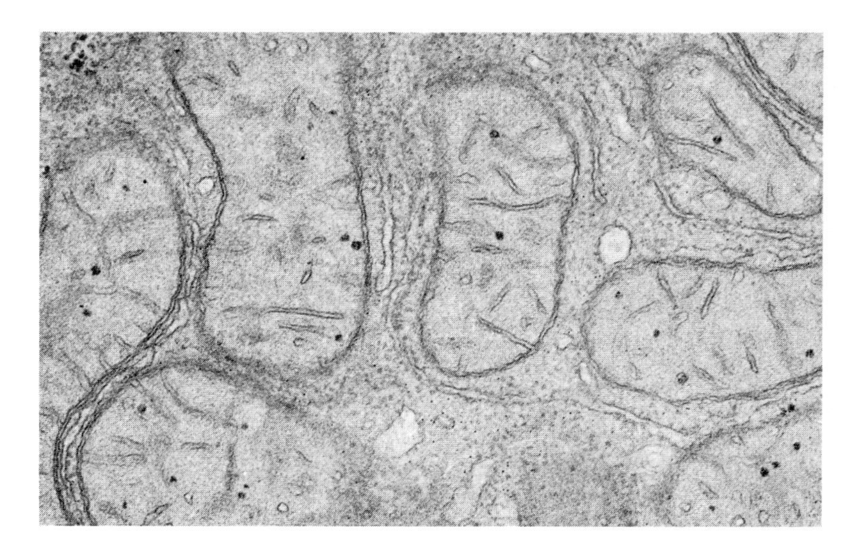

fig. 2-20. Mitochondria from the liver cell of a Sprague-Dawley rat. The connection of the cristae to the inner lamina of the bounding unit membrane can be seen in many places. The mitochondria contain typical dark granules. Magnification 35,000. (Courtesy of Dr. Thomas P. Ashford.)

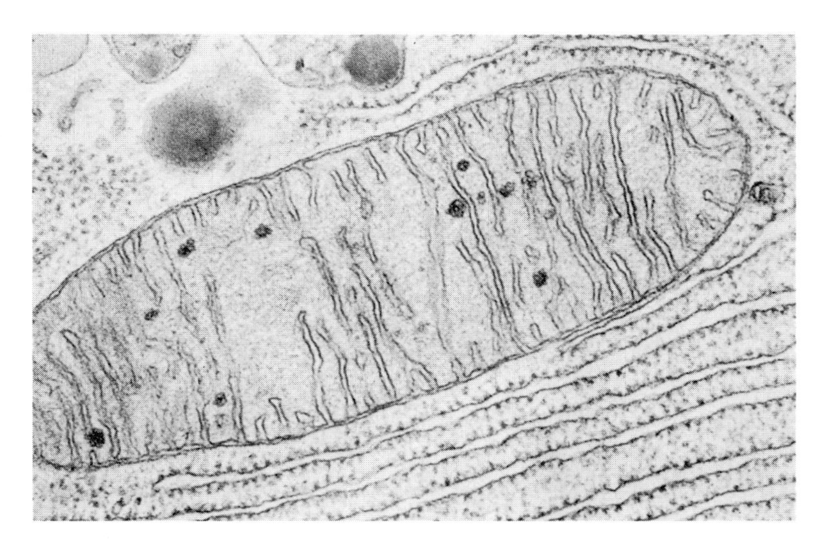

fig. 2-21. Mitochondrion from the pancreas of a bat showing the limiting membranes, the membranes of the cristae, and the dense particles. Magnification 44,000. (Courtesy of Dr. Keith R. Porter.)

synthesis. Endoplasmic reticulum covered with many ribosomes is called *granular reticulum* or *rough endoplasmic reticulum* (Fig. 2-22), while endoplasmic reticulum devoid of ribosomes is called *agranular reticulum* or *smooth endoplasmic reticulum* (Fig. 2-23).

The rough endoplasmic reticulum tends to occur in *lamellae*; when cross sections of these are cut, a system of parallel double membranes is seen. When granular reticulum

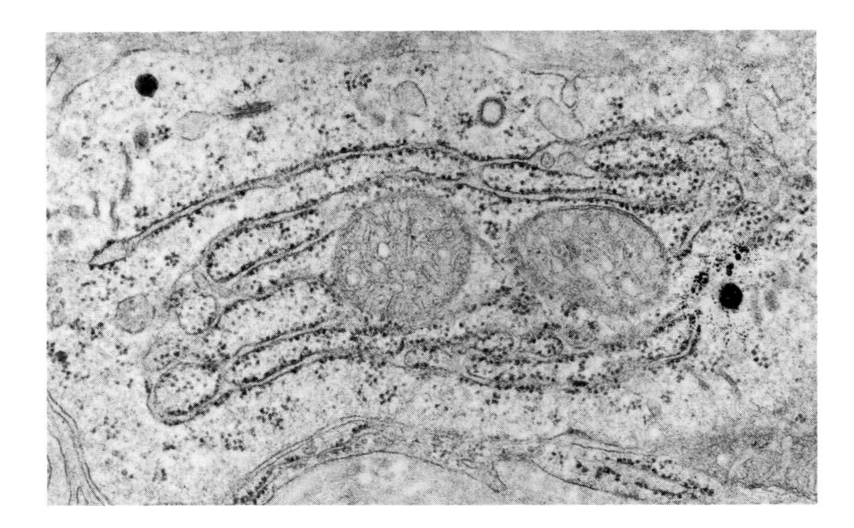

fig. 2-22. Mucosal cell from the rat duodenum showing connections between the lumina of rough endoplasmic reticulum. Just above the rough endoplasmic reticulum is a chorded vesicle. Magnification 18,000. (Courtesy of Dr. Thomas P. Ashford.)

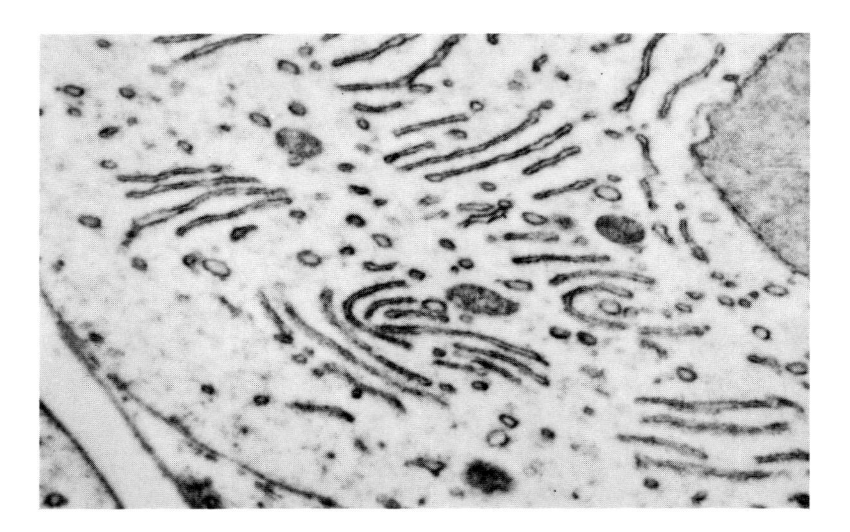

fig. 2-23. Smooth endoplasmic reticulum in the liver of a starved animal. Magnification 44,000. (Courtesy of Dr. Keith R. Porter.)

is sectioned tangentially, whorls or saccules are seen. Smooth endoplasmic reticulum tends to appear as smooth vesicles 300 to 700 Å in diameter, bounded by unit membranes. Smooth endoplasmic reticulum can be converted into the rough form and vice versa,[8] depending upon the protein requirements of the cell. Granular and agranular reticulum may be found in a single cell, and in such cells the two forms are

---

[8] Dallner, G., Siekevitz, P., and Palade, G. *J. Cell Biol.*, *30*, 73 (1966).

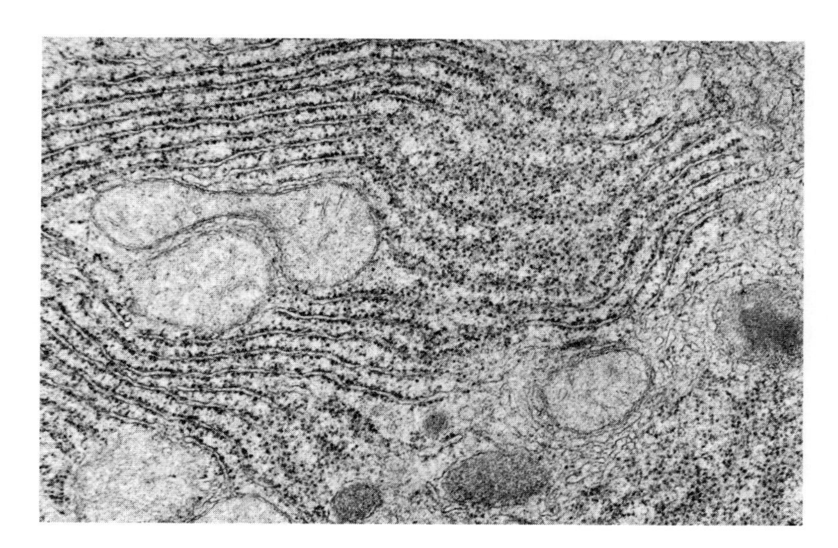

fig. 2-24. Liver cell from a Sprague-Dawley rat showing rough endoplasmic reticulum and adjacent mitochondria, and the merging of rough and smooth endoplasmic reticulum. Magnification 17,000. (Courtesy of Dr. Thomas P. Ashford.)

continuous (Fig. 2-24). The granular reticulum stains basophilic because of the high RNA content and corresponds to the structure called the *ergastoplasm* by light microscopists.

The nuclear membrane is also studded with ribosomes on the cytoplasmic side, and at many points it is continuous with the membrane system of the endoplasmic reticulum. At these points, the matrix of the nucleus is thought to open through *nuclear pores* to the cisternae of the endoplasmic reticulum, although the exact nature of the continuity is still not entirely known. These structures are believed to play an important role in the movement of substances from the nucleus into the cytoplasm, and perhaps vice versa. Similar points of continuity may occur between the endoplasmic reticulum and the cell membrane, although this idea has not been verified at the present time.

The granular reticulum varies in its degree of development and complexity from cell type to cell type and sometimes varies with the functional states of a given cell type. Generally, the endoplasmic reticulum is most prominent and most highly developed in cells actively synthesizing large amounts of protein, such as the secretory cells of various glands. Usually, mitochondria tend to cluster around these areas of well-developed granular reticulum. At times, the cavities of the reticular vesicles and saccules, the *cisternae*, become distended with accumulated protein. Similarly, the cavities of smooth endoplasmic reticulum may be distended by lipids, melanin, or other materials. In cells like the mammalian erythrocyte, which lose their nuclei through involution, after a short time the endoplasmic reticulum also disappears. The agranular reticulum is well developed in cells that synthesize steroid hormones, such as the testes, and can be stimulated to develop in liver cells by the administration of certain drugs, for example, phenobarbital.

The *Golgi apparatus* was discovered by Camillo Golgi in 1898. He observed a network of anastomosing, dense filaments in the juxtanuclear region of neural cells which had been stained by metal impregnation (Fig. 2-25). In glandular cells, the Golgi apparatus is more compact and is situated at the apical pole of the nucleus, surrounded

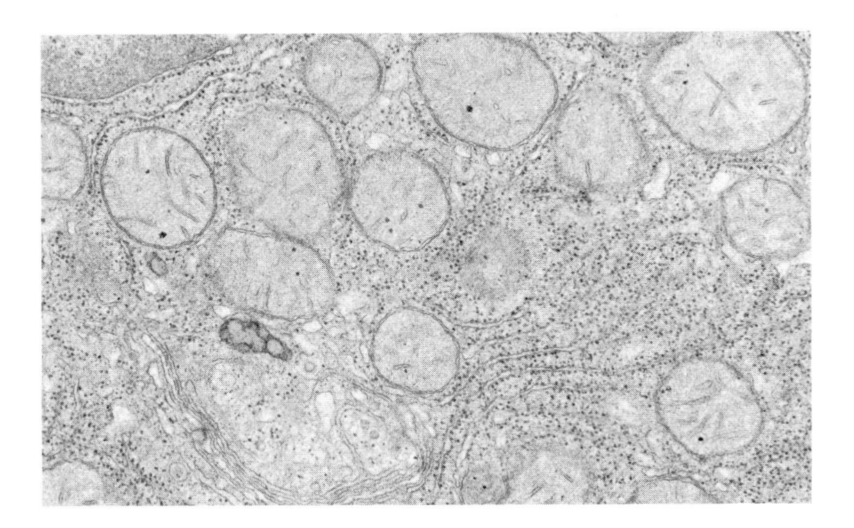

fig. 2-25. Liver cell from a Sprague-Dawley rat showing a Golgi apparatus surrounded by mitochondria and radiating rough endoplasmic reticulum. Magnification 20,000. (Courtesy of Dr. Thomas P. Ashford.)

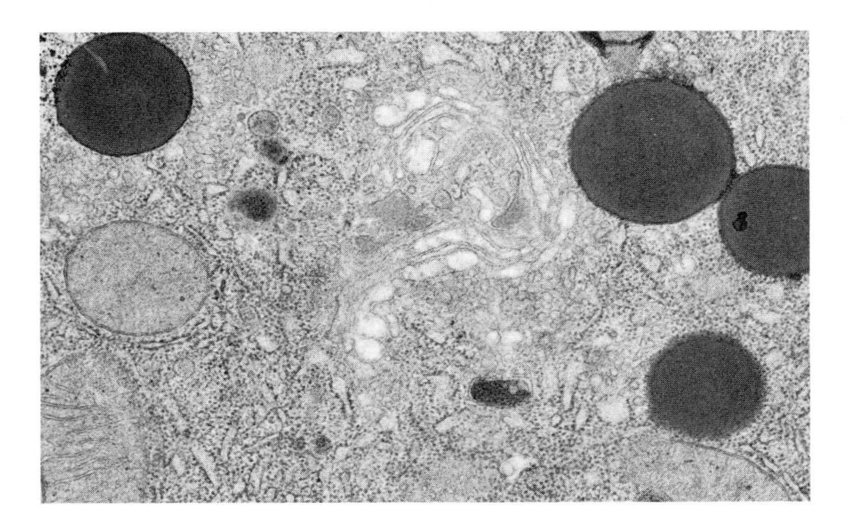

fig. 2-26. Golgi apparatus and zymogen granules from an acinar cell of the rat pancreas. Magnification 18,000. (Courtesy of Dr. Thomas P. Ashford.)

by secretory granules[9] (Fig. 2-26). Studies with the electron microscope have shown the Golgi apparatus to consist of a membrane-limited structure that can be divided into three parts: (1) flattened cisternae, which appear as a system of roughly parallel membranes enclosing a space of 60 to 90 Å, with a distance of about 200 Å between them; (2) clusters of vesicles around the ends and outer surfaces of the cisternae; and (3) large, clear vacuoles, which are associated with the inner cisternae, particularly in glandular cells. Commonly, groups of four to eight flat or curved cisternae are found,

[9] Caro, L. *J. Biophys. Biochem. Cytol.*, *10*, 37 (1961).

and at times, particularly in plant and invertebrate cells, the cisternae are arranged to outline an elliptical or spheroidal Golgi apparatus, enclosing a number of vacuoles or vesicles. The outer lamellae, which extend into the cytoplasm, are called *dictyosomes.* As is true of the endoplasmic reticulum, to which the Golgi apparatus is related, the development and complexity of the Golgi apparatus varies from cell type to cell type and often with the functional state of a given cell type. While the Golgi apparatus is very developed in secretory cells and is believed to play an important role in the accumulation and storage of secreted products, it is also well developed in cells that do not carry on any known secretory activity.

Centrioles are hollow, cylindrical cups approximately 4000 Å long and 1500 Å in diameter. Cells usually contain two centrioles located in the juxtanuclear region of the cytoplasm, often arranged so that the axis of one is perpendicular to the axis of the other (Fig. 2-27). The wall of the centriole appears to be composed of nine hollow

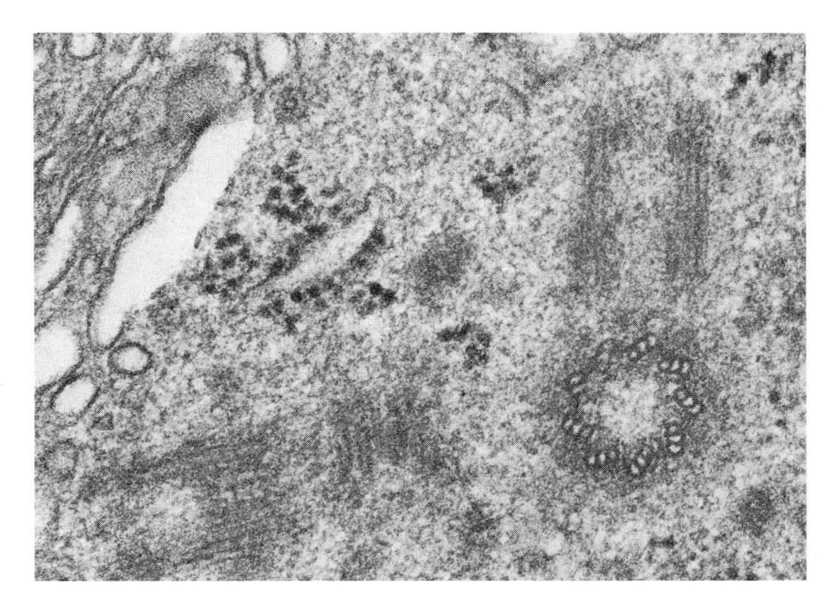

fig. 2-27. Centrioles from rat liver embryo. Note the orientation at almost right angles to one another. Magnification 65,000. (Courtesy of Dr. Keith R. Porter.)

tubules embedded in a dense, granular matrix. Sometimes, there appear to be granular discs around the centriole; these are the so-called *satellites.* Centrioles were recognized by light microscopists as two densely staining rods, referred to as the *diplosome,* which they regarded as an indicator of the axis of cellular symmetry. The area of cytoplasm around the centriole is called the *centrosome,* or cell center, and a line connecting the nucleus and centrosome is sometimes called the *cell axis.*

Plant cells contain a group of inclusions collectively called *plastids.* Of these, the *chloroplast* is the most important biologically, because chloroplasts are the organelles responsible for photosynthesis. Their number, shape, size, and distribution vary with the cell type and species, and often with the time of year and stage of development. Chloroplasts are surrounded by a unit membrane and contain an inner membranous structure. *Grana* are cylindrical structures made up of stacks of discs bounded by unit membranes (Figs. 2-28 and 2-29). A spinach chloroplast, for example, contains 40 to 60 grana, each about 5000 Å in diameter. Often the grana extend across the entire thickness of the chloroplast. Adjacent grana are interconnected by a network of almost parallel, anastomosing tubules in the manner illustrated diagrammatically in

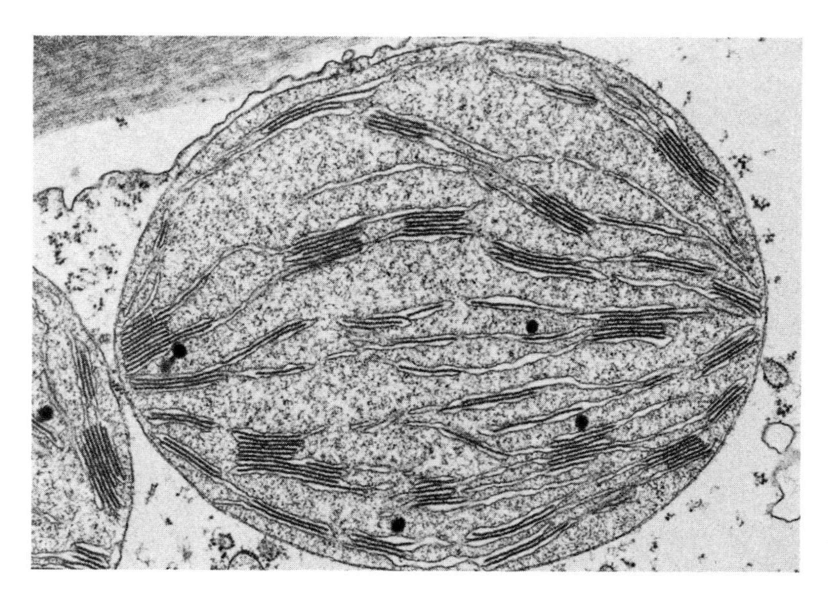

fig. 2-28. A chloroplast from the alga *Nitella* showing the membrane of the envelope, the membranes of the grana, and the intergranal membranes. The dense bodies are lipid inclusions. Magnification 41,000. (Courtesy of Dr. Myron C. Ledbetter.)

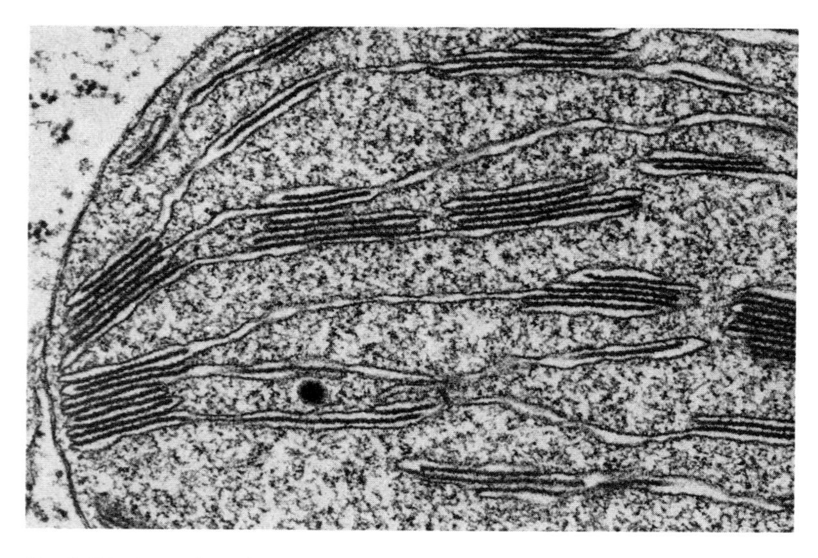

fig. 2-29. A portion of a chloroplast showing the arrangement of the membranes in the grana and intergranal membranes. The small dense particles in the stroma are ribosomes of the chloroplast. Magnification 78,000. (Courtesy of Dr. Myron C. Ledbetter.)

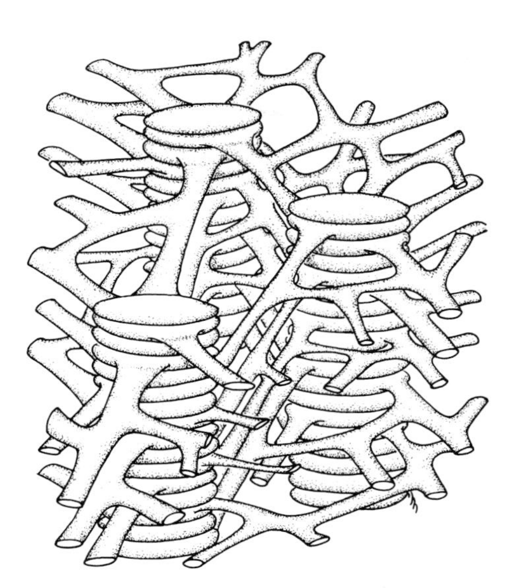

fig. 2-30. A schematic representation by Dr. T. E. Weier of the membranes in a tobacco chloroplast showing the stacks of membranes in the grana and the intergranal connections. (From Weier, T. E., Stocking, C. R., Thomson, W. W., and Drever, H. J. *J. Ultrastruct. Res.*, *8*, 141 [1963]. Copyright Academic Press; reprinted by permission.)

Fig. 2-30. On cross section, the grana appear as stacks of parallel double membranes, with roughly parallel extensions of some of the membranes to adjacent grana. In lower plants, the tubular system is more prominent and the grana may be absent. Chloroplasts resemble mitochondria in many ways; both are the site of membrane-oriented sequences of metabolic reactions.

Leucoplasts are colorless rodlike or spheroidal plastids which are frequently found in embryonic and sexual plant cells and which resemble mitochondria to the casual observer. At times, leucoplasts elaborate starch granules and are then called *amyloplasts*. In addition to chloroplasts, there are other colored plastids called *chromoplasts*, which contain various pigments, such as the phycoerythrin- or phycocyan-containing chromoplasts in algae and the lycopene-containing chromoplasts in the tomato, which give the fruit its characteristic color.

The term *lysosome* was originally an operational designation for tissue elements containing several hydrolytic enzymes with *p*H optima well on the acid side of neutrality. Lysosomes may be best studied in animal cells. Lysosome fractions obtained by differential centrifugation of homogenized cells when examined with the electron microscope, revealed (in addition to mitochondria, fragments of endoplasmic reticulum and other structures) characteristic dense bodies limited by a membrane which give the histochemical staining reaction for acid phosphatase. In liver cells, similar dense bodies are found in association with the bile canaliculi and Golgi apparatus (Fig. 2-31). Sometimes lysosomes contain fragments of intracellular organelles such as those seen in Fig. 2-32.

In some cells, there are *digestive vacuoles* of low density which result from the phagocytosis or pinocytosis of foreign material. They stain for acid phosphatase and resemble lysosomes in enzyme composition. In some cells (protozoa, for example), there are *residual bodies*, the end stage of digestive vacuoles containing undigestible

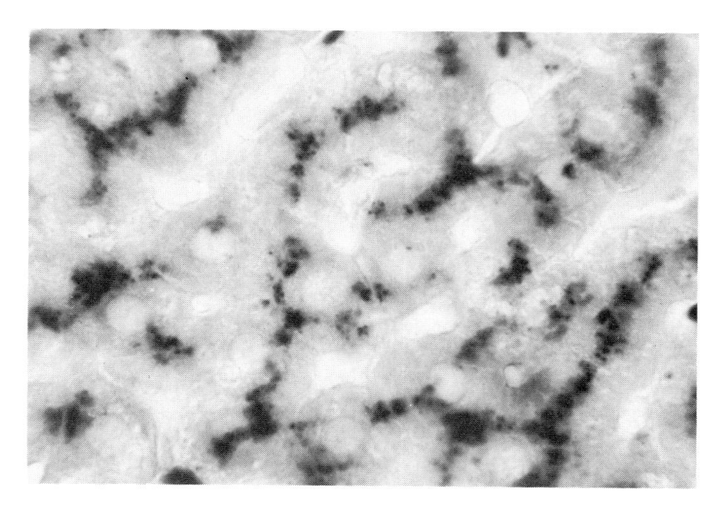

fig. 2-31. Histochemical localization of β-glucuronidase in lysosomes of rat liver parenchymal cells using (6-bromo,2-hydroxy, 3-naphthoyl-*o*-anisidine)-acetobromotrimethyl-β-D-glucuronidate as substrate and hexazonium-*p*-rosanilin as color developer. Magnification 1000. (Courtesy of Dr. M. Hayashi.)

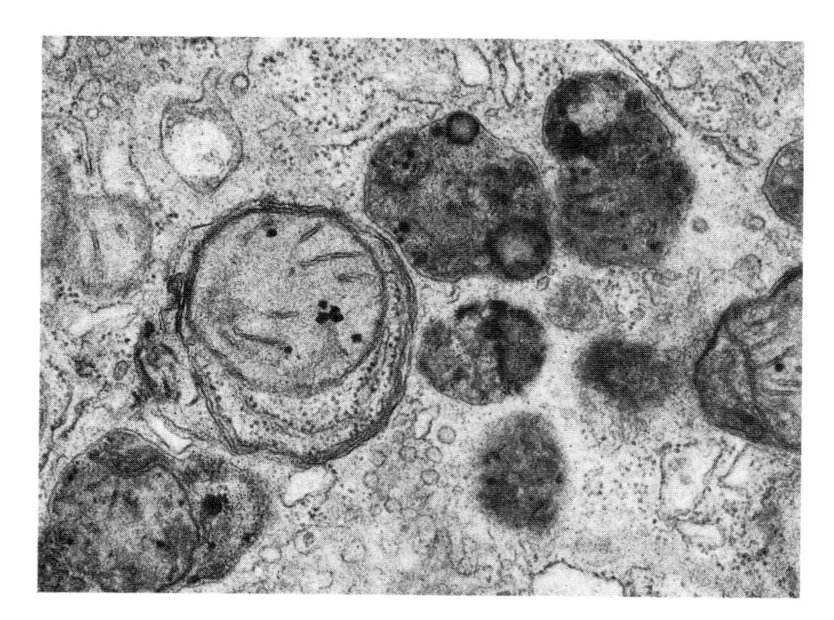

fig. 2-32. Lysosome ingesting a mitochrondrion, and other lysosomes containing fragments of intracellular organelles. Rat liver 4 hours after glucagon administration. Magnification 34,000. (Courtesy of Dr. Keith R. Porter and Dr. Thomas P. Ashford.)

material. Often the residual bodies are extruded from the cell. *Microbodies* are a different kind of membrane-limited organelle. They are smaller than mitochondria and contain a very dense crystalline material in a dense granular matrix. There is some evidence that microbodies contain the enzymes urate oxidase, catalase, and D-amino acid oxidase. Many cells contain *microtubules* in the matrix of the cytoplasm; they consist of cylinders about 200 Å in diameter composed of 12 to 14 filaments. The filaments often seem to be made up of rows of globular subunits 35 Å in diameter.

Cells also contain a variety of inclusions: *zymogen granules* containing material synthesized by the cell awaiting secretion (Fig. 2-26); *pigment granules*, particularly abundant in melanocytes; granules of *glycogen*, representing stored carbodydrates; *lipid* droplets, frequently associated with mitochondria (Fig. 2-33); and various kinds

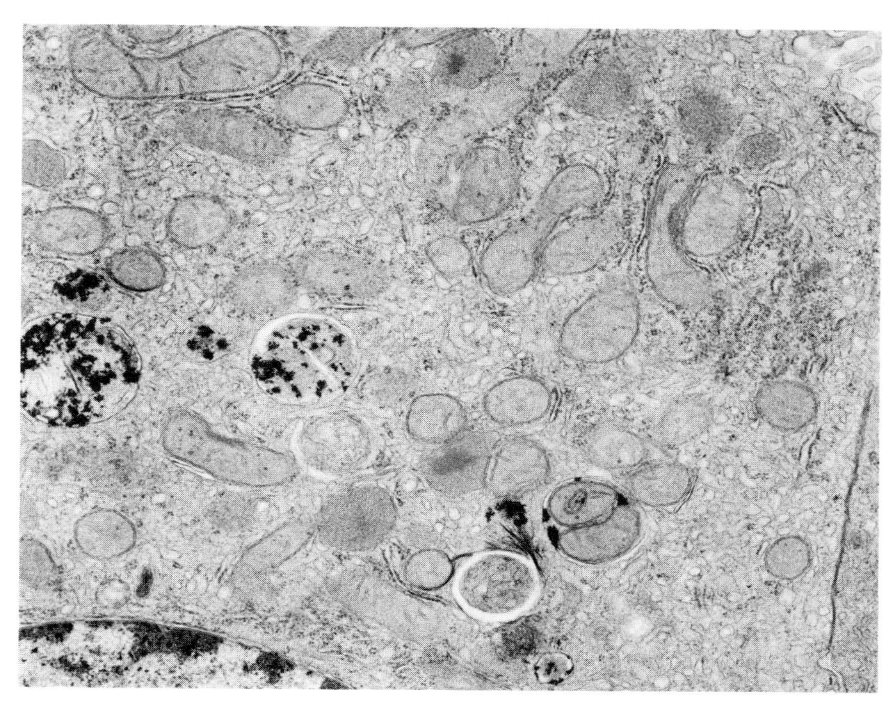

fig. 2-33. Rat liver stained histochemically for acid phosphatase activity prior to fixation. The black electron-opaque material is lead phosphate generated by the enzyme; it is localized in lysosomes except for a small amount in the nucleus considered to be an adsorption artifact. Magnification 17,000 (Courtesy of Dr. Alex B. Novikoff.)

of intracellular crystals. Plant cells frequently contain a large *vacuole* which is separated from the bulk of the cytoplasm by a unit membrane, the *tonoplast membrane*.

The ultrastructure of certain specialized cells, such as muscle and Schwann cells, and certain specialized cellular structures, such as motor end plates, will be considered later.

specializations of the cell surface

A number of specializations of the cell membrane have been recognized. The free surface of epithelial cells is often made up of *microvilli*, cytoplasmic projections covered by cell membrane which measure about 1000 Å in diameter and 6000 to 9000 Å in length (Fig. 2-34). A single intestinal epithelial cell may have several thousand microvilli facing the gut lumen. The effective surface area of the cell is greatly increased by the microvilli, and it is thought that they are important in absorption. In the case of

fig. 2-34. Cells from the duodenum of a Sprague-Dawley rat, showing microvilli and a junctional complex between two adjacent cells. Magnification 57,000. (Courtesy of Dr. Thomas P. Ashford.)

intestinal epithelial cells, a dense mat of delicate, branching, tangled filaments approximately 25 Å thick cover the surfaces of the microvilli, to which they appear to be firmly attached, and fill the spaces between them. This filamentous surface layer has the staining properties of mucopolysaccharide and appears to resist attack from proteolytic and mucolytic enzymes.

Epithelial cells are usually separated from the connective tissue on which they rest by the *basement membrane*, a moderately dense layer on electron micrographs, about 600 Å thick, which follows the contour of the epithelial cells and is separated from them by a clear zone of about 300 Å (Fig. 2-35). The basement membrane contains fine collagen filaments embedded in a mucopolysaccharide matrix. Evidence from immunological and other studies indicates that the basement membrane is not a product of the connective tissue but is elaborated by the epithelial cells.

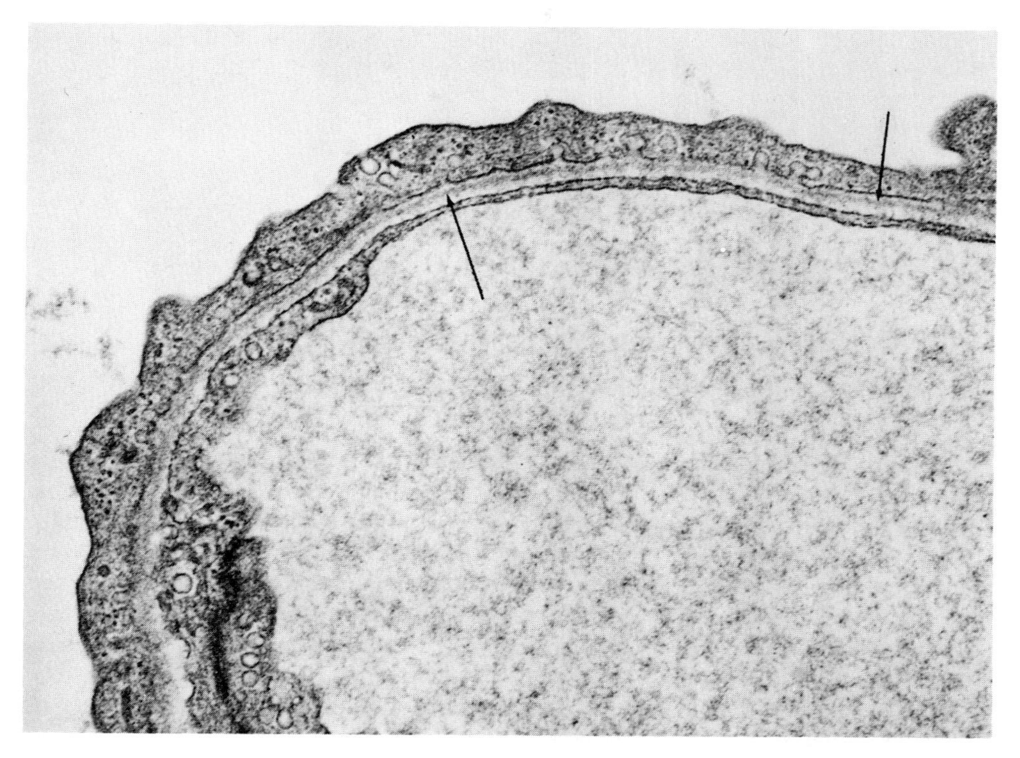

fig. 2-35. A portion of an alveolus from rabbit lung showing epithelial and endothelial cells and a basement membrane (arrows). Magnification 34,000. (Courtesy of Dr. Thomas P. Ashford.)

The cell membranes of adjoining cells are parallel to each other, separated by an intercellular space of remarkably uniform width (Fig. 2-36). The exact width appears to depend on the tonicity of the environment and on other physiological circumstances.[10] Setälä and his associates[11] observed the development of intercellular edema in the basal layer of mouse epidermis after the application of a nonionic detergent, Tween 60. Wide intercellular gaps which gave the impression that the cells had been stretched apart were seen with the electron microscope. While rupture of such stretched cell parts was seen at times, adjacent desmosomes (see below) remained intact.

Several localized developments of the opposing cell membranes have been recognized which are thought to represent specialized sites of firmer intercellular attachment. A

[10] Nilsson, O. *J. Ultrastruct. Res.*, *2*, 73, 185 (1958).
[11] Setälä, K., Merenmies, L., Stjernvall, L., Nijholm, M., and Aho, Y. *J. Natl. Cancer Inst.*, *24*, 329 (1960).

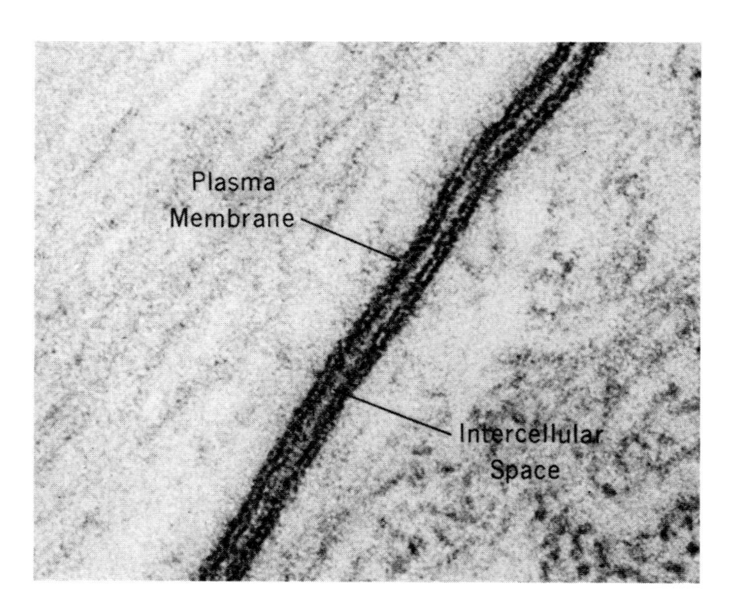

fig. 2-36. The intercellular space between two glial cells of an annelid, *Aphrodite.* Magnification 220,000. (From Fawcett, D. W. *An Atlas of Fine Structure.* Philadelphia: Saunders, 1966, p. 341.)

sequence of three specialized structures frequently is seen at the junction of adjacent epithelial cells near the free surface of the tissue facing a body cavity or the exterior. Nearest the free surface, the two cell membranes appear to fuse for a short distance, obliterating the intercellular space to form the *tight junction*. Adjacent to the tight junction is the *intermediary junction*, where the intercellular space is slightly widened and filled with low-density amorphous material; the adjacent cytoplasm often appears to have condensed into a dense, filamentous mat. Next in line is the *desmosome*. Here, there is a widening of the intercellular space, which contains a discoid structure. The inner line of the cell membrane is thickened and very dense, and a dense layer of filaments radiates into the adjoining cytoplasm. Taken together, the tight junction, intermediary junction, and desmosome represent the junctional complex, or *terminal bar*, observed by light microscopy (Fig. 2-37). Desmosomes, however, are not confined to junctional complexes but are widely distributed. At times the junctional complex is polarized, that is, it is not symmetric across the two adjacent cells. A junctional complex is thought to provide not only firmer adhesion between the two cells but also a barrier to the entry of substances from the exterior. On the other hand, desmosomes appear to be the sites of intercellular communications.

Cilia and *flagella* are long, hairlike, vibrating processes of cells which are continuous with the cell membrane at their bases. When the processes are few in number and long in proportion to the cell, they are called flagella, while when they are numerous and relatively short, they are called cilia. A unit membrane is found at the edge of the cilia. Light microscopists observed a single dense line in the center of flagella, which they called the *axial filament*. Ultrastructure studies using the electron microscope have disclosed the curious fact that almost all cilia and flagella throughout the animal and plant kingdoms possess a uniform pattern of internal fibrils, nine fibrils arranged in a circle around two central fibrils. This pattern of eleven fibrils is called the *axial filament complex* (Fig. 2-38). The retinal connecting cilium is an interesting exception;

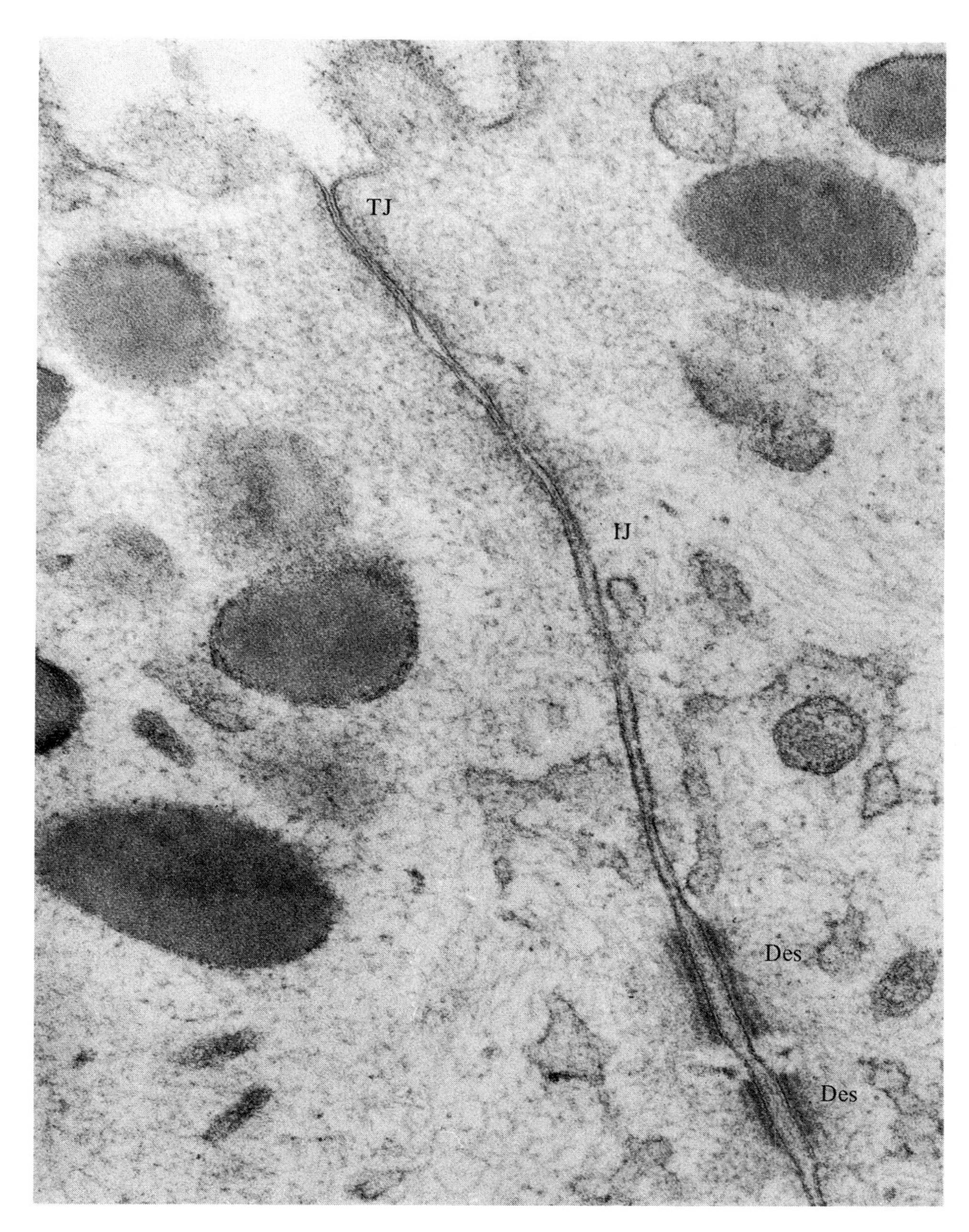

Fig. 2-37. The junctional complex between two epithelial cells in the gastric mucosa of the bat. The tight junction is labeled TJ; the intermediate junction, IJ; and the desmosomes, Des. Magnification 83,000. (Courtesy of Dr. Keith R. Porter.)

it has the nine circumferential fibrils, but the two central fibrils are missing. At the base of the axial filament complex is the *basal corpuscle*, which resembles a centriole (see above). It is thought that the basal corpuscles of cilia and flagella are formed by the reduplication of centrioles. The cilia beat in a direction perpendicular to an axis through the two central fibers.

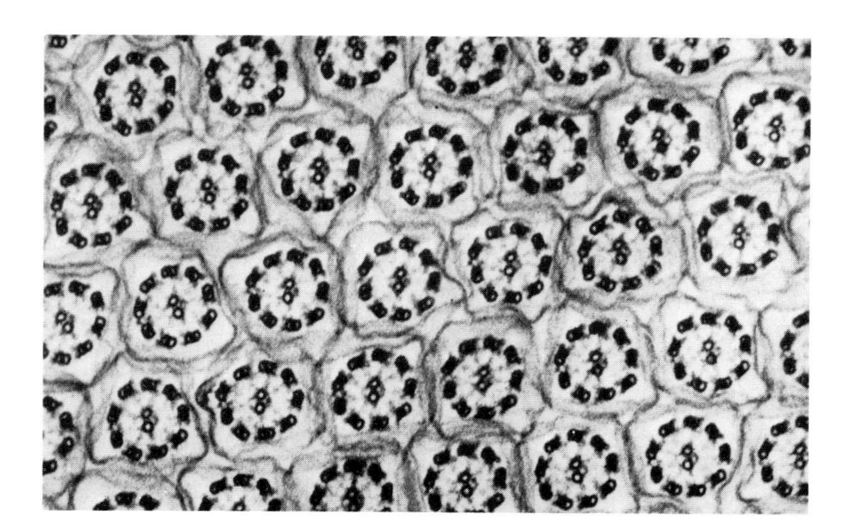

fig. 2-38. Lateral cilia from the gill of a mussel, *Anodonta cataracta.* Magnification 70,000. (From Gibbons, I. R. *J. Biophys. Biochem. Cytol., 11,* 183 [1961].)

Plant cells are surrounded by a *cell wall,* which is secreted by the cell. The cell wall is rather rigid but somewhat elastic, strong, and quite porous. It consists of an external, thin *primary wall* and a thicker, inner *secondary wall* (Fig. 2-39). The primary walls of two adjacent cells are often separated by the *middle lamella.* In the development of cell walls, the middle lamella is formed first. At the end of mitosis, material appears in the area of division between the daughter cells. Granules which increase in size and number continue to be secreted by the cells. The middle lamella is composed of viscous, gelatinous material which probably is principally calcium pectinate and which

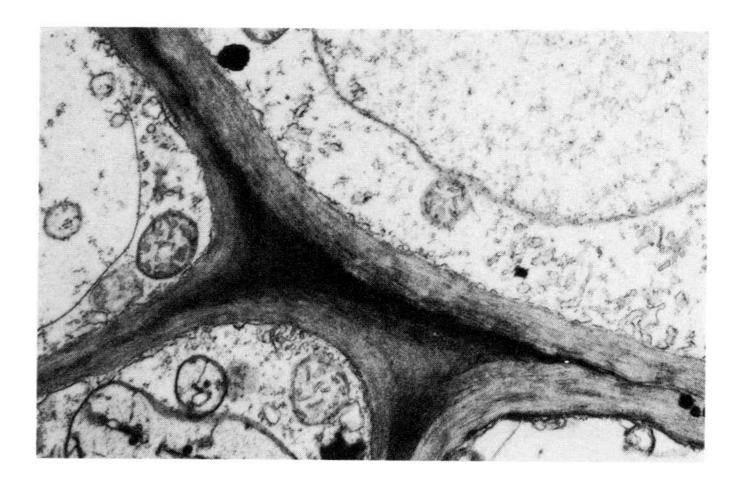

fig. 2-39. Cells from the developing phloem of *Robinia pseudo-acacia* showing the thick primary wall immediately surrounding the cells and the dense middle lamella lying between adjacent walls. At the lower right is a maturing sieve cell which has lost most of its protoplasm. Magnification 16,000. (Courtesy of Dr. Myron C. Ledbetter.)

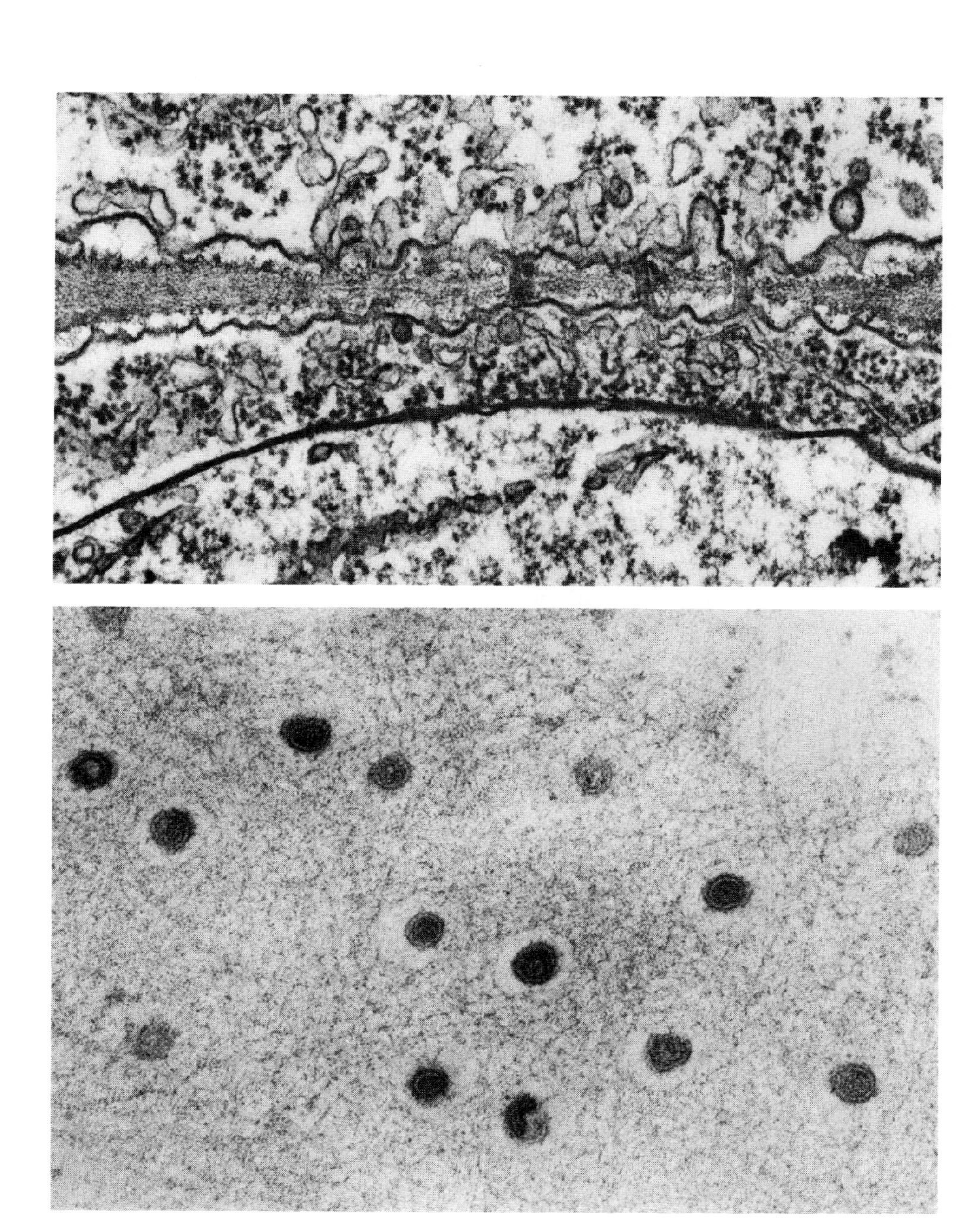

fig. 2-40. Plasmadesmata, continuities in the plasma membrane between adjacent cells showing the association of the smooth endoplasmic reticulum to these structures. Upper plate: longitudinal sections of plasmadesmata from a young wheat leaf. Magnification 24,000. Lower plate: transverse sections of plasmadesmata from the filament of the anther of wheat. Microfibrils of the cell wall can be seen around the plasmadesmata. Magnification 130,000. (Courtesy of Dr. Myron C. Ledbetter.)

stains with ruthenium red, a characteristic reaction of pectins. The primary wall, which is subsequently secreted against the middle lamella, consists of intertwined cellulose fibers. The cellulose is laid down in layers of parallel fibers. In successive layers, the fiber direction shifts through 120°, so that the orientation is the same in every fourth layer.

At first the primary wall is rather plastic and able to extend as the cell grows, but as more cellulose is deposited, it becomes increasingly rigid. In cells with a relatively thick cell wall, a secondary cell wall is secreted between the cell and the primary wall. The secondary wall contains cellulose, pectins and other noncellulose polysaccharides, and lignin, a phenolic polymer which endows wood with its hardness and mechanical rigidity. The outer surfaces of epidermal cells, for example in leaves, may have a *cuticle* rich in fats and waxes, which tends to limit water loss.

Most plant cells have thin areas in the cell wall called *pits*. Many pits appear to have very small pores, through which delicate strands of cytoplasm, *plasmadesmata* (Fig. 2-40), form bridges between adjacent protoplasts. Although the cell walls are quite porous and water and various solutes freely penetrate them, the plasmadesmata form much more intimate intercellular connections.

cell adhesion

While the numerous cells that make up a complex organism operate to some degree as independent individuals, it is clearly necessary that they also act in concert. Before considering the morphological aspects of cell aggregation for the formation of tissues and organs, let us consider some of the more intimate aspects of cellular association, even though our understanding of these phenomena is very sketchy. Cellular association can be examined from several points of view. First, one might inquire into the forces and mechanisms at work in the adhesion of cells to surfaces in general and to other cells in particular. Second, there is the question of cellular associations and the mechanisms of recognition. Last, there is the question of when cells migrate and where they go.

In the previous section, it was noted that adjacent cells are usually separated by a uniform gap of 150 to 200 Å. In places, adjacent cells appear to have structural connections, sometimes consisting of entire junctional complexes or, more frequently, of isolated desmosomes. In addition to the structural connections, physical surface forces appear to play an important role in cellular adhesion. These forces, collectively referred to as weak molecular interactions, will be considered in greater detail in Chapter 3. The action of these forces can be demonstrated by, for example, the rise in temperature which occurs when a solid is wetted by a liquid. Thus, when aluminum powder is added to water, the temperature of the suspension rises dramatically. Where appreciable weak molecular interactions exist across a phase boundary, there is a lowering of surface tension, which is called "wettability" in everyday language. Cell surfaces bear a net negative charge. The coloumbic forces which occur when two cells approach closely are repulsive. The distance of cell separation, about 200 Å, probably represents the distance at which the attractive weak molecular interactions are just offset by the repulsive forces.

When two surfaces are in contact, the degree of adhesion is a function of the relative fit. One of the ways in which glues increase adhesion is by filling in the empty spaces which result from slight unevenness, thereby increasing the area of contact between two surfaces. Glues also tend to prevent separation if they are very viscous. It has been tempting to surmise that the intercellular gap is filled with a cement. The presence of an intercellular substance seems likely,[12] even though recent attempts to isolate it have not been successful. It probably does not just act as a mechanical glue. The material is most likely a polyelectrolyte present in colloidal solution. While a detailed consideration of the properties of colloidal polyelectrolytes is postponed to a later section, it is worth noting some general effects. Increasing the ionic strength, decreasing the *p*H, or using cations with higher valence in the bathing medium all tend to increase cell adhesion. Proteolytic enzymes, which might degrade a protein intercellular cement substance, reduce adhesiveness, while phospholipases are without effect. The addition of certain proteins, which tend to lower the effective negative surface charge of cells, increases adhesion. A number of observations indicate that there is a real space between cells. For example, large molecules, such as hemoglobin, can diffuse freely between cells in the living animal,[13] and Ambrose and Jones[14] have determined by interference microscopy that a definite gap exists between the surface of cells and a glass slide upon which they are placed.

For the living cell, the process of adhesion appears to have a component of active participation in addition. Cells can be observed to spread on the surface of glass slides in a stepwise manner as the apparent result of rhythmic, undulating pulses across the cell surface. It has been proposed that the cell surface is, in fact, corrugated, and thus makes only intermittent contacts with surfaces.[15] Cells move along surfaces partly as a result of these undulating movements and partly as a result of pseudopod formation. Pseudopods appear to form particularly strong adhesions. When cells make secure contact with a surface, pseudopod formation and the undulations of the cell surface disappear. This phenomenon is called *contact inhibition*.[16] It may be that the active phenomena are important for cell adhesion over short periods of time, while the physical interactions described above result in more stable, long-term adhesion.

One aspect of cellular interactions that attracts immediate attention is the specificity which is frequently manifested. Like cells tend to associate. This is particularly apparent in embryonic development. In fact, cells dissociated from embryonic chick tissues and injected into the blood stream of host embryos almost invariably come to rest in the proper organ.[17] Similarly, when two types of dissociated embryonic cells are mixed, they will tend to reassociate according to type.[18] The remarkable specificity of cell association is also demonstrated in wound healing.

For a time, it was thought that the specificity of cellular association was based on an immunological mechanism, that is, that it resembled an antigen-antibody reaction. This explanation was based primarily on the tendency of mixtures of sponge cells or slime mold cells from different variants to separate and reaggregate according to the variant or species from which they were derived.[19] However, immunological agglutination reactions tend to be highly specific and very stable, while mixtures of heterologous cells tend to separate and reaggregate in homogeneous groups by what appears to be a trial-and-error process. There has not been any direct demonstration of an

---

[12] Moscona, A. A. *J. Cellular Comp. Physiol.*, *60*, suppl. 1, 65 (1962); Steinberg, M. *Exptl. Cell Res.*, *30*, 257 (1963).
[13] Miller, F. *J. Biophys. Biochem. Cytol.*, *9*, 157 (1961).
[14] Ambrose, E. J. *Rec. Progr. Surface Sci.*, *1*, 338 (1964).
[15] Abercrombie, M., and Ambrose, E. J. *Cancer Res.*, *22*, 525 (1962).
[16] Abercrombie, M. *Exptl. Cell Res.*, suppl. 8, 188 (1961).
[17] Weiss, P., and Andres, G. *J. Exptl. Zool.*, *121*, 449 (1952).
[18] Moscona, A. *Proc. Natl. Acad. Sci.*, *43*, 184 (1957).
[19] Spiegel, M. *Biol. Bull.*, *107*, 130 (1954); Elbers, P. F. *Rec. Progr. Surface Sci.*, *2*, 443 (1964).

antigen-antibody reaction. More recent theories of cell recognition hypothesize structural patterns on the cell surface of a more subtle variety which lead to somewhat increased intermolecular forces between homologous cells.[20] These theories propose a uniqueness of the mosaic of proteins in the cell surface for various cell types. Association occurs by recognition of an identical pattern by like cells. Weak intermolecular forces will be greater between two surfaces that are complementary for the arrangement of donor and receptor hydrogen bonding sites, etc.

Cell movement is an integral part of the development of complex organisms. After observing developing nerve fibers, P. Weiss[21] concluded that growth is directed by mechanical factors, in addition to chemotaxis. These ideas have been further developed by Abercrombie and his coworkers,[22] who believe that the most important mechanical factors are related to the phenomenon of contact inhibition. They observed that fibroblasts move randomly in an amoeboid fashion but react to contact with other cells by moving away. When confronted by a sheet of cells, the fibroblasts come to a standstill. Mesenchymal cells in adult organisms are continually migrating. Leucocytes often leave blood capillaries, pushing their way between the epithelial cells of the capillary wall, a process called *diapedesis* (Fig. 2-41). The extreme instance of freedom

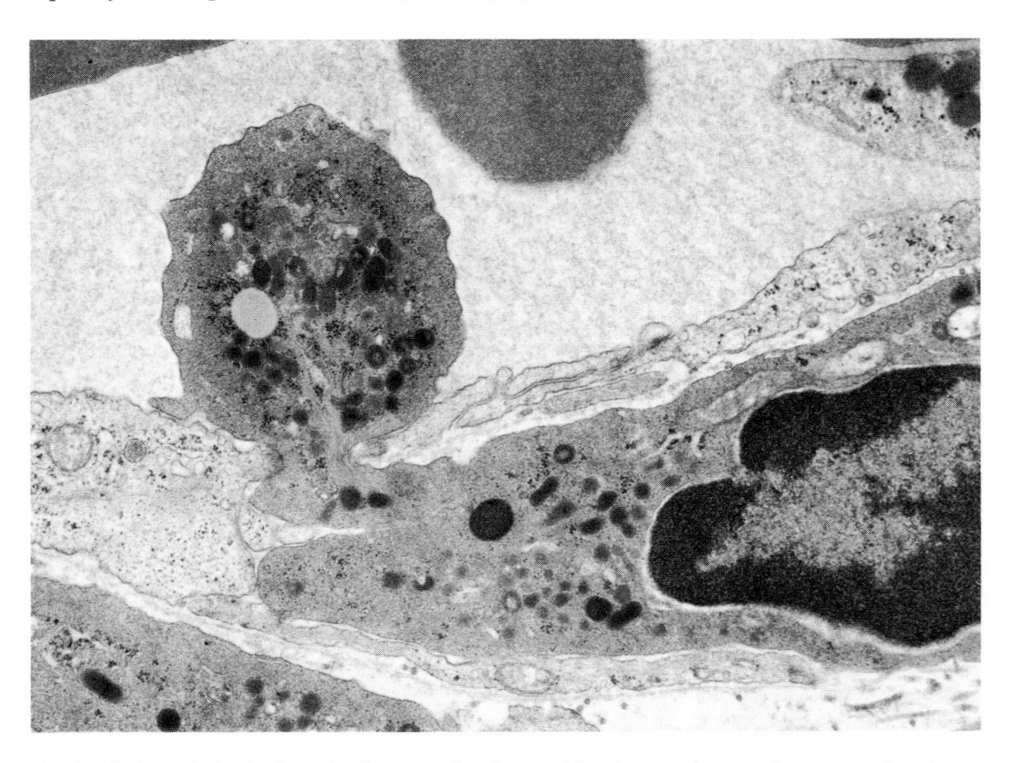

fig. 2-41. Venule in the leg of a Sprague-Dawley rat 10 minutes after gentle trauma, showing a polymorphonuclear leucocyte penetrating the vessel wall between two endothelial cells, a second leucocyte lying between two laminae of epithelium which have been forced apart, and a third leucocyte (lower right-hand corner) which lies below the epithelium. Magnification 23,000. (Courtesy of Dr. Thomas P. Ashford.)

[20] Steinberg, M. S. *Am. Naturalist*, *92*, 68 (1958).

[21] Weiss, P. *J. Exptl. Zool.*, *68*, 393 (1934); Weiss, P., and Garber, B. *Proc. Natl. Acad. Sci.*, *38*, 264 (1952).

[22] Abercrombie, M., Heaysman, J. E. M., and Karthauser, H. M. *Exptl. Cell Res.*, *13*, 276 (1957).

of cell movement in adult organisms is, of course, the cancer cells. These cells are patently invasive of other tissues. A high degree of amoeboid movement is characteristic of malignant cells in tissue culture.[23] The mutual adhesiveness of cells in a malignant growth is much less than the mutual adhesiveness of cells in the parent tissue. Cancer cells also appear to have a greater negative charge density on their surfaces than the cells of the parent tissues.[24]

Calcium and other divalent cations appear to play an important role in cellular adhesion. The embryonic cells of sea urchin blastomeres disperse in calcium-free sea water. Perfusion of vertebrate organs with calcium-chelating agents permits easy dispersion of the cells. Similarly, the adhesion of cultured cells to glass appears to depend upon the presence of calcium. Malignant tissue often appears to have significantly less calcium than its normal counterpart. Yet the mode and site of action of calcium is still unknown. Perhaps calcium forms bridges between anionic sites on macromolecules. Calcium is very effective in forming pectate gels by this mechanism. Also, divalent cations are very effective in reducing the effective surface potentials and may act by reducing the electrostatic repulsive forces, thereby permitting a closer approach by adjacent cells.

tissues

In most complex organisms, cells differentiate into various forms. Cells of a given type which all perform similar functions are found together in large numbers in structures called *tissues*, which in turn are assembled in functional units called *organs*. The cells in a tissue are surrounded by *extracellular fluid*, from which they acquire nutrients and oxygen and into which they deposit wastes and carbon dioxide. The term *tissu*, which is derived from a Greek word meaning "a woven material" and was sometimes used to designate a particularly rich cloth, was introduced by M. F. X. Bichat (1771–1802) and later used by Richard Owen (1844). At first the term was applied to the loose areolar tissue which fills the spaces between closely packed cells of various organs. Later the term was extended to aggregations of various cell types, each of which tends to present a specific appearance and texture.

The variety of cell types in a fully developed organism arises through progressive differentiation from the primitive cells of the embryo. Particularly in higher organisms, development proceeds through a complex series of processes in which cell division is accompanied by cell migration; by cell aggregation with the formation of masses, sheets, or cords of cells; by the folding of cell layers; by cavitation; and by a variety of rearrangements, so that the origin of a given cell type in the adult organism is not always immediately apparent. At times the circuitous development of some organs can be understood in terms of von Baer's *law of recapitulation*, which was epitomized in Haeckel's dictum (1866), "ontogeny recapitulates phylogeny," that is to say, the development of an individual complex animal reflects, in part, its evolutionary development.

Epithelium consists of sheets of cells which closely abut against each other. The face which the organism presents to the environment, either external or internal, usually is lined with epithelial cells. Thus, the skin and the lining of the gastrointestinal tract are epithelium. Other hollow organs and secretory glands are also lined with epithelium.

---

[23] Coman, D. R. *Cancer Res.*, *13*, 397 (1953).
[24] Purdom, L., Ambrose, E. J., and Klein, G. *Nature*, *181*, 1586 (1958).

The cells may be flat (squamous), cuboidal, or columnar, and may be single-layered (simple epithelium), or multilayered (stratified epithelium) like that of the skin. Epithelial cells in various organs may arise from any of the three embryonic germ layers: ectoderm, mesoderm, or endoderm. The ectoderm proper keeps its epithelial character, giving rise to the epidermis, to the lining of the oral cavity, and to parts of sense organs. The endoderm gives rise to the epithelial lining of the gastrointestinal tract and respiratory tract and the glands associated with these organ systems. Epithelium of mesodermal origin is found in the urinary and genital tracts and the linings of the peritoneal, pleural, and pericardial cavities of the body.

In a hollow organ (Fig. 2-42), the epithelium may be surrounded by a layer of *muscle fibers*. In the gastrointestinal tract, for example, the muscle fibers are responsible

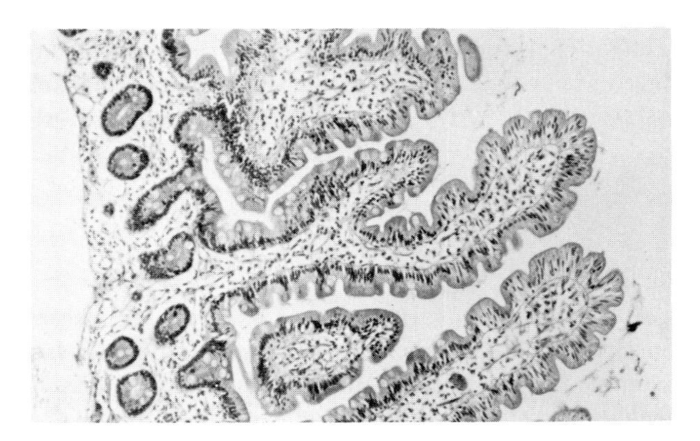

Fig. 2.42. Human duodenum, biopsy specimen, showing the villi lined with columnar epithelial cells among which are occasional pale, goblet-shaped mucus-secreting cells. In the connective tissue in the center of the villi are capillaries. At the base of the crypts of Lieberkühn between the villi, the epithelial cells are proliferating rapidly. The biopsy has been stripped off the muscularis layer on which the tissue rested. Magnification 200.

for the peristaltic activity which propels the contents along its length as digestion proceeds. Within the epithelial layer, some of the cells may have specialized functions; for instance, there are mucus-secreting cells in the intestinal mucosa and acid-secreting cells in the gastric mucosa. The blood vessels and nerves to the organ enter from the outer surface, over which they ramify by successive divisions to supply every part of the organ.

Connective tissue is mesodermal in origin and penetrates into organs to provide structural integrity; in a loose form, it fills in the spaces between the organs. The bulk of connective tissue is made up of intercellular *collagen fibers* and *elastic fibers* embedded in amorphous *ground substance*, while cells are relatively few. The collagen fibers are very flexible but offer considerable resistance to pulling forces. The brilliant, highly refractive elastic fibers yield to stretching but resume their former length when released. The ground substance stains metachromatically with dyes such as toluidine blue and appears to contain large amounts of mucopolysaccharide material. Within the connective tissue are undifferentiated mesenchymal cells, fibroblasts, macrophages, pigment cells, fat cells, lymphoid cells, and other cell types.

Three types of muscle tissue are found in higher organisms. Smooth muscle is found in the walls of the gut, of blood vessels, and in sphincters of various ducts. The cells are spindle-shaped and contain one or a few nuclei. Skeletal muscle, as one might guess, is attached to parts of the skeleton and is used for purposeful movement. It is composed of cylindrical cells with alternate light and dark bands, the *cross striations*, which give it a striped appearance. Cardiac muscle is composed of cell units that have specialized boundaries, the *intercalated discs*, which makes this type of structure a functional *syncytium*.

Neurons (Fig. 2-43), the functional cells of the nervous system, differ from other cells in that they possess long processes which are involved in the transmisson of nerve impulses. The processes which carry impulses toward the nerve-cell body are called *dendrites*, while those which carry impulses away from the nerve-cell body are called *axons*. Axons are usually longer than dendrities, although they tend to be less complex in their arborization. Axons can reach a length of several feet.

Blood (Fig. 2-44) consists of a dense suspension of individual cells in extracellular

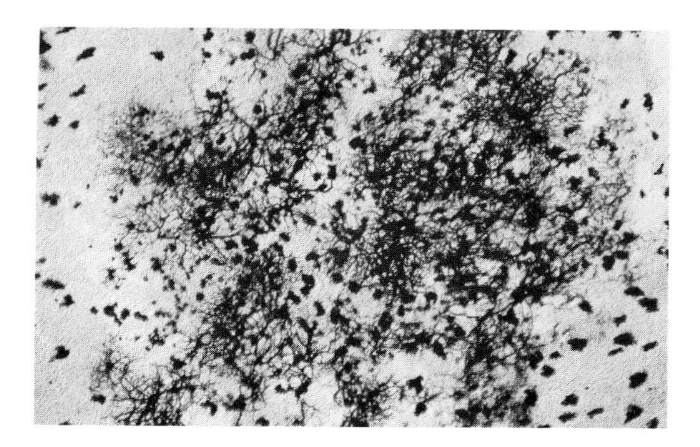

fig. 2-43. Cat cerebellum, silver impregnation, showing cell bodies and many of the cell processes. Magnification 150. (Courtesy of Dr. Joel Brown.)

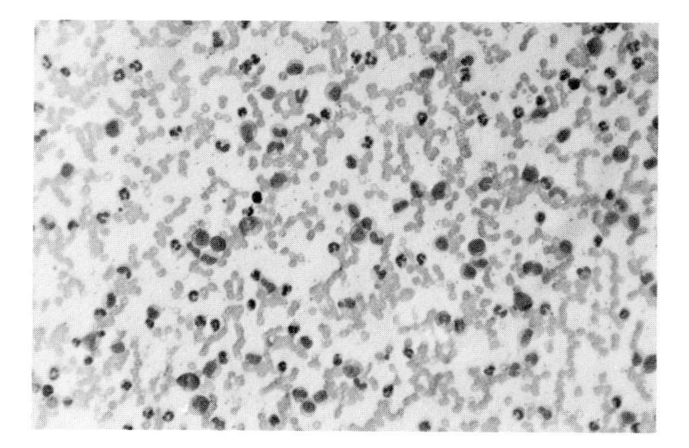

fig. 2-44. Smear of blood from a patient with myelocytic leukemia. In addition to (1) the polymorphonuclear leucocytes with lobulated nuclei and (2) lymphocytes, larger nucleated cells are seen which are immature forms. Magnification 330.

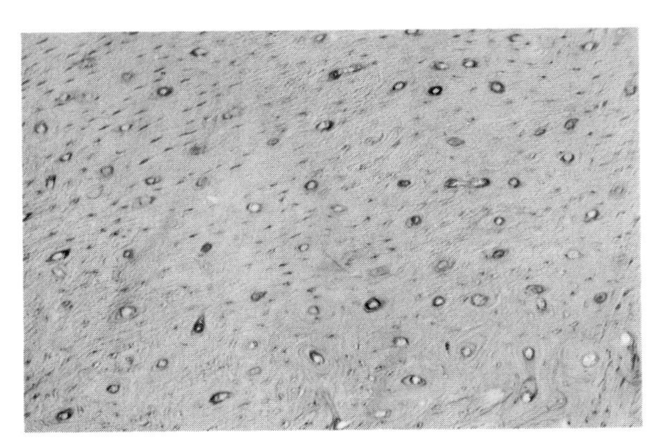

fig. 2-45. Bone, decalcified, showing cells and the Haversian canals, and the deposition of bone in lamellae. Magnification 200.

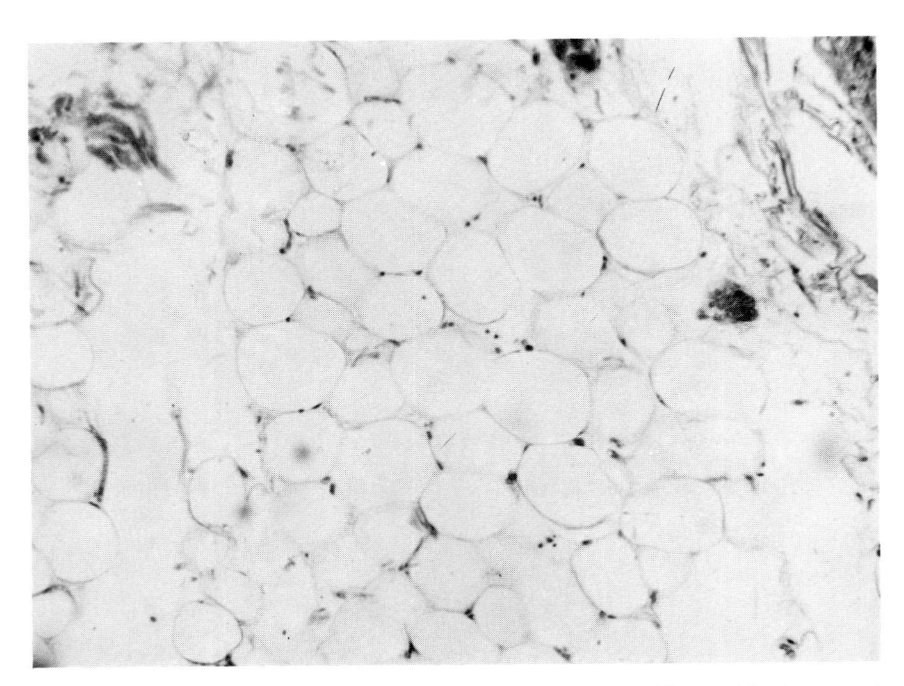

fig. 2-46. Areolar fat. The cytoplasm and nucleus are squeezed into a thin rim around the periphery of cell by the fat, giving the cell the appearance of a signet ring. Magnification 300.

fluid. The cells, which amount to about 45 percent of the volume, consist of three main types in vertebrates. The *erythrocytes*, or red blood cells, contain large amounts of hemoglobin and are charged with the function of transporting oxygen to the peripheral tissues. In lower vertebrates, the erythrocytes are large and nucleated. In mammals, mature erythrocytes lose their nuclei and assume the shape of biconcave discs, approximately 8 μ in diameter. There are about 5×10^6 erythrocytes per cubic millimeter in human blood. There are several types of white blood cells or *leucocytes*. The *polymorphonuclear leucocytes* have nuclei constricted in one or more places, dividing them into two or more lobes. A small projection may be seen from some of the nuclei, the *Barr body*. The Barr body is seen only in cells from female individuals and is thought to contain a segregated X chromosome. Tiny, lightly basophilic granules are present in the cytoplasm. The *eosinophilic leucocytes* resemble polymorphonuclear leucocytes except that the cytoplasm contains large, brightly eosinophilic granules. Normally, the eosinophilic leucocytes comprise 1 to 2 percent of the total leucocytes, but in allergic or immune responses, they may increase to 10 to 20 percent. The *lymphocytes* are smaller cells, about 5 to 8 μ in diameter, with a large, densely staining nucleus surrounded by a thin rim of cytoplasm. The *mononuclear leucocytes* are large cells, about 20 μ in diameter, with an eccentrically placed oval- or crescent-shaped nucleus, surrounded by an abundant, pale cytoplasm largely devoid of granules. All types of white blood cells taken together usually amount to 8×10^3 per cubic millimeter in human blood. Lastly, there are the *platelets*, small nonnucleated cells that play an important role in blood clotting.

Bone (Fig. 2-45) contains relatively few cells in a complex matrix in which calcium salts, mainly hydroxyapatite, are deposited. The insoluble calcium salts are in equilibrium with the dissolved ions in the extracellular fluid. Numerous blood vessels and nerves ramify through bone. Often, blood vessels are surrounded by concentric lamellae of bone, forming the *Haversian canals*.

Adipose cells (Fig. 2-46) make up the fat of the organism. They consist of a thin layer of cytoplasm surrounding a huge fat droplet. The cell nucleus is squeezed to one side, giving adipose cells an appearance which resembles a signet ring. The amount of fat, of course, depends on the nutritional status of the animal.

The complex organism includes other highly organized organs and tissues, including the nervous system and its specialized appendages, the kidney, the lung, the various glands, and the blood-forming tissue. The organization of some of these will be discussed later as an introduction to considering their function. The preceding figures (2-42 through 2-46) illustrate the organization of some organs and tissues and show the variety of cell types from a strictly morphological point of view.

composition of cells

Water is far and away the most abundant constituent of cells; it accounts for 75 to 85 percent of their total weight. It acts as a solvent for many of the cellular constituents and as a dispersion medium for the colloidal suspension of others. Water not only serves as the medium in which most metabolic reactions take place; it also takes part in many of them either as a reactant or by providing hydrogen or hydroxyl ions. Water is an end product of cellular metabolism, and the water so produced results in a small net efflux of water from cells. While some of the intracellular water is "bound" to proteins and other cellular constituents, it does not appear to be compartmentalized. It is known from microinjection studies that injected solutions quickly diffuse to all parts of the cell. By virtue of its high coefficient of specific heat, water acts as a sort of temperature buffer, minimizing sudden changes in temperature.

Inorganic salts are a vital constituent of all cells (Fig. 2-47) and are present in such quantities that the total concentration of salts is about 200 mEq/L. Potassium and magnesium are the most abundant intracellular cations, and smaller amounts of sodium and calcium are present. The most abundant intracellular anions are phosphate, bicarbonate and organic anions, proteins, and metabolic intermediates such as lactate. In contrast to the composition of the intracellular phase, the extracellular fluid contains

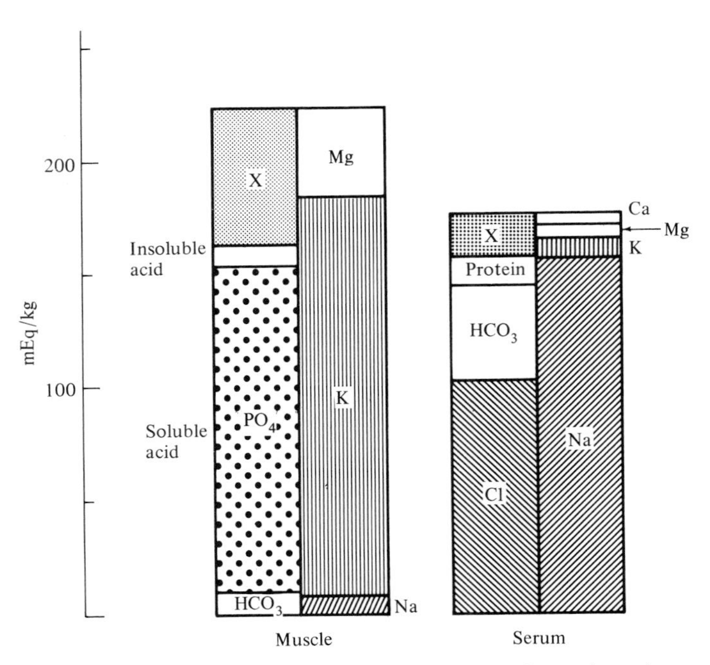

fig. 2-47. Ionic composition of mammalian skeletal muscle and blood serum.

large concentrations of sodium and chloride and small concentrations of potassium, magnesium, and phosphate. It is noteworthy that the ionic composition of the extracellular fluid bears a marked similarity to that of ocean water. Many scientists have made the conjecture that when marine organisms became land animals, principally in the Cambrian period, they brought with them a *milieu intérieur*, blood and extracellular fluid, that resembled the ancient ocean in its composition. A proper proportion of potassium, sodium, magnesium, and calcium ions is necessary in both the extracellular and intracellular fluids for cellular function and viability. Cellular irritability and contractility are particularly sensitive to slight abnormalities in the concentrations of these ions, and larger abnormalities in cation concentrations may result in the death of higher animals because of cessation of cardiac contraction. The heart may stop beating either in a state of relaxation or in a maintained contraction, depending upon the nature of the cation abnormality. Within the cell, a relatively high concentration of sodium ions is found in the nucleus. Sodium appears to be necessary for some specific nuclear biochemical reactions.[25] Cells contain a number of inorganic constituents in minor or trace quantities, among them iron, manganese, copper, iodine, vanadium, zinc, cobalt, nickel, molybdenum, and cadmium. Most of these trace elements are required as cofactors for enzymes which catalyze essential metabolic reactions.

Organic matter constitutes 15 to 20 percent of the cell weight (Figs. 2-48 and 2-49). About 85 percent of the organic matter is in the form of macromolecules. DNA makes up about 0.3 percent of the cell weight. The exceptions are anucleate cells, such as the mature mammalian erythrocyte and platelets, which contain no DNA, and sperm,

[25] Allfrey, V. G., Meudt, R., Hopkins, J. W., and Mirsky, A. E. *Proc. Natl. Acad. Sci.*, *47*, 907, 1961.

fig. 2-48. Composition of rat cells. (Data from Campbell, R. M., and Kosterlitz, H. W. *J. Physiol., 106,* 13 P [1947]; Altman, P. L., and Dittmer, D. S., in *Biology Data Book.* Washington, D.C.: Federation of American Societies for Experimental Biology, 1964.)

SUBSTANCE	LIVER PERCENT	CARDIAC MUSCLE PERCENT	SKELETAL MUSCLE PERCENT
Water	69.0	78.0	75.0
DNA	0.2	1.0	0.3
RNA	1.0	1.5	1.0
Protein	16.4	8.5	7.6
Phospholipids	3.1	2.0	1.8
Neutral lipids	1.6	4.6	9.0
Glycogen	3.4	3.2	4.3
Other materials	5.3	0.8	1.2

fig. 2-49. Composition of a myxomycete protoplast. (Data from Lepeshkin, V. V. *Kolloidchemie des Protoplasmas.* Berlin: Springer, 1924.)

SUBSTANCE	PERCENT OF TOTAL DRY MATTER
Soluble sugars	14.2
Soluble nitrogenous compounds	24.3
Proteins	2.2
Inorganic substances	4.4
Nucleoprotein	32.3
Nucleotides	2.5
Lipoprotein	4.8
Neutral lipids	6.8
Phospholipids	1.3
Other materials	9.0

where DNA comprises more than half the total cell solids. DNA carries the genetic information for protein synthesis and, therefore, occupies a central position in cellular organization and function. Upon experimental enucleation of cells by microsurgery, using protozoa or tissue-cultured cells, for example, protein synthesis ceases and after a time the cell dies. Replacement of the nucleus before death restores the vital processes. There are some viruses, such as the poliomyelitis and tobacco mosaic, that are devoid of DNA but instead contain RNA. Almost all the DNA is in the nucleus; a small amount is found in mitochondria and chloroplasts. In the nucleus, the DNA is closely associated with basic proteins, histones, or protamines. RNA makes up about 0.7 percent of the cell weight. It is found in the nucleolus, in the ribosomes, and to some extent free in the cytoplasm and nuclear ground substance.

Proteins constitute the bulk of the organic material and the bulk of the macromolecules found in cells; they amount to 12 to 14 percent of the cell weight. The word protein literally means "of the first importance." Proteins are responsible for cellular structure and for many of the physical and chemical properties of protoplasm. With the exception of bacteria, intracellular proteins can also be degraded and catabolized for the production of energy. Proteins are not only highly specific polymers, in which the sequence of the 20 constituent amino acids is duplicated exactly for each protein molecule of a given type, but they also have highly specific three-dimensional arrangements of their atoms. Of course, not all 20 amino acids are present in all proteins. While many of the physical and chemical properties of proteins result from their three-dimensional configuration (secondary and tertiary structure), it is now generally believed that the three-dimensional configuration is a direct consequence of the sequence of amino acids in the protein molecule. Some proteins (the globular ones) are soluble in water or dilute salt solutions, while others (the fibrous proteins and scleroproteins) are not. The globular proteins probably are found in solution in the cell, while the insoluble proteins are the structural proteins making up the cell membranes and various cellular organelles and inclusions. An important unsolved physiological problem is how the insoluble structural proteins move from the ribosomes, where they are synthesized, to the organelles, where they are found in a highly organized structure. Both the globular and the insoluble proteins possess enzymatic activity; that is, they catalize the metabolic reactions of the cell. Some enzymes, although they are globular, soluble proteins after they have been extracted from the cell and purified, seem to be firmly attached to a cellular organelle in vivo. Certain proteins may be firmly associated with nucleic acids, with lipids, or with carbohydrates, and are known as nucleoproteins, lipoproteins, or glycoproteins, respectively. The physical and chemical properties of an intact lipoprotein, for example, are usually very different from those of the protein portion alone after the lipid has been dissociated.

Cells usually contain a variable amount of polysaccharide macromolecules such as starch and glycogen, the former in plant cells and the latter in animal cells. These polysaccharides are segregated in insoluble granules in the cell and serve as a food reserve, which can be degraded in times of need for energy production. In addition, cells synthesize a variety of other polysaccharides. Some of these are the type-specific blood group antigens; polysaccharides that form the basement membrane and intercellular ground substance; cellulose, which forms the cell walls of plant cells; pectins and related intercellular materials found in plants; polysaccharides that together with proteins make up the mucoproteins which coat the gastrointestinal tract and are present in other glandular secretions; and chitin, a polyacetylglucosamine, which makes up the exoskeleton of arthropods (crustaceans, insects, spiders, etc.).

A final 0.5 percent of the cell weight is a very large variety of low-molecular-weight organic compounds. Included in this group are all purines, pyrimidines, amino acids, and sugars, the monomeric building blocks of the nucleic acids, the proteins, and the polysaccharides. In addition, there are a large variety of fatty acids, lipids, and steroids; vitamins and cofactors for various enzymes; and a large variety of metabolic intermediates. Many of the small organic molecules are present in the cell in ionized form, usually as anions.

cell fractionation

One of the main objects of cell physiology is the biochemical characterization of the cellular organelles or, stated conversely, the assignment of a cellular location to the various molecular constituents. Cell fractionation has proven to be a potent technique for obtaining such information. Although electrophoresis, phase partition, and chromatography have been used successfully on rare occasions to separate cellular components, the method almost always employed is differential centrifugation, in which the cellular components are separated according to differences in the sedimentation rates or differences in their densities. The first step in cell fractionation is the homogenization of a cell suspension or of a solid tissue suspended in a liquid medium. This is done by means of a grinder with a clearance between the pestle and tube of such dimensions that almost all the cells are disrupted with but minimal damage to the cellular components. The cell homogenate obtained in this way is then subjected to one of two types of procedures. It may be layered on a solution with a density gradient and, after centrifugation until equilibrium, the gradient is divided into fractions. This procedure separates the intracellular components according to their density. Alternatively, the cellular homogenate is subjected to a series of centrifugations, each successive centrifugation having a greater force-time product. The various sediments and the final supernate constitute the fractions separated according to their sedimentation rates.

Centrifugation, of course, produces forces much greater than gravity. The centrifugal force, expressed as a multiple of gravity (980 cm/sec^2), is given by

$$G = \omega^2 r = \left(\frac{2\pi \text{ rpm}}{60}\right)^2 r \qquad (2\text{-}1)$$

where ω is the angular velocity in radians per second, r is the distance from the center of revolution, and rpm is the number of revolutions per minute. Under the influence of a centrifugal force, particles that differ in density (or in shape or size) will sediment at different rates. The time in seconds required for a spherical particle to move from the top of a centrifuge tube to the bottom is given by

$$t = \frac{9}{2} \frac{\eta}{\omega^2 r_p^2(\delta_p - \delta)} \ln \frac{r_t}{r_b} \qquad (2\text{-}2)$$

where r_p is the radius of the particle, r_t and r_b are the distances from the center of revolution to the top and bottom of the centrifuge tube, respectively, η is the viscosity of the medium, and δ_p and δ are the densities of the particles and of the suspending medium. Thus, at a constant rotor speed, the time required to sediment spherical particles is inversely proportional to the difference between their density and that of the suspending medium, directly proportional to the viscosity of the medium, and inversely proportional to the square of their radius. For nonspherical particles, the sedimentation time increases as their asymmetry increases. A typical fractionation scheme is outlined in Fig. 2-50. The major cell components are sedimented in the following order: nuclei first, then mitochondria, lysosomes, and microsomes. A supernatant fraction remains after very high-speed centrifugation which contains materials in solution in the cytoplasm.

It should be noted again that most animal tissues contain several types of cells, and the intracellular components isolated from them are heterogenous. In rat liver which has not been perfused with saline or sucrose, erythrocytes in the blood vessels amount to approximately 10 percent of the gross weight, and in mouse liver they amount to 15 percent. In addition to the hepatic parenchymal cells, there are Kupfer cells (reticuloendothelial cells), epithelial cells of blood vessels and biliary system ducts, and small numbers of miscellaneous cells, including smooth muscle and fibroblasts. The hepatic parenchymal cells themselves are a heterogeneous population which differ in

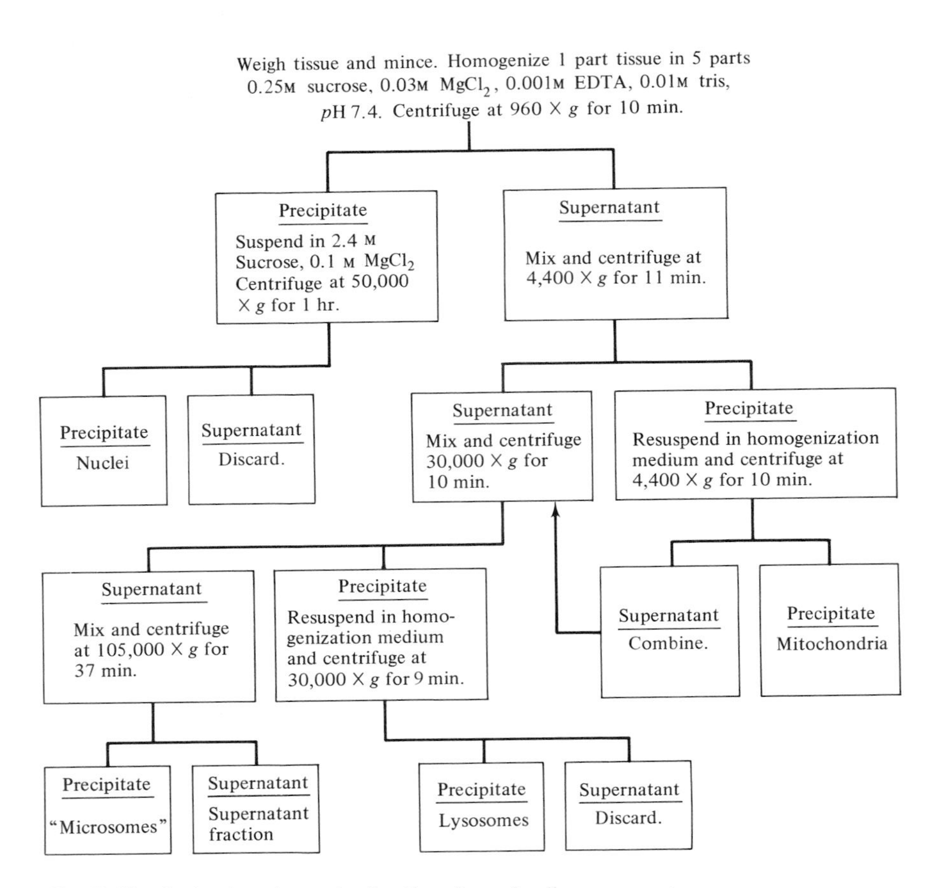

fig. 2-50. A simple scheme for fractionation of cell components.

the content of chromosomes, glycogen, lipid, etc. This fact should be borne in mind when assessing data on cell-component composition.

The composition, ionic strength or osmolarity, and *p*H of the suspension medium are important in the final appearance and functional integrity of the components finally isolated. If the cells are suspended and homogenized in an aqueous medium, water-soluble materials are extracted from the nuclei and cytoplasmic organelles. Isotonic sucrose (0.25 to 0.32 M) appears to be a particularly good medium for suspension and homogenization. The sucrose seems to result in greater functional integrity than isotonic salt solutions of NaCl, potassium phosphate, etc. Binary organic mixtures are used sometimes; for example, benzene-carbon tetrachloride or cyclohexane-carbon tetrachloride.

In the original technique described by Albert Claude[26] the fractions were examined by electron microscopy and on this basis were divided into nuclei and unbroken cells, mitochondria, microsomes, and cell sap. It has been found subsequently that Occam's razor has been applied to the intracellular localization of most enzymes; that is, most enzymes are associated with a single cellular component or are present in solution in the cell sap. Conversely, it appears that all granules of a singular cellular component have the same enzymatic composition. For example, nicotinamide-

[26] Claude, A. *J. Exptl. Med.*, *84*, 51, 61 (1946).

mononucleotide-adenyltransferase has been found essentially only in the nuclear fraction; cytochrome oxidase has been found essentially only in the mitochondrial fraction; glucose-6-phosphatase has been found essentially only in the microsomal fraction; and aldolase only in the remaining supernatant fraction after very high-speed centrifugation. Some minor cellular components were discovered because of the anomalous distribution of some enzymes upon cell fractionation, coupled with the hypothesis that they were localized in a singular cellular component and acted as a label for it. Thus, the anomalous pattern for acid phosphatase led to the discovery of the lysosomes, and the anomalous pattern for urate oxidase, catalase, and D-amino acid oxidase led to the discovery of the microbodies. It appears, therefore, that the homogeneity and composition of a fraction can be determined not only from its morphology in the electron microscope but also from the enzymatic activity it shows. There are, of course, enzymes that are found in more than one cell fraction. In some cases, however, the finding of a given enzymatic activity in two cellular fractions has been shown to result from two different but homologous enzymes, each located in a different cell component, as for example in the case of malate dehydrogenase in ox heart[27] and aspartate aminotransferase in rat liver.[28] The intracellular location of a given enzyme may vary from the cells of one tissue to those of another. Thus, aconitate hydratase is found in the high-speed supernatant fraction of liver but in the mitochondria of brain.[29] It should be noted that binding of soluble enzymes to organelles may cause misleading results.

In the course of cell-fractionation experiments, it became apparent that many enzymes associated with cellular organelles behave as though they were partially masked. Some enzymes, such as chymotrypsin and thrombin, are present as inactive zymogens. Many other enzymes could be liberated from the insoluble structured organelle and solubilized by treatment with detergents. An increase in apparent enzymatic activity was frequently found to accompany the solubilization of such enzymes. About 80 percent of acid phosphatase activity is not apparent in a rat liver lysosomal fraction until it is treated with 0.02 percent final concentration digitonin, a surface-active steroid. Similarly, 80 percent of the catalase activity of a rat liver microbody fraction is not apparent until it is treated with 0.2 percent final concentration digitonin. It is noteworthy that a higher concentration of digitonin is required to liberate catalase from microbodies than is required to liberate acid phosphatase from lysosomes. Mitochondrial enzymes such as glutamate dehydrogenase can be solubilized and the apparent activity increased, but even higher concentrations of detergents are required.

composition of cellular components

While nuclei contain almost all the intracellular DNA, the amount varies in different species. The nuclei of bird erythrocytes contain approximately 2.5×10^{-9} mg of DNA per nucleus, which accounts for about 20 percent of the solids. In any given species, all interphase cells contain a given amount of DNA, or an integer multiple of that amount, or in the case of gametes, one-half that amount, regardless of the size of the cell. Gametes, of course, contain only one set of chromosomes, instead of the two sets

[27] Wieland, T., Pfleiderer, G., Haupt, I., and Wörmer, W. *Biochem. Z.*, *332*, 1 (1959).
[28] Eichel, H. J., and Bukovsky, J. *Nature*, *191*, 243 (1961).
[29] Shepherd, J. A., and Kalnitsky, G. *J. Biol. Chem.*, *207*, 605 (1954).

fig. 2-51. Intracellular location of enzymes. (References compiled in de Duve, C., Wattiaux, R., and Baudhuin, P. *Advan. Enzymol.*, *24*, 291 [1962].)

ECC NUMBER	NAME	TISSUE	NUCLEI	MITO-CHONDRIA	LYSOSOMES, MICRO-BODIES	MICRO-SOMES	HIGH-SPEED SUPERNATE
1.1.1.1	Alcohol dehydrogenase	Rat liver	—	—	—	—	++++
1.1.1.8	Glycerylphosphate dehydrogenase *NAD-linked (see also 1.1.2.1)	Fly muscle	—	—	—	—	++++
1.1.1.20	Glucuronolactone reductase	Rat liver	—	—	—	++++	—
1.1.1.27	Lactate dehydrogenase	Rat liver	—	—	—	++	++
	Lactate dehydrogenase	Rat brain	—	—	—	—	++++
1.1.1.30	β-Hydroxybutyrate dehydrogenase	Rat liver	—	++++	—	—	—
1.1.1.37	Malate dehydrogenase (NAD-linked)	Rat liver	—	++	—	—	++
1.1.1.40	Malate dehydrogenase	Pigeon liver	—	—	—	—	++++
1.1.1.41	Isocitrate dehydrogenase	Rat liver	—	++++	—	—	—
1.1.1.49	Glucose-6-phosphate dehydrogenase	Rat liver	—	—	—	—	++++
1.1.1.51	β-Hydroxysteroid dehydrogenase (NAD-linked)	Guinea pig liver	—	++++	—	—	—
	β-Hydroxysteroid dehydrogenase (NADP-linked)	Guinea pig liver	—	—	—	—	++++
1.1.2.1	Glycerylphosphate-cytochrome reductase *(see also 1.1.1.8)	Fly muscle	—	++++	—	—	—
1.2.1.12	Triosephosphate dehydrogenase	Rat brain	—	—	—	—	++++
1.2.3.2	Xanthine oxidase	Rat liver	—	—	—	—	++++
1.3.99.1	Succinate-cytochrome *c* reductase	Rat liver	—	++++	—	—	—

1.4.3.2	L-Amino acid oxidase	Chicken liver	—	—	—	++++	—
1.4.3.3	D-Amino acid oxidase	Rat liver	—	+	+++	—	—
1.4.3.4	Monamine oxidase	Rat liver	—	+++	—	++	—
1.5.1.3	Tetrahydrofolate dehydrogenase	Rat liver (sucrose medium)	—	+++	—	—	+
	Tetrahydrofolate dehydrogenase	Rat liver (saline medium)	—	+	—	—	+++
1.9.3.1	Cytochrome *c* oxidase	Rat liver	—	++++	—	—	—
1.11.1.6	Catalase	Rat liver	—	—	+++	—	++
2.4.1.17	UDP-glycuronyltransferase	Guinea pig liver	—	—	—	++++	—
2.6.1.1	Aspartate aminotransferase (probably two distinct enzymes)	Rat liver	—	+++	—	—	+++
2.7.7.1	NAD-pyrophosphorylase	Mouse liver	+++	—	—	—	+
2.7.7.10	Galactose-1-phosphate uridyltransferase	Pigeon liver	++	±	—	+	+++
3.1.3.2	Acid phosphatase	Rat liver	—	—	++++	—	—
3.1.3.9	Glucose-6-phosphatase	Rat liver	—	—	—	++++	—
3.1.4.3	Phospholipase-C	Rat liver	—	—	—	—	++++
3.2.1.23	β-Galactosidase	Rat liver	—	—	++++	—	—
3.2.1.31	β-Glucuronidase	Rat liver	—	—	++++	+	—
4.1.2.7	Aldolase	Rat liver	+	—	—	—	++++

found in somatic cell nuclei. It is evident that the nuclear DNA is a measure of the number of chromosomes present. Thus, skin cells, liver cells, kidney cells, etc., contain the same amount of DNA, even though their sizes and functions may be different, unless the cells are polyploid. Polyploid cells contain an even-multiple amount of DNA. The amount of nuclear DNA remains constant during starvation and other gross physiological stresses. In general, the amount of DNA per cell tends to increase with increasing complexity of the organism or its position on the phylogenetic scale.

Protein accounts for about 70 percent of the nuclear solids. While the amount of DNA per nucleus is quite constant, the quantity of nuclear protein is very variable in the cells of different tissues, and the protein-to-DNA ratio varies from 2.6 to 7.0. The protamines and histones, proteins closely associated with DNA, contain large proportions of arginine and lysine and, therefore, are quite basic. Salmine and clupeine, two protamines isolated from fish sperm, contain about 80 percent arginine. These proteins contain relatively few aromatic amino acids and often are totally lacking in many amino acids. The quantity of protein not associated with DNA in the nucleus is relatively small, and it has not been well studied.

The nuclear RNA per cell varies considerably in different tissues of a given species, but in general it accounts for about 1.0 percent of the nuclear solids. The majority of the nuclear RNA resides in the nucleolus. The RNA content and nucleolus size are large in cells undergoing rapid multiplication or synthesizing large amounts of protein, and decrease during starvation. Nuclei contain small amounts of lipid that are bound to protein. Calf thymus nuclei contain 0.115 mg magnesium and 0.024 mg calcium per 100 g dry, fat-free solid. These divalent cations are strongly bound to DNA and are liberated in stoichiometric amounts upon hydrolysis of DNA. The most important nuclear enzymes are those involved in nucleic acid metabolism. The nucleus contains DNA polymerase and RNA polymerase, enzymes which catalyze the synthesis of DNA and messenger RNA, respectively, from a primer (or template) and the four deoxyribonucleotides or ribonucleotides, respectively. Other related enzymes include adenosine deaminase, nucleoside phosphorylase, and guanase. Nuclei also contain the glycolytic enzymes and appear to carry on anaerobic glycolysis with the production of ATP. The intracellular distribution of a number of key enzymes is tabulated in Fig. 2-51.

In rat liver, mitochondria account for about one-third of the tissue protein. About 25 to 30 percent of the mitochondrial solids are lipids, mainly the phospholipids lecithin and cephalin, with small amounts of cholesterol and neutral fats. Mitochondria with few contaminating granules by electron microscopy contain about 0.5 percent of their dry weight of RNA, which amounts to approximately 5 percent of the total cellular RNA in rat liver. Small amounts of DNA are constantly present as well. Cell fractionation and histochemical studies confirmed the prediction made by early cytologists that the mitochondria are the seat of cellular oxidation. They are the main repository for cytochrome *c* and the Krebs-cycle enzymes and contain the full complement of enzymes necessary to link the phosphorylation of adenosine diphosphate (ADP) to adenosine triphosphate (ATP) with oxidation and to oxidize fatty acids and amino acids. In addition, mitochondria contain the enzymes necessary to synthesize phospholipids, and they synthesize some protein. The economical performance of the large number of sequential reactions constituting the process of oxidative phosphorylation requires a degree of integration that has suggested a structural organization of the multienzyme system. Evidence, mainly indirect in nature, has been accumulating to support the idea that mitochondrial enzymes are organized in submicroscopic structural units, and it has been possible to fragment mitochondria into small particles which show a trilaminar structure in the electron microscope and are still able to carry out oxidative phosphorylation. However, if meticulous care is not observed in the isolation and preparation of mitochondria, they lose the ability to carry out the complete sequence of reactions in an integrated fashion.

The lysosome was recognized as a result of cell-fractionation studies, which yielded a unique fraction sedimenting between mitochondria and microsomes characteristically rich in hydrolytic enzymes with *p*H optima in the acid range. These enzymes included acid ribonuclease, acid deoxyribonuclease, acid phosphatase, cathepsins, collagenase, β-glucuronidase, β-galactosidase, α-mannosidase, α-glucosidase, β-N-acetylglucosaminidase, and aryl sulfatase. Examination of this fraction in the electron microscope revealed that it was composed mainly of rounded vesicles bounded by a unit membrane. Such vesicles can be recognized in electron photomicrographs of intact cells, and their morphology has been discussed above. Lysosomes contain the bulk of the cellular ferritin and are rich in phospholipids. Therefore, they stain with the periodic acid–Schiff reagent stain. Microbodies are another cellular component that was first recognized as a unique fraction in cell-fractionation experiments containing the enzymes catalase, urate oxidase, and D-amino acid oxidase. This fraction was found, when examined by electron microscopy, to contain mainly rounded, dense vesicles bounded by a unit membrane—organelles that did not resemble lysosomes. Many lysosomal enzymes also are found in the high-speed supernatant fraction.

The microsomal fraction appears to contain the fragmented endoplasmic reticulum with its associated ribosomes and perhaps other components of the tubular system, such as the Golgi apparatus. The microsomal fraction constitutes 15 to 20 percent of the cellular mass. It contains little or no DNA when uncontaminated with nuclear material, but it does contain about two-thirds of the cellular RNA and has a high phospholipid content. Treatment of the microsomal fraction with deoxycholate or a similar detergent results in solubilization of the membranous material and liberation of the ribosomes. Ribosomes separated in this fashion contain almost all the RNA of the microsomal fraction, only about one-fifth of the protein, and almost none of the phospholipid, cytochrome b_5 or the NADH–cytochrome *c* reductase system. While the ribosomes carry on protein synthesis, the membranous portion of the microsomal fraction contains the enzyme systems which carry on the synthesis of triglycerides, phosphates, glycolipids, and phospholipids (fatty acids are synthesized largely in the soluble cytoplasm). Steroid biosynthesis and drug-detoxification reactions, including hydroxylation, deamination, oxidation (often by molecular oxygen); and uronic acid and sulfate conjugation reactions are also carried on by the membranous portion of the microsomal fraction. The membranous portion also contains a number of characteristic enzymes, including alkaline phosphatase, glucose-6-phosphatase, acetylcholinesterase, the Na^+-K^+- Mg^{2+} activated ATPase that has been implicated in active cation transport, and NADH–cytochrome *c* reductase system.

While the same basic pattern of metabolism seems to be used by all living forms and, therefore, in the main, the same enzyme composition and localization is found in all types of cells, differences in the complement of enzymes and their distributions have been observed between cells of different tissues of a given type of organism (Fig. 2-52) and between cells of different species (Fig. 2-53). These differences are the presence, or the deletion, or a difference in abundance, or a difference in location of one enzyme here and there, rather than a wholesale change in the pattern of enzymes. These differences reflect differences in genetic expression and they give rise, no doubt, to the unique, distinguishing characteristics of a given cell type. Of course, organisms farther apart on the phylogenetic scale are likely to have more differences than closely related organisms.

fig. 2-52. Comparison of enzyme activities in liver, kidney, and fat pad. (From Weber, G. *Advan. Enzyme Regul., 1,* 15 [1963]. Copyright 1963, Pergamon Press; reprinted by permission.)

The mean values and standard errors represent four or more rats in each group. The enzyme activities are expressed in μmoles of substrate metabolized per hour per *average cell* $\times 10^{-7}$ at 37°C. Numbers in parentheses express the data in percentages taking the value of phosphohexose isomerase arbitrarily as 100 percent.

ENZYMES	LIVER	KIDNEY	FAT PAD
Phosphohexose isomerase	685 ± 66 (100)	811 ± 58 (100)	450 (100)
Lactic dehydrogenase	593 ± 19 (87)	140 ± 14 (17)	248 (55)
Phosphoglucomutase	127 ± 11 (19)	2.8 ± 0.2 (0.3)	24.9 (6)
Glucose-6-phosphatase	36.3 ± 2.1 (5)	26.9 ± 4.9 (3)	absent (0)
Fructose-1,6-diphosphatase	26.5 ± 2.8 (4)	8.3 ± 1.4 (1)	absent (0)
Glucose-6-phosphate dehydrogenase	4.4 ± 0.4 (0.6)	0.3 ± 0.03 (0.04)	72.0 (16)
6-Phosphogluconate dehydrogenase	12.3 ± 0.8 (2)	1.0 ± 0 (0.1)	49.2 (11)
Cellularity[a]	178 ± 5	281 ± 20	10
Supernatant nitrogen[b]	0.9 ± 0.02	0.47 ± 0.06	2.4

[a] Expressed in millions of nuclei counted/g wet weight of tissue.
[b] Calculated as mg nitrogen/cell $\times 10^{-8}$.

fig. 2-53. Species difference in liver carbohydrate enzyme activities. (From Weber, G. *Advan. Enzyme Regul., 1,* 13 [1963]. Copyright 1963, Pergamon Press; reprinted by permission.)

Means and standard errors of four or more samples are given. Activities are expressed in μmoles of substrate metabolized per hour per gram wet weight at 37°C. Numbers in parentheses express the data in percentages, taking the value of phosphohexose isomerase arbitrarily at 100 percent.

ENZYMES	AVIAN	RODENT	HUMAN
Phosphohexose isomerase	18,300 ± 1,006 (100)	8,166 ± 337 (100)	15,630 ± 5,241 (100)
Lactic dehydrogenase	10,628 ± 629 (58)	14,229 ± 959 (174)	4,249 ± 1,609 (27)
Phosphoglucomutase	428 ± 44 (2.3)	467 ± 27 (6)	10,149 ± 5,046 (65)
Glucose-6-phosphatase	638 ± 35 (3.0)	645 ± 21 (8)	255 ± 118 (1.6)
Fructose-1,6-diphosphatase	305 ± 22 (1.7)	382 ± 17 (5)	157 ± 93 (1.0)
6-Phosphogluconate dehydrogenase	127 ± 3 (0.7)	477 ± 20 (6)	300 ± 21 (2.0)
Glucose-6-phosphate dehydrogenase	5.8 ± 1 (0.3)	68 ± 24 (0.8)	90 ± 24 (0.6)

For example, the animal kingdom is distinguished by a lack of enzymes required for photosynthesis and for the formation of aromatic benzene rings.

However, prominent differences have been observed even between closely related species. For example, all mammals except man and some other primates possess urate oxidase in their tissues. This enzyme is also absent in birds. Allantoin is the end product of purine metabolism in most mammals, while man, monkeys, and birds excrete uric acid. The Dalmatian coach hound also excretes uric acid, but the mechanism is a defect of renal tubular reabsorption rather than the absence of urate oxidase. Histidine decarboxylase is present in the kidneys of rabbits and guinea pigs but not in the kidneys of horses, oxen, dogs, cats, sheep, or men. The specific activity of amphibian liver carbamate kinase increases *pari passu* with the degree of developmental complexity.

Species are more apt to vary in the relative amounts of enzymes present than to exhibit all-or-none differences. For example, sheep kidney contains roughly 50-fold as much D-amino acid oxidase per unit weight as does rat kidney, while rat kidney contains large quantities of L-amino acid oxidase, in contrast to barely detectable amounts in the kidneys of other mammals tested. Different cell types in a given species also show differences in the amount of enzymes present. Thus, a high concentration of alkaline phosphatase is characteristic of intestinal epithelial cells, a high concentration of acid phosphatase is characteristic of prostate gland cells, and a high concentration of glutamine synthetase is found in neuronal (brain) tissue.

The role of these and other cell components in the general metabolism and their association with the functional aspects of organisms will be discussed in greater detail in subsequent chapters.

references

Allfrey, V. The isolation of subcellular components, in Brachet, J., and Mirsky, A. E., eds. *The Cell.* New York: Academic Press, 1959, vol. 1, pp. 193–290.

Baker, J. R. The cell theory: a restatement, history, and critique. *Quart. J. Microscop. Sci.*, *89*, 103 (1948); *90*, 87 (1949); *93*, 157 (1952); *94*, 407 (1953); *96*, 449 (1955).

Bloom, W., and Fawcett, D. W. *A Textbook of Histology*, 8th ed. Philadelphia: Saunders, 1962.

Curtis, A. S. G. Cell contact and adhesion. *Biol. Rev.*, *37*, 82 (1962).

de Duve, C. Principles of tissue fractionation. *J. Theoret. Biol.*, *6*, 33 (1964).

de Duve, C., Wattiaux, R., and Baudhuin, P. Distribution of enzymes between subcellular fractions in animal tissues. *Advan. Enzymol.*, *24*, 291 (1962).

De Robertis, E. D. P., Nowinski, W. W., and Salz, F. A. *Cell Biology*, 4th ed. Philadelphia: Saunders, 1965.

Fawcett, D. W. *An Atlas of Fine Structure. The Cell.* Philadelphia: Saunders, 1966.

Goodwin, T. W., and Lindberg, O., eds. *Biological Structure and Function.* New York: Academic Press, 1961.

Grant, J. K., ed. *Methods of Separation of Subcellular Structural Components.* London: Cambridge University Press, Biochemical Society Symposium No. 23, 1963.

Haguenan, F. The ergastoplasm: its history, ultrastructure, and biochemistry. *Intern. Rev. Cytol.*, *7*, 425 (1958).

Harris, R. J. C. *The Interpretation of Ultrastructure.* New York: Academic Press, 1962.

Hughes, A. *History of Cytology.* London: Abelard-Schuman, 1959.
Kennedy, D., ed. *The Living Cell.* San Francisco: Freeman, 1965.
Lehninger, A. *The Mitochondrion.* New York: W. A. Benjamin, 1964.
Pearse, A. G. E. *Histochemistry.* Boston: Little, Brown, 1960.
Porter, K. R., and Bonneville, M. A. *An Introduction to the Structure of Cells and Tissues.* Philadelphia: Lea & Febiger, 1963.
Robertson, J. D. The ultrastructure of cell membranes and their derivatives. *Biochem. Soc. Symp., 16,* 3 (1959).
Singer, C. *A History of Biology,* 3rd ed. London: Abelard-Schuman, 1959.
Weiss, L. The adhesion of cells. *Intern. Rev. Cytol., 9,* 187 (1960).

chapter 3

molecular constituents of biological systems

molecular forces; strong bonds

Before launching into a discussion on the molecular constitutents of biological systems and their organization at a molecular level, it seems worthwhile to review briefly some aspects of the forces which act on atoms and molecules. It is convenient to divide the forces which act at the molecular level into two sorts: (1) strong forces, or primary forces, or chemical (valence) forces, and (2) weak forces, or secondary forces, or physical (cohesive) forces. A rough criterion that may be used to distinguish strong forces from weak forces is whether or not the union of particles which results from the action of the force can be disrupted by thermal agitation at ambient temperatures. One should bear in mind, of course, that in the interaction of large molecules, many weak forces may act cooperatively to establish a fairly firm union, such as the multiple hydrogen bonds formed between two complementary DNA molecules. In the example cited, one can easily rupture the hydrogen bonds and separate the two strands without breaking any chemical bonds, that is, without hydrolysis and breakdown in each polynucleotide chain.

Although it is not possible to measure molecular forces absolutely, it is possible to evaluate the *interaction energy*, the loss of potential energy which occurs when two particles approach each other. A useful general expression for the molecular interaction energy, U_i, of an isolated pair of atoms separated by a distance, r, was proposed by Mie.[1]

$$U_i = Ar^{-n} - Br^{-m} \tag{3-1}$$

where A and B are positive constants, and n and m are positive integers with $n > m$. The first term is a positive force and represents a repulsion; the second term is a negative force and represents an attraction. Exact expressions can be assigned to the various constants in terms of considerations of quantum mechanics, particularly for the forces of attraction. Lennard-Jones[2] introduced a convention of plotting interaction energies as a function of distance of separation using a specific form of Mie's equation in which $n = 12$ and $m = 6$. The interaction energy is commonly depicted as a plot of potential energy against distance of separation (Lennard-Jones potential plot). The potential energy between two hydrogen atoms as a function of interatomic distance is plotted in Fig. 3-1. In this figure it is seen that there will be an equilibrium

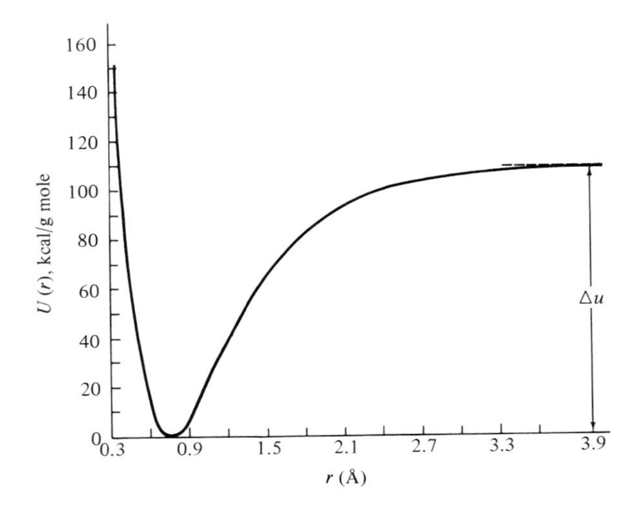

fig. 3-1. Potential energy of two hydrogen atoms *versus* interatomic distance.

at one distance, r_e, where the attractive and repulsive forces balance each other. This is the most stable state and is a potential energy minimum. The interatomic distances (bond distances) for some common covalent bonds are listed in Fig. 3-2. The force between the two atoms is given by

$$F = \nabla U_i = nAr^{-(n+1)} - mBr^{-(m+1)} \tag{3-2}$$

A simple example of a strong interatomic force is the interaction of two hydrogen atoms to form a hydrogen molecule. The system of two hydrogen atoms consists of two massive, positively charged nuclei and two negatively charged electrons. When the atoms are far apart, the interaction energy is zero for practical purposes. On the other hand, an external force of great magnitude is required to force the atoms closer than

[1] Mie, G. *Ann. Physik.*, *11*, 657 (1903).
[2] Lennard-Jones, J. E. *Proc. Roy. Soc.*, *A 112*, 214 (1926).

fig. 3-2. Bond distances and energies. (Data from Sutton, L. E. *Tables of Interatomic Distances and Configurations in Molecules and Ions.* London: Chemical Society, 1958.)

BOND	ENTHALPY (KCAL/MOLE)	DISTANCE (Å)
C—C	58.6	1.543
C—H	87.3	1.098
C—O	70.0	1.44
C—N	48.6	1.48
C=O	152	1.215
C=C		1.271
C=N		1.265
C≡C		1.21
N—H	83.7	1.014
O—H	110.2	0.96
C—S		1.81
H—S	87.5	1.334

about 0.5 Å because of a large repulsive force between the two positively charged nuclei. Between these limits, two hydrogen atoms will unite to form a stable hydrogen molecule with a dissociation energy of 109.5 kcal/mole. It is possible for the two electrons to fill the lowest energy orbital around each hydrogen nucleus. In the stable molecular configuration, each electron of both atoms occupies a larger domain which results in lower kinetic energy and greater stability. The larger electron domain results in an increased electron density around and between the protons; the protons are strongly attracted by the increased negative electron density between them. Thus, the apposition of two hydrogen atoms results in a more stable configuration as a result of a decrease in the electron energy and the electrostatic potential energy. The *covalent bond* which has been described for the hydrogen molecule is the prototype of covalent bonds generally which derive their stability from the decrease in potential energy which occurs when two atoms approach each other and share electrons. For two hydrogen atoms, Mie's equation becomes

$$U_i = \frac{3.91 \times 10^{-80}}{r^9} - \frac{1.21 \times 10^{-59}}{r^6} \text{ ergs} \tag{3-3}$$

A detailed discussion of the energy considerations on the basis of wave functions or molecular orbitals is beyond the scope of this presentation. However, several points should be made which are important for the biologist. The first is that electrons have an angular momentum or spin, and the Pauli exclusion principle states that two electrons can occupy the same energy state only if their spins are antiparallel. The formation of a covalent bond, then, requires that the spins of the electrons of the two atoms be antiparallel. Furthermore, additional stability, that is, a lower kinetic energy, is achieved when an energy state is filled by two electrons with antiparallel spins. If the electrons of two approaching atoms have parallel spins, there is only repulsion as they approach. In the case of two approaching hydrogen atoms, because of the requirement of antiparallel spins, there is only about one chance in two that they will attract each other. Electron spin is important in excitation and electron-transfer effects, which will be discussed later.

Another point of importance concerns molecules with resonance. In such molecules, benzene being the classical example (Fig. 3-3), several structural configurations of the

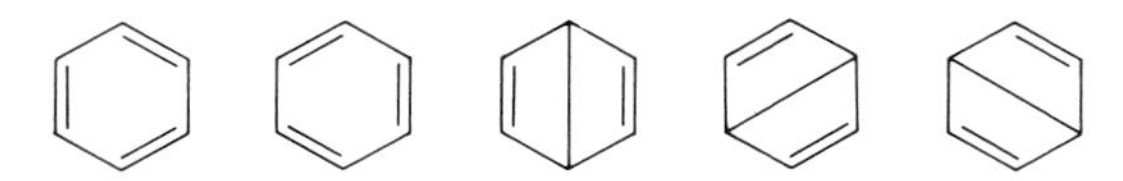

fig. 3-3. Canonical resonance forms of benzene.

atoms are possible. Of course, resonant structures can differ only in the distributions of the electrons; substances which differ in the positions of the atoms are chemical isomers. Isomers can be distinguished as distinct chemical compounds by their chemical and physical properties. It is important to remember that the practice of writing several distinct structures in equilibrium for molecules with resonance is a convenient device of notation; in actuality there is one intermediate electron distribution for each molecule which is a resultant derived from the various resonance structures. Thus, for benzene, there is a ring of electron density above and below the planar ring of carbon nuclei (Fig. 3-4). These rings, the first π orbitals of benzene, can participate in weak interactions with other molecules.

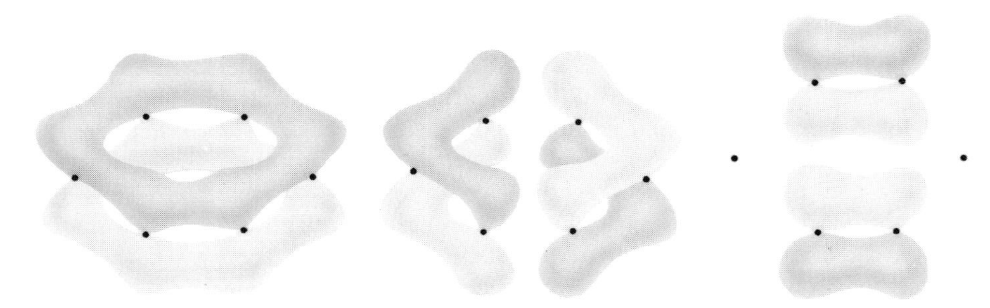

fig. 3-4. First-, second-, and third-order π orbital electron distribution for benzene.

The *ionic bond* represents, in a sense, a limiting case of a covalent bond. The electrons in an ionic bond are shared in an extremely asymmetrical fashion, so that the force between the atoms is almost entirely electrostatic. If the ions are forced very close together and an overlap of the electron densities occurs, the result is a mutual repulsion between the positively charged nuclei. The interaction of two charged ions is given by Coulomb's law. Substitution into Mie's equation gives

$$U_i = Ar^{-n} + \frac{z_A z_B q^2}{\varepsilon r} \qquad (3\text{-}4)$$

where z_A and z_B denote the magnitude of the valence and sign of the charge of ions A and B, q is the unit charge, and ε is the dielectric constant of the medium ($\varepsilon = 1$ for a vacuum). It is apparent that an attraction occurs only when the ions have opposite signs. The potential energy function of a sodium atom and a chloride atom and of a sodium ion and a chloride ion are plotted in Fig. 3-5. It should be noted that at large distances of separation, sodium and chloride atoms comprise a more stable system than sodium and chloride ions.

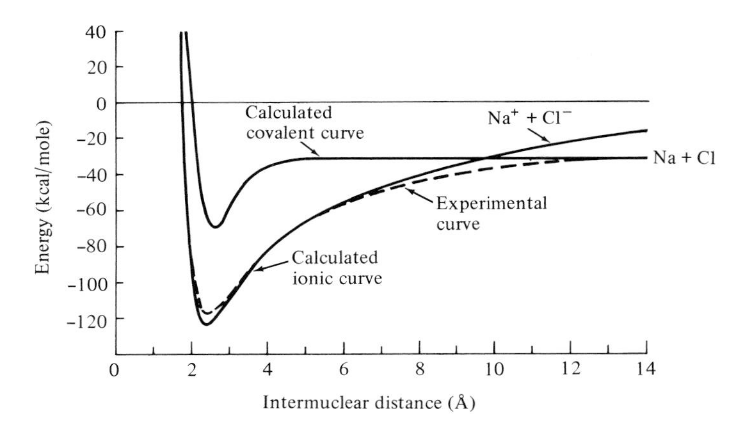

fig. 3-5. Potential energy of NaCl *versus* distance of separation compared to the calculated curves for sodium and chloride atoms and sodium and chloride ions.

Another important, though less common, type of strong bond is the *coordination bond.* These bonds are sometimes called *semipolar* or *dative* bonds. They resemble ordinary covalent bonds in that two electrons are shared by the atoms forming the bond, but they differ in that both electrons are contributed by only one of the atoms forming a coordination bond. Atoms with unshared pairs of electrons in the valence shell, such as nitrogen and sulfur, can act as donor atoms in coordination bonds.

·N̈·   :S̈·

An arrow pointing away from the donor atom is often used as the symbol for a coordination bond.

(pyridine ring)N→O   R—O—S(→O)(→O)—OH

Coordination bonds have a strong polar character; the donor atom possesses a relative positive charge and the recipient atom possesses a relative negative charge. Sometimes electrons of the recipient atom must move into higher orbitals in order to accommodate the electrons of the donor atom. This is frequently the case in *chelates*, a type of compound with coordination bonds that commonly occurs in living organisms and drugs. The iron-porphyrin complex of heme and the copper-salicylaldehyde complex are examples of chelates (Fig. 3-6).

In the polyatomic molecules, adjacent bonds connecting series of atoms tend to form definite angles which are characteristic of the atoms involved. Some common bond angles are listed in Fig. 3-7. Relatively small deviations from the characteristic bond angles or the characteristic interatomic distances require a considerable increase in molecular energy. Because these parameters are relatively fixed, they impose constraints upon possible steric configurations of atoms in molecules.

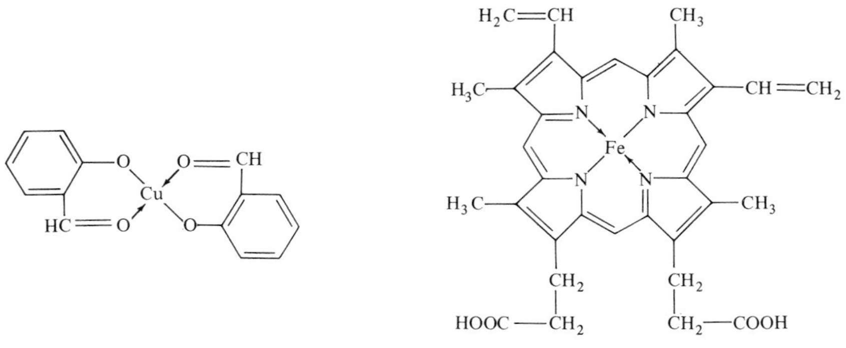

a

b

fig. 3-6. Chelates with coordination bonds: (*a*) copper-salicylaldehyde complex, and (*b*) iron-protoporphyrin IX complex (heme).

fig. 3-7. Bond angles. (Data from Sutton, L. E. *Tables of Interatomic Distances and Configurations in Molecules and Ions.* London: Chemical Society, 1958.)

BOND	ANGLE	BOND	ANGLE
C—C—C	109°28′	—C(=O)—O	125° (all)
C—N—C	110°		
CN—H	108°		
N—CN	109°28′		
C—C—H	109°28′	C—S—C	104°
N=C—N	125°16′	C—C—S	109°28′
C=C—C	124°45′		

some electronic properties of molecules

If two atoms of different electronegativity form a covalent bond, an asymmetry of electron distribution between the atoms results, with a relative negative charge accumulating on the more electronegative atom; as a consequence, the less electronegative atom has an equal positive charge. A *dipole* may be defined as equal negative and positive charges, $\pm q$, separated by a distance, r. The dipoles which occur in many covalent bonds can be characterized by vector quantities, qr, which have the direction of lines joining the charges. The quantity qr is called the *dipole moment* and is measured in units of 10^{-18} esu cm called the *debye* (μ). If a polyatomic molecule contains two or more dipoles in different bonds, the net dipole moment of the molecule is the resultant of the vector addition of the individual dipole moments of each bond (Fig. 3-8).

A molecule which does not normally have a dipole moment behaves like an insulator or *dielectric*. In the presence of an electric field, there is a polarization of the dielectric, that is, a tendency for the electrons to become slightly displaced from their equilibrium

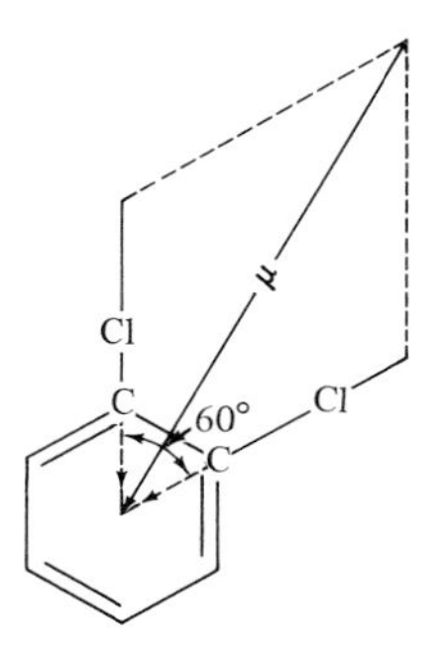

fig. 3-8. Dipole moment of *o*-dichlorobenzene representing the vector addition of the dipole moments of the individual bonds.

positions, resulting in a separation of charges. An electric field always induces dipoles in molecules, whether or not they contain dipoles in its absence. If a molecule contains a permanent dipole, the dipole tends to align itself in the direction of the electric field. This tendency toward orientation with the field is counteracted by the thermal motion of the molecules. When a molecule is placed in an electric field E, the induced dipole moment is given by

$$\mu = \alpha E \tag{3-5}$$

The proportionality factor, α, called the *polarizability*, has the dimensions of a volume and is a good approximation of the effective volume of an atom or ion.

The *dielectric constant* may be defined as the reciprocal of electric field strength in a substance interposed between two charges compared to the field strength in a vacuum.

$$\varepsilon = E_{\text{vac}}/E = 1 + 4\pi\alpha/E \tag{3-6}$$

where ε is the dielectric constant of a substance, and E is the electric field strength produced in that material by a field of strength E_{vac} in a vacuum, and α is the polarizability as defined in eq. 3-5. The molecular mechanism is the polarization of charges and a resultant distortion which also is responsible for the induction of a molecular dipole. In the case of substances where there are no permanent dipoles and where molecular interactions other than induced dipole–induced dipole interactions can be neglected, the dielectric constant can be defined solely in terms of the polarizability. The derivation is due to Debye,[3] and the statement is the Clausius-Mossotti relation which was deduced empirically

$$\frac{\varepsilon - 1}{\varepsilon + 2} = \frac{4\pi N_0}{3}\alpha \tag{3-7}$$

where N_0 is the number of molecules per cm^3.

G. N. Lewis[4] first proposed that the unequal sharing of electrons, which gives rise to the partial ionic character of covalent bonds, could be propagated in a chain of atoms by a mechanism involving electrostatic induction. Thus, a chlorine-carbon bond is polarized with the electrons displaced toward the more electronegative chlorine atom. If the first carbon atom is linked to a second carbon atom, the electrons in the

[3] Debye, P. *Phys. Z.*, *13*, 97 (1912).
[4] Lewis, G. N. *Valence and the Structure of Atoms and Molecules*. New York: Reinhold, 1923.

carbon-carbon bond will be displaced toward the carbon atom linked to the chlorine, and so on. Such electron displacements resulting from the *inductive effect* influence the physical properties of organic compounds.

Lewis first used this idea to explain the higher acidity constant of chloracetic acid compared to acetic acid. In chloracetic acid, electrons in the Cl-C bond are displaced toward the chlorine atom, and, by induction, the electrons in the C-C and then in the C-O bonds are displaced in the direction of the chlorine atom. This leaves the oxygen atom relatively more positively charged in chloracetic acid than in acetic acid and makes the proton dissociate more readily in chloracetic acid. It follows that the more chlorine atoms there are on the α-carbon atom, the stronger the acid; in fact, trichloracetic acid is a much stronger acid than dichloracetic acid which, in turn, is a stronger acid than monochloracetic acid. The inductive effect decreases rapidly with distance as shown by the chlorobutyric acids; α-chlorobutyric acid is stronger than β-chlorobutyric acid which, in turn, is stronger than γ-chlorobutyric acid.

Molecules can absorb energy in a number of ways. The heat evolved in a chemical reaction represents increased kinetic energy of the individual molecules. *Excitation* represents an increase in molecular energy content confined essentially to one or more electrons while the atomic nuclei are relatively stable. *Ionization* occurs when an electron acquires sufficient energy to escape from a molecule, leaving an ion. The energy required to abstract an electron (usually given in volts) is known as the *ionization potential.*

Electrons can occupy only certain discrete (allowed) energy levels. In the *ground state*, the electrons of a molecule fill the lowest possible energy levels consistent with the Pauli exclusion principle. Excitation involves the transition of an electron from the ground state to a higher allowed energy level. Excitation commonly involves nonbonding electrons (n), that is, electrons which do not play an important role in the bonding of atomic nuclei. Nonbonding electrons, such as the unpaired electrons of nitrogen or oxygen in amino or carbonyl groups, occupy orbitals which do not make appreciable contributions to the electron density between nuclei. Another type of electron that is frequently excited is the π-orbital. These are molecular electrons similar to atomic p-orbitals which extend over at least two atoms; they may be bonding if the electron density tends to build up between nuclei, or antibonding if a node of electron charge forms between the nuclei. Excitation of π-electrons is important particularly in systems with conjugated double bonds. The higher level to which a transition takes place is usually a π-antibonding orbital. The common transitions of excitation, therefore, are n-π^* and π-π^* transitions (Fig. 3-9).

Because the energy levels of electron orbitals are fixed, definite increments of energy corresponding to light of certain wavelengths tend to be absorbed in the process of excitation. At room or body temperature, thermal energy is insufficient to excite more than a negligible fraction of molecules. When the electron of an excited molecule drops from the higher energy level back to the ground state, this discrete difference in energy is radiated as a quantum of light, a phenomenon known as *fluorescence.* Excited compounds show two spectra, an absorption spectrum and an emission spectrum, which are characteristic of the compound (Fig. 3-10). The emission spectrum is shifted to the red of the absorption spectrum. Absorption is a process that takes place in about 10^{-14} sec. This time is short compared to the times required for various molecular processes. The excited state, on the other hand, has an average lifetime of 10^{-9} to 3×10^{-8} sec, long compared to the time between molecular collisions and those required for many molecular processes. Chemical bonds are longer and weaker in excited molecules. Bond distances may be longer by 15 percent or more, and bond angles may change by

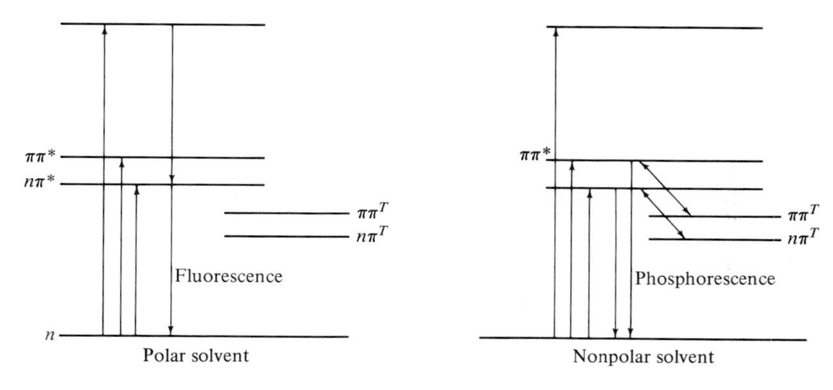

fig. 3-9. Transitions corresponding to excitation of a hypothetical compound. Transitions to the triplet state are more likely to occur in nonpolar solvents.

as much as 80°. Excited molecules are much more reactive chemically than molecules in the ground state.

At energy levels above the ground state, additional electronic configurations are possible. Under certain conditions, an excited molecule may pass from one electronic configuration in which there are no spin unpaired electrons into an electronic configuration with a different net electron spin. This gives rise to a *triplet*, which is so called because its spectrum contains a characteristic band of three closely placed lines. Because of the quantum mechanical selection rules, the original spin orientations must be restored before decay can occur, and this process is slow. The average lifetime of a triplet is of the order of 10^{-2} sec and in some cases may be as long as several minutes. Radiative decay of the triplet state is called *phosphoresence* and gives an emission spectrum farther toward the red than the fluorescence spectrum.

The energy of excitation can be transferred from one molecule to another. The energy increment in the excited donor molecule must be equal or greater than that required to excite the acceptor. Such excitation transfers can occur over distances of 25 to 50 Å. At times two stable molecular entities can form a complex in which there tends to be a transfer of an electron from one component to the other. Such *charge-transfer complexes* give a unique spectrum which is different from the spectrum of

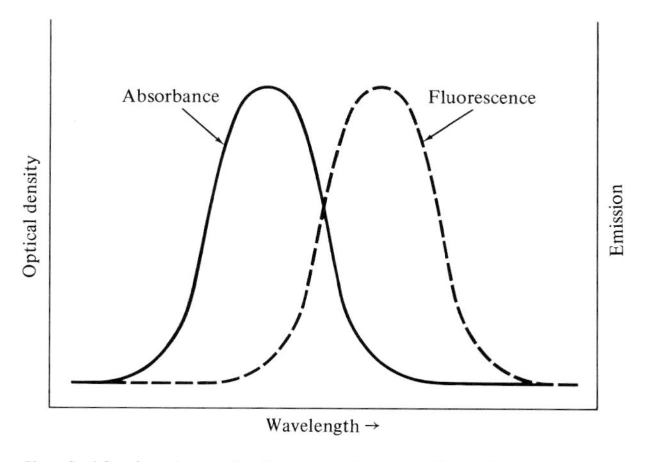

fig. 3-10. A schematic diagram showing the relation between the absorption and emission spectra.

either component. Charge-transfer complexes have overlapping orbitals. Frequently charge-transfer complexes occur between compounds with planar rings; an attractive interaction between the molecules occurs with the energy of stabilization coming from a resonance effect of the electron displacement. Actual transfer of an electron from a donor to an acceptor may result in the formation of a *free radical*, a molecule with a single, unpaired electron. Many biological materials, particularly charge-transfer complexes, act as organic semiconductors,[5] and light-induced charge separation or photoconductivity may play important roles in biological processes. Free radicals appear as intermediates in some metabolic processes.

Excitation is an important feature of many biological processes including photosynthesis, bioluminescence, and various photodynamic processes. A large number of compounds of biological origin, including nucleic acids, proteins, and coenzymes, are fluorescent. These compounds have a large amount of resonance energy which results in their stabilization. For example, compounds with high resonance stabilization are much more resistant to decomposition by ultraviolet or ionizing radiation than compounds that do not have a large amount of resonance energy. Such stability and resistance to destruction were particularly important under conditions that existed in the primitive earth. Charge-transfer complexes may play an important role in the transfer of energy in nicotinamide adenine dinucleotide and nicotinamide adenine trinucleotide dependent enzymes, in enzymes in which pyridoxal phosphate is a coenzyme, and between flavin adenine dinucleotide and the flavoproteins.[6] Carcinogenic compounds are good electron donors and tend to form charge-transfer complexes.[7] Similarly, convulsant drugs tend to be excellent electron donors, as are certain tranquilizers. Their specific pharmacological activity may result from their propensity to form charge-transfer complexes with compounds which normally are involved in the metabolism of the nervous system.

The absorption spectrum of a substance in solution shows a red shift compared to the absorption spectrum of that substance in the gaseous state. The spectral shift results from weak interactions between the substance and solvent molecules. In the case of the fluorescence spectrum, the red shift is greater and is related in magnitude to a parameter Δf, which depends upon the dielectric constant and refractive index n of the solvent.[8]

$$\Delta f = \frac{\varepsilon - 1}{2\varepsilon - 1} - \frac{n^2 - 1}{2n^2 - 1} \tag{3-8}$$

The fluorescence spectrum can often be used to determine the polarity of the solvent. The solvent also may play an important role in quenching fluorescence. The quantum yield of fluorescence is greater in nonpolar solvents, that is, solvents with low dielectric constants. Solvents such as water with high dielectric constants tend to quench fluorescence.

---

[5] Arnold, W., and Sherwood, H. K. *Proc. Natl. Acad. Sci.*, *43*, 105 (1957); Eley, D., in Kasha, M., and Pullman, B., eds. *Horizons in Biochemistry.* New York: Academic Press, 1962, p. 341; Isenberg, I. *Physiol. Rev.*, *44*, 487 (1964).

[6] Shifrin, S. *Biochim. Biophys. Acta*, *81*, 205 (1964).

[7] Pullman, B., ed. *Electronic Aspects of Biochemistry.* New York: Academic Press, 1964; Karreman, G., in Enslein, K., ed. *Data Acquisition and Processing in Biology and Medicine.* New York: Pergamon Press, 1962.

[8] Lippert, E., Lüder, W., Prigge, H., and Seibold-Blankenstein, I. *Angew. Chem.*, *21*, 695 (1961); Wetlaufer, D. *Advan. Protein Chem.*, *17*, 303 (1962).

properties of gases

Gases are the simplest molecular systems. Their bulk properties are described in terms of pressure (P), volume (V), and absolute temperature (T) by the *ideal gas law*

$$P = \frac{nRT}{V} \tag{3-9}$$

where n is the number of moles of the material. A remarkable feature of gases is that the size or weight of the molecules does not enter into the ideal gas law. Thus, regardless of its molecular weight, one mole of any gas occupies 22.4 L at 0°C and 1 atm pressure. The molecular weight of a gas M, therefore, can be determined by use of the relation

$$\lim_{P \to 0} \frac{wRT}{PV} = M \tag{3-10}$$

where w is the weight of the gas in grams. The relation is given as a limit because many observations indicate that gases tend to deviate from the ideal gas law as the pressure increases, that is, as molecules tend to become more tightly packed together. The bulk properties of gases can be better described by a relation which takes these deviations into account, such as

$$P = \frac{RT}{V}\left[1 + \frac{A}{V} + \frac{B}{V^2} + \frac{C}{V^3} + \cdots\right] \tag{3-11}$$

The deviations from the ideal gas law that occur as the gas molecules tend to become more tightly packed have two major causes: (1) the actual volume occupied by the molecules becomes comparable to the volume of the gas, and the molecules can no longer be regarded as infinitesimally small points; and (2) there are attractive forces between the molecules. Johannes D. van der Waals proposed a relation in 1873 which bears his name and which describes the properties of gases in terms of these considerations.

$$P = \frac{nRT}{V - nb} - \frac{n^2 a}{V^2} \tag{3-12}$$

It corresponds to eq. 3-11 if higher than second-order terms are omitted; $A = (b - a/RT)$ and $B = (ab/RT)$. It can be analyzed, however, in terms of the considerations stated above. The term nb accounts for the volume effectively occupied by the gas molecules and $(V - nb)$ represents the free volume not occupied by the molecules. The term n^2a/V^2 qualitatively accounts for the effect of the attractive forces between molecules; it represents the "internal pressure." Inspection of the van der Waals equation and the Mie equation reveals a general resemblance between the two.

weak interactions

There are a variety of weak interactions between atoms and molecules. These interactions give rise, in part, to the deviations from the ideal gas law displayed by real gases. Because the experimental data obtained from real gases can be described by the van der Waals equation, the weak interactions are often called van der Waals interactions.

In solids and liquids any given molecule is close to several other molecules and interacts simultaneously with all of them. If the molecules are considered to be point charges, an approximation which holds up quite well except at high pressures where tight molecular packing occurs, the total potential energy of a group of molecules is equal to the sum of the pair potential energies. For a set of four molecules, for example,

$$U \cong u_{12} + u_{13} + u_{14} + u_{23} + u_{24} + u_{34} \tag{3-13}$$

It is appropriate, therefore, to consider interactions of pairs of molecules, since these can be extended to molecules in bulk. The types of interactions, which are outlined below, are not mutually exclusive, and, in fact, it is common for atoms, ions, or molecules to interact in more than one way simultaneously.

The simplest type of interaction is the charge-charge interaction. A special case of this type of interaction, the ionic bond, has already been considered. It is well to bear the general type of interaction in mind, since it can occur under situations (for example, in solutions of electrolytes) where it results not in a chemical bond but rather in a bond easily disrupted by thermal agitation.

Somewhat more complex is the charge-dipole interaction, which can be described in terms of Coulomb's law. The potential energy depends on the distance of separation, r; the dipole moment, μ; and θ, the angle of the axis of the dipole with the vector between the dipole and the charge (Fig. 3-11). For such an interaction, the Mie equation is

$$U = Ar^{-n} - \frac{Z_A q \mu_B \cos\theta}{\varepsilon r^2} \tag{3-14}$$

For molecules in bulk, the orientation of the dipoles relative to the charges will follow a Boltzmann distribution which permits the derivation of an average expression for the

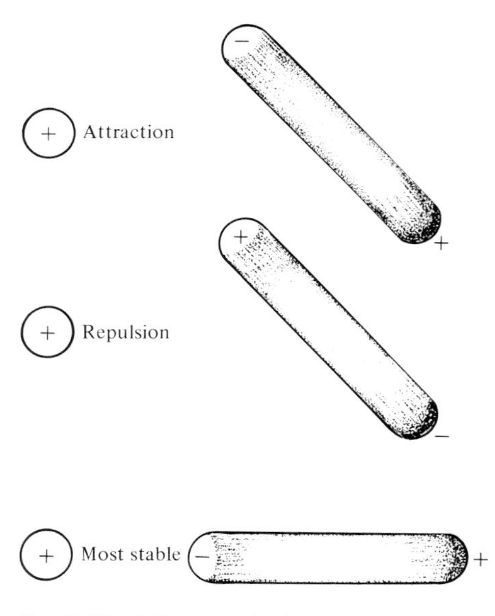

fig. 3-11. Influence of orientation on the interaction energy between an ion and a dipole.

attraction term

$$U = -\frac{1}{3kT} \cdot \frac{(Z_A q)^2 (\mu_B)^2}{\varepsilon r^4} \tag{3-15}$$

where k is the Boltzmann constant. In this averaging, it is assumed that the displacement of the charges in the dipole is small compared with the distance of separation of the dipole from the charge and that the temperature is high enough so that the thermal energy is high compared with the interaction energy. However, when the temperature is very high, random thermal motion results in complete randomness of orientation of the dipole, and the average potential energy becomes zero. An example of a charge dipole interaction occurs between an ion (formed by dissolving an electrolyte) and a water molecule, a dipole.

Somewhat similar to the above type of interaction is the interaction between two dipoles. In this case two angles of orientation with the vector of separation must be considered. For such an interaction, we can write

$$U = Ar^{-n} - \frac{\mu_A \mu_B}{\varepsilon r^3}(2 \cos \theta_A \cos \theta_B - \sin \theta_A \sin \theta_B \cos \psi) \tag{3-16}$$

where θ_A and θ_B are the angles of orientation and ψ is the angle of inclination of the planes in which the dipole axes lie. Averaging all possible orientations according to a Boltzmann distribution, an average expression for the attractive term can be obtained:

$$U = -\frac{2}{3kT} \frac{\mu_A^2 \mu_B^2}{\varepsilon r^6} \tag{3-17}$$

The interaction between water molecules is an example of this type of interaction. The torque which results from these types of interactions creates a tendency for a dipole to align itself so that its axis points to an interacting ion, while two dipoles tend to align themselves so that their axes are parallel. Of course, thermal energy tends to overcome the orientation in favored positions.

A charge induces a dipole in a neutral molecule, and an interaction between the charge and the induced dipole results. From Coulomb's law, attractive interaction energy is given by

$$U = -\frac{(Z_A q)^2 \alpha}{\varepsilon 2 r^4} \tag{3-18}$$

where α is the polarizability of the neutral molecule. An example of this type of interaction is one between an ion and a nonelectrolyte molecule in solution, for instance, the interaction between a K^+ ion and a N_2 molecule in an aqueous solution. Water, the solvent, has a permanent dipole moment. Ions formed by the solution of an electrolyte tend to induce an additional dipole moment, so that the interaction of an ion and a water molecule is more properly the sum of a charge dipole and a charge-induced dipole interaction. The attractive force in the latter case is expressed by the sum of eqs. 3-17 and 3-18. A permanent dipole may also induce a dipole in a neutral molecule, and the interaction energy depends upon the orientation of the permanent dipole and the induced dipole. Upon averaging orientations, the following expression for the average interaction energy can be derived:

$$U = -\frac{\mu^2 \alpha}{\varepsilon r^6} \tag{3-19}$$

An example of such an interaction is the one which occurs between N_2 and water molecules in a solution of nitrogen in water.

There are two other types of interactions where the energy varies with r^{-6}. The first of these is the induced dipole–induced dipole interaction which occurs between permanent dipoles that are free to rotate. For two dipoles of moments μ_A and μ_B and polarizability α_A and α_B, the interaction energy is given by

$$U = -\frac{(\mu_A^2 \alpha_B) + (\mu_B^2 \alpha_A)}{\varepsilon r^6} \tag{3-20}$$

Quantitatively this type of interaction is not important. A very much more important related attraction energy, particularly between nonpolar molecules, is that due to the coupling of electronic oscillators. The orbital electrons can be considered as electronic oscillators, and an attractive coupling force can occur between them. From quantum mechanical considerations, London[9] derived the following expression for this type of attractive force:

$$U = -\frac{3}{2} \cdot \left(\frac{h\nu_{iA} h\nu_{iB}}{h\nu_{iA} + h\nu_{iB}} \right) \frac{\alpha_A \alpha_B}{r^6} \tag{3-21}$$

where $h\nu_i$ is the ionization potential, that is, the energy required to remove one electron from the shell of an atom or molecule. It should be noted that this type of interaction, which is sometimes called the dispersion force or London force, is proportional to the product of the polarizability of the molecules and always is a force of attraction. The polarizability depends approximately upon the size of the molecules, and therefore large molecules tend to have large dispersion interactions.

The dielectric constant, ε, has appeared as a term in many of the electrostatic interaction equations, and it should be considered briefly. Of course, the dielectric constant of a vacuum is 1, and when the interaction energies between molecules in a system containing only one species of molecules is considered, the term ε drops out. However, when one molecular species is dispersed in a medium composed of a second molecular species, such as a solute in a solution, the dielectric constant of the medium may become very important. It should be pointed out that medium molecules must be interposed between solute molecules in order to produce a dielectric effect. The weak van der Waals interactions, those where the interaction energy varies as a function of $1/r^4$ or $1/r^6$, are effective only at short range, that is, at distances of separation so small that they do not admit interstitial solvent molecules.

The repulsive force which becomes manifest when two molecules make a very close approach has been mentioned briefly. This force becomes important when the electron clouds overlap and increases precipitously in magnitude as the overlap increases, that is, when $r < r_e$, where r_e is the separation at minimal potential energy. When the overlap is so great that the nuclei begin to approach each other, there is a large contribution to the repulsion from the Coulombic repulsion of two positive charges. The effect of these repulsive forces is to give each molecule a space-filling quality which corresponds roughly to the space filled by the electron clouds around each molecule. In effect, two molecules cannot occupy the same space at the same time. The quantity $r_e/2$ is called the *van der Waals radius* of a molecule and is intimately related to the constant b in the van der Waals equation of state (Fig. 3-12). A number of important considerations

[9] London, F. *Trans. Faraday Soc.*, *33*, 8 (1937).

arise in considering dispersion force interactions between macromolecules which will be considered later. The relative importance of the various weak interactions for representative small molecules is listed in Fig. 3-13.

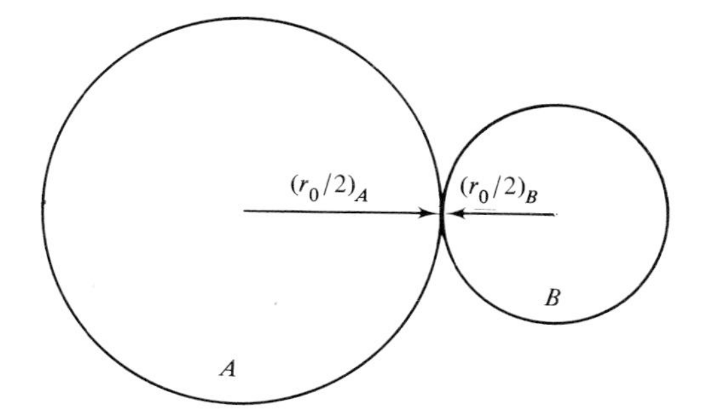

Molecule	r^* (in Å)	r_0 (in Å)
He	2.87	2.56
H_2	3.29	2.93
Ne	3.12	2.78
Ar	3.82	3.40
Kr	4.04	3.60
Xe	4.60	4.10
N_2	4.15	3.70
O_2	3.88	3.46
CH_4	4.28	3.82
CCl_4	6.61	5.88

fig. 3-12. Diagram showing two atoms in contact and their *van der Waals radii*, $r_0/2$. Values for r_0 and r^* (distance of separation for minimum potential energy) of a number of typical molecules are listed.

fig. 3-13. Lengths and energies of some hydrogen bonds. (Data from Pimental, George C., and McClellan, Aubrey L. *The Hydrogen Bond.* San Francisco: W. H. Freeman and Company, copyright © 1960; reprinted by permission.)

BOND	SUBSTANCE	LENGTH (Å)	ENERGY (KCAL/MOLE)
OH—O	H_2O	2.76	4.5
OH—O	CH_3OH	—	6.2
OH—O	$(CH_3COOH)_2$	—	8.2
CH—N	$(HCN)_2$	—	3.28
NH—N	NH_3	3.38	1.3
OH—N	Peptides	2.79	—
NH—F	NH_4F	2.63	5.0

The *hydrogen bond* is a special case of the dipole-dipole interaction; it occurs when one of the dipoles contains a hydrogen atom. One special feature of this interaction is that the length of the dipole and the distance of separation, r, become comparable. This results from the extremely small size of the hydrogen atom which allows a very close approach to the other dipole. The hydrogen atom which forms a hydrogen bond is usually covalently linked to a highly electronegative atom such as F, O, or N. Such a hydrogen atom will be strongly attracted by another F, O, or N atom. Hydrogen bonds have energies of 2 to 8 kcal/mole, bonds with more electronegative atoms being stronger. Because of their large size and lesser electronegativity, Cl, S, and P form very weak hydrogen bonds. Another consequence of the small size of the hydrogen atom is that it can only rarely associate with more than two electronegative atoms and it usually forms a linear sequence; that is, a hydrogen atom is covalently linked to one electronegative atom and, for steric reasons, is hydrogen-bonded to only one other electronegative atom. An anomolous feature of hydrogen bonds is that the interaction energy tends to vary as $1/r^2$.

The dipole of the covalent hydrogen bond is usually restricted in its freedom of rotation. This is particularly true in relatively large molecules. Here, through cooperative effects of multiple hydrogen bonds, they may play a key role in three-dimensional structure. The electronegative atoms to which hydrogens bond tend to form bonds in a tetrahedral array. For valence reasons, the tetrahedral array is incomplete when only covalent bonds are allowed. Hydrogen bonds permit the completion of the tetrahedral array and the propagation of a three-dimensional structure such as occurs extensively in water and in a rudimentary form in ammonia and hydrogen fluoride.

A final type of weak interaction that is important in biological systems is the *stacking interaction* between molecules containing conjugated, planar ring systems. Such molecules tend to orient themselves with the planar rings parallel to one another, thus forming stacks of molecules. In this configuration there tends to be an overlap of the π-orbitals which gives rise to some stabilization of the configuration by resonance energy. Many molecules of biological importance contain conjugated rings. The mutagenic dyes, acridine orange and related compounds, tend to associate with DNA in large part through stacking interactions, and they tend to bind to DNA in stacks when large amounts of dye are present.

water

Water constitutes about 75 percent or more of living organisms, and its properties have great relevance to life processes. The only exceptions which contain less water are inactive tissues or forms, such as hair or bone, or seeds or spores. Water is the matrix in which all the other substances present in living tissues are dissolved or dispersed. It enters into numerous metabolic reactions and is a product of others. Water is a very unusual liquid, and its chemical properties present many anomalies. While our present ideas about the structure of water are tentative and uncertain, the importance of water in living systems makes it worthwhile considering them.

If the melting points, boiling points, and heats of vaporization of homologous series of compounds having the general formula RH_n are plotted, these physical properties are found to increase almost in a straight line as the atomic number of R increases, excepting the first members of each series NH_3, H_2O, and HF. The values observed for these three compounds are far greater than would be predicted by extrapolation from the values of higher members of the series. The deviations from the expected values are greater for water than for ammonia or hydrogen fluoride. Thus, by extrapolation from H_2S, H_2Se, and H_2Te, a boiling point for water of -80°C would be expected instead of $+100$°C; a melting point of $-110°$ would be expected instead of 0°; and a heat of vaporization of about 4.3 kcal/mole would be expected instead of the actual heat of vaporization of 9.7 kcal/mole (Figs. 3-14, 3-15, and 3-16).

Water has a very high specific heat. Water, of course, is the standard on which the calorie is based; that is, the amount of heat required to raise the temperature of 1 g water from 15° to 16° is exactly 1 calorie. Most organic liquids have specific heats in the neighborhood of 0.5 cal/g. The specific heats of solids are even smaller: 0.5 cal/g for ice, approximately 0.3 cal/g for most organic solids, and 0.1 or less for metals. Only the specific heat of liquid ammonia, 1.23 cal/g, exceeds that of water. The heat of vaporization of water at the boiling point is 540 cal/g, higher than for any other substance liquid at room temperature. Methyl alcohol, which resembles water more closely than any other organic liquid, is next with a heat of vaporization at its boiling point of 263 cal/g. Most organic liquids have heats of vaporization in the neighborhood

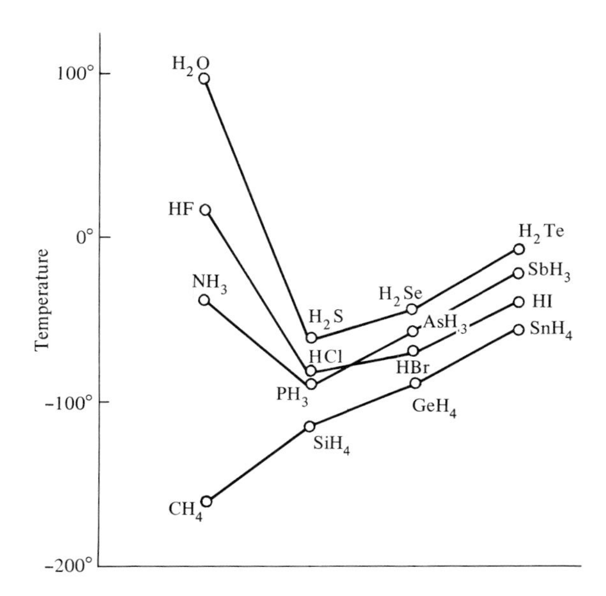

fig. 3-14. The boiling points of isoelectronic sequences of hydride molecules. (From Pauling, L. *The Nature of the Chemical Bond,* 3rd ed. Ithaca, N.Y.: Cornell University Press, 1960, p. 455. Copyright 1939 and 1940 by Cornell University. Third edition © 1960 by Cornell University. Reprinted by permission of the Cornell University Press.)

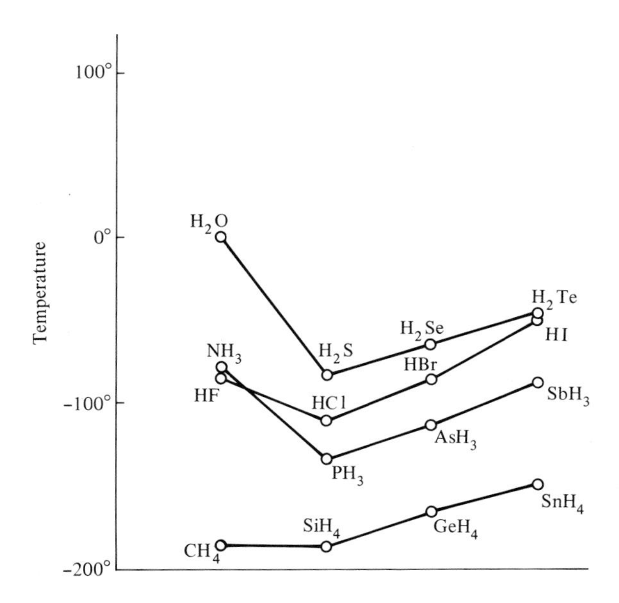

fig. 3-15. The melting points of isoelectronic sequences of hydride molecules. (From Pauling, L. *The Nature of the Chemical Bond,* 3rd ed. Ithaca, N.Y.: Cornell University Press, 1960, p. 455. Copyright 1939 and 1940 by Cornell University. Third edition © 1960 by Cornell University. Used by permission of the Cornell University Press.)

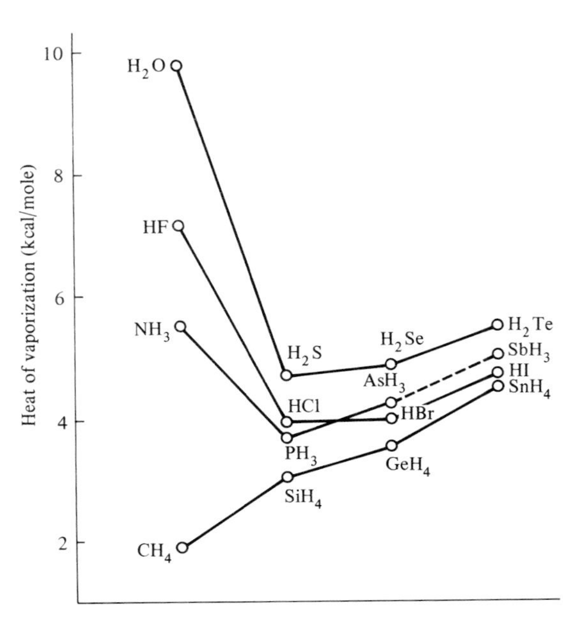

fig. 3-16. Heats of vaporization of isoelectronic sequences of hydride molecules. (From Pauling, L. *The Nature of the Chemical Bond,* 3rd ed. Ithaca, N.Y.: Cornell University Press, 1960, p. 456. Copyright 1939 and 1940 by Cornell University. Third edition © 1960 by Cornell University. Used by permission of the Cornell University Press.)

of 100 cal/g. At 40°, the heat of vaporization of water is 574 cal/g. The heat of fusion of water is 80 cal/g. In this physical property, water is exceeded by ammonia, which has a heat of fusion of 108 cal/g, and by a number of inorganic salts. The high melting point, high boiling point, and high heat of vaporization are direct indications of the presence of strong intermolecular forces in water.

A water molecule is shaped like an isosceles triangle. The legs of the triangle are the two O-H bonds which have an internuclear distance of 0.99 Å, and the angle subtended between the bonds is very close to 105°. Because oxygen is very electronegative, the water molecule is a permanent dipole with a moment of 1.84 μ (debye units). Molecular orbital calculations indicate the four pairs of electrons in the water oxygen are highly localized within four tetrahedrally directed hybrid orbitals, two of them on the side of the oxygen atom opposite to the hydrogen atoms. The water molecules tend to orient themselves so that the positive side of one water molecule faces the negative sides of adjacent molecules. In this way, there tends to arise a propagated structure of hydrogen-bonded molecules in water.

The crystal structure of water in the solid form, ice I, resembles that of the hexagonal form of SiO_2, which is known as tridymite (Fig. 3-17). The oxygen atoms of each water molecule are covalently bonded to two hydrogen atoms, and in addition, participate in two hydrogen bonds. Each oxygen atom is surrounded by four other oxygen atoms 2.76 Å distant in a tetrahedral array. The hydrogen atoms lie on lines connecting the oxygen atoms but are closer to the oxygen atom to which they are covalently bonded than to the oxygen atom to which they are hydrogen-bonded. The distances between oxygen atoms are large compared to the van der Waals radii of the atoms, and the crystal structure has a very open centrosymmetric form. The oxygen atoms lie in layers, each a network of hexagons in which alternate oxygen atoms are

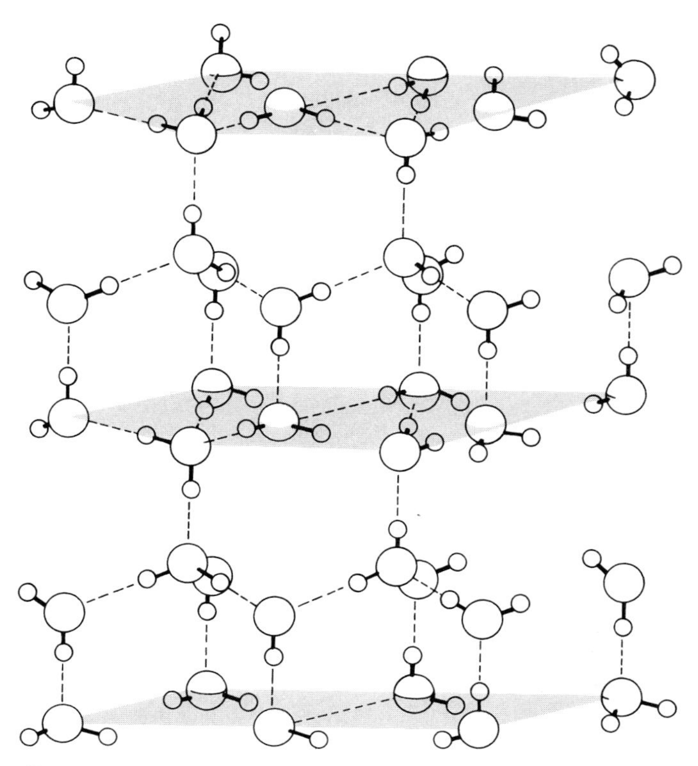

fig. 3-17. The arrangement of water molecules in normal ice.

raised or lowered. Alternate layers are mirror images of each other. Pauling has estimated the energy of the hydrogen bonds in ice from the difference between the heat of sublimation of ice, 12.2 kcal/mole, and the heat of sublimation of methane and related molecules which do not form hydrogen bonds. He obtained a value of approximately 4.5 kcal/mole. This is about one–twenty-fifth the energy of the O-H bond in water which is 110 kcal/mole, but it is sufficient to account for the extensive intermolecular interactions and the high degree of organization in water and other hydrogen-bonded liquids. Additional stabilization of the hydrogen-bonded configuration comes from resonance forms which are possible in this configuration (Fig. 3-18).

Thus, the distinctive properties of water are ascribed to the partial retention of the crystalline, hydrogen-bonded structure of ice. The heat of fusion of ice, 1.44 kcal/mole, leads to the conclusion that only about 15 percent of the hydrogen bonds in ice are broken when it melts. It is common knowledge that ice is less dense than water at the

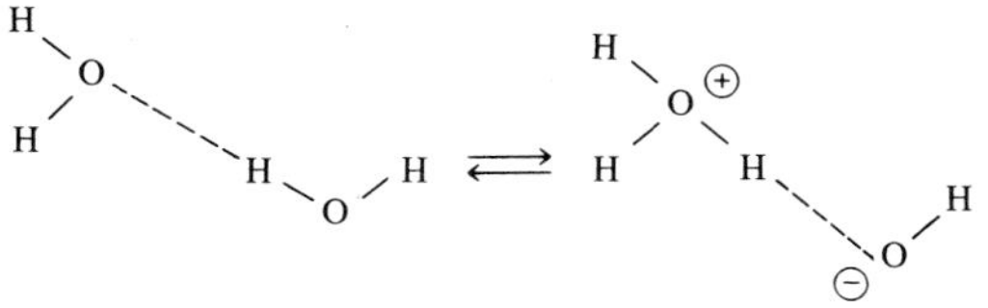

H
O
H
H O H ⇌ H
O ⊕
H
H
O
⊖

fig. 3-18. Resonance of hydrogen bonds in water. The separation of charges may be followed by separation into ions.

freezing point and that water reaches its maximum density at 4°C. *X*-ray diffraction studies indicate that upon melting the nearest-neighbor distance between atoms increases slightly to about 2.9 Å. This is more than offset, however, by an increase in the number of nearest neighbors of each oxygen atom from 4 in ice to 4.4–4.6 in water at the melting point, reflecting a denser packing of the water molecules than the open crystal structure in ice even though only a portion of the crystalline bonds have broken. As the temperature rises above 4°, the increased thermal energy results in increased breaking down of the crystalline structure and continued expansion of the structure.

The fact that ice is less dense than water has very important implications for the biologist, because it is difficult to visualize the development of life if this were not the case.[10] If ice were heavier than water, it would sink to the bottom. The oceans, lakes, and rivers would fill up with ice in cold weather. In warm weather the ice would remain at the bottom and not melt if the body of water were deep enough. It is well known that it is possible to boil water by applying heat at the surface while not appreciably melting a piece of ice held at the bottom of the container. Because ice forms at the surface, it protects the water below from further cooling, and when it is exposed to warmth, the ice melts. Water sinking as it cools until it reaches 4°, but, upon further cooling, rising to the surface, tends to augment the current flows in large bodies of water and thus to increase their efficiency as environmental thermostats.

Röntgen,[11] in 1892, advanced the notion, which he claimed was not new even at that time, that water was a mixture, a solution of ice in a denser, truly liquid species of water. Röntgen proposed that water represents an equilibrium of the following chemical reaction:

$$(H_2O)_d \leftrightarrows (H_2O)_b \qquad H_2O \leftrightarrows \frac{1}{n}(H_2O)_n \tag{3-22}$$

where $(H_2O)_d$ and $(H_2O)_b$ are the dense and bulky forms, respectively. For this reaction $\Delta H^\circ < 0$, $\Delta V^\circ > 0$, and the dense form of water flows more freely than does the bulky form. These assumptions taken together with the principle of le Chatelier made it possible for Röntgen to account for phenomena of water he had discovered: the temperature of maximum density is lowered when the pressure is increased, and an increase in pressure is accompanied by a decrease in the viscosity of cold water (see Chapter 4). The right-hand form expresses the reaction in terms of a polymerization.

Because of the negative ΔH°, the equilibrium will shift to the left with increasing temperature, producing a negative term in $(\partial V/\partial T)_P$. The magnitude of this term is greater at low temperatures; at high temperatures it is small compared to expansion of $(H_2O)_d + (H_2O)_b$. The specific volume will reach a minimum at the temperature where the two effects are equal. The temperature of minimum density can be explained on the basis of these assumptions without invoking a phase change or another transformation. H. S. Frank[12] points out that the abnormally low expansibility of water at higher temperatures is just as remarkable as its negative expansibility below 4°, and that increased pressure not only lowers the temperature of maximum density but also increases the expansibility of water at higher temperatures instead of lowering it as it does in other liquids.

Several theories of water structure have been proposed which account for the bulky

[10] Henderson, L. J. *The Fitness of the Environment*. New York: Macmillan, 1913.
[11] Röntgen, W. K. *Ann. Phys. Chem.*, *45*, 91 (1892).
[12] Frank, H. S. *Federation Proc.*, *24*, suppl. 15, 1 (1965).

form; the *flickering-cluster* model of Frank and Wen appears to satisfy many experimental observations. Frank and Wen[13] postulated that the formation of hydrogen bonds in water is a cooperative phenomenon; that is, the formation of one hydrogen bond between two water molecules enhances the probability that each will in turn hydrogen bond to other adjacent water molecules. The greater tendency of a hydrogen-bonded molecule to form an additional hydrogen bond is thought to arise from the existence of three resonance forms for the hydrogen bond, one of which requires a charge separation between the two oxygen atoms. Although it is quite different from complete dissociation into hydroxyl and hydronium ions, the formation of a hydrogen bond between two water molecules may be regarded as a Lewis-type acid-base interaction resulting in a polarization which makes one molecule more acidic and the other more basic than the nonbonded monomers. The hydrogen bonds in water, then, are made and broken not singly, but in groups; they give rise to short-lived clusters of hydrogen-bonded water molecules. Because of the tetrahedral orientation of the hybrid orbitals around the oxygen atoms, end-to-end chains of hydrogen-bonded molecules will not be favored, but rather the clusters will be approximately spherical in shape and will consist of as compact tetrahedrally oriented structures as is possible. While there is a statistical distribution of cluster size around a large average size, there is no appreciable population of small clusters, dimers, trimers, tetramers, etc. Using published values of the dielectric relaxation time, Frank estimated the half-life of a cluster to be in the range of 10^{-10} to 10^{-11} sec or about two to three orders of magnitude greater than the period of molecular vibration—a half-time great enough to make their existence significant.

Némethy and Scheraga[14] have been able to carry out a statistical mechanical analysis of the flickering-cluster model assuming that only clusters and monomers will exist (Fig. 3-19). Within the clusters there are four species of molecules, molecules with four hydrogen bonds in the interior, and molecules participating in one, two, or three hydrogen bonds at the surface of the clusters. Of course, the relative proportions of each species depend upon the size of the clusters and their surface-to-volume ratios. An energy level can be assigned to each species of water molecule depending on the number of hydrogen bonds in which it participates. The nonhydrogen-bonded molecules must be considered, too, because they participate in other molecular interactions due to dipole forces. The difference in energy levels assigned to the nonbonded and four-hydrogen–bonded molecules represents the difference between the energy required to break four hydrogen bonds and the gain in energy by dipole and dispersion force interactions with eight near neighbors as a nonbonded molecule. They also deduced a second parameter, the "free volume" for translational motion of nonbonded molecules. They then obtained an expression for the partition function from which the thermodynamic properties U, S, G and C_V could be obtained. The best agreement with experimentally observed values of the thermodynamic properties was obtained with an energy difference between the nonbonded and four-hydrogen–bonded forms of 1.32 kcal/mole. Némethy and Scheraga also calculated the average cluster size and the mole fraction of water molecules participating in clusters as a function of temperature. The results are given in Fig. 3-20. While the mole fraction of nonbonded water molecules increases slowly with increasing temperatures, there is a precipitous drop

[13] Frank, H. S., and Wen, W. Y. *Discussions Faraday Soc.*, *24*, 133 (1957); Frank, H. S., and Quist, A. S. *J. Chem. Phys.*, *34*, 604 (1961).

[14] Némethy, G., and Scheraga, H. A. *J. Chem. Phys.*, *36*, 3382, 3401 (1962); *J. Phys. Chem.*, *66*, 1773 (1962).

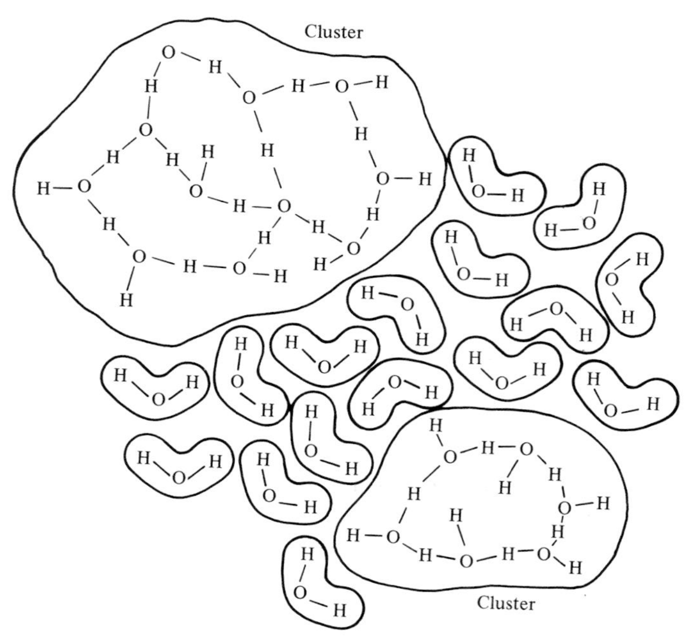

fig. 3-19. Schematic representation of the Frank and Wen–Némethy and Scheraga *flickering cluster* model of water, showing hydrogen-bonded clusters and unbonded molecules. (From Némethy, G., and Scheraga, H. A. *J. Chem. Phys., 36,* 3387 [1962].)

fig. 3-20. Temperature-dependence of cluster size and the mole fraction of nonhydrogen-bonded molecules in liquid H_2O and D_2O. (Data from Némethy, G., and Scheraga, H. A. *J. Chem. Phys., 36,* 3394 [1962]; *41,* 685 [1964].)

	MOLECULES PER CLUSTER		MOLE FRACTION	
TEMPERATURE, °C	H_2O	D_2O	H_2O	D_2O
0	91	—	0.24	—
4	—	117	—	0.23
10	72	97	0.27	0.25
20	57	72	0.29	0.27
30	47	56	0.32	0.30
40	38	44	0.34	0.32
50	32	35	0.36	0.34
60	28	29	0.38	0.36

in the cluster size. This means that as the temperature increases, the number of four-hydrogen–bonded species decreases. However, the doubly and singly hydrogen-bonded species go through maxima of concentration at 50° and 80°, respectively.

The ease with which water can be supercooled, that is, the difficulty in forming crystallization nuclei spontaneously in supercooled, dust-free water, has been one of the most persuasive arguments against the existence of fragments with icelike structure in liquid water. The failure of neighboring clusters to coalesce and propagate the ordered structure further upon cooling may be explained in the following manner. The faces of a hydrogen-bonded cluster will display a pattern of partial charge separation on hydrogen atoms and lone pair electrons. The faces of two clusters will be able to coalesce only if their opposing faces have the correct tetrahedral geometry and matching patterns of hydrogen atoms and lone pair electrons. The clusters form randomly and separately, and the possibilities of face patterns are vast, so that the likelihood of two opposing faces matching would be extremely rare. On the other hand, the probability of the presence of clusters of the sizes required from water compressibility data is not very high.

Pauling[15] proposed another model for the bulky species of water in which single water molecules are surrounded by a clathrate framework. The basic unit in such frameworks is the pentagonal dodecahedron; the oxygen atoms of the 20 participating water molecules are located at each of the vertices of the dodecahedron. Three of the four tetrahedrally oriented bonds of each oxygen atom form the edges of the polyhedron, while the fourth projects directly outward from the vertex formed by the oxygen atom. Of the 40 hydrogen atoms, 30 are found in hydrogen bonds in the edges of the dodecahedron. The remaining 10 hydrogens are available to form a lattice with other polyhedra. The polyhedra enclose cavities 5 to 7 Å in diameter which can be filled by unreactive molecules such as a molecule of one of the rare gases or a hydrocarbon (Fig. 3-21).

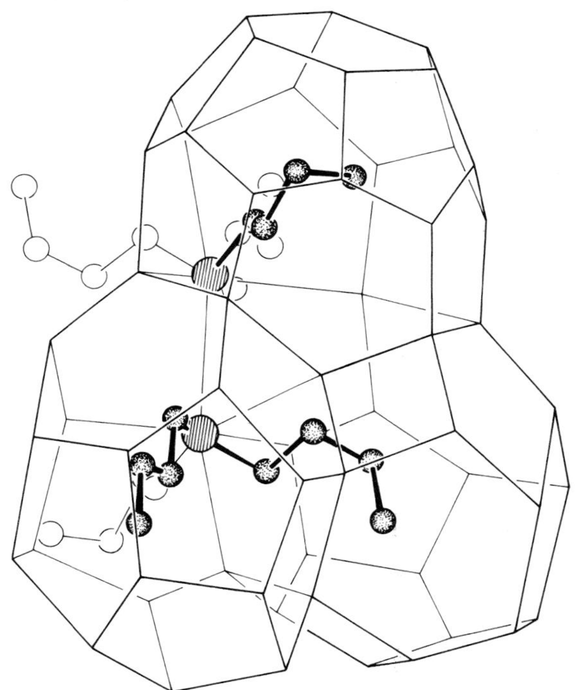

fig. 3-21. A schematic drawing of a clathrate containing two tributylsulfonium ions in the cavity. (From Beurskens, P. T., and Jeffrey, G. A. *J. Chem. Phys., 40,* 2805 [1964].)

The energy of the hydrogen bonds alone is not sufficient to stabilize the clathrate structure. However, the presence of an unreactive molecule in the cavity permits permanent dipole-induced–dipole and transient dipole-induced–dipole interactions

[15] Pauling, L., and Marsh, R. E. *Proc. Natl. Acad. Sci., 38*, 112 (1952).

between the entrapped molecule and the water molecules in the framework. An empty 11.88 Å clathrate framework has a calculated enthalpy of 160 cal/mole greater than ice at 0° and a free energy of 167 cal/mole greater than ice at 0°. This leads to the conclusion that there is little entropy difference between the water molecules in the clathrate framework and in ordinary ice at 0°. The stabilizing effect of the guest molecule is shown by the measured enthalpy of formation of the xenon clathrate from gaseous xenon and ice at 0° of 8.4 kcal/mole. Pauling suggested that the bulky phase of water could consist of dodecahedral clathrate frameworks in which a twenty-first water molecule occupied a central position inside the cage and did not participate in any hydrogen bonds. Clusters of dodecahedra might occur joining each other through hydrogen bonds or even sharing pentagonal faces. The dodecahedral complex might be more stable because it contains 71.5 percent of the maximum number of possible hydrogen bonds, while no tridymite-like cluster of 21 water molecules can be constructed in which there are formed as many as 60 percent of the maximum possible number of hydrogen bonds. In a sense, the water-clathrate structure can be regarded as a specific type of flickering cluster, and the model has been analyzed in such terms.

A variation of the water hydrate model has been proposed recently by Danford and Levy[16] on the basis of *x*-ray diffraction analysis. In their view, the oxygen atoms are arranged in layers of puckered, six-membered rings. Between two adjacent layers, mirror images of each other, virtual polyhedral cavities are formed, some of which are occupied by lone interstitial water molecules. In their view, the interstitial water molecules (representing the bulky form) may be hydrogen-bonded to the lattice, possibly coupled to protonic defects which should occur relatively easily in the expanded lattice. If this conjecture is correct, diffusion should occur by means of propagation of protonic defects, either as an empty bond or as a doubly occupied bond, and will be coupled to the dielectric relaxation time. Dielectric relaxation times calculated from diffusion rates agree remarkably well with relaxation times observed experimentally. A similar model has been proposed by Berendsen[17] in which 15 molecules are arranged to form a cage between two parallel planar pentagons, so joined that three puckered, six-membered rings are formed (Fig. 3-22). The cage can be filled by an interstitial molecule without disturbing the lattice. Actually, the structured elements of water may be very

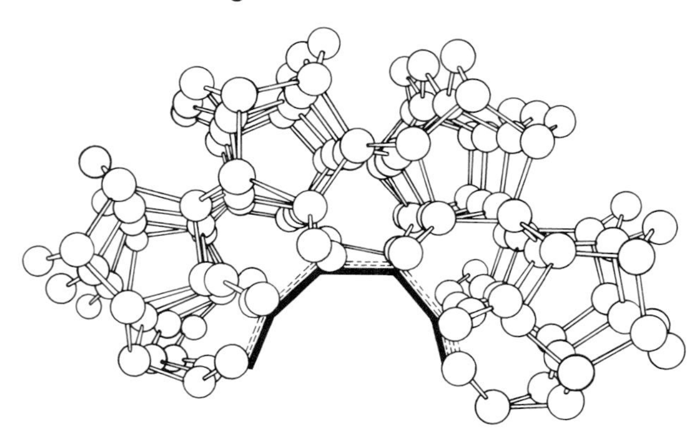

fig. 3-22. A diagram of water molecules arranged in pentagonal cages, a structure intermediate between icelike structures and clathrates, clustered around a model of collagen to which they might be attached by hydrogen bonding. (From Berendsen, H. J. C. *Quart. Progr. Rep., R. L. E., Mass. Inst. Techn., 58*, 249 [1960].)

[16] Danford, M. D., and Levy, H. A. *J. Am. Chem. Soc., 84*, 3965 (1962).
[17] Berendsen, H. J. C. *Federation Proc., 25*, 971 (1966).

complex and contain all these forms with local variations depending upon the nature of surface boundaries and surfaces presented by macromolecules.

The present views concerning the dense species of water are even more speculative. From one viewpoint, it is difficult to conceive of the existence of some water molecules, with their large dipole moment and propensity to form hydrogen bonds, in the liquid without their being subject to the same intermolecular forces as the molecules in the bulky structures. Lennard-Jones and Pople[18] proposed that no water molecules are "free," but rather that the hydrogen bonds, are "bent," that is, the hydrogen atom does not lie on the axis joining adjacent oxygen atoms. Many, though not all, of the infra-red spectroscopic studies indicate that there are few broken bonds in water. Water of this type might well be the interstitial water between flickering clusters or hydrate structures. A bolder proposal has also been made for the dense species which has considerable merit. Because of its small moment of inertia and the consequence that quantal effects are important in its rotational motion, it has been proposed that the molecules of interstitial water act as effectively free rotators. There is some evidence from cold neutron scattering experiments that supports this view.[19] Such a freely rotating monomer would probably be "nonhydrophilic" because the dipole moment should be averaged out over the various rotational states.

The viscosity, melting point, temperature of maximum density, and molar heat capacity of heavy water are all higher than for ordinary water, indicating that there is more structural order in D_2O than in H_2O. Némethy and Scheraga[20] extended their treatment of the flickering-cluster model of water to heavy water by taking the energy of breaking a hydrogen bond in D_2O to be 230 cal/mole higher than in H_2O. The results of their calculations give clusters of larger size and a greater fraction of molecules in the clusters for heavy water.

aqueous solutions

A solution may be defined as a homogeneous, one-phase mixture of two or more substances. Although there is no fundamental qualitative difference in the contributions of the various constituents to the system as a whole, it is convenient to call the substance present in excess the *solvent* and to call the other constituents of the system *solutes*, that is, dissolved substances. The biologist is generally concerned with systems in which water is the solvent, and the solutes are nonvolatile solids whose vapor pressures are negligible. A number of the physical properties of solutions compared to solvents alone—the osmotic pressure, the elevation of the boiling point, the depression of the freezing point, and the depression of the vapor pressure—depend upon the number of nonvolatile solute particles in solution. Together these properties are sometimes called the *colligative properties* of solutions.

In 1748 the Abbé Nollet found that when a vial containing an aqueous solution of alcohol was covered with an animal bladder and immersed in pure water, some of the water passed through the bladder. The Abbé correctly interpreted the seeming paradox of water moving into a sealed vial and increasing the internal pressure in the process by assuming that the bladder was more permeable to water than to ethanol. In 1827 Dutrochet introduced the manometer into osmotic pressure experiments and coined

[18] Lennard-Jones, J., and Pople, J. A. *Proc. Roy. Soc.*, *A 205*, 155, 163 (1951).
[19] Hughes, D. J., Palevsky, H., Kley, W., and Tunkelo, E. *Phys. Rev.*, *119*, 872 (1960).
[20] Némethy, G., and Scheraga, H. A. *J. Chem. Phys.*, *41*, 680 (1964).

the term "osmose" to describe the phenomenon. There followed a period of intense fascination and observation of osmotic phenomena in living systems, the swelling of cells transferred to hypotonic media, and the shrinkage after immersion in hypertonic solutions. This interest culminated in the careful, quantitative experiments of Hugo de Vries (1848–1935) on the osmotic behavior of plant cells, and the experiments of H. J. Hamburger (1859–1924) on osmotic phenomena in animal cells. The results of their studies and the experiments of Wilhelm Pfeffer (1845–1920), who used artificial osmometers made by precipitating a copper ferrocyanide membrane in a porous plate, led Jacobus H. van't Hoff (1852–1911) to his formulation of the laws of solutions.

Van't Hoff's monumental contribution consisted of demonstrating that at constant temperature the osmotic pressure of dilute solutions depended only upon the concentration of solute particles and not upon their size or molecular weight. He showed that the osmotic pressure was proportional to the absolute temperature if the concentration of solute remained constant. Furthermore, he observed that the osmotic pressure of a solution at 0°C containing one mole of solute per liter of solvent was 22.4 atmospheres. In short, van't Hoff discovered that dilute or "ideal" solutions could be described by an equation analogous to the ideal gas law:

$$\Pi = \frac{nRT}{V} \tag{3-23}$$

where Π is the osmotic pressure, n the number of moles of solutes, and V the volume of solvent. Just as gases tend to deviate from the ideal gas law as the pressure increases, solutions tend to deviate from ideality as the concentrations of solutes increase. These deviations from ideality result from interactions between the solute molecules themselves, between solvent molecules themselves, and between solute molecules and solvent molecules. These interactions result in a marked concentration dependence of the osmotic pressure. Just as the van der Waals equation of state can be used to describe a nonideal gas, an analogous equation can be used to describe the osmotic pressure of nonideal solution:

$$\Pi/c = RT(1/M + Bc + Cc^2 + \cdots) \tag{3-24}$$

where M is the molecular weight of the solute, and $c/M = n/V$.

Let us examine briefly the effects of molecular interactions upon the properties of solutions. Because of the unique structure of water, most aqueous solutions deviate markedly from ideality. It is convenient for purposes of discussion to divide aqueous solutions into four classes according to the properties of the solute: (1) nonpolar nonelectrolytes such as hydrocarbons, which do not form hydrogen bonds; (2) polar nonelectrolytes, such as sugars, which may participate in hydrogen bonds; (3) solutions of electrolytes; and (4) solutions of macromolecules.

Solutions of hydrocarbons in water interest the biologist because the results can be applied by analogy, for instance, to the nonpolar amino acid side chains in proteins. If aqueous solutions of hydrocarbons were ideal, there would be no change in volume or enthalpy upon mixing, and the free energy and entropy of mixing would be comparable to the values found for the solution of hydrocarbons in nonpolar solvents. In point of fact, the dissolution of hydrocarbons in water is accompanied by a decrease in the partial molal volume; mixing is exothermic, and there is a negative enthalpy of mixing. This negative enthalpy is more than offset by a large negative entropy of solution which results in a large positive free energy of mixing and corresponds to the low solubility of hydrocarbons in water. While the thermodynamic considerations are discussed in Chapter 4, the general events which occur upon the dissolution of a hydrocarbon can be explained tentatively in the following manner.

When a solute molecule is introduced into water, it will displace a water molecule as a neighbor to solvent water molecules. Because a water molecule is a much stronger dipole than a hydrocarbon molecule, the sum of the van der Waals forces between two water molecules will be greater than between a water molecule and a hydrocarbon molecule. The displacement of a water molecule by a solute molecule, therefore, will be an unfavorable event. Many water molecules already have as many as four hydrogen-bonded neighbor water molecules. Sometimes it is possible for a water molecule to acquire a hydrocarbon solute molecule as a fifth neighbor; the solute molecule occupies a partial void in the water structure. The latter arrangement is possible only if the solute molecule is inert; that is, it does not disturb the orientation of water molecules, either by electrostatic forces or by hydrogen bonding. Because the hydrocarbon molecules occupy space in the water structure which was largely empty, there is a decrease in volume upon mixing. The presence of a fifth solute neighbor results in a lowering of the potential energy level of the four-hydrogen–bonded water molecule. In the case of water molecules with less than four hydrogen bonds, the solute molecule displaces a neighbor water molecule, a substitution which, as stated above, is energetically not favorable. The presence of solute molecules, therefore, tends to increase the number of four-hydrogen–bonded water molecules and thereby increases the structural order in the solvent water. In this way, a large negative entropy of mixing is brought about. In the ultimate case, the presence of hydrocarbon solutes results in a stabilization and extension of the polyhedral hydrate cages. But in general, the displacement of water molecules is so unfavorable that two apolar molecules in an aqueous solution tend to come out of the water environment and associate with each other. The resistance to disruption of the hydrogen-bonded structure in water is greater than the tendency for water and hydrocarbons to mix, and therefore the solubility of hydrocarbons in water is small.

In the case of polar nonelectrolytes, particularly molecules that are able to participate in hydrogen bonds, the displacement of a water molecule by the introduction of a solute molecule results in a molecular substitution where the van der Waals interaction forces are comparable. Such solutes are highly soluble in water, and they seem to produce little change in the extent of the water structure. An important exception to this rule is urea, which appears to be a strong structure-breaking solute. The structure breaking action of urea seems to originate for steric reasons, which makes it difficult for urea to participate in extended tetrahedrally oriented hydrogen-bonded structures.[21]

solutions of electrolytes

Electrolytes may be defined as substances which conduct electricity and where the passage of an electric current is accompanied by a transport of matter. In the latter respect, electrolytes differ from electronic conductors. The transport of matter in electrolytes upon the passage of an electric current is best observed at the discontinuities of the electrolyte phase. For example, Nicholson and Carlisle found in 1800 that upon connecting to a battery two platinum wires immersed in a dilute aqueous solution of acid, bubbles of hydrogen and oxygen appeared at the platinum wires;

[21] Rupley, J. A. *J. Phys. Chem.*, *68*, 2002 (1964).

hydrogen at the wire connected to the negative pole of the battery (cathode) and oxygen at the wire connected to the positive pole of the battery (anode).[22]

Michael Faraday (1791–1867) observed that if the electrolyte solution contained a salt such as copper sulfate or silver nitrate, the corresponding metal was plated out on the cathode instead of hydrogen being liberated. Faraday also observed that if the anode was made of a base metal such as iron, zinc, or copper, the metal tended to dissolve with passage of an electric current. To account for these observations, Faraday proposed that the electric current was conducted by means of charged particles moving in the electrolyte, which he called *ions* (Gk., "wanderer"). The particles carrying a positive charge and moving toward the cathode were called *cations*, while those carrying a negative charge and moving towards the anode were called *anions*. Faraday thought that the charges on the ions were neutralized at the electrodes, releasing uncharged atoms or molecules.

Relying on van't Hoff's observations that the colligative properties of electrolytes in solution were far in excess of those expected from their mole fraction, Svante A. Arrhenius (1859–1927) put forward the theory of electrolytic dissociation in 1887. When an acid, base, or salt is dissolved in water, a considerable portion of it spontaneously dissociates into cations and anions.

$$AB \rightarrow A^+ + B^- \tag{3-25}$$

The ions formed in the solution are free to move independently and tend to move to electrodes of opposite sign under the influence of an applied electric field. The nineteenth-century chemists were so impressed with the stability of inorganic molecules that the idea of ionic dissociation eluded them for a long time. Thus Arrhenius's theory was a bold step forward.

Electrolyte solutions can be considered quantitatively by introducing the *dissociation coefficient*, α, to describe the stoichiometry of eq. 3-25. If n moles of AB are dissolved in a solution

$$n(1-\alpha)AB \rightarrow n\alpha A^+ + n\alpha B^- \tag{3-26}$$

and the equilibrium constant is given by

$$K = \frac{[A^+][B^-]}{[AB]} = \frac{(n\alpha)(n\alpha)}{1-\alpha} = \frac{n^2\alpha^2}{1-\alpha} \tag{3-27}$$

for an electrolyte of the type AB_2, the following expressions can be written:

$$n(1-\alpha)AB_2 \rightarrow n\alpha A^{++} + 2n\alpha B^- \tag{3-28}$$

$$K = \frac{[A^{++}][B^-]^2}{[AB]} = \frac{(n\alpha)(2n\alpha)^2}{n(1-\alpha)} = \frac{4n^2\alpha^3}{1-\alpha} \tag{3-29}$$

Similar relations can be written for other types of electrolytes.

The osmotic pressure and other colligative properties of an ideal electrolyte solution, that is, a solution where the individual components do not interact with each other, are a function of the mole fraction of solutes. The dissociation of electrolytes results in a greater effective mole fraction than if dissociation did not occur. Van't Hoff

[22] The system of nomenclature used in the chemistry of electrolytes was devised by Michael Faraday in consultation with W. Whewell and used in Faraday's definitive papers on this subject, *Experimental Researches in Electricity, Seventh Series*, 1833–1834.

designated the required correction factor i

$$\frac{\text{Observed osmotic pressure}}{\text{Expected osmotic pressure}} = i \tag{3-30}$$

This same correction factor applies to the greater freezing-point depression, boiling-point elevation, and vapor-pressure depression of electrolyte solutes. If an electrolyte molecule gives v ions upon dissociating, 2 in the case of eq. 3-25 and 3 in the case of eq. 3-28, the factor, i, is given by

$$i = \frac{n(1 - \alpha) + vn\alpha}{n} = 1 + (v - 1)\alpha \tag{3-31}$$

The dissociation coefficient can be obtained from any of the colligative properties by the following relation:

$$\alpha = \frac{i - 1}{v - 1} \tag{3-32}$$

In dealing with electrolyte solutions, it is also of interest to know the combined effects of multiple electrolyte solutes. It is convenient to express the effects of a multicomponent electrolyte solution in terms of the ionic strength, $\boldsymbol{u}$. The ionic strength is defined by the following relationship:

$$\boldsymbol{u} = \tfrac{1}{2} \sum n_i Z_i^2 \tag{3-33}$$

where n is the mole fraction of the ith ion (regardless of the polarity of its charge) and Z_i is the number of its charge. For the salt AB:

$$\boldsymbol{u} = \tfrac{1}{2}[n(1)^2 + n(1)^2] = n \tag{3-34}$$

For the salt AB_2

$$\boldsymbol{u} = \tfrac{1}{2}[n(2)^2 + 2n(1)^2] = 3n \tag{3-35}$$

For a multicomponent solution, the contribution of the ions of all components must be summed.

In Arrhenius's theory of electrolyte solutions, dissolving an electrolyte in water led to a dissociation of the molecules into ions. He was able to explain electrolytic conduction and the higher colligative properties of electrolyte solutions. A number of difficulties arose, however, with the simple form of his theory. The degree of dissociation, α, often did not agree with the van't Hoff i factor. Sometimes α was greater than unity. When electrolytes are dissolved, there is very little heat absorbed or evolved—a fact that had been noted by Hess before Arrhenius stated his theory. This generalization led to the conjecture that solid electrolytes are already dissociated and that no chemical dissociation reaction, but rather only a separation of ions, occurs upon mixing. Direct evidence supporting this conjecture came from x-ray diffraction studies of electrolyte crystals. A remarkable deficiency in the original theory of Arrhenius was the fact that the participation of the solvent in the dissociation process was neglected completely. Because of the high dielectric constant of water, the attractive interaction energy between two ions of opposite charge (given by eq. 3-4) is about 1/80 in aqueous solution of the energy in the solid crystal.

Although it has been known for more than half a century that ion-solvent interactions occur, the details are still fragmentary and their quantification is still uncertain. In addition to the marked diminution of interionic attractive forces by the interposition of bulk water with its high dielectric constant, ions interact with water molecules directly, principally as a result of charge-dipole attraction and, to a lesser extent, as a result of other weak interactions. Thus a number of water molecules tend to become intimately associated with a dissolved ion, a phenomenon known as *solvation* or *hydration*. For water molecules immediately adjacent to the ion, the bulk dielectric constant for water is not relevant in applying eq. 3-14. The interaction energy is proportional to $1/r^2$, and ions with the smallest radii will have the largest and most tenaciously held primary layer of water molecules (Fig. 3-23). The interaction energy

fig. 3-23. Radii and hydration of alkali earth ions.

ION	CRYSTAL RADIUS (Å)	HYDRATED RADIUS (Å)	HYDRATION (NUMBER OF WATER MOLECULES)
Li^+	0.68	2.51	6.0
Na^+	1.01	2.25	4.6
K^+	1.30	1.86	2.3
Rb^+	1.50	1.75	1.7
Cs^+	1.75	1.56	—

will be greater than RT (about 0.6 kcal/mole) for $r^2 < 25$ Å^2. The interaction energy is greater than the hydrogen-bond or dipole-dipole interaction energies between the water molecules themselves. In a few instances, the first sheath of water molecules are firmly held in a long-term sense. Hunt and Traube[23] using O^{18} as a tracer have shown in a series of elegant experiments that the water molecules in the $[Cr(H_2O)_6]^{+++}$ ion, for example, have a half-time of exchange with solvent water of about 40 hours. The water surrounding most ions, even such small, multiply charged ions as Al^{+++} and Th^{++++}, exchanges within a few minutes. Although water molecules exchange readily with solvent water in the hydration shell, it can be regarded as a permanent structure compared to the times of Brownian motion, even though there is probably a statistical variation in its size and energy. While the interaction energy of the water molecules in the first layer is large compared with RT, more peripheral water is loosely bound. In addition to the larger distance of separation (r), there is some interposition of bulk solvent with an increase in the effective dielectric constant. It seems likely that the water molecules in the secondary layer have interaction energies comparable to their thermal energies only in the case of small, polyvalent, monatomic ions.

In addition to the solvent-structuring action of ions by the process of hydration, ions also have a structure-breaking effect. Actually, in large part, the structure-breaking action of ions is a consequence of hydration. In order for water molecules to arrange themselves in a tetrahedrally oriented, hydrogen-bonded structure, the direction of the dipole must alternate. In contrast, an ion gives rise to an intense, radially oriented field which tends to orient the water molecules in the hydration shell with their dipole axes directed toward the central ion. The two arrangements are depicted in Fig. 3-24. The water molecules in the hydration shell, therefore, have only limited opportunity for hydrogen bonding to other water molecules in the bulk of the solvent. In addition,

[23] Hunt, J. P., and Traube, H. *J. Chem. Phys.*, *18*, 757 (1950); *19*, 602 (1951).

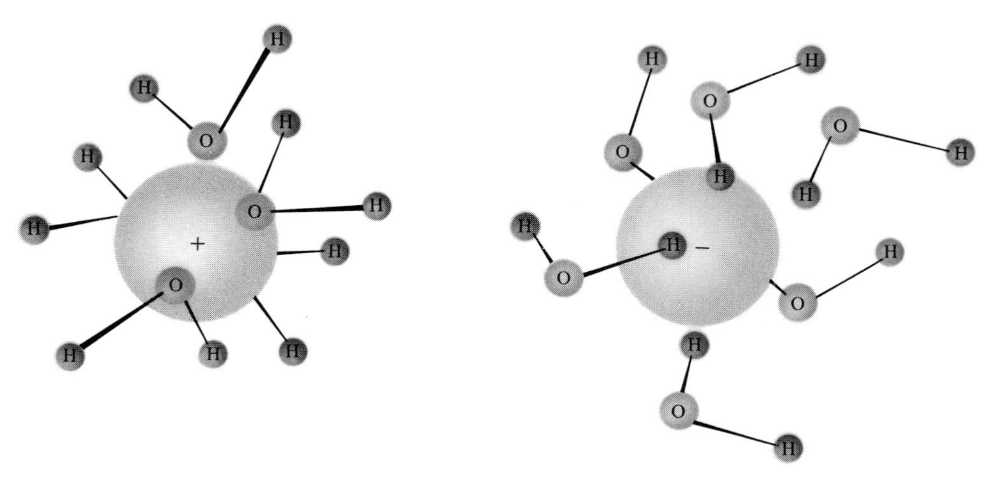

fig. 3-24. Schematic representation of the orientation of water molecules around ions.

the electric field of the ion may create sufficient torque on water dipoles farther removed to result in orientations unfavorable for participation in hydrogen-bonded structures. Experimental evidence for the structure-breaking action of ions comes, for example, from their influence on the self-diffusion of water. The rate of diffusion of labeled water molecules in an electrolyte solution will be greater or less than the rate of diffusion of water molecules in pure water depending upon whether the ions decrease or increase the amount of structure in the water. The rate of diffusion of labeled water in a 1 M potassium iodide solution at 10°, for instance, is about 13 percent greater than for pure water at that temperature.[24]

There has been considerable effort to evaluate the structure-stabilizing and structure-breaking effects of ions vis-à-vis each other. In general, monatomic anions appear to give smaller spheres of hydration than cations of similar size. It has been suggested that water molecules around anions tend to orient with one O-H bond directed toward the anion; this leaves them with a greater degree of rotational freedom and the possibility of participating more readily in hydrogen bonds with other water molecules.[25] The entropy contributions by the formation of a highly oriented hydration shell and by disruption of water structure have been evaluated by Frank and Evans.[26] The large monovalent ions generally have a net structure-breaking effect as evidenced by a positive entropy of mixing and a decrease in the viscosity of the solution. The small polyvalent ions, in contrast, tend to have a net structuring effect. The hydrated diameters of ions can be evaluated approximately from diffusion rates using Stokes' law and from mobility measurements in an electric field. The latter measurements give only relative values because the mobility of an ion probably also involves energy to disrupt relatively larger elements of structure. Measurements give a series of hydrated diameters for monovalent cations $Li^+ > Na^+ > K^+ > NH_4^+ > Rb^+ > Cs^+$. This is approximately the reverse of the van der Waals radii for the ions themselves.

Two water molecules dissociate into hydronium (H_3O^+) and hydroxyl ions ($K = 10^{-7}$ at 20°). It appears that hydronium ions are formed by the jump of a

[24] Wang, J. H. *J. Phys. Chem.*, *58*, 686 (1954); Podolsky, R. J. *J. Am. Chem. Soc.*, *80*, 4442 (1958).
[25] Haggis, G. H., Hasted, J. B., and Buchanan, T. J. *J. Chem. Phys.*, *20*, 1452 (1952).
[26] Frank, H. S., and Evans, M. W. *J. Chem. Phys.*, *13*, 507 (1945).

proton from one water molecule to another so that the reaction is

$$H_2O + H_2O \rightleftarrows HO^- + H_3O^+ \tag{3-36}$$

The proton does not exist as such but with varying numbers of water molecules of hydration: H_3O^+, $H_9O_4^+$, etc. The existence of these hydrated protons is supported by several lines of evidence but particularly by spectroscopic data. Protons diffuse through water not in the ordinary sense, but by a series of sequential reactions involving proton jumps from water molecule to water molecule (Fig. 3-25). As might be expected from this type of conduction, the mobility of protons in ice is *greater* than it is in liquid water (Fig. 3-26).

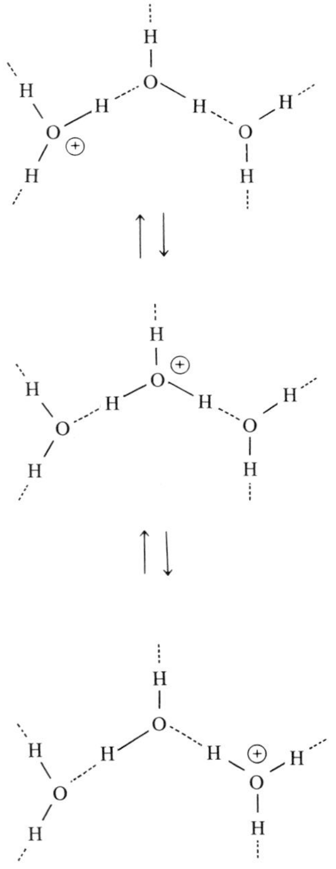

fig. 3-25. Mechanism of proton conduction through water.

amphiphilic systems

Biological membranes have a high content of *amphiphilic* lipids, compounds with both hydrophilic and hydrophobic properties. In the presence of water, many of these lipids tend to arrange themselves in a highly characteristic pattern of bimolecular sheets or cylinders. These highly organized structures are ubiquitous in biological

fig. 3-26. Apparent mobilities of protons and lithium ions in ice and water.

	WATER[a]	ICE[a]
H^+	0.0036	0.3
Li^+	0.0004	$<10^{-8}$

[a] Mobilities are given in $cm^2 \cdot volt^{-1} \cdot sec^{-1}$.

systems and arise, at least in part, because of the inherent tendency of the lipids to orient themselves in characteristic patterns with respect to the aqueous phase and with respect to themselves. These properties of lipids are also important in the digestion, absorption, and transport of lipids. Lastly, lipid interfaces provide specialized surfaces which may act to activate a chemical or enzymic reaction or to protect substrates from attack by an enzyme.

One group of interesting phenomena arises from the ionic properties of amphiphilic lipids, particularly when the charges are spatially oriented at an interface. The ionic species is most frequently strongly anionic because of the phosphoric acid residues, but weakly anionic or cationic groups may be present or there may be Zwitterions. The thermodynamics of the resulting electrostatic phenomena will be considered in a subsequent section.

It has been pointed out above (p. 107) that the tendency of nonpolar compounds to be "squeezed" out of water is the result of the much greater interaction energy between water molecules themselves than between water molecules and nonpolar molecules, and thus is not due to any direct repulsive forces between water and the nonpolar molecules. In general, the tendency of lipids to be squeezed out of aqueous solution depends upon the balance between their hydrophobic and hydrophilic properties. If an aqueous solution of amphiphilic lipids is anywhere bounded by an air or oil phase, the lipid molecules will tend to accumulate at the interface and form an adsorbed layer. The thermodynamics of these phenomena will be considered in Chapter 7. Soaps and amphiphiles are miscible with water only above a critical temperature. This temperature, called the *Krafft point*, has a characteristic value for each type of lipid and is relatively independent of concentration. Thus, sodium linoleate is miscible with water at 0°, sodium myristate dissolves only above 55°, and sodium oleate has a Krafft point of 15°. The Krafft point represents a phase change similar to melting.

The thermodynamic expression for the adsorption isotherm implies that the unadsorbed molecules of lipid in the bulk water phase are in free solution. This is true for very dilute solutions. As the relative amount of lipid is increased, a concentration is reached where bulk aggregation suddenly occurs, the *critical micelle concentration*. The units of bulk aggregation are called *micelles*. Each micelle consists of several to several hundred lipid molecules, usually arranged in the form of a sphere. The term *micelle* was introduced by Nägeli, who played an important part in developing the membrane concept, to designate a polymolecular aggregate with a quasicrystalline structure. The hydrophobic ends of the lipid molecules tend to be buried in the micelle, while the hydrophilic ends are at the surface in intimate contact with the aqueous phase (Fig. 3-27). Because the micellar dimensions are usually small compared to the wavelength of visible light, the mixture is isotropic and appears transparent. However, light-scattering techniques are particularly suited for studying the shape, size, number, and other properties of micellar suspensions. As further lipid is added, more micelles form. These are similar in size and shape to those first formed at the critical micelle concentration. Finally, a concentration of lipid is reached, at approximately 55 to 70 percent lipid, when the micelles are closely packed and additional

fig. 3-27. Schematic diagram of the arrangement of amphophile molecules in micelles.

micelles cannot be accommodated.

If the concentration of lipid is increased still further, anisotropy, an abrupt increase in viscosity, and optical birefringence suddenly occur. These changes indicate that a structural reorganization of the system has taken place. The systems which are thus formed have been called liquid crystalline or *smectic* because in *x*-ray diffraction studies a regular crystalline array is present in one or two coordinates but not in all three, and the system has the flow and other physical properties of a liquid. These systems present a number of structures,[27] some of which are shown in Fig. 3-28. As the concentration of lipid increases, the forms of organization tend to appear in the following order: micellar, middle, deformed middle, rectangular, complex hexagonal, cubic, neat. The chemical structure of the lipid has some effect on the relative stability of these structures: lipids with a prominent hydrophobic portion tend to have an extended neat type of organization while lipids with a prominent hydrophilic portion tend to have an extended middle phase. The presence of double bonds in the hydrocarbon chains tends to increase the water solubility of the lipids. At times there may be phase reversal, and, rarely, both phases may exist in equilibrium (Fig. 3-28). Of particular relevance to the structure of biological membranes and the role of lipids in their

[27] Luzzati, V., and Husson, F. *J. Cell Biol.*, *12*, 207 (1962).

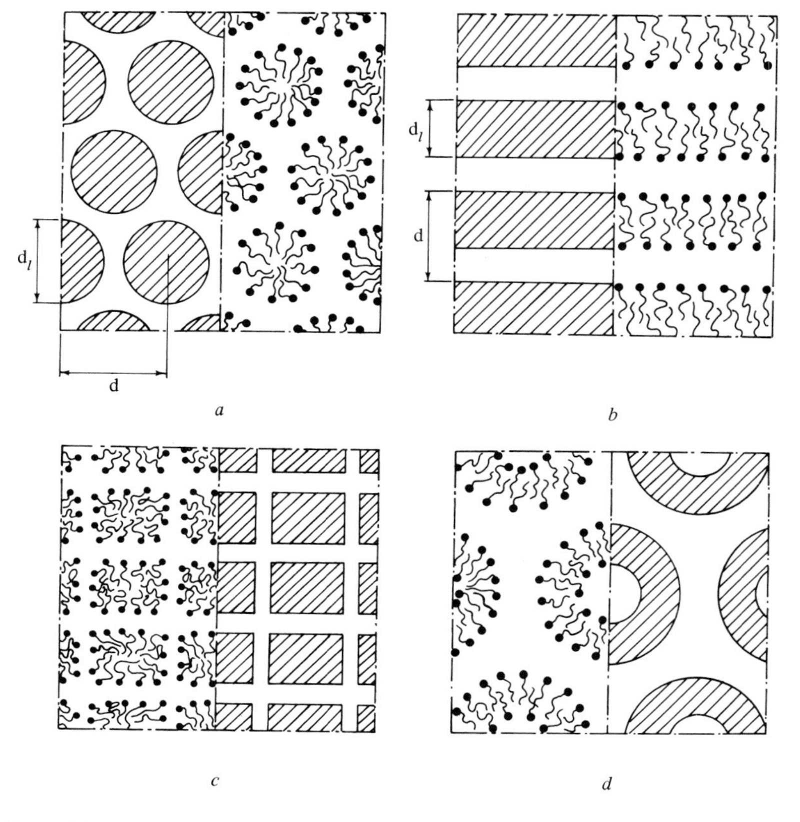

fig. 3-28. Structure of some liquid-crystalline phases of simple lipid-water systems: (*a*) middle, (*b*) neat, (*c*) rectangular, and (*d*) complex hexagonal. (From Luzzati, V., and Husson, F. *J. Cell Biol.*, *12*, 210 [1962].)

formation, of course, is the spontaneous formation of extended sheets of bimolecular lipids. It should be pointed out that temperature is a very critical parameter in the formation of these various phases at given lipid concentrations.

When pure lipid substances are heated, they are observed to undergo several phase transitions before finally melting into a clear, isotropic liquid. These phases are types of liquid crystalline structures which arise from partial disruption of the solid crystal lattice in one coordinate axis at a time. Lipid molecules are generally long and narrow. The transition from the solid to smectic structure results from a breakdown of the end-to-end cohesion of molecules with the application of heat before there is any appreciable disturbance in the lateral attractive forces. This permits a sliding of sheets in one plane only, giving rise to a liquid of high residual viscosity.[28]

Phospholipids are very hygroscopic substances. Phospholipid crystals contain small amounts of water which are tenaciously held. Removal of this "water of crystallization" often results in marked changes in the *x*-ray crystallographic pattern. Absorption isotherms can be plotted which have an S-shape. Lecithin fixes 44 g water per 100 g lipid at 25° and 44 g water per 100 g lipid at 40°. When certain phospholipids are dispersed in water, concentric bimolecular tubes or spheres of lipid separated by thin

[28] Brown, G. H., and Shaw, W. G. *Chem. Rev.*, *57*, 1049 (1957).

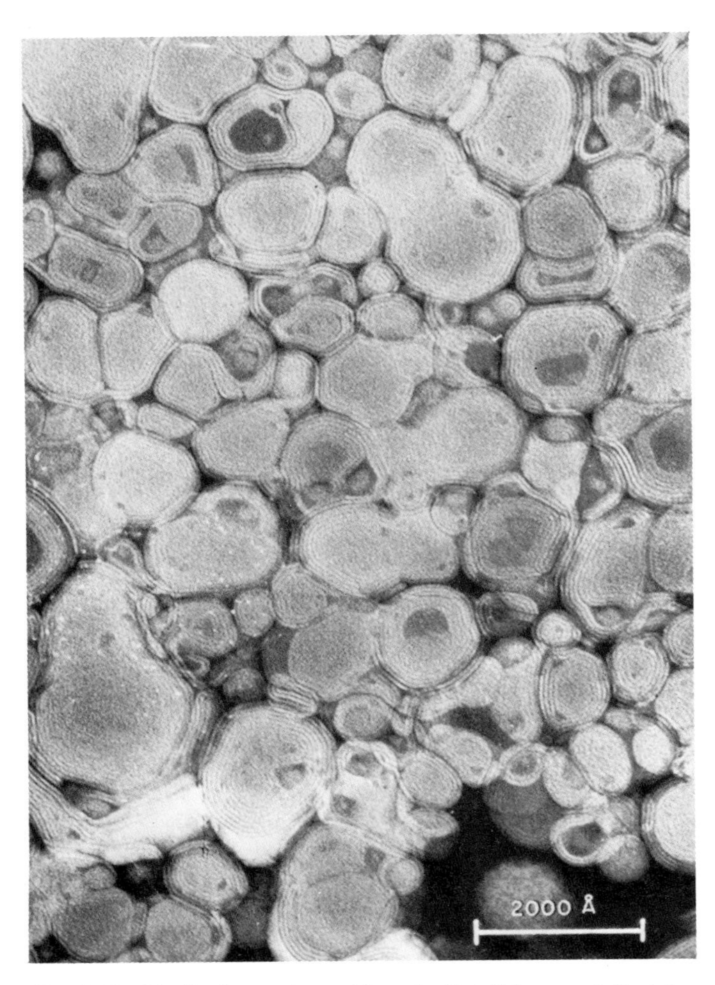

fig. 3-29. Myelin figures formed from lecithin/10 percent dicetyl phosphoric acid dispersed in 2 percent potassium phosphotungstate. (From Bangham, A. D., Standish, M. M., and Watkins, J. C. *J. Mol. Biol., 13,* 241 [1965]. Copyright Academic Press; reprinted by permission.)

layers of water are sometimes obtained. These structures are called *myelin figures* (Fig. 3-29).

If one considers a solution to which phospholipid is being added continually, more and more lipid will be adsorbed at the interface with a consequent drop in the surface tension. If the free energy of adsorption is negative and sufficiently large, the interfacial tension will approach zero at relatively low concentrations of lipid. Once the interfacial tension reaches a minimum value, further addition of lipid results in expansion of the interfacial surface. In this way, phospholipids spontaneously expand their interfaces with water to form extensive systems of bimolecular leaflets separated by thin films of water. The interfacial tension of these leaflets is close to zero, and the phenomenological reaction is driven by a large favorable free energy change which accompanies the transfer of the lipid polar end from the lipid phase to the aqueous phase. Phospholipid molecules are approximately cylinder-shaped, because the cross section of the two fatty acid residues comprising the nonpolar end of the molecule is almost the same as the cross section of the polar end. A bimolecular leaflet is the most favored configuration because it provides the closest packing of the nonpolar hydrocarbon chains and at the same time provides the greatest surface area for the polar ends. If the polar ends are ionized in addition, a repulsive force between the polar ends comes into play and there is a tendency for the system to form spheres of radially oriented molecules. For lipids with a net ionic charge to assume bimolecular leaflet orientation, either the presence of counterions or the presence of neutral lipids to permit adequate charge separation is necessary. Lecithin is micellar in concentrations as low as 10^{-5} g/ml, and light-scattering data[29] suggest that the micelles are smectic lamellae 69 Å thick (a bimolecular leaflet) and 910 Å in diameter.

proteins

Proteins are the most versatile and varied class of biological macromolecules; they are responsible for the fundamental features of structure and function which underlie all living systems as well as for the tremendous diversity found in such systems. Proteins are composed of repeating peptide bonds separated by a single carbon atom. A variety of side chains, 20 in all, or a hydrogen atom may be attached to the α-carbon atom (Fig. 3-30). The character of the protein chain is profoundly influenced by the sequence of amino acids from which it is condensed.

X-ray analysis of simple polypeptides reveals that the peptide bonds between a variety of amino acids have uniform dimensions (Fig. 3-31). The C-N amide bond has an observed distance of 1.32 Å, a value between the expected single-bond spacing of 1.47 Å and the expected double-bond spacing of 1.28 Å. The C-O carbonyl bond has an observed spacing of 1.24 Å, a value larger than the expected double-bond spacing of 1.21 Å. These findings have been interpreted to result from resonance between two forms of the peptide bond

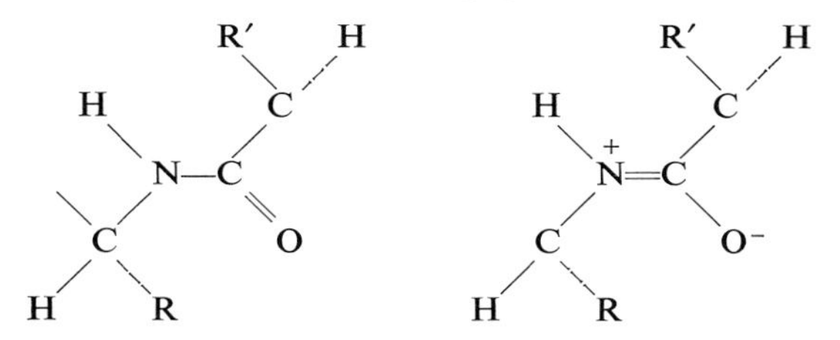

which gives the C-N amide bond approximately a 40 percent double-bond character and the carbonyl bond approximately a 60 percent double-bond character. Because of the partial double-bond character of the amide bond, the most stable configuration for the peptide group is close to planar. In all peptide linkages examined experimentally the structure is within a few degrees of being planar. In addition, all small peptides examined showed a *trans*-configuration for the side chains of the α-carbon atoms on either side of the peptide linkage. It has been deduced from infrared absorption studies that the *trans*-configuration is more stable than the *cis*-configuration by about 2 kcal/mole.

A very important feature of the peptide group is that the hydrogen atom attached to the nitrogen is capable of forming a hydrogen bond, and the oxygen atom of the

[29] Robinson, N. *Trans. Faraday Soc.*, *56*, 1260 (1960).

Name	Symbol	Structure
Glycine	Gly	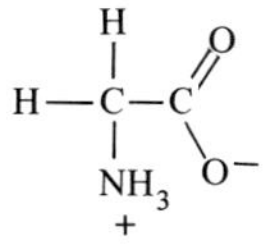 $H-C(H)(NH_3^+)-C(=O)O^-$
Alanine	Ala	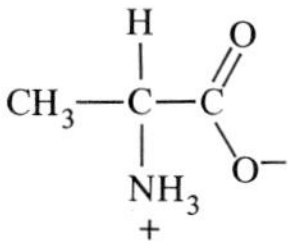 $CH_3-C(H)(NH_3^+)-C(=O)O^-$
Valine	Val	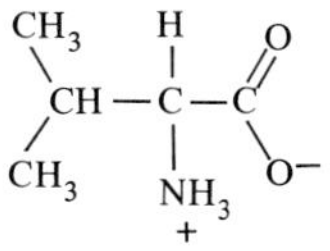 $(CH_3)_2CH-C(H)(NH_3^+)-C(=O)O^-$
Leucine	Leu	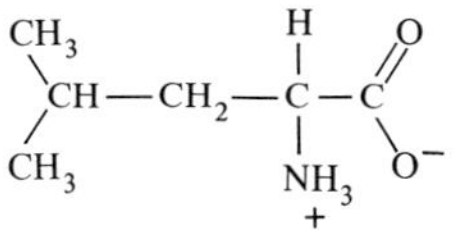 $(CH_3)_2CH-CH_2-C(H)(NH_3^+)-C(=O)O^-$
Isoleucine	Ileu	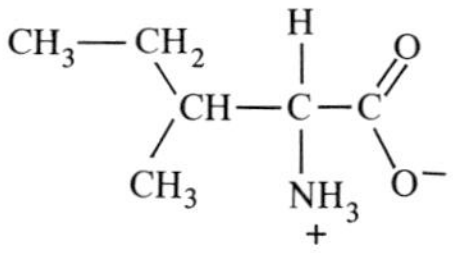 $CH_3-CH_2-CH(CH_3)-C(H)(NH_3^+)-C(=O)O^-$
Cystine	$(CyS)_2$	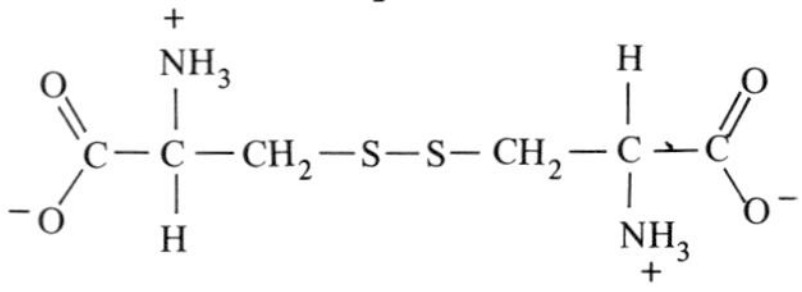 $^-O(O=)C-C(H)(NH_3^+)-CH_2-S-S-CH_2-C(H)(NH_3^+)-C(=O)O^-$
Serine	Ser	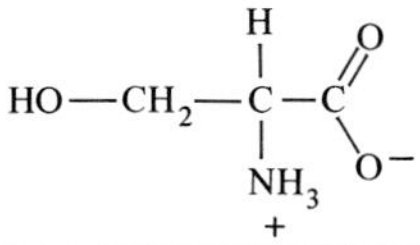 $HO-CH_2-C(H)(NH_3^+)-C(=O)O^-$
Threonine	Thr	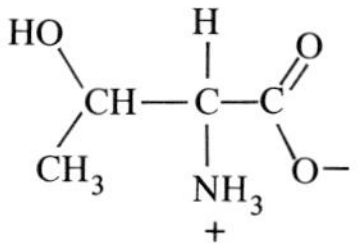 $HO(CH_3)CH-C(H)(NH_3^+)-C(=O)O^-$
Phenylalanine	Phe	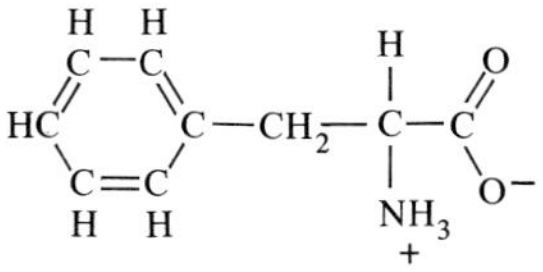 $C_6H_5-CH_2-C(H)(NH_3^+)-C(=O)O^-$
Tyrosine	Tyr	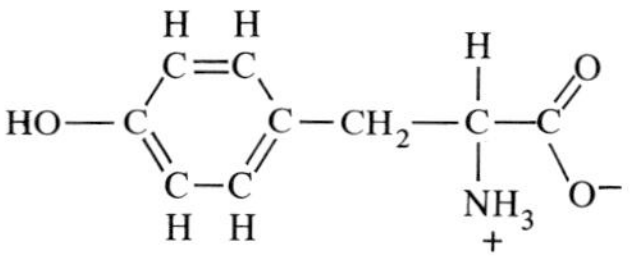 $HO-C_6H_4-CH_2-C(H)(NH_3^+)-C(=O)O^-$
Tryptophane	Try	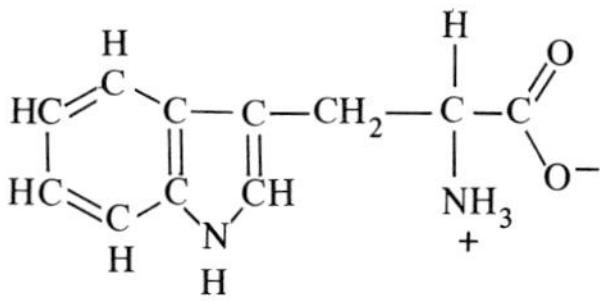 $C_8H_6N-CH_2-C(H)(NH_3^+)-C(=O)O^-$ (indole ring)
Glutamic Acid	Glu	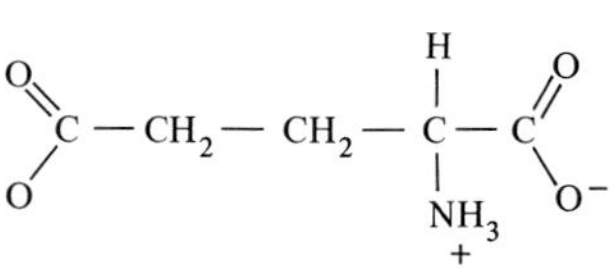 $O{=}C(O)-CH_2-CH_2-C(H)(NH_3^+)-C(=O)O^-$

fig. 3-30. Structure of the amino acids.

Name	Symbol	Structure
Cysteine	CySH	$HS-CH_2-CH(NH_3^+)-C(=O)O^-$
Methionine	Met	$CH_3-S-CH_2-CH_2-CH(NH_3^+)-C(=O)O^-$
Proline	Pro	$CH_2-CH_2-CH_2-CH(-C(=O)O^-)-N^+H_2$ (ring)
Hydroxyproline	Hypro	$HO-CH-CH_2-CH(-C(=O)O^-)-N^+H_2-CH_2$ (ring)
Aspartic Acid	Asp	$^-O(O=)C-CH_2-CH(NH_3^+)-C(=O)O^-$
Asparagine	$Asp\text{-}NH_2$	$H_2N-C(=O)-CH_2-CH(NH_3^+)-C(=O)O^-$
Glutamine	$Glu\text{-}NH_2$	$H_2N-C(=O)-CH_2-CH_2-CH(NH_3^+)-C(=O)O^-$
Histidine	His	$HC=C(-CH_2-CH(NH_3^+)-C(=O)O^-)-NH-CH=N$ (ring)
Arginine	Arg	$(H_2N)_2C-NH-CH_2-CH_2-CH(NH_3^+)-C(=O)O^-$
Lysine	Lys	$H_3N^+-CH_2-CH_2-CH_2-CH_2-CH(NH_3^+)-C(=O)O^-$

carbonyl group is capable of acting as an acceptor of a hydrogen bond. It is surmised from infrared absorption and other data that polypeptides have a maximum possible number of hydrogen bonds. Clearly, a configuration which allowed the maximum number of hydrogen bonds would have the greatest stability. Hydrogen bonds are within a few degrees of being linear and have a bond length of very close to 2.79 Å. The rotational freedom around the α-carbon atoms depends upon the side-chain substituents, and the rotational barrier in certain pairs of amino acids may amount to 3 kcal/mole. Relatively few stable configurations of polypeptides are possible that will satisfy the constraints outlined above.

The simplest possible configuration for a polypeptide chain is one in which the polypeptide chain is extended with all of the planar peptide linkages lying in a common plane. Adjacent amino acids are related by a distance of translation of 3.6 Å and a rotation of 180°. Polyglycine has a configuration of this type although the measured

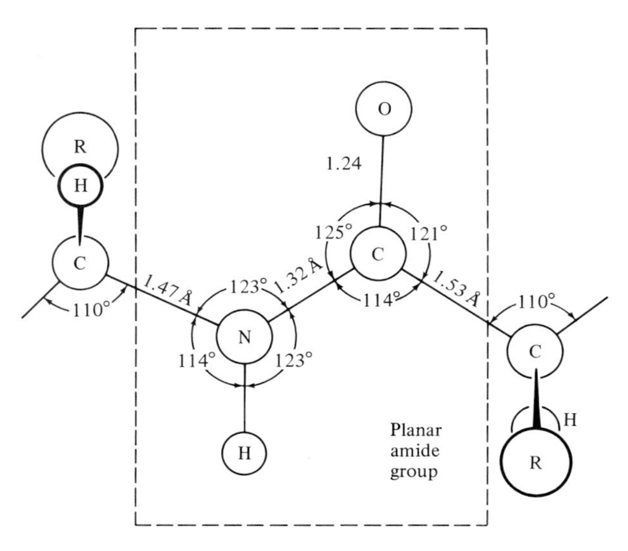

fig. 3-31. Dimensions of the peptide bond derived from *x*-ray analysis of simple peptides. (From Pauling, L., Corey, R. B., and Branson, H. R. *Proc. Natl. Acad. Sci.*, *37*, 206 [1951].)

repeat unit is somewhat less than the expected 7.2 Å, indicating that the chains are almost, but not fully, extended. Chains of polyglycine can hydrogen-bond to one another to form a sheet in which alternate chains lie antiparallel (Fig. 3-32). A configuration of this type is not possible with amino acids other than glycine because side chains (instead of hydrogen atoms) attached to the α-carbon could not be accommodated.

Silk fibroin, a member of the class of β-keratins, is an example of a protein with a related structure. Silk fibroin has an unusual amino acid composition; almost half the amino acid residues are glycine, and almost all the remainder are alanine or serine. Silk fibroin appears to contain long sequences in which glycine alternates with either alanine or serine. The β-keratins give side chains on the α-carbon atoms and are arranged in a configuration such that the β-carbon atoms project alternately from either side of the polypeptide backbone. The chain of polypeptide linkages has a zigzag rather than a fully extended form with adjacent units related by a translation of 3.5 Å and a rotation of 180°. The polypeptide linkages lie in planes which are perpendicular to the plane of the side chains extending from the α-carbons. A series of polypeptide chains with this configuration can form hydrogen bonds to each other when they lie side by side, with alternate chains oriented in opposite directions, so that alternate imino and carbonyl groups on a given chain are hydrogen-bonded to chains lying on either side. This alignment of polypeptide chains results in what has been called the "pleated-sheet" structure. Polarized infrared absorption data supports the idea that the hydrogen bonds are formed between polypeptide chains. The side chains appear in phase on adjacent fibers in their projections from either side of the sheet, resulting in large transverse grooves. In the case of silk fibroin, since every other amino acid residue is glycine, only every other amino acid residue has a β-carbon atom, and the projections from the pleated sheet occur on one side only. With the side chains extending from only one side of the sheet and deep transverse grooves between the side chains, it is possible to pack pairs of sheets so that the bulky side chains face each other and interdigitate (Fig. 3-33). The distance between two sheets on the side

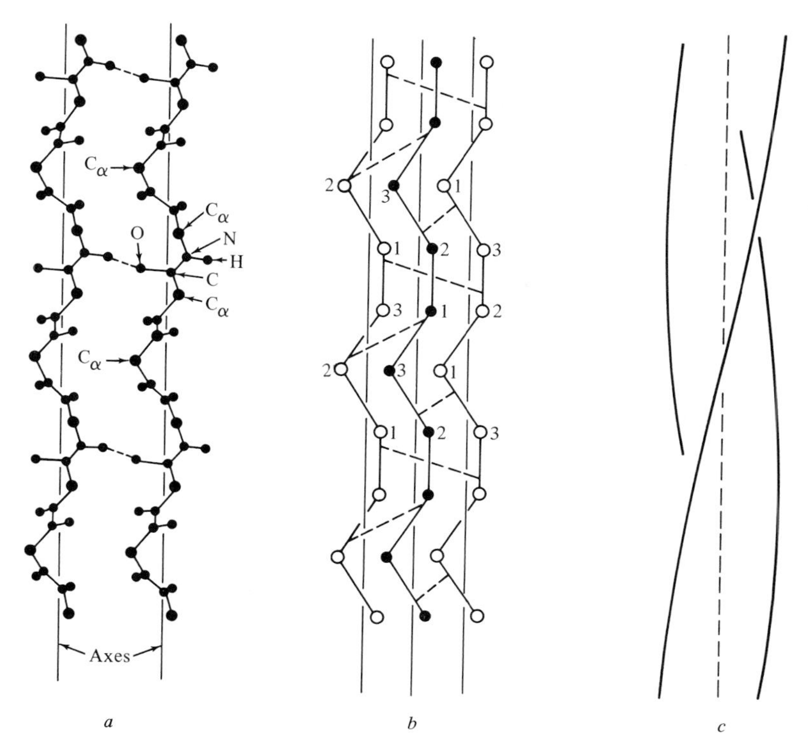

fig. 3-32. A schematic diagram illustrating the structure of collagen: (*a*) two chains of polyglycine II, (*b*) three chains showing only the α-carbon atoms and hydrogen bonds, and (*c*) the coiling of the three chains of collagen. (From Rich, A., and Crick, F. H. C. *Recent Advances in Gelatine and Glue Research, 1,* 21 [1957].)

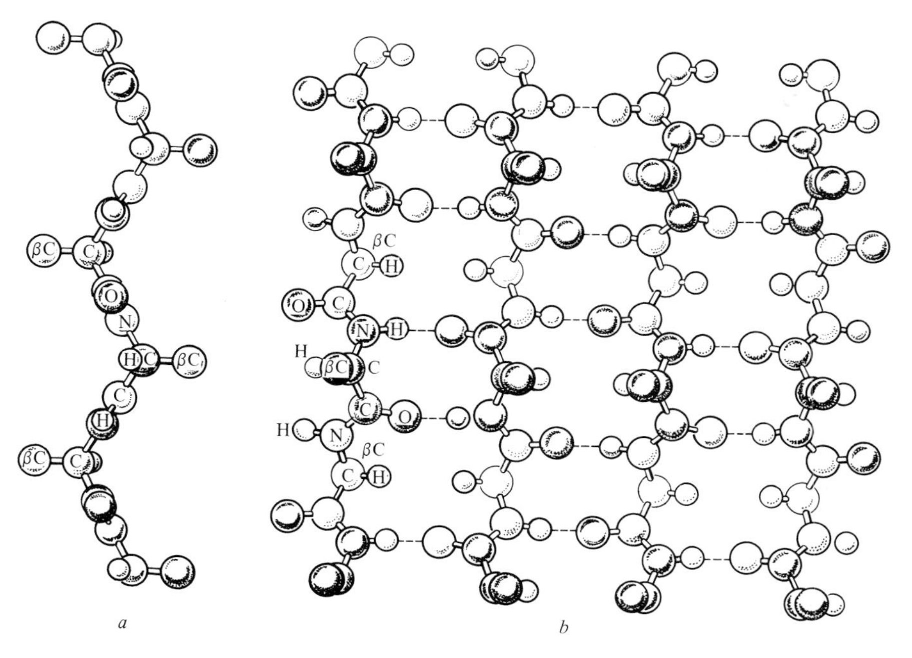

fig. 3-33. A drawing of (*a*) a single polypeptide chain and (*b*) several polypeptide chains lying in a sheet, showing antiparallel pleating. Silk fibroin is a protein with this structure. (From Marsh, R. E., Corey, R. B., and Pauling, L. *Biochim. Biophys. Acta, 16,* 13 [1955].)

with β-carbon extensions is 5.7 Å and between sheets with the glycine residues in contact is 3.5 Å; this gives a repeating unit of 9.2 Å between pairs of sheets. The x-ray diffraction pattern can be accounted for by an orthogonal unit cell with dimensions of 9.20 Å and 9.40 Å at right angles to the fiber and a fiber-axis repeat of 6.97 Å.[30]

A somewhat more complex type of molecular organization is illustrated by the protein collagen, the major structural component of skin, tendon, and connective tissue. Glycine accounts for approximately one-third of the amino acid residues of collagen, and proline plus hydroxyproline make up another one-fourth of the amino acid residues. Collagen consists of three polypeptide chains with parallel orientation but with the glycine of every triplet of amino acids displaced one residue compared to the register of the other two chains. The three chains are wound around in a coil so that hydrogen bonding occurs between the glycine residues adjacent to each other in adjacent chains.[31] While the α-carbons of the glycine residues tend to be oriented toward each other and the center of the three-stranded unit, the other two-thirds of the amino acid residues are oriented with the amino acid side chains facing outward. The pyrrolidine rings tend to be closely packed, producing a helical ridge on the outer surface of the molecule. Adjacent amino acid residues in a chain are related by a translation of 2.86 Å and a rotation of 108°.

Collagen also displays a complex pattern organization at the next level of structure. Collagen is composed of long, thin, rodlike molecular units, *tropocollagen*, with a molecular weight of about 340,000. Electron photomicrographs and x-ray diffraction of collagen fibers show a major repeat distance of 640–700 Å, approximately one-fourth the estimated length of 2820 Å for tropocollagen molecules in electron photomicrographs. Schmitt *et al.*[32] showed that the addition of ATP to tropocollagen solutions results in a precipitation of ordered aggregates in which the molecules are packed in a side-to-side, polarized fashion, giving an electron microscopic pattern called *segmented long spacing* (SLS). Glycoproteins also induce an orderly lateral aggregation, but the molecules are not polarized and thus give an electron microscopic pattern called *fibrous long spacing* (FLS). The tropocollagen molecules in native collagen occur in a laterally oriented structure in which the molecules are polarized. However, while all the molecular "heads" face in the same direction, units are displaced longitudinally from adjacent units by one-fourth of their length; thus displacement gives rise to the *quarter-staggered spacing*.[33] High resolution electron microscopy shows that the tropocollagen units do not lie with their ends opposed, one to the next, but are separated by a space of 170 to 270 Å[34] (Fig. 3-34).

Of the various structures into which polypeptide chains can condense, the α-helix is the one structure that makes minimal constraints for side-chain substitution on the α-carbon atoms.[35] In the α-helix, the peptide linkages are oriented in a sequence of planes tangential to an axial cylinder (Fig. 3-35). Adjacent amino acid residues are related by a translation of 1.5 Å along the axis and a rotation of 100° around the axis. The number of amino acid residues per turn is not integral but 3.6 to 3.7. Slight differences in the hydrogen-bonding pattern change the arrangement slightly. The total rise of the helix per turn is approximately 5.4 Å. The amide hydrogen of each peptide linkage is hydrogen-bonded to the carbonyl group of the third linkage farther along

[30] Marsh, R. E., Corey, R. B., and Pauling, L. *Biochim. Biophys. Acta*, *16*, 1 (1955).
[31] Rich, A., and Crick, F. H. C. *Nature*, *176*, 915 (1955).
[32] Schmitt, F. O., Gross, J., and Highberger, J. H. *Proc. Natl. Acad. Sci.*, *39*, 459 (1953).
[33] Hodge, A. J., and Schmitt, F. O. *Proc. Natl. Acad. Sci.*, *46*, 186 (1960).
[34] Petruska, J. A., and Hodge, A. J. *Proc. Natl. Acad. Sci.*, *51*, 871 (1964).
[35] Pauling, L., and Corey, R. B. *Proc. Natl. Acad. Sci.*, *37*, 241 (1951).

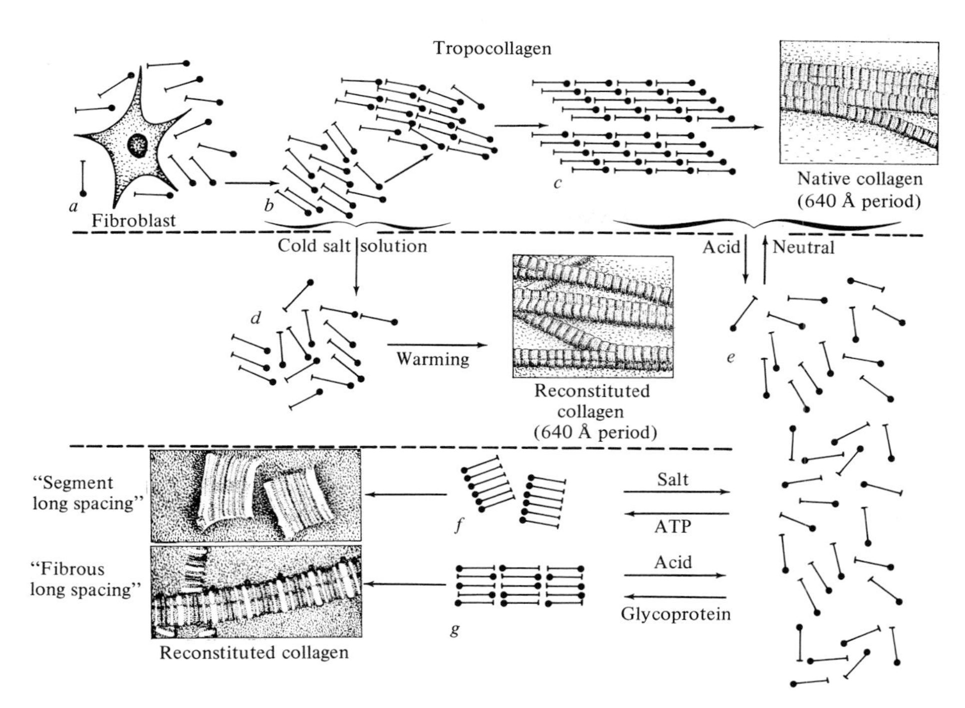

fig. 3-34. Reconstitution of collagen can take place in three basic ways. In an animal, tropocollagen molecules (*b*), manufactured by cells called fibroblasts (*a*), overlap to form native collagen (*c*). Newly formed molecules are soluble in cold salt solution (*d*); simple warming yields reconstituted fibrils duplicating the native form. Alternately, native collagen can be dissolved in acetic acid (*e*). Treating the resulting solution with adenosine triphosphoric acid produces the nonoverlapping, segment long-spacing form of collagen *(f)*. Treating the solution with glycoprotein produces the fibrous long-spacing form *(g)*, in which molecules are nonoverlapping and face randomly. The fine structure reflects the asymmetry of the tropocollagen molecule. (From Gross, J. Collagen. *Sci. Am., 204*, 126 [May, 1961]. Copyright © 1961 by Scientific American, Inc. All rights reserved.)

the chain. The 1.5 Å repeat spacing has been found in a number of proteins.[36] In some proteins, such as α-keratin, a number of helical strands are arranged to form a multistranded helical cable.

One of the striking properties of macromolecular solutions is their high viscosity. The viscosity of a solution is a function of the concentration of the solute. Because of molecular interactions, the viscosity change is frequently not linear, but can be expressed in terms of a power function:

$$\eta = \eta_0[1 + Ac + Bc^2 + \cdots] \tag{3-37}$$

where η is the viscosity of the solution and η_0 is the viscosity of the solvent. The intrinsic viscosity may be defined

$$[\eta] = \lim_{c \to 0} \left(\frac{[\eta/\eta_0] - 1}{c} \right) = A \tag{3-38}$$

[36] Perutz, M. F. *Nature*, *167*, 1053 (1951).

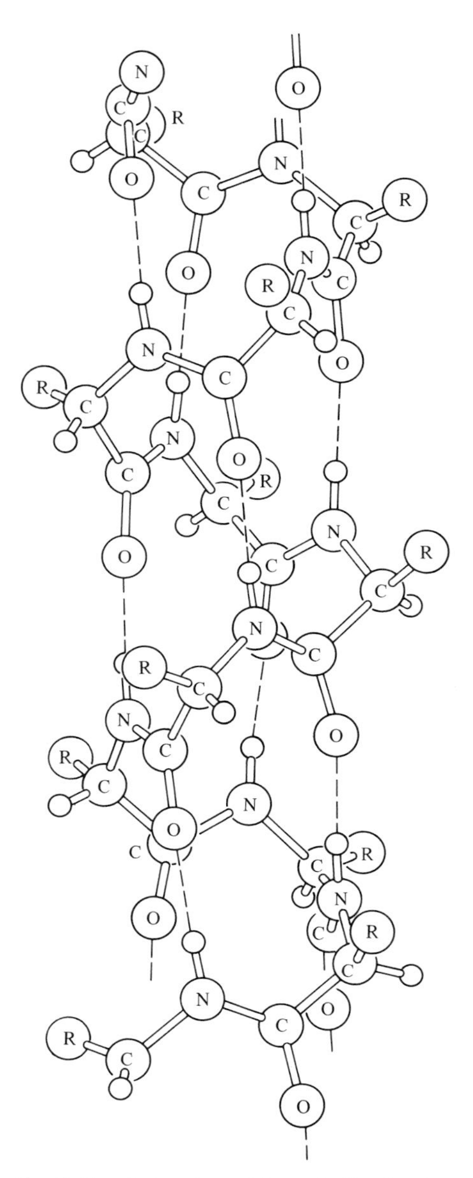

fig. 3-35. A drawing of the α-helix of polypeptides.

It was shown by Einstein that for rigid, spherical particles $A = 5/2$, and therefore $[\eta] = 5/2$. As molecules deviate from the spherical shape, the value for A increases. The values of $[\eta]$ for many native proteins is close to 2.5 cc/g, evidence that they are present in solution as compact, approximately spherical molecules. Upon denaturation following treatment with urea or upon unfolding following the rupture of disulfide bonds, the intrinsic viscosity increases markedly as the proteins assume a random-coil configuration (Fig. 3-36). On the other hand, the intrinsic viscosities of rodlike structural proteins such as fibrinogen, myosin, and collagen are very high.

Several soluble, compact, globular proteins in crystalline form, particularly myoglobin, hemoglobin, and lysozyme, have been analyzed by x-ray crystallographic

fig. 3-36. Intrinsic viscosities of macromolecules. (From Schachman, H. K. *Cold Spring Harbor Symp. Quant. Biol., 28,* 410 [1963].)

COMPACT GLOBULAR PARTICLES			RANDOMLY COILED CHAINS			RODLIKE PARTICLES		
MACROMOLECULE	MOLECULAR WEIGHT	$[\eta]$ CC/G	MACROMOLECULE	MOLECULAR WEIGHT	$[\eta]$ CC/G	MACROMOLECULE	MOLECULAR WEIGHT	$[\eta]$ CC/G
Polystyrene latex particles	10^9	2.4	Polystyrene in toluene	45,000	28	Fibrinogen	330,000	27
Ribonuclease	13,700	3.3	Polystyrene in toluene	70,000	37	Collagen	345,000	1,150
Lysozyme	14,400	3.0	Reduced ribonuclease	13,700	14.4	Myosin	620,000	230
Myoglobin	17,000	3.1	Oxidized ribonuclease	14,100	11.6	DNA	5×10^6	5,000
β-Lactoglobulin	35,000	3.4	Oxidized ribonuclease in urea	14,100	13.9	TMV	4×10^7	29
Ovalbumin	44,000	4.0	Ovalbumin in urea	44,000	34			
Serum albumin	65,000	3.7	Serum albumin in urea	66,000	22			
Hemoglobin	67,000	3.6	Reduced serum albumin in urea	66,000	53			
Liver alcohol dehydrogenase	83,000	4.0	Myosin in guanidine-hydrochloride	200,000	93			
Hemerythrin	107,000	3.6	RNA	1.5×10^6	100			
Aldolase	142,000	3.8						
Ribosomes (yeast)	3.5×10^6	5.0						
Bushy stunt virus	8.9×10^6	4.0						

techniques that permit resolution down to a few Ångstroms.[37] These analyses have shown the location of all but the hydrogen atoms (Fig. 3-37). The structural characteristics revealed can be summarized as follows. The molecules are very compact and generally globular in form with space for not more than a few solvent molecules in the interior. Nonpolar (hydrophobic) residues are largely oriented toward the interior of the molecule. Polar residues tend to face the external surface of the molecule and are exposed to the solvent. Water appears to be bound to many polar groups at the surface. The helical portions of the polypeptide chain occur in separate segments. Of course, there is some uncertainty about the equivalence of protein structure in the crystalline form and protein structure in solutions.

polysaccharides

Another important class of polymers are the polysaccharides, which are composed of either repeating units of a single type of sugar or an alternation between two types of monosaccharides (Fig. 3-38). The glycosidic linkages between the monomers have a characteristic, simple pattern in a given polysaccharide. They may occur between any

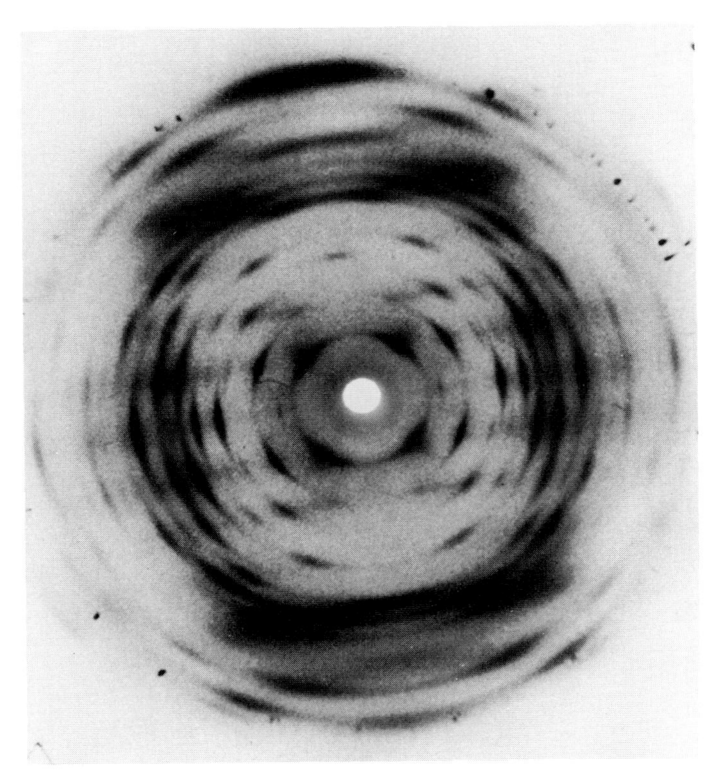

fig. 3-37. A typical *x*-ray diffraction pattern. (Courtesy of Dr. A. Rich.)

[37] Kendrew, J. C., Dickerson, R. E., Strandberg, B. E., Hart, R. G., Davies, D. R., Phillips, D. C., and Shore, V. C. *Nature, 185*, 422 (1960); Kendrew, J. C., Watson, H. C., Strandberg, B. E., Dickerson, R. E., Phillips, D. C., and Shore, V. C. *Nature, 190*, 666 (1961); Muirhead, H., and Perutz, M. F. *Nature, 199*, 633 (1963); Blake, C. C. F., Koenig, D. F., Mair, G. A., North, A. C. T., Phillips, D. C., and Sarma, V. R. *Nature, 206*, 757 (1965).

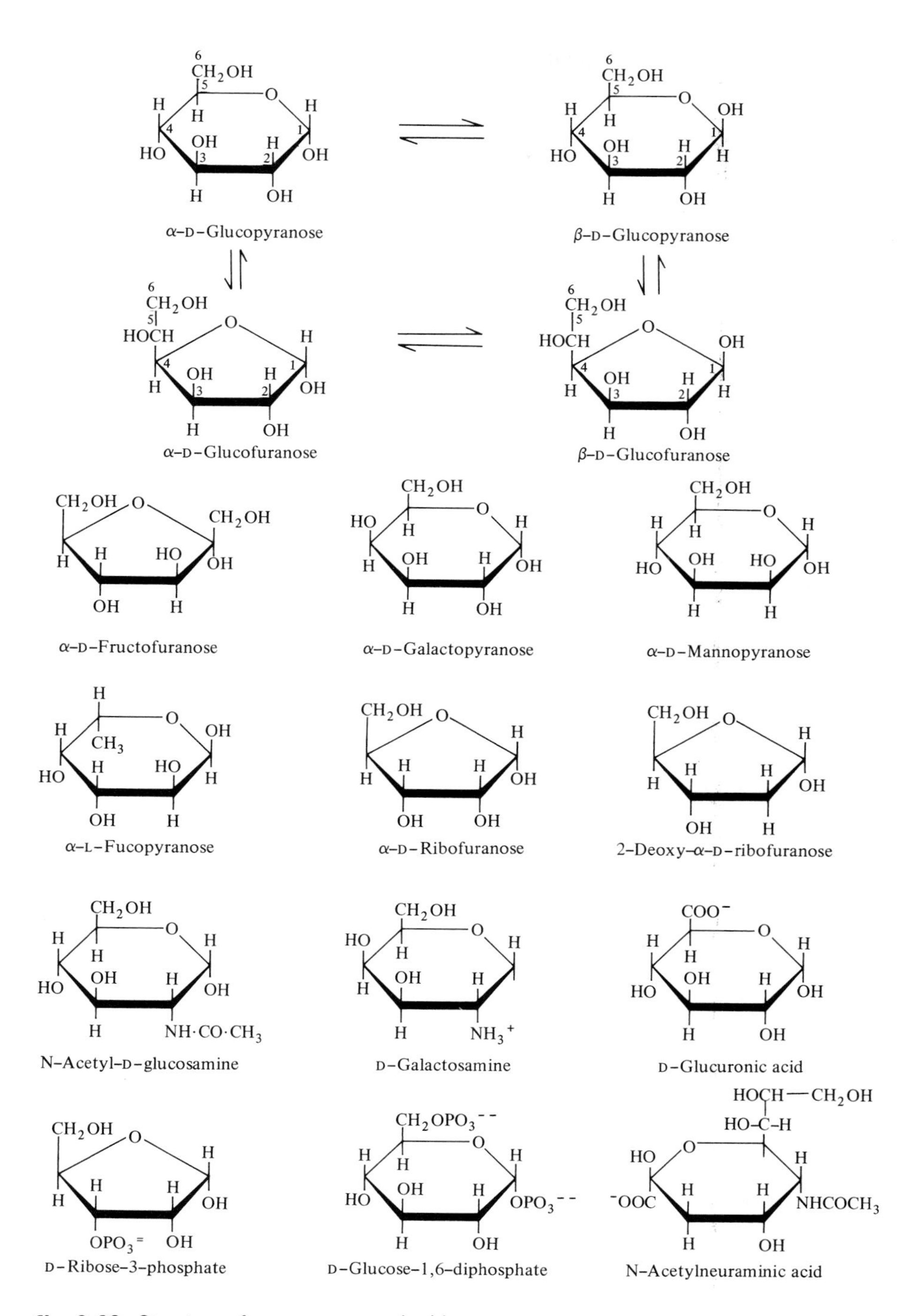

fig. 3-38. Structure of some monosaccharides.

pair of hydroxyl groups and may be oriented either below (α) or above (β) the plane of the monosaccharide ring. Polysaccharides are not synthesized on a template; they do not have a specified structure and do not carry information. Unlike the proteins, polysaccharides do not contain a definite number of monomer units, and they commonly display heterogeneity of molecular weights and other physical properties.

Cellulose and amylose are two common polysaccharides (Fig. 3-39). They are both composed of D-glucose residues with $1 \rightarrow 4$ linkages between the monomer units. In cellulose, the linkages have the β configuration; amylose has α linkages. Thus, cellulose is made up of repeating units of the disaccharide cellobiose while amylose is made up of maltose units. The polysaccharides of glucose with α-glucosidic bonds tend to assume a helical arrangement while the β configuration results in linear polymers. The helical arrangement minimizes adhesion between polymer strands; linear polymers tend to adhere as a result of weak molecular interactions.

X-ray diffraction studies of natural fibers show that the flat cellulose strands are

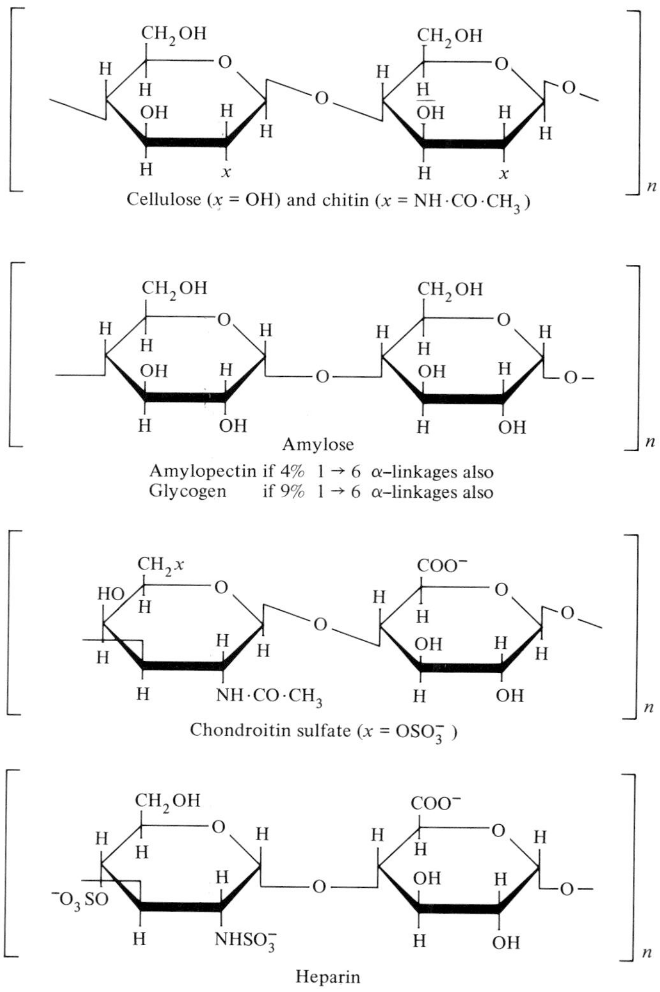

Cellulose (x = OH) and chitin (x = $NH \cdot CO \cdot CH_3$)

Amylose

Amylopectin if 4% $1 \rightarrow 6$ α-linkages also
Glycogen if 9% $1 \rightarrow 6$ α-linkages also

Chondroitin sulfate (x = OSO_3^-)

Heparin

fig. 3-39. Disaccharide repeating units in several polysaccharides.

arranged in a quasi-crystalline pattern with a unit cell corresponding to a lateral distance of 8.35 Å between strands, 7.9 Å separation perpendicular to the axis of the strands, and an axial repeat of 10.3 Å representing disaccharide-repeating units. There is some diffuseness of the spots in the pattern which has been attributed to discontinuities between bundles of crystallized strands. Birefringence studies suggest a micellar structure. On the basis of chemical studies, a single polymer chain of cellulose is thought to be made up of from 200 to 1000 glucose residues.

Amylopectin and glycogen have a basic structure similar to that of amylose; but about 5 percent of the residues form a branching by means of $1 \rightarrow 6$ α-glycosidic bonds in the amylopectins, while in the glycogens about 9 percent of the residues are involved in branching bonds (Fig. 3-40). The average distance between branch points is six glucose residues in glycogen; in the amylopectins it is twelve glucose residues.

A particularly interesting group of polysaccharide polymers is the mucopolysaccharides, macromolecules isolated principally from alkaline extracts or proteolytic digests of connective tissue. In general, these are unbranched polymers of alternating hexuronidic acid and N-acetylhexosamine residues. The N-acetylhexosamine residues

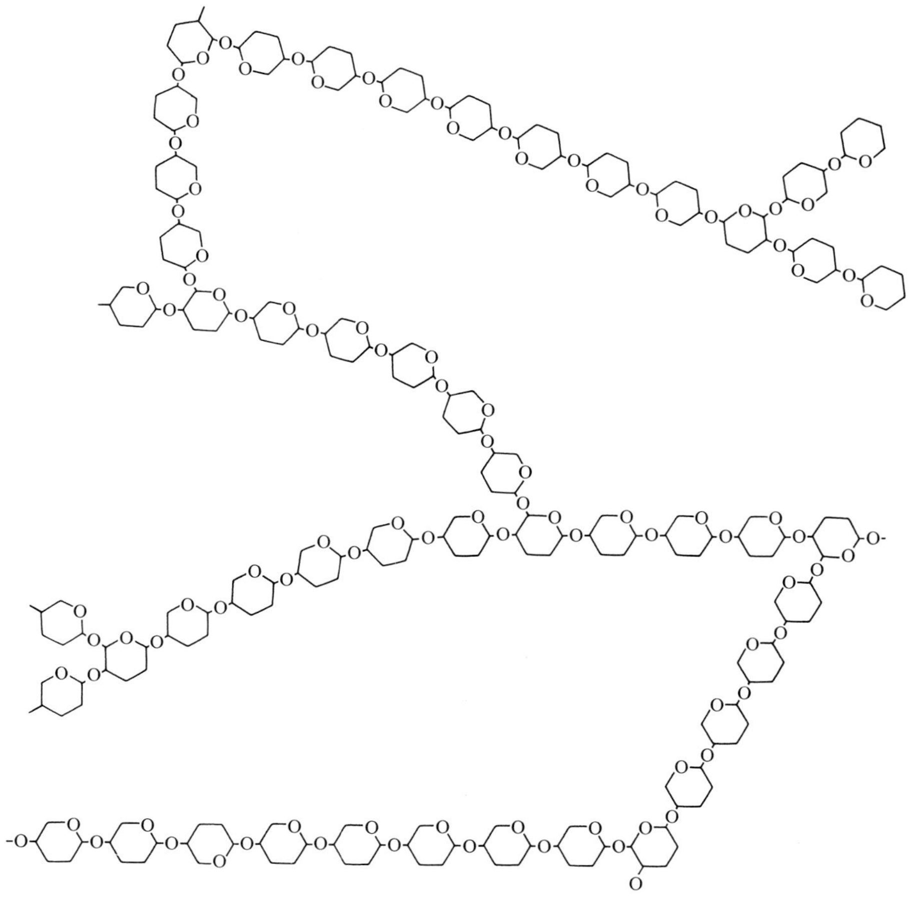

fig. 3-40. Diagram of a portion of a branching polysaccharide molecule such as glycogen or amylopectin. (From Oncley, J. L. *Biophysical Sciences—A Study Program.* New York: Wiley, 1959, p. 46.)

fig. 3-41. Biosynthesis of di-, oligo-, and polysaccharides. (From Table 10.3 in Mahler, Henry R., and Cordes, Eugene H. *Biological Chemistry.* New York: Harper & Row, 1966, p. 468. Copyright © 1966 by Henry R. Mahler and Eugene H. Cordes. Reprinted by permission of Harper & Row, Publishers.)

DI-, OLIGO-, OR POLY-SACCHARIDE FORMED	SOURCE OF ENZYME SYSTEM	ACCEPTOR OR REPEATING UNIT	LINKAGES	MONOMERIC NUCLEOTIDE GLYCOSYL DONOR
Sucrose (-P)	Plants	D-Fructose (-6-P)	α,1 → 2	UDP-D-Glucose
Lactose (-P)	Mammals	D-Glucose (-1-P)	β,1 → 4	UDP-Galactose
Sialyl-lactose	Mammals	Lactose	α,1 → 3 (galactose)	CMP-N-Acetylneuraminic acid
Fucosyl-lactose	Mammals	Lactose	α,1 → 3 (galactose)	GDP-L-Fucose
α-1,4-Glucan (starch amylose)	Plants	D-Glucose	α,1 → 4	ADP-D-Glucose
α-1,4-Glucan (glycogen amylose)	Mammalian liver	D-Glucose	α,1 → 4	UDP-D-Glucose
β-1,3-Glucan (callose)	Beans	D-Glucose	β,1 → 3	UDP-D-Glucose
β-1,4-Glucan (cellulose)	Mung beans, bacteria	D-Glucose	β,1 → 4	UDP-D-Glucose
β-1,4-Xylan	Plants	D-Xylose	β,1 → 4	UDP-D-Xylose
Chitin	*Neurospora crassa*	N-Acetyl-D-glucosamine	α,1 → 4	UDP-N-Acetyl-D-glucosamine
Colominic acid	*E. coli*	N-Acetylneuraminic acid	α,1 → 5	CMP-N-Acetylneuraminic acid
Hyaluronic acid	Bacteria, animals (umbilicus, vitreous humor, etc)	D-Glucuronic acid; N-acetylglucosamine	β,1 → 3 β,1 → 4	UDP-D-Glucuronic acid UDP-N-Acetyl-D-glucosamine
Chondroitin	Mammalian cornea	D-Glucuronic acid; N-acetyl-D-galactosamine	β,1 → 3 β,1 → 4	UDP-D-Glucuronic acid UDP-N-Acetyl-D-galactosamine
Chondroitin sulfates	Mammalian connective tissue	D-Glucuronic acid; N-acetyl-D-galactosamine-4-, or -6-sulfate	β,1 → 3 β,1 → 4	UDP derivatives
Dermatan sulfate	Mammalian skin	L-Iduronic acid; N-acetyl-D-galactosamine-2-sulfate	α,1 → 3	UDP derivatives

Heparin	Mammalian liver, lung, arterial walls	D-Glucuronic acid 2-sulfate;	α,1 → 4	UDP derivatives
		D-galactosamine-N, C-6-disulfate	α,1 → 4	
Capsular polysaccharide	Type III pneumonococci	D-Glucuronic acid;	β,1 → 4	UDP-D-Glucuronic acid
		D-glucose	β,1 → 3	UDP-D-glucose
Capsular polysaccharide	Type VIII pneumonococci	D-Glucuronic acid		UDP-D-Glucuronic acid
		D-Glucose		UDP-D-Glucose
		D-Galactose		UDP-D-Galactose
Teichoic acids	Bacteria	Polyribitol or polyglycerol-P with D-glucose or N-acetyl-glucosamine in glycosidic linkage	α,1 → 2	CDP-L-Ribitol or L-glycerol UDP-D-glucose or UDP-N-acetyl-D-glucosamine
Murein	Bacterial cell walls	N-Acetyl-D-glucosamine	β,1 → 6	UDP-N-Acetyl-D-glucosamine
		N-Acetylmuropeptides	β,1 → 4	UDP-N-Acetylmuropeptides
Glycoproteins	Mammalian submaxillary gland	N-Acetylneuraminic acid	α,2 → 6	CMP-N-Acetylneuraminic acid
		N-Acetyl-D-galactosamine disaccharide		UDP-N-Acetyl-D-galactosamine
Glycoproteins	Mammalian plasma: fetuin, orosomucoid	N-Acetylneuraminic acid	α,2 → 6	CMP-N-Acetylneuraminic acid
		N-Acetyl-D-glucosamine		UDP-N-Acetyl-D-glucose
		D-Mannose		GDP-D-Mannose
		D-Galactose		UDP-D-Galactose
Blood group substances	Animals	L-Fucose, N-acetyl-D-galactosamine, D-galactose		

are sulfated, giving these polymers the properties of strong polyanions. In the natural state, the mucopolysaccharides appear to be associated with specific proteins, even though, at least in some cases, the polysaccharides are not covalently bound to the protein moiety.

The properties of other polysaccharides are listed in Fig. 3-41. The pectins are polysaccharides composed of D-galacturonic-acid monomers joined in $1 \rightarrow 4$ α-glycosidic linkages. The repeat unit of the pectins is 4.35 Å, indicating some folding of the ring structure. Lignins are complex polymers of a variety of phenylpropane derivatives. Both of these polysaccharides are found in plants. Chitin, which forms the exoskeleton of the arthropods, is a polysaccharide composed of N-acetylglucosamine units. Alternate polymer strands, which are unbranched, are condensed in a crystalline structure in antiparallel orientation. *X*-ray diffraction studies show a unit cell corresponding to a lateral distance of 9.13 Å between strands, a separation of 9.4 Å perpendicular to the fiber axis, and a repeat of 10.46 Å along the fiber axis representing disaccharide units.

nucleic acids

The nucleic acids are polymers composed of nucleotide monomers, each nucleotide consisting of a pyrimidine or purine base, a sugar, and a phosphoric acid residue. The two important classes of nucleic acids, ribonucleic acid (RNA) and deoxyribonucleic acid (DNA), are distinguished by the fact that the nucleotides of the former contain ribose and those of the latter contain 2-deoxyribose as the sugar. The bases in DNA are adenine, thymine, guanine, and cytosine, while in RNA uracil is found in place of thymine (Fig. 3-42). Additional types of bases which occur only rarely are also found;

fig 3-42. Components of the nucleic acids.

DNA	RNA
Adenine (A)	Adenine (A)
Thymine (T)	Uracil (U)
Guanine (G)	Guanine (G)
Cytosine (C)	Cytosine (C)
2-Deoxy-D-ribose	D-Ribose
Phosphate	Phosphate

these will be discussed in later sections. The bases are attached to the 1′ carbon atom, and the phosphoric acid residue is attached to the 5′ carbon atom of the sugar. Adjacent nucleotides are connected by a linkage between the phosphoric acid residue of one nucleotide and the 3′ carbon atom on the next nucleotide.

Both the bases and the sugars have approximately planar structures, and in the nucleotides the planes are oriented with respect to one another at an angle of 70° to 75°. In DNA, the molar ratios of adenine to thymine and of guanine to cytosine are both about one ($A/T = 1$; $G/C = 1$). However, the ratio $(A + T)/(G + C)$ varies from about 0.4 to about 1.9. The order of the bases in the polynucleotide chains is highly irregular. DNA with a lower $(A + T)/(G + C)$ ratio is often found in microorganisms, while higher animals have DNA with a high ratio. DNA may be very large; some preparations have been obtained with molecular weights of about 1.3×10^8 containing about 4.3×10^5 nucleotides.

Watson and Crick[38] were the first to propose that native DNA occurred usually as two intertwined strands wound in a right-handed helix. The chains are oriented in opposite directions so that the 3′-end of one chain corresponds to the 5′-end of the other chain. The nucleotides in the two strands contain complementary bases, so that at any given point an adenine in one chain corresponds to a thymine in the other chain, or a cytosine corresponds to a guanine, thus accounting for the A/T and G/C ratios of unity.

The two chains are joined together by hydrogen bonds between the complementary bases. In order to permit a regular helix, a purine must always be paired with a pyrimidine. (Were two purine bases hydrogen-bonded, the distance would be greater than for a purine-pyrimidine combination, while for a pyrimidine pair, the distance would be smaller. Fortunately, the most favorable hydrogen-bonded base pairs occur between

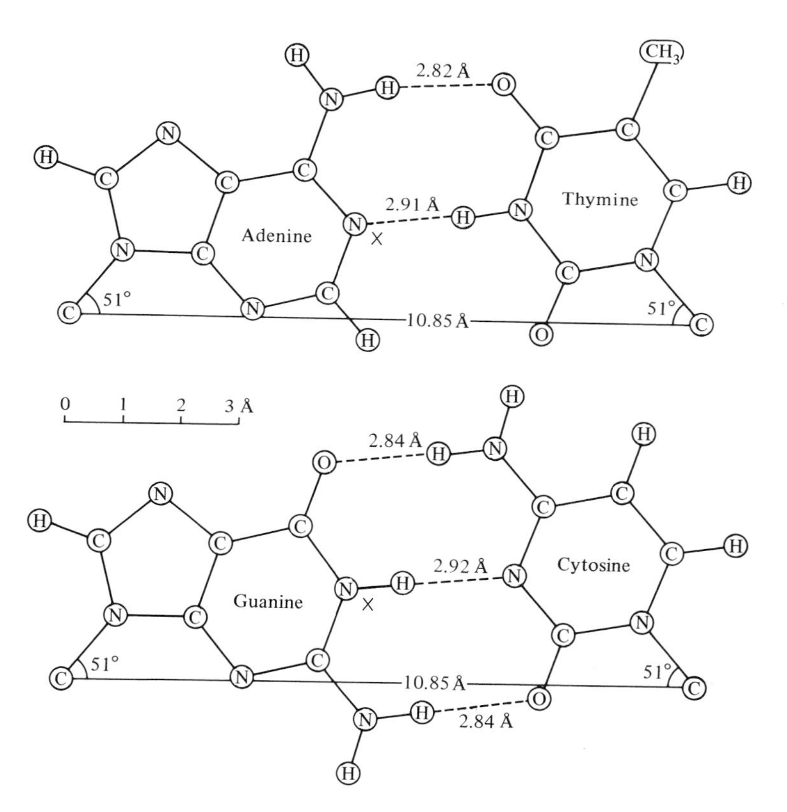

fig. 3-43. Watson-Crick pairing of bases by hydrogen bonding. The position of the helix axis of DNA is shown by the *X*. (From Arnott, S., Wilkins, M. F., Hamilton, L. D., and Langridge, R. *J. Mol. Biol., 11*, 391 [1965]. Copyright Academic Press; reprinted by permission.)

[38] Watson, J. D., and Crick, F. H. C. *Nature*, *171*, 737, 964 (1953).

a purine and a pyrimidine.) The hydrogen-bonded structures are shown in Fig. 3-43. Thus, the bases of the nucleotides are oriented inward with a distance of about 11 Å between the two 1′ carbon atoms of the two sugar molecules. The rings of the two bases are coplanar and are oriented at right angles to the helix axis. Thus, the rings of successive bases are stacked one upon the next with a distance of about 3.4 Å between base pairs. There are 10 bases per turn of the double helix, and each turn has a height of 34 Å. The highly polar phosphodiester backbone faces outward and interacts with the solvent environment. The double helix has two grooves: a narrow groove between complementary bases of the two strands and a wide groove between turns. There are rare forms of DNA such as that found in the bacteriophage ϕX 174 which is single-stranded and in a random configuration. It is of interest that during replication, the DNA develops a complementary strand and takes the form of a circular coiled double helix.

The nucleotide bases can exist in two tautomeric forms, an *enol* and a *keto* form. In solution, single bases or nucleotides exist in an equilibrium between these forms. Only the keto forms can exist in DNA. The various bases have characteristic absorptions in the ultraviolet region of the spectrum (Fig. 3-44). The spectrum and molar

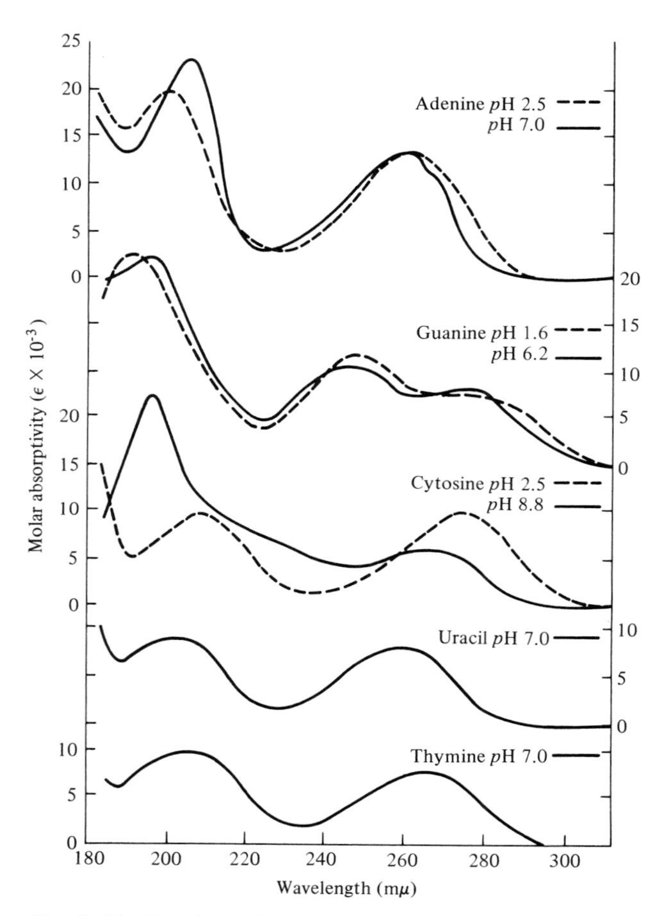

fig. 3-44. The absorption spectra of the common nucleotide bases. (From Voet, D., Gratzer, W. B., Cox, R. A., and Doty, P. *Biopolymers, 1,* 198 [1963].)

extinction coefficient of absorption depend upon the relative amounts of bases in the two tautomeric forms and upon the degree of ionization of the bases; they thus depend upon concentration, *p*H, ionic strength of dissolved salts, and temperature. One of the most characteristic features of all polynucleotides which have an ordered structure, and particularly those organized in a double helix, is *hypochromicity*, the phenomenon that the polynucleotide absorbs less light than would be expected by summing the absorption expected from the content of free bases. The actual absorbance may be as much as 40 to 45 percent less than expected from that of the free bases. The stacking interactions between the bases resulting in additional resonance forms is thought to change the π-orbitals and result in hypochromicity. Relatively little ordered structure appears necessary to produce hypochromicity; the hypochromatic effect was found to be high for synthetic purine dinucleotides and was as high as 30 percent for trinucleotides.

Because of their very high molecular weight and great molecular asymmetry, solutions of polynucleotides have very high viscosities, and the intrinsic viscosities are much greater than 2.5 cc/g. DNAs are so highly asymmetric that they are easily degraded by mild shearing forces, for example, in vigorous pipetting.

An important property of DNA is *denaturation*, the separation of the complementary strands and subsequent loss of the highly ordered structure. Denaturation can be brought about at the extremes of *p*H, by lowering the salt concentration, and by heat. If a DNA solution is heated, the transition from the native to the denatured form is remarkably sharp, occurring over a 5° range. During the transition, the absorbancy of the solution increases, which is to say that the degree of hypochromicity decreases, and this permits the process to be monitored easily (Fig. 3-45). The change from the highly ordered double helix to separated, uncoiled strands corresponds to melting of a one-dimensional crystal, and the process frequently is referred to as *melting* of the DNA. The temperature at the midpoint of the transition is known as the melting

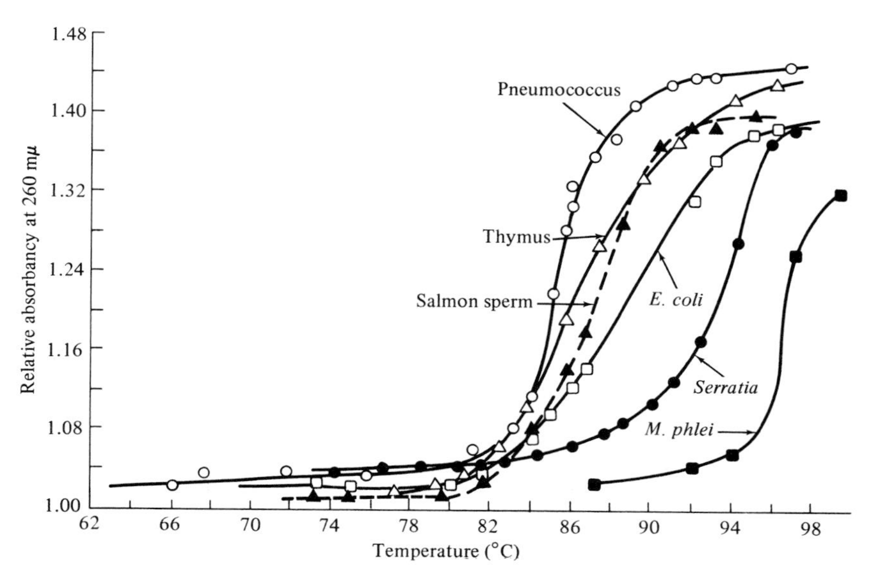

fig. 3-45. Plots of absorbance *versus* temperature for various DNA samples showing "melting." (From Snell, F. M., Shulman, S., Spencer, R. P., and Moos, C. *Biophysical Principles of Structure and Function.* Reading, Mass.: Addison-Wesley, 1965, p. 123.)

temperature (T_m). The melting temperature for a given DNA preparation depends upon the pH and ionic strength of the solvent. For different DNA preparations, the melting temperature at a given pH and ionic strength depends upon the base composition. The greater the content of G + C and the less the A + T, the higher the melting temperature (Fig. 3-46).

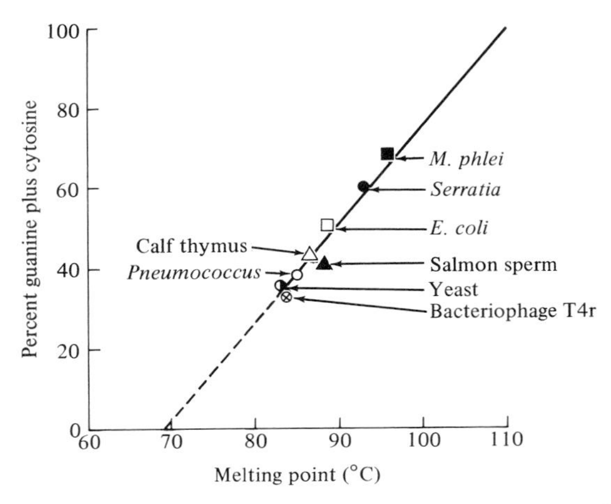

fig. 3-46. Relation between the melting temperature (T_m) and the guanine + cytosine content of various DNA samples. (From Snell, F. M., Shulman, S., Spencer, R. P., and Moos, C. *Biophysical Principles of Structure and Function.* Reading, Mass.: Addison-Wesley, 1965, p. 123.)

If a heated solution of DNA above the melting temperature is cooled, two phenomena may occur. If the solution is cooled rapidly, almost all of the DNA will remain in the form of random coils of single strands, and significant irreversible changes may occur. If the solution is cooled very slowly, the individual strands will recombine and a double helical structure will reform. The latter process is called *annealing*, and the DNA is often referred to as *renatured*. Annealing requires almost perfect complementarity between DNA strands, and the process is a sensitive technique for demonstrating homology between polynucleotides.

colloids

Thomas Graham (1805–1869) recognized that soluble materials could be divided into two classes, those like table salt and sugar which readily form crystals in the solid state, the *crystalloids*, and another group of substances like albumin, starch, and glue which tend to precipitate as amorphous masses, the *colloids* (Gk., "gluelike"). Crystalloids give "true solutions" while colloids give "colloidal solutions." Graham got to the heart of the matter when he discovered that colloids diffuse very much less rapidly in solution than crystalloids, and while crystalloids in solution would penetrate a parchment membrane, colloids in solution would not.

Berzelius, Selmi, and Faraday, all early nineteenth-century scientists, observed that it was possible to make colloidal solutions of substances like sulfur, silicic acid, Prussian blue, or silver chloride, and that even gold could be dispersed in a seeming solution under certain conditions. When these normally insoluble materials were solubilized, they resembled colloids like albumin and glue in their behavior. For a spherical particle, the diffusion constant is inversely proportional to the radius of the particle. The slow diffusion of colloids in solution was explained by assuming that they were large particles, either because the individual molecules were very large or because the individual particles consisted of aggregates of many small molecules. Until the development of the physical chemistry of solutions in the latter part of the nineteenth century, colloids were an enigma because they showed hardly any osmotic pressure or raising of the boiling point or lowering of the freezing point. In our present view, these observations are consistent with the fact that colloidal solutions contain larger but fewer particles. There is no clear-cut division between true solutions and colloidal solutions, and many systems with intermediate properties are known.

Colloidal solutions can be classified into two main groups, *lyophilic systems* and *lyophobic systems.* Their classification depends upon the interaction between the dispersed particles and their dispersion medium. In terms of water as the solvent, these two categories of colloidal solutions are *hydrophilic colloids* and *hydrophobic colloids.* These two kinds of colloidal solutions can be distinguished by a number of properties (Fig. 3-47). Hydrophilic colloidal solutions can be obtained by simply dissolving the

fig. 3-47. Properties that differentiate lyophobic and lyophilic sols.

LYOPHOBIC SOLS	LYOPHILIC SOLS
Viscosity close to that of the solvent	Viscosity higher than that of the solvent
Surface tension close to that of the solvent	Surface tension often lower than that of the solvent
Particles easily detected in the ultramicroscope	Particles not easily detected in the ultramicroscope
Little or no colloid osmotic pressure	Colloid osmotic pressure present
Small amounts of electrolytes cause precipitation	Small amounts of electrolytes have little effect; large amounts cause salting out

material, such as protein, polysaccharide, or soap in water; the dispersion of hydrophilic colloids occurs spontaneously when the solid material is shaken with water. Solutions of hydrophobic colloids can be made only by indirect means, for example, the electrolytic formation of a colloidal gold sol or the precipitation of finely dispersed sulfur particles from an acidified solution of sodium thiosulfate. While the addition of electrolytes to hydrophilic colloids does not produce any dramatic changes, hydrophobic sols are very sensitive to electrolytes; and the addition of a very small quantity of an inorganic salt will usually result in the coagulation of the dispersed phase. If the dispersed phase of a hydrophobic sol is precipitated by the addition of a salt or by evaporation of the solvent, a colloidal solution cannot be obtained again by mixing the solid with the solvent. When a hydrophilic colloidal solution is formed, there is a large change in surface tension and viscosity as well as smaller but definite changes in the vapor pressure and other physical properties of the solvent. In the case of hydrophobic sols, on the other hand, the surface tension, viscosity, and other physical properties of the colloidal solution are practically the same as those of water. In the ultramicroscope, hydrophobic colloids give a well-differentiated diffraction pattern while hydrophilic colloids tend to give a diffuse spot of light.

In true solutions, the solute is presumed to be dispersed in particles of molecular size. Suspensions or emulsions, on the other hand, contain particles large enough to be seen with the naked eye, or at least through a microscope. Most colloidal solutions are perfectly clear, and no large particles can be observed with even the most powerful light microscope. This observation was disturbing to early investigators who tried to explain the properties of colloids by assuming that they were composed of large particles. Of course, most colloidal particles, though large compared to ordinary low-molecular-weight solutes, are small compared to the wavelength of light.

The problem was resolved by the use of the ultramicroscope by H. Siedentopf and R. Zsigmondy. In this instrument, a beam of light is passed through a solution while the solution is observed through a microscope mounted at right angles to the beam of light. Nothing is seen in the ultramicroscope unless a particle is in the beam of light and creates a diffraction pattern against the dark background. The diffraction tends to be greater for light of shorter wavelengths, and if white light is used in the ultramicroscope, the scattered light seen tends to be blue. The scattering of light by submicroscopic particles is called the *Tyndall phenomenon.* In the ultramicroscope, the light scattered from individual particles is observed, permitting one to detect particles considerably smaller than the wavelength of light. Of course, it is the light scattered by the particles which is seen and not the particles themselves. While the size, form, and color of the diffraction pattern is not a direct indication of the size, form, and color of the colloidal particles, it is possible to obtain some information about the particles from the ultramicroscope image. Because of their small size, colloidal particles, as seen in the ultramicroscope, display vigorous Brownian movement resulting from thermal agitation.

lyophobic colloids

Lyophobic sols represent a nonequilibrium state of a system containing two or more phases. Every sol of this type will eventually flocculate, although under favorable circumstances the process may take years. A lyophobic sol, once formed, has a unique "life history"; extremely rapidly moving particles gradually overcome the repulsive forces which tend to separate them, and the sol finally "dies" by complete flocculation. The process may occur so slowly that the sol gives an impression of stability. Lyophobic sols are dispersions of essentially insoluble substances, such as metals, sulfur, sulfides, and silver halides. While these substances appear to be amorphous when they precipitate, *x*-ray diffraction studies show that they are actually microcrystalline in structure. Hydrophobic sols may be prepared by means of a chemical reaction which results in a supersaturated solution with dispersed particles of molecular or slightly supramolecular size (such as mixing saturated solutions of hydrogen sulfide and arsenic trioxide to form an arsenic trisulfide sol), or by dispersion (for example, of metals) by an electric arc or by ultrasound. Lyophobic sols can be formed in nonaqueous media either directly or by dialyzing an aqueous sol against an organic solvent which is miscible with water.

It is obvious that some repulsive force must exist between the dispersed particles of a lyophobic sol which prevents them from coalescing and precipitating. The repulsive force has its origin in the fact that the dispersed particles of a hydrophobic sol are all electrically charged. The charge may be either positive or negative, but in either case the particles repel each other so successfully that collisions resulting in combination and aggregation are very rare events and the sols show remarkable stability. Were it not for the repulsive forces of like charged particles, there would be a tendency to aggregate and diminish the surface area of the dispersed phase and, therefore, lower the total free energy of the system. The charged double layer on colloidal particles will be discussed quantitatively in Chapter 4.

If a dilute solution of a silver salt is added to an excess of a dilute potassium iodide solution, a negatively charged silver iodide sol is obtained; if the silver salt is in excess, a positively charged silver iodide sol is obtained. If stoichiometric amounts of the silver salt and potassium iodide are mixed, the sol is unstable and complete precipitation occurs. The negatively charged sol is stabilized by the adsorption of iodide ions on the surface of the particles, while the positively charged sol is stabilized by the adsorption of silver ions on the surface of the particles. As a general rule, electrolytes show a preference for adsorbing an ion of which it is composed as a result of the tendency for a crystal to extend its own lattice. Sols of the noble metals usually consist of negatively charged particles. In summary, the behavior of the colloidal particles depends upon two opposing forces, attractive van der Waals forces which vary inversely as r^7 (potential energy varies inversely as r^6), and Coulombic repulsive forces which vary inversely as r^2 (potential energy varies inversely with r). A composite potential energy curve can be constructed which shows a net repulsion at relatively short distances of separation even though there is a net attraction when the particles approach each other extremely closely. In order for particles to coalesce, the potential energy barrier of the repulsive forces must be overcome. If the potential energy barrier is high compared to the kinetic energy of the particles, the sol will be stable; instability usually occurs at a ζ potential of 0.02–0.03 volts. The ζ potential or electrokinetic potential is a potential difference found in the boundary layer of a liquid in contact with a solid. Its magnitude depends upon the substances, the rate of flow of liquid, and other variables.

While traces of salts are often essential to the stability of sols, particularly in water somewhat larger amounts will cause the particles to aggregate. The flocculating effect of electrolytes depends upon the extent to which they lower the ζ potential, that is, the extent to which they compress the double layer (the ions adsorbed on the surface of the particles and their counter ions). By carefully standardizing the experimental

fig. 3-48. Precipitating effects of various ions. (From Glasstone, S. *Textbook of Physical Chemistry,* 2nd ed. Princeton, N.J.: Van Nostrand, 1946, p. 1244.)

FERRIC OXIDE (POSITIVE) SOL			ARSENIOUS SULFIDE (NEGATIVE) SOL		
ELECTROLYTE	ANION VALENCE	MINIMUM CONCENTRATION	ELECTROLYTE	CATION VALENCE	MINIMUM CONCENTRATION
KCl	1	103	NaCl	1	51
KBr	1	138	KNO_3	1	50
KNO_3	1	131	$\frac{1}{2}K_2SO_4$	1	63
$KBrO_3$	1	31	HCl	1	31
K_2CrO_4	2	0.325	$MgSO_4$	2	0.81
K_2SO_4	2	0.219	$BaCl_2$	2	0.69
$K_2C_2O_4$	2	0.238	$ZnCl_2$	2	0.68
$K_3Fe(CN)_6$	3	0.096	$AlCl_3$	3	0.093

conditions, it is possible to determine, for purposes of comparison, the concentration of various electrolytes that will just cause precipitation of a sol. A number of investigators studied the precipitation of sols by electrolytes, and their results are summarized in the *Schulze-Hardy* rule (which is analogous to Perrin's rule for electrosmosis). The Schulze-Hardy rule states that the ion which brings about flocculation bears the charge of opposite sign to that of the charge on the colloidal particles (cations for negatively charged sols and *vice versa*), and that the coagulating power increases considerably with the valence of the ion (Fig. 3-48). The precipitating effect of a tervalent ion is roughly three orders of magnitude greater than that of an univalent ion. If two sols composed of particles carrying charges of opposite signs are mixed in approximately stoichiometric proportions, Coulombic repulsion is replaced by attraction, and flocculation occurs.

In the example of the silver iodide sol given above, an excess of either potassium iodide or of the silver salt was required to form a stable sol. In this case, the presence of a salt is required for the formation of a stable sol, and such substances are known as *peptizing agents.* Almost all sols require a very small amount of an electrolyte for stability; and if the peptizing agent is removed by dialysis, the sol will flocculate. In general, ionic peptizing agents act to enhance the double layer around the colloidal particles. Hydrophobic sols can be *protected* against flocculation in many cases by the addition of a small quantity of a hydrophilic sol generally bearing a net charge of the same sign. It has been supposed, at times, that the hydrophilic material coats the lyophobic particles in the process of protection, and that the protected sol acts like a hydrophilic sol. However, maximum protection is often achieved with quantities of hydrophilic material too small to coat the hydrophobic particles, and often the hydrophilic and hydrophobic particles are comparable in size. Also, the addition of a small quantity of a hydrophilic sol bearing a net charge of opposite sign to a hydrophobic sol may result in *sensitization* to flocculation.

In the preceding discussion, it has been assumed that the colloidal particles are approximately spherical in shape. While this is generally the case, at times astonishing deviations from a spherical shape occur. Vanadium pentoxide sols consist of long, needle-shaped particles, and ferric oxide sols are composed of flat plates. Both sols show birefringence of flow, a phenomenon characteristic of sols containing markedly anisometric particles. The actual particles in sols can be visualized in electron photomicrographs.

lyophilic colloids

The colloidal systems in living tissues are almost entirely lyophilic colloids or, more specifically, hydrophilic colloids. In contrast to lyophobic sols, the particles of lyophilic colloids have a uniform mass which is constant through time. The colloidal solution forms spontaneously, and it represents a true equilibrium state. In general, lyophilic colloids can be divided into two classes: (1) true solutions of single macromolecules and (2) *association colloids.* The first class, even though it consists of true solutions of single molecules, merits consideration as colloidal solutions simply because the molecules are very large and therefore endow the solutions with special properties. These macromolecular solutions can be divided into solutions of electrolyte macromolecules and solutions of nonelectrolyte macromolecules. A suspension of soap, detergent, or other amphophile micelles is an example of an association colloid. Even though the solution contains small molecules, it is the micelle containing many molecules, a large unit compared to the size of ordinary molecules, which behaves as the unit of solute. Furthermore, each micelle may contain several different molecular species, yet the micelles behave as identical, single solute units.

Solutions of lyophilic colloids are formed as a result of the same kinds of interactions that occur between small ions or small nonelectrolyte molecules and solvent molecules. The macromolecule, of course, has multiple functional groups which can participate in hydrogen bonds and multiple dipoles. If it is an ionic macromolecule, it has multiple charged groups, often some of each sign. Very often two distinct stages can be distinguished in the formation of a lyophilic colloid. First there is *swelling* of the solute as it imbibes solvent molecules. *Solvation*, the intimate association of solvent molecules with the dispersed particles during swelling, is a characteristic property of lyophilic sols. Swelling is followed by *dissolution.*

Many macromolecules, notably proteins and nucleic acids, are homogeneous, all the molecules being absolutely identical in composition even though they are composed of many monomers. Other macromolecules, however, are heterogeneous. For example, the starches are composed of hexose monomers which are polymerized to varying extents, and a single type of starch consists of a population of molecular species with a range of molecular weights. The formation of a starch can be described by the following:

$$xM_o \leftrightarrows M_x \qquad (3\text{-}39)$$

The molecular weight of the polymer depends upon the degree of advancement of reaction 3-39. The number average molecular weight of such a polymer population is given by

$$\overline{M}_x = \frac{\Sigma N_i M_i}{\Sigma N_i} = \Sigma n_i M_i \qquad (3\text{-}40)$$

where N_i is the number of molecules of the ith species, n_i is its mole fraction, and M_i is its molecular weight.

In addition to the heterogeneity of molecular weight, many of these macromolecules are very flexible and can assume a variety of three-dimensional configurations. The properties of such macromolecular solutions must be treated statistically by averaging out contributions from all possible conformations of a given molecular species. Important properties in such considerations are the *end-to-end distance* of a macromolecule, h, and the *radius of gyration*, R_G, which is defined as the root mean square of the individual radii from the center of mass of the polymer molecule to the center of each structural unit. It has been shown[39] that the average of the squares of all possible end-to-end distances, $\overline{h^2}$, is given by the following relation:

$$\overline{h^2} = \alpha^2\beta^2 M/M_0 = \alpha^2\beta^2\sigma \qquad (3\text{-}41)$$

where M is the molecular weight of the polymer, M_0 is the number average molecular weight of the structural units composing the polymer, σ is the number of structural units, and α and β are parameters which depend upon the system. The parameter β depends principally upon the polymer itself and represents the effective length of an average structural unit. For a polymer with free rotation and no steric hindrance, $\beta/1_{av} = 2^{1/2}$, while for many polymers of biological interest, $\beta/1_{av} \cong 3$, where 1_{av} is the actual average length of a structural unit. The quantity $\beta/1_{av}$ is a measure of the

[39] Flory, P. J., and Fox, T. G., Jr. *J. Am. Chem. Soc.*, *73*, 1904 (1951).

"stiffness" of the macromolecule. While the parameter α depends to a slight extent on the molecular weight of the macromolecule, its value is determined largely by the solvent in which the macromolecule is suspended; it is slightly less than one for "poor" solvents and greater than one for "good" solvents. The radius of gyration is related to the end-to-end distance in the following way:[40]

$$R_G^2 = \overline{h^2}/6 = \alpha^2\beta^2\sigma/6 = \alpha^2\beta^2 M/6M_0 \tag{3-42}$$

The density of a typical macromolecule in solution can be assessed from the average distribution of all segments relative to the center of mass. The density of mass of a single macromolecule in a given volume is reflected by the segment density, ρ, that is, the number of segments per cubic centimeter. This problem was treated by Debye and Bueche[41] who obtained the following relation:

$$\rho = \sigma(3/2\pi R_G^2)^{3/2} e^{-3r^2/2R_G^2} \tag{3-43}$$

where r is the distance from the center of mass of the polymer to the volume unit. Examination of eq. 3-43 indicates that the segment density decreases with increasing chain length (ρ is inversely proportional to $\sigma^{1/2}$ at the center of mass). In addition, ρ is larger in a poor solvent ($\alpha < 1$) than in a good solvent ($\alpha > 1$). The fraction of space occupied by the polymer molecule can be obtained by multiplying ρ by the average volume of a segment, 100 to 200 Å^3 for most macromolecules. The calculations indicate that a flexible macromolecule occupies only a small fraction of the volume which it fills, less in good solvents than in poor solvents but in most cases not more than a few percent of the volume subtended by the radius of gyration.

Carrying these considerations further, it is apparent that it is difficult to place a second macromolecule in the immediate vicinity of the first macromolecule. Put another way, every molecule of a flexible polymer has a domain from which other polymer molecules are excluded. The domain of a polymer molecule from which a second polymer is excluded (Fig. 3-49) may be regarded as a sphere whose volume, V, is a function of the radius of gyration:

$$V = (32/3)\pi\gamma^3 R_G^3 \tag{3-44}$$

where γ is a parameter which depends largely upon the solvent and is related to α. This consideration of the excluded volume of a macromolecule does not take into account either attractive or repulsive forces between molecules. These properties of macromolecular solutions are very important to the biologist who deals with concentrated solutions of macromolecules.

Macromolecules, like small-molecule solutes, raise the boiling point of solutions, lower the freezing point, etc. Except for the osmotic pressure, the changes in colligative properties are so small for most macromolecular solutions that they are difficult to measure. Osmotic pressure measurements are also advantageous for another reason. Using membranes prepared from cellophane or collodion which are permeable not only to solvent molecules but to all low-molecular-weight solutes, it is possible to measure the *colloid osmotic pressure*, that is, the osmotic pressure due to the macromolecules alone rather than the total osmotic pressure due to all solutes. At infinitely

[40] Zimm, B. H., and Stockmayer, W. H. *J. Chem. Phys.*, *17*, 1301 (1949).
[41] Debye, P., and Bueche, F. *J. Chem. Phys.*, *20*, 1337 (1952).

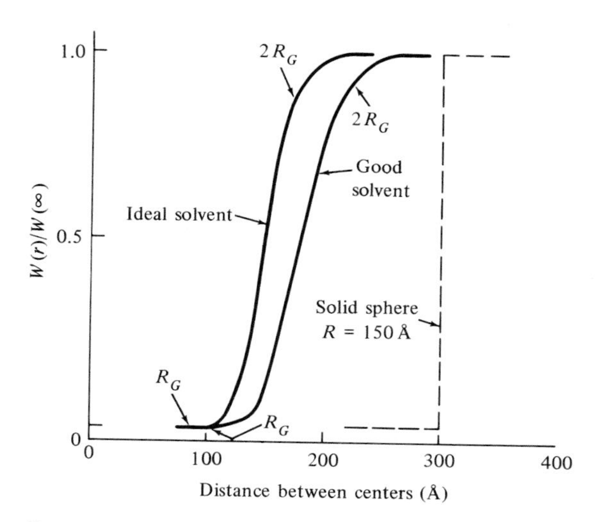

fig. 3-49. The probability of being able to locate a flexible polymer near another one. The corresponding behavior of solid spheres is shown for comparison. (From Tanford, C. *Physical Chemistry of Macromolecules.* New York: Wiley, 1961, p. 199.)

dilute concentrations the colloid osmotic pressure is given by van't Hoff's limiting law which resembles the equation of state for an ideal gas.

$$\lim_{c\to 0} \frac{\Pi}{c} = \frac{RT}{M} \tag{3-45}$$

where Π is the colloid osmotic pressure, c is the concentration in grams per liter of solvent, and M is the molecular weight. For a mixture of macromolecules with molecular weights M_1, M_2, etc., M becomes $\overline{M}_x$, the number average molecular weight defined in eq. 3-40.

Macromolecular solutions, particularly aqueous solutions, deviate markedly from ideality because of interactions between the solvent molecules themselves, between solute molecules themselves, and between solvent and solute molecules. These interactions result in a noticeable concentration dependence of the osmotic pressure. The value of the second virial coefficient, B, of eq. 3-24 can be obtained from the limiting slope of a plot of Π/c versus c. It can be shown that

$$B \cong \left(\frac{2}{3}\right)^{5/2} \frac{\pi N \alpha^3 \beta^3 \gamma^3}{M_0^{3/2} M^{1/2}} \tag{3-46}$$

for flexible linear polymers.

In the case of *polyelectrolytes*, macromolecules which possess charged ionic groups in solution, there are additional contributions to the colligative properties from the ionic groups and from the counterions which are associated with them. Assuming that every structural unit has one potentially ionizable group, the degree of ionization of the polyelectrolyte can be defined by $\alpha = \nu/\sigma$, where ν is the number of ionized groups on a polyelectrolyte molecule. The molal concentration of counterions is then given by

$$m_c = \alpha c/M_0 = \frac{\nu}{\sigma}\frac{c}{M_0} = \nu m_x \tag{3-47}$$

where c/M_0 is the molal concentration of monomer structural units. A salt-free solution of a polyelectrolyte will have a total osmotic pressure due in part to the polyelectrolyte molecules themselves and in part to the counterions carried along with the polymer molecule.

$$\Pi = RT(m_x + m_c) = RT(m_x + \nu m_x \varphi) \cong \varphi RT \nu m_x \tag{3-48}$$

where the *practical osmotic coefficient* is defined by the relationship, $\varphi = \Pi_{\text{observed}}/\Pi_{\text{ideal}}$. The last approximation of the right-hand side of eq. 3-48 was made because $\nu m_x \gg m_x$.

It has been shown by Alexandrowicz[42] that for all but low-molecular-weight polyelectrolytes, φ is essentially independent of the molecular weight of the polymer and relatively independent of the polyelectrolyte concentration. In contrast to strong electrolytes of low molecular weight, φ tends to *decrease* slightly rather than increase upon dilution of the solution. It appears that φ depends primarily upon the charge density along the polyelectrolyte chain; it decreases with increasing charge density. For polyacrylic acids, by way of example, under conditions when $\alpha = 1$, only about 12 to 15 percent of the counterions are osmotically active; the remainder behave as associated ion pairs. When an acidic polyelectrolyte is partially neutralized by the addition of alkali, even though the number of counterions in solution is increased, the observed osmotic pressure remains essentially constant (Fig. 3-50). The nature of the neutralizing

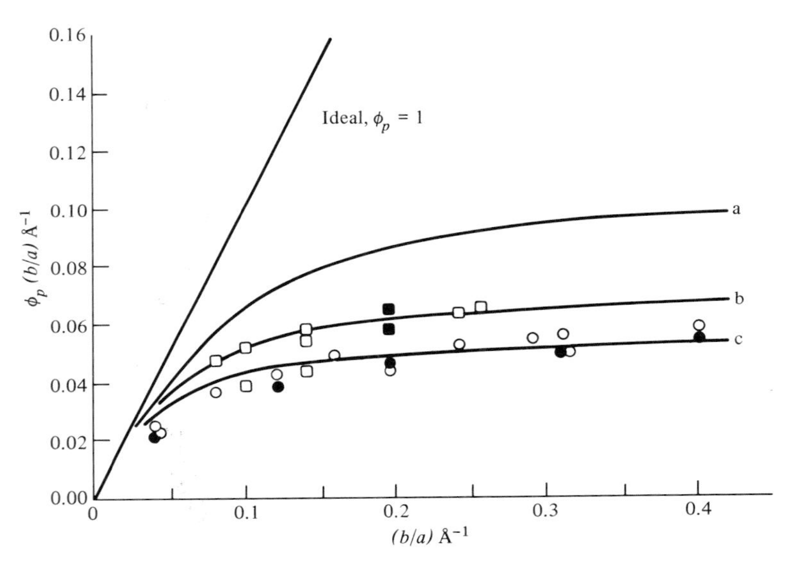

fig. 3-50. The osmotic coefficient, φ_p, *divided by* the intercharge distance, b/a, *plotted against* the reciprocal intercharge distance, a/b, for several polyelectrolytes: ○––– ○ polyacrylates, ●–––● polymethacrylates, □–––□ carboxymethyl cellulose, and ■–––■ alginates. (From Alexandrowicz, Z., and Katchalsky, A. *J. Polymer Sci., A 1*, 3251 [1963].)

cation (Na, K, Li) seems to have little effect on φ unless it is bulky; φ increases if the polymer is neutralized by tetraethylammonium hydroxide. As a result, polyelectrolytes in solution behave as *osmotic buffers* over a wide range of degrees of ionization.

[42] Alexandrowicz, Z. *J. Polymer Sci.*, *40*, 91 (1959); *A-1*, 3231 (1963).

This phenomenon is of possible far-reaching importance for the osmotic homeostasis of living systems. The observed osmotic pressure of a ternary mixture comprising a polyelectrolyte, a low-molecular-weight salt, and water is approximately the sum of the osmotic pressure of a polyelectrolyte solution alone at the same concentration (Π_P) and the osmotic pressure of a salt solution alone at the same concentration (Π_S).[43]

$$\Pi = \Pi_P + \Pi_S \qquad (3\text{-}49)$$

The effectively associated counterions which move along with the polyelectrolyte give it an electrical double layer similar to the electrical double layer around lyophobic sol particles.

One of the striking properties of lyophilic colloids is their high viscosity. The effect of dispersing approximately spherical solid particles upon the viscosity of a liquid was treated theoretically by Einstein, who deduced the relation

$$\eta = \eta_0\left(1 + \frac{5}{2}\,\overline{V}\right) \qquad (3\text{-}50)$$

where η is the viscosity of the mixture, η_0 is the viscosity of the solvent alone, and $\overline{V}$ is the volume fraction of the dispersed substance (eq. 3-37 for "ideal" solutes). While the equation holds reasonably well for lyophobic sols, the particles of lyophilic colloids appear to occupy a much larger volume fraction than their dry volume would indicate. In part, the larger effective volume fraction may be due to deviations in the shape of the particles from spheres. An important contribution to the larger effective volume, however, is solvent molecules which appear to be intimately associated with the colloidal particles. The contribution of solvation to the viscosity can be evaluated by measurements of viscosity in several solvents. For example, the value of $\overline{V}$ obtained from viscosity measurements of agar solutions in water is about 150 times higher than the value obtained from agar solutions in ethanol. The conclusion to be drawn from these data is that agar is much more highly solvated in water than in ethanol. The concept of a solvated hydrodynamic particle has been discussed *in extenso* by J. L. Oncley.[44] The particles of macromolecular colloids also behave as though they are solvated when their sedimentation or diffusion is measured.

The addition of a small quantity of an electrolyte to a lyophilic colloid produces a marked decrease in viscosity. This is the *electro-viscous effect*. Further addition of electrolytes, however, does not change the viscosity appreciably. The electro-viscous effect appears to be related to the electrical double layer around the colloidal particles. The addition of large amounts of electrolyte results in precipitation of the colloidal particles, *salting out*. The salting out effect depends upon the nature of the electrolyte added. Ions can be arranged in the *lyotropic series*, a series of decreasing effectiveness in removing lyophilic colloids from solution first described by Franz Hofmeister. The cation lyotropic series is

$Mg^{++} > Ca^{++} > Sr^{++} > Ba^{++} > Li^{+} > Na^{+} > K^{+} > NH_4^{+} > Rb^{+} > Cs^{+}$

and the anion series is

$HPO_4^{--} > SO_4^{--} > Cl^{-} > Br^{-} > I^{-} > NO_3 > SCN^{-}$

---

[43] Alexandrowicz, Z. *J. Polymer Sci.*, *43*, 337 (1960); *56*, 97, 115 (1962).

[44] Oncley, J. L., in Cohn, E. J., and Edsall, J. T., eds. *Proteins, Amino Acids and Peptides*. New York: Reinhold, 1943.

coacervates and gels

Under certain conditions, often when an electrolyte is added judiciously to a concentrated hydrophilic colloid, the particles do not flocculate, but instead the solution separates into two layers: a colloid-poor layer and a colloid-rich layer. This phenomenon is called *coacervation*, and the term *coacervate* is applied to the colloid-rich layer (Fig. 3-51). The colloidal systems which form coacervates are two-phase systems,

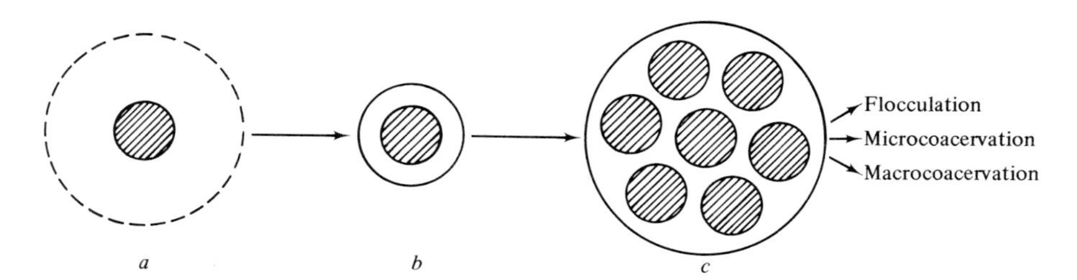

fig. 3-51. Schematic representation of the mechanism of coacervate formation: *(a)* sol particles with diffuse solvated coating, *(b)* particles with condensed solvated coating, and *(c)* fusion of particles with condensed solvated coating into a coacervate. (From Bungenberg de Jong, H. G., in Kruyt, H. R., ed. *Colloid Science.* Amsterdam: Elsevier, 1949, vol. 2, p. 246.)

and the apparent separation into layers does not represent an increase in the number of phases. Coacervates also are amorphous and are not spontaneously birefringent. Coacervates behave as liquids and obey Poiseuille's law of flow. Just prior to coacervation, there is usually a sharp drop in the specific viscosity, $\eta_{sp} = (\eta - \eta_0)/\eta_0$. The drop in specific viscosity is thought to reflect intermolecular association between the colloidal particles. Because the coacervate is liquid in character, the intermolecular associations must be dynamic rather than fixed. Water of occlusion and solvation is present in the coacervate, but the solvent plays a passive role in the formation of the coacervate. Coacervates can be separated into two classes: (1) *simple coacervates* in which no ionic bonds are involved in the intermolecular association, and (2) *complex coacervates* in which ionic forces are involved. Not only will the addition of a salt to a hydrophilic colloid sometimes lead to coacervate formation, but the addition of a nonionic solute of low molecular weight, ethanol for instance, or of a second hydrophilic colloid may also result in coacervation. For example, mixing sols of gum arabic and gelatin will result in coacervation. If concentrated solutions at a *p*H greater than the isoelectric point of the gelatin are mixed, two layers are formed, each of which contains principally one of the two types of colloidal particles. This system is a simple coacervate. If, on the other hand, more dilute sols at a *p*H less than the isoelectric point of gelatin are mixed, complex coacervation occurs. The properties of the two coacervates are outlined in Fig. 3-52. Many complex coacervates have extraordinarily low surface tensions, so low that surface tension is difficult to measure. Coacervates tend to wet glass and at the same time to take up drops of oily liquids. In addition, many coacervates tend to imbibe insoluble particles such as powdered charcoal, dye particles, or pollen grains. Under certain conditions, for instance, as a result of loss of solvent, coacervate droplets tend to form vacuoles. The vacuoles may coalesce to form hollow spheres (Fig. 3-53). The amount of solvent held in a coacervate

fig. 3-52. Conditions for simple and complex coacervation on mixing gelatin and gum arabic sols. (From Bungenberg de Jong, H. G. Crystallization—Coacervation—Flocculation, in Kruyt, H. R., ed. *Colloid Science,* Amsterdam: Elsevier, 1949, vol. 2, p. 256.)

SIMPLE COACERVATION	COMPLEX COACERVATION
Principal Condition	
Water deficit in the total system.	Adequate charge opposition between the two colloids.
Other Properties	
Also occurs at pH > I.E.P.[a] of the gelatin (at which both colloids are negatively charged).	Only occurs at pH < I.E.P. of the gelatin (at which the two colloids have opposite charges).
Is only possible on mixing concentrated sols. The coacervation disappears on adding water.	Does not occur in concentrated sols; occurs, however, after dilution with water. Still occurs even on mixing 0.001 percent sols.
Added indifferent salts do not suppress coacervation, appear rather to promote coacervation in certain cases. Ions arrange themselves in their effectiveness in lyotropic series.	Indifferent salts suppress coacervation. Valency of both ions is of primary importance in the matter. Position of the ions in the lyotropic series is of very minor significance.
Coacervate drops exhibit no disintegration phenomena in a d-c electric field.	Coacervate drops exhibit disintegration phenomena in a d-c electric field.
Both liquid layers are rich in colloid, each layer containing in the main one of the colloids.	One layer, the coacervate, is rich in colloids; the second layer is poor in colloid. Both layers contain gelatin and gum arabic in not far different ratios.

[a] I.E.P. is the isoelectric potential.

is variable, depending upon temperature, salt concentration, additions to the system, and other parameters.

Gels may be regarded as solid colloidal solutions. Hermans[45] gives three criteria which define the gel state: (1) it is a coherent colloidal system of at least two phases, (2) it exhibits the mechanical properties characteristic of the solid state (for example, the system shows mechanical strain and has a yield value), and (3) the constituent phases

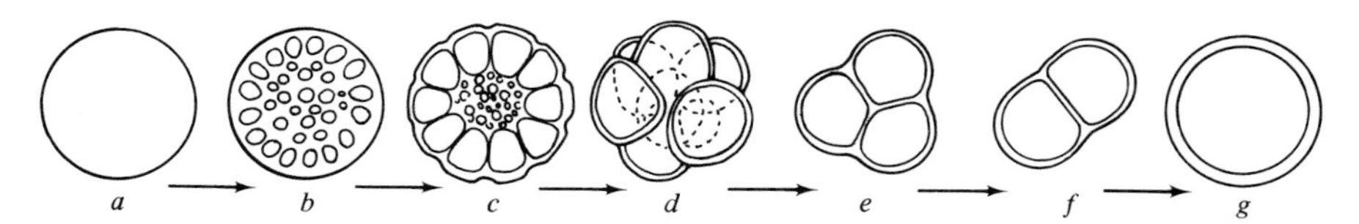

fig. 3-53. Development of hollow spheres from a negatively charged coacervate drop of the complex coacervate gum arabic-gelatin. (From Bungenberg de Jong, H. G., in Kruyt, H. R., ed. *Colloid Science.* Amsterdam: Elsevier, 1949, vol. 2, p. 460.)

[45] Hermans, P. H., in Kruyt, H. R., ed. *Colloid Science*. Amsterdam: Elsevier, 1949, vol. 2, p. 484.

are continuous throughout the system. The last characteristic differentiates gels from frozen colloidal solutions. Gelation may be regarded as forming by a process of coagulation in which the dispersed phase consisting of the colloidal macromolecules does not separate out of solution as particulate aggregates but rather coalesces into a continuous network in the spaces of which the solvent becomes occluded. The cooling curves of solutions of low-molecular-weight solutes show breaks when the solute begins to crystallize and separate out of solution. The onset of gelation is also marked by a small but definite break and arrest in the cooling curve which is evidence that the sol-gel transformation is accompanied by the liberation of heat. From polarized light and x-ray diffraction studies, some gels appear to contain small, localized domains of crystalline structure distributed randomly throughout. Hysteresis in sol-gel transformation is commonly observed; the temperature of liquefaction may be considerably higher than the temperature of gelation. Thus, a 2 percent solution of agar gels at approximately 55°. The gel, however, does not liquefy until it is heated to 90°. In many cases the sol-gel transformation is accompanied by an increased light scattering which indicates that an increase in particle size takes place. The particle size and the intermicellar cavities in the particle network have dimensions much smaller than the wavelength of visible light in most gels; this results in an optically isotropic appearance even though appreciable light scattering takes place. Usually gels are not double-refracting unless stressed by elongation, compression, or shear. It is interesting that the rates of diffusion of low-molecular-weight solutes in gels are not far different from their rates of diffusion in solvent alone. In gels containing electrolytes, the electrical conductivity, and therefore, the mobility of the ions, also are not very different from their conductivity and mobility in solvent alone. These findings indicate that an anastomosing system of channels filled with liquid solvent must be present in the gel.

Newton is credited with showing that the velocity of flow of a liquid is directly proportional to the pressure applied for most liquids, $P = \eta v$, and those liquids that demonstrate a proportionality between pressure and velocity of flow are known as *Newtonian liquids*. Viscosity, η, which sometimes is called the coefficient of viscosity, is the proportionality constant. Many colloidal solutions behave as Newtonian liquids. Some, however, such as the vanadium pentoxide sol or myosin solutions, are non-Newtonian; that is, the v/P function is not linear. In these liquids the dispersed particles are asymmetrical, and they become oriented in the direction of flow. The viscosity is not constant but becomes a function of the rate of flow. Gels display yet another type of viscous flow; it is necessary to apply a critical pressure characteristic of the gel, the *yield value*, before flow begins. For pressures greater than the yield value, the velocity of flow is approximately a linear function of the pressure applied. The application of pressure up to the yield value is thought to break some internal bonds in the network of the dispersed phase after which flow occurs. Such substances are said to be *plastic*. If the yield value of a gel is sufficiently small, vigorous shaking will cause it to liquefy; this phenomenon is called *thixotropy*. Some colloids show *dilatancy* or inverse plasticity; the viscosity increases with increasing shear stress. In such colloids, mixing results in less close packing of the disperse phase with adsorption of all the solvent present. Some gels when placed in a liquid take up appreciable quantities of it. If the liquid is taken up by the gel with little or no change in the volume of the gel, the phenomenon is called *imbibition*. If the volume of gel increases as the liquid is taken up, the phenomenon is called *swelling*. In general, the swelling of polyelectrolyte gels is least at the isoelectric point and greatest in acid or alkaline solutions. If a gel is permitted to set in a glass tube and the tube above the gel is filled with mercury, a swelling pressure can be measured. The swelling pressure is clearly an osmotic pressure with the gel acting as its own semipermeable membrane. The usual limiting law of van't Hoff holds in this case:

$$\Pi = \frac{RT}{\bar{V}} \ln \frac{P_0}{P} \tag{3-51}$$

where $\bar{V}$ is the partial molar volume of the solvent phase, and P_0 and P are the vapor pressures of the pure solvent and gel respectively. Some gels display the phenomenon of *syneresis*; that is, upon standing they extrude solvent and diminish in volume—a process which appears to be the reverse of swelling.

There is a vast literature in which the properties of cytoplasm have been compared to simple colloidal solutions. In many cell types, there is an outer cortical layer of cytoplasm which appears to be a gel while the interior of the cell contains fluid cytoplasm. Stimulation of the cell by sudden changes in the environment is often accompanied by a liquefaction of the cortical gel together with a movement of calcium into the central sol. The viscosity of the cytoplasm of various cell types varies widely from cells in which the cytoplasm is relatively nonviscous to those in which it is a gel with a yield value. The cytoplasm from many cell types behaves as a Newtonian liquid, while from others it is thixotropic and from still others (usually cells with a very high content of granules), the cytoplasm shows the phenomenon of dilatancy. In a given cell type, the viscosity appears to vary with the stage of the cell cycle and other physiological variables. For example, the viscosity of an amoeba is high at temperatures below 12°. Above this temperature, the viscosity falls rapidly. It reaches a minimum at about 18° and then rises to a plateau between 22° and 26° and then falls again. The drop in viscosity between 12° and 18° is thought to result from disruption of intermolecular interactions; the increase at somewhat higher temperatures may be ascribed to syneresis. Oxygen deprivation and immersion in hypotonic solutions result in a lowering of viscosity, while immersion in hypertonic solutions causes an increase in viscosity.

The idea, held for many years, that the cytoplasm is a homogeneous colloid has been dispelled by ultrastructure studies with the electron microscope. From the discussions in Chapter 2, it is clear that the cytoplasm contains many structured organelles of assorted types as well as an extensive system of membranes. This does not diminish the importance of colloid chemistry to the biologist. The concepts can be applied to the matrix of the cytoplasm and organelles and to the boundary layers of the liquid phases. Furthermore, it is becoming increasingly apparent that colloidal systems can develop a high degree of structural organization. This interface between biology and physical chemistry promises to be a fruitful area for inquiry.

the nature of the intracellular water

A question which has concerned physiologists for a good many years is whether or not intracellular water, or a part of it, exists in a different physical state than ordinary water. The idea that intracellular water is "bound" was advanced by Gortner[46] among others, but the theory has been viewed with skepticism for lack of confirmatory evidence. Although the evidence that intracellular water, or at least part of it, has

[46] Gortner, R. A. *Selected Topics in Colloid Chemistry*. Ithaca, N.Y.: Cornell University Press, 1937, chap. 8.

different physical properties than ordinary water is still very meager, physiologists find the concept attractive. Today we might prefer to think of the difference in terms of the physical properties of water, such as increased structuredness or unavailability of some water as solvent, rather than a "binding" of the water to macromolecules. Such "bound" water is associated not only with proteins but with other types of macromolecules as well.

Several mechanisms may be responsible for the association of water to macromolecules. (1) Ionic groups may be surrounded by water of hydration, as are small, free ions. Beyond the layer of water of hydration, however, ionic groups could have a structure-breaking effect on solvent water. (2) Nonpolar side chains directed outward on the exterior of the molecules, like hydrocarbons, will tend to order water in their environment, particularly if the dimensions of the side chain are such that they will fit easily into clathrate structures. (3) Areas on the surface of the macromolecule that are able to participate in hydrogen bonds will have either structure-promoting or structure-breaking effects depending upon whether or not the geometry of the hydrogen bonding sites is compatible with the bulky, hydrogen-bonded species of water.

Many macromolecules, particularly proteins, tend to adsorb water tenaciously. Evaluation of the adsorbed water gives values of 0.2 to 0.5 g water adsorbed per g protein for most proteins. In *x*-ray diffraction studies very dry proteins give a diffuse, uncharacteristic diffraction pattern, while the same proteins with a little adsorbed water give clear, crystalline diffraction patterns. When the amount of water adsorbed by a pure, solid protein is plotted against the vapor pressure, an S-shaped curve consistent with the formation of a multilayered adsorbate is obtained. For many proteins, the data fit an absorption isotherm of the type derived by Bradley[47] for the adsorption of inert gases to solids by dipole interactions.

$$\log \frac{P_0}{P} = K_1 \cdot K_3^a + K_4 \qquad \textit{(3-52)}$$

where a is the amount of adsorbate at partial pressure P, and P_0 is the partial pressure of the vapor at saturation. The constants K_1, K_3, and K_4 depend upon the system under the conditions studied. Water vapor adsorption on wool and collagen are plotted as a *versus* $\log [\log (P_0/P) - K_4] + K$ in Figs. 3-54 and 3-55.

For some proteins it has been possible to evaluate the adsorbed water by study of the water protons in oriented protein samples with nuclear magnetic resonance. In the case of collagen, the adsorbed water molecules appear to rotate anisotropically, with the main axis of anisotropy parallel to the collagen fiber direction.[48] The adsorbed water molecules appear to be hydrogen-bonded to the collagen and hydrogen-bonded to each other, lying in chains along the fiber axis. The half-life of a water molecule in a given position was estimated to be in the microsecond range. This relaxation time is five orders of magnitude greater than that of liquid water molecules and is taken to indicate a high degree of order in the adsorbed water. In the case of DNA, the adsorbed

---

[47] de Boer, J. H., and Zwikker, C. *Z. phys. Chem.*, *B3*, 407 (1929); Bradley, R. S. *J. Chem. Soc.*, 1467, 1799 (1936); Hoover, S. R., and Mellon, E. F. *J. Am. Chem. Soc.*, *72*, 2562 (1950); Ling, G. N. *Ann. N.Y. Acad. Sci.*, *125*, 401 (1965). An alternative adsorption isotherm, an extension of the Langmuir adsorption isotherm, has been suggested for the adsorption of inert gases on solids where London dispersion forces are most prominent by Brunauer, S., Emmett, P. H., and Teller, E. *J. Am. Chem. Soc.*, *60*, 309 (1938). For most proteins, the adsorption of water vapor fits the Bradley adsorption isotherm better than the Brunauer-Emmett-Teller adsorption isotherm, particularly above 50 percent vapor saturation.

[48] Berendsen, H. J. C., and Migchelsen, C. *Ann. N.Y. Acad. Sci.*, *125*, 365 (1965).

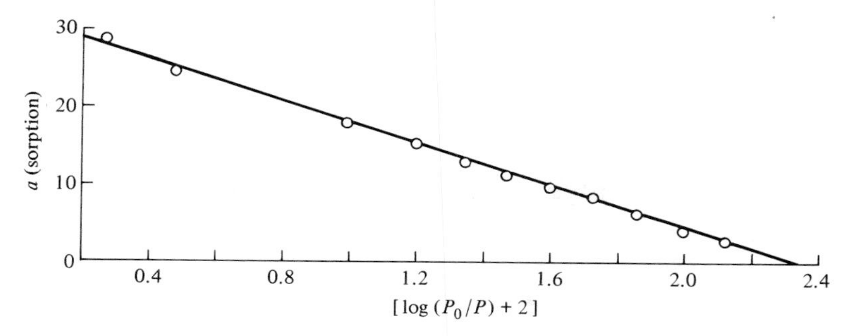

fig. 3-54. Water vapor adsorbed on sheep's wool, plotted according to the Bradley isotherm. (From Ling, G. N. *Ann. N.Y. Acad. Sci., 125,* 405 [1965]. Copyright 1965 by The New York Academy of Sciences; reprinted by permission.)

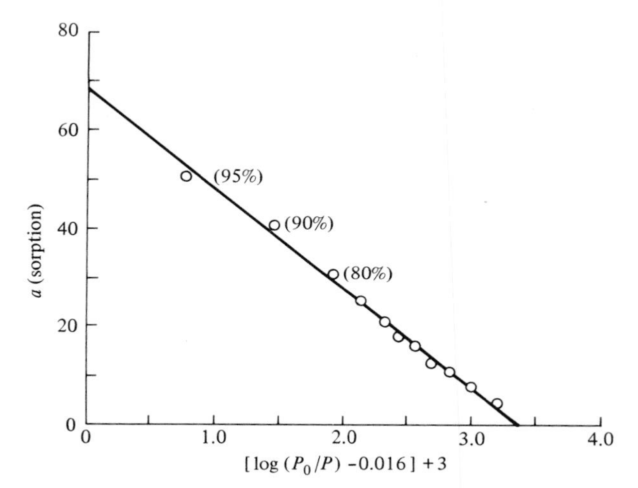

fig. 3-55. Water vapor adsorbed on collagen, plotted according to the Bradley isotherm. (From Ling, G. N. *Ann. N.Y. Acad. Sci., 125,* 405 [1965]. Copyright 1965 by The New York Academy of Sciences; reprinted by permission.)

water shows a perpendicular type of anisotropy. By way of contrast, silk fibroin and keratin adsorb water which does not display a high degree of directional orientation.

Similarly, the electrical conductivity of dry proteins is increased when water is adsorbed.[49] If the increased conductivity were due to proton jumps in hydrated protein, differences in conductivity might be expected with deuterated proteins and deuterium vapor. Experimentally, significant differences were not observed in this instance, and it appears that the adsorbed water alters the electronic properties of the protein.

It has already been said that macromolecules in solution behave as though they were larger particles than might be expected from evaluation of their molecular composition. This increase in molecular size appears in measurements of viscosity, light scattering, migration in an electric field, and sedimentation. For randomly coiled, long-chain

[49] Eley, D. D., and Leslie, R. B., in Pullman, B., ed. *Electronic Aspects of Biochemistry.* New York: Academic Press, 1964, p. 105.

particles, the effective size might correspond to the molecular domain of the polymer molecule in solution (see p. 141). Nevertheless, compact, globular macromolecules contain little solvent water in the interior. In the case of polynucleotides, the associated water may act to stabilize the structure, as may be deduced from the increased melting temperatures of DNA in heavy water.[50]

The water associated with macromolecules appears to be unavailable as a solvent for sucrose and other low-molecular-weight solutes.[51] Sucrose is excluded from cupric ferrocyanide, gum arabic, and gelatin gels as well as from water surrounding proteins such as bovine plasma albumin and polysaccharides like hyaluronic acid. Similarly, sucrose, galactose, xylose, and other low-molecular-weight solutes appear to be excluded from a portion of the intracellular water. The idea that a portion of the intracellular water exists in a highly ordered form with a structure intermediate between those of ordinary liquid water and ice has been a very attractive notion,[52] although the evidence put forward in support of this view is very indirect, and at the present time the idea must be regarded as an interesting speculation.

The reader has probably gathered from the foregoing discussion that the solvent associated with macromolecules in solution cannot be determined quantitatively at the present time. The situation is complicated by the fact that intracellularly, and in most physiological solutions, salts and other low-molecular-weight solutes are present that compete with solvent for adsorption; and the low-molecular-weight solutes alter the adsorption characteristics of the macromolecule. Recent studies by Clark and Schachman[53] provide a method for evaluation of adsorption in complex systems. Consider a three-component system containing a macromolecule, solvent (S), and low-molecular-weight solute (Y). The macromolecule will adsorb both solvent and solute in amounts that will depend upon their relative concentrations and will be described by the following relations:

$$a_S = a_{S_0} - a_{Y_0}(\bar{c}_S/\bar{c}_Y)_{\text{free}} \tag{3-53}$$

$$a_Y = a_{Y_0} - a_{S_0}(\bar{c}_Y/\bar{c}_S)_{\text{free}} \tag{3-54}$$

where a_S and a_Y are the weight fractions of solvent and solute actually adsorbed by the macromolecule in the system under study, a_{S_0} and a_{Y_0} are the weight fractions of solvent and solute adsorbed at saturation, and $\bar{c}_S$ and $\bar{c}_Y$ are the weight fractions of solvent and solute. It has been possible to evaluate a_S and a_Y by measuring the refraction with an interferometer during sedimentation of a macromolecule solution in an ultracentrifuge and comparing it with that of solvent and solute without the macromolecule. The effect of adding the macromolecule upon the solvent composition is measured in this technique. Selected results from this type of measurement are shown in Fig. 3-56. Interesting findings that emerged from these studies were the observation of increased amounts of adsorbed water with increasing salt concentration in many cases, and sharp diminution of total solvation preceding denaturation as the concentration of agents such as guanidine hydrochloride was increased.

---

[50] Lewis, S. *Arch. Biochem. Biophys.*, *115*, 62 (1966).

[51] Hartung, E. J., Kelly, F. H. C., and Wertheim, J. *Trans. Faraday Soc.*, *33*, 398 (1937); Troshin, A. S. *Das Problem der Zellpermeabilität.* Jena: Fischer, 1958; Beeman, W. W., Geil, P., Shurman, M., and Malmon, A. G. *Acta Cryst.*, *10*, 818 (1957); Hechter, O., and Lester, G. *Recent Progr. Hormone Res.*, *16*, 139 (1960); Ling, G. N. *Ann. N.Y. Acad. Sci.*, *125*, 401 (1965).

[52] Jacobson, B. *Nature*, *172*, 666 (1953); Szent-Györgyi, A. *Bioenergetics.* New York: Academic Press, 1957; Klotz, I. M. *Science*, *128*, 815 (1958).

[53] Clark, J. B., *Solvation of Macromolecules.* Ph.D. thesis, Berkeley, Calif.: University of California at Berkeley, 1964.

fig. 3-56. Solvation of macromolecules. (Data from Clark, J. B., Ph.D. thesis, University of California at Berkeley, copyright 1964.)

MACRO-MOLECULE (P)	SOLVENT (S)	LOW-MOLECULAR-WEIGHT SOLUTE (Y)	WEIGHT FRACTION FREE SOLVENT g/g	COMPLEX FOUND		RANGE OF POSSIBLE SOLVATION COMPLEXES					
				PS_jY_k S/P	(g/g) Y/P	MAX	a_{s0}	MIN	MAX	a_{y0}	MIN
Bovine plasma albumin	Water	Glycerol	0.10	0.23	0.003						
〃	〃	〃	0.50	0.12	0.003						
〃	〃	$(NH_4)_2SO_4$	0.01			1.1		0.27	0.01		0.01
〃	〃	〃	0.05			1.1		0.30	0.05		0.01
〃	〃	〃	0.25			1.1		0.48	0.24		0.01
〃	〃	LiBr	0.10			1.26		0.14	0.13		0.004
〃	〃	Guanidine HCl	0.01			0.926			0.007		
〃	〃	〃	0.25			0.12			0.09		

mechanism of action of anesthetics

The reversible failure to respond to painful stimuli and loss of consciousness constitute a dramatic response of higher organisms to anesthetic agents. While an enormous number of substances are known to produce the temporary state of suspended animation characteristic of anesthesia, the toxic side effects, low aqueous solubility, or high vapor pressure of most of these compounds prohibit their use as clinical anesthetic agents. The inhalation anesthetics include a diverse group of compounds: nitrous oxide, ether, chloroform, ethylene, cyclopropane, trichlorethylene, halothane (2-bromo,2-chloro,1,1,1-trifluoroethane), methoxyfluorane (2,2-dichloro,1,1-difluoroethyl methyl ether), and xenon. In general, they are gases or volatile liquids that are inert chemically. Although Joseph Priestly discovered the anesthetic action of nitrous oxide in 1776, Humphry Davy suggested its use during surgical operations to abolish pain in 1799, and Michael Faraday described the anesthetic action of diethyl ether in 1818, the use of anesthesia during surgery was not widespread until after a demonstration of ether anesthesia in the Massachusetts General Hospital in 1846. Since then, many scientists have sought a rational explanation for the mechanism of anesthesia.

Claude Bernard[54] suggested that an aggregation of intracellular colloids or proteins accompanies anesthesia, and that the reversibility of this effect enables recovery to occur. The evidence for this theory rested largely on the increase in optical density of muscle tissue which followed its immersion in chloroform. Later, Meyer and Overton[55] called attention to the correlation between anesthetic potency and the solubility of the agent in olive oil. Meyer believed that anesthesia occurred when the concentration of anesthetic agents in the cellular lipids reached a critical concentration. While this theory was highly regarded for many years, it did not explain the mechanism of anesthesia and did not admit a number of effective agents such as xenon which are not very soluble in lipids. A number of investigators have suggested that anesthetic agents alter cellular permeability and alter the ionic movements that accompany membrane depolarization.[56] Other investigators have pointed to a depression of respiration and oxygen consumption during anesthesia.[57] All these theories fail to provide a mechanism of action that admits the chemical diversity of anesthetic agents or such remarkably unreactive anesthetics as xenon and the other noble gases.

A molecular basis for anesthetic action was simultaneously and independently proposed by Linus Pauling and S. L. Miller[58] in 1961. They called attention to the striking correlation between anesthetic potency and the ability of these substances to form hydrates of the clathrate type (Fig. 3-57). Most anesthetic agents have a molecular configuration which makes them suitable guest molecules in the cavities of the pentagonal dodecahedral and hexakaidecahedral clathrates described earlier. Xenon, of course, is unable to form covalent or ionic chemical bonds or even hydrogen bonds, and its ability to form stable hydrates by acting as a guest molecule in a clathrate cavity is one of its few known chemical effects. In part, the stability of such hydrates results

---

[54] Bernard, C. Leçons sur les anésthesiques et sur l'asphyxie. Paris: Baillière, 1875.

[55] Meyer, H. H. *Arch. exptl. Pathol. Pharmakol.*, *42*, 109 (1899); *46*, 338 (1901); Overton, E. Studien über die Narkose zugleich ein Beitrag zur algemeinen Pharmakologie. Jena: Fischer, 1901.

[56] Höber, R. *Arch. ges. Physiol.*, *120*, 492 (1907); Lillie, R. S. *Am. J. Physiol.*, *24*, 14 (1909); Loewe, S. *Biochem. Z.*, *57*, 161 (1913); Yamaguchi, T., and Okumura, H. *Ann. Zool. Japan.*, *36*, 109 (1963).

[57] Quastel, J. H. *Current Res. Anesthesia Analgesia*, *31*, 151 (1952).

[58] Pauling, L. *Science*, *134*, 15 (1961); Miller, S. L. *Proc. Natl. Acad. Sci.*, *47*, 1515 (1961).

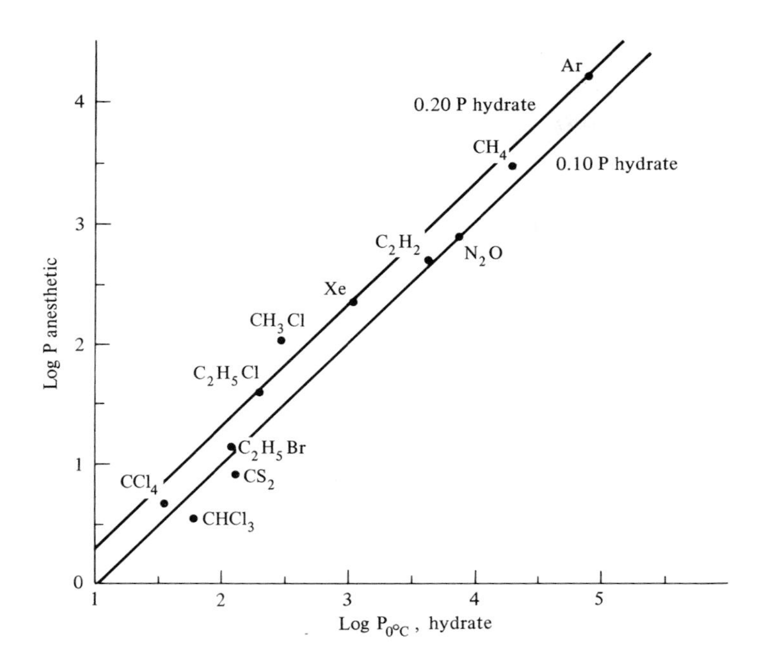

fig. 3-57. Logarithm of the partial pressure of several agents at which anesthesia occurs plotted against the equilibrium partial pressure of their hydrate crystals at 0°. (From Pauling, L. *Science, 134,* 19 [1961]. Copyright 1961 by the American Association for the Advancement of Science; reprinted by permission.)

from the weak molecular interactions (van der Waals forces) between the guest anesthetic molecules and the water molecules forming the cage.[59]

The hydrates formed by chloroform, xenon, and the other anesthetic agents are stable at atmospheric pressure only for a few degrees above the melting point of ice. Pauling proposed that the anesthetics act in concert with the intracellular proteins to increase the stability of structured water around protein and to propagate and extend ordered water in the vicinity of proteins. Tetra-*n*-butylammonium fluoride, which resembles in a general way the lysine side chains of proteins, forms a clathrate with the composition $(C_4H_9)_4NF \cdot 32\ H_2O$ which melts at 24.9°C at atmospheric pressure. Pauling speculated that if the remaining small cavities in the tetrabutylammonium-fluoride clathrate were filled with xenon, it might very well be stable at temperatures as high as 37°. The chloroform clathrate melts at about 2°, but a mixed chloroform-xenon clathrate formed in a xenon environment at atmospheric pressure melts at 14.8°. The extension and reinforcement of structured water in cells might alter the properties of irritability and excitation and transmission of nerve impulses across synapses.

If anesthesia resulted from a chemical reaction, anesthetic potency might be expected to increase with temperature, roughly doubling or tripling with every 10° rise like

[59] Wulf, R. J., and Featherstone, R. M., *Anesthesiology, 18,* 97 (1957), noted a correlation between anesthetic potency and the van der Waals constants *a* and *b* and between anesthetic potency and polarizability. The polarizability (mole refraction) is related to the van der Waals forces. The basic evidence for the Pauling-Miller theory is the correlation between anesthetic potency and polarizability; alternative explanations which depend upon van der Waals forces could be supported just as well.

other chemical reactions. On the other hand, if anesthesia resulted from clathrate formation, anesthetic potency would be expected to increase upon *decreasing* the temperature. This question was subjected to experimental test by Cherkin and Catchpool,[60] who used goldfish acclimated to various temperatures. The potency of a given anesthetic agent increased as the temperature was lowered from 30° to 5°. Extrapolation back to 37° gave the same anesthetic potency as was observed for mice. If mammals are subjected to hypothermia, they develop anesthesia spontaneously when the body temperature falls to 25–27°, and goldfish develop spontaneous anesthesia at about 2°. Pauling conjectured that the spontaneous anesthesia resulted from the extension of structured water around intracellular proteins as the temperature was lowered.

The actual effect of anesthetic agents may be more complicated. Featherstone[61] observed that more cyclopropane, ethylene, and nitrous oxide is present in a saturated blood sample than can be accounted for by summing the amount of gas that would be expected to dissolve in the blood water and the blood lipids. Thus, 53 percent of the cyclopropane dissolved in blood cannot be accounted for by its solubility in blood water and lipid. Featherstone suggested that the excess anesthetic agent was intimately associated with protein. Schoenborn, Watson, and Kendrew[62] found that xenon develops a large induced dipole and binds to hemoglobin and myoglobin at a site about equidistant from the heme-linked histidine and a heme pyrrole ring. The site is located between the charged areas and the nonpolar areas. Calculation of the charge-induced dipole, dipole-induced dipole, and London interaction energies indicate that they are in excess of 10.2 kcal/mole.

The action of a number of narcotic agents cannot be explained by the clathrate stabilization theory. The barbiturates, for instance, are substituted pyridines. These compounds may very well form hydrogen-bonded complexes with adenosine triphosphate. The ATP-barbiturate complexes might prevent ATP from acting as a substrate in certain critical reactions such as in the sodium-potassium activated ATPase, which is thought to be involved in the active transport of cations.

antigen-antibody interactions

Immune phenomena are an important physiological response of higher animals. Included in immune phenomena is the protection against viral and bacterial disease agents which results either after an attack of the disease or after the deliberate administration of a modified form of the disease-producing agent, *immunization*. In addition to such beneficial manifestations of the immune response, there are deleterious manifestations, such as the rejection of tissue or organ grafts, and certain diseases, such as allergies, nephritis, or lupus erythematosis, which are characterized by an abnormal immune response. The hallmark of the immune response is its high degree of specificity which results from the three-dimensional array of weak molecular interactions. Thus, recovery from one infectious disease is followed by immunity to that disease, but not to other infectious diseases.

The fundamental immune response consists in the appearance in the blood of higher organisms of specific proteins, *antibodies*, in response to the entry of an *antigen* into

[60] Cherkin, A., and Catchpool, J. F. *Science*, *144*, 1460 (1964).
[61] Featherstone, R. M., Muehlbaecher, C. A., de Bon, F. L., and Forsaith, J. A. *Anesthesiology*, *22*, 977 (1961).
[62] Schoenborn, B. P., Watson, H. C., and Kendrew, J. C. *Nature*, *207*, 28 (1965).

the animal. There are two types of antibodies which can be distinguished by their sedimentation constants in the ultracentrifuge, 7 *S* and 19 *S*. The sequence of antibody production after injection of an antigen has been studied *in extenso*; a typical pattern is shown in Fig. 3-58. The injection of antigen is followed by a latent period of several

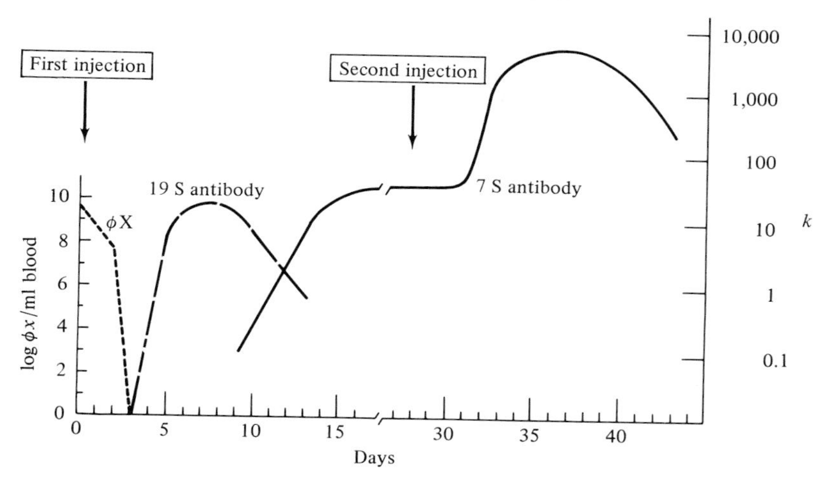

fig. 3-58. Sequence of antibody response by a guinea pig to two intravenous injections of 10^{11} plaque-forming units of bacteriophage ϕX-174 given 1 month apart. (From Uhr, J. W. *Science, 145,* 456 [1964]. Copyright 1964 by the American Association for the Advancement of Science; reprinted by permission.)

days. Antibodies of the 19 *S* type appear in an exponentially increasing concentration for about four days. This is followed by continuing synthesis but at a decreasing rate for another 4 to 6 days, after which the 19 *S* antibody disappears at an approximately logarithmic rate with a half-life of about 24 hours. Antibodies of the 7 *S* type appear about 1 week after injection of antigen and increase in concentration exponentially for a period of 4 to 6 days. This period is followed by a period in which the concentration remains approximately constant. If a second injection of antigen is made about 1 month after the first, during the period of plateau of the 7 *S* antibodies, it produces a *secondary response* in the synthesis of 7 *S* antibody which subsequently reaches very high levels in the circulation. Unless the second dose of antigen is given within about a week of the first injection, no secondary response of 19 *S* antibody is seen.

Antibodies are produced, by and large, in the spleen, lymph nodes, bone marrow, and other lymphoid tissue by lymphocytes and plasma cells (see Chapter 2). There is compelling evidence that macrophages take up antibodies,[63] although it is not clear that this process is essential for the ultimate production of antibodies and there is no evidence that macrophages themselves form antibodies. The capacity to form antibodies belongs to *immunologically competent cells*, which appear to be mainly small lymphocytes.[64] The small lymphocytes both circulate in the blood and dwell in lymphoid

[63] Garvey, J. S., and Campbell, D. H. *J. Exptl. Med., 105*, 361 (1957).
[64] Gowans, J. L., and McGregor, D. D., in Graber, P., and Miescher, P. A., eds. *Third International Symposium of Immunopathology*. Basel: Benno Schwabe, 1963, p. 89.

tissue for variable periods. The population of lymphoid cells is in a dynamic state and constantly moves from one lymphoid organ to another via the circulation. Probably as a result of stimulation by antigen, immunologically competent lymphocytes appear to mature into plasma cells. In addition, antigen seems to stimulate increased division of immunologically competent cells.[65] Plasma cells have a very highly developed endoplasmic reticulum and are thought to produce antibodies at high rates. Single plasma cells appear capable of synthesizing antibodies to interact with more than one antigen,[66] although cells obtained from an animal injected simultaneously with two unrelated antigens produce antibodies to either one or the other antigen.

Antigens capable of eliciting an immune response comprise a remarkably diverse group of substances including proteins, polysaccharides, lipids, nucleic acids, and synthetic organic materials. Contrariwise, not all naturally occurring substances, particularly not all proteins, are antigenic, and substances which are antigenic in one species may not be antigenic in another. Effective antigens are foreign to the circulation of the animal to be immunized. In addition, an animal will not produce antibody to a normally antigenic material if the antigen is injected in an adequate dose at an early stage in the animal's development. Such an animal will not respond usually to a challenge with the same antigen in adult life; this phenomenon is called *immune tolerance*.

There appears to be an approximate minimum molecular weight of several thousand for effective antigens. On the other hand, a large variety of naturally occurring and synthetic substances of low molecular weight will elicit antibodies if they are coupled to high-molecular-weight substances before injection. Such small molecules are called *haptens*. Although haptens are incapable of provoking an immune response directly, they are able to combine with their specific antibodies. Most of the information about the nature of the antigen-antibody interaction has come from studies of hapten interactions with their specific antibodies. Challenge with a hapten-protein complex will produce two types of antibodies, one type which reacts with the hapten and one type which reacts with the protein moiety. The protein has many kinds of functional groups, each of which acts as an antigenic determinant. The protein, being an antigenic mosaic, may provoke antibodies with a variety of specificities.

The 7 *S* antibodies have a molecular weight of about 160,000 and contain about 1500 amino acid residues. About 3 percent of the weight is carbohydrate covalently linked to the protein. The 7 *S* antibodies migrate as γ-globulins upon electrophoresis. Optical rotatory dispersion studies[67] suggest that they have practically no helical structure. The molecules appear to be flexible and able to assume a variety of conformations as indicated by polarization of fluoresence,[68] potentiometric titrations,[69] and viscosity determinations[70] of specific antibodies. Not only do antibodies display a remarkable heterogeneity in their ability to react with various antigens; they are also heterogeneous in their physical properties, as indicated by reversible boundary

[65] Dutton, R. W., and Eady, J. D. *Immunology*, *7*, 40 (1964); Jerne, N. K., and Nordin, A. A. *Science*, *140*, 405 (1963).
[66] Nossal, G. J. V., and Mäkelä, O. *J. Exptl. Med.*, *115*, 209 (1962); Attardi, G., Cohn, M., Horibata, K., and Lennox, E. S. *J. Immunol.*, *92*, 335 (1964).
[67] Jirgensons, B. *Arch. Biochem. Biophys.*, *89*, 48 (1960); *96*, 314 (1962); Winkler, M., and Doty, P. *Biochim. Biophys. Acta*, *54*, 448 (1961).
[68] Steiner, R. F., and Edelhoch, H. *J. Am. Chem. Soc.*, *84*, 2139 (1962).
[69] Weltman, J. K., and Sela, M. *Biochim. Biophys. Acta*, *93*, 553 (1964).
[70] Noelken, M. E., Nelson, C. A., Buckley, C. E., and Tanford, C. *J. Biol. Chem.*, *240*, 218 (1965).

spreading in moving-boundary electrophoresis[71] and fractionation by column chromatography.[72] On the other hand, in certain respects the 7 *S* antibodies display remarkable uniformity. Thus, the various antibodies of one species seem to have a common antigenic determinant, and when injected into another species, they produce a common antibody which cannot be resolved by such powerful techniques as immunoelectrophoresis. Peptide fingerprints of antibodies to different antigens show extensive regions of common amino acid identity.[73]

The 7 *S* antibody molecule appears to be composed to two pairs of subunits held together by disulfide bonds. Mild reduction with β-mercaptoethanol, followed by treatment with dilute hydrochloric acid[74] leads to a dissociation into identical half molecules, each with one antibody-combining site. Reduction of the disulfide bonds followed by treatment with 6 M urea or propionic acid leads to the dissociation of the 7 *S* antibody into two subunits (*H*) with a molecular weight of 60,000 and two subunits (*L*) with a molecular weight of 20,000.[75] Edelman and Gally[76] suggested a model for the 7 *S* antibody which fits these data and the results of other experiments; it is illustrated in Fig. 3-59.

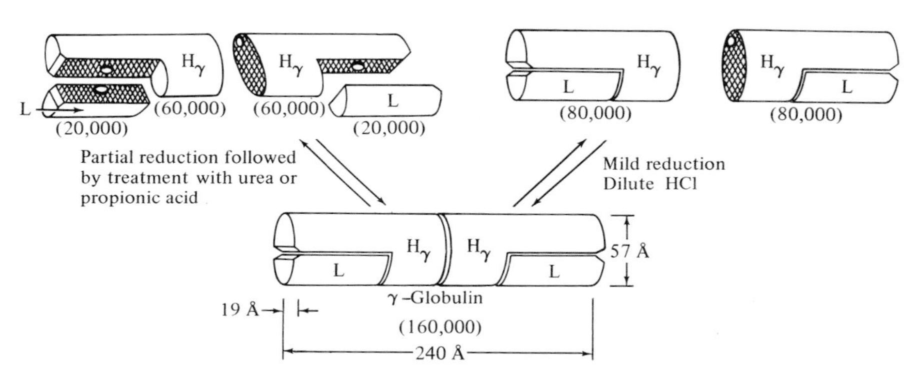

fig. 3-59. A schematic drawing of the model of 7*S* antibody suggested by Edelman, G. M., and Gally, J. A. *Proc. Natl. Acad. Sci*, *51*, 849 (1964), using the molecular dimensions of Kratky, O., Porod, G., Sekora, A., and Paletta, B. *J. Polymer Sci.*, *16*, 163 (1955).

The combination of antibody with antigen is manifested in several ways. If the antigen is a macromolecule, the reaction with antibody results in coprecipitation under appropriate circumstances. Precipitation is most complete when equivalent amounts of antigen and antibody are mixed. Incomplete precipitation occurs if either antibody

[71] Alberty, R. A. *J. Am. Chem. Soc.*, *70*, 1675 (1948).
[72] Peterson, E. A., and Sober, H. A., in Putnam, F. W., ed. *Plasma Proteins*. New York: Academic Press, 1960, vol. 1, p. 105.
[73] Edelman, G. M., Heremans, J. F., Heremans, M. T., and Kunkel, H. G. *J. Exptl. Med.*, *112*, 203 (1960); Gitlin, D., and Merler, E. *J. Exptl. Med.*, *114*, 217 (1961); Putnam, F. W., Migita, S., and Easley, C. W., in Peeters, H., ed. *Protides of the Biological Fluids*. Amsterdam: Elsevier, 1963, vol. 10, p. 93.
[74] Palmer, J. L., and Nisonoff, A. *Biochemistry*, *3*, 863 (1964).
[75] Edelman, G. M., and Poulik, M. D. *J. Exptl. Med.*, *113*, 861 (1961); Edelman, G. M., and Benacerraf, B. *Proc. Natl. Acad. Sci.*, *48*, 1035 (1962); Fleischman, J. B., Porter, R. R., and Press, E. M. *Biochem. J.*, *88*, 220 (1963).
[76] Edelman, G. M., and Gally, J. A. *Proc. Natl. Acad. Sci.*, *51*, 846 (1964).

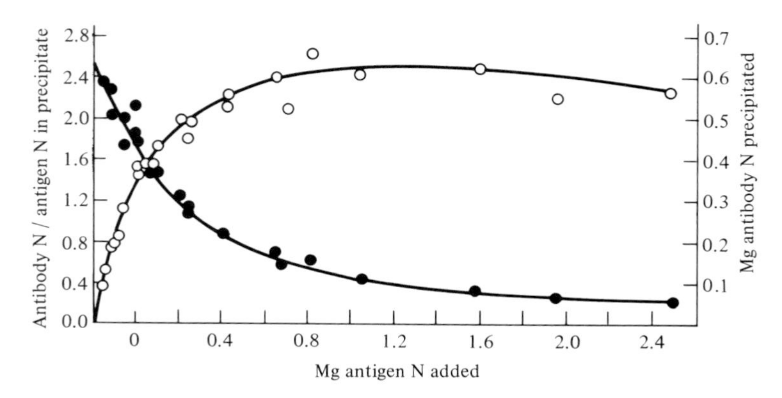

fig. 3-60. Quantitative precipitin reaction of tobacco mosaic virus and rabbit antiserum: O––– O antibody nitrogen precipitated and ●–––● ratio of antibody nitrogen to antigen nitrogen in the precipitate. (From Rappaport, I. *J. Immunol, 78,* 247 [1957]. Copyright 1957, The Williams & Wilkins Co., Baltimore, Md. 21202, U.S.A.; reprinted by permission.)

or antigen is present in excess (Fig. 3-60). The precipitation reaction can be understood qualitatively in terms of the framework theory.[77] Each molecule of both antigen and antibody is thought to possess more than one combining site. The interaction of antigens and antibodies with each other results in the formation of an extensive cross-linked aggregate which is insoluble. The precipitate which forms, however, does not contain a fixed proportion of antigen to antibody. The most extensive framework occurs at equivalence. When a large excess of antigen is present, each antibody molecule will combine with as many antigen molecules as it has combining sites. In this way, the valence of 7 *S* antibodies was found to be two. Correspondingly, the valence of antigens can be determined in the presence of excess antibodies. The antigenic valences of several proteins are given in Fig. 3-61.

fig. 3-61. Effective valences of some protein antigens. (From Singer, S. J., in Neurath, H., ed. *The Proteins,* 2nd ed. New York: Academic Press, 1965, vol. 3, p. 292. Copyright Academic Press; reprinted by permission.)

ANTIGEN	MOLECULAR WEIGHT	EFFECTIVE VALENCE
Bovine ribonuclease	13,400	2.8
Ovalbumin	42,000	5
Horse serum albumin	67,000	6
Human γ-globulin	160,000	7
Horse apoferritin	465,000	26
Thyroglobulin	700,000	40
Tomato bushy stunt virus	8,000,000	90
Tobacco mosaic virus	40,700,000	650

[77] Marrack, J. R. *Chemistry of Antigens and Antibodies.* London: Medical Research Council, 1938.

If the antigen is attached to the surface of cells, the antigen-antibody reaction results in *agglutination* of the cells. When blood or immune serum is used, additional components of serum called *complement* coprecipitate with the antigen-antibody aggregate. If the antigen is attached to a cell surface, reaction with antibody in the presence of complement often results in cell lysis. In addition, there are many more manifestations of the immune response.

The interaction of an antigen and an antibody requires a high degree of geometric complementarity at the combining sites. An immune *cross reaction*, that is, the reaction of an antibody with a substance other than the original antigen, signifies great similarity between the original antigen and the cross-reacting material, at least at one site. The specificity of the interactions was studied in a series of pioneering studies by Landsteiner[78] in which compounds such as *p*-aminobenzoic acid, *p*-aminobenzenesulfonic acid, and *p*-aminobenzenearsonic acid were used as haptens. The amino groups were diazotized and coupled to serum proteins to produce an antigen. The antibodies produced were reacted with the original hapten-protein conjugate in the presence of compounds related chemically to the hapten. When the related compounds reacted with the antibody, the precipitin reaction was inhibited.

From experiments using the haptens cited above, the following conclusions were drawn:

1. The presence of an acidic group on the hapten was required for interaction.
2. The acidic group had to bear the same relation to the amino group on the hapten, *para*, *meta*, or *ortho*, as the groups had on the challenging antigen for interaction.
3. The antibodies were able to distinguish between carboxyl, sulfonic acid, and arsonic acid groups on the hapten. The results are summarized in Fig. 3-62.
4. Replacement of a hydrogen atom on the benzene ring with a methyl group, halogen, nitro, or other uncharged group had only a minor effect on the intensity of interaction.

From similar experiments, the following additional conclusions were drawn:

5. Antibodies distinguish between haptens which are optical isomers or which are *cis-trans* isomers.
6. The size and nature of the protein or other bulk group to which a hapten was attached had only a minor effect on the intensity of interaction.
7. Environmental factors, such as *p*H and the nature of the solvent, affect the intensity of the interaction.

The schematic diagram of Fig. 3-63 may help the reader visualize the relationships involved in the antigen-antibody interaction. Undoubtedly, the interaction results from the intermolecular forces described earlier in this chapter. Electrostatic interactions occur between a hapten possessing an ionic group and an ionic group of opposite charge on the antibody. While ion pairs do not tend to occur in aqueous solutions of simple electrolytes, ion pair formation between polyelectrolytes and counterions does occur as judged by fewer effective particles than expected in observed colligative properties (see p. 196). Ion pair formation is even more favorable if water, a solvent

[78] Landsteiner, K. *The Specificity of Serological Reactions.* Cambridge, Mass.: Harvard University Press, 1945; Pressman, D. *Advan. Biol. Med. Phys.*, *3*, 99 (1953).

Hapten Coupled to Chick Serum Used for Precipitin Reaction	Hapten Coupled to Horse Serum Used To Prepare Antibody: N—R, N, p-phenyl COO^-	N—R, N, p-phenyl SO_3^-
R—N=N—phenyl	0	0
R—N=N—phenyl-p-COO^-	+++	0
R—N=N—phenyl (Cl, COO^-)	++++	0
R—N=N—phenyl (CH_3, COO^-)	+++	0
R—N=N—phenyl-m-COO^-	0	0
R—N=N—phenyl-p-SO_3^-	+	++++

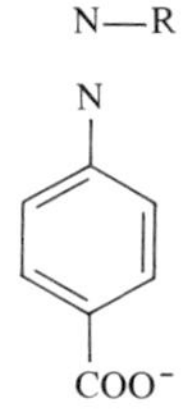

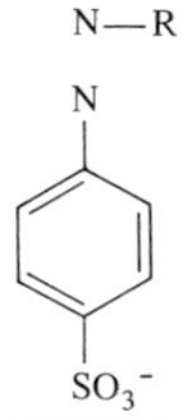

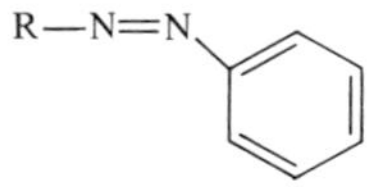

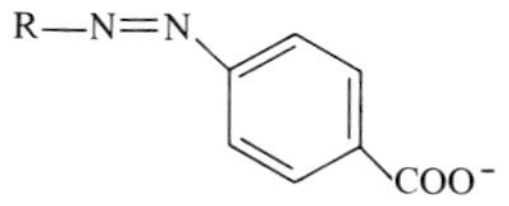

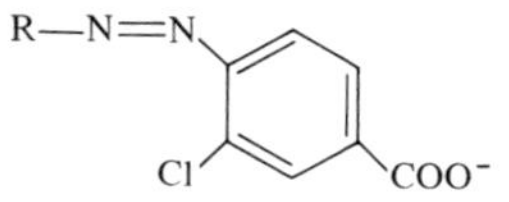

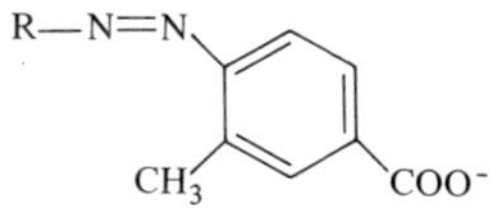

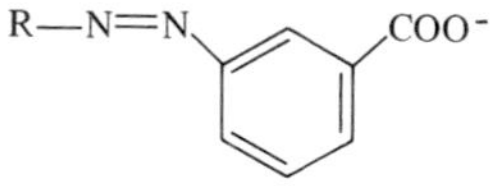

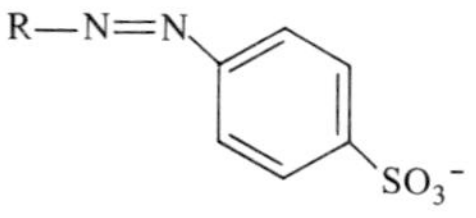

fig. 3-62. Effect of structure of hapten on antibody interaction. Intensity of precipitin reaction is estimated qualitatively as +, ++, +++, ++++, or 0. (Adapted from Landsteiner, K. *The Specificity of Serological Reactions.* Cambridge, Mass.: Harvard University Press, 1945; Pressman, D. *Advan. Biol. Med. Phys., 3,* 99 [1953]. Copyright Academic Press; reprinted by permission.)

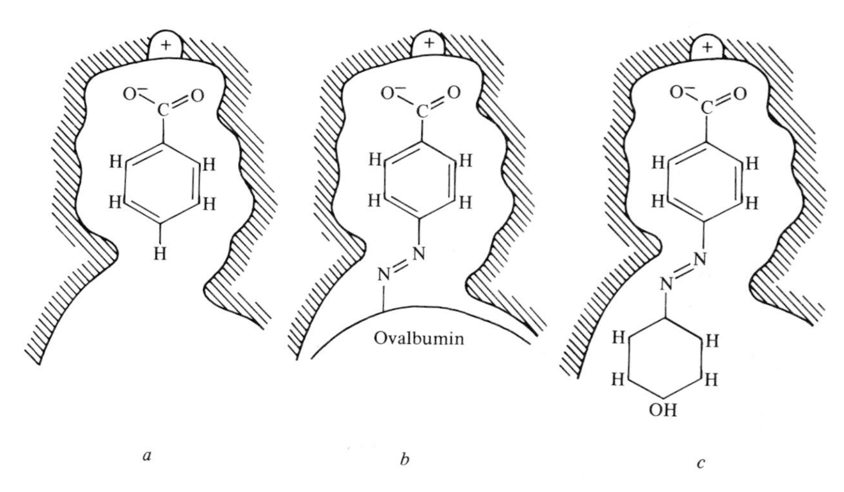

fig. 3-63. Schematic representation of the binding of antigen by antibody: *(a)* binding of benzoate, *(b)* binding of diazotized *p*-aminobenzoate coupled to ovalbumin, and *(c)* binding of *p*-hydroxyphenylazobenzoate to antibody prepared to diazotized *p*-aminobenzoate coupled to ovalbumin. (Adapted from Kauzmann, W., in Oncley, J. L., ed. *Biophysical Sciences—A Study Program.* New York: Wiley, 1959, p. 552.)

with a high dielectric constant, is excluded from the region of the electrostatic interaction.[79] Unlike electrostatic interactions between simple electrolytes, ion pair formation shows structural preferences (see Chapter 4) which could contribute to specificity.

In addition, all the weak intermolecular forces contribute to the interaction, including hydrophobic interactions. These forces act primarily at short distances; they are thought to be responsible for the great specificity of the immune reactions because they can only come into play when the complementarity of sites provides a fit good enough that there is close molecular approximation. The free energy of binding can be evaluated from determination of the antigen-antibody dissociation constants (Chapter 4). The values obtained are of the order of 8 to 10 kcal/mole. The overall free energy change of the antigen-antibody reaction is derived from the cooperative action of many weak interactions. In part the favorable free energy change results from hydrophobic interactions, the tendency for nonpolar surfaces in the antigen and antibody to come together and in the process exclude solvent water that formerly occupied the domain. It has not been possible yet to analyze nor quantify the individual forces involved in a specific interaction.

The immune reaction is an area of great interest to biologists and presents many different aspects that are being studied. The affinity, energetic and kinetics of the interaction, and the mechanisms of antibody production will be considered in later sections.

references

Castellan, G. W. *Physical Chemistry.* Reading, Mass.: Addison-Wesley, 1964.

Dervichian, D. G. The physical chemistry of phospholipids. *Progr. Biophys. Biophys. Chem., 14,* 265 (1964).

[79] Fuoss, R. M. *J. Am. Chem. Soc., 80,* 5059 (1958).

Edsall, J. T., and Wyman, J. *Biophysical Chemistry.* New York: Academic Press, 1958.

Energy transfer with special reference to biological systems. *Discussions Faraday Soc.*, no. 27 (1960).

Featherstone, R. M., and Muehlbaecher, C. A. The current role of inert gases in the search for anesthesia mechanisms. *Pharmacol. Rev.*, *15*, 97 (1963).

Hayashi, T., and Szent-Györgyi, A. G., eds. *Molecular Architecture in Cell Physiology.* Englewood Cliffs, N.J.: Prentice-Hall, 1966.

Kabat, E. A. *Experimental Immunochemistry*, 2nd ed. Springfield, Ill.: Charles C Thomas, 1961.

Kruyt, H. R., ed. *Colloid Science.* Amsterdam: Elsevier, 1949, 1952.

Moelwyn-Hughes, E. A. *States of Matter.* Edinburgh: Oliver and Boyd, 1961.

Murrell, J. N. *Theory of Electronic Spectra of Organic Molecules.* London: Methuen, 1963.

Pauling, L. *The Nature of the Chemical Bond*, 3rd ed. Ithaca, N.Y.: Cornell University Press, 1960.

Seliger, H. H., and McElroy, W. D. *Light: Physical and Biological Action.* New York: Academic Press, 1965.

Stowell, R. E., ed. Cryobiology. *Federation Proc.*, *24*, suppl. 15 (1965).

Szent-Györgyi, A. *Introduction to a Submolecular Biology.* New York: Academic Press, 1960.

Tanford, C. *Physical Chemistry of Macromolecules.* New York: Wiley, 1961.

chapter 4

physical chemical principles

physical chemistry in biology

It is an article of faith among contemporary biologists that the operations of living systems are governed by the same laws that govern the nonliving, purely physical world. That biologists have long subscribed to this idea is attested to by the large number of fundamental contributions to physics and chemistry that were made by scientists with biological training. Franciscus Sylvius (1614–1672), a Dutch physician, recognized that salts were formed by the union of acids and bases and developed the idea of chemical affinity. Sylvius also proposed that living systems maintained an acid-base balance. Thomas Young (1773–1829), an English physician, demonstrated the diffraction of light passing through narrow slits—important evidence that supported the wave theory of light. William Prout (1785–1850), an English physiologist who discovered the presence of hydrochloric acid in the gastric juice and is responsible for the classification of food into carbohydrates, proteins, and fats, was the first to point out that the atom weights of the elements are approximate integer multiples of the atom weight of hydrogen. Jean L. M. Poiseuille (1799–1869), who made important contributions concerning viscosity and viscous flow, and Adolph Fick (1829–1901), who did fundamental work on diffusion, were trained as physicians.

As a matter of fact, in Germany formal energetics developed from experiments on animal metabolism. J. R. von Mayer (1814–1887) was a ship's surgeon when he noticed that blood was brighter when drawn in the tropics than when drawn in colder climates. This observation eventually led von Mayer to consider both the relationship between work and heat and the intermediary processes of metabolism. He built upon the studies of Lavoisier, who had demonstrated a correlation between the heat an animal evolved and the food it consumed, showing that additional food was consumed corresponding to work performed. With brilliant insight, von Mayer enunciated the law of conservation of energy in the twenty-eighth year of his life, five years before James P. Joule (1818–1889) published his meticulous experiments on the mechanical equivalence of heat. Although von Mayer's papers were couched in metaphysical language, he was responsible to a large degree for clarifying the concepts of energy and for pointing out that radiant energy from the sun was the primary source of energy on the earth.

Hermann L. F. von Helmholtz (1821–1894), one of the most versatile geniuses in the annals of science, began his career as a military surgeon (see Fig. 4-1). Though frequently thought of as a physical chemist, from 1847 to 1871 von Helmholtz held chairs in physiology successively at Königsberg, Bonn, and Heidelberg, and he

fig. 4-1. Hermann L. F. von Helmholtz (1821–1894). (Courtesy of the Countway Library of Medicine.)

regarded medicine as his intellectual home. He invented the ophthalmoscope for examining the interior of the eye and the ophthalmometer for measuring the optical characteristics of the eye. Von Helmholtz was an accomplished musician and made many contributions to acoustics and the physiology of hearing. His first research concerned the neuroanatomy of leeches, and in later life he was the first to measure the speed of the nerve impulse. Von Helmholtz gave the clearest statement of the law of conservation of energy and made many other contributions to thermodynamics and physical chemistry.

Work on osmosis and plasmolysis by W. F. P. Pfeffer (1845–1920), a botanist, Hugo de Vries (1848–1935), another botanist, and H. J. Hamburger (1859–1924), a physiologist, led to the development of the theory of solutions by Jacobus van't Hoff (1852–1911). Van't Hoff was the son of a physician, as was Svante Arrhenius (1859–1927). Arrhenius extended van't Hoff's theory to electrolyte solutions by assuming that electrolytes dissociate into ions in solution.

The understanding of cellular processes in molecular terms is one of the main goals of general physiology. This requires an understanding of the principles of physics and chemistry, although often a restatement to make them more useful for the biologist is required. For example, the biologist is concerned with many kinds of work, not just expansion work, and with open systems which exchange heat and matter with the environment.

thermodynamics: its nature and terminology

The physiological processes of living systems require transfers of energy and matter. Thermodynamics permits quantification of such transfers, enables more precise and satisfying descriptions of them, and provides insights that otherwise might not be apparent.

A *system* in thermodynamics is a circumscribed space, limited by well-defined boundaries, including all matter contained therein. Usually the systems under study are separated from their environment by physical barriers which limit the possible interactions with the surroundings. An *isolated system* cannot exchange matter or energy with its surroundings. A *closed system* is surrounded by a barrier which prevents the exchange of matter between the system and the environment, but allows the exchange of energy. An *adiabatic system* is a closed system which cannot exchange heat with the surroundings. In an *isochoric system*, heat but not work can be exchanged. An *open system* can exchange both energy and matter with the environment. Although the analysis of open systems is more complex than closed systems, open systems are particularly interesting to biologists because living systems continually exchange both matter and energy with the environment.

The fundamental principles of thermodynamics can be formulated without reference to the mechanical properties of molecules. Specification of the *thermodynamic state* of a system requires knowledge only of the kind and quantity of matter and its distribution between phases (gas, liquid, solid, etc.). The thermodynamic state of a system is defined in terms of variables which are measured on a *macroscopic scale*. These variables fall into two classes. *Extensive variables*, such as volume and heat capacity, depend on the size of the system. The magnitude of *intensive variables*, on the other hand, is independent of the size of the system. Intensive variables include pressure, temperature, viscosity, electric-field density, concentration, and molal heat capacity.

Among the intensive variables, temperature occupies a somewhat special position in that it is the variable most easily used to define a state of equilibrium between two closed systems in contact. The tendency for closed systems in contact to reach *thermal equilibrium* is sometimes called the *Zeroth Law of Thermodynamics*. Temperature may be defined in terms of the volume of a gas using the equation of state (eq. 3-9):

$$\frac{T}{T_0} = \lim_{P \to 0} \frac{(PV)_T}{(PV)_{T_0}} \tag{4-1}$$

where T_0 is the reference temperature, usually 273.15°K (the ice point = 0°C).

It is necessary to distinguish between *exact differentials* (denoted by the symbol d) and *inexact differentials* (denoted by the symbol $đ$). The integral of an exact differential depends only on the initial and final states and not on the path used to go from the initial to the final state. The integral of an inexact differential, on the other hand, depends on the path. For example, the change in the potential energy of moving a boulder depends only on the initial and final heights, while the quantity of work required to lift it depends on the method used to move the boulder (for example, dragging it up a hill *versus* using a cart or wheelbarrow). For an exact differential, the integral over a *closed path*, that is, over a *cyclical change of state*, is zero.

$$\oint d\,f(x, y) = 0 \qquad \oint đ\,f(x, y) \neq 0 \tag{4-2}$$

If the differential of a thermodynamic function is exact, then the function is called a *thermodynamic property*[1] (state function).

first law of thermodynamics

The First Law of Thermodynamics is a statement about the *transfer* of energy by means of heat and work. *Work* is defined as that *transfer* of energy from a thermodynamic system to the environment which causes some *macroscopic displacement*. Work may be mechanical (displaced mass), electrical (displaced charge), etc. *Expansion work* is an important example of work which is performed by a gas whenever it expands against an external pressure. Pressure (P) equals the force (F) per unit area ($\mathfrak{A}$), and $\mathfrak{A}dl = dV$.

$$đW = Fdl = P\mathfrak{A}dl = PdV \tag{4-3}$$

For a perfect gas

$$\Delta W = \int_{V_1}^{V_2} PdV = \int_{V_1}^{V_2} \frac{RT}{V}\,dV \tag{4-4}$$

using eq. 3-9 to eliminate P. The value of ΔW depends on the path (relation between T and V during expansion).

[1] The reader who is uncertain of the derivations of the following equations may refresh his memory by consulting Guggenheim, E. A. *Thermodynamics*, 3rd ed. Amsterdam: North Holland Publishing Company, 1957, or Wall, F. T. *Chemical Thermodynamics*. San Francisco: Freeman, 1958. For a more rigorous treatment of the mathematics involved, the reader may refer to Margenau, H., and Murphy, G. M. *The Mathematics of Physics and Chemistry*, 2nd ed. Princeton: Van Nostrand, 1956, or Chisholm, J. S. R., and Morris, R. M. *Mathematical Methods in Physics*. Amsterdam: North Holland Publishing Company, 1965.

Heat is defined as that *transfer* of energy to the system from the environment which does not cause any macroscopic displacement (only microscopic molecular displacements are involved). A rise in temperature is generally *not* a reliable indicator of heat since an adiabatic compression produces a temperature increase. If no work is done during a process, however, then

$$đQ = C_V \, dT \tag{4-5}$$

where C_V is the *heat capacity* at *constant volume*. Thus "heating" and "making hot" are synonymous only for isochoric processes.

The change in the *internal energy*, dU, of the system is defined as the *heat*, $đQ$, *absorbed* by the system, less the *work*, $đW$, *performed* by the system *on the environment*.

$$dU = đQ - đW \tag{4-6}$$

The *First Law of Thermodynamics* states that

$$\oint dU = 0 \tag{4-7}$$

In other words, the internal energy of a system is a thermodynamic property (state function).

An important thermodynamic property related to the First Law is the *enthalpy*, H, which is defined as

$$H = U + PV \tag{4-8}$$

Differentiating eq. 4-8 and substituting eq. 4-6 gives

$$dH = đQ - đW + PdV + VdP \tag{4-9}$$

If, as in most systems of interest to the biologist, the pressure is constant (atmospheric pressure) and no work other than expansion work is performed (e.g., against the atmosphere), then $đW = PdV$, $dP = 0$, and consequently

$$dH_P = đQ_P \tag{4-10}$$

The enthalpy is sometimes referred to as the *heat content* since at constant pressure the change in enthalpy which accompanies a reaction (change of state) is equal to the heat absorbed, the heat of reaction. Because enthalpy is a thermodynamic property, the change of H depends only upon the nature and state of the initial reactants and the final products and is independent of the nature of the reactions leading from the initial to the final state. A special case of this principle is Hess's Law, which states that the heats of reaction for a sequence of reactions are additive. This law is particularly pertinent in biochemistry where a large number of different metabolic processes can accomplish the same overall result.

second law of thermodynamics

Because most spontaneous reactions at constant pressure are accompanied by a loss of heat, it was believed for a time that an enthalpy decrease always indicated spontaneity. With more experience and better experimental techniques, however, it soon became obvious that many reactions which proceed spontaneously are accompanied in fact by an absorption of heat ($\Delta H > 0$). These seemingly anomalous results are explained by the *Second Law of Thermodynamics*. Lord Kelvin's formulation of this law was, "It is impossible by means of inanimate material agency to derive mechanical effect from any portion of matter by cooling it below the temperature of the coldest of the surrounding objects."[2]

Consider the simplest model system, an ideal gas. One distinguishing feature of an ideal gas is that

$$dU = C_V\, dT \tag{4-11}$$

From eqs. 4-5, 4-6, and 4-11, we find that, considering expansion work only,

$$đQ = dU + đW = C_V\, dT + PdV = C_V\, dT + \frac{RT}{V}\, dV \tag{4-12}$$

The fact that $đQ$ is an inexact differential is clear from an examination of the right side of eq. 4-12 because it cannot be integrated unless a path (relation between T and V) is specified. However, if eq. 4-12 is multiplied by the *integration factor* $1/T$ and the equation of state is used, an equation is obtained where the right side is a perfect differential:

$$\frac{đQ_{\text{rev}}}{T} = C_V \frac{dT}{T} + R\frac{dV}{V} = d(C_V \ln T + R \ln V) \tag{4-13}$$

The restriction of eq. 4-13 to reversible processes is necessary because *the equation of state is valid only near equilibrium*. The quantity $đQ_{\text{rev}}/T$ is an exact differential even though $đQ$ alone is not. The quantity $đQ_{\text{rev}}/T$ defines the change in a new thermodynamic property, S, the *entropy*.

$$dS = \frac{đQ_{\text{rev}}}{T} \tag{4-14}$$

Equation 4-14 may be considered as a statement of the *Second Law of Thermodynamics*. An implicit assumption of the Second Law of Thermodynamics is that eq. 4-14 applies to all systems, not just to perfect gases.

Now consider the flow of heat from a reservoir at a higher temperature, T_1, to a reservoir at a lower temperature, T_2. For such a process, the changes in entropies for reservoir 1 and reservoir 2 are given by

$$dS_1 = -\frac{đQ}{T_1} \qquad dS_2 = +\frac{đQ}{T_2} \tag{4-15}$$

Because $đQ$ is positive and $T_2 < T_1$, the entropy change for the isolated system as a whole is positive.

$$dS = dS_1 + dS_2 = đQ\left(\frac{1}{T_2} - \frac{1}{T_1}\right) > 0 \tag{4-16}$$

Entropy, therefore, is not a conserved quantity; by this we mean that it is not constant for an isolated system.

For a closed system in contact with a heat source, the Second Law of Thermodynamics may be stated as

$$TdS \geq đQ \tag{4-17}$$

[2] Thomson, W. *Trans. Roy. Soc. Edinburgh*, *20*, 261 (1853).

where T is the temperature of the heat source. Equality holds *by definition* for *reversible* processes, while for *irreversible* processes, the inequality sign must be applied. It is apparent from eq. 4-17 that the entropy of a closed system can never decrease during an adiabatic change in state.

$$dS_{(\text{adiabatic})} \geq 0 \tag{4-18}$$

Note that eq. 4-14 is a special case of eq. 4-17 and that eq. 4-16 is a special case of eq. 4-18 (internal heat flow is an adiabatic process with respect to the environment).

It should be noted that the transformation produced by an irreversible process *can be reversed* if heat is transferred to the environment. For example, a free isothermal expansion is reversed by compression and cooling. The reversal of an irreversible process must always be "paid for" by an entropy increase in the environment. These considerations are fundamental to an understanding of the role of metabolism in physiological processes.

For *reversible* transformations, an expression for the *combined First and Second Laws* can be obtained from eqs. 4-6 and 4-17:

$$dU = TdS - đW \tag{4-19}$$

It is not uncommon to consider primarily expansion work in thermodynamic discussions. As stated above, however, there are many other forms of work including mechanical work, $-Fdl$, such as might be performed by a contracting muscle shortening through a distance, $-dl$, with a force, F; electrical work, $-Ed\mathfrak{F}$, performed by an increment of charge, $-d\mathfrak{F}$, moving through an electrical potential, E; etc. The force is always an intensive variable which does not depend on the size of the system, while the conjugate displacement is an extensive variable.

The notion of work leads intuitively to the idea of *chemical work* first proposed by Willard Gibbs. If $-dn_i$ moles of the ith chemical species are lost from a system either by chemical reaction or by transport to the surroundings, an energy change equal to $-\mu_i dn_i$ occurs in the system. Gibbs called this energy change *chemical work* and called the intensive variable, μ, the *chemical potential.* On the basis of these considerations, work can be formulated as

$$đW = PdV - Fdl - Ed\mathfrak{F} - \sum_{i=1}^{k} \mu_i dn_i + \cdots \tag{4-20}$$

In the last term, total chemical work is evaluated by a summation over all chemical species present in the system. Upon substituting eq. 4-20 into eq. 4-19, a more explicit combined statement of the First and Second Laws for reversible systems is obtained.

$$dU = TdS - PdV + Fdl + Ed\mathfrak{F} + \sum_{i=1}^{k} \mu_i dn_i + \cdots \tag{4-21}$$

From eq. 4-21, it is evident that the chemical potential may be defined as the change in energy of a system resulting from the addition of dn_i moles of component i to the system while S, V, l, $\mathfrak{F}$, and n_j are maintained constant, j denoting all components of the system other than i.

$$\mu_i = \left(\frac{\partial U}{\partial n_i}\right)_{S, V, l, \mathfrak{F}, n_j, j \neq i} \tag{4-22}$$

a mathematical interlude

At this point, a brief discussion of a few mathematical points may be helpful to the reader. A composite function of one variable can be differentiated by application of the *chain rule*. Consider two functions f and g such that

$$y = f(g(x)) \tag{a}$$

Introducing an *auxiliary variable*, u, eq. **a** can be restated

$$y = f(u) \qquad u = g(x) \tag{b}$$

Applying the chain rule, the derivative of y with respect to x can be written

$$\frac{dy}{dx} = \left(\frac{dy}{du}\right)\left(\frac{du}{dx}\right) \tag{c}$$

The chain rule can be generalized to composite functions of more than one variable by the use of *partial derivatives*. Their proper use requires an understanding of *explicit* and *implicit* functional dependence. Let us write

$$z = f(x, y) = z(x, y) \tag{d}$$

to indicate that z will be treated as an explicit function of x and y. The expressions $f(x, y)$ or $z(x, y)$ mean that values of z are specified in terms of values of both x and y. The partial derivative of z with respect to x is obtained by treating y as a constant during differentiation. This is represented by the expression

$$\frac{\partial z(x, y)}{\partial x} = \lim_{h \to 0} \frac{z(x + h, y) - z(x, y)}{h} \tag{e}$$

using h as an increment of x.

Now let us suppose that y also depends explicitly on x:

$$y = y(x) \tag{f}$$

Under these conditions, the process of changing x while holding y constant cannot be realized. The quantity $\dfrac{\partial z(x, y)}{\partial x}$ exists all the same, the change in x being called a *virtual displacement. Partial derivatives must not be regarded as total derivatives for special realizable processes.* In the example cited here, z depends explicitly on x, and also *implicitly* on x through y. Partial differentiation of z with respect to x is sensitive to the explicit functional dependence on x but ignores the implicit functional dependence through y.

The *total derivative* of $z(x, y)$ with respect to x, of course, is sensitive to both explicit and implicit functional dependences. It is given by

$$\frac{dz(x, y)}{dx} = \frac{\partial z(x, y)}{\partial x} + \left(\frac{\partial z(x, y)}{\partial y}\right)\frac{dy}{dx} \tag{g}$$

The general relation between total and partial derivatives can be expressed as

$$dz = \sum_i \frac{\partial z(\{x_i\})}{\partial x_i}\, dx_i \tag{h}$$

where $\{x_i\}$ denotes the complete set of quantities upon which z depends explicitly.

Because the quantities dx_i are virtual displacements which can be made independently regardless of implicit functional relations between various x_i's, it follows that the equation

$$dz = \sum_i A_i \, dx_i \qquad (i)$$

implies the set of equations

$$\frac{\partial z(\{x_i\})}{\partial x_i} = A_i \qquad (j)$$

It is always possible to transform an implicit functional dependence into an explicit one. In the example cited above, y may simply be replaced by $y(x)$, the explicit function of x. Doing this, the following expressions are obtained:

$$z = z(x) \qquad (k)$$

$$\frac{\partial z(x)}{\partial x} = \frac{dz}{dx} \qquad (l)$$

$$\frac{\partial z(x)}{\partial y} = 0 \qquad (m)$$

Alternatively consider the functional relation given by unit circle equation:

$$1 = x^2 + y^2 \qquad (n)$$

for which the following partial derivative can be written:

$$\frac{\partial 1(x, y)}{\partial x} = 2x \qquad (o)$$

Obviously, the forms $\left(\frac{\partial 1}{\partial x}\right)$ and $\left(\frac{\partial 1}{\partial x}\right)_y$ do not have a meaningful numerical solution. These examples underscore the fact that partial differentiation expresses explicit functional relations rather than quantitative variations.

These sequences show that the quantity $(\partial z/\partial x)$ is meaningless by itself; the functional form of z must always be specified. An exceedingly deceptive convention has developed in the literature on thermodynamics in which the notation $\left(\frac{\partial z}{\partial x}\right)_y$ is used to represent $\left(\frac{\partial z(x, y)}{\partial x}\right)$. The use of the notation $\left(\frac{\partial z}{\partial x}\right)_y$ often gives rise to the *misconception* that y actually can be held constant while x is being changed. Given a dependence of y upon x, as seen in the example cited above, this may be impossible to carry out in practice.

To summarize, total differentiation operates on the numerical value of a function while partial differentiation operates on its explicit functional dependence on other quantities.

Thermodynamic properties are exact differentials. An important mathematical consequence of this fact is that the *reciprocity characteristic* of Cauchy applies to thermodynamic properties. If the differential $dz(x, y)$ is exact, then

$$dz(x, y) = \left(\frac{\partial z(x, y)}{\partial x}\right) dx + \left(\frac{\partial z(x, y)}{\partial y}\right) dy \qquad (p)$$

Further differentiation yields

$$\frac{\partial}{\partial y}\left(\frac{\partial z(x, y)}{\partial x}\right) = \frac{\partial^2 z(x, y)}{\partial y\, \partial x} = \frac{\partial}{\partial x}\left(\frac{\partial z(x, y)}{\partial y}\right) \qquad (q)$$

For a function

$$d\Phi = Ldw + Mdx + Ndy \qquad (r)$$

where $d\Phi$ is a total differential

$$L = \left(\frac{\partial \Phi}{\partial w}\right)_{x,\, y} \qquad M = \left(\frac{\partial \Phi}{\partial x}\right)_{w,\, y} \qquad N = \left(\frac{\partial \Phi}{\partial y}\right)_{w,\, x} \qquad (s)$$

and by analogy with eq. **q**, we obtain

$$\frac{\partial L}{\partial x} = \frac{\partial M}{\partial w} \qquad \frac{\partial M}{\partial y} = \frac{\partial N}{\partial x} \qquad \frac{\partial L}{\partial y} = \frac{\partial N}{\partial w} \qquad (t)$$

Nonequilibrium thermodynamics involves mathematical analyses using differentiable volume elements to quantify flows and variations of the thermodynamic properties with position and time. The *density* of an extensive quantity Y is a point function of position coordinates defined by

$$\rho = \lim_{V \to 0} \frac{Y}{V} = \frac{dY}{dV} \qquad (u)$$

The *flow vector* $\mathfrak{J}$ of a quantity Y, also called the *flux density*, is a vector function of the position variables such that the quantity dY crossing a plane surface of area $\mathfrak{A}$ in the direction of its normal vector $\boldsymbol{n}$ in a time dt is given by

$$dY = \mathfrak{J} \cdot \boldsymbol{n}\, d\mathfrak{A}\, dt \qquad (v)$$

The vector $\boldsymbol{n}$ is defined to have unit magnitude, and dY may be positive or negative, depending upon which side of the surface element $\boldsymbol{n}$ projects. The *flux* of a quantity through a macroscopic surface is defined as the total amount per unit time passing through the surface and is given by

$$\Phi = \int_{\mathfrak{A}} \mathfrak{J} \cdot \boldsymbol{n}\, d\mathfrak{A} \qquad (w)$$

If the area differential is made a vector with a direction of the normal and a magnitude of the scalar differential, this formula becomes

$$\Phi = \int_{\mathfrak{A}} \mathfrak{J} \cdot d\mathfrak{A} \qquad (x)$$

The operator ∇ is known as the *gradient* and is defined as

$$\text{grad } \varphi = \nabla\varphi = \boldsymbol{i}\frac{\partial\varphi}{\partial x} + \boldsymbol{j}\frac{\partial\varphi}{\partial y} + \boldsymbol{k}\frac{\partial\varphi}{\partial z} \tag{y}$$

where $\boldsymbol{i}$, $\boldsymbol{j}$, and $\boldsymbol{k}$ are unit vectors pointing along the x, y, and z axes. The physical meaning of eq. y can be understood as follows. At an arbitrary point in space, the quantity φ has some unique value which will change by some increment $d\varphi$ if one moves away a small distance dr. The rate of change $d\varphi/dr$ will depend on the direction chosen. The quantity $\nabla\varphi$ will have the direction in which $d\varphi/dr$ is maximum and a magnitude of this maximal value of $d\varphi/dr$.

The *divergence* of a flow vector is defined in terms of the net flux through a closed surface about an infinitesimal volume element

$$\text{div } \mathfrak{J} = \lim_{V \to 0} \frac{\Phi_i}{V} \tag{z}$$

The physical meaning of divergence may be appreciated by the following explanation. An arbitrary point in space at which a flow of matter occurs is contained within a tiny volume. The divergence of a flow (div $\mathfrak{J}_i$) is a scalar quantity which describes the net rate of entry of the ith constituent into the volume element. Applying the chain rule with respect to a coordinate system,

$$\text{div } \mathfrak{J}_i = \left(\frac{dc}{dt}\right)_{x,y,z} = \frac{\partial c}{\partial x}\cdot\frac{dx}{dt} + \frac{\partial c}{\partial y}\cdot\frac{dy}{dt} + \frac{\partial c}{\partial z}\cdot\frac{dz}{dt} \tag{aa}$$

$$= \nabla c_i \cdot \boldsymbol{v} \tag{bb}$$

$$= \nabla \cdot c_i \boldsymbol{v} = \nabla \cdot \mathfrak{J}_i \tag{cc}$$

where dr/dt is a velocity vector. It should be noted that $\nabla \cdot \dfrac{dr}{dt} = 0$ because dr/dt is never an explicit function of the coordinates.

A basic theorem of vector analysis, known as the *divergence theorem* or *Gauss's theorem*, asserts that

$$\Phi_T = \oint_{\mathfrak{A}} \mathfrak{J} \cdot d\mathfrak{A} = \int_V \text{div } \mathfrak{J}\, dV \tag{dd}$$

Since the total flux in a volume element can be expressed as the difference between the amount created and the change in the amount present (assuming that the quantity is mathematically conserved), we can also write

$$\Phi_T = \int_V \left(\frac{d\rho}{dt} - \frac{\partial\rho}{\partial t}\right) dV \tag{ee}$$

and

$$\int_V \left(\frac{d\rho}{dt} - \frac{\partial\rho}{\partial t}\right) dV = \int_V \text{div } \mathfrak{J}\, dV \tag{ff}$$

The explicit dependence of ρ on time, detected by $(\partial\rho/\partial t)$, denotes creation of matter (or energy), such as the creation of a chemical species by a chemical reaction. The volume element's shape is entirely arbitrary; if we assume that the flow and density are continuous, we must have, upon integration,

$$\int_V \left(\frac{d\rho}{dt} - \frac{\partial \rho}{\partial t} - \text{div}\,\mathfrak{J} \right) dV = 0 \tag{gg}$$

The equation

$$\frac{d\rho}{dt} = \frac{\partial \rho}{\partial t} + \text{div}\,\mathfrak{J} \tag{hh}$$

is often termed the *equation of continuity*. It states that the change in density of a quantity ($d\rho/dt$) can be separated into two contributions, that introduced by the creation or destruction of the quantity ($\partial\rho/\partial t$) and that introduced by its flow, ($-\text{div}\,\mathfrak{J}$).

Lastly, the reader's attention is directed to *Euler's theorem*, which states that if in a function f, when every parameter is multiplied by an arbitrary factor λ,

$$f(\lambda x_1, \lambda x_2, \lambda x_3, \ldots, \lambda x_k) = \lambda^{\nu} f(x_1, x_2, x_3, \ldots, x_k) \tag{ii}$$

then

$$\sum_k x_k \left(\frac{\partial f}{\partial x_k} \right) = \nu f(x_k) \tag{jj}$$

Any function which satisfies eq. **ii** is called a homogeneous function of degree ν.

free energy

Because many important processes occur under nonadiabatic conditions, and because the entropy content of a system is difficult to determine experimentally, entropy generally does not serve directly as an index of spontaneity. In order to deal practically and easily with the question of the spontaneity of a chemical or physical transformation, certain new thermodynamic functions have been introduced, the free energy functions. The two most commonly used free energy functions are the *Helmholtz free energy*, A, and the *Gibbs free energy*, G, which are defined as

$$A = U - TS \tag{4-23}$$

$$G = A + PV = U + PV - TS \tag{4-24}$$

Both the Helmholtz free energy and the Gibbs free energy are thermodynamic properties, and their differentials are exact.

Differentiating eq. 4-23 yields

$$dA = dU - TdS - SdT \tag{4-25}$$

For an isochoric, isothermal process, eqs. 4-17, 4-19, and 4-25 can be combined to give an alternate criterion for the spontaneity of a transformation:

$$dA = đQ - TdS \geq 0 \tag{4-26}$$

While eq. 4-26 is more easily applied than eq. 4-18 as a criterion of spontaneity, it still is not widely applicable because isothermal, isochoric heat exchange occurs only in a limited number of processes, such as during a phase transition.

Differentiating eq. 4-24 gives

$$dG = dU + PdV - TdS + VdP - SdT \tag{4-27}$$

For an isothermal, isobaric process in which expansion work is the only form of work which occurs, eqs. 4-9, 4-10, 4-17, and 4-27 can be combined, yielding

$$dG = đQ - TdS \leq 0 \tag{4-28}$$

Equation 4-28 provides a more useful criterion for spontaneity than eq. 4-26 because the conditions required for its application are met more frequently. For example, in many chemical and engineering applications, the restriction to expansion work is not limiting.

In physiological systems many other forms of work than expansion work are encountered, such as mechanical work in muscle contraction, electrical work in active transport, or chemical work in metabolic processes. In these cases, eq. 4-28 is not applicable. For analysis of physiological processes, it is useful to define a new thermodynamic property, the *total free energy*, Θ.

$$\Theta = A - \sum_i Y_i\left(\frac{\partial U}{\partial Y_i}\right) \tag{4-29}$$

where Y_i represents all extensive thermodynamic variables in the system on which U depends explicitly. Equation 4-20 can be rewritten in this notation as

$$đW = -\sum_i \left(\frac{\partial U}{\partial Y_i}\right) dY_i \tag{4-30}$$

The conjugate forces exerted on the environment in the system (intensive variables associated with a particular extensive variable) are denoted by

$$X_i = -\left(\frac{\partial U}{\partial Y_i}\right) \tag{4-31}$$

Differentiating eq. 4-29 yields

$$d\Theta = \left[dU - \sum_i \left(\frac{\partial U}{\partial Y_i}\right) dY_i\right] - TdS - \left[SdT + \sum_i Y_i\left(\frac{\partial U}{\partial Y_i}\right)\right] \tag{4-32}$$

From eqs. 4-30 and 4-32 it is evident that for any isothermal process in which all the forces in the system remain constant,

$$d\Theta = đQ - TdS \leq 0 \tag{4-33}$$

Because many forms of work occur simultaneously in biological processes, total free energy is the most useful function for the analysis of living systems. The relation expressed in eq. 4-32 is fundamental to the application of thermodynamics in physiology.

The following relations can be derived by inspection from eq. 4-32 remembering that $d\Theta$ is an exact differential and a homogeneous function of the first degree.

$$\frac{\partial \Theta}{\partial U} = 1 \tag{4-34}$$

$$\frac{\partial \Theta}{\partial Y_i} = -\frac{\partial U}{\partial Y_i} = X_i \tag{4-35}$$

$$\frac{\partial \Theta}{\partial T} = -S \tag{4-36}$$

$$\frac{\partial \Theta}{\partial S} = -T \tag{4-37}$$

It follows from eqs. 4-31 and 4-32 that

$$\frac{\partial \Theta}{\partial X_i} = Y_i \tag{4-38}$$

Because $d\Theta$ is an exact differential and the Cauchy condition holds, further differentiation of the above expressions leads to the *Maxwell reciprocity relations.* For example, eqs. 4-35 and 4-36 imply

$$\left(\frac{\partial X_i}{\partial T}\right) = \frac{\partial^2 \Theta}{\partial T \, \partial Y_i} \tag{4-39}$$

and

$$-\left(\frac{\partial S}{\partial Y_i}\right) = \frac{\partial^2 \Theta}{\partial Y_i \, \partial T} \tag{4-40}$$

Equating the two partial derivatives of Θ (eqs. 4-39 and 4-40) gives

$$\left(\frac{\partial X_i}{\partial T}\right) = -\left(\frac{\partial S}{\partial Y_i}\right) \tag{4-41}$$

The other Maxwell reciprocity relations can be derived in similar fashion.[3] For example,

$$\left(\frac{\partial T}{\partial Y_i}\right) = -\left(\frac{\partial X_i}{\partial S}\right) \tag{4-42}$$

The Maxwell reciprocity relations are useful for analyzing systems undergoing a reversible change of state. Their use can be illustrated by comparing the stretching of a steel spring and a rubber band using the relation expressed in eq. 4-42, substituting F (force exerted) for X_i, and l (length) for Y_i. A steel spring heats slightly when it undergoes reversible adiabatic stretching, so that $(\partial T/\partial l)_S$ is positive. It follows that $(\partial F/\partial S)_l$ is negative; experimentally, the tension in a spring is found to decrease when its entropy is increased by heating. In a rubber band, on the other hand, $(\partial T/\partial l)_S$ is negative because the rubber band is found to cool when it undergoes reversible adiabatic stretching. From eq. 4-42, it follows that $(\partial F/\partial S)_l$ is positive. In fact, the isometric tension in a rubber band is found to increase as its entropy increases—for example, upon heating or while being dissolved by a rubber solvent. The action of the rubber solvent occurs because it ruptures cross links between the long-chain rubber molecules. This is accompanied by a transfer of a portion of the thermal kinetic energy into transverse molecular vibrations. The tension in the rubber band then increases just as the tension in a string increases when it vibrates. Obviously, the effect vanishes when the rubber structure is destroyed completely.

[3] These relations have been developed in the most general terms, and any set of intensive and extensive variables can be used for X_i and Y_i, such as P and V (pressure, volume), F and l (force, length), E and $\mathfrak{F}$ (electric potential, charge), Γ and $\mathfrak{A}$ (surface tension, area), μ_j and n_j (chemical potential, moles of substance), or A_k and ξ_k (affinity of reaction, advancement of reaction). When P or A is used for X_i, the sign must be reversed to preserve the convention that work is performed on the environment.

A very important use of the partial derivatives of the free energy function is the *characterization of equilibrium*. Equation 4-33 holds for all paths that lead, at constant T and $\{X_i\}$, to a given equilibrium state. If the set $\{X_i\}$ includes *all* forces tending to change the $\{Y_i\}$, then it follows that at equilibrium the free energy, Θ, must reach a minimum with respect to changes in the $\{Y_i\}$. At internal equilibrium in an isolated system

$$X_i = \frac{\partial \Theta}{\partial Y_i} = 0 \qquad \textit{(4-43)}$$

$$\frac{\partial X_i}{\partial Y_i} = \frac{\partial^2 \Theta}{\partial X_i \, \partial Y_i} \geq 0 \qquad \textit{(4-44)}$$

Equation 4-43 is a relation which is fundamental to the discussion of phase and chemical equilibria below.

In using eq. 4-43, it should be noted that if, for example, volume is used for Y_i, the *net* pressure will be zero at equilibrium because all pressure terms must be included. Thus, the equilibrium shape of a balloon is reached when the net pressure on the balloon surface is zero. The total free energy of the enclosed gas, the total free energy of the atmospheric gas, and the total free energy of the rubber all must be known in order to be able to predict the equilibrium shape of the balloon.

The formalisms developed here are stated in general terms where X_i and Y_i represent any pair of an intensive force and its conjugated extensive thermodynamic variable. The use of particular variables is a matter of convenience for dealing with a particular system. The reader may find a list of commonly used pairs of variables helpful at this point.

	X_i, INTENSIVE FORCE		Y_i, EXTENSIVE VARIABLE
$-P$	Pressure	V	Volume
F	Force	l	Length
E	Electric potential	$\mathfrak{F}$	Electric charge
Γ	Surface tension	$\mathfrak{A}$	Surface area
μ_j	Chemical potential	n_j	Mole number
$-A$	Affinity of reaction	Ξ	Advancement of reaction
$-B$	Affinity of phase transition	$\mathcal{N}$	Advancement of phase transition

partial molal quantities

A very important subset of extensive variables consists of the *mole numbers* $\{n_j\}$ which specify the number of moles of each chemical species present in the system. The extensive variables in eq. 4-29 can be segregated so that the set $\{Y_i\}$ does not include the set $\{n_j\}$. Then

$$\Theta = U - TS - \Sigma X_i Y_i - \Sigma \mu_j n_j \qquad \textit{(4-45)}$$

where μ_j is the chemical potential of the jth species. If the system is homogeneous, at equilibrium the equation of state specifies each extensive variable Y_i as a function of T, $\{X_k\}$, and $\{n_j\}$. Therefore, for any reversible process in a homogeneous system

$$dY_i = \frac{\partial Y_i}{\partial T} dT + \sum_k \frac{\partial Y_i}{\partial X_k} dX_k + \sum_j \frac{\partial Y_i}{\partial n_j} dn_j, \qquad i \neq j \neq k \tag{4-46}$$

The quantities $(\partial Y_i/\partial n_j)$ are called *partial molal quantities* and usually are denoted as

$$\overline{Y}_{ij} = \frac{\partial Y_i}{\partial n_j} \tag{4-47}$$

where $\overline{Y}_{ij}$ is the partial molal quantity of the ith extensive variable attributable to the jth chemical species. The partial molal volume $\overline{V}_j$ frequently appears in discussions of partial molal quantities because it is common to restrict attention to systems which do only expansion work on the environment.

The use of partial molal quantities permits some important properties of systems to be deduced even without knowing the equation of state. The basis for the deduction is that at constant values of the intensive variables (T and $\{X_i\}$), multiplication of all mole numbers ($\{n_j\}$) by some factor must multiply all the extensive variables ($\{Y_i\}$) by the same factor. For example, doubling the quantities of all species in a gaseous mixture requires that the volume double if the pressure and temperature are to remain constant. This property of $\{Y_i\}$ is just a precise statement of the fact that these variables are chosen to be extensive. Applying the Euler theorem (eqs. **u** and **v**) to eq. 4-44 (identifying Y_i with f and n_j with x_k), we have

$$\sum_j n_j \overline{Y}_i = Y_i \tag{4-48}$$

Further partial differentiation of eq. 4-48 with respect to some n_k gives

$$\overline{Y}_{ik} = \frac{\partial Y_i}{\partial n_k} = \overline{Y}_{ik} + \sum_j n_j \frac{\partial \overline{Y}_{ij}}{\partial_{n_k}} \tag{4-49}$$

from which it follows that

$$\sum_j n_j \frac{\partial \overline{Y}_{ij}}{\partial n_k} = 0 \tag{4-50}$$

The relation expressed by eq. 4-50 is known as the *Gibbs-Duhem equation*, when $\overline{Y}_{ij}$ is the partial molal free energy, which is the same as the chemical potential, $\overline{\Theta}_j = \mu_j$. The set of equations represented relates the changes in the chemical potentials of all components in a system upon the addition or removal of an amount of one component.

Equation 4-50 may be rewritten as

$$n_k \frac{\partial \overline{Y}_{ik}}{\partial n_k} = -\frac{\partial}{\partial n_k} \sum_{j \neq k} n_j \overline{Y}_{ij} \tag{4-51}$$

Equation 4-51 is often applied to solutions, in which case n_k is conveniently chosen to be the number of moles of solvent. The term $\sum_{j \neq k} n_j \overline{Y}_{ij}$ is then the solute contribution to Y_i. Equation 4-51 applies to any extensive thermodynamic variable. When applied to free energy it becomes

$$n_k \frac{\partial \mu_k}{\partial n_k} = -\frac{\partial}{\partial n_k} \Sigma n_j \mu_j \tag{4-52}$$

chemical reactions and phase transitions

In analyzing complex chemical systems, it is often more convenient to use entire chemical reactions rather than changes in the amounts of individual chemical species as the elementary processes. This is particularly true in biological systems where the rates of chemical reactions are controlled by highly specific enzymes. For such an analysis the *extent of advancement*[4] of the ith reaction, Ξ_i, is used as an extensive variable in place of Y_i in eq. 4-29. The extent of advancement of a reaction is defined so that in a closed system it satisfies the relation

$$\sum_i m_{ij} \frac{d\Xi_i}{dt} = \frac{dn_j}{dt} \tag{4-53}$$

where n_j is the number of moles of the jth chemical species present in the system, and m_{ij} is the stoichiometric coefficient of the jth species in the ith reaction. The sign of m_{ij} is positive for reaction products and negative for reactants.

It follows from eq. 4-53 that the rate of change in Θ due to all chemical reactions is

$$\left(\frac{d\Theta}{dt}\right)_{\text{chemical}} = \sum_j \left(\frac{\partial\Theta}{\partial n_j}\right) \frac{dn_j}{dt} \tag{4-54}$$

$$= \sum_j \sum_i m_{ij} \left(\frac{d\Xi_i}{dt}\right) \frac{\partial\Theta}{\partial n_j} \tag{4-55}$$

The coefficient of $(d\Xi_i/dt)$ gives the expression for $(\partial\Theta/\partial\Xi_i)$

$$\frac{\partial\Theta}{\partial\Xi_i} = \sum_j m_{ij} \frac{\partial\Theta}{\partial n_j} \tag{4-56}$$

If the system consists of a single phase, eqs. 4-22 and 4-35 permit us to identify $(\partial\Theta/\partial n_j)$ as μ_j. The conjugate driving force or *affinity* of the ith reaction in a single-phase closed system is given by the relation

$$A_i = -\frac{\partial\Theta}{\partial\Xi_i} = -\sum_j m_{ij}\mu_j \tag{4-57}$$

For a multiphase system, these relations are applied to each phase. Letting a superscript denote the phase of each component in a multiphase system, eqs. 4-53, 4-55, and 4-57 become

$$\frac{dn_j^k}{dt} = \sum_i m_{ij} \frac{d\Xi_i^k}{dt} \tag{4-58}$$

$$\left(\frac{d\Theta}{dt}\right)_{\substack{\text{chemical reaction}\\ \text{phase transition}}} = -\sum_k \sum_j \sum_i m_{ij} \frac{d\Xi_i^k}{dt} \mu_j^k \tag{4-59}$$

$$A_i^k = -\sum_j m_{ij}\mu_j^k \tag{4-60}$$

[4] de Donder, T., and van Rysselberghe, P. *Thermodynamic Theory of Affinity*. Stanford, Cal.: Stanford University Press, 1936.

The extent to which the jth chemical species has passed from phase k' to phase k, $\mathcal{N}_j^{k',k}$, should satisfy the relation

$$\frac{dn_j^k}{dt} = \sum_{k'} \frac{d\mathcal{N}_j^{k',k}}{dt} \tag{4-61}$$

by analogy to eq. 4-53. The thermodynamic force, $B_j^{k',k}$, tending to drive the phase transition of a single chemical species, then, is given by

$$B_j^{k',k} = -\frac{\partial \Theta}{\partial \mathcal{N}_j^{k',k}} = \mu_j^k - \mu_j^{k'} \tag{4-62}$$

The conditions for *internal chemical equilibrium* follow immediately from eq. 4-43:

$$\sum_j m_{ij} \mu_j^k = 0 \tag{4-63}$$

Similarly, the conditions for *internal phase equilibrium* are given by

$$\mu_j^k - \mu_j^{k'} = 0 \tag{4-64}$$

Studies on the pressure and temperature dependence of chemical and phase equilibria are facilitated by use of the following reciprocity relations for the chemical potentials

$$\left(\frac{\partial \mu_j^k}{\partial T}\right) = -\left(\frac{\partial S^k}{\partial n_j}\right) = -\bar{S}_j^k \tag{4-65}$$

$$\left(\frac{\partial \mu_j^k}{\partial P}\right) = \left(\frac{\partial V^k}{\partial n_j}\right) = \bar{V}_j^k \tag{4-66}$$

For the three major states of a substance at any temperature, $\bar{S}_{\text{gas}} \gg \bar{S}_{\text{liq}} > \bar{S}_{\text{solid}}$. A spontaneous change of state will occur only when a component moves from a higher to a lower chemical potential. At any temperature, it follows that the substance will tend to exist in that state which has the lowest chemical potential. Thus, if μ versus T is plotted for each of the three states (Fig. 4-2) at a given constant pressure, the

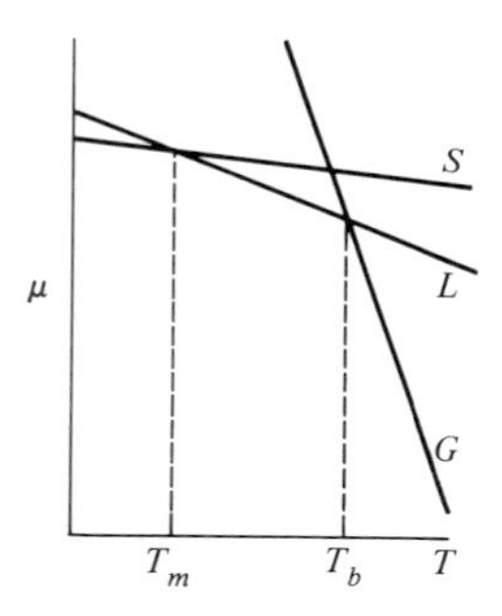

fig. 4-2. A plot of chemical potential μ *versus* T at constant pressure for the solid (S), liquid (L), and gas (G) phases of a model compound.

temperatures at which the curves intersect are the melting point (T_m) and boiling point (T_b). That is, at temperatures above the T_b, the gas has the lowest chemical potential; between the T_b and T_m the liquid form has the lowest chemical potential; and below the T_m the solid form has the lowest chemical potential. At the melting point $\mu_{\text{solid}} = \mu_{\text{liq}}$, and at the boiling point $\mu_{\text{liq}} = \mu_{\text{gas}}$.

From eq. 4-32, in terms of partial molal quantities

$$d\mu_j^k = \bar{V}_j^k \, dP - \bar{S}_j^k \, dT \qquad d\mu_j^{k'} = \bar{V}_j^{k'} \, dP - \bar{S}_j^{k'} \, dT \tag{4-67}$$

Equation 4-64 implies that at equilibrium,

$$\frac{dP}{dT} = \frac{\Delta S}{\Delta V} = \frac{\bar{S}_j^{k'} - \bar{S}_j^k}{\bar{V}_j^{k'} - \bar{V}_j^k} \tag{4-68}$$

For an isothermal, reversible reaction, such as any system at equilibrium, eq. 4-14 can be integrated to give

$$\Delta S = \int_k^{k'} \frac{(đQ)_P}{T} = \frac{1}{T} \int_k^{k'} (đQ)_P = \frac{(\Delta Q)_P}{T} \tag{4-69}$$

Substituting eqs. 4-8 and 4-69 into eq. 4-68, the following expression is obtained which is known as the *Clapeyron equation*:

$$\frac{dP}{dT} = \frac{\Delta H}{T \Delta V} \tag{4-70}$$

In the case of an ideal gas, eq. 3-9 may be substituted to obtain

$$\frac{dP}{dT} = \frac{P \Delta H}{(RT)T} \tag{4-71}$$

$$\frac{1}{P} \frac{dP}{dT} = \frac{d \ln P}{dT} = \frac{\Delta H}{RT^2} \tag{4-72}$$

Equation 4-72 is called the *Clausius-Clapeyron equation*. It can be used to predict the vapor pressure of a liquid or solid when the heat of vaporization or sublimation and one vapor pressure are known.

third law of thermodynamics

For a reversible temperature change in a substance at constant pressure,

$$d(S)_P = \frac{đ(Q)_P}{T} = \frac{C_P \, dT}{T} \tag{4-73}$$

where C_P is the isobaric heat capacity. Integrating eq. 4-73 gives

$$S_T = \int_0^T C_P \frac{dT}{T} + S_0 \tag{4-74}$$

For each phase transition that the substance undergoes between the temperature of 0 and T, it is necessary to add the entropy change for the phase transition. The entropy of transition, $\Delta S_{tr} = \Delta H_{tr}/T$, and eq. 4-74 becomes

$$S_T = \int_0^T C_p \, d \ln T + \sum \frac{\Delta H_{tr}}{T_{tr}} + S_0 \tag{4-75}$$

Phase transitions include transitions from one crystalline form to another. The

Third Law of Thermodynamics enunciated by Nernst and Planck states that *the entropy of a pure, crystalline substance at 0°K is zero.*

$$S_0 = \lim_{T \to 0} S_T = 0 \qquad \lim_{T \to 0} (\Delta G - \Delta H) = 0 \tag{4-76}$$

The entropy value obtained experimentally using eqs. 4-75 and 4-76 is frequently called the *absolute entropy* and is designated S_T^0. Absolute entropies can also be calculated from spectroscopic data using the considerations of statistical thermodynamics. The absolute entropies of various compounds are listed in Fig. 4-3.

fig. 4-3. Entropy of certain compounds. (From Huffman, H. M., Parkes, G. S., and Barmore, M. *J. Am. Chem. Soc.*, *53*, 3884 [1931]. Copyright 1931 by the American Chemical Society; reprinted by permission.)

COMPOUND	ENTROPY (CAL/MOLE/°C)
α-D-Glucose (solid)	50.7
α-D-Glucose (solid)(1/6 mole)	8.45
Oxygen (gas)	49.0
Water (liquid)	16.75
Carbon dioxide (gas)	51.1
n-Octane[a]	86.6
2,2-Dimethylhexane[a]	77.6
2,2-Dimethyl-3,3-dimethylbutane[a]	68.6
Maleic acid (*cis*-butene di-acid)	38.1
Fumaric acid (*trans*-butene di-acid)	39.7

[a] Calculated from formula $S = 25 \cdot 0 + 7 \cdot 7\,\boldsymbol{n} - 4 \cdot 5\,\boldsymbol{r}$, where $\boldsymbol{n}$ is the number of carbon atoms and $\boldsymbol{r}$ is the number of branches.

There are numerous apparent exceptions to the Third Law of Thermodynamics. For example, hydrogen molecules exist in two forms, *ortho* and *para*, which differ in the relative orientation of their nuclear spins. Discrepancies in the entropy values calculated from heat-capacity measurements are due to the persistence of both forms at low temperatures. For many other substances, several molecular orientations can exist simultaneously at low temperatures, causing exceptions to the Third Law. These examples show that the Third Law is generally inapplicable because most substances do not assume a "pure crystalline form."

coupled processes

The analysis of a complex system frequently begins by dissecting it into its component structural parts. This approach, frequently used in biology, yields subunits more amenable to analysis by reducing the *structural complexity*. *Functional complexity* is an important, albeit different, aspect of biological systems. In many cases, the fractionation methods which reduce the structural complexity either destroy or fail to simplify the complex functional process of interest. For the analysis of the *function* of complex systems, it is important to consider methods which fractionate the system into its component *processes*.

Under conditions when the temperature and the forces X_i are constant, eq. 4-33 determines the direction of a complex process. Furthermore, eq. 4-32 separates the complex process into its component processes, each involving a change of U, S, or Y_i. A component process is said to *run forward* (occur spontaneously or run downhill) if it contributes to a decrease in Θ. Thus, decreasing internal energy and increasing entropy are forward processes. For a forward process, $X_i\,(dY_i/dt)$ must be negative. A component process is said to *run backward* (be driven uphill) if it contributes to an increase in Θ. Increasing internal energy, decreasing entropy, and changes in Y_i such that $X_i\,(dY_i/dt)$ is positive are characteristic of backward processes.

Within a system, a backward-running process is said to be *thermodynamically coupled* to a simultaneously occurring forward process. The importance of thermodynamic coupling in physiology cannot be overemphasized. So many of the readily observed processes in biological systems run backward that the Second Law of Thermodynamics has sometimes been suspected of failing in living systems.

The following example based on the special properties of rubber may help to clarify the concept of thermodynamic coupling. Let us tie one end of a rubber band to a support and the other end to a weight which hangs free. If, under isothermal conditions, rubber solvent is placed on the rubber band, the tension will begin to increase and will lift the weight to a new stationary height. The total free energy of the rubber band must decrease because the actual tension in the rubber band will remain essentially constant, and hence eq. 4-42 applies. Lifting the weight is obviously an uphill process; $F(dl/dt)$ is positive, tending to increase the total free energy, Θ, of the rubber band. This is offset by a negative contribution to Θ from the quantity $-T(dS/dt)$. The process of lifting the weight is thermodynamically coupled to the entropy-increasing process which accompanies the dissolution of the rubber.

The biologist frequently deals with open systems in which a steady state is maintained in part of the system at the expense of energy utilization in another part of the system. Living systems characteristically involve departures from equilibrium. Systems which are maintained in a state of continuous disequilibrium by coupling to processes which utilize energy can be analyzed by a set of formalisms, sometimes called *nonequilibrium thermodynamics*, derived from an extension of classical principles.

The general mathematical description of thermodynamic coupling in heterogeneous systems begins with the selection of local regions of fixed volume. The volume of such a region is required to be so small that it can be treated without appreciable error as a differential volume element in the subsequent mathematical development. The fluctuations of the thermodynamic variables within the confines of the region always can be smoothed out by time averaging. The volume element is assigned unit volume, and the extensive thermodynamic variables which apply to it are treated as *local* densities (amount per unit volume). The local density associated with any thermodynamic variable Y_i is generally designated by the corresponding lower-case character y_i. An important exception to this is the local molar concentration c_j^k which is the local density associated with the mole number n_j^k.

The usual treatment of nonequilibrium thermodynamics is based on an analysis of the local internal entropy production $đs_i$ defined in terms of the equation of continuity (eq. **hh**) for entropy density

$$ds = ds_e + ds_i = \frac{đq}{T} + ds_i \qquad \textit{(4-77)}$$

where ds is the total local entropy production and ds_e is the local entropy transferred to the environment. Generally it is assumed that

$$\text{đ}s_i \geq 0 \tag{4-78}$$

However, one must recognize that $\text{đ}s_i$ *can be negative* if not all the forces are constant and work is done by the environment. Moreover, $\text{đ}s_i$ is not an exact differential and consequently one cannot proceed in the analysis without the additional assumption of local equilibrium. Therefore, it seems preferable to adopt a more general approach based on an analysis of the total free energy density θ. Under isothermal conditions at constant values for all the forces

$$T\,\text{đ}s_i = -d\theta \geq 0 \tag{4-79}$$

Furthermore, the use of eq. 4-79 in place of eq. 4-78 avoids the restriction of equilibrium in the local volume elements.

To illustrate the above considerations, let us again examine the behavior of a rubber band. The isometric tension of a stretched rubber band increases with increasing temperature. From the Maxwell relation

$$\frac{\partial F}{\partial T} = -\frac{\partial S}{\partial l} \tag{4-41}$$

we conclude that the entropy of the rubber band decreases during isothermal stretching. Moreover we have already noted that a rubber band cools during adiabatic stretching, so that heat must flow into the rubber band during isothermal stretching. Therefore, in terms of eq. 4-77, the isothermal stretching of a rubber band causes a *negative entropy production* in violation of eq. 4-78. The example just considered of thermodynamic coupling in a rubber band illustrates the utility of the free energy formulation of nonequilibrium thermodynamics in a situation where the local equilibrium assumption fails. Generally, whenever chemical reactions are displaced from equilibrium to a considerable extent (a frequent situation in biological systems), the local equilibrium assumption fails while the free energy formulation is applicable.

The change in the total free energy density θ of a fixed volume element at constant temperature and constant values for all forces acting on the system $\{X_i\}$ can be divided into contributions from local chemical reactions, local phase transitions, and flows of matter.

$$\left(\frac{d\theta}{dt}\right)_{\text{total}} = \left(\frac{d\theta}{dt}\right)_{\text{chemical}} + \left(\frac{d\theta}{dt}\right)_{\text{phase}} + \left(\frac{d\theta}{dt}\right)_{\text{flow}} \leq 0 \tag{4-80}$$

Applying the chain rule to the change in total free energy due to chemical reactions with respect to individual chemical species, one can write

$$\left(\frac{d\theta}{dt}\right)_{\text{chemical}} = \sum_j \sum_k \left(\frac{\partial \theta}{\partial c_j^k}\right) \frac{dc_j^k}{dt} \tag{4-81}$$

Equation 4-53 can be rewritten in terms of local densities:

$$\frac{dc_j^k}{dt} = \sum_i m_{ij} \frac{d\xi_i^k}{dt} \tag{4-82}$$

Substituting eqs. 4-60 and 4-82 into eq. 4-81 gives

$$\left(\frac{d\theta}{dt}\right)_{\text{chemical}} = -\sum_k \sum_i A_i^k \frac{d\xi_i^k}{dt} \tag{4-83}$$

Similarly the expression for the change of total free energy density due to phase transitions can be written

$$\left(\frac{d\theta}{dt}\right)_{\text{phase}} = -\sum_k \sum_{k'} \sum_j B_j^{k',k} \frac{dv_j^{k',k}}{dt} \tag{4-84}$$

The change of θ due to flows of matter, by a similar derivation, can be written as[5]

$$\left(\frac{d\theta}{dt}\right)_{\text{flow}} = \sum_k \sum_j \nabla(c_j^k \mu_j^k) \cdot \frac{d\mathbf{r}_j^k}{dt} \tag{4-85}$$

where $(d\mathbf{r}_j^k/dt)$ is a vector denoting the average local flow velocity. A flux of matter is defined by the relation

$$\mathfrak{J}_j^k = c_j^k \frac{d\mathbf{r}_j^k}{dt} \tag{4-86}$$

Introducing eq. 4-86 into eq. 4-85 gives

$$\left(\frac{d\theta}{dt}\right)_{\text{flow}} = \sum_k \sum_j (\nabla\mu_j^k + \mu_j^k \nabla \ln c_j^k) \cdot \mathfrak{J}_j^k \tag{4-87}$$

The force associated with the flux $\mathfrak{J}_j^k$, therefore, is given by

$$\mathbf{C}_j^k = -(\nabla\mu_j^k + \mu_j^k \nabla \ln c_j^k) \tag{4-88}$$

The formulation outlined above shows that the change of total free energy density depends upon the sum of products of forces and the rates of processes which they drive. The forces are the intensive quantities A_i^k, $B_j^{k',k}$, and $\mathbf{C}_j^k$, and the rates conjugated to them are the extensive quantities $(d\xi_i^k/dt)$, $(dv_j^{k',k}/dt)$, and $\mathfrak{J}_j^k$ respectively. Equations 4-83, 4-84, and 4-87 can be combined into a single expression:

$$\left(\frac{d\theta}{dt}\right) = -\sum_i X_i v_i \leq 0 \tag{4-89}$$

where X_i is the force acting on the local volume element and v_i is the corresponding rate associated with the ith chemical reaction, phase transition, or directional component of the flow of matter. Equation 4-89 serves to evaluate spontaneity in a system of processes when the temperature and all forces acting on the system are constant.

A thermodynamic force may affect not only the velocity of the process with which it is associated but also the velocities of any or all other processes in the system. The action of a force on nonconjugated process rates is expressed by *local thermodynamic coupling coefficients* which may be defined as

$$\lambda_{ij} = \frac{\partial v_i}{\partial X_j} \tag{4-90}$$

[5] See the Mathematical Interlude section (pp. 174–175) of this chapter for an explanation of gradient and divergence.

If the volume element is *near steady state* (meaning that $\boldsymbol{v}_i$ is almost zero), then to a good approximation

$$\boldsymbol{v}_i \approx \lambda_{ii}\,\Delta X_i + \sum_j \lambda_{ij}\,\Delta X_j \tag{4-91}$$

where ΔX_j denotes the departure of X_j from its steady-state value. If the volume element is near equilibrium, a condition rarely encountered in living systems, then eq. 4-91 reduces to

$$\boldsymbol{v}_i \approx \lambda_{ii} X_i + \sum_{j \neq i} \lambda_{ij} X_j \tag{4-92}$$

A composite process is said to be *stationary* with respect to a substance if its local molar concentration c_j^k remains unchanged. Since all terms in $(d\theta/dt)_{\text{chemical}}$ and $(d\theta/dt)_{\text{phase}}$ are proportional to (dc_j^k/dt), we can conclude that

$$\left(\frac{d\theta}{dt}\right)_{\text{stationary}} = \left(\frac{d\theta}{dt}\right)_{\text{flow}} \tag{4-93}$$

A flow is called stationary if it does not contribute to a change of c_j^k. For a stationary flow, $\boldsymbol{\nabla} \cdot \mathfrak{J}_j^k$ must be zero, from which it follows that

$$\left(\frac{d\theta}{dt}\right)_{\substack{\text{stationary}\\ \text{flow}}} = \sum_k \sum_j \boldsymbol{\nabla}\mu_j^k \cdot \mathfrak{J}_j^k \tag{4-94}$$

Thus, the force associated with a stationary flow $\mathfrak{J}_j^k$ is just $-\boldsymbol{\nabla}\mu_j^k$. Applying eq. 4-92 to a stationary flow *near equilibrium* in an isotropic system yields

$$\mathfrak{J}_j^k \approx -\sum_{k'} \sum_{j'} \lambda_{jj'}^{kk'}\, \boldsymbol{\nabla}\mu_j^k \tag{4-95}$$

There are a number of familiar physical laws for transport which are special cases of eq. 4-95.

Fick's Law (diffusion)	$\mathfrak{J} = -D \text{ grad } c$	(4-96)
Ohm's Law (electric current)	$\mathfrak{J} = -\kappa \text{ grad } \psi$	(4-97)
Fourier's Law (heat flow)	$\mathfrak{J} = -\kappa_T \text{ grad } T$	(4-98)
Poiseuille's Law (flow of viscous fluids)	$\mathfrak{J} = -C \text{ grad } P$	(4-99)

In dealing with the various flows and forces encountered in complex systems it is important to remember the principle first discovered by Pierre Curie and developed in a more general form by Prigogine.[6] The *Curie-Prigogine principle* states that *entities whose tensorial characters differ by an odd integer cannot interact* (fail to couple) *in isotropic systems*. This principle says that vector flow $\mathfrak{J}_i$ cannot couple with a scalar flow $\mathfrak{J}_j$ in an isotropic system. On the other hand, vector flows can be coupled one to another, and scalar flows can be coupled one to another. Thus, coupling between the diffusion flows of the various components of an isotropic system or between diffusion flows and heat flow can occur because they are all vector flows; but coupling between

[6] Curie, P. *J. de Phys.* (*Paris*), series 3, *3*, 393 (1894); Prigogine, I., and Wiame, M. *Experientia*, *2*, 451 (1946).

such vector flows and chemical reactions or viscous flows which are scalars cannot occur.

However, *flows whose forces have tensorial ranks differing by an odd integer can interact in an anisotropic system.* Coupling between scalar flows such as chemical reactions and vector flows such as diffusion flows, heat flows, and electric currents can occur only in anisotropic systems. The fact that chemical reactions in cells are coupled to transmembrane mass transport processes is a powerful argument in favor of the existence of a substantive structure at the cell boundary[7] (see p. 456). Whether or not the functional cell membrane corresponds to the structure seen in electron micrographs is not known at present. An analysis of the transport properties of the cell membrane in terms of nonequilibrium thermodynamics does not require a detailed knowledge of its structure. However, analyzing the cell membrane as a biological machine (Chapter 8) and discovering the mechanisms through which the cross-coupling coefficients actually operate does require detailed information about its structure.

For analyzing physiological systems, one must generally begin with eq. 4-91. Most physiological systems, such as the cell membrane, maintain at least one *nonstationary* flow, and the chemical reactions are maintained far from equilibrium locally. For example, the process of active transport which maintains a nonequilibrium steady-state concentration gradient of sodium ions across a muscle or nerve membrane is driven by the enzyme-catalyzed hydrolysis of ATP. The hydrolysis of ATP takes place spontaneously because it is far from chemical equilibrium with ADP. Furthermore, the continuous replenishment of ATP which maintains a relatively constant ATP concentration requires some nonstationary flow.

Onsager symmetry

The number of coupling coefficients leaves a cumbersome set of formalisms with which to deal. The simplest statement of a diffusion process with a completely ionized solute requires that nine coefficients be measured, even in an isothermal medium. A substantial reduction in this complexity was introduced by Onsager,[8] who found that the linear coefficients satisfy the relationship

$$L_{ij} = L_{ji} \qquad \textit{(4-100)}$$

The sign reverses when the forces or fluxes involve angular momentum such as is found with magnetic fields or Coriolus forces.

This remarkable set of relationships, resulting in a symmetric matrix of linear coefficients, provided an important stimulus to the development of a consistent theory of nonequilibrium processes. It is usually derived from a limited application of statistical mechanics, not from any macroscopic principles; and although an indication of the derivation will be given, a full treatment of it is beyond the scope of this presentation. In any case, the ultimate justification for the use of Onsager symmetry rests on experimental verification; and many rather intricate experiments have been performed to test it and find its limits of validity.[9]

---

[7] Acland, J. D. *J. Theoret. Biol.*, *13*, 318 (1966).
[8] Onsager, L. *Phys. Rev.*, *37*, 405 (1931); *38*, 2265 (1931).
[9] An extensive review of experimental data has been published by Miller, D. G., *Chem. Rev.*, *60*, 15 (1960). Miller concludes that for diffusion processes with "gentle" concentration grad units, the Onsager relations may be regarded as a law of nature.

We begin an indication of the statistical basis for the Onsager relations[10] by considering the macroscopic state variables $[b_i^0]$ at equilibrium. Let $[a_i]$ measure their departures from equilibrium value.

$$b_i = b_i^0 + a_i \tag{4-101}$$

Since equilibrium is given, through the Second Law, as the state of maximum entropy[11]

$$\Delta S = \sum_{ij} \left(\frac{\partial^2 S}{\partial a_i \, \partial a_j} \right) a_i a_j \leq 0 \tag{4-102}$$

Setting

$$-2 \frac{\partial^2 S}{\partial a_i \, \partial a_j} = g_{ij} \tag{4-103}$$

g_{ij} must be positive definite. Applying the Boltzmann equation, we can evaluate the probability of the perturbed state.

$$\Delta S = k \ln P \tag{4-104}$$

$$P \prod da_i = \frac{\exp\left(\frac{\Delta S}{k}\right) \prod da_i}{I} \tag{4-105}$$

with

$$I = \int \exp\left(\frac{\Delta S}{k}\right) \prod da_i \tag{4-106}$$

Setting

$$X_k = \frac{\partial(\Delta S)}{\partial a_k} = \frac{\partial(k \ln P)}{\partial a_k} \tag{4-107}$$

$$X_k = -\sum_j g_{kj} a_j \tag{4-108}$$

We obtain a weighted average of $a_i X_j$

$$\overline{a_i X_j} = \int a_i X_j P \prod da_k \tag{4-109}$$

$$= k \int a_i P \frac{\partial \ln P}{\partial a_j} \prod da_k \tag{4-110}$$

$$= k \int a_i \frac{\partial P}{\partial a_j} \prod da_k \tag{4-111}$$

$$= \left[P a_i k \int \prod_{k \neq 1} da_k \right] - k\delta_{ij} \int P \prod da_k \tag{4-112}$$

$$\overline{a_i X_j} = -k\delta_{ij} \tag{4-113}$$

Because the Lagrange equations governing molecular interactions contain only the second derivative of time, if we take the average over time in a system or

[10] This discussion relies heavily on de Groot, S. R. *Thermodynamics of Irreversible Processes*. Amsterdam: North Holland Publishing Company, 1952, pp. 13–19.
[11] The following expression is merely the third term in a Taylor expansion.

an ensemble of some state variable, after the system has been unchanged for a "long" time, the choice of origin of time will not matter, and in fact

$$\overline{a_i(t+\tau)} = \overline{a_i(t-\tau)} \qquad (4\text{-}114)$$

This statement is called the *law of microscopic reversibility*, indicating that molecular interactions at equilibrium are equiprobable with respect to the direction of time. It is important to realize that the law of microscopic reversibility may not hold universally in biological systems (see Chapter 8). We can, on the same basis, assert that the average product of any two functions has the same property.

$$\overline{a_i(t)a_j(t+\tau)} = \overline{a_i(t+\tau)a_j(t)} \qquad (4\text{-}115)$$

It is easy to show that

$$\overline{a_i(t)[\overline{a_j(t+\tau)} - a_j(t)]} = \overline{a_j(t)[\overline{a_i(t+\tau)} - a_i(t)]} \qquad (4\text{-}116)$$

by manipulating eqs. 4-114 and 4-115.

We write the fluxes assuming the a_i have been chosen from extensive densities

$$\mathfrak{J}_i = \frac{\overline{da_i}}{dt} = \sum_k L_{ik} X_i \qquad (4\text{-}117)$$

with vector flows assumed linear for simplicity. This is the Onsager hypothesis; it links fluxes with the decay of molecular fluctuations.[12] It requires that deviations from equilibrium not be large compared to equilibrium mean free path and mean free time if thermodynamic equilibrium is to be continuously maintained.

Writing the time derivative for small τ

$$\overline{\left(\frac{a_i(t+\tau) - a_i(t)}{\tau}\right)} = \sum_k L_{ik} X_k \qquad (4\text{-}118)$$

We can substitute eq. 4-118 into eq. 4-116 and, multiplying by τ, obtain

$$\overline{a_i(t) \sum_k L_{jk} X_k} = \overline{a_j(t) \sum_k L_{ik} X_k} \qquad (4\text{-}119)$$

Inserting eq. 4-113,

$$-k \sum_k L_{jk} \delta_{ik} = -k \sum_k L_{ik} \delta_{jk} \qquad (4\text{-}120)$$

$$L_{ji} = L_{ij} \qquad (4\text{-}100)$$

It is significant to note that this derivation is independent of a kinetic model except for the general form of the Lagrangian function. While local equilibrium is assumed for this proof, Onsager reciprocity frequently applies under conditions where microscopic reversibility does not obtain—for example, in tunneling.[13]

---

[12] The limits of validity of this time averaging of a time derivative are discussed by Casimir, H. B. *Rev. Mod. Phys.*, *17*, 343 (1945).

[13] Onsager reciprocity holds only near equilibrium. For some biological processes far from equilibrium, the assumptions may not be valid.

The free energy of a substance is usually quantified in terms of the *standard free energy of formation*, ΔGf^0, which is defined as the change in free energy accompanying the formation of the substance in its standard state from its elements in their standard states. The standard state is the most stable form of the substance at 1 atm pressure and 0°C. From these data, the *standard free energy change*, ΔG^0, for any chemical reaction occurring under standard conditions can be derived by the following expression:

$$\Delta G^0 = \sum \Delta Gf^0(\text{products}) - \sum \Delta Gf^0(\text{reactants}) \tag{4-121}$$

The standard free energies of formation of a number of compounds are listed in Fig. 4-4.

For an ideal gas at an arbitrarily chosen constant temperature, eq. 4-27 becomes

$$dG = V\,dP = \frac{RT}{P}\,dP \tag{4-122}$$

Integrating, we obtain

$$\Delta G = RT \ln \frac{P_2}{P_1} \tag{4-123}$$

Consider now a chemical reaction involving two reactants and two products, all ideal gases. At equilibrium

$$a\mathrm{A}(P_\mathrm{A}) + b\mathrm{B}(P_\mathrm{B}) \rightleftarrows c\mathrm{C}(P_\mathrm{C}) + d\mathrm{D}(P_\mathrm{D}) \tag{4-124}$$

when a, b, c, and d represent the number of moles of substances A, B, C, and D which are at partial pressures P_A, P_B, P_C, and P_D. In order to calculate the standard free energy of this reaction, a series of corrections must be added to the free energy change accompanying the reaction so that each substance is considered at 1 atm pressure rather than at its partial pressure.

$$\Delta G^0 = \Delta G + aRT \ln \frac{P_\mathrm{A}}{1} + bTR \ln \frac{P_\mathrm{B}}{1} + cRT \ln \frac{1}{P_\mathrm{C}} + dRT \ln \frac{1}{P_\mathrm{D}} \tag{4-125}$$

Equation 4-125 can be simplified to

$$\Delta G^0 = \Delta G - RT \ln \frac{(P_\mathrm{C})^c (P_\mathrm{D})^d}{(P_\mathrm{A})^a (P_\mathrm{B})^b} \tag{4-126}$$

But the equilibrium constant of the reaction given by eq. 4-124 is defined as

$$K = \frac{(P_\mathrm{C})^c (P_\mathrm{D})^d}{(P_\mathrm{A})^a (P_\mathrm{B})^b} \tag{4-127}$$

It follows, therefore, that

$$\Delta G^0 = \Delta G - RT \ln K \tag{4-128}$$

fig. 4-4. Free energies of formation in kcals/mole at 25° and at atmospheric pressure in aqueous solution at one molal activity unless otherwise stated. (From Bull, H. B. *An Introduction to Physical Biochemistry.* Philadelphia: Davis, 1964, p. 52.)

COMPOUND	ΔG^o	COMPOUND	ΔG^o
Acetaldehyde	−33.38	Glyoxylate$^-$	−112.00
Acetic Acid	−95.48	Hydrogen (ion)	0.00
anion$^-$	−88.99	Hydrogen chloride	−31.35
Acetoacetate$^-$	−118.00	Hydrogen peroxide	−32.67
Acetone	−38.52	Hydrogen sulfide	−6.54
cis Aconitate^{3-}	−220.51	anion$^-$	+3.00
DL-Alanine	−89.11	Hydroxide ion	−37.60
L-Alanine	−88.75	β-Hydroxybutyric acid	−127.00
L-Alanylglycine	−114.57	anion$^-$	−121.00
Ammonia (gas)	−3.98	Isocitrate^{3-}	−277.65
Ammonia (NH_3)	−6.37	Isopropanol	−44.44
(NH_4)	−19.00	α-Ketoglutarate$^-$	−190.62
L-Asparagine	−125.86	Lactate	−123.76
L-Aspartic acid	−172.31	α-Lactose	−362.15
anion$^-$	−166.99	β-Lactose	−375.76
anion^{2-}	−154.99	DL-Leucine	−81.76
n-Butanol	−41.07	L-Leucine	−81.68
Butyric acid	−90.86	DL-Leucylglycine	−110.90
anion$^-$	−84.28	Lithium ion$^+$	−70.22
Calcium ion^{2+}	−132.18	L-Malate^{2-}	−201.98
Carbon dioxide (gas)	−94.26	β-Maltose	−357.80
Carbon dioxide	−92.31	Mannitol	−225.29
Carbonic acid	−149.00	Methanol	−41.88
anion$^-$	−140.31	Nitrate$^-$	−26.41
anion^{2-}	−126.22	Nitrite$^-$	−8.25
Carbon monoxide (gas)	−32.81	Oxalacetate^{2-}	−190.53
Chloride ion$^-$	−40.02	Oxalate^{2-}	−161.30
Citrate^{3-}	−279.24	Palmitic acid (solid)	−82.9
Creatine	−63.17	L-Phenylalanine (solid)	−50.6
Creatinine	−6.91	Potassium ion$^+$	−67.47
L-Cysteine	−81.21	Potassium chloride	−97.59
L-Cystine	−159.00	*n*-Propanol	−42.02
Ethanol	−43.39	Pyruvate$^-$	−113.44
Formaldehyde	−31.20	Sodium ion$^+$	−62.59
Fructose	−218.78	Sodium chloride	−93.94
Formic acid	−85.10	Sorbitol	−225.31
anion$^-$	−80.00	Succinic acid	−178.39
Fumaric acid	−154.67	anion^{2-}	−164.97
anion^{2-}	−144.41	Sucrose	−370.90
α-D-Galactose	−220.73	Sulfate^{2-}	−177.34
α-D-Glucose	−219.22	L-Threonine	−123.00
L-Glutamic acid	−171.76	L-Tryptophane (solid)	−28.5
anion^{2-}	−165.87	L-Tyrosine (solid)	−92.2
Glycerol	−116.76	Urea	−48.72
Glycine	−89.26	Water (gas)	−54.64
Glycogen (per glucose unit)	−158.30	Water (liquid)	−56.69
Glycolate$^-$	−126.90		

If the pressures in eq. 4-124 are values at equilibrium and the transformation is isothermal and isobaric, $\Delta G = 0$, and eq. 4-128 becomes $\Delta G^0 = -RT \ln K$. For any component in reaction 4-128

$$\mu_j = \mu_j^0 + RT \ln P_j \tag{4-129}$$

The dependence of the equilibrium constant on temperature can be derived from the relation of ΔG and ΔH. Equations analogous to eqs. 4-70 and 4-72 can be derived starting with eq. 4-24:

$$\left(\frac{\partial[\Delta G/T]}{\partial T}\right)_P = -\frac{\Delta H}{T^2} \tag{4-130}$$

$$R\left(\frac{\partial \ln K}{\partial T}\right)_P = \frac{\Delta H^0}{T^2} \tag{4-131}$$

If neither ΔG^0 nor K depends on the pressure, then eq. 4-131 becomes

$$\frac{d \ln K}{dT} = \frac{\Delta H^0}{RT^2} \tag{4-132}$$

Equations 4-130 and 4-132 are forms of the Gibbs-Helmholtz equations. Equation 4-132 can be rearranged to give

$$d \ln K = \frac{\Delta H^0}{R}\left(\frac{dT}{T^2}\right) = -\frac{\Delta H^0}{R}\, d\left(\frac{1}{T}\right) \tag{4-133}$$

$$\frac{d \ln K}{d(1/T)} = -\frac{\Delta H^0}{R} \tag{4-134}$$

For moderate ranges of temperature, ΔH^0 is very nearly constant. Therefore, a plot of $\ln K$ *versus* $1/T$ is approximately linear and gives a line with a slope of $-\Delta H^0/R$. Thus, ΔH^0 of a reaction can be evaluated from the change in equilibrium constant as a function of temperature. Equation 4-134, sometimes called the van't Hoff equation, is useful as a means of determining the standard enthalpies experimentally.

In order to extend the above equations to nonideal gases, it will be helpful to introduce the concept of *fugacity*, f, which was originally suggested by G. N. Lewis in 1901. Fugacity replaces pressure in eq. 4-123, so that the equation

$$\ln \frac{f_1}{f_2} = \frac{\Delta G}{RT} \tag{4-135}$$

expresses a definition. Equations 4-125 through 4-134 are then correct if pressure is everywhere replaced by fugacity. The definition of fugacity can be applied to liquid and solid phases as well as to the gaseous state. Every liquid and solid is in equilibrium with its vapor because every substance has a finite vapor pressure. At equilibrium $(\Delta G)_{T,P} = 0$, and the fugacity of the liquid or solid and its vapor are the same.

The *standard state of a solution* which may be used to define μ^0 is a 1-molal solution at 25°C. For biologists, a much more useful reference point is the *specific chemical potential*, μ', which is a solution at pH 7.5 equilibrated with CO_2 and O_2 at partial pressures of 0.05 and 0.2 atm respectively; the solvent is assigned unit fugacity, and all solutes are present at concentrations of 0.01 m.

solutions

A mixture may be regarded as an ideal solution if it obeys the generalized form of Raoult's Law, which is analogous to Dalton's Law of partial pressure. Raoult's Law states that the fugacity of any component is equal to the fugacity of the pure substance times its mole fraction.

$$(f_i)_T = (f_i^0)_T \bar{n}_i \tag{4-136}$$

It can be shown that there is *no change in volume upon mixing pure components which form an ideal solution.* Equation 4-136 stated in the logarithmic form is

$$\ln f_i = \ln f_i^0 + \ln \bar{n}_i \tag{4-137}$$

At any fixed mole fraction

$$\left(\frac{\partial \ln f_i}{\partial P}\right)_T = \left(\frac{\partial \ln f_i^0}{\partial P}\right)_T = \frac{\bar{V}_i}{RT} \tag{4-138}$$

The following identity appears from eq. 4-138:

$$\bar{V}_i = \bar{V}_i^0 = V_i \tag{4-139}$$

$$\Delta V = V_{\text{final}} - V_{\text{initial}} = \sum n_i \bar{V}_i - \sum n_i V_i = 0 \tag{4-140}$$

Thus, the partial molal volume of each constituent of a solution is the same as the molal volume of the pure material alone.

By a similar argument, it can be shown that there is *no evolution of heat when substances which form an ideal solution are mixed.*

The change in free energy which accompanies the formation of an ideal solution is best visualized in terms of diluting a solution with pure solvent. An ideal solution follows Raoult's Law (eq. 4-91), and in terms of the partial molar free energy change,

$$\Delta\bar{G} = \sum (\mu_i)_2 - (\mu_i)_1$$

$$= RT \sum_i \ln (f_i)_2(\bar{n}_i)_2 - RT \sum_i \ln (f_i)_1(\bar{n}_i)_1 \tag{4-141}$$

But $f_{i1} = f_{i2}$. It is evident, therefore, that

$$\Delta\bar{G} = RT \sum_i \ln \frac{(\bar{n}_i)_2}{(\bar{n}_i)_1} \tag{4-142}$$

It can be appreciated that $\Delta\bar{G} < 0$ for diluting a solution or dissolving a solute because $\bar{n}_{i2} < \bar{n}_{i1}$. This corresponds to our daily experience of the spontaneity of dissolution.

The entropy of diluting an ideal solution or of dissolving a solute can be obtained from the following considerations. For any isothermal process,

$$\Delta\bar{G} = \Delta\bar{H} - T\Delta\bar{S} \tag{4-143}$$

However, there is no change in enthalpy upon dilution or formation of an ideal solution. Substitution into eq. 4-142 gives

$$\Delta\bar{S} = -\frac{\Delta\bar{G}}{T} = -R \ln \frac{(\bar{n}_i)_2}{(\bar{n}_i)_1} \tag{4-144}$$

From a consideration of eq. 4-144, it can be appreciated that $\Delta\bar{S} > 0$ for diluting a solution or dissolving a solute. This again corresponds to our daily experience of the spontaneity of such processes.

The biologist is generally concerned with solutions in which water or, less often, another volatile liquid is the solvent, and nonvolatile solids with negligible vapor pressures are the solutes. In such a solution the vapor pressure of the solution will be determined essentially by the mole fraction of solvent and will fall as more nonvolatile solutes are dissolved. Observations of this phenomenon had been made from the beginning of the nineteenth century, but a quantitative relationship was not shown until F. M. Raoult's deduction in 1887. For a solution of a nonvolatile solute, the following relationship can be derived from the identity of fugacities of liquid and vapor and the use of eq. 4-136 to describe the relative fall in vapor pressure of the solution

$$\lim_{\bar{n}_{\text{solv}} \to 1} \frac{\Delta P_{\text{soln}}}{P^0} = \frac{P^0 - P_{\text{soln}}}{P^0} = \sum \bar{n}_j \qquad (4\text{-}145)$$

where P^0 is the vapor pressure of the solvent alone and $\sum \bar{n}_j$ is the sum of the mole fractions of the *nonvolatile* solutes.

The effect of dissolving a nonvolatile solute on the boiling point of the solution may be evaluated as follows. At the boiling point of pure solvent the fugacity of the vapor phase is equal to that of the liquid phase and also to that of the atmosphere. If solute is added, the fugacity of the solution is lowered and it no longer boils. However, the temperature may be raised until it boils again. At the boiling point of the solution, the fugacities of the pure solvent and solution are both increased, but they are now equal.

$$(d \ln f^0)_P = (d \ln f_{\text{soln}})_P \qquad (4\text{-}146)$$

The fugacity of the solvent alone depends on the temperature only while that of the solution depends on both the temperature and the sum of mole fractions of non-volatile solutes. Equation 4-146 may be expressed in terms of the partial derivatives:

$$\left(\frac{\partial \ln f^0}{\partial T}\right)_P dT = \left(\frac{\partial \ln f_{\text{soln}}}{\partial T}\right)_{P, \bar{n}_j} dT + \left(\frac{\partial \ln f_{\text{soln}}}{\partial \bar{n}_j}\right)_{P, T} d \sum \bar{n}_j \qquad (4\text{-}147)$$

where f^0 is the fugacity of the pure solvent. Equation 4-146 may be stated in the logarithmic form (similar to eq. 4-137).

$$\ln f_{\text{soln}} = \ln f^0 + \ln(1 - \sum \bar{n}_j) \qquad (4\text{-}148)$$

Differentiating eq. 4-148 at constant temperature and pressure, we obtain

$$d \ln f_{\text{soln}} = d \ln(1 - \sum \bar{n}_j) = -\frac{d\Sigma\bar{n}_j}{1 - \Sigma\bar{n}_j} \qquad (4\text{-}149)$$

Since for very dilute solutions $(1 - \sum \bar{n}_j)$ is almost equal to 1, eq. 4-149 becomes

$$\left(\frac{\partial \ln f_{\text{soln}}}{\partial \Sigma\, \bar{n}_j}\right)_{T, P} = -1 \qquad (4\text{-}150)$$

At the boiling point of the pure solvent at atmospheric pressure, $f \approx 1$ and the left-hand term of eq. 4-147 is ≈ 0. Substituting eqs. 4-72 and 4-150 into eq. 4-147 gives

$$0 = \frac{\overline{H}_{\text{vap}}}{RT^2}\, dT - d \sum \bar{n}_j \qquad (4\text{-}151)$$

$$dT = \frac{RT^2}{\overline{H}_{\text{vap}}}\, d \sum \bar{n}_j \qquad (4\text{-}152)$$

For dilute solutions the elevation in boiling point is small and T and $\overline{H}$ are approximately constant. Equation 4-152 can be integrated to give

$$\Delta T_b = \frac{RT^2}{\overline{H}_{\text{vap}}} \sum \bar{n}_j \qquad (4\text{-}153)$$

It is evident that $RT^2/\overline{H}_{\text{vap}}$ is a constant with a unique value for each solvent. Equation 4-153 can also be written in the form

$$\Delta T_b = K_e \cdot m \qquad (4\text{-}154)$$

where K_e is the *ebulloscopic constant* or molal boiling-point elevation constant for the solvent and m is the molality of the solution (Fig. 4-5).

fig. 4-5. Ebulloscopic (K_e) and cryoscopic (K_f) constants.

COMPOUND	MOLECULAR WEIGHT	BOILING POINT (°C)	K_e	MELTING POINT (°C)	K_f
Water	18.0	100.0	0.51	0.0	1.86
Ethanol	46.1	78.5	1.23	—	—
Acetone	58.1	56.1	1.71	—	—
Acetic acid	60.0	118.3	3.07	16.6	3.57
Benzene	78.1	80.2	2.53	5.45	5.07
Dioxane	88.1			11.7	4.71
p-Dichlorobenzene	147.0			52.7	7.11
Camphor	152.2			178.4	37.7

By analogous reasoning, the effect of dissolving a nonvolatile solute on the freezing-point depression of the solution can be evaluated. It is assumed that the solute is not soluble in the solid solvent phase. This is true, of course, for almost all aqueous solutions of interest to the biologist; when a dilute aqueous solution begins to freeze, pure ice forms, and the remaining liquid solution becomes more concentrated. As solute is added to a solution, the fugacity falls, and the temperature must be lowered before freezing begins. At the freezing point of the solution, the fugacities of the pure solvent and the solution are both decreased, but they are now equal. An equation similar to eq. 4-147 can be written:

$$\left(\frac{\partial \ln f^0{}_{\text{solid}}}{\partial T}\right)_P = \left(\frac{\partial \ln f_{\text{soln}}}{\partial T}\right)_{P,\bar{n}_j} dT + \left(\frac{\partial \ln f_{\text{soln}}}{\partial \Sigma \bar{n}_j}\right)_{P,T} d \sum \bar{n}_j \qquad (4\text{-}155)$$

Using eqs. 4-72 and 4-147 gives

$$\frac{\overline{H}_{\text{subl}}}{RT^2} = \frac{\overline{H}_{\text{vap}}}{RT^2} - d \sum \bar{n}_j \tag{4-156}$$

At the freezing point of the solvent, the heat of sublimation is equal to the heat of fusion plus the heat of vaporization ($\overline{H}_{\text{subl}} = \overline{H}_{\text{fusion}} + \overline{H}_{\text{vap}}$). Substitution into eq. 4-156, rearrangement and integration, assuming T and $\overline{H}_{\text{fusion}}$ to be constant, yields

$$\Delta T_f = -\frac{RT^2}{\overline{H}_{\text{fusion}}} \sum \bar{n}_j \tag{4-157}$$

It is evident that $RT^2/\overline{H}_{\text{fusion}}$ is a constant with a unique value for each solvent. Equation 4-157 can also be written in the form

$$\Delta T_f = -K_f \cdot m \tag{4-158}$$

where K_f is the *cryoscopic constant* or molal freezing-point depression constant and m is the molality of the solution (see Fig. 4-5).

Let us now consider a perfect semipermeable membrane separating two chambers, one containing pure solvent and the other containing a solution. The membrane permits solvent molecules to pass through freely while it acts as a barrier to solute molecules. There is less likelihood for solvent molecules to pass from the solution side of the membrane than from the pure solvent side because the concentration of solvent is diminished in the solution side. This results in a tendency for a net flow of solvent from the pure solvent side to the solution side. The flow of solvent can be stopped by the application of a hydrostatic pressure to the solution side. This counterpressure is equal to the osmotic pressure of the solution. With adequate pressure compensation

$$f^0_{\text{solvent}} = f_{\text{soln}} + \Delta P \tag{4-159}$$

At constant temperature the fugacity of the solution depends upon the externally applied pressure and the quantity of solute.

$$d \ln f_{\text{soln}} = \left(\frac{\partial \ln f_{\text{soln}}}{\partial P}\right)_{T, \bar{n}_j} dP + \left(\frac{\partial \ln f_{\text{soln}}}{\partial \bar{n}_j}\right)_{T, P} d \sum \bar{n}_j \tag{4-160}$$

If equilibrium is maintained there is no change if f_{soln} and the left-hand term is equal to zero. Substituting eqs. 4-137 and 4-150 into eq. 4-160 and rearranging gives

$$\overline{V}_{\text{solvent}}\, dP = RT \sum \bar{n}_j \tag{4-161}$$

For dilute solutions the partial molal volume of the solution and pure solvent are almost identical. Assuming $\overline{V}_{\text{solvent}}$ to be constant and equal to $\overline{V}^0_{\text{solvent}}$, eq. 4-161 can be integrated to give

$$\Delta P = \frac{RT}{\overline{V}^0_{\text{solvent}}} \sum \bar{n}_j = \Pi \tag{4-162}$$

where Π is the osmotic pressure, the pressure required to maintain equilibrium.

Equation 4-162 is sometimes written in terms of the molality of the solution and the volume of solvent

$$\Pi = \frac{RT}{V} \cdot m \qquad (4\text{-}163)$$

The laws describing the colligative properties of solutions which have been developed above apply only to ideal solutions of nonelectrolytes. These laws hold for real (nonideal) nonelectrolyte solutions as they approach infinite dilution. More concentrated nonideal solutions, however, may be described in terms of precise, observed measurements. G. N. Lewis also introduced the concept of *activity* and *activity coefficient* as a means of applying the laws of ideal solutions to nonideal solutions. The activity, a, of a component of a solution may be defined as its apparent or effective fugacity. It is evident that for infinitely dilute solutions the activity and fugacity are equal.

$$\lim_{\bar{n}\to 0} \frac{a}{f} = 1 \qquad (4\text{-}164)$$

For a nonideal solution, eq. 4-129 becomes

$$\mu_j = \mu_j^0 + RT \ln a \qquad (4\text{-}165)$$

For many purposes it is convenient to use the activity coefficient, γ, which may be defined

$$\gamma_j = a_j/\bar{n}_j \approx a_j/m \qquad (4\text{-}166)$$

The right-hand term applies to very dilute solutions; m is the molality of the solution. It is evident that

$$\lim_{\bar{n}_j\to 0} \gamma_j = 1 \qquad (4\text{-}167)$$

It has been assumed tacitly that the components of an ideal solution do not interact with each other, and therefore the chemical potential of any one component is independent of the concentrations of all other components

$$\left(\frac{\partial \mu_j}{\partial n_k}\right)_{T,P,n_1} = 0 \qquad j \neq k \qquad (4\text{-}168)$$

This is not the case, however, for nonideal solutions. The activity and activity coefficient of the jth component, which express the deviations from ideality, including deviations which result from interactions with other components, may depend not only on the concentration of the jth component but also on the concentration of all other components as well. To evaluate the effect of other components on the activity of the jth component, the following expression can be derived from eq. 4-163:

$$\left(\frac{\partial \mu_j}{\partial n_k}\right)_{T,P,n_1} = RT\left(\frac{\partial \ln \gamma_j}{\partial n_k}\right)_{T,P,n_1} \qquad (4\text{-}169)$$

The following reciprocity can be written from the differential form of eq. 4-45:

$$\left(\frac{\partial \mu_j}{\partial n_k}\right)_{T,P,n_1} = \left(\frac{\partial \mu_k}{\partial n_j}\right)_{T,P,n_1} \qquad (4\text{-}170)$$

Introducing eq. 4-169 into eq. 4-170 gives

$$\left(\frac{\partial \ln \gamma_j}{\partial n_k}\right)_{T,\,P,\,n_1} = \left(\frac{\partial \ln \gamma_k}{\partial n_j}\right)_{T,\,P,\,n_1} \qquad (4\text{-}171)$$

Living systems are extraordinarily sensitive to changes in osmotic pressure, and the biologist is concerned frequently with the *osmolarity* of solutions. It should be remembered that the colligative properties, of which the freezing-point depression and the osmotic pressure are measured most frequently, depend upon the effective concentration of solute particles. Deviations from ideality, particularly in the case of electrolytes where effective dissociation may not be complete, frequently lead to fewer effective solute particles than might be expected from the weight of solute present. Thus, measurement of the colligative properties and chemical analysis yield different sorts of information. Yet, because the colligative properties depend upon the number of particles, extrapolation to zero concentration (reduced osmotic pressure, for instance, eq. 3-45) offers a means of evaluating the molecular weight of a substance.

While the use of activity and the activity coefficient is a convenient means of dealing with departures from ideality by a component of a solution, when dealing with the properties of the solution as a whole it may be useful to employ a series of excess functions.[14] The free energy of mixing of a number of components to form an ideal solution, $\Delta G_{\text{mix}}^{\text{ideal}}$, is given by eq. 4-141. In an observed system, the actual free energy of mixing, ΔG_{mix}, may differ from $\Delta G_{\text{mix}}^{\text{ideal}}$; the difference is defined as the *excess free energy of mixing*, $\Delta G_{\text{mix}}^{\text{ex}}$. It is evident that

$$\Delta G_{\text{mix}}^{\text{ex}} = \Delta G_{\text{mix}} - \Delta G_{\text{mix}}^{\text{ideal}} = \Delta G_{\text{mix}} - \sum n_i RT \ln \bar{n}_i \qquad (4\text{-}172)$$

Similarly, the following expression can be written for the *excess entropy of mixing*:

$$\Delta S_{\text{mix}}^{\text{ex}} + \Delta S_{\text{mix}} - \Delta S_{\text{mix}}^{\text{ideal}} = \Delta S_{\text{mix}} + \sum n_i R \ln \bar{n}_i \qquad (4\text{-}173)$$

The enthalpy of mixing for an ideal solution is zero, and therefore the excess enthalpy of mixing is the same as the actual enthalpy of mixing, $\Delta H_{\text{mix}}^{\text{ex}} = \Delta H_{\text{mix}}$. The following useful relations can be derived:

$$\Delta S_{\text{mix}}^{\text{ex}} = -\frac{\partial \Delta G_{\text{mix}}^{\text{ex}}}{\partial T} \qquad (4\text{-}174)$$

$$\Delta H_{\text{mix}}^{\text{ex}} = \Delta G_{\text{mix}}^{\text{ex}} - T\frac{\partial \Delta G_{\text{mix}}^{\text{ex}}}{\partial T} \qquad (4\text{-}175)$$

For nonideal electrolyte solutions, the concepts of activity and activity coefficients apply as they do to nonideal nonelectrolytes, except that eqs. 4-164 and 4-166 become

$$\lim_{\bar{n}^\nu \to 0} \frac{a}{f} = 1 \qquad (4\text{-}176)$$

$$a = a_\pm^\nu = \gamma_\pm^\nu m_\pm^\nu = \gamma_\pm^\nu[(\nu_+)^{\nu_+}(\nu_-)^{\nu_-}]m^\nu \qquad (4\text{-}177)$$

where ν is the number of ions formed upon dissociation of each molecule of electrolyte.

[14] Scatchard, G., and Raymond, C. L. *J. Am. Chem. Soc.*, *60*, 1278 (1938).

Substitution into eq. 4-142 gives

$$\mu_j = \mu_j^0 + \nu RT \ln m + \nu RT \ln \gamma_\pm \tag{4-178}$$

for the chemical potential of a dilute electrolyte solution. The far right-hand term represents the difference between the electrostatic contribution to the chemical potential and the same contribution calculated at infinite dilution of all ions (see Fig. 4-6).

fig. 4-6. Activity coefficients of strong electrolytes. (From Latimer, W. M. *The Oxidation States of the Elements and Their Potentials in Aqueous Solutions,* 2nd ed. Englewood Cliffs, N.J.: Prentice-Hall, 1952, pp. 354–356.)

m	0.001	0.005	0.01	0.05	0.1	0.5	1.0
HCl	0.966	0.928	0.904	0.830	0.796	0.758	0.809
NaOH	—	—	—	0.82	—	0.69	0.68
KOH	—	0.92	0.90	0.82	0.80	0.73	0.76
KCl	0.965	0.927	0.901	0.815	0.769	0.651	0.606
NaBr	0.966	0.934	0.914	0.844	0.800	0.695	0.686
H_2SO_4	0.830	0.639	0.544	0.340	0.265	0.154	0.130
K_2SO_4	0.89	0.78	0.71	0.52	0.43	—	—
$Ca(NO_3)_2$	0.88	0.77	0.71	0.54	0.48	0.38	0.35
$CuSO_4$	0.74	0.53	0.41	0.21	0.16	0.068	0.047
$MgSO_4$	—	—	0.40	0.22	0.18	0.088	0.064
$La(NO_3)_3$	—	—	0.57	0.39	0.33	—	—
$In_2(SO_4)_3$	—	—	0.142	0.054	0.035	—	—

theory of electrolyte solutions

The Debye-Hückel theory of electrolyte solutions is based upon consideration of the electrostatic interactions of ions. The electrostatic attractive forces will cause a relative excess of positive ions to be present in the immediate neighborhood of a negative ion and vice versa. The difference at any point between the local concentrations of positive and negative ions results in a net charge density. Debye and Hückel assumed that the distribution of ions, the number of ions per unit volume in an electrostatic field, is given by the Boltzmann distribution equation

$$N = N_0 \, e^{Zq\psi/kT} \tag{4-179}$$

where N_0 is the number of ions per unit volume in the absence of an electrostatic potential ψ, $\boldsymbol{q}$ is the electronic charge, Z is the valence of the ion, and k is the Boltzmann constant. If the central reference ion is an anion, the sign of the exponent is positive for cations and negative for anions. The term $Z\boldsymbol{q}\psi$ represents the electrostatic energy of the ions, and kT represents the kinetic energy. The charge density per unit volume is equal to the difference between the concentrations of cations and anions in the volume.

$$\rho = N_+ - N_- = Z_+ \boldsymbol{q} N_0 \, e^{Z_+ q\psi/kT} - Z_- \boldsymbol{q} N_0 \, e^{-Z_- q\psi/kT} \tag{4-180}$$

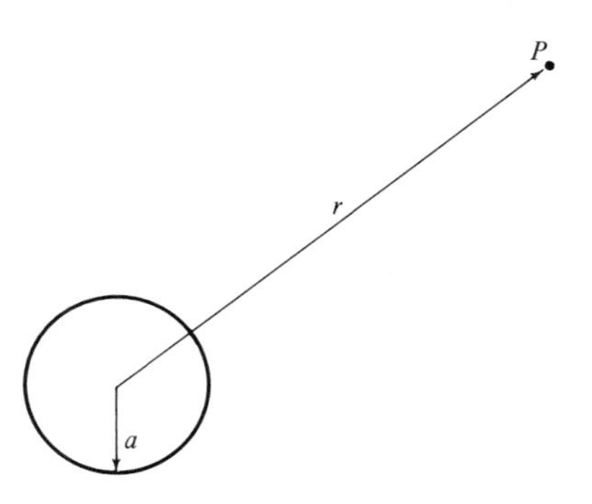

fig. 4-7. The coordinate system used in the development of the Debye-Hückel theory.

Let us now consider the space charge surrounding an ion. At a point in the environment of an ion, but removed from its center by a distance r (see Fig. 4-7), the potential is given by the Poisson equation:[15]

$$\nabla^2\psi = \frac{1}{r^2}\frac{d}{dr}\left(r^2\frac{d\psi}{dr}\right) = -\frac{4\pi\rho}{\varepsilon} \tag{4-181}$$

Substitution of ρ obtained from the Boltzmann equation (eq. 4-180) into the Poisson equation (eq. 4-181) unfortunately results in a nonlinear differential equation that cannot be integrated. Debye and Hückel used an expansion of the Boltzmann equation and neglected higher order terms:

$$\rho = \sum N_i Z_i \boldsymbol{q} - \sum N_i Z_i \boldsymbol{q}\left(\frac{Z_i \boldsymbol{q}\psi}{kT}\right) + \frac{\Sigma N_i Z_i \boldsymbol{q}}{Z}\left(\frac{Z_i \boldsymbol{q}\psi}{kT}\right)^2 + \cdots \tag{4-182}$$

Solutions are neutral with an equal number of positive and negative ions; therefore, the term $\sum N_i Z_i \boldsymbol{q}$ vanishes. If $kT \gg Z_i \boldsymbol{q}\psi$, second-order and higher terms can be neglected and eq. 4-182 reduces to

$$\rho = -\frac{\Sigma N_i Z_i^2 \boldsymbol{q}^2 \psi}{KT} \tag{4-183}$$

Substituting eq. 4-183 into eq. 4-181 gives[16]

$$\frac{1}{r^2}\frac{d}{dr}\left(r^2\frac{d\psi}{dr}\right) = \frac{4\pi\boldsymbol{q}^2}{\varepsilon kT}\sum N_i Z_i \psi = \kappa^2\psi \tag{4-184}$$

---

[15] The expression used for the *Laplacian operator* is in polar coordinates for a system with spherical symmetry where ψ is independent of θ and φ. See Chisholm, J. S. R., and Morris, R. M. *Mathematical Methods in Physics.* Amsterdam: North Holland Publishing Company, 1965, pp. 628 ff.; Margenau, H., and Murphy, G. M. *The Mathematics of Physics and Chemistry.* Princeton: Van Nostrand, 1943, p. 186.

[16] From eq. 4-180, it is appreciated that

$$\kappa = \left(\frac{8\pi N^2 \boldsymbol{q}^2}{1000\varepsilon RT}\right)^{1/2} \boldsymbol{u}^{1/2} \tag{4-180'}$$

where $\boldsymbol{u}$ is the ionic strength defined in eq. 3-33. Substituting numerical values for the constants, at 25°C

$$\kappa = (3.282 \times 10^7)\boldsymbol{u}^{1/2} \tag{4-180''}$$

Equation 4-184 has the following solution:[17]

$$\psi = A\frac{e^{-\kappa r}}{r} + B\frac{e^{\kappa r}}{r} \tag{4-185}$$

where A and B are integration constants. As r increases and approaches infinity, the term $(e^{\kappa r})/r$ approaches infinity. At infinity, however, the potential is zero, and, therefore, $B = 0$. Equation 4-185 becomes

$$\psi = A\frac{e^{-\kappa r}}{r} \tag{4-186}$$

Substituting κ and eq. 4-186 into eq. 4-183 gives

$$\rho = A\frac{\kappa^2\varepsilon}{4\pi}\frac{e^{-\kappa r}}{r} \tag{4-187}$$

The charge on the ion must be equal and opposite to the net charge of the atmosphere surrounding the central ion. This can be stated

$$\int_a^{\infty} \pi r^2 \rho \, dr = -Z\boldsymbol{q} \tag{4-188}$$

where a is the radius of the central ion. Combining eqs. 4-187 and 4-188 gives

$$A\kappa^2\varepsilon \int_a^{\infty} re^{-\kappa r} \, dr = Z\boldsymbol{q} \tag{4-189}$$

which upon integration leads to

$$A = \frac{Z\boldsymbol{q}}{\varepsilon}\frac{e^{\kappa a}}{1 + \kappa a} \tag{4-190}$$

Substituting eq. 4-190 into eq. 4-186 yields

$$\psi = \frac{Z\boldsymbol{q}e^{\kappa(a-r)}}{\varepsilon(1 - ka)r} \tag{4-191}$$

At the surface of the ion, $r = a$, and

$$\psi_a = \frac{Z\boldsymbol{q}}{\varepsilon a} - \frac{Z\boldsymbol{q}\kappa}{\varepsilon(1 + \kappa a)} \tag{4-192}$$

---

[17] Equation 4-180 is rearranged to

$$\frac{1}{r^2}\frac{d}{dr}\left(r^2\frac{d\psi}{dr}\right) - \kappa^2\psi = 0 \tag{4–180‴}$$

Substituting $\psi = v/r$ into eq. 4-180′ gives

$$\frac{d^2v}{dr^2} - \kappa^2\psi = 0 \tag{4–180⁗}$$

Integration of eq. 4-180″ and substituting $v = \psi r$ gives eq. 4-181.

The first term on the right side of eq. 4-192 is the potential of an isolated charged sphere, while the second term represents the potential of the ion atmosphere. A plot of ψ as a function of distance from the surface of an ion discloses enormous potential gradients in the immediate vicinity of an ion which may amount to several million volts per centimeter at the ion surface (see Fig. 4-8).

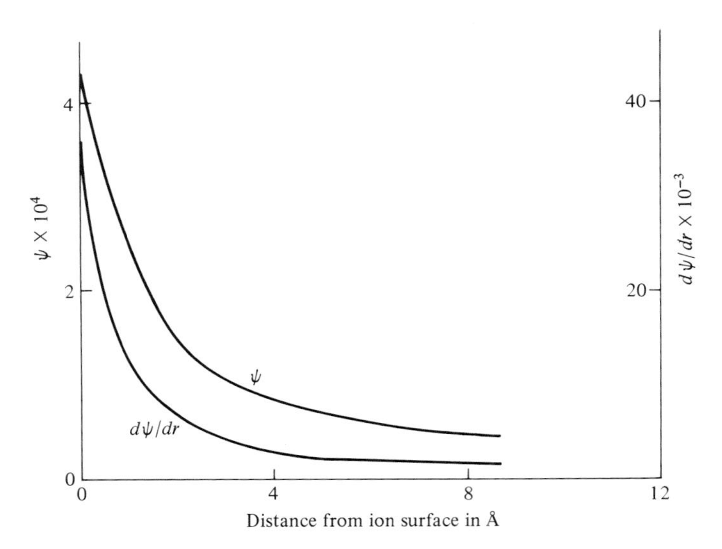

fig. 4-8. A plot of the potential ψ in electrostatic volts and the field strength $d\psi/dr$ *versus* the distance from the surface of a potassium ion. Ionic strength 0.01 at 25°C ($1/\kappa = 30.5$Å). (From Bull, H. B. *An Introduction to Physical Biochemistry.* Philadelphia: Davis, 1964, p. 70.)

The work of charging the atmosphere around a central ion can be calculated in the following way:

$$W = \int_0^{\boldsymbol{q}} \psi_a \, d\boldsymbol{q} \qquad \textbf{(4-193)}$$

The potential of the ion atmosphere is given by the far right-hand term of eq. 4-192. Substituting this term into eq. 4-193 and integrating the combined equations leads to the following solution:

$$W = kT \ln \gamma = -\frac{Z^2 \boldsymbol{q}^2}{2\varepsilon} \left(\frac{\kappa}{1 + \kappa a} \right) \qquad \textbf{(4-194)}$$

where k is Boltzmann's constant ($R/\boldsymbol{N}$ where $\boldsymbol{N}$ is Avogadro's number). Rearranging eq. 4-194, substituting the values of the constants at 25°C, and converting to ordinary logarithms gives

$$\log \gamma_{\pm} = -0.509 \, Z_- Z_+ \boldsymbol{u}^{1/2} \qquad \textbf{(4-195)}$$

Equation 4-195 is known as the *Debye-Hückel limiting law.* One deduces from this relation that the logarithm of the activity coefficient should be a linear function of the ionic strength with a slope proportional to the product of the valences of the cations and anions. The free energy of electrolyte solutions varies directly as the total ionic strength with a proportionality factor that depends only on the temperature and dielectric constant of the solvent. Agreement between theory and experiment is limited to very dilute solutions—less than 0.01 M for univalent-univalent salts and less than 0.001 M for multivalent salts.[18]

Bjerrum[19] proposed an explanation for the failure of the Debye-Hückel limiting law to represent the activity coefficient as the salt concentration is increased. He suggested that when two ions of opposite sign approach more closely than a critical distance, Λ, the coulombic forces are strong enough to form an associated ion pair. Such an ion pair exists for a time long enough to act as a kinetic unit in a number of collisions with other ions and molecules of solvent. The effective charge of an ion pair is zero. Ion pairs do not contribute to the conductance of a solution nor to ionic interactions. In the case of multivalent ions, ionic association leads to the formation of new ion species with a lower effective charge and results in a lesser contribution to the ionic conductance and other ionic interactions. Therefore, ionic association leading to ion pair formation always results in lower ionic conductance and mean activity coefficients than otherwise would be expected. Bjerrum's theory negates the assumption in the Debye-Hückel theory that strong electrolytes are completely dissociated.

Bjerrum's critical distance of approach Λ can be evaluated from the Boltzmann distribution function (eq. 4-179). The probability of finding an ion of opposite charge close to a central ion is high because of attractive coulombic forces; the probability decreases as the distance of separation r increases. On the other hand, the probability of finding an ion of opposite charge within the sphere subtended by r increases as r increases simply because the volume of the sphere increases. The critical distance Λ corresponds to the value of r at which the probability of finding an ion of opposite sign is at a minimum and is given by

$$\Lambda = -\frac{Z_- Z_+ \boldsymbol{q}^2}{2\varepsilon kT} \tag{4-196}$$

The association constant for ion pair formation is given by

$$\frac{1}{K_c} = \frac{4\pi N_\pm}{V} \int_a^q \exp\left(-\frac{Z_- Z_+ \boldsymbol{q}^2}{\varepsilon kTr}\right) r^2\, dr \tag{4-197}$$

$$= \frac{4\pi N_\pm}{V}\left(-\frac{Z_- Z_+ \boldsymbol{q}^2}{\varepsilon kT}\right) Q(b) \tag{4-198}$$

where $N_\pm$ is the number of ions in volume V, a is the distance of closest approach and is equal to the sum of the van der Waals radii, and $b = -(Z_- Z_+ \boldsymbol{q}^2)/(\varepsilon kTa)$. Values of the function $Q(b)$ for a number of values of b are given in Fig. 4-9. The fraction of a

[18] The lack of agreement between the theory and experimental data for more concentrated solutions no doubt prompted the unkind remark that the Debye-Hückel treatment is little more than a theory of slightly polluted water. This view is unjustified since this approach has had a profound influence on the development of our understanding of electrolyte solutions, and particularly of polyelectrolyte solutions.

[19] Bjerrum, N. *Kgl. Danske Videnskab. Selskab Mat. Fys. Medd.*, *7*, no. 9, 1 (1926).

fig. 4-9. Values of $Q(b) \equiv \int_2^b e^y y^{-4}$ for the calculation of the degree of Bjerrum association. (From Kortüm, G. *Treatise on Electrochemistry*, 2nd ed. Amsterdam: Elsevier, 1965, p. 620.)

b	$\log Q(b)$	b	$\log Q(b)$	b	$\log Q(b)$
2.0	—	5	−0.124	17	2.59
2.1	−1.357	6	0.016	20	3.59
2.2	−1.074	7	0.152	25	5.35
2.4	−0.808	8	0.300	30	7.19
2.6	−0.662	9	0.470	40	11.01
2.8	−0.562	10	0.655	50	14.96
3.0	−0.487	12	1.125	60	18.98
3.5	−0.355	14	1.680	70	23.05
4.0	−0.260	15	1.96	80	27.15

univalent-univalent salt in aqueous solution existing as ion pairs for several values of a and several values of salt concentration are given in Fig. 4-10. When $a > \Lambda$, salts are completely dissociated.

Numerous studies have shown that Bjerrum's theory accounts very satisfactorily for deviations from the Debye-Hückel theory at high salt concentrations and in solvents with a low dielectric constant.

fig. 4-10. Degree of association of 1,1-valent ions in an aqueous solution at 18°C, according to Bjerrum. (From Kortüm, G. *Treatise on Electrochemistry*, 2nd ed. Amsterdam: Elsevier, 1965, p. 226.)

α-PARAMETER (MINIMUM IONIC DISTANCE)	c_0[MOL/L]				
	10^{-4}	$5 \cdot 10^{-4}$	10^{-3}	$5 \cdot 10^{-3}$	10^{-2}
2.82 Å	0	0	0	0.002	0.005
2.35 Å	0	0	0.001	0.004	0.008
1.76 Å	0	0	0.001	0.007	0.012
1.01 Å	0	0.002	0.004	0.016	0.030
0.70 Å	0.001	0.006	0.011	0.048	0.083
0.47 Å	0.027	0.106	0.177	0.418	0.529

electrochemical cells

Electrochemical cells are described by a formal notation which can be described in terms of an example. Consider a cell consisting of a zinc electrode immersed in a 0.5 m Zn^{++} solution in one beaker and a copper electrode immersed in a 1.0 m Cu^{++} solution in another beaker. The anion of the salts may be any soluble anion such as Cl^- or SO_4^{--} (see Fig. 4-11). The two beakers are connected by a salt bridge, a 4 percent agar gel containing 3 M KCl. The formal notation describing this cell is

$$Zn(s)\,|Zn^{++}(0.5\,m)|\,|Cu^{++}(1.0\,m)|\,Cu(s) \qquad \textit{(4-199)}$$

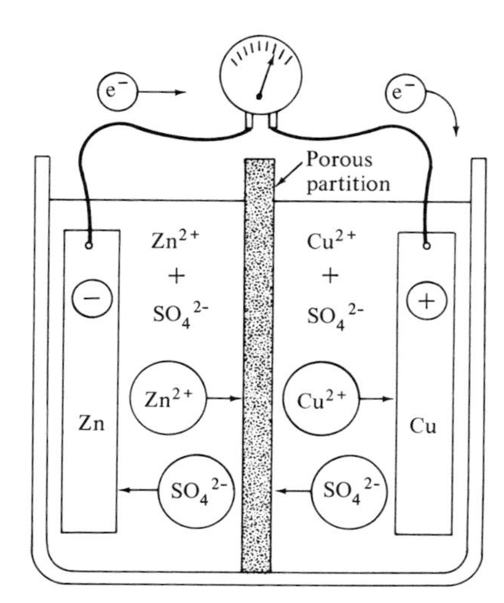

fig. 4-11. An electrochemical cell.

A number of standard half-cell potentials are given in Fig. 4-12. The convention employed in this formalism is that electrons leave the electrochemical cell by the left electrode and enter by the right electrode. Whether these changes occur spontaneously and whether an external potential is required to drive on electric current in this direction are not considered. In any case, an oxidation reaction occurs in the left-hand half-cell and a reduction reaction occurs in the right-hand half-cell. In the example of eq. 4-199

$$\mathrm{Zn} \rightarrow \mathrm{Zn}^{++} + 2\mathrm{e}^- \qquad \mathrm{Cu}^{++} + 2\mathrm{e}^- \rightarrow \mathrm{Cu} \tag{4-200}$$

or, for the whole electrochemical cell,

$$\mathrm{Zn} + \mathrm{Cu}^{++} \rightarrow \mathrm{Zn}^{++} + \mathrm{Cu} \tag{4-201}$$

The following expression describes the free energy changes

$$\Delta G = \Delta G^0 + RT \ln \frac{a_{(\mathrm{Zn}^{++})}\, a_{(\mathrm{Cu})}}{a_{(\mathrm{Zn})}\, a_{(\mathrm{Cu}^{++})}} \tag{4-202}$$

If reaction 4-201 is permitted to proceed, the following expression can be derived from eqs. 4-20 and 4-56 to describe the useful, reversible electrical work performed by the cell:

$$đW_{\mathrm{useful,\,rev}} = -(dG)_{T,P} = -nE\mathfrak{F}\, d\Xi \tag{4-203}$$

where $\mathfrak{F}$ is the faraday and E is the voltage across the cell. If the electrochemical cell is connected to an equal opposing potential, reaction 4-201 occurs reversibly, and at equilibrium

$$\Delta G = -nE\mathfrak{F} \tag{4-204}$$

Substituting eq. 4-204 into eq. 4-202, the following expression can be derived for the cell potential:

$$E = E^0 + \frac{RT}{n\mathfrak{F}} \ln \frac{a_{(\mathrm{Zn}^{++})}\, a_{(\mathrm{Cu})}}{a_{(\mathrm{Zn})}\, a_{(\mathrm{Cu}^{++})}} \tag{4-205}$$

fig. 4-12. Standard electrode potentials at 25°C. (From Latimer, W. M. *The Oxidation States of the Elements and Their Potentials in Aqueous Solution,* 2nd ed. Englewood Cliffs, N.J.: Prentice-Hall, 1952.)

ELECTRODE REACTION	VOLTS
$K^+ + e^- = K$	—2.925
$Na^+ + e^- = Na$	−2.714
$H_2 + 2e^- = 2H^-$	−2.25
$Al^{3+} + 3e^- = Al$	−1.66
$Zn(CN)_4^{2-} + 2e^- = Zn + 4CN^-$	−1.26
$ZnO_2^{2-} + 2H_2O + 2e^- = Zn + 4OH^-$	−1.216
$Zn(NH_3)_4^{2+} + 2e^- = Zn + 4NH_3$	−1.03
$Sn(OH)_6^{2-} + 2e^- = HSnO_2^- + H_2O + 3OH$	−0.90
$Fe(OH)_2 + 2e^- = Fe + 2OH$	−0.877
$2H_2O + 2e^- = H_2 + 2OH^-$	−0.828
$Fe(OH)_3 + 3e^- = Fe + 3OH^-$	−0.77
$Zn^{2+} + 2e^- = Zn$	−0.763
$Ag_2S + 2e^- = 2Ag + S^{2-}$	−0.69
$FE^{2+} + 2e^- = Fe$	−0.440
$Bi_2O_3 + 3H_2O + 6e^- = 2Bi + 6OH^-$	−0.44
$PbSO_4 + 2e^- = Pb + SO_4^{2-}$	−0.356
$Ag(CN)_2^- + e^- = Ag + 2CN^-$	−0.31
$Ni^{2+} + 2e^- = Ni$	−0.250
$AgI + e^- = Ag + I^-$	−0.151
$Sn^{2+} + 2e^- = Sn$	−0.136
$Pb^{2+} + 2e^- = Pb$	−0.126
$Cu(NH_3)_4^{2+} + 2e^- = Cu + 4NH_3$	−0.12
$Fe^{3+} + 3e^- = Fe$	−0.036
$2H^+ + 2e^- = H_2$	0.000
$AgBr + e^- = Ag + Br^-$	0.095
$HgO(red) + H_2O + 2e^- = Hg + 2OH^-$	0.098
$Sn^{4+} + 2e^- = Sn^{2+}$	0.15
$AgCl + e^- = Ag + Cl^-$	0.222
$Hg_2Cl_2 + 2e^- = 2Hg + 2Cl^-$	0.2676
$Cu^{2+} + 2e^- = Cu$	0.337
$Ag(NH_3)_2^+ + e^- = Ag + 2NH_3$	0.373
$Hg_2SO_4 + 2e^- = 2Hg + SO_4^{2-}$	0.6151
$Fe^{3+} + e^- = Fe^{2+}$	0.771
$Ag^+ + e^- = Ag$	0.7991
$O_2 + 4H^+ + 4e^- = 2H_2O$	1.229
$PbO_2 + SO_4^{2-} + 4H^+ + 2e^- = PbSO_4 + 2H_2O$	1.685
$O_3 + 2H^+ + 2e^- = O_2 + H_2O$	2.07

Since the activities of solid copper and solid zinc are very close to 1, substituting these values and eq. 4-166 into eq. 4-205 gives

$$E = E^0 + \frac{RT}{n\mathfrak{F}} \ln \frac{m_{Zn^{++}}}{m_{Cu^{++}}} + \frac{RT}{n\mathfrak{F}} \ln \frac{\gamma_{Zn^{++}}}{\gamma_{Cu^{++}}} \quad \textit{(4-206)}$$

It is possible to assign a standard potential to every possible electrochemical half-cell. The standard potential of any complete electrochemical cell, then, is the difference between the standard half-cell potentials of the two component half-cells. In this formalism, the standard hydrogen electrode, a hydrogen electrode in which hydrogen gas at 1 atm pressure is in equilibrium with 1 *m* hydrogen ions, is used as the reference and assigned a potential of zero. For any other reversible half-cell, a zinc-zinc ion half-cell for instance, the standard half-cell potential is given by the potential of a cell such as

$$\text{Pt, H}_2(1\text{ atm})\,|\text{H}^+(1\,m)||\text{Zn}^{++}(1\,m)|\text{Zn(s)} \qquad E^0_{25°C} = -0.763\text{ volt} \tag{4-207}$$

$$\text{Pt, H}_2(1\text{ atm})\,|\text{H}^+(1\,m)||\text{Cu}^{++}(1\,m)|\text{Cu(s)} \qquad E^0_{25°C} = +0.337\text{ volt} \tag{4-208}$$

$$\text{Zn(s)}\,|\text{Zn}^{++}(1\,m)||\text{Cu}^{++}(1\,m)|\text{Cu(s)} \qquad E^0_{25°C} = +1.100\text{ volt} \tag{4-209}$$

As stated above, an oxidation reaction always occurs in the left-hand half-cell, and a reduction reaction always occurs in the right-hand half-cell. Oxidation-reduction cells comprise an important class of half-cells in which the electrode is inert and in which the electrochemical reaction involves an oxidation or reduction of the electrolyte. An example of such a cell is

$$\text{Pt}\,|\text{Fe}^{+++}, \text{Fe}^{++}||\text{Sn}^{++++}, \text{Sn}^{++}|\,\text{Pt} \tag{4-210}$$

Oxidation-reduction half-cells have a characteristic standard potential and can be treated as ordinary half-cells (see Fig. 4-13).

fig. 4-13. Oxidation-reduction potentials and r'H values at *p*H 7. (From Bray, H. G., and White, K. *Kinetics and Thermodynamics in Biochemistry*. London: J. & A. Churchill, 1966, p. 101.)

SYSTEM	E_0' (VOLTS)	r'H	TEMPERATURE (°C)
Fe^{3+}/Fe^{2+}	0.77	39.6	25
Heme: Fe^{3+}/Fe^{2+}	−0.23	6.4	30
Cytochrome *b*: Fe^{3+}/Fe^{2+}	−0.04	12.6	20
Cytochrome *c*: Fe^{3+}/Fe^{2+}	0.26	22.7	25
Cytochrome *a*: Fe^{3+}/Fe^{2+}	0.29	23.8	20
Hydrogen ion (hydrated)/hydrogen atom	0	14.0	25
Hydrogen peroxide/water	−2.19	59.0	25
Oxygen/hydrogen peroxide	0.26	22.7	25
Oxygen/water	0.82	27.7	25
NAD^+/NADH	−0.28	4.8	30
Riboflavin: ox/red	−0.18	7.8	20
Quinone/quinol	0.28	23.3	25
Luciferin: ox/red	−0.05	12.3	18
Adrenaline: ox/red	0.38	26.3	30
Cystine/cysteine	−0.14	9.3	25
Glutathione: ox/red	0.04	15.4	25
Pyruvate/lactate	−0.18	8.2	35
Fumarate/succinate	0	14.0	25

It is evident that two identical half-cells will produce a potential if the concentrations and, therefore, the activities of the electrolytes differ in the two half-cells. An example of such a *concentration cell* is

$$\underbrace{Zn(s)\,|Zn^{++}(1\ m)|}_{\text{half-cell 2}}\ \underbrace{|Zn^{++}(0.01\ m)|\ Zn^{++}}_{\text{half-cell 1}} \tag{4-211}$$

For this cell eq. 4-205 becomes

$$E = \frac{RT}{n\mathfrak{F}} \ln \frac{a_2}{a_1} \tag{4-212}$$

In a soluble oxidation-reduction system such as ferrocyanide-ferricyanide salts the concentrations of the oxidant and reductant can be adjusted to any desired values. The free energy change for an oxidation reaction is given by

$$\Delta G = \Delta G^0 + RT \ln \frac{a_{\text{oxidant}}}{a_{\text{reductant}}} \tag{4-213}$$

If the reaction is conducted in such a manner that a reversible potential can be produced, eq. 4-205 becomes

$$E = E^0 + \frac{RT}{n\mathfrak{F}} \ln \frac{a_{\text{oxidant}}}{a_{\text{reductant}}} \tag{4-214}$$

Redox (oxidation-reduction) potentials can often be measured by inserting a bright platinum electrode into the solution and connecting the solution to a reference half-cell such as a silver-silver chloride or calomel half-cell by means of a salt bridge. Frequently it is necessary carefully to exclude all oxygen from the system.

The dependence of the cell potential on temperature can be evaluated by an expression derived from eqs. 4-36 and 4-204

$$\left(\frac{\partial E}{\partial T}\right)_P = \frac{\Delta S}{n\mathfrak{F}} \tag{4-215}$$

It is possible, therefore, to calculate ΔS^0 for a half-cell from the temperature dependence of the half-cell potential. An expression for the dependence of the enthalpy on temperature can be derived from eqs. 4-24 and 4-215:

$$\Delta H = n\mathfrak{F}\left[T\left(\frac{\partial E}{\partial T}\right)_P - E\right] = n\mathfrak{F}T^2\left(\frac{\partial[E/T]}{\partial T}\right)_P \tag{4-216}$$

Equation 4-216 is another form of eq. 4-130, the Gibbs-Helmholtz equation.

chemical potential—a recapitulation

The chemical potential occupies a key position in the practical application of thermodynamics; it is defined in terms of the equations of state of various systems. The most frequently used definitions of the chemical potential are listed here; most of them have been derived above.

System	*Chemical Potential*	
Ideal gas	$\mu_i = \mu_i^0(T) + RT \ln P_i$	*(4-129)*
Ideal solution	$\mu_i = \mu_i^0(T, X_j) + RT \ln c_i$	*(4-142)*
Nonideal solution	$\mu_i = \mu_i^0(T, X_j) + RT \ln a$	*(4-165)*

The first term on the right-hand side of the above equations can be evaluated from the general expression for the total free energy (eq. 4-45) because the chemical potential is the partial molal free energy, $\overline{\Theta} = (\partial\Theta/\partial n_i) = \mu_i$. The differential form of the substituted expression showing the dependence on all intensive thermodynamic variables in the system can be written as

$$d\mu_i = \left(\frac{\partial\mu_i}{\partial T}\right) dT + \left(\frac{\partial\mu_i}{\partial P}\right) dP + \left(\frac{\partial\mu_i}{\partial\psi}\right) d\psi + \cdots + RT\, d \ln c_i \qquad (4\text{-}217)$$

The partial differentials in parentheses in the first two terms on the right side of eq. 4-217 can be identified as $-\overline{S}$ and $\overline{V}$ from eqs. 4-65 and 4-66. Similarly, the partial in the third term can be identified as $Z_i\mathfrak{F}$. Substituting these into eq. 4-217 gives

$$d\mu_i = -\overline{S}\, dT + \overline{V}\, dP + Z_i \mathfrak{F}\, d\psi + \cdots + RT\, d \ln c_i \qquad (4\text{-}218)$$

acid-base and oxidation-reduction equilibria

An acid, according to Brønsted, may be defined as a material which will give off a proton, leaving its conjugate base

$$\text{HA (acid)} \rightleftarrows H^+ + A^- \text{ (base)} \qquad (4\text{-}219)$$

Actually, when an acid is dissolved in an amphiprotic solvent such as water or alcohol, it dissociates partially

$$HA + H_2O \rightleftarrows H_3O^+ + A^- \qquad (4\text{-}220)$$

Or for a base, such as an amine, one can write

$$RNH_3^+ + OH^- \rightleftarrows RNH_2 + H_2O \qquad (4\text{-}221)$$

The equilibrium constant of dissociation is

$$K_a = \frac{a_{H_3O} + a_{\bar{A}}}{a_{HA}} \qquad (4\text{-}222)$$

Sørensen suggested the use of pH as a simple means of expressing the hydrogen-ion concentration; it is defined by $p\text{H} = -\log [H^+]$. The equilibrium constant for the dissociation of water is about 10^{-7} at 20°. Neutrality, therefore, is pH 7; a 1 M solution of a completely dissociated acid is pH 0; and a 1 M solution of a completely dissociated base is pH 14. Similarly, one can define $pK_a = -\log K_a$. Substituting these terms into the logarithmic form of eq. 4-222 gives the Henderson-Hasselbach equation:

$$pH = pK_a + \log \frac{[A^-]}{[HA]} = pK_a + \log \frac{\alpha}{1 - \alpha} \qquad (4\text{-}223)$$

where α is the fraction of the acid that is neutralized (that is, the salt), and $1 - \alpha$ is the fraction of the acid present that is not neutralized.

Equation 4-223 may be used to calculate pH upon addition of a strong base to a solution of a weak acid. In a solvent in which the ionic strength is maintained constant throughout the titration, eq. 4-223 describes the titration curves rather accurately after corrections have been made for changes in volume (and therefore, concentration). The titration curves of various weak acids are similar in shape and differ only by a displacement which depends upon the pK_a of the acid. A characteristic feature of these curves is that to produce a small change in pH, a relatively large amount of acid or base must be added when α is near 0.5, that is, at a pH near the pK_a. This phenomenon is called *buffer action* and plays an important role in the homeostasis of living organisms. The rates of many metabolic reactions are altered profoundly by relatively small changes in pH. As a result, the pH of biological fluids is regulated within narrow limits. For example, blood pH of vertebrates must be within the limits of 6.9 and 7.8 to be compatible with viability, and in health, the arterial blood pH varies within the limits of 7.39 and 7.44. Organic acids, such as carbonic, lactic, and pyruvic acids, are end products of metabolic reactions, and living organisms must be able to handle large and sometimes erratic additions or removal of such materials (such as occurs with sudden exercise) without appreciable pH shifts.

The *buffer value* of van Slyke is a means of readily evaluating the resistance of a system to pH change upon the addition of acid or alkali. The slope of the titration curve is a good index for this purpose. Since $\Delta\alpha = \Delta[A^-]/c$

$$\frac{d[A^-]}{d\,pH} = \left(\frac{d[A^-]}{d\alpha}\right)\left(\frac{d\alpha}{d\,pH}\right) = c\,\frac{d\alpha}{d\,pH} \qquad (4\text{-}224)$$

Differentiation of eq. 4-223 gives

$$d\,pH = d\log\frac{\alpha}{1-\alpha} = \frac{1}{2.303}\,d\ln\frac{\alpha}{1-\alpha} = \frac{d\alpha}{2.303\,\alpha(1-\alpha)} \qquad (4\text{-}225)$$

Substitution of eq. 4-225 into eq. 4-224 gives

$$\frac{d[A^-]}{d\,pH} = 2.303\,\alpha(1-\alpha)\cdot c \qquad (4\text{-}226)$$

The addition of acid can be considered the negative of addition of base.

Amino acids, proteins, phospholipids, and other substances have both positively and negatively charged groups and form Zwitterions. The isoelectric point of a Zwitterion is the pH at which there are an equal number of positively and negatively charged groups. Incidentally, although the charges in Zwitterions cancel out, they have a discrete distance of separation which gives these molecules very high dipole moments. Consider the ionization of a simple Zwitterion, glycine:

$$\underset{R^+}{\overset{COOH}{\underset{|}{H_2CNH_3^+}}} \xrightarrow[K_1]{-H^+} \underset{R^\pm}{\overset{COO^-}{\underset{|}{H_2CNH_3^+}}} \xrightarrow[K_2]{-H^+} \underset{R^-}{\overset{COO^-}{\underset{|}{H_2CNH_2}}} \qquad (4\text{-}227)$$

where R^+ is the cation, $R^\pm$ is the Zwitterion, and R^- is the anion. The two ionization constants and their product are given by

$$K_1 = \frac{[H^+][R^\pm]}{[R^+]} \qquad K_2 = \frac{[H^+][R^-]}{[R^\pm]} \qquad (4\text{-}228)$$

$$K_1 \cdot K_2 = \frac{[H^+]^2[R^-]}{[R^+]} \qquad (4\text{-}229)$$

At the isoelectric point, $[R^+] = [R^-]$. Canceling these terms in eq. 4-229 and taking negative logarithms, we obtain

$$pI = \frac{pK_1 + pK_2}{2} \qquad (4\text{-}230)$$

where pI is the pH at the isoelectric point.

In many systems the reduced form of a compound can be maintained in equilibrium with molecular hydrogen in the presence of a catalyst such as platinum black or an appropriate enzyme. Because the concentration of molecular hydrogen in solution is associated with a definite partial pressure of hydrogen in the vapor phase, the partial pressure of hydrogen required to maintain equilibrium can be used as a measure of the reducing power of a substance. For the same reasons that it is convenient to measure the hydrogen-ion concentration as a logarithm, it is convenient to use the negative logarithm of the hydrogen partial pressure as an indication of the redox potential. In this case, the function is called rH ($r\text{H} = -\log\,[H_2]$), and the scale extends from 0, which corresponds to a solution in equilibrium with 1 atm hydrogen, to 41, which corresponds to a solution in equilibrium with 1 atm oxygen. The rH is related to the ratios of oxidized and reduced forms, and an expression analogous to eq. 4-223 can be written:

$$r\text{H} = r\text{H}_a + \log \frac{[\text{oxidized}]}{[\text{reduced}]} \qquad (4\text{-}231)$$

donnan equilibrium

If a membrane separates two compartments, both of which contain a solution of a permeable salt such as NaCl, and one compartment contains a nonpermeable ion such as protein anions, the permeable salt will distribute itself unequally on the two sides of the membrane. Assuming that the solutions are sufficiently dilute so that concentrations can be substituted for activities, at equilibrium we can write for an exemplary cell:

	Na^+	Cl^- ⋮	Na^+	R^-	Cl^-	
Initial Concentration:	c_1	c_1	c_2	c_2	0	(4-232)
Equilibrium Concentration:	$c_1 - x$	$c_1 - x$	$c_2 + x$	c_2	x	

$$\mu^0_{Na^+} + RT \ln c_{Na_1{}^+} + \mu^0_{Cl^-} + RT \ln c_{Cl_1{}^-} = \mu^0_{Na^+} + RT \ln c_{Na_2{}^+} + \mu^0_{Cl^-} + RT \ln c_{Cl_2{}^-} \qquad (4\text{-}233)$$

$$(c_{Na_1^+})(c_{Cl_1^-}) = (c_{Na_2^+})(c_{Cl_2^-}) \tag{4-234}$$

$$(c_1 - x)(c_1 - x) = (c_2 + x)(x) \tag{4-235}$$

$$\frac{x}{c_1} = \frac{c_1}{c_2 + 2c_1} \tag{4-236}$$

The fraction x/c_1 is the fraction of sodium chloride initially present which has diffused through the membrane to the side containing the nonpermeable anion, protein. Similarly, for another example, one can write

	H^+	Cl^-	⋮	H^+	HR^+	Cl^-	R	
Equilibrium concentration:	w	w		x	b	$y + x$	a	(4-237)

where R is a partially dissociated protein with R nonionized residues and HR^+ ionized residues. If it contains n basic groups per molecule, then $y = n \cdot b$. Using an analysis similar to that above, one can write

$$(w)(w) = (x)(x + y) \qquad y = (w^2 - x^2)/x \tag{4-238}$$

The total concentration of particles on the left side is $2w$ while on the right side it is $(2x + y + a + b)$. If the membrane is part of an osmometer, a pressure will be developed given by (from eq. 4-163)

$$\Pi = RT(m + 2x + y - 2w) \tag{4-239}$$

where the molal concentration of the nonpermeable substance is $m = a + b$. Using eq. 4-238 to eliminate either x or y gives

$$\Pi = RT(\sqrt{4w^2 + y^2} - 2w) \qquad \Pi = RT(w - x)^2/x \tag{4-240}$$

When w is large, as for instance in the presence of concentrated acid in the example given, the term $\sqrt{4w^2 + y^2}$ is not much larger than $2w$, and the osmotic pressure across the membrane will be small. As w decreases, the osmotic pressure will increase, go through a maximum, and decrease again as x approaches w in magnitude.

If two glass electrodes (reversible to hydrogen ions) are inserted into the two chambers of the cell described in eq. 4-237, no potential is measured. Yet, if solution is removed from each side of the chamber and the pH is measured, a difference in pH between the two chambers will be found.

$$(\text{Pt})\ H_2\ |H^+(HR^+, Cl^-)\ \vdots\ (Cl^-)\ H^+|\ H_2\ (\text{Pt}) \qquad E = 0 \tag{4-241}$$

$$(\text{Pt})\ H_2\ |H^+\ (HR^+, Cl^-)|\ \text{KCl(sat'd)}\ |(Cl^-)\ H^+|\ H_2\ (\text{Pt}) \qquad E < 0 \tag{4-242}$$

It is clear, then, that a potential is created across the semipermeable membrane which is equal to, and opposite in sign to, that in eq. 4-242.

multiple equilibria and binding to macromolecules

Let us consider briefly the application of the principles of equilibrium to the binding of hydrogen ions or other small ions or molecules to a protein or other macromolecule. Let the state of equilibrium at a single reacting site on the macromolecule be represented by the *degree of association* θ which may be defined as the probability that this site has combined with the reacting substance A. It is evident that θ represents the fraction of such sites on all macromolecules which have combined with A. The fraction of A which is free or not combined is $(1 - \theta)$, and the equilibrium condition is given by

$$kc = \frac{\theta}{1 - \theta} \tag{4-243}$$

where k is the *association constant*. Substituting eq. 4-243 into eq. 4-128 gives

$$\Delta G = \Delta G^0 + RT \ln \frac{\theta}{c(1 - \theta)} \tag{4-244}$$

It is important to remember that the ΔG and ΔG^0 are the free energy changes of *association* per mole of *combining sites.*

If the macromolecule has n sites which are identical, completely independent of one another, and therefore, indistinguishable,

$$kc = \frac{n\theta}{n - n\theta} = \frac{\bar{v}}{n - \bar{v}} \tag{4-245}$$

where

$$\bar{v} = n\theta = \frac{\text{moles A combined}}{\text{moles macromolecule}} \tag{4-246}$$

The equilibria may be evaluated in terms of dissociation. If α is the *degree of dissociation,*

$$\frac{\alpha}{1 - \alpha} = \frac{\bar{r}}{n - \bar{r}} = \frac{K}{c} \tag{4-247}$$

where K is the dissociation constant and $\bar{r} = n - \bar{v}$.

Frequently, a macromolecule may have n identical sites which interact, however, so that binding at one site will affect the binding affinity at other sites. It is possible to take such interaction into account by permitting k and ΔG^0 in eqs. 4-243 and 4-244 to vary as $\bar{v}$ changes. Let us define an *intrinsic association constant*, k_{int}, and an *intrinsic standard free energy change*, ΔG^0_{int}, such that

$$\lim_{\bar{v} \to 0} k = k_{\text{int}} \qquad \lim_{\bar{v} \to 0} \Delta G^0 = \Delta G^0_{\text{int}} \tag{4-248}$$

The interaction can be accounted for by means of an arbitrary function φ, such that, for $\bar{v} > 0$,

$$\Delta G^0 = \Delta G^0_{\text{int}} + RT\varphi(\bar{v}) \tag{4-249}$$

$$k = k_{\text{int}} e^{-\varphi(\bar{v})} \tag{4-250}$$

If the function $\varphi(\bar{v})$ increases as $\bar{v}$ increases, the interaction becomes less as more ligand is bound. On the other hand, if $\varphi(\bar{v})$ decreases as $\bar{v}$ increases, a cooperative interaction takes place between binding sites. Combining eqs. 4-250 and 4-245 gives

$$\frac{\bar{v}}{n - \bar{v}} = kc = k_{\text{int}} e^{-\varphi(\bar{v})} c \tag{4-251}$$

which, in the logarithmic form, is

$$\log \frac{\bar{v}}{n - \bar{v}} - \log c = \log k_{\text{int}} - 0.434\ \varphi(\bar{v}) \tag{4-252}$$

If the combining sites are reasonably identical and n is known, the relation in eq. 4-252 can be used to determine the qualitative nature of the interaction between binding sites. For example, Fig. 4-14 shows a plot of $[\log \bar{v}/(n - \bar{v}) - \log P_{O_2}]$ *versus* $\bar{v}$ for

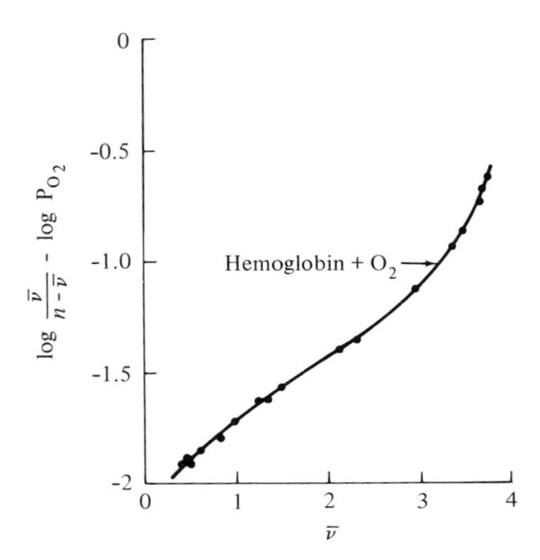

fig. 4-14. Binding of oxygen by hemoglobin. (Data from Wyman, J., Jr. *Advan. Protein Chem., 4,* 407 [1948]. Copyright Academic Press, reprinted by permission.)

the binding of oxygen by hemoglobin. Hemoglobin has four binding sites per molecule at each of the porphyrin iron atoms, each of which should have an identical intrinsic affinity for binding an oxygen atom. The slope $-0.434\ \varphi(\bar{v})$ is positive; $\varphi(\bar{v})$ is negative, indicating a cooperative interaction. In fact, binding of an oxygen atom by hemoglobin increases the affinity of the remaining sites for binding additional oxygen atoms.

If the low-molecular-weight ligand is an ion, the most important interaction between binding sites will be electrostatic. Of course, most molecules have, in addition to the ion ligands, charged groups which play a role in electrostatic interactions; and it is necessary to take all charges of the macromolecule into account in evaluating electrostatic interactions. The interaction function is $\varphi(\bar{Z})$. In considering electrostatic interactions, therefore, the intrinsic properties are redefined in terms of the *absence of all charges* on the macromolecule. Equation 4-248 becomes

$$\lim_{Z \to 0} k = k_{\text{int}} \qquad \lim_{Z \to 0} \Delta G^0 = \Delta G^0_{\text{int}} \tag{4-253}$$

where $\bar{Z}$ is the average net charge per macromolecule.

The free energy change now can be stated in terms of the sum of the intrinsic standard free energy change and the work required to move an ion from the solution to the macromolecule; the macromolecule may be regarded as the central ion held at a constant potential.

$$\Delta G^0 = \Delta G^0_{\text{int}} + q\psi \tag{4-254}$$

The electrical work is the product of q, the electrostatic charge on the small ion, times

ψ, the potential of the central ion and its ion atmosphere. The free energy change of ionization per molecule is equal to 2.3 $kTpK$. An equation analogous to eq. 4-252 can be written in the case of hydrogen-ion binding.

$$\log \frac{\alpha}{1-\alpha} - \mathrm{pH} = -pK_{\mathrm{int}} + 0.434 \frac{q\psi}{kT} \qquad (4\text{-}255)$$

The far right-hand term can be expressed in terms of $\varphi(\bar{Z})$ by evaluating φ by eq. 4-191 and the electrostatic interaction factor, $W = (q^2N)/(2\varepsilon RT \cdot [1 + \kappa a]r)$, giving

$$p\mathrm{H} - \log \frac{\alpha}{1-\alpha} = pK_{\mathrm{int}} - 0.868\ W\bar{Z} \qquad (4\text{-}256)$$

reaction kinetics

The biologist is concerned not only with the energetics of a reaction but with its rate as well. A marvel of living cells is the fact that the multitude of reactions that are simultaneously occurring proceed with such fine quantitative adjustment to each other. Rapid and precise adjustment of rates follow changes in environmental conditions. The rate of a chemical reaction is evaluated by following the disappearance of reactants or the accumulation of products as a function of time. Chemical reactions are divided into a number of types depending upon the number of reactant molecules whose concentration influences the velocity of the reaction.

Reactions which have a velocity proportional to the concentration of only one component are *first-order reactions*, and their velocity is described by

$$\frac{d[\mathrm{A}]}{dt} = -k[\mathrm{A}] \qquad (4\text{-}257)$$

which, upon integration, gives

$$\ln [\mathrm{A}] = \ln [\mathrm{A}]_0 - kt \qquad [\mathrm{A}] = [\mathrm{A}]_0 e^{-kt} \qquad (4\text{-}258)$$

where [A] is the concentration of the rate-controlling reactant at time t, and $[\mathrm{A}]_0$ is the concentration at $t = 0$. The rate constant for a first-order reaction k has the dimensions of time^{-1}. For a first-order reaction, a plot of ln [A] *versus* time gives a straight line with a slope of $-k$ (see Fig. 4-15). One of the earliest first-order reactions that was studied thoroughly (by L. F. Wilhelmy in 1850) was the inversion of sucrose, that is, the hydrolysis of sucrose into glucose and fructose, a reaction that is observed readily by watching the shift of rotation of plane-polarized light from a clockwise rotation to a counterclockwise rotation. The decay of radioactive isotopes is another example of a first-order reaction.

After a lag following innoculation, a bacterial culture exhibits a period of exponential growth. During this phase of growth, the rate of increase of bacteria is proportional to the number of bacteria present, and

$$\frac{dN}{dt} = kN \qquad (4\text{-}259)$$

The rate constant k is the reciprocal of the mean generation time t_{gen}, the mean time required between cell divisions of a single bacterium. Assuming random cell divisions,

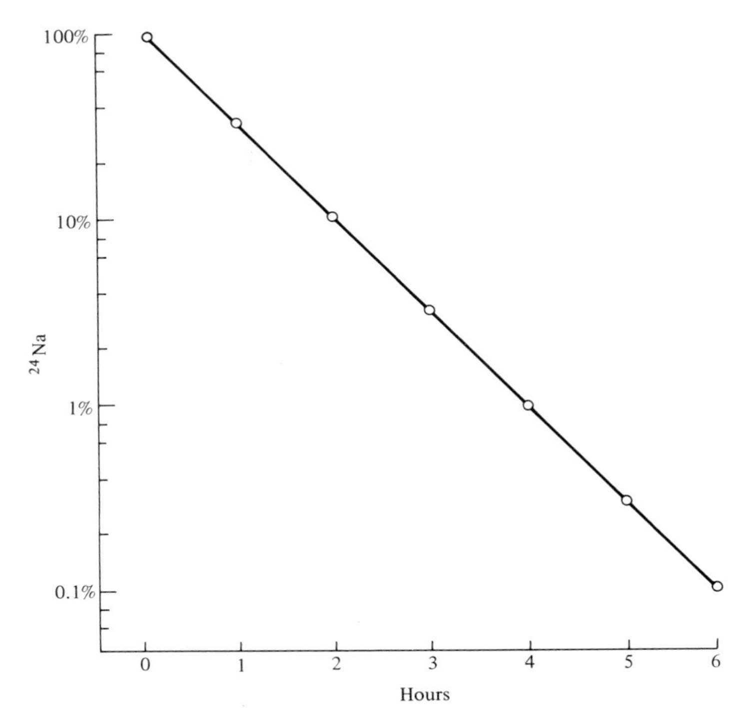

fig. 4-15. A plot of the decay of radioactivity of ^{24}Na, a first-order reaction.

t_{gen} is related to the doubling time t_d, the time at which $N = 2N_0$, by the following expression:

$$t_{gen} = t_d \ln \frac{N_0}{N} = \frac{t_d}{\ln 2} \tag{4-260}$$

The decay of radioactive isotopes is a *unimolecular reaction*; that is, there is only one species of reactant molecules, and the reactant molecules react singly. The inversion of sucrose, however, is a *bimolecular reaction.*

$$C_{12}H_{22}O_{11} + H_2O \rightarrow C_6H_{12}O_6 + C_6H_{12}O_6 \tag{4-261}$$

Under ordinary circumstances, only the concentration of sucrose affects the reaction rate. One needs to distinguish, therefore, between the *order of a reaction* and its *molecularity*.

The rate of *second-order reactions* depends upon the concentrations of two reactant molecules, which may be identical or different. The reaction velocity is given by

$$\frac{d[A]}{dt} = -k[A][B] \tag{4-262}$$

Equation 4-262 is more easily integrated if it is put in a form with a single variable. Let x represent the moles of A that have reacted at time t. The concentrations of A and B reactants at time t will be $([A]_0 - x)$ and $([B]_0 - rx)$ where r is a factor determined by the stoichiometry of the reaction. Making these substitutions, eq. 4-262 becomes

$$\frac{d[A]}{dt} = -k([A]_0 - x)([B]_0 - rx) \tag{4-263}$$

Integrating eq. 4-263 and evaluating the constant of integration by substituting the initial conditions, $x = 0$ at $t = 0$, gives

$$kt = \frac{1}{[B]_0 - r[A]_0}\left[\ln\left(\frac{[A]_0}{[A]_0 - x}\right) - \ln\left(\frac{[B]_0}{[B]_0 - rx}\right)\right] \tag{4-264}$$

$$t = \frac{2.303}{k(r[A]_0 - [B]_0)} \log \frac{[B]_0([A]_0 - x)}{[A]_0([B]_0 - rx)} \tag{4-265}$$

A plot of $\log [B]_0([A]_0 - x)/[A]_0([B]_0 - rx)$ versus t yields a straight line whose slope is $-k([A]_0 - [B]_0)/2.303$. An example of a second-order reaction is the saponification of esters by alkali (Fig. 4-16).

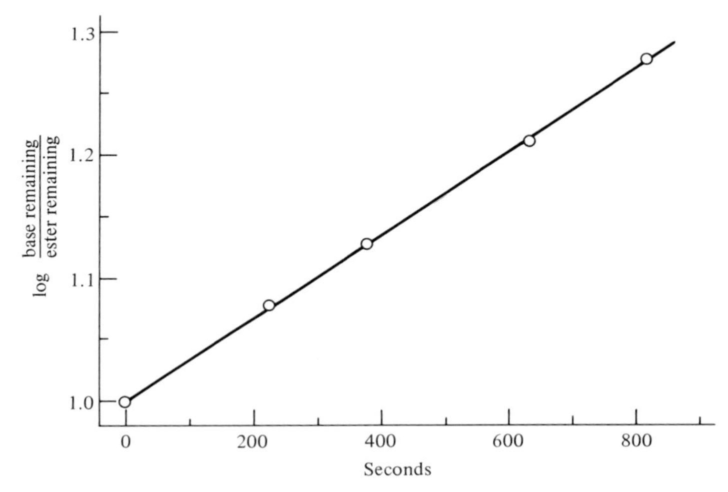

fig. 4-16. A plot of the saponification of ethyl acetate by sodium hydroxide at 16°C, a second-order reaction.

Occasionally reactions of even higher order are important. For a reaction of the general type

$$qA + rB + sC + \cdots \rightarrow \text{Products} \tag{4-266}$$

the reaction velocity will be given by

$$\frac{d[A]}{dt} = -k[A]^q[B]^r[C]^s \cdots \tag{4-267}$$

Occasionally reactions are encountered where the rate of reaction is independent of the concentration of all reactants, and $d[A]/dt = -k$. A plot of [A] *versus* t gives a straight line whose slope is $-k$. Reactions with these kinetics are called *zero-order* reactions and are typified by reactions which occur at the interface between two phases at concentrations of reactants in excess of that required to saturate the surface. Surface denaturation of proteins displays these kinetics.

Let us now consider a reversible reaction such as

$$A + B \underset{k_2}{\overset{k_1}{\rightleftarrows}} C + D \tag{4-268}$$

The rate of reaction is described by the following relation

$$v = -\frac{d[\mathrm{A}]}{dt} = \frac{d[\mathrm{C}]}{dt} = k_1[\mathrm{A}][\mathrm{B}] - k_2[\mathrm{C}][\mathrm{D}] \tag{4-269}$$

At equilibrium, the forward and backward reactions occur at equal velocities so that there is no net change in the concentrations of either reactants or products and $d[\mathrm{C}]/dt = 0$. It was shown by Guldberg and Waage[20] that the relation of the rate constants could be determined at equilibrium where the law of mass action held (eq. 4-127).

$$K_{\mathrm{eq}} = \frac{k_1}{k_2} = \frac{[\mathrm{C}][\mathrm{D}]}{[\mathrm{A}][\mathrm{B}]} \tag{4-270}$$

Integrating eq. 4-269 and evaluating the constant of integration at the initial and equilibrium conditions for the case where $[\mathrm{A}]_0 = [\mathrm{B}]_0$ and $[\mathrm{C}]_e = [\mathrm{D}]_e$ gives

$$k_1 t = \frac{[\mathrm{C}]_e}{[\mathrm{A}]_0^2 - [\mathrm{C}]_e^2} \ln \frac{[\mathrm{A}]_0^2[\mathrm{C}]_e - [\mathrm{C}]_e^2[\mathrm{C}]}{[\mathrm{A}]_0^2[\mathrm{C}]_e - [\mathrm{A}]_0^2[\mathrm{C}]} \tag{4-271}$$

For the sequence of reactions

$$\mathrm{A} + \mathrm{B} \underset{k_2}{\overset{k_1}{\rightleftarrows}} \mathrm{X} \overset{k_3}{\rightarrow} \mathrm{P} \tag{4-272}$$

three differential equations are required to describe the system:

$$\frac{d[\mathrm{A}]}{dt} = \frac{d[\mathrm{B}]}{dt} = k_2[\mathrm{X}] - k_1[\mathrm{A}][\mathrm{B}] \tag{4-273}$$

$$\frac{d[\mathrm{X}]}{dt} = k_1[\mathrm{A}][\mathrm{B}] - (k_2 + k_3)[\mathrm{X}] \tag{4-274}$$

$$\frac{d[\mathrm{P}]}{dt} = k_3[\mathrm{X}] \tag{4-275}$$

At any time t,

$$[\mathrm{A}]_0 - [\mathrm{A}] = [\mathrm{B}]_0 - [\mathrm{B}] \tag{4-276}$$

In the most general case where no restriction exists with respect to the relative magnitudes of the rate constants k_1, k_2, and k_3, an explicit solution is not possible; the equations can only be integrated numerically with the aid of a computer. A typical solution is shown in Fig. 4-17.

Where $k_3 \ll k_2$, the rate of formation of product is determined by the monomolecular breakdown of X (which is formed rapidly and reversibly from A and B); and

$$\frac{d[\mathrm{P}]}{dt} = -\frac{d[\mathrm{A}]}{dt} = k_3 K_{\mathrm{eq}}[\mathrm{A}][\mathrm{B}] \tag{4-277}$$

where $K_{\mathrm{eq}} = k_1/k_2$.

Where $k_3 \gg k_2 \approx k_1$, X is converted to P as rapidly as it is formed and relatively

[20] Guldberg, C. M., and Waage, P., reprinted in Ostwald, W. *Klassiker der exakten Wissenschaften.* Leipzig: W. Engelmann, 1899, no. 104.

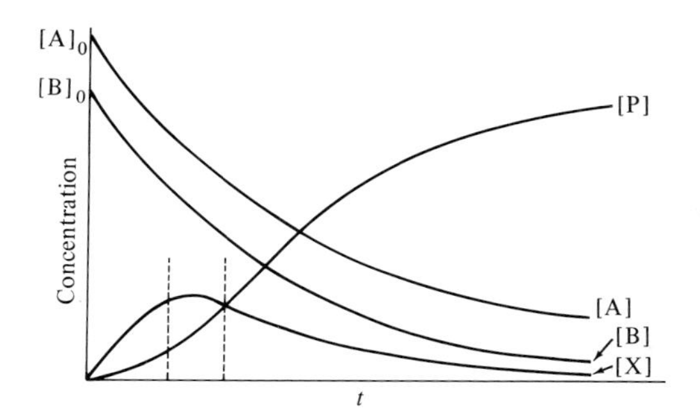

fig. 4-17. Progress curve for the reaction sequence of eq. 4-272. (Program from Cleland, W. W. *Nature, 198*, 463 [1963]; *Advan. Enzymol., 29*, 1 [1967].)

little X decomposes into the original reactants. Because the rate of formation of X is rate-limiting,

$$\frac{d[P]}{dt} = k_1[A][B] \tag{4-278}$$

kinetics of enzyme reactions

Enzyme reactions are characterized by a catalyst (the enzyme) which combines with the reactant (the substrate) to form an intermediate; the intermediate decomposes to form the product, regenerating the catalyst in the process. The intermediate X is the enzyme-substitute complex. The sequence of reactions is

$$A + C \underset{k_2}{\overset{k_1}{\rightleftarrows}} X \overset{k_3}{\rightarrow} P + C \tag{4-279}$$

The velocities of the reactions are:

$$\frac{d[A]}{dt} = k_2[X] - k_1[A][C] \tag{4-280}$$

$$\frac{d[X]}{dt} = k_1[A][C] - (k_2 + k_3)[X] \tag{4-281}$$

$$\frac{d[C]}{dt} = (k_2 + k_3)[X] - k_1[A][C] \tag{4-282}$$

$$\frac{d[P]}{dt} = k_3[X] \tag{4-283}$$

$$[C]_0 = [C] + [X] \tag{4-284}$$

Although an explicit solution of these equations is not possible, a numerical solution can be obtained with the aid of a computer; a generalized solution is shown in

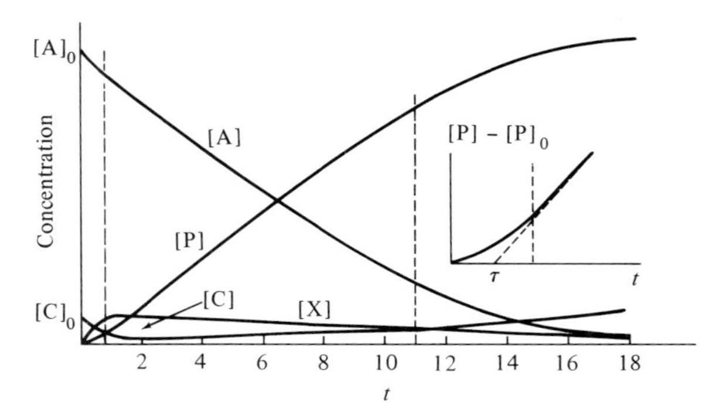

fig. 4-18. Progress curve for the reaction sequence of eq. 4-279. (Program from Cleland, W. W. *Nature, 198,* 463 [1963]; *Advan. Enzymol., 29,* 1 [1967].)

Fig. 4-18. After the initial period of reaction and for a considerable period of time, sometimes until equilibrium is reached, the slopes of the progress curves for [X] and [C] are virtually zero. During this period, the steady-state approximations $d[X]/dt \approx 0$ and $d[C]/dt \approx 0$ hold. The larger the ratio $[A]_0/[C]_0$, the shorter the period required to reach steady-state conditions. From eq. 4-282,

$$k_1[A][C] \approx (k_2 + k_3)[X] \tag{4-285}$$

Substituting eq. 4-284 into eq. 4-285,

$$[X] = \frac{k_1[A][C]_0}{k_1[A] + k_2 + k_3} \tag{4-286}$$

Substituting eq. 4-283 into eq. 4-286 gives

$$v = -\frac{d[A]}{dt} = \frac{d[P]}{dt} = k_3[X] = \frac{k_1k_3[A][C]_0}{k_1[A] + k_2 + k_3} = \frac{k_3[A][C]_0}{(k_2 + k_3)/k_1 + [A]} \tag{4-287}$$

If one defines *maximal velocity*, V_M, as k_3 $[C]_0$ and a rate constant, k_M, as $(k_2 + k_3)/k_1$, eq. 4-287 can be rewritten as the well-known *Michaelis-Menten equation*,

$$v = \frac{V_M[S]}{k_M + [S]} \tag{4-288}$$

in which the catalyst is an enzyme and S is the substrate. Equation 4-288 can be rewritten so that linear plots of data can be obtained.

$$\frac{1}{v} = \frac{k_M}{V_M} \cdot \frac{1}{[S]} + \frac{1}{V_M} \tag{4-289}$$

$$\frac{[S]}{v} = \frac{[S]}{V_M} + \frac{k_M}{V_M} \tag{4-290}$$

$$v + k_M\frac{V_M}{[S]} = V_M \tag{4-291}$$

Plots of these equations are shown in Fig. 4-19.

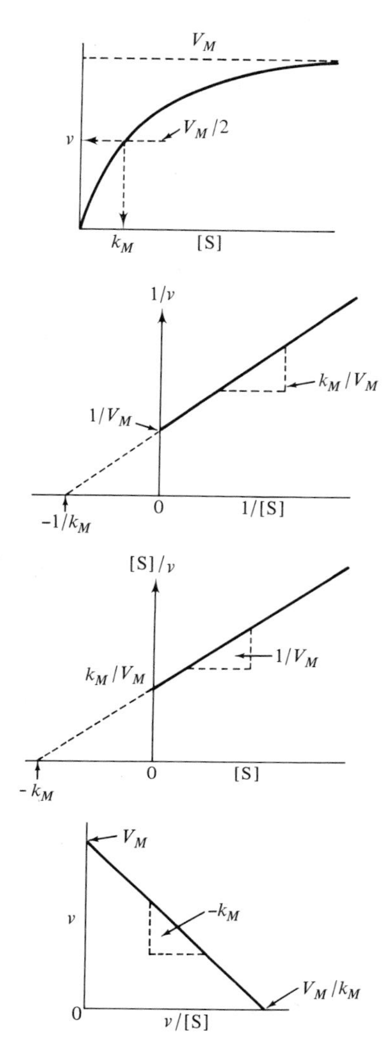

fig. 4-19. Common plots of Michaelis-Menten kinetics.

Actually, most enzymes catalyze reactions involving more than one substrate. In many cases, one substrate is present in large excess and is not rate-limiting or the rate depends only on one substrate. In other instances, the concentrations of both substrates must be taken into account. The reactions and equilibria for a two-substrate reaction are given by

$$\mathrm{E + A \rightleftharpoons EA} \qquad k_{\mathrm{A}} = \frac{[\mathrm{E}][\mathrm{A}]}{[\mathrm{EA}]} \tag{4-292}$$

$$\mathrm{E + B \rightleftharpoons EB} \qquad k_{\mathrm{B}} = \frac{[\mathrm{E}][\mathrm{B}]}{[\mathrm{EB}]} \tag{4-293}$$

$$\mathrm{EA + B \rightleftharpoons EAB} \qquad k'_{\mathrm{B}} = \frac{[\mathrm{EA}][\mathrm{B}]}{[\mathrm{EAB}]} \tag{4-294}$$

$$\mathrm{EB + A \rightleftharpoons EAB} \qquad k'_{\mathrm{A}} = \frac{[\mathrm{EB}][\mathrm{A}]}{[\mathrm{EAB}]} \tag{4-295}$$

$$\text{EAB} \rightarrow \text{E} + \text{Products} \tag{4-296}$$

$$[\text{E}]_0 = [\text{E}] + [\text{EA}] + [\text{EB}] + [\text{EAB}] \tag{4-297}$$

The overall velocity of the reaction will be given by

$$v = k[\text{EAB}] \qquad V_M = k[\text{E}]_0 \tag{4-298}$$

Eliminating [E], [EA], and [EB] from eqs. 4-292 through

$$V_M = \left[\left(\frac{k_A k'_B}{[B]} + k'_A\right)\frac{1}{[A]} + \frac{k'_B}{[B]} + 1\right]v \tag{4-299}$$

or

$$\frac{1}{v} = \left(\frac{k_A k'_B}{[B]} + k'_A\right)\frac{1}{V_M[A]} + \left(\frac{k'_B}{[B]} + 1\right)\frac{1}{V_M} \tag{4-300}$$

If $[B] \gg k'_B$, eqs. 4-299 and 4-300 can be approximated by the Michaelis-Menten equation (4-288). By keeping [B] constant, a family of straight lines can be obtained by plotting $1/v$ *versus* $1/[A]$ for various values of [B] (see Fig. 4-20). In the model

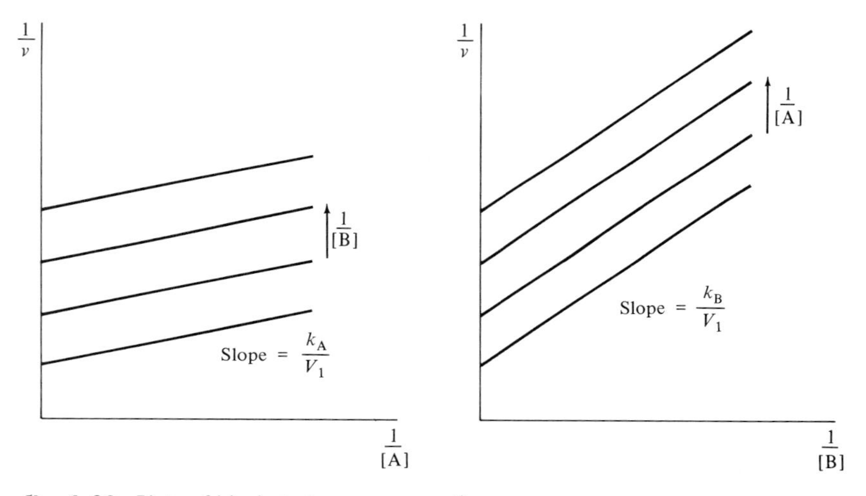

fig. 4-20. Plots of bisubstrate enzyme reactions.

considered above, the two substrates combine independently with their specific sites, $k_A \approx k'_A$ and $k_B \approx k'_B$, and

$$\frac{v}{V_M} = \frac{\dfrac{[A]}{k_A}\cdot\dfrac{[B]}{k_B}}{\left(1 + \dfrac{[A]}{k_A}\right)\left(1 + \dfrac{[B]}{k_B}\right)} \tag{4-301}$$

It is seen that eq. 4-301 is the product of two Michaelis-Menten equations.

In the development outlined above, it was implied that the order of combination of either substrate with enzyme was not material. Frequently this is not the case, and an order of combination is required if the reaction is to proceed. In addition, it is frequently necessary to consider more than one ternary complex. While the outline above should help the reader to understand the aspects of control at the enzymatic level considered in Chapter 5, it is oversimplified. The kinetics of complex enzymes has received considerable attention, and the interested reader is referred to the more rigorous analyses that have been made.[21]

reaction rates and the activated complex

While studying the rate of sucrose inversion as a function of temperature, Arrhenius observed that the rate increased faster than could be accounted for just on the basis of the increased kinetic energy of all the particles or a change in the dissociation constant of the acid catalyst (see van't Hoff's equation, 4-134). Arrhenius suggested that only a fraction of the molecules, those with an internal energy greater than a threshold value, could enter into a reaction. These molecules are said to be in an *activated* state. Arrhenius's equation is

$$k_r = Ae^{-U^{\ddagger}/RT} \qquad \frac{d \ln k_r}{dT} = -\frac{U^{\ddagger}}{RT^2} \tag{4-302}$$

where k_r is the rate constant, A is the *frequency factor* which may have a value $0 < A < 1$, and $U^{\ddagger}$ is the *energy of activation*, that is, the difference between the average energy of the active molecules and the average energy of all molecules.

The *theory of absolute reaction rates*, developed in large part by Eyring and his collaborators,[22] leads to an a-priori prediction of the rate of a chemical reaction. The theory is based on the concept that a chemical reaction involves the formation of an intermediate complex, the *transition state* or *activated complex*, which has an energy content greater than either the reactants or the products. The activated complex presents an energy barrier which separates the reactants from the products.

The concept can be visualized in terms of a hypothetical reaction

$$AB + C \underset{k_2}{\overset{k_1}{\rightleftharpoons}} ABC^{\ddagger} \underset{k_4}{\overset{k_3}{\rightleftharpoons}} A + BC \tag{4-303}$$

in which $ABC^{\ddagger}$ represents the activated complex. A potential energy curve as a function of interatomic distance, like that in Fig. 3-1, can be drawn for the two diatomic molecules AB and BC. A composite contour diagram for the whole reaction can be constructed by extension of the potential energy curves for the reaction 4-303 (see Figs. 4-21 and 4-22). The reaction occurs along the lowest energy level in the surface. A potential energy curve for the reaction can be drawn along this path (see Fig. 4-23).

---

[21] King, E. L., and Altman, C. *J. Phys. Chem.*, *60*, 1375, 1378 (1956); Alberty, R. A. *Advan. Enzymol.*, *17*, 1 (1956); Dalziel, K. *Acta Chem. Scand.*, *11*, 1706 (1957); Alberty, R. A. *J. Am. Chem. Soc.*, *80*, 1777 (1958); Wong, J. T. F., and Hanes, C. S. *Can. J. Biochem. Physiol.*, *40*, 763 (1962); Cleland, W. W. *Biochim. Biophys. Acta*, *67*, 104 173, 188 (1963).

[22] Glasstone, S., Laidler, K. J., and Eyring, H. *The Theory of Rate Processes*. New York: McGraw-Hill, 1941.

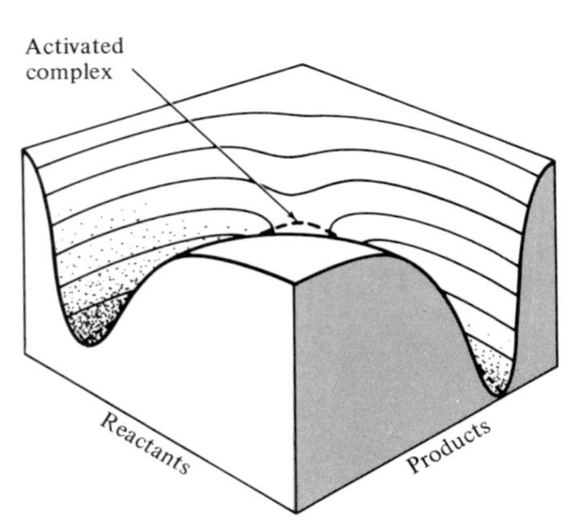

fig. 4-21. Three-dimensional contour model for the energy relations of the reaction sequence of eq. 4-273. (From Dawes, E. A., in Florkin, M., and Stotz, E. H., eds. *Comprehensive Biochemistry.* Amsterdam: Elsevier, 1964, vol. 12, p. 108.)

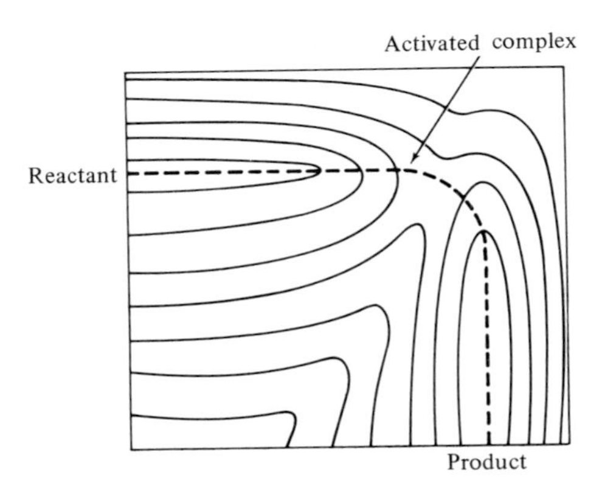

fig. 4-22. Contour map of Fig. 4-21 showing the reaction path (dotted line) from the reactants, via the activated complex, to the products. (From Dawes, E. A., in Florkin, M., and Stotz, E. H., eds. *Comprehensive Biochemistry.* Amsterdam: Elsevier, 1964, vol. 12, p. 108.)

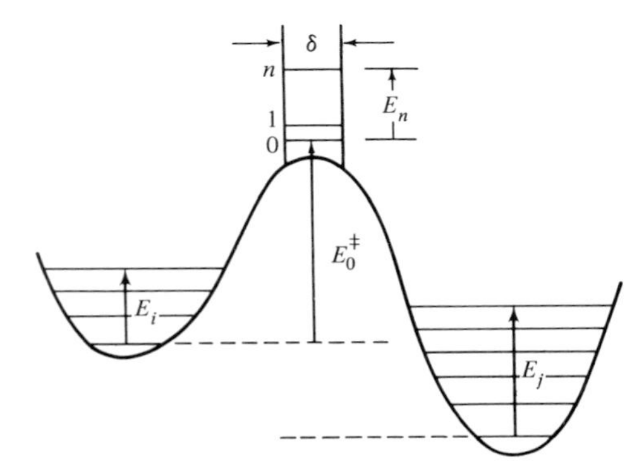

fig. 4-23. A view of the reaction path with the activated complex at the top of the energy barrier. (From Eyring, H., and Eyring, E. M. *Modern Chemical Kinetics.* New York: Reinhold, 1963, p. 46.)

The activated complex can be regarded as an ordinary chemical species possessing all the usual thermodynamic properties. In terms of eqs. 4-24 and 4-128, one can write

$$\Delta G^‡ = \Delta H^‡ - T\Delta S^‡ = -RT \ln K^‡ \quad \textbf{(4-304)}$$

where $K^‡$ is the equilibrium constant and $\Delta G^‡$, $\Delta H^‡$, and $\Delta S^‡$ are the standard-state changes associated with the formation of the activated state.

The rate of a chemical reaction will equal the product of the concentration of the activated complex and the frequency of crossing the energy barrier. Let C* equal the number of activated complexes per unit volume along length δ, and v be the mean velocity of transversing δ. The frequency of crossing the barrier is equal to v/δ. Since only half the activated complexes will be moving in the forward direction of the chemical reaction,

$$\text{reaction rate} = k[\text{AB}][\text{C}] = \tfrac{1}{2}\text{C}^* \frac{v}{\delta}\kappa \tag{4-305}$$

where κ is a transmission coefficient representing the probability that an activated complex having crossed the barrier will continue on to yield the products. The magnitude of C*, κ, v, and δ can be evaluated from statistical mechanical considerations:

$$\text{C}^* = [\text{ABC}](2\pi m^{\ddagger} kT)^{1/2}\,\delta/h \tag{4-306}$$

$$v = (2kT/\pi m^{\ddagger})^{1/2} \tag{4-307}$$

where k is Boltzmann's constant and h is Planck's constant. It may be assumed that the activated complex is in equilibrium with the reactants A and B, and

$$K^{\ddagger} = [\text{ABC}]/[\text{A}][\text{B}] \qquad \text{reaction rate} = k_r[\text{A}][\text{B}] \tag{4-308}$$

Upon the appropriate substitutions of eqs. 4-306, 4-307, and 4-308 into eq. 4-305

$$k_r = \kappa \frac{kT}{h} K^{\ddagger} \tag{4-309}$$

For reactions in a homogeneous medium which involve simple bond rearrangements such as hydration, hydrolysis, and group-transfer reactions, the transmission coefficient κ is close to unity. For reactions that involve changes in the electronic states of the atoms during reaction, or reactions that proceed by tunneling through the potential energy barrier, κ may have a value significantly less than one. If κ is taken as one, the equilibrium constant can be related to the standard free energy change by eq. 4-304; and from eq. 4-309

$$\Delta G^{\ddagger} = -RT \ln \frac{k_r h}{kT} = \Delta H^{\ddagger} - T\Delta S^{\ddagger} \tag{4-310}$$

or

$$k_r = \frac{kT}{h} e^{-\Delta G^{\ddagger}/RT} = \frac{kT}{h} e^{\Delta S^{\ddagger}/R} e^{-\Delta H^{\ddagger}/RT} \tag{4-311}$$

Assuming that $\Delta S^{\ddagger}$ is independent of temperature, taking logarithms of eq. 4-311 and differentiating gives

$$\frac{d \ln k_r}{dT} = \frac{\Delta H^{\ddagger}}{RT^2} = \frac{1}{T} = \frac{\Delta H^{\ddagger} + RT}{RT^2} \tag{4-312}$$

Comparison of eqs. 4-302 and 4-312 leads to

$$U^{\ddagger} = \Delta H^{\ddagger} + RT \tag{4-313}$$

Although there is a difference between the two of 0.6 kcal/mole at ordinary temperatures, it is not uncommon to equate $\Delta H^{\ddagger}$ and $\Delta U^{\ddagger}$. If these two are equated, one can obtain an approximate value for A:

$$A = \frac{kT}{h} e^{\Delta S^{\ddagger}/R} \tag{4-314}$$

Clearly, the magnitude of the frequency factor A is determined largely by the magnitude of the entropy of activation; the smaller the decrease in entropy required in forming the activated complex, the faster the reaction will proceed. Even though a reaction may have a very large heat of activation, if the entropy of activation is not very large, the reaction will proceed very slowly—perhaps even not be observable. On the other hand, reactions with very large entropies of activation and small enthalpies of activation may proceed very rapidly. A property of reactions with high heats of activation is that the rate increases very rapidly with temperature.

It should be realized that the enzyme-substrate complex of enzyme reactions is not an activated complex. Rather, an activated complex is an intermediate step in the formation of the enzyme-substrate complex. The enzyme-substrate complex proceeds through the formation of a second activated complex before dissociating into enzyme and product. The overall energy profile for the fumarase reaction is illustrated in Fig. 4-24. The enzyme forms two substrate complexes in this reaction: one with

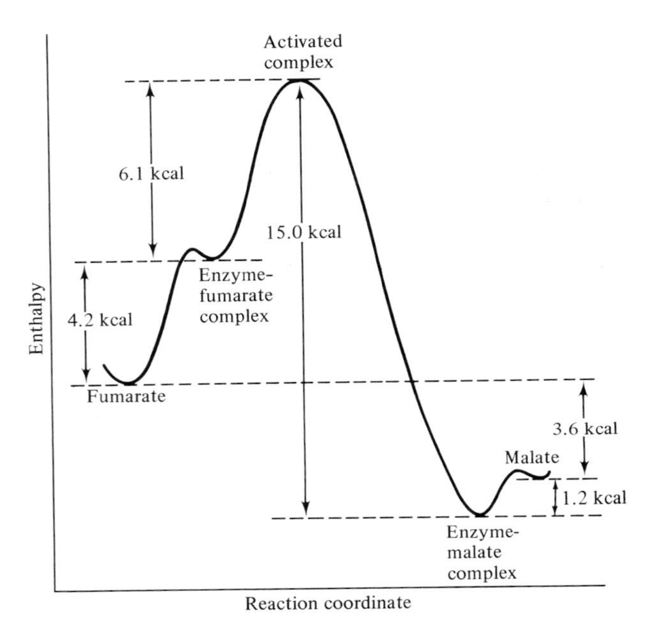

fig. 4-24. Enthalpy profile for the reaction catalyzed by fumarase. (From Massey, V. *Biochem. J., 53,* 77 [1953].)

fumarate and one with malate. Each of these enzyme-substrate complexes requires thermal activation in order to form an activated complex which is able to proceed with the chemical reaction. Nevertheless, an analogy does exist between the enzyme-substrate complex and the activated complex, and approximate evaluations of the energy of activation of enzyme-catalyzed reactions have been made from analyses of the temperature dependence of Michaelis-Menten kinetic data.

protein denaturation

It was pointed out in Chapter 3 that proteins possess unique conformation in their native form which is required for expression of their catalytic or structural properties. A loss of this native conformation is called *denaturation* and is accompanied by a loss of enzymatic activity. The native conformation of proteins is maintained as a result of a number of types of weak attractive forces. For a long time it was held that intramolecular hydrogen bonds were principally responsible for the maintenance of conformational integrity of proteins. It was first pointed out by Kauzmann[23] that the energy of peptide hydrogen bonds in water is much less than the 8 kcal/mole usually ascribed to them because rupture involves an exchange reaction with the subsequent formation of hydrogen bonds with water. Schellman[24] estimated the energy of peptide hydrogen bonds to be about 1.5 kcal/mole. In a model system using N-methylacetamine, Klotz and Franzen[25] found aggregation in carbon tetrachloride and evaluated the hydrogen bond ΔH to be about -4.2 kcal/mole. In water, on the other hand, hydrogen-bond formation between N-methylacetamide molecules was practically zero. The interior of the protein molecule, however, has a preponderance of apolar residues, and the enthalpy values of hydrogen bonds in the interior of the protein molecule may be expected to lie between the values in a hydrocarbon solvent and in water.

About 35 to 40 percent of the amino acid residues in proteins have apolar side chains. It was pointed out by Kauzmann[26] that these residues tend to associate with themselves, pointing inward toward the center of the molecule, and tend to avoid contact with the aqueous solvent. The process is envisioned as analogous to the tendency for hydrocarbon molecules to come out of aqueous solution. Kauzmann called this phenomenon *apolar bonding* or *hydrophobic bonding*. As shown in Fig. 4-25,

fig. 4-25. Thermodynamic changes in the transfer of hydrocarbons from a nonpolar solvent to water. (From Kauzmann, W. *Advan. Protein Chem., 14,* 39 [1959]. Copyright Academic Press; reprinted by permission.)

PROCESS	TEMPERATURE (°K)	ΔS (ELECTROSTATIC UNITS)	ΔH (CAL/MOLE)	ΔG (CAL/MOLE)
C_4 in benzene → CH_4 in H_2O	298	−18	−2800	2600
CH_4 in ether → CH_4 in H_2O	298	−19	−2400	3300
CH_4 in CCl_4 → CH_4 in H_2O	298	−18	−2500	2900
C_2H_6 in benzene → C_2H_6 in H_2O	298	−20	−2200	3800
C_2H_6 in CCl_4 → C_2H_6 in H_2O	298	−18	−1700	3700
C_2H_4 in benzene → C_2H_4 in H_2O	298	−15	−1610	2920
C_2H_2 in benzene → C_2H_2 in H_2O	298	−7	−190	1870
Liquid propane → C_3H_8 in H_2O	298	−23	−1800	5050
Liquid *n*-butane → C_4H_{10} in H_2O	298	−23	−1000	5850
Liquid benzene → C_6H_6 in H_2O	291	−14	0	4070
Liquid toluene → C_7H_8 in H_2O	291	−16	0	4650
Liquid ethyl benzene → C_8H_{10} in H_2O	291	−19	0	5500
Liquid *m*- or *p*-xylene → C_8H_{10} in H_2O	291	−20	0	5800

[23] Kauzmann, W., in McElroy, W. D., and Glass, B., eds. *The Mechanism of Enzyme Action.* Baltimore: Johns Hopkins Press, 1954, p. 70.
[24] Schellman, J. A. *Compt. Rend. Trav. Lab. Carlsberg, Ser. Chim., 29,* 223, 230 (1955).
[25] Klotz, I. M., and Franzen, J. S. *J. Am. Chem. Soc., 84,* 3461 (1962).
[26] Kauzmann, W. *Advan. Protein Chem., 14,* 1 (1959).

the dissolution of hydrocarbons in water is unfavored because the process is accompanied by a positive free energy change. Although dissolution of hydrocarbons is exothermic ($\Delta H < 0$), this is more than offset by the large decrease in entropy ($\Delta S > 0$) which results from a tendency toward increased order in water clusters (see Chapter 3).

Klotz[27] has stressed the tendency for apolar side chains on proteins to form envelopes of ordered water analogous to clathrates. While x-ray crystallographic and other data indicate that apolar residues tend to point to the interior of the molecule where they may be expected to participate in hydrophobic bonds, for many proteins not all the apolar side chains can be accommodated in the interior of the molecule. Those apolar residues that face the aqueous solvent may, indeed, tend to interact with water molecules to form a clathrate-type cage. Here, the unfavorable entropy change ($\Delta S < 0$) is more than offset by the favorable enthalpy ($\Delta H < 0$) change of the process. The various noncovalent bonds involved in stabilizing the native state of proteins are listed in Fig. 4-26 together with the free energies of stabilization for a hypothetical protein of 100 residues.[28]

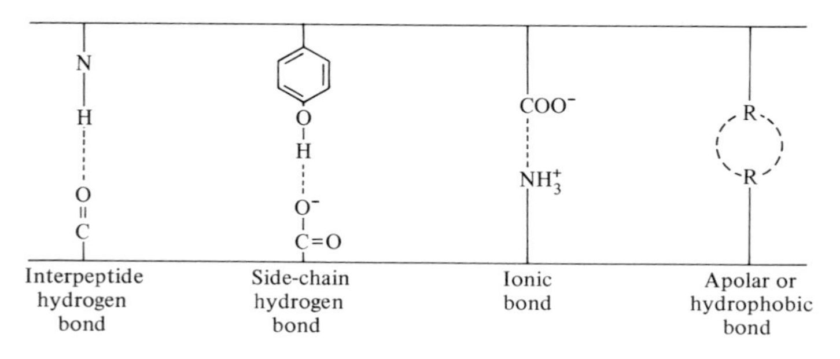

Unfolded chains $\rightleftharpoons$ Native structure

		ΔG (cal)
Conformation entropy	∿	$+1.5 \times 10^5$
Interpeptide hydrogen bonds	∿	-0.5×10^5
Apolar or hydrophobic bonds	∿	-1.0×10^5
Side-chain hydrogen bonds	∿	-0.03×10^5
Ionic bonds	∿	-0.1×10^5
Total:		-0.1×10^5

fig. 4-26. A diagram illustrating the types of noncovalent bonds involved in maintaining the native conformation of proteins together with estimates of the free energy terms involved for a hypothetical protein of 100 residues. (From Schachman, H. K. *Cold Spring Harbor Symp. Quant. Biol., 28,* 418 [1963].)

The thermodynamic constants for the reversible denaturation of several proteins are listed in Fig. 4-27. Typically, the denaturation reaction is accompanied by a very large increase in entropy. This is consistent with the idea that the protein molecule can assume a large number of different conformations in the denatured form while in the native state its conformation is relatively fixed.

[27] Klotz, I. M. *Science, 128,* 815 (1948); *Brookhaven Symp. Biol., 13,* 25 (1960).
[28] Schachman, H. K. *Cold Spring Harbor Symp. Quant. Biol., 28,* 409 (1963).

fig. 4-27. Values of thermodynamic constants for the reversible denaturation of certain proteins.

CONSTANT	TRYPSIN[a]	CRYSTALLINE TRYPSIN SOYBEAN INHIBITOR[b]	CHYMOTRYPSIN[c]
pH	2.0	3.0	2.0
T (°C)	47	50	47
ΔG_1° [d]	−1.3	−0.9	−1.4
ΔH_1°	67.6	57.3	99.6
$\Delta H_1^\ddagger$	40.2	55.3	84.5
$\Delta H_{-1}^\ddagger$	−27.4	−1.9	−15.7
ΔS_1°	213	180	316
$\Delta S_1^\ddagger$	45	95	202
$\Delta S_{-1}^\ddagger$	−168	−84	−116

[a] Values from Anson, M. L., and Mirsky, A. E. *J. Gen. Physiol.*, *17*, 396 (1934).
[b] Values from Kunitz, M. *J. Gen. Physiol.*, *32*, 241 (1948).
[c] Values from Eisenberg, M. A., and Schwert, G. W. *J. Gen. Physiol.*, *34*, 583 (1951).
[d] The subscripts 1 and −1 refer to the forward and reverse reactions respectively.

intracellular *p*H

While the *p*H of the extracellular fluid (or blood) of higher organisms can be measured with relative ease and is found to be maintained within relatively narrow limits (7.39 to 7.44 in healthy humans) measurement of intracellular *p*H has presented formidable technical difficulties. Early studies made use of the CO_2-HCO_3^- buffer system.[29] This technique assumed that the P_{CO_2} in a muscle fiber is identical to that in venous blood. The bicarbonate content of muscle was taken to be the total CO_2 less the CO_2 calculated for the blood contained in muscle and the extracellular space. At the time of these studies, the evaluation of the extracellular space was not very reliable. Using the carbon dioxide method, values for the intracellular *p*H of 6.9 to 7.0 were obtained. Conway and Fearon[30] argued that only the CO_2 precipitable by barium chloride should be used to calculate the intracellular *p*H by the Henderson-Hasselbach equation; the remaining CO_2 was thought to be combined and not available for buffer action. Conway and Fearon obtained an intracellular *p*H of 6.0 which supported the contention of these authors that the distribution of hydrogen ions followed a Donnan equilibrium.

A number of investigators have employed indicator dyes to evaluate intracellular *p*H.[31] Many of these dyes act as vital stains and are taken up preferentially by cells. Alternatively, the indicator dyes may be introduced into the cells by the Chambers microinjection technique. A dye which changes color in the intracellular *p*H range is selected, and the color in the cell is compared with standards. Proteins are known to

[29] Fenn, W. O., and Maurer, F. W. *Protoplasma*, *24*, 337 (1935); Wallace, W. M., and Hastings, A. B. *J. Biol. Chem.*, *144*, 637 (1942).
[30] Conway, E. J., and Fearon, P. J. *J. Physiol.* (*London*), *103*, 274 (1944).
[31] Small, J., and Wiercinski, F. J., in Heilbrunn, L. V., and Weber, F., eds. *Protoplasmatologia*. Vienna: Springer, 1955, vol. 2 B; Caldwell, P. C. *Intern. Rev. Cytol.*, *5*, 229 (1956).

cause errors of 1 *p*H unit or more with many dyes as a result of binding of the dyes. Many measurements of this type have been performed giving intracellular *p*H's in the range of 5.6 to 7.2 depending on the cell type, the dye, and the technique of measurement.

Recently, 5,5-dimethyl-2,4-oxazolidinedione (DMO) has been used as an indicator of intracellular *p*H.[32] The use of DMO is based on several assumptions. DMO is a weak acid with a pK_a of 6.13 at 37°. It exists in two forms, ionized and nonionized, when in solution:

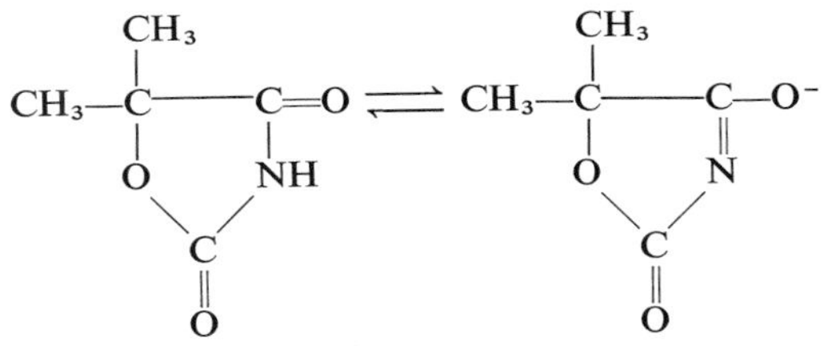

```
     CH3                          CH3
      |                            |
CH3—C————C=O  ⇌  CH3—C————C—O⁻
      |       |                    |       ||
      O      NH                    O       N
       \     /                      \     /
          C                            C
          ||                           ||
          O                            O
```

The compound is inert, and it is believed to be bound neither to plasma albumin nor to proteins of muscle-cell sap. The excretion of DMO by the kidneys is very slow. It is thought that cellular membrane is relatively impermeable to the ionized form of DMO but highly permeable to the nonionized form, so that the intracellular and extracellular concentrations of nonionized DMO are taken to be equal. Although dissociation constants vary with other solutes, the pK_a of DMO within the cell and the pK_a in the extracellular fluid are taken to be the same.

The following formula has been deduced from the Henderson-Hasselbach equation (eq. 4-223) for calculating the intracellular *p*H:

$$\text{pH}_i = pK_a + \log\left\{\left[\frac{C_t}{C_e}\left(1 + \frac{V_e}{V_i}\right) + \frac{V_e}{V_i}\right][10^{(p\text{H}_e - pK_a)} + 1] - 1\right\} \qquad (4\text{-}315)$$

where V_e is the volume of extracellular water calculated from the inulin space,[33] V_i is the volume of intracellular water calculated by subtracting V_i from the total water, C_t is the concentration of DMO in the total tissue sample, and C_e is the concentration of DMO in the extracellular fluid. The concentrations of DMO can be determined by its ultraviolet absorption or by use of radioactive ^{14}C-DMO. Values of intracellular *p*H between 6.90 and 7.08 have been obtained for mammalian muscle by this method.

The use of indicators for the measuremert of intracellular *p*H has been challenged on the basis that the cell contains a large number of organelles and is not an internally homogeneous medium. In a recent study, 85 percent of intracellular DMO was found to be bound to a small fraction of basic intracellular proteins.[34]

Intracellular *p*H has also been measured directly by the use of glass electrodes. An intracellular *p*H in crab muscle of 7.15 was obtained using a *p*H electrode with a 30 μ tip diameter.[35] Finer *p*H electrodes with tip diameters less than 1 μ were subse-

[32] Waddell, W. J., and Butler, T. C. *J. Clin. Invest.*, *38*, 720 (1959); Irvine, R. O. H., Saunders, S. J., Milne, M. D., and Crawford, M. A. *Clin. Sci.*, *20*, 1 (1961); Bittar, E. E., Watt, M. F., Pateras, V. R., and Parrish, A. E. *Clin. Sci.*, *23*, 265 (1962); Miller, R. B., Tyson, I., and Relman, A. S. *Am. J. Physiol.*, *204*, 1048 (1963); Adler, S., Roy, A., and Relman, A. S. *J. Clin. Invest.*, *44*, 8, 21 (1965).

[33] There is evidence that inulin, a large polysaccharide, does not penetrate the cell membrane. After adding a known quantity of inulin to a tissue, the extracellular space can be estimated by determining its concentration in the extracellular fluid.

[34] Campion, D. S., Carter, N. W., Rector, F. C., Jr., and Seldin, D. W. *Clin. Res.*, *46*, 353 (1967).

[35] Caldwell, P. C. *J. Physiol. (London)*, *142*, 22 (1958).

quently constructed which are presumed to minimize leakage and not to cause injury to the cell membrane;[36] these *p*H electrodes led to measurements of 7.12 and 6.78 for the intracellular *p*H in frog and rat muscle respectively. Recently, these results have been criticized on the basis of technical aspects of electrode construction and measurement techniques.[37] Using *p*H electrodes of about 1 μ tip diameter, Carter and his coworkers obtained a value of 5.99 for the intracellular *p*H of rat muscle.

Thus, some uncertainty about the intracellular *p*H of muscle remains, and the experimental data cluster around two values, 6.0 and 7.0. The difference is of some importance with regard to the question of whether or not a Donnan equilibrium for hydrogen ions exists across the cell membrane (see Chapter 8).

structure and function

In thermodynamics an engine is always described by its *effect* on some other thermodynamically characterized system. For example, a heat engine is defined as an entity which removes heat from a high-temperature source, transforms part of it into environmental work, and returns the remainder to a low-temperature reservoir. *The thermodynamic state of the engine itself is not considered.* In fact the thermodynamic state of an engine may not even be relevant to a consideration of its operation. For example, the entropy content of a piece of steel and a machined gear may be virtually the same. The detailed *shape* of a homogeneous gear is not a thermodynamic parameter, but it may be crucial to the operation of the engine. Conversely, the *entropy* of the gear, one of its basic thermodynamic properties, is not related to the gear's ability to transfer torque. *The order (or information content) expressed by the coherent functioning of the parts of an engine is not described by its thermodynamic state variables.* In particular, there is not a direct relation between the internal order of an engine and its entropy content. One should be cognizant of these limitations in extrapolating the statistical mechanical interpretation of entropy.

An important type of order in biological systems is that expressed by the parts of a functioning engine. In the case of coded polymers such as DNA, RNA, and proteins, the entropy changes associated with permutations of the sequences of monomers are unrelated to the resulting changes in the functional capacity of the polymer. Thus two sequences of DNA containing the same number of nucleotides may have the same internal entropy, yet one will code for a functioning enzyme while the other will not. Similar arguments apply to the membrane structures which perform active transport, the contractile structures which perform mechanical work, the nerve nets which generate and recognize patterns, etc. Consequently, *there are significant functional aspects of biological systems which cannot be described in terms of the equilibrium thermodynamic properties of the component structures.*[38]

For the physiologist the most important aspect of thermodynamic coupling coefficients is their direct relevance to structure-function relations in physiological systems. In mechanics, structure-function relations describe how the movements of some parts of a machine produce movements in other parts of the machine. In physiology, one must consider not only spatial movements but also chemical reactions and phase

[36] Kostyuk, P. G., and Sorokina, Z. A., in Kleinzeller, A., and Kotyk, A., eds. *Membrane Transport and Metabolism.* New York: Academic Press, 1961, p. 193; Carter, N. W. *Clin. Res.*, *9*, 177 (1961).
[37] Carter, N. W., Rector, F. C., Jr., Campion, D. S., and Seldin, D. W. *J. Clin. Invest.*, *46*, 920 (1967).
[38] Linschitz, H., in Quastler, H., ed. *Information Theory in Biology.* Urbana, Ill.: The University of Illinois Press, 1953, pp. 14 and 251.

transitions. The thermodynamic coupling coefficients describe how one type of "displacement"—be it spatial, chemical, or phase—produces another displacement in a different "direction." The directional aspect of the thermodynamic coupling coefficients defines the functional significance of the underlying physical structures.

An especially clear example of these generalities is the structural specialization of biological membranes leading to active transport. The forward-running (driving) process is a chemical reaction in the membrane while the backward-running (driven) process is a spatial displacement of molecules across the membrane. The chemical reaction has no spatial direction, and the transmembrane movement has no chemical direction. Therefore, the thermodynamic coupling coefficient which relates transport to a chemical reaction must have mixed spatial and chemical aspects; hence it describes an *anisotropic* chemical structure in the membrane. Moreover, thermodynamic coupling coefficients describe only the functionally (physiologically) significant aspects of the membrane anisotropy—an important simplification considering the great structural complexity of biological membranes.

Another basic example concerns the structure-function relations for enzymes. Most enzymes are not simply catalysts. Frequently enzyme reactions serve to couple a forward-running reaction to another reaction which is then driven away from equilibrium. Thermodynamic coupling coefficients directly describe such physiologically significant aspects of enzyme structure.

It must be admitted that thermodynamic coupling coefficients only describe and do not explain the function of biological structures. For an explanation one needs a statistical theory of thermodynamic coupling. A useful theory must be applicable to processes which occur far from equilibrium and must not require randomness in the underlying sequence of molecular states. The development of such a theory is one of the most urgent tasks in the field of theoretical biology.

references

Castellan, G. W. *Physical Chemistry.* Reading, Mass.: Addison-Wesley, 1964.

Dixon, M., and Webb, E. C. *Enzymes*, 2nd ed. New York: Academic Press, 1964.

Edsall, J. T., and Wyman, J. *Biophysical Chemistry.* New York: Academic Press, 1958.

Fitts, D. D. *Nonequilibrium Thermodynamics.* New York: McGraw-Hill, 1962.

Glasstone, S. *The Elements of Physical Chemistry*, 2nd ed. Princeton, N.J.: Van Nostrand, 1946.

de Groot, S. R. *Thermodynamics of Irreversible Processes.* Amsterdam: North Holland Publishing Company, 1952.

Guggenheim, E. A. *Chemical Thermodynamics*, 4th ed. New York: Wiley (Interscience), 1960.

Katchalsky, A., and Curran, P. F. *Nonequilibrium Thermodynamics in Biophysics.* Cambridge, Mass.: Harvard University Press, 1965.

Klotz, I. M. *Chemical Thermodynamics.* New York: W. A. Benjamin, 1964.

Moore, W. J. *Physical Chemistry*, 3rd ed. Englewood Cliffs, N.J.: Prentice-Hall, 1962.

Prigogine, I. *Introduction to Thermodynamics of Irreversible Processes.* Springfield, Ill.: Charles C Thomas, 1955.

Tanford, C. *Physical Chemistry of Macromolecules.* New York: Wiley, 1961.

Wall, F. T. *Chemical Thermodynamics*, 2nd ed. San Francisco: Freeman, 1965.

chapter 5

energetics and regulation of metabolic processes

flow of energy in living systems

Like functioning machines in general, living organisms are open systems which take up energy from the environment and utilize a portion of it for the useful work of carrying on those processes which are characteristic of life. By and large, the energy utilized is derived from specific types of chemical fuels which comprise the *food* of the organism. Living organisms vary in their food requirements; some are fastidious with a narrow range of acceptable foods or with idiosyncrasies of diet while others can utilize a wide variety of substances as food. The utilization of food is accompanied by the liberation of heat, which represents the part of the energy not used for work.

A number of kinds of living organisms, the *autotrophs*, are able to utilize the radiant energy of sunlight to synthesize complex organic substances from inorganic materials by the process of *photosynthesis*. Autotrophs, in the main, belong to the plant kingdom. Many microorganisms can utilize hydrocarbons as energy sources for the synthesis of required complex organic compounds from carbon dioxide, ammonia, and water. The *chemosynthetic* bacteria can couple synthetic reactions to the oxidation of inorganic compounds including sulfur, hydrogen sulfide, thiosulfate, ammonia, hydrogen gas, ferrous and manganous compounds, and nitrites.[1] But quantitatively, photosynthesis

[1] Starkey, R. L., ed. *Bacteriol. Rev.*, *26*, 142 (1962).

is the major process in living systems which incorporates energy from outside sources. Photosynthesis results in the formation of a variety of compounds, but the largest fraction of the newly synthesized material is carbohydrate. The photosynthetic process can be summarized, although in a somewhat oversimplified statement, by the following reaction:[2]

$$6\ CO_2 + 6\ H_2O \rightarrow C_6H_{12}O_6 + 6\ O_2 \qquad \Delta G' = +686\ \text{kcal/mole} \qquad (5\text{-}1)$$

The energy in sunlight is used to form glucose from carbon dioxide and water, and molecular oxygen is liberated as a by-product. Although as much as 20 percent efficiency of conversion of radiant energy into chemical energy has been obtained in the laboratory using algae or sections of leaves, the highest efficiency of photosynthesis in field crops has been estimated to be about 2 percent.[3]

All multicellular animals and some plants are *heterotrophs*; that is, they require for food preformed organic compounds which are available only from other living organisms. While many heterotrophs feed upon other heterotrophs, all food utilized by living organisms originates in photosynthesis, the relatively small amount made by the chemosynthetic microorganisms excepted. Heterotrophs can be regarded as carrying out the reverse of reaction 5-1 by the process of *glycolysis* and *respiration*. A number of organisms can live without oxygen, but they and the products of their metabolism are ultimately further oxidized by other heterotrophs to carbon dioxide and water. Some of the energy which is liberated during the oxidation of glucose is utilized in the form of work. Thus, a cycle exists (see Fig. 5-1) in which autotrophs on the balance remove carbon dioxide from the atmosphere for the synthesis of glucose and liberate molecular

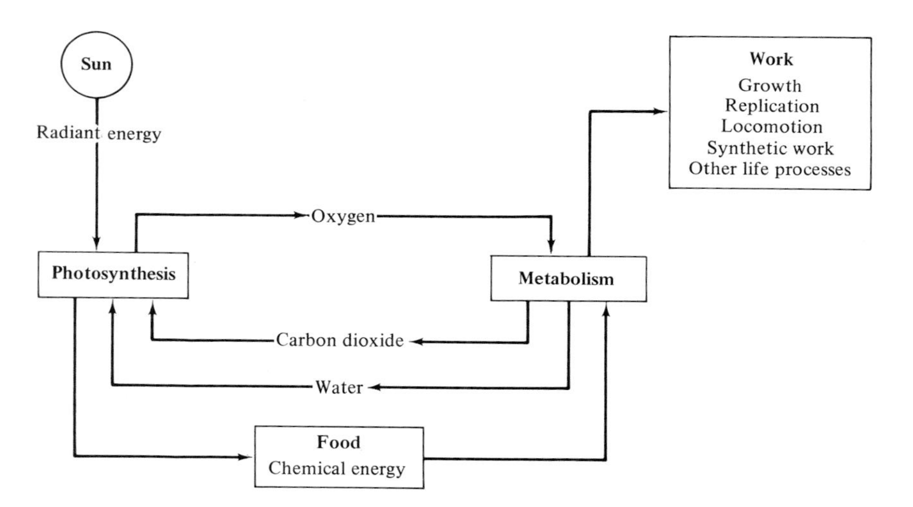

fig. 5-1. A diagram illustrating the energy cycle in the biosphere.

[2] Because the conditions which prevail in living systems differ markedly from the ordinary standard-state conditions, the specific free energy changes of reactions ($\Delta G'$) will be used in this chapter in terms of the following conditions: (1) solvent is at an activity of unity, (2) *p*H is 7.0, (3) standard solute concentrations are 0.01 *m*, (4) equilibrated with oxygen at a partial pressure of 0.2 atm, and (5) equilibrated with carbon dioxide at a partial pressure of 0.05 atm.

[3] Fry, B. A., and Peel, J. L., eds. *Autotrophic Microorganisms*. London: Cambridge University Press, 1954.

oxygen, while heterotrophs oxidize the glucose from plant sources, using molecular oxygen and, in the process, liberating carbon dioxide. Energy derived from sunlight enters this cycle, and energy leaves the cycle in the form of complex organic substances synthesized, useful work accomplished, and heat.

Some notion of the magnitude of the exchange in the cycle can be gleaned from the estimate that the entire content of carbon dioxide in the atmosphere would be removed by photosynthetic processes in the earth's vegetation in two to three years if it were not replenished. The total amount of carbon fixed by photosynthesis is enormous, about 3.3×10^{10} tons per year. Air contains about 0.03 percent carbon dioxide, which limits photosynthesis at a submaximal level. There may have been periods when the carbon-dioxide content of the atmosphere was greater and when the earth was richer in terms of total living matter. The amount present today is about equally divided between photosynthetic plants on the land surfaces, mainly forests and cultivated land, and photosynthetic organisms in the oceans. The energy capture in the total photosynthetic process is about 10^{18} kcal per year. For purposes of comparison, the total energy used as fuel by man in fires and engines is about 10^{16} kcal per year for which mostly mineral fuel is used. Actually, less than 0.1 percent of the energy from solar radiation falling on the surface of the earth is used for photosynthesis.

The ideas set out above are, in fact, very old. Jan B. van Helmont (1578–1644) planted a young willow which weighed 16 pounds in a bucket containing 200 pounds of dry earth. The dirt was covered, except when the tree was watered, to prevent the inadvertent addition of extraneous dust or dirt. After five years, the willow had grown to weigh 180 pounds, but, surprisingly, the earth still weighed 200 pounds. Van Helmont deduced that the additional 164 pounds of wood, roots, and leaves had their origin in the water. Of course, he was only partly right. How pleased van Helmont probably would have been to know that the additional weight of tree had been elaborated not only from the water but also in part from his *blas*, carbon dioxide.

Joseph Priestley (1733–1804) discovered a gas given off by plants kept under water. He noted that this gas could revitalize air which had been spent by burning a candle in it, and thus enable the candle to burn on. Subscribing to the then-current phlogiston theory, Priestley called his gas "dephlogisticated air." Jan Ingenhousz (1730–1799) introduced the concept of balance between the plant kingdom and the animal kingdom. The experiments of Jan Ingenhousz and Jean Senebier (1742–1809) demonstrated that the green parts of plants absorb carbon dioxide while exposed to sunlight, while, in the dark, plants, like animals, give off carbon dioxide. Carbon dioxide was already well known, it being the major component of van Helmont's blas.

Nicolas de Saussure (1767–1845) did careful experiments which indicated that plants gained more weight than could be accounted for by the weight difference between the carbon dioxide fixed and oxygen evolved. He concluded that water was incorporated into the plant. De Saussure's careful experiments established the fact that the volumes of carbon dioxide fixed and oxygen evolved during photosynthesis were equal.

To Antoine Lavoisier (1743–1794) must go the credit of recognizing the true role of oxygen in combustion. Lavoisier quantified the amount of oxygen taken up during combustion with the amount of oxide formed. With the help of Pierre de Laplace (1749–1827), Lavoisier built a calorimeter to measure heat evolved and showed that this was related to the oxygen taken up during combustion. Lavoisier measured the heat evolved by animals in his calorimeter and demonstrated that respiration in animals is a combustion accompanied by the uptake of oxygen and evolution of carbon dioxide with the expected amount of heat liberated (Fig. 5-2). Lavoisier even observed the specific dynamic action of proteins (see p. 242), but he did not realize its significance.

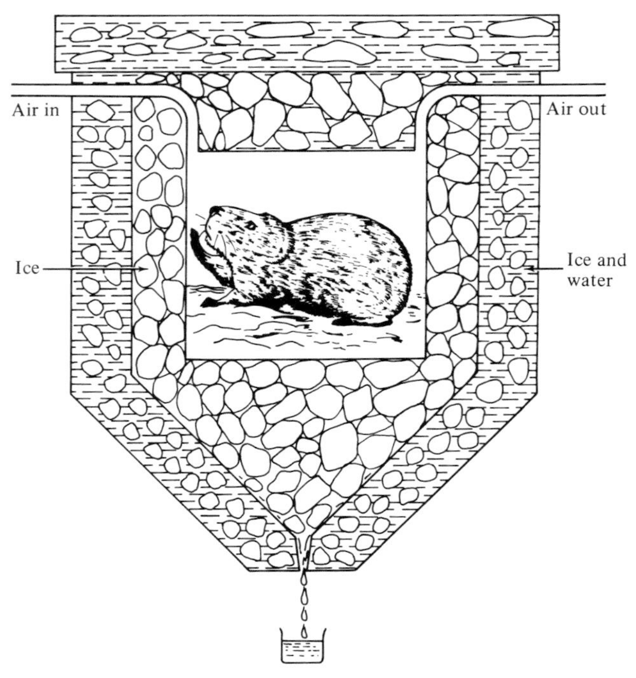

fig. 5-2. An artist's conception of the animal calorimeter built by Lavoisier. The heat evolved by the animal melts the ice in the inner jacket, and the water formed flows out of the apparatus. A mixture of ice and water in the outer jacket forms an adiabatic wall preventing heat flow into or out of the calorimeter because it is at the same temperature as the inner jacket.

general aspects of metabolism

Foods—the carbohydrates derived in the first instance from photosynthesis, and carbohydrates, fats, and proteins produced secondarily by living organisms—represent the form in which energy is stored until it is needed and utilized to carry out the life processes. The overall metabolism of foods in living organisms can be evaluated by measurement of oxygen consumption; by measurement of carbon dioxide liberated; and, because almost all the energy is ultimately liberated as heat, by measurement of the heat produced by an animal or by the combustion of food in a calorimeter. The heat of combustion of glucose, a representative carbohydrate, by the following reaction, is given below:

$$C_6H_{12}O_6 + 6\ O_2 \rightarrow 6\ H_2O + 6\ CO_2 \qquad \Delta H' = -673\ \text{kcal/mole} \qquad (5\text{-}2)$$

or 3.7 kcal/g. The heat of combustion of glycogen is about 4.3 kcal/g. Triolein, a representative fat, is oxidized by the following reaction:

$$C_{57}H_{104}O_6 + 80\ O_2 \rightarrow 52\ H_2O + 57\ CO_2 \qquad \Delta H' = -9700\ \text{kcal/mole} \qquad (5\text{-}3)$$

or a heat of combustion of 9.3 kcal/g. Protein is not completely oxidized in living organisms, and the estimation of heat liberated from protein foods is based on their metabolism to urea and other products. On this basis, the metabolism of proteins should yield about 4.1 kcal/g. The heat produced can also be evaluated in terms of the oxygen consumed and carbon dioxide liberated; these data are listed in Fig. 5-3.

fig. 5-3. Average metabolic energy derived from food.

TYPE OF FOOD	KCAL/G	KCAL/L O_2 CONSUMED	KCAL/L CO_2 EVOLVED	RESPIRATORY QUOTIENT
Carbohydrate	4.1	5.0	5.0	1.00
Fat	9.3	4.7	6.6	0.71
Protein	4.1	4.5	5.6	0.80

Many organisms utilize all three major types of food simultaneously. The relative proportions of carbohydrate, fat, and protein food utilized by an organism are reflected in the ratio of the volume of carbon dioxide evolved during metabolism to the volume of oxygen used, a ratio known as the *respiratory quotient.*

$$\text{Respiratory quotient (R.Q.)} = \frac{\text{volume } CO_2 \text{ evolved}}{\text{volume } O_2 \text{ consumed}} \qquad (5\text{-}4)$$

For carbohydrates, the respiratory quotient is 1.00, while for fats it is 0.71 and for proteins it is 0.80. The proportions of the various types of food consumed can be calculated in the following manner. The amount of protein consumed can be estimated from the amount of urinary nitrogen excreted. Each gram of excreted nitrogen is equivalent to approximately 6.25 grams protein metabolized, and is equivalent to the consumption of 5.94 liters oxygen and the evolution of 4.76 liters carbon dioxide. The oxygen consumed and carbon dioxide evolved calculated from the metabolism of protein can be subtracted from the total volumes measured, leaving the oxygen consumed and carbon dioxide evolved from the metabolism of nonprotein foods. The ratio of carbohydrate to fat in the nonprotein foods can be calculated from the respiratory quotient. Some sample values are given in Fig. 5-4.

fig. 5-4. Relation of nonprotein respiratory quotient to the percentages of carbohydrate and fat metabolized.

NONPROTEIN RESPIRATORY QUOTIENT	KCAL/L OXYGEN CONSUMED	CALORIES DERIVED FROM	
		CARBOHYDRATE PERCENT	FAT PERCENT
0.707	4.686	0	100.0
0.720	4.702	4.8	95.2
0.760	4.751	19.2	80.8
0.800	4.801	33.4	66.6
0.840	4.850	47.2	52.8
0.880	4.899	60.8	39.2
0.920	4.948	74.1	25.9
0.960	4.998	87.2	12.8
1.000	5.047	100.0	0

The metabolic rates of a variety of organisms have been determined. In general, the metabolic rate varies with the surface area of the organism. Microorganisms have the largest ratio of surface area to mass, and it is not surprising, therefore, that they have the highest rates of oxygen consumption per gram dry weight (Fig. 5-5). The

fig. 5-5. Respiration rates of various organisms and tissues. (From Giese, A. C. *Cell Physiology*, 3rd ed. Philadelphia: Saunders, 1964, p. 404.)

GROUP	ORGANISM	°C	Q_{O_2}[a]
Microorganisms	*Bacillus mesentericus vulgatus*	16	12.1
	Azotobacter chroococcum	28	500–1000
	Bacillus florescens non liquefaciens		4100
	Neurospora crassa	26	6.4
	Saccharomyces cereviseae	26	8–14.5
	Paramecium	20	0.5
Plants	*Verbascum thapsus* (leaf)	23	0.093
	(pistil)		0.204
	(stamen)		0.190
	Papaver Rhoeas (leaf)	22	0.803
	(pistil)		0.172
	(stamen)		0.280
Invertebrates	*Anemonia sulcata*	18	0.0134
	Asterias rubens	15	0.03
	Nereis virens	15	0.026
	Mytilus (mussel)	20	0.02
	Astacus (crayfish)	20	0.047
	Vanessa (butterfly)	20	0.06
Vertebrates	Carp	20	0.1
	Mouse	37	2.5
	Man	37	0.2
Animal tissues	Rat liver	37.5	2.2–3.3
	Rat kidney cortex	37.5	5.2–9.0
	Rat brain cortex	37.5	2.7
	Rat voluntary muscle	37	1.5
	Frog nerve	15	0.02
	Rabbit nerve	37	0.29

[a] Q_{O_2} is given in milliliters per gram of wet weight per hour.

relation of oxygen consumption to cell size in protozoans is depicted in Fig. 5-6. Comparison of the metabolic rates of microorganisms with those of larger animals reveals marked differences. In large part, the very high metabolic rates for microorganisms are the result of the method of measurement. The oxygen consumption of microorganisms is measured generally under conditions of active growth and normal activity.

The metabolic rates of larger organisms, on the other hand, are measured under conditions when the energy requirements are minimal. The measurements are made during inactivity in a well-fed animal after a period of rest. These circumstances are called *basal conditions*, and the metabolic rate obtained is called the *basal metabolic*

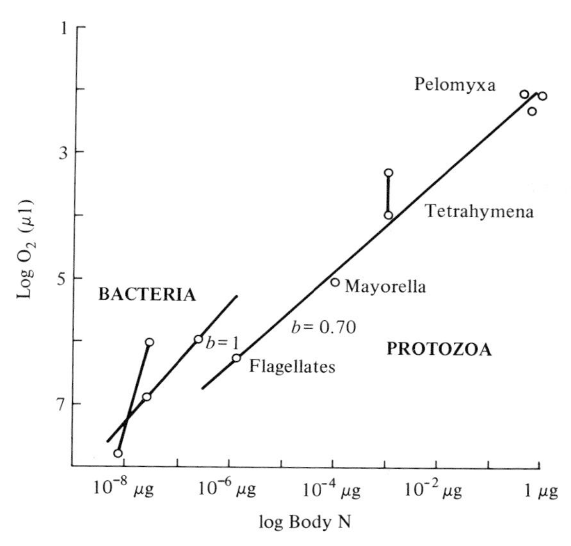

fig. 5-6. A diagram showing the relation between cell size (indicated by the nitrogen content per cell) and the oxygen consumption. (From Zeuthen, E. *Quart. Rev. Biol., 28*, 3 [1953].)

rate. The basal metabolic rate has great practical value in animal nutrition and husbandry and in the practice of clinical medicine. Activity will result in an oxygen consumption which may be as much as two orders of magnitude greater than the basal rate. Under conditions of maximal activity, the rate of oxygen consumption of mammals may approach that of microorganisms. In *homoiotherms*, animals that maintain a constant temperature somewhat above the ambient temperature (about 37° in mammals and about 42° in birds), a large fraction of the basal metabolic rate is required to maintain the body temperature. By contrast, *poikilotherms*, organisms which have no mechanism for maintaining a constant internal temperature and whose temperature follows that of the surroundings, have lower metabolic rates.

The constancy of the basal metabolic rate per unit of surface area is particularly striking among homoiotherms (Fig. 5-7). The metabolic rates of phylogenetically

fig. 5-7. Relation of daily basal heat production to body weight and surface area. (From Voit, E. *Z. f. Biol., 41*,120 [1901].)

	BODY WEIGHT (KG)	METABOLISM PER KG OF BODY WEIGHT PER DAY (CAL)	METABOLISM PER M^2 OF BODY SURFACE PER DAY (CAL)
Horse	441.0	11.3	948
Pig	128.0	19.1	1078
Man	64.3	32.1	1042
Dog	15.2	51.5	1039
Goose	3.5	66.7	969
Fowl	2.0	71.0	943
Mouse	0.018	212.0	1188

distant animals of the same size are nearly equal while the metabolic rates of closely related species of different size show marked differences. The relationship of the metabolic rate to surface area has been held to result in large part from the necessity of maintaining the body temperature in the face of heat losses. The heat losses of an animal vary with the surface area. The metabolic rate varies approximately as the ¾ power of the body weight in mammals (Fig. 5-8). The effect of activity on the metabolic rate in man is given in Fig. 5-9. Various tissues of higher organisms differ in their metabolic rates; some representative values are given in Fig. 5-10.

effect of temperature on metabolism

Within the temperature limits that permit the life processes to function (0° to 42° for most organisms), the rate of respiration (oxygen consumption) of cells or organisms increases with temperature, usually by a factor of 2 to 4 for a 10° rise in temperature. The rate of respiration of very young mammals who are not yet able to regulate their body temperature varies with the ambient temperature like that of poikilotherms. In the case of adult homoiotherms, however, the rate of respiration may increase with a drop in ambient temperature as the animal is forced to provide more heat to maintain its temperature.

M. Rubner (1902) described the increase in metabolic rate which follows the ingestion of food. The degree of increase in metabolic rate, which is called the *specific dynamic effect*, depends upon the nature of the food; it is much greater for protein than for carbohydrate or fat. Rubner attributed the specific dynamic effect to the work required to digest the food. The specific dynamic effect depends upon the size of the meal and on the nature of the food but is approximately 30 percent of the ingested calories for protein, 12.5 percent for fat, and 10 percent for carbohydrate. The specific dynamic effect in homoiotherms is lower when the ambient temperature is low because the additional metabolism produces heat to raise the body temperature and offsets, in part, the need for metabolism to produce the heat required to maintain the body temperature.

There have been a multitude of observations that many complex biological phenomena occur more rapidly at higher than at lower temperatures. During the 1920s, W. J. Crozier and his collaborators[4] found that such diverse processes as the frequency of chirping of a cricket, the rate of creeping of ants, the rate of ciliary movement on clam gill epithelium, or the heart rate of the silkworm give a linear plot of the logarithm of rate *versus* temperature for a large temperature range. These investigators also found that these Arrhenius type plots sometimes showed more or less sharply defined "breaks." On the basis of their studies, Crozier and his colleagues proposed a theory which may be summarized as follows: (1) Complex physiological phenomena result from a catenary series of reactions, each with a unique temperature characteristic which resembles the Arrhenius energy of activation; (2) the overall process is limited over a finite temperature range by the slowest reaction (master reaction); (3) at certain critical temperatures, a different reaction may become rate-limiting, producing a break in the Arrhenius plots; and (4) the rate-limiting reactions might be identified in some cases by their temperature characteristic.

---

[4] Crozier, W. J. *J. Gen. Physiol.*, *7*, 123, 189 (1924); Crozier, W. J., and Federighi, H. *J. Gen. Physiol.*, *7*, 137, 565 (1924); Crozier, W. J., and Stier, T. B. *J. Gen. Physiol.*, *7*, 429, 571, 699, 705 (1925); Crozier, W. J. *J. Gen. Physiol.*, *9*, 531 (1926).

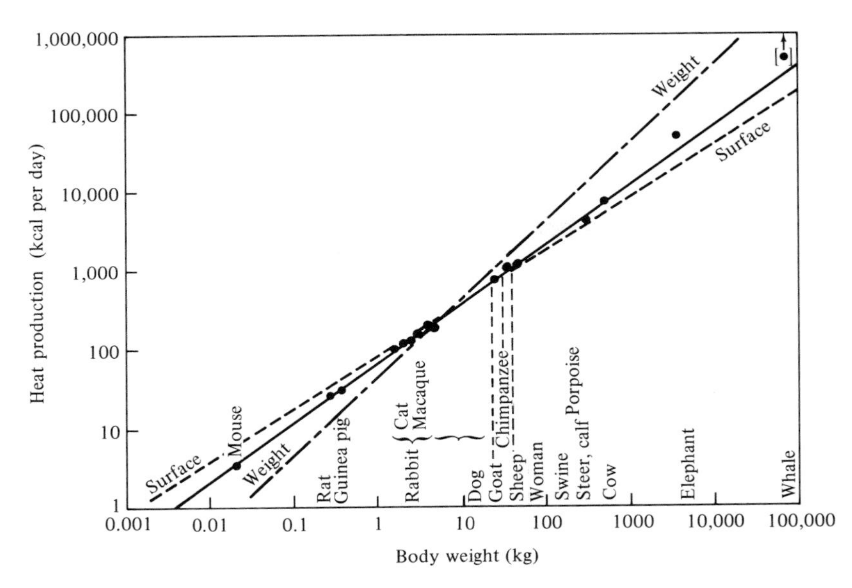

fig. 5-8. A graph showing the approximately linear relationship between the logarithms of basal metabolic rate and body weight. (From Kleiber, M. *Physiol. Rev., 27,* 530 [1947].)

fig. 5-9. Metabolic rate of man as a function of activity.

TYPE OF ACTIVITY	KCAL/HR
Sleeping	65
Awake, lying quietly	77
Awake, sitting quietly	100
Standing, relaxed	110
Light muscular exercise	170
Heavy muscular exercise	600

fig. 5-10. Respiration of various tissues. (From White, A., Handler, P., and Smith, E. L. *Principles of Biochemistry,* 3rd ed. New York: McGraw-Hill, 1959, p. 334.)

TISSUE	Q_{O_2} [a]	TISSUE	Q_{O_2}
Retina	31	Lung	8
Kidney	21	Placenta	7
Liver (fasted animal)	17	Myeloid bone marrow	6
Liver (fed animal)	12	Thymus	6
Jejunal mucosa	15	Pancreas	6
Thyroid	13	Diaphragm	6
Testis	12	Heart	5
Cerebral cortex	12	Ileal mucosa	5
Hypothysis	12	Lymph node	4
Spleen	12	Skeletal muscle	3
Adrenal gland	10	Cornea	2
Erythroid bone marrow	9	Skin	0.8
Duodenal mucosa	9	Lens	0.5

[a] Q_{O_2} = microliters O_2 per milligram dry weight per hour. All values are for rat tissue slices in Ringer's phosphate + glucose.

Typical data of Crozier are shown in Fig. 5-11. A temperature curve which shows a supposed break is shown in Fig. 5-12. Many of the plots showing breaks, it has been argued, could just as well be fitted by a smooth curve (Fig. 5-13), which might lead to the interpretation that the rate dependence upon temperature is a continuous function.[5] In view of the complex metabolic pathways that we now know exist in cells, the master reaction concept is probably an oversimplification, and it is doubtful that the critical temperature breaks have any real meaning in most cases. Even purified enzyme systems show breaks in their rate dependence on temperature when assayed in vitro.[6] Never-

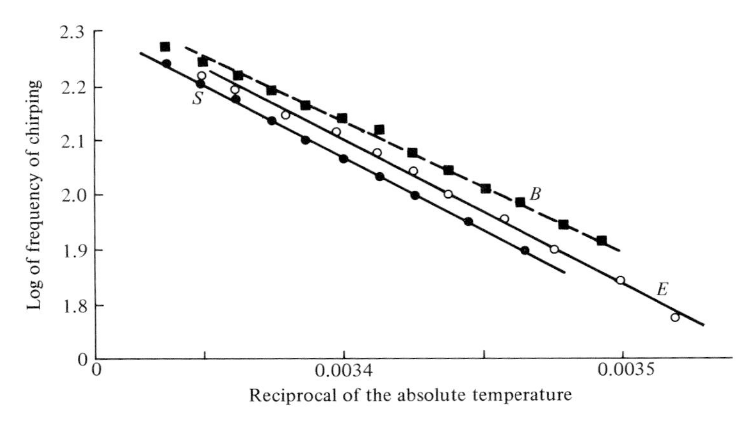

fig. 5-11. Temperature dependence of the frequency of chirping of the tree cricket, *Oecanthus.* (From Crozier, W. J. *J. Gen. Physiol., 7,* 133 [1924].)

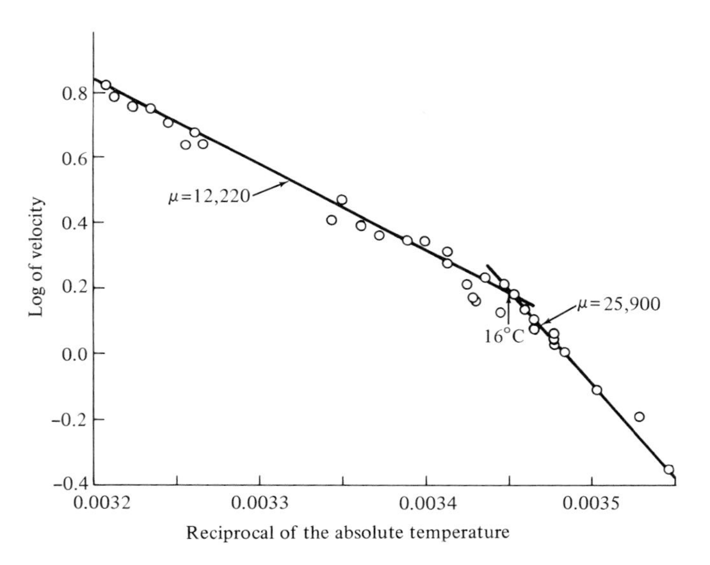

fig. 5-12. Temperature dependence of the rate of creeping of ants. (From Crozier, W. J. *J. Gen. Physiol., 7,* 131 [1924].)

---

[5] Buchanan, R. E., and Fulmer, E. I. *Physiology and Biochemistry of Bacteria*. Baltimore: Williams and Wilkins, 1930, vol. 2, p. 46.

[6] Sizer, I. W. *J. Biol. Chem., 145*, 405 (1942); *Advan. Enzymol., 3*, 35 (1943); Kistiakowsky, G. B., and Lumry, R. *J. Am. Chem. Soc., 71*, 2006 (1949).

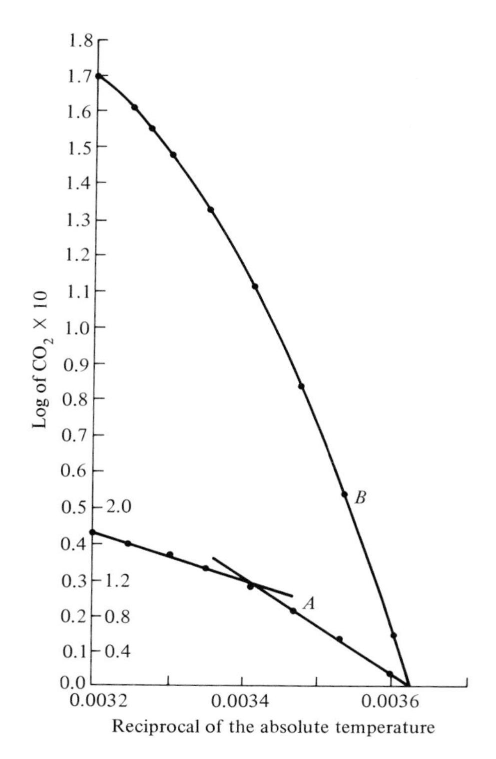

fig. 5-13. The rate of CO_2 production in alcoholic fermentation plotted on two different scales of ordinate. The two linear sections appearing in curve *A* are seen to be a continuous curve when plotted on an expanded ordinate scale in *B*. (From Buchanan, R. E., and Fulmer, E. I. *Physiology and Biochemistry of Bacteria.* Baltimore: Williams & Wilkins, 1930, vol. 2, p. 46. Copyright © 1930, The Williams & Wilkins Co., Baltimore, Md. 21202, U.S.A.)

theless, the fact that many complex physiological processes conform to an Arrhenius relationship provides some support for the idea that one reaction is largely rate-limiting. The curved or nonlinear plots may be due in some instances to a shift in the rate-limiting reaction from one step to another. In other instances, the nonlinearity may be the result of temperature effects on the enzyme system of the rate-limiting step which change its rate characteristics with temperature, for instance, by alterations in the enzyme itself with temperature.[6]

Although the environmental temperature range for living organisms in general is rather narrow, a number of species have evolved that live at the extremes of temperature. Bacteria which grow at ordinary temperatures, 10 to 45°, are called *mesophiles*, while bacteria which grow at temperatures above 55° are called *thermophiles*, and those which grow well only at temperatures below 20° are called *psychrophiles.* For a considerable temperature range, the growth rate of bacteria adheres to an Arrhenius plot. At low temperatures, however, the curves are nonlinear and fall off rapidly as the temperature is lowered; and at high temperatures the growth rates pass through a maximum and then fall off rapidly again. The growth rate maximum was explained by Hinshelwood by the proposition that two types of competitive processes, synthetic processes leading to cell growth, and destructive processes such as the denaturation of intracellular proteins, occur simultaneously.[7] Growth rate plots as a function of temperature for a mesophile and a psychrophile are shown in Fig. 5-14. Note the general similarity in the shape of the curves and the displacement along the temperature scale.

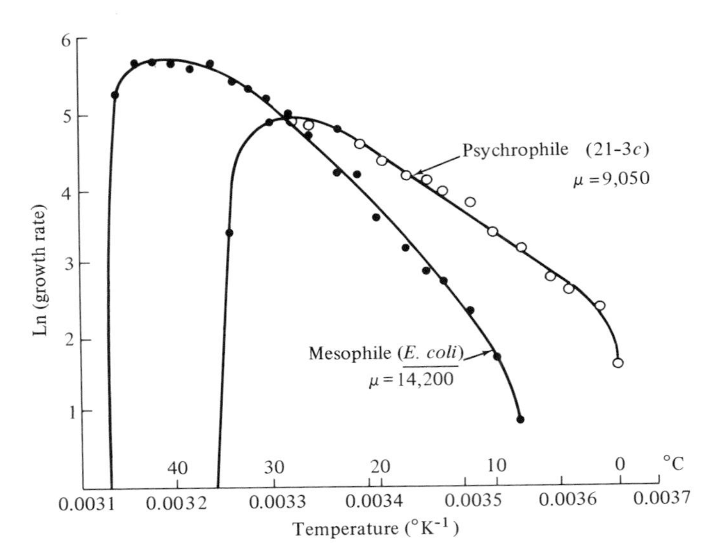

fig. 5-14. A plot showing the dependence of growth rate on temperature for a mesophilic bacterium, *E. coli,* and a psychrophile, 21-3*c*. (From Ingraham, J. L. *J. Bacteriol., 76,* 78 [1958].)

energy-rich compounds

One of the marvels of cellular function is the system of stepwise reactions in which energy is liberated with precise control. The energy thus liberated is coupled to the synthetic reactions which maintain the cellular constituents and sustain secretion, growth, and reproduction with remarkable efficiency by the formation and hydrolysis of so-called *energy-rich compounds.* Energy-rich compounds are low-molecular-weight esters with a high free energy of hydrolysis. Energy liberation is also coupled to processes leading to mechanical work, such as muscular contraction, or to electrical work, such as relaying nerve impulses, by means of these energy-rich compounds. The requirement for energy-rich compounds in the coupling has been shown in many ways, some of which will be described later. Lundsgaard[8] showed that a muscle poisoned by iodoacetate, although glucose breakdown was abolished, could contract 40 to 50 times. In the process, inorganic phosphate was liberated, phosphorylcreatine was virtually completely hydrolyzed, and adenosine triphosphate was largely hydrolyzed.

The more important energy-rich compounds and some of their properties are listed in Fig. 5-15. Structurally, these compounds are anhydride, amidine, or thioester derivatives of a phosphoric acid or a carboxylic acid. Phosphate anhydrides tend to have

[7] Hinshelwood, C. N. *The Chemical Kinetics of the Bacterial Cell,* 2nd ed. London: Oxford University Press, 1965.
[8] Lundsgaard, E. *Biochem. Z., 217,* 162 (1930); *227,* 51 (1930).

fig. 5-15. Approximate ΔG^0 values for hydrolysis of "energy-rich" compounds. (From Huennekens, F. M., and Whiteley, H. R., in Florkin, M., and Mason, H. S., eds. *Comparative Biochemistry.* New York: Academic Press, 1960, vol. 1, p. 121. Copyright Academic Press; reprinted by permission.)

COMPOUNDS	$-\Delta G^0$ KCAL/MOLE
Pyrophosphate	6.0
Acetyl-coenzyme A	6.3
Adenosine diphosphate	6.5
Adenosine triphosphate[a]	7.0
Adenosine triphosphate[b,c]	8.6
Acetyl phosphate	8.7
S-Phosphoryl-coenzyme A	9.0
Phosphocreatine	9.8
Glycerylphosphate	11.3
Phospho*enol*pyruvate	12.4
Acetyl adenylate	13.0
Acetyl imidazole	13.3
Adenosine phosphosulfate	18.0

[a] $ATP \rightarrow ADP + P_i$.
[b] $ATP \rightarrow AMP + PP$.
[c] Calculated from ΔG^0 values for hydrolysis of ATP, ADP, and PP.

high energies of activation, and, therefore, tend to be resistant to nonenzymatic hydrolysis. Lipmann[9] has called attention to the ease with which acetic anhydride hydrolyzes at *p*H 7, while acetylphosphate is more stable, and pyrophosphates are resistant to hydrolysis near neutrality. Whenever hydrolysis occurs, the liberation of energy accompanies the hydrolysis of these bonds. These compounds are so widely and nearly universally found in living systems that, viruses and rickettsia excepted, the presence of energy-rich compounds may be regarded as a fundamental attribute of living systems.

Adenosine triphosphate occupies a key position because, more than any of the other energy-rich compounds, it couples to energy-producing and energy-requiring reactions. Some of the more important reactions that lead to its formation or that require adenosine triphosphate to drive them will be outlined (see p. 248). Phosphorylcreatine is an energy-rich compound that appears to function as a reservoir of chemical energy in the cell, much like a storage battery functions as a reservoir of electrical energy in an automobile. Phosphorylcreatine can regenerate adenosine triphosphate from adenosine diphosphate in times of need, and in turn, phosphorylcreatine is resynthesized at times when excess adenosine triphosphate is available. In some animals,

[9] Lipmann, F., in McElroy, W. D., and Glass, B., eds. *Phosphorus Metabolism.* Baltimore: Johns Hopkins Press, 1951, vol. 1, p. 521.

phosphorylarginine is the energy-rich reservoir instead of phosphorylcreatine, and in a few species other phosphorylguanidinium compounds are found. Some interrelations of energy-rich compounds are shown in Fig. 5-16.

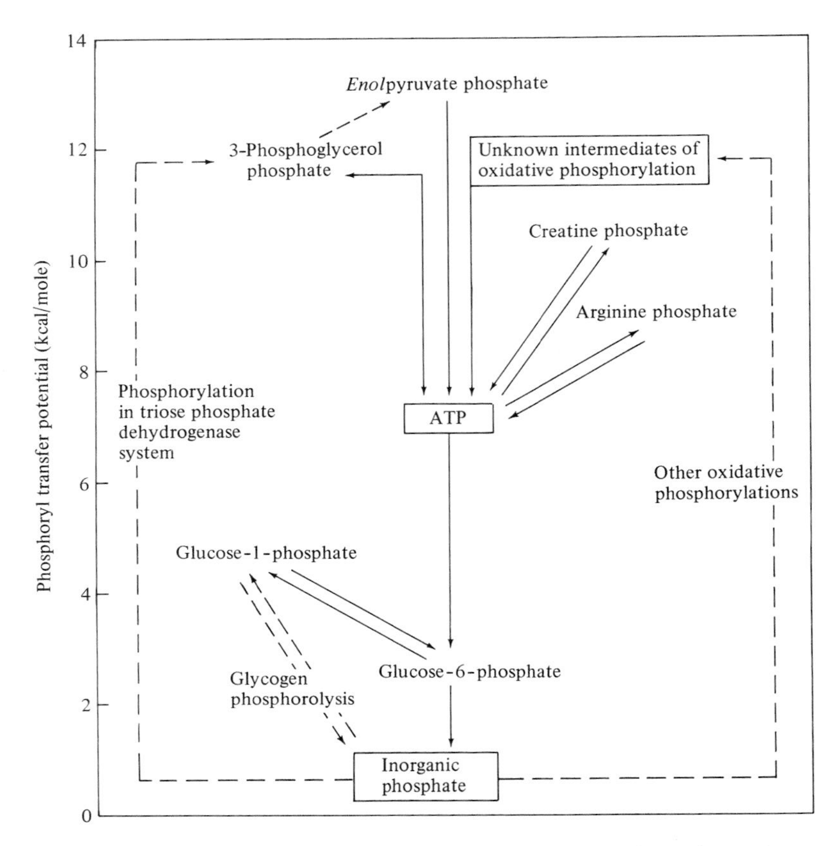

fig. 5-16. A diagram showing some reactions leading to the formation and utilization of ATP in terms of ΔG^0 of the energy-rich compounds involved. (From Atkinson, M. R., and Morton, R. K., in Florkin, M., and Mason, H. S., eds. *Comparative Biochemistry.* New York: Academic Press, 1960, vol. 2, p. 74. Copyright Academic Press; reprinted by permission.)

The hydrolysis of most O-P bonds, as in α-glycerylphosphate or adenosine monophosphate (AMP), has a standard free energy of about −2 kcal/mole. The explanation of the energy-rich nature of compounds like adenosine triphosphate, ATP, or carboxylphosphates in chemical terms is a matter of some interest. Kalckar[10] was the first to draw attention to the fact that the hydrolysis products of energy-rich compounds have a great deal more resonance stabilization than the parent compound. Not only do the products have a greater total number of resonance forms than the reactant, but also the parent energy-rich compound shows *opposing resonance.* This last consideration was first suggested by C. D. Coryell. In opposing resonance there is a tendency for electrons on a single atom to shift in opposite directions (Fig. 5-17). In addition to the free energy attributable to resonance stabilization in the hydrolysis products, which

[10] Kalckar, H. M. *Chem. Rev.*, *28*, 71 (1941).

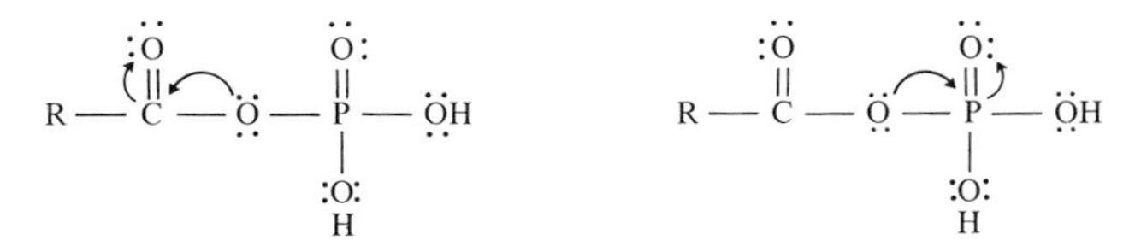

fig. 5-17. A diagram showing opposing resonance in an energy-rich ester.

appears to be a characteristic of all energy-rich compounds, Oesper[11] pointed out that an additional free energy change occurred in going from an acid reactant or an acid hydrolysis product to a mixture of acid and anion. For a typical energy-rich phosphate, the following reactions can be written:

$$\begin{array}{ccccccc} X{-}PO_3^{2-} & + & H_2O & \underset{}{\overset{K_h}{\rightleftharpoons}} & HX & + & HPO_4^{2-} \\ + & & & & \updownarrow K_2 & & + \\ H^+ & & & & H^+ + X^- & & H^+ \\ K_1 \updownarrow & & & & & & \updownarrow K_3 \\ X{-}PO_3H^- & & & & & & H_2PO_4^- \end{array} \tag{5-5}$$

Hill and Morales[12] treated the free energy contributions of the dissociation reactions as corrections to the primary reaction, the hydrolysis of the energy-rich phosphate. The free energy change for the actual equilibrium mixture of the various ionized forms of reactants and products, $\Delta G'$, is given by

$$\Delta G' = \Delta G_h' + \Delta G_2' + \Delta G_3' - \Delta G_1' \tag{5-6}$$

For the free energy contribution from ionization of the carboxyl group, Hill and Morales derived the following expression:

$$\Delta G_2 = -RT \ln (1 + K_2/[H^+]) \tag{5-7}$$

It can be seen that for $[H^+] \gg K_2, \Delta G_2 = 0$, and for $[H^+] \ll K_2$, $\Delta G_2 = RT \ln ([H^+]/K_2)$. The actual free energy contribution of the hydrolysis reaction depends, then, upon the equilibrium constant of the hydrolysis reaction and the pH of the actual reaction mixture. Assuming a dissociation constant, K_2, of the carboxyl group of 2×10^{-5}, when the hydrolysis is carried out at pH 7, it contributes approximately -3 kcal/mole to the total free energy of hydrolysis. At neutral pH, $(\Delta G_3 - \Delta G_1)$ is relatively small.

In the case of energy-rich compounds with an N-P bond, the greater stability of the O-P bond compared to the N-P bond, approximately 28 kcal/mole, is almost exactly offset by the greater stability of the O-H bond in the product, approximately 26.5 kcal/mole. In addition to the free energy contributions of resonance stabilization and ionization, Hill and Morales suggested a contribution from electrostatic repulsion of negative charges on adjacent phosphorus atoms of polyphosphates. From theoretical considerations, the electrostatic repulsion in the parent energy-rich compound might

---

[11] Oesper, P. *Arch. Biochem.*, *27*, 255 (1950).
[12] Hill, T. L., and Morales, M. F. *J. Am. Chem. Soc.*, *73*, 1656 (1951).

be expected to amount to approximately −3 to −4 kcal/mole for adenosine diphosphate or phospho*enol*pyruvate and −5 to −6 kcal/mole for ATP.

Under physiological conditions, the actual free energy of hydrolysis must be corrected by a term which takes into consideration the concentrations of the reactants and products. Thus, for ATP,

$$\Delta G = \Delta G' + RT \ln \frac{[\text{ADP}][\text{P}_i]}{[\text{ATP}]} \qquad (5\text{-}8)$$

In frog muscle, for example, the concentrations in the cell water are approximately 0.008 M for inorganic phosphate, 0.0005 M for adenosine diphosphate, and 0.003 M for ATP. These data give a value of about −4.0 kcal/mole for the far right term of eq. 5-8.

oxidative phosphorylation

Let us turn now to another important type of intermediate which serves to couple metabolic reactions so that the energy liberated by oxidation can be utilized to advantage. These intermediates are the *redox coenzymes*, typified by nicotinamide adenine dinucleotide, NAD; nicotinamide adenine dinucleotide phosphate, NADP; their reduced forms, NADH and NADPH, respectively; and flavine adenine dinucleotide,

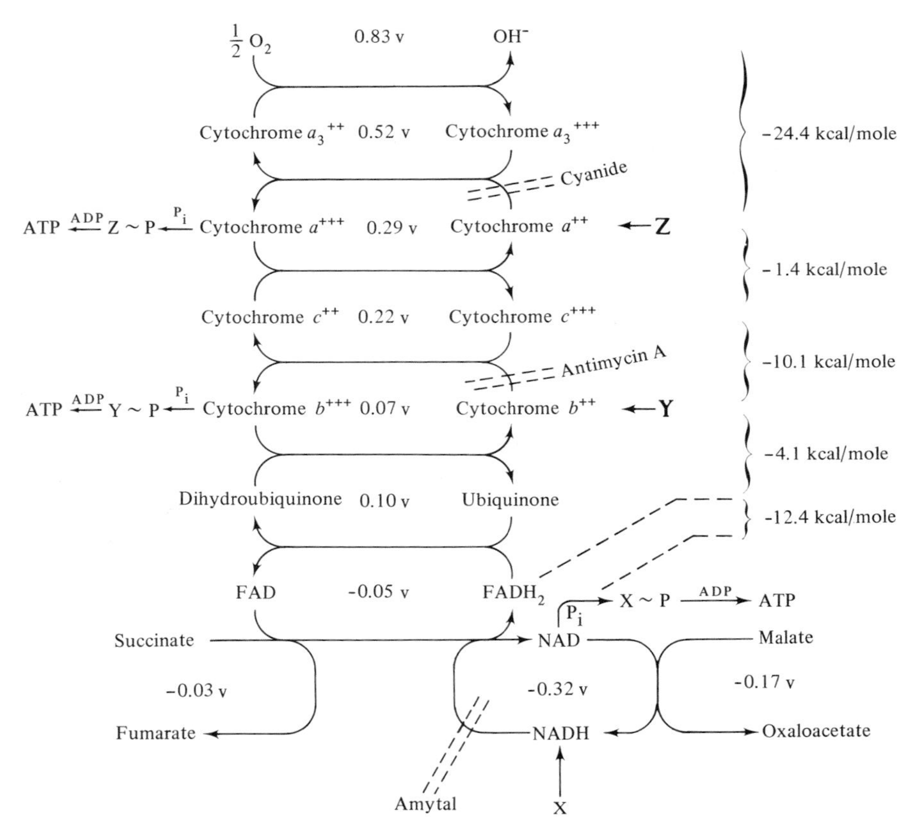

fig. 5-18. A schematic representation of a hypothetical organization of the sequential electron transport in mitochondria. The apparent sites of action of various inhibitors are also shown. Approximate values for E' and $\Delta G'$ are given for the various reactions. X, Y, and Z are hypothetical intermediates supposedly involved in the coupling of oxidation and phosphorylation.

FAD, and its reduced form, FADH (the latter occurring in association with specific proteins). These coenzymes are coupled to a variety of reactions in which they are either reduced or oxidized, permitting the transfer of energy to take place in an orderly fashion. Thus, there is efficient coupling of reactions in which there is oxidation to reactions in which there is reduction. On the balance, the metabolic processes of the cell are oxidative. Because many of these reactions are coupled to the redox coenzymes, a net reduction of coenzymes takes place.

The mitochondria perform a unique function in carrying on the orderly oxidation of the reduced coenzymes through a series of intermediates, ending in the oxidation by molecular oxygen. These intermediates occur only in mitochondria where they are arranged functionally, and probably also architecturally, according to their oxidation-reduction potentials to form a chain of electron carriers from the pyridine nucleotide coenzymes to molecular oxygen (Fig. 5-18). This sequence of oxidations in mitochondria is coupled to the phosphorylation of adenosine diphosphate to form ATP, so that most of the energy liberated during the oxidation reactions is utilized to form energy-rich compounds. This reservoir of energy-rich intermediates, in turn, makes energy available for other cellular processes. The reaction complex of oxidation coupled to the phosphorylation of adenosine diphosphate is called *oxidative phosphorylation.*

Mitochondria can be disrupted by ultrasound, by freezing and thawing, or by treatment with dilute ethanol or concentrated salt solutions. Such disruption liberates many of their constituents in soluble form, including the enzymes of the Krebs

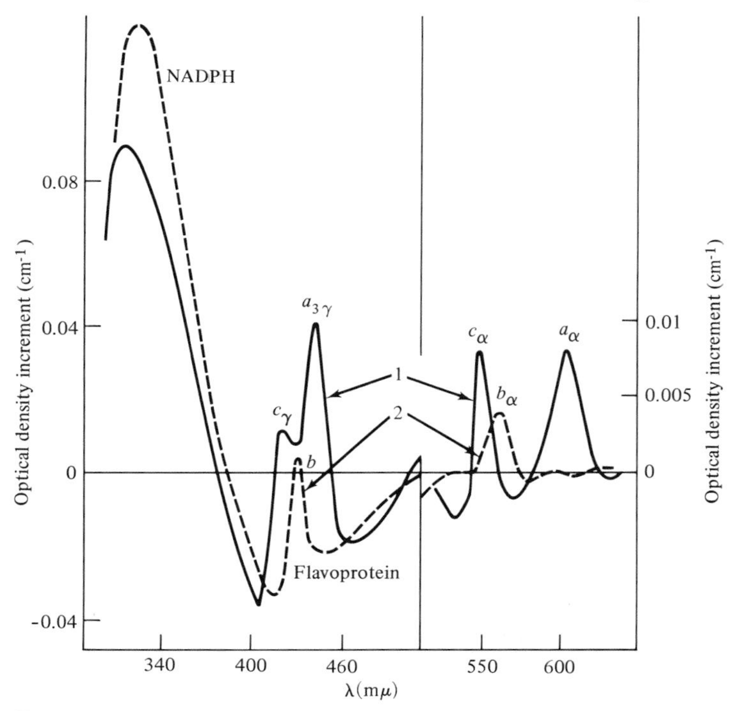

fig. 5-19. Difference spectra of the electron carriers in rat liver mitochondria. The solid line indicates the difference in absorbancy produced by excess substrate under anaerobic conditions. The dashed line indicates the difference in absorbancy produced by excess substrate in the presence of antimycin A. The control cuvette used for comparison is under aerobic conditions. (From Chance, B., and Williams, G. R. *Advan. Enzymol., 17,* 74 [1956].)

tricarboxylic acid cycle to be described below. The insoluble particles that remain are rich in lipid and contain almost all the cytochromes and other intermediates in the electron transport chain. The various members of the chain have been identified by comparing the absorption spectrum of a suspension of oxidized mitochondria with that of a suspension of mitochondria to which a reducing agent was added. The difference spectra so obtained show characteristic peaks for the compounds in the electron transport chain. A typical difference spectrum of this type is shown in Fig. 5-19. A variety of cytochromes are important members of this sequence. The cytochromes are proteins which contain *heme*, a tetrapyrrole compound in which an iron atom is complexed; their properties are tabulated in Fig. 5-20. Other important intermediates are

fig. 5-20. Properties of the cytochromes from mitochondria.

	SPECTRA (λ MAX)								
	REDUCED			OXIDIZED		MOLECULAR WEIGHT	REACTS WITH		
TYPE	α	β	γ	γ	E_0'	(MW $\times 10^3$)	O_2	CO	CN^-, F^-, N_3^-
a	600	—	439	425	+0.28	240			
a_3	603.5	—	443	—	+0.30	—	+	+	+
b	563	532	429	415	+0.05	30	—	—	—
c	550	521	415	407	+0.254	13	—	—	slow
f	555	525	423	413	+0.365	110			

ubiquinone, plastoquinone, and vitamin K. The structural formulas of these compounds are depicted in Fig. 5-21.

Ubiquinone is also found in nuclei and microsomes, probably as a constituent of their membranes. It is noteworthy that the various constituents of the chain are present in mitochondria in almost even integer multiples of one another (Fig. 5-22). The respiratory chain can accept electrons from either the pyridine nucleotide coenzymes or succinate, an intermediate of the Krebs tricarboxylic acid cycle. After sonication or extraction with ethanol or salt solutions, treatment of the insoluble residue of mitochondria by detergents yields four types of particles, each of which is able to carry on only a part of the electron-transfer process. The functions of the chain which the four types of particles are able to carry out are:

1. Oxidation of NADH coupled to the reduction of ubiquinone
2. Oxidation of succinate coupled to the reduction of ubiquinone
3. Oxidation of ubiquinone coupled to the reduction of cytochrome *c*
4. Oxidation of cytochrome *c* by molecular oxygen

A hypothetical arrangement of the particles to form a complete transport chain is shown in Fig. 5-23. The sequence of electron carriers in the chain can be determined by a variety of experiments. One method is to reduce a mitochondrial suspension and determine the changes in the difference spectra as a function of time after oxygen is admitted to the system. In such an experiment, it was found that cytochrome *a* was oxidized first, followed by cytochrome *c*, then by cytochrome *b*, and lastly by the flavoproteins. Another approach utilizes specific inhibitors. Barbiturates such as amytal inhibit the reaction between NADH and flavoprotein, and mitochondria treated

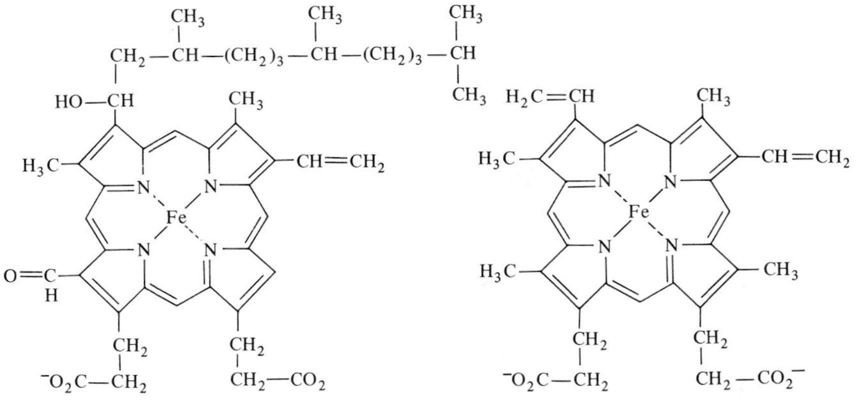

Heme A

Heme B

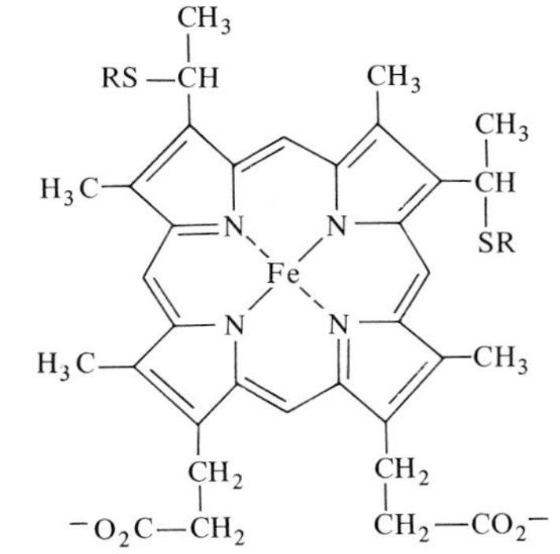

Heme C

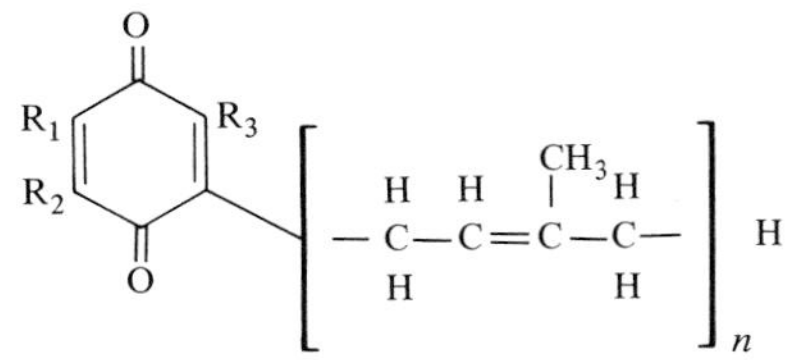

	n	R_1	R_2	R_3
Coenzyme Q_{6-10}	6–10	$-OCH_3$	$-OCH_3$	$-CH_2$
Plastoquinone	9	$-CH_3$	$-CH_3$	H
Vitamin K_2	4–7	CH ‖ CH	CH ‖ CH	CH_2

fig. 5-21. Structural formulas of the heme moieties of the cytochromes and the coenzyme Q compounds.

fig. 5-22. Constituents of beef heart mitochondria.

CONSTITUENT	μ MOLES/G PROTEIN
Cytochrome *a*	0.80
Cytochrome a_3	1.13
Cytochrome *b*	0.60
Cytochrome $c + c_1$	0.65
Cytochromes total	3.18
FMN	0.08
FAD	0.26
Flavins other	0.11
Flavins total	0.45
Coenzyme Q	3.8
Iron	8.85×10^3
Copper	1.46×10^3
Phospholipid	35 percent

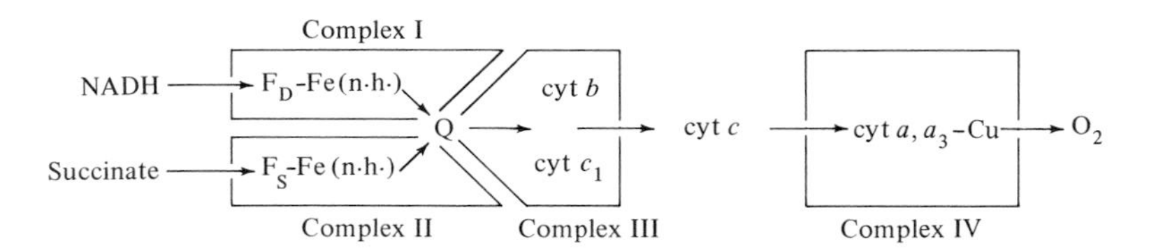

fig. 5-23. A diagram of the four functional complexes of the electron transfer system and their functional arrangement. (From Hatefi, Y., Haavik, A. G., Fowler, L. R., and Griffiths, D. E. *J. Biol. Chem.*, *237*, 2668 [1962].)

with amytal contain pyridine nucleotides in the reduced form while the other members of the electron transport chain are in the oxidized form. Cyanide combines with the oxidized form of cytochrome oxidase, the last step in the chain, and results in the accumulation of reduced forms of all intermediates. The antibiotic antimycin A acts upon the transfer between cytochrome b and cytochrome c, and results in the accumulation of reduced members of the chain below this site and oxidized members above the site. BAL (2,3-dimercaptopropanol) and hydroxyquinoline-N-oxide also block at this site.

The phosphorylation of adenosine diphosphate bears a definite stoichiometry to the oxidation of various substrates. Thus, the ratio of ATP molecules formed per oxygen molecule utilized is 2.0 when succinate is the substrate, 3.0 when $NADH_2$ is the substrate, and 4.0 when α-ketoglutarate is the substrate. A number of compounds, the so-called *uncouplers* of oxidative phosphorylation, inhibit the formation of ATP without appreciably affecting the transport of electrons and oxidation of substrates. These compounds include dinitrophenol, dicoumarol (anti-vitamin K compound), and certain polypeptide antibiotics such as gramicidin D and tyrocidin. Oxidative phosphorylation requires reasonably intact structure of the mitochondria, and it is lost if the organelles are subjected to anything but the most gentle treatment. Gentle disruption in digitonin, a steroid with detergent properties, yields mitochondrial fragments with a particle weight of about 1×10^9 that are capable of carrying on oxidative phosphorylation, albeit at somewhat reduced efficiency. Recently, indirect evidence has been accumulated indicating that the inner mitochondrial membrane is composed of repeating units, each of which contains the complete complement of protein molecules required to carry on oxidative phosphorylation, arranged in space so that the reactions can take place sequentially.

It is thought that the coupling of oxidation to phosphorylation proceeds through a high-energy intermediate which as yet has not been isolated. The hypothetical energy-rich intermediate has been invoked to explain (1) control of respiration by the concentration of ADP or P_i, (2) uncoupling of phosphorylation from oxidation by dinitrophenol, (3) inhibition of phosphorylation and oxidation by oligomycin, (4) relief of oligomycin inhibition by concomitant administration of dinitrophenol, and (5) energy conservation in the absence of ADP or P_i.

A coupled oxidation may be formulated as a two-step reaction[13]

$$AH_2 + B + C \rightleftharpoons A \sim C + BH_2 \quad \textit{(5-9)}$$

$$A \sim C + P_i + ADP \rightleftharpoons A + C + ATP \quad \textit{(5-10)}$$

$$AH_2 + B + P_i + ADP \rightleftharpoons A + BH_2 + ATP \quad \textit{(5-11)}$$

[13] Slater, E. C. *Bull. Soc. Chim. Biol.*, *48*, 1151 (1966).

where ~ represents the energy-rich bond in the hypothetical compound A ~ C. Dinitrophenol is thought to act by substituting the following reaction for reaction 5-10.

$$A \sim C \rightarrow A + C \tag{5-12}$$

Oligomycin supposedly acts by blocking reaction 5-10. Van Dam[14] has suggested from indirect evidence that the amount of an energy-rich intermediate that might be present in tissue is extremely small and that it is not surprising that it has not been isolated.

On the other hand, Mitchell[15] has proposed an alternative hypothesis to account for these observations. Mitchell proposed that phosphorylation takes place because the oxidative steps in respiration are accompanied by the net translocation of hydrogen ions from the interior to the exterior and the net transport of the same number of electrons from the exterior to the interior across the mitochondrial membrane which is relatively impermeable to other ions. Mitchell evaluated the stoichiometry of the P_i incorporating system as approximately 2 H^+ ions transported for each P_i incorporated. The quotients of H^+ ions per $\frac{1}{2}\,O_2$ utilized is approximately 4 for succinate and 6 for β-hydroxybutyrate. This possible mechanism will be discussed further in Chapter 7.

Oxidative phosphorylation is a freely reversible process. This was demonstrated by Klingenberg and Schollmeyer,[16] who found that the oxidation-reduction state of all components of the entire respiratory chain becomes reduced when ATP is added to the system in the absence of adenosine diphosphate and inorganic phosphate. Furthermore, it appears that the ratio of oxidized to reduced mitochondrial cytochrome *c* depends upon the ratio (ATP)/(ADP)(P_i), and from this relationship they were able to calculate the standard free energy of hydrolysis of the energy-rich precursor of ATP as about −12 kcal/mole.

photosynthesis

Prior to the 1930s, photosynthesis was regarded as a direct reversal of the process of respiration, as shown in eq. 5-1. Sunlight was believed to provide the energy needed to operate these reactions in the reverse direction. It was the view of R. Willstätter and others that light energy acted through chlorophyll to substitute H_2O for the oxygen of CO_2. C. B. van Niel was the first to suggest that water might act as a hydrogen donor in photosynthesis and that carbon dioxide molecules were incorporated intact into carbohydrates. He based his argument on the reactions which occur in photosynthetic bacteria which utilize reducing substances in place of water. For example, in the sulfur bacteria, photosynthesis can be summarized by the following reaction:

$$2\,H_2S + CO_2 \rightarrow H_2O + (CH_2O) + 2\,S \tag{5-13}$$

Reasoning by analogy, van Niel proposed that in green plants water substitutes for hydrogen sulfide.[17] Other kinds of microorganisms are able to utilize thiosulfate, selenium compounds, hydrogen gas, or a variety of organic compounds as hydrogen donors in place of hydrogen sulfide. Convincing proof for van Niel's conjecture came from experiments with water labeled with the stable isotope of oxygen, ^{18}O, by

---

[14] Van Dam, K. *Biochim. Biophys. Acta*, *92*, 181 (1964); *128*, 337 (1966).
[15] Mitchell, P. *Nature*, *191*, 144 (1961); *208*, 147 (1965).
[16] Klingenberg, M., and Schollmeyer, P. *Biochem. Z.*, *333*, 335 (1960); *335*, 231, 243 (1961).
[17] van Niel, C. B., in Frank, J., and Loomis, W., eds. *Photosynthesis in Plants*. Ames, Iowa: Iowa State College Press, 1949, p. 437.

Samuel Ruben and Martin Kamen.[18] They observed that cultures of algae exposed to light in the presence of ^{18}O water liberated oxygen containing the isotope while no label was found in the carbohydrate produced. When labeled carbon dioxide was used, half of the isotope was found in the carbohydrate while the other half was found in the water. In the case of green plants, then, eq. 5-13 can be rewritten

$$2\ H_2O^* + CO_2 \rightarrow H_2O + (CH_2O) + O_2^*$$
$$2\ H_2O + CO_2^* \rightarrow H_2O^* + (CH_2O^*) + O_2 \quad (5\text{-}14)$$

As a result of such observations, it appears that photosynthesis in all its diverse forms in various organisms operates essentially by a single mechanism. These observations also suggest that photosynthesis developed in a remote era in microorganisms utilizing hydrogen donors then available in the environment. When reducing substrates were exhausted, photosynthetic plants appear to have developed which were able to utilize water as the hydrogen donor.

Obviously, the statements of photosynthesis in eqs. 5-1 and 5-14 are oversimplifications. Insight into the more detailed mechanism can be gleaned from the following observations. Robert Hill[19] discovered that fresh ground leaves, in which the incorporation of carbon dioxide into carbohydrates has been disrupted, were able, nevertheless, to reduce certain hydrogen acceptors and give off molecular oxygen when exposed to light. A large number of substances can be reduced in the Hill reaction including quinone, reducible dyes, methemoglobin, ferric ions, etc. The oxygen liberated has been shown to come from water. Approximately the same number of light quanta are required to liberate a molecule of oxygen in the Hill reaction as are required during photosynthesis in the intact cell. The Hill reaction demonstrates that the decomposition of water is a photochemical process and that it can be separated from carbon dioxide fixation.

In microorganisms, photosynthesis coupled to the decomposition of water requires about twice the light energy of photosynthesis coupled to the decomposition of hydrogen sulfide (eq. 5-13). It is possible to adapt certain algae to utilize hydrogen gas in photosynthesis.[20] In this circumstance, carbon dioxide fixation is not accompanied by the release of oxygen. However, an equivalent amount of hydrogen gas is absorbed and incorporated into carbohydrate. The algae which are able to utilize hydrogen gas contain a specific enzyme, hydrogenase, in a latent form. This enyzme is activated during the process of adaptation. The adaptation is enhanced by darkness or very subdued illumination, while strong illumination results in a reversion to photolysis of water. The incorporation of hydrogen is a photochemical process which does not proceed in the absence of light. Far-red light, 705 mμ, is far more effectively utilized than shorter wavelength light for the photoreduction of carbon dioxide by hydrogen gas. Furthermore, red light does not produce the deadaptation characteristic of illumination by shorter wavelength light. The reversion is also blocked by the herbicide DCMU [3-(3,4-dichlorophenyl)-1,1-dimethylurea]. It seems likely, therefore, that there are two separate photochemical processes, one involving the formation of a stable oxidant, as isolated in the Hill reaction, and the other leading to the formation of a stable reductant, as isolated in hydrogen-adapted algae and bacteria.

A number of investigators, principally Arnon and his colleagues, have shown that the phosphorylation of adenosine diphosphate to form adenosine triphosphate and the

[18] Ruben, S., Randall, M., Kamen, M. D., and Hyde, J. L. *J. Am. Chem. Soc.*, *63*, 877 (1941).
[19] Hill, R. *Proc. Roy. Soc.*, *B 127*, 192 (1939); *Advan. Enzymol.*, *12*, 1 (1951).
[20] Gaffron, H. *Am. J. Botany*, *27*, 273 (1940); *Biol. Rev.*, *19*, 1 (1944).

reduction of coenzymes such as NADP occur in association with the photochemical reactions.[21] Presumably the energy needed to drive these processes arises from light-excited chlorophyll molecules; the electrons so generated supposedly fall through a series of cytochromes and give up their energy in a sequence of steps coupled to phosphorylation forming ATP, or coupled to the formation of NADPH. This sequence of reactions is analogous to the sequence of steps in mitochondrial oxidative phosphorylation except that photophosphorylation does not require the presence of oxygen or Krebs-cycle intermediates. Chloroplasts, unlike mitochondria, are not able to form ATP by oxidizing hydrogen donors with molecular oxygen. Photophosphorylation proceeds in the absence of CO_2 and CO_2 fixation. In chloroplasts treated with iodoacetamide or other inhibitors of CO_2 fixation, photophosphorylation leads to the accumulation of substantial amounts of ATP and reduced coenzymes. Photophosphorylation requires FAD and vitamin K as cofactors. The formation of reduced coenzymes requires the presence of a specific iron-rich, water-soluble protein, photosynthetic pyridine nucleotide reductase[22] or *ferredoxin.*

In addition to photochemical reactions, photosynthesis involves thermochemical or "dark" reactions. In general, the photochemical reactions proceed at a rate which is approximately proportional to the absolute temperature. On the other hand, the thermochemical reactions of photosynthesis, like other chemical reactions, double or triple their rates for every 10° rise in temperature. At low intensities of illumination, the photochemical reactions are rate-limiting. Under these circumstances the temperature may be varied over wide limits without appreciably altering the rate of photosynthesis. The efficiency of absorption, transmission, and utilization of light energy is not appreciably increased by raising the temperature. However, when the intensity of illumination is high enough to saturate the photosynthetic apparatus, the rate of photosynthesis approximately doubles for every 10° rise in temperature between 5° and 32°C.

Another observation of interest is the fact that plants exposed to intermittent flashes of light carry on more photosynthetic activity per unit of light than plants continuously exposed to light. It appears that light is used more efficiently if the period of exposure is quite short and if it is followed by a period of darkness. If brief flashes of light are followed by dark periods of variable duration, the efficiency of light utilization increases as the periods of darkness are lengthened until a maximum is reached. This observation is explained by assuming that thermochemical reactions occur in the dark which require finite time for completion after illumination stops. This interpretation is supported by the fact that the dark period necessary to achieve maximum efficiency must be longer when the ambient temperature is lowered, indicating that the dark reactions proceed at an appreciably slower rate at lower temperatures. The dark reactions, sometimes called the Blackman reaction, utilize the products of the photochemical reactions to assimilate carbon dioxide.

Thus, the overall reactions of photosynthesis can be regarded as occurring in three phases: (1) the photodecomposition of water leading to a stable reduced intermediate and the evolution of molecular oxygen, (2) photophosphorylation, and (3) the assimilation of carbon dioxide and metabolic reactions leading to the synthesis of carbohydrate.

---

[21] Arnon, D. I., Whatley, F. R., and Allen, M. B. *Science, 127,* 1026 (1958); Arnon, D. I. *Nature, 184,* 10 (1959); Whatley, F. R., and Losada, M., in Giese, A. C., ed. *Photophysiology.* New York: Academic Press, 1964, vol. 1, p. 111.
[22] San Pietro, A., and Lang, H. M. *J. Biol. Chem., 231,* 211 (1958).

the photosynthetic unit

The chloroplasts, whose morphology was described in Chapter 2, are the physiological units in which photosynthesis takes place. Isolated chloroplasts can carry on the same photosynthetic reactions that occur in whole leaves provided the required cofactors are supplied. The chloroplasts are made up of subunits, the *grana*, which are membranous structures that tend to occur in stacks. The structural integrity of the grana appears to be required for photosynthesis; and it is believed, therefore, that they are the site of the first reactions of photosynthesis. If the membranous surface of a stack of grana is carefully stripped away, a layer of elements, the *quantasomes*,[23] is revealed (Fig. 5-24). These units are plates or ellipsoids about 200 Å in diameter and 100 Å

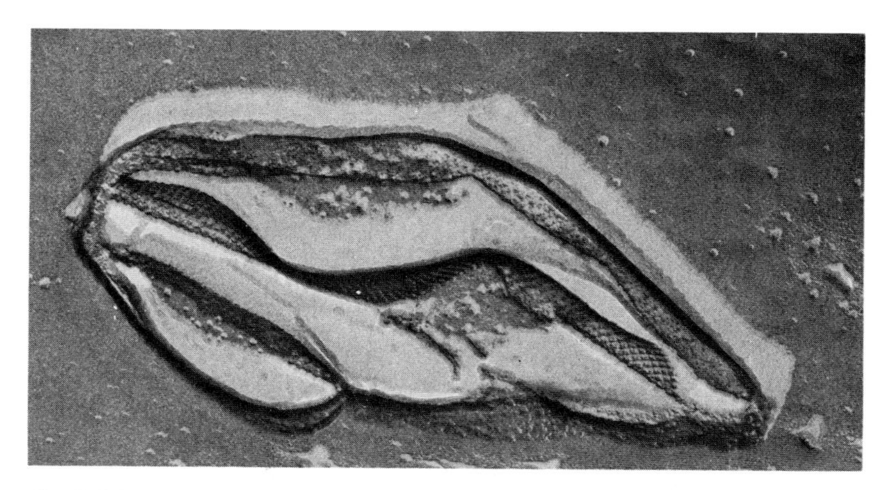

fig. 5-24. A spinach chloroplast; freeze-etched preparation showing cobblestone-appearing paracrystalline array on the thylakoid surface. Magnification 70,000. (Courtesy of Dr. Roderick B. Park.)

thick, arranged in a regular, lateral array which gives the appearance of a cobblestone street. Quantasomes from spinach have an approximate molecular weight of 2×10^6; their composition is given in Fig. 5-25.

In bacteria and other unicellular organisms, less highly organized structures carry on photosynthesis. After disrupting photosynthetic bacteria, roughly spherical particles approximately 300 Å in diameter called *chromatophores* are obtained which contain all the photosynthetic pigments and enzymes required for photosynthesis. It is not clear whether these units exist in the same structural form within the bacterial cell. It may be that the chromatophores are attached to, or even an integral part of, the protoplast membrane or other intracellular structures, and that they take the form of small vesicles during the process of isolation in much the same way that microsomes are formed from the endoplasmic reticulum.

The photosynthetic pigments are an essential requirement for function. Chlorophylls are present in all photosynthetic cells. They are phytol esters of dihydroporphyrin carboxylic acids, the *chlorophyllins* (Fig. 5-26); that is, one of the double bonds on

[23] Park, R. B., and Pon, N. G. *J. Mol. Biol.*, *3*, 1 (1961); *6*, 105 (1963); Park, R. B., and Biggins, J. *Science*, *144*, 1009 (1964).

fig. 5-25. Composition of spinach quantasomes.

CONSTITUENT	MOLECULES PER QUANTASOME
Chlorophyll *a*	160
Chlorophyll *b*	70
β-Carotene	14
Lutein	22
Violaxanthin	6
Neoxanthin	6
Plastoquinone *a*	16
Plastoquinone *b*	8
Plastoquinone *c*	4
α-Tocopherol	10
α-Tocopherylquinone	4
Vitamin K_1	4
Phospholipids	116
Galactosylglycerides	500
Sulfolipids	48
Sterols and other lipids	uncertain

the porphyrin ring is reduced by two hydrogens. The porphyrin nucleus consisting of four pyrrole rings is similar to that of heme. In the chlorophylls, magnesium is the metal ion chelated by the porphyrin nitrogen atoms. *Protochlorophyll*, which is formed in green plants not exposed to light, contains a porphyrin nucleus with all double bonds present. Upon exposure to light, one double bond is reduced. Phytol is a straight-chain alcohol with a single double bond which may be regarded as hydrogenated carotene (vitamin A).

The various chlorophylls differ from one another only by the side chains attached to the porphyrin nucleus. Chlorophyll *a* and chlorophyll *b* are the types predominantly found in green plants and algae. They have absorption maxima in vivo at about 675 mμ and 650 mμ respectively. Within the plant cell, apparently several functional types of chlorophyll *a* are present, each with a slightly different absorption maximum. The purple photosynthetic bacteria have a chlorophyll, *bacteriochlorophyll*, which exhibits several absorption bands between 800 and 890 mμ in vivo. Upon extraction, a solution of bacteriochlorophyll in an organic solvent shows a single absorption band at 770 mμ. The multiple absorption bands of bacteriochlorophyll in vivo are probably due to the heterogeneity of the molecular environment. The green photosynthetic bacteria possess two pigments, chlorobium-chlorophylls *a* and *b*, which have absorption maxima in vivo at 725 mμ and 747 mμ respectively. In addition, the various chlorophylls have Soret bands, absorption maxima in the blue or near ultraviolet region of the spectrum. The spectra of various pigments are shown in Fig. 5-27. A characteristic property of the chlorophylls is a brilliant fluorescent band in the red portion of the spectrum which persists for minutes after the cessation of illumination. This phosphorescence may be associated with the formation of an excited triplet.

A variety of accessory pigments is also found. The carotenols and xanthophylls absorb strongly with characteristic triple bands in the blue-violet and near ultraviolet portions of the spectrum. Carotene itself appears to protect against photooxidation.

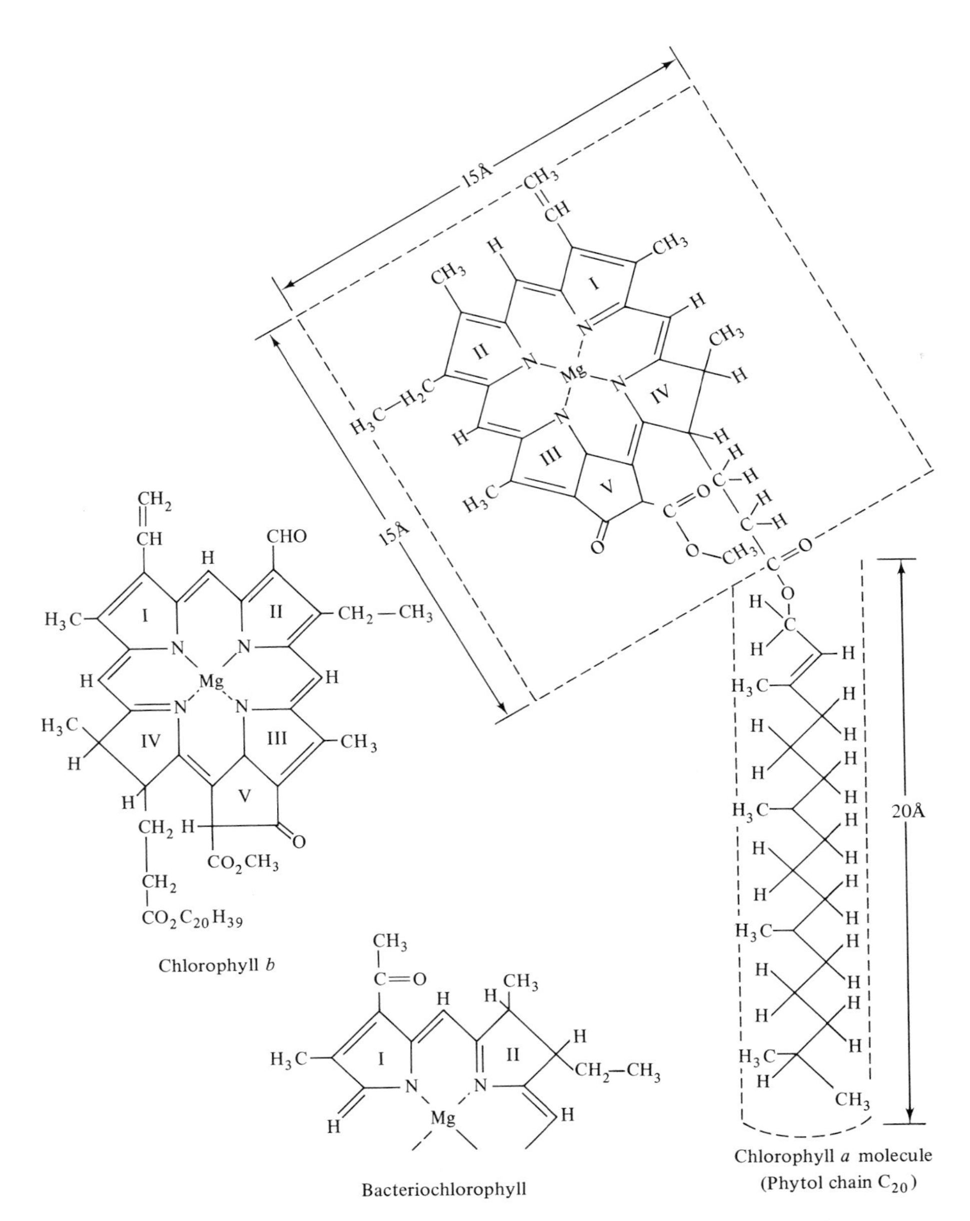

fig. 5-26. Structures of chlorophyll *a*, chlorophyll *b*, and bacteriochlorophyll. The approximate dimensions of the molecule are shown. The phytol residue can rotate with respect to the heme head. Presumably the phytol residue is embedded in the phospholipid of the membranous structure.

The phycobilins, mainly phycocyanin in the blue-green algae and phycoerythrin in the red algae, are another set of accessory pigments which absorb in the region between 500 and 650 mμ, while green plants contain anthocyans. The accessory pigments do not participate in photosynthesis but can transfer absorbed light energy to chlorophyll. Lastly, there are the cytochromes, iron-containing porphyrins, and ferredoxin. The changes in the absorption spectrum under various conditions of lighting have been important experimentally in elucidating the changes in the pigments during photosynthesis.

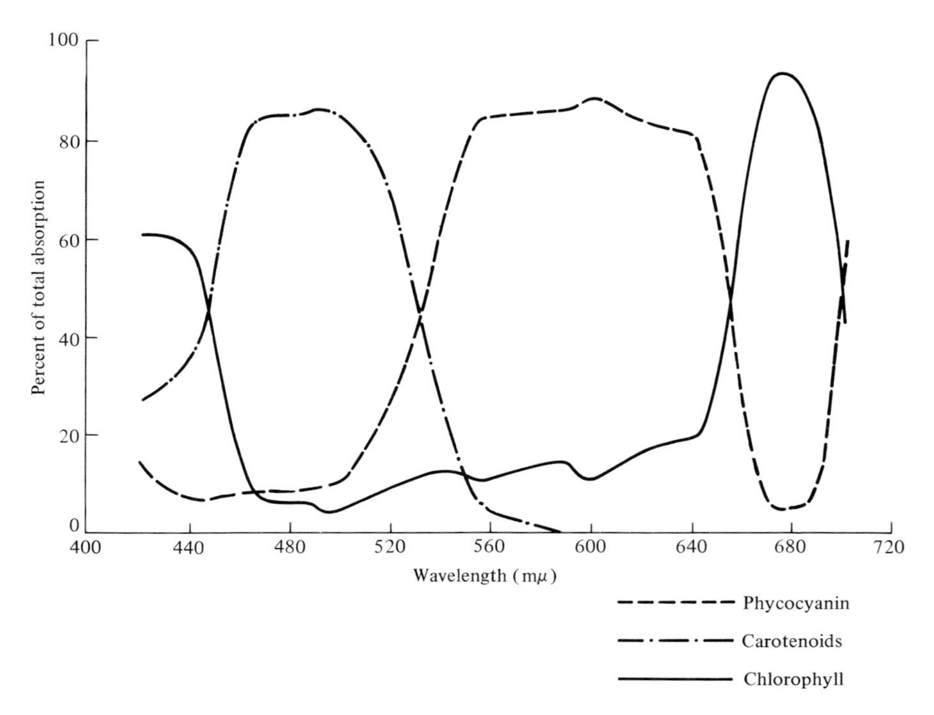

fig. 5-27. The absorption spectra of the pigments of the blue-green alga *Chroöcoccus.* (From Emerson, R., and Lewis, C. M. *Am. J. Botany, 30,* 165 [1943]; and Emerson, R., and Lewis, C. M. *J. Gen. Physiol., 25,* 587 [1942].)

In general, the relative effectiveness of monochromatic illumination of various wavelengths corresponds to the absorption spectrum of the chloroplasts; the highest efficiency of photosynthesis results with monochromatic light of the wavelength of the absorption maxima (Fig. 5-28).[24] Regardless of the wavelength of the exciting light, the wavelength of fluorescence of the chloroplast is that of chlorophyll *a*, even if the wavelength of the exciting light is one that is not appreciably absorbed by chlorophyll.[25] This observation suggests that light energy absorbed by various pigments in the chloroplast is transferred to chlorophyll *a*. In general, illumination by light of wavelength longer than 700 mμ is not effective in photosynthesis.

If plants are illuminated with long wavelength light of about 700 mμ, the efficiency of photosynthesis can be markedly increased by simultaneous illumination with shorter wavelength light. This phenomenon is called the Emerson effect. Thus, the simultaneous exposure of cells to 700 mμ light and light of a shorter wavelength results in a rate of photosynthesis greater than the sum of photosynthesis which results from illumination at each wavelength separately. A related phenomenon is the Blinks effect, which is the transient enhancement of photosynthesis which occurs upon shifting the wavelength of illumination from 700 mμ to a shorter wavelength. These phenomena are depicted graphically in Fig. 5-29. The Blinks effect is still observed when a brief period of darkness intervenes between the exposure to the two wavelengths of light, or when the plant is exposed to the shorter wavelength light first and to the 700 mμ

[24] Haxo, F. T., and Blinks, L. R. *J. Gen. Physiol., 33,* 389 (1950).
[25] Franck, J., French, C. S., and Puck, T. T. *J. Phys. Chem., 45,* 1268 (1941); Duysens, L. N. M. *Nature, 168,* 548 (1951).

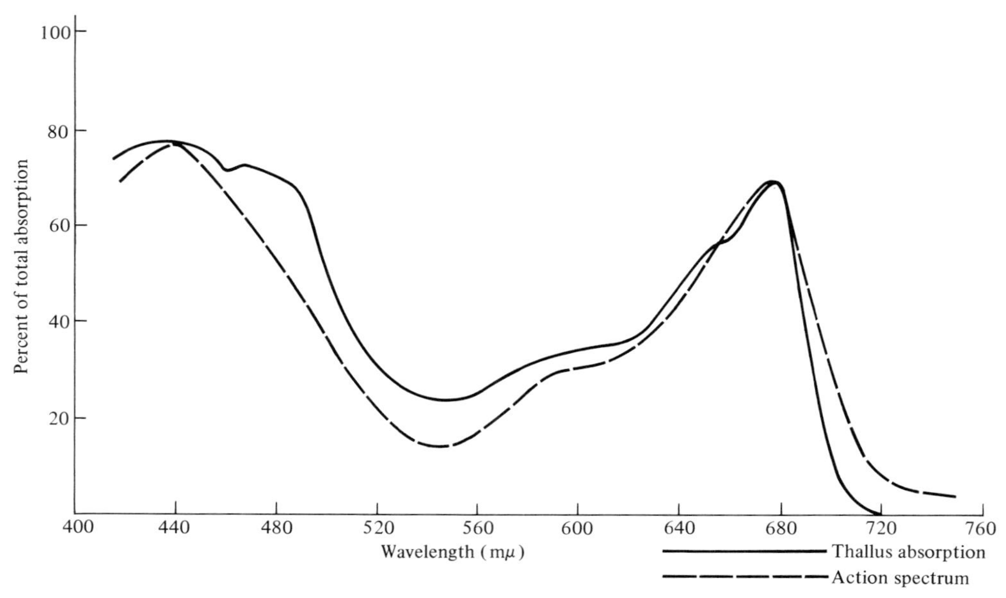

fig. 5-28. The absorption spectrum and action spectrum of a green alga *Ulva taeniata*, showing their similarity (From Haxo, F. T., and Blinks, L. R. *J. Gen. Physiol.*, *33*, 404 [1950].)

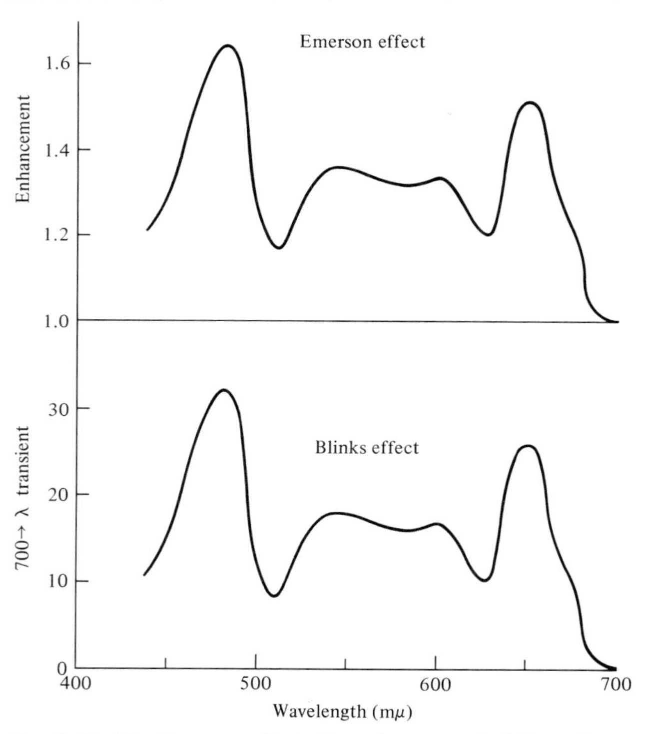

fig. 5-29. The Emerson effect, the enhancement of the action spectrum obtained by illuminating a plant with 700 mμ light together with light of shorter wavelength. The Blinks effect, the increase in photosynthesis obtained by following illumination with 700 mμ light by illumination with light of a shorter wavelength. (From French, C. S., in McElroy, W. D., and Glass, B., eds. *Light and Life.* Baltimore: Johns Hopkins University Press, 1961, p. 447.)

light afterward. These findings indicate that more than one pigment may be involved in the photochemical reactions.

Let us now present some evidence supporting the view that a photosynthetic unit exists in terms of function. The photolysis of one water molecule liberating one molecule of oxygen and the photoreduction and assimilation of one carbon dioxide molecule requires the transfer of four electrons. Numerous measurements of the quantum efficiency of this process have been made. With the notable exception of O. Warburg and his colleagues, who have repeatedly reported one carbon dioxide molecule fixed per four quanta of light absorbed, most investigators have found a light requirement of six to ten quanta for each carbon dioxide molecule fixed. From the energetic point of view, eight quanta would be a more logical requirement than four quanta for each carbon dioxide molecule fixed. The matter is not settled, however, and while it is attractive to suppose an integer multiple of four (the number of electrons transferred) on esthetic grounds and for easy formulations of mechanisms, there is no assurance at the present time that eight (or four) is the precise number of quanta required.

The energetic considerations can be summarized in the following way. The free energy difference between one mole of carbon dioxide and $\frac{1}{6}$ mole of glucose is 118 kcal. In addition, there must exist an energy barrier of some sort which prevents the immediate recombination of the primary reductant and the primary oxidant which are formed in the initial photochemical reaction. It is difficult to evaluate the magnitude of this barrier precisely with the present uncertainties about the details of the photosynthetic processes, but it is at least 0.3 ev or 28 kcal/mole CO_2. In addition, there are other processes in which energy is required. The formation and utilization of ATP in carbon dioxide assimilation requires perhaps 18 kcal/mole. Approximately 20 kcal/mole or more are required for oxygen evolution. Thus, the minimum total energy requirement is 184 kcal/mole CO_2 absorbed. The energy provided by four einsteins (mole quanta) of light at 680 mμ is 164 kcal which clearly is insufficient, while eight einsteins would provide 328 kcal, a more than adequate amount. These considerations are summarized in Fig. 5-30.

fig. 5-30. Energy budget of photosynthesis. (From Franck, J. *Arch. Biochem. Biophys.*, *23*, 297 [1949]; *45*, 198 [1953]. Copyright Academic Press; reprinted by permission.)

BUDGET ENTRIES	4 QUANTA (KCAL)	2.7 QUANTA[a] (KCAL)
Energy income for process with:		
Singlet-singlet transition at 41 kcal	164	111
Singlet-triplet transition at about 26 kcal	104	71
Energy expenditure:		
Free energy stored per CH_2O	117	117
Losses in photochemical steps at 7 kcal	28	19
Losses for evolution of one O_2	20	20
Losses for radical transmutation at 1.5 kcal	6	4
Losses for carboxylation with one CO_2 + phosphorylation	13	13
Total energy demand:	184	173

[a] Highest efficiency (= smallest quantum number) reported.

If approximately eight quanta of light are required for the reduction of one molecule of carbon dioxide and the evolution of one oxygen molecule, one might expect a sufficiently intense flash of light to bring about the fixation of one molecule of CO_2 and the evolution of one molecule of O_2 for every eight molecules of chlorophyll exposed to the light. Of course, this assumes that the conditions are such that the subsequent dark reactions can utilize all the products of the photochemical reactions produced by the flash. This experiment was actually performed by Emerson and Arnold[26] using the green alga *Chlorella*. They found a maximum yield of one oxygen molecule per 2500 chlorophyll molecules after intense, brief (10^{-5} sec) flashes of light. This limiting value was about 1/300th of that expected. Furthermore, it could be achieved with flashes not nearly intense enough to excite all the chlorophyll molecules present. Incidentally, a dark period of at least 0.04 sec was required between flashes for subsequent flashes to produce the maximum effect.

The conclusion drawn from this and other similar experiments is that chloroplasts consist of photosynthetic units. Each unit contains a reaction center capable of carrying out the photochemical reactions, surrounded by light-harvesting pigment molecules. Each unit might be expected to contain approximately 600 chlorophyll molecules. The energy from a quantum of light absorbed anywhere in this ensemble of pigment molecules would be transmitted to the reaction center where the initial stable products of photosynthesis would be produced within 0.04 sec. A unit of 600 chlorophyll molecules is chosen to accommodate the two-quantum sequence to be described in the next section; a 300-molecule unit would serve equally well for a single quantum process. The migration of energy occurs, undoubtedly, by means of the energy-transfer reactions described in Chapter 3.

An early argument supporting the existence of a functional photosynthetic unit came from the theoretical deductions of Gaffron and Wohl.[27] Gaffron and Wohl pointed out that a quantum of light would hit a single chlorophyll molecule in a dimly illuminated plant only once in several minutes. At this rate, almost an hour might elapse before the chlorophyll molecule would absorb the eight quanta needed for the fixation of one carbon dioxide molecule. In point of fact, maximal rates of photosynthesis *were* obtained with such low intensities of light and the maximal rates of oxygen evolution and CO_2 fixation were established almost immediately. They, too, concluded that light energy is harvested by a collection of chlorophyll molecules and transmitted to a reaction center.

More recent evidence for a functional photosynthetic unit comes from studies with herbicides such as DCMU which inhibit photosynthesis completely in relative concentrations of about one herbicide molecule for every 200 chlorophyll molecules.[28] It was pointed out above that the Hill reaction, the photosynthetic evolution of oxygen in the presence of an oxidant, can be carried out by cell fragments. The yield of the Hill reaction, however, drops markedly when the cells are so thoroughly disrupted that the fragments contain less than 200 to 250 chlorophyll molecules.[29] Lastly, a light-reacting cytochrome and a chlorophyll molecule with a unique absorbance appear to be involved in the photochemical reactions. The stoichiometry appears to be approximately 300 chlorophyll molecules for every light-reacting cytochrome and one special

[26] Emerson, R., and Arnold, W. *J. Gen. Physiol.*, *15*, 391 (1932); Kok, B. *Biochim. Biophys. Acta*, *21*, 245 (1956).
[27] Gaffron, H., and Wohl, K. *Naturwissenschaften*, *24*, 81, 103 (1936).
[28] Wessels, J. S. C., and van der Veen, R. *Biochim. Biophys. Acta*, *19*, 548 (1956).
[29] Thomas, J. B., Blaauw, O. H., and Duysens, L. N. M. *Biochim. Biophys. Acta*, *10*, 230 (1953); Gross, J. A., Becker, M. J., and Schefner, A. M. *Nature*, *203*, 1263 (1964).

chlorophyll in green plants and algae. By way of contrast, the chromatophores of bacteria appear to contain photosynthetic units with approximately 60 chlorophyll molecules.

The absorption of a photon by any molecule in a photosynthetic unit results in an excited molecule with an average lifetime of about 5×10^{-9} sec. Resonance transfer of excitation can occur between identical molecules and also between molecules which are dissimilar chemically if the receiving molecule absorbs at the same or a slightly longer wavelength than the emitter molecule, that is, if the two molecules act as coupled oscillators. If the molecules lie adjacent to one another, resonance transfer of excitation occurs with such ease that a quantum of light can "visit" several hundred molecules within the brief lifetime of excitation. If a pigment molecule with an absorption at a slightly higher wavelength, or whose excited state is at a slightly lower energy level, is present in the ensemble, it will serve as a sink to trap photons because, once excited, the energy cannot be transferred back to a neighboring molecule. In this way, the photosynthetic unit acts as a light-gathering system.

In addition, there is evidence that a portion of the photosynthetic pigments are present in fixed spatial orientation. Sauer and Calvin[30] found that the principal absorption band of chlorophyll *a* in spinach lamellae was at 678 mμ, but that a peak in the dichroic ratio spectrum occurred at 695 mμ. This observation was interpreted as indicating that about 5 percent of the chlorophyll *a* was spatially oriented. Olson[31] illuminated immobilized cells by plane-polarized light. The fluorescent light emitted was plane polarized, with a single band at 720 mμ. When the plane of polarization of the exciting light was varied, the plane of polarization of the emitted light remained unchanged. These experiments indicate that the light absorbed by various pigments is transferred to a single type of pigment consisting of spatially oriented and fixed molecules.

the photochemical reactions

It is not possible at the present time to give a secure formulation of the photochemical reactions that is consistent with all known observations. Because of the complexity of the photosynthetic units and the photosynthetic processes, progress in elucidating the details of function has been slow, but it has been steady. The scheme outlined below should be regarded as tentative and subject to modification as more data become available. Alternative formulations have been proposed to account for the experimental observations thus far made. In part, the present uncertainty results from the fact that many intermediates in the photochemical reactions are not known chemically with certainty, but are known in terms of their absorption spectra. Duysens[32] was the first to show a reversible change in the absorption spectrum of bacteriochlorophyll by illumination. Exposure of bacteriochlorophyll from *R. rubrum* resulted in a bleaching of the 890 mμ absorption band accompanied by increased absorption at 800 mμ. It was shown later[33] that similar changes in the absorption of bacteriochlorophyll could be brought about by chemical oxidation. The bleaching reactions also occur at liquid

[30] Sauer, K., and Calvin, M. *J. Mol. Biol.*, *4*, 451 (1962).
[31] Olson, R. A., in *Mechanisms of Photosynthesis in Green Plants.* Washington: National Research Council, publ. no. 1145, 1963, p. 545.
[32] Duysens, L. N. M. *Transfer of Excitation Energy in Photosynthesis.* Utrecht: thesis, 1952; *Biochim. Biophys. Acta*, *19*, 1 (1956).
[33] Goedheer, J. C. *Biochim. Biophys. Acta*, *27*, 478 (1958); *28*, 278 (1958).

nitrogen temperature; this indicates that they are photochemical reactions. It should be said that the maximum change in absorbance at 890 mμ is only a few percent of the total absorbance at that wavelength. If the decrease in absorbance at 890 mμ accompanying illumination represents an oxidation, some substance should be reduced.

It has been observed that the bleaching at 890 mμ is accompanied by a change in absorbance at 275 mμ which would correspond to the concomitant reduction of ubiquinone. At low intensities of illumination in intact cells, or in chromatophores placed in a mildly reducing environment such as a dilute, buffered, reduced glutathione solution, spectral changes corresponding to an oxidation of cytochromes are observed. A slight red shift in the absorption spectrum of bacteriochlorophyll has been observed in cells at low intensities of illumination. This shift corresponds to a photochemical reduction of bacteriochlorophyll. All these data have been interpreted to mean that the primary photochemical event in the intact cell is the simultaneous oxidation of cytochrome and reduction of bacteriochlorophyll. At high light intensities, there is an oxidation of bacteriochlorophyll and a reduction of ubiquinone.

Differential spectrophotometry is much more difficult in plants and algae because the chloroplasts contain a much greater percentage of inert pigments and the spectral changes are correspondingly smaller. Kok[34] and others, however, have demonstrated undoubted absorption changes at 700 mμ in plants that correspond to the changes observed at 890 mμ (and 870 mμ) in bacterial systems. When green leaves are illuminated, the absorption of reduced cytochrome *f* decreases, indicating further oxidation of this compound. Very careful spectrophotometric measurements have shown that the absorption changes in plant cells are actually dual, one absorption change occurring in 700 mμ mainly as a result of far-red illumination, and another occurring at 670 mμ mainly as a result of exposure to shorter-wavelength light. The pigments responsible for these light-induced changes are thought to reside in different centers which can be excited separately. These centers are designated System I for the center that absorbs at 700 mμ and System II for the center that absorbs at 670 mμ. The chlorophyll in the two centers appears to be associated with different accessory pigments; cytochrome *f* and plastocyanin in System I, and cytochrome b_6 and plastoquinone in System II.

A hypothetical though yet unproved formulation of the sequence of events which fits the experimental data is schematized in Fig. 5-31. Light absorbed by a System II center generates a strong oxidant and a weak reductant, possibly reduced plastoquinone.

$$4\,X + 4\,Y + 4h\nu_{(670)} \rightarrow 4\,X^{-}_{(red)} + 4\,Y^{+}_{(ox)} \qquad (5\text{-}15)$$

This reaction results in the evolution of oxygen by green plants, or the oxidation of other acceptors than water in bacteria.

$$4\,Y^{+}_{(ox)} + 2\,H_2O \rightarrow O_2 + 4\,Y + 4\,H^+ \qquad (5\text{-}16)$$

Manganese ions are required, and the reaction is inhibited by DCMU and other related herbicides. This sequence involves a change in redox potential from 0.8 volt to about 0 volt.

The reductant generated in System II is oxidized by the oxidant generated by System I in reactions involving plastocyanine and/or cytochrome b_6 and coupled to the phosphorylation of ADP to form ATP. This sequence involves a change in the redox potential from about 0 volt to 0.4 volt.

Light absorbed by a System I center generates a weak oxidant and a strong reductant.

$$4\,X + 4\,Y + 4\,h\nu_{(700)} \rightarrow 4\,X^{-}_{(red)} + 4\,Y^{+}_{(ox)} \qquad (5\text{-}17)$$

[34] Kok, B. *Acta Botan. Neerl.*, *6*, 316 (1957).

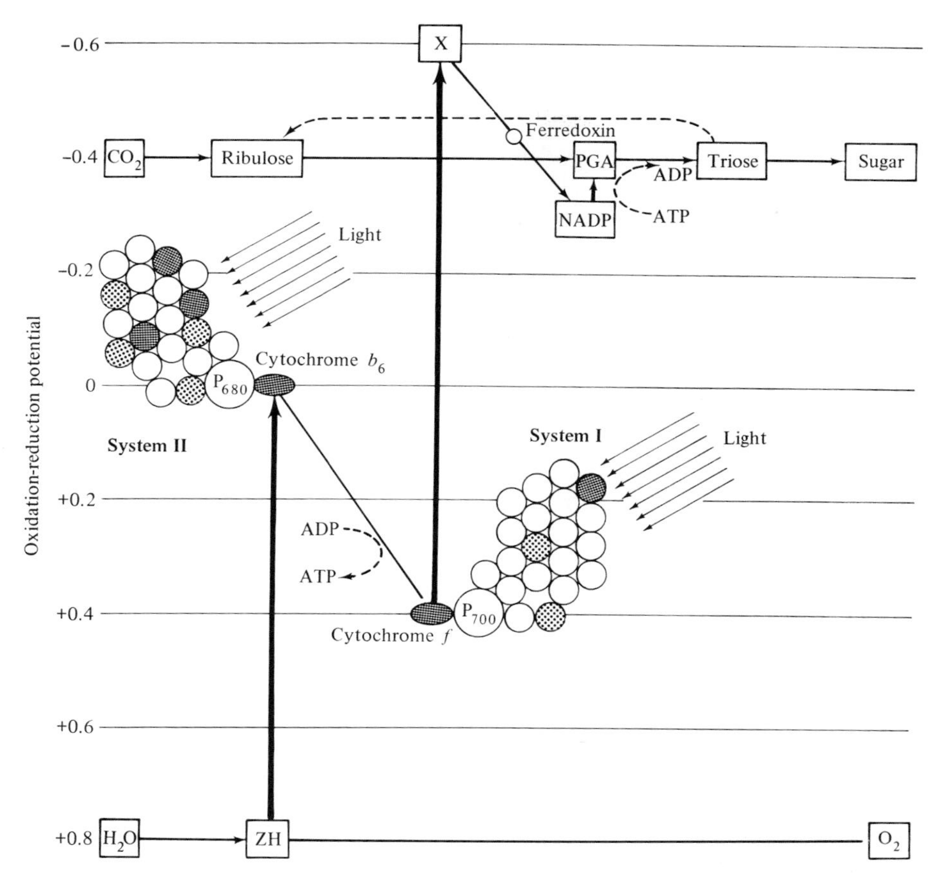

fig. 5-31. A schematic diagram of photosynthesis as a two-step process involving two pigment systems. Hydrogen atoms (or electrons) from the donor ZH are boosted to cytochrome b_6 by energy collected in System II and trapped by pigment P_{680}. The pigments of System II include chlorophyll a_{670} and the accessory pigments chlorophyll *b* or *c*, phycoerythrin or phycocyanin, depending upon the species. The electrons are then passed "downhill" to cytochrome *f*, synthesizing ATP in the process. Energy from System I, which contains chlorophyll *a* and accessory pigments, is trapped by pigment P_{700} and boosts the electrons to a receptor substance X, from which they are transferred by ferredoxin to NADP. The reduced NADPH and ATP generated are utilized in the conversion of phosphoglyceric acid to triose phosphate. (From Rabinowitch, E. I., and Govindjee. The role of chlorophyll in photosynthesis. *Sci. Am., 213,* 80 [July, 1965]. Copyright © 1965 by Scientific American. All rights reserved.)

System I can also be bleached by potassium ferricyanide. The weak oxidant generated is possibly cytochrome *f* which interacts with the weak reductant generated by System II as indicated above. The strong reductant generated by System I reduces ferredoxin, which in turn reduces NADP by the following sequence of reactions:

$$X_{(red)}^{-} + \text{ferredoxin}_{(ox)} \rightarrow X + \text{ferredoxin}_{(red)} \qquad (5\text{-}18)$$

$$\text{ferredoxin}_{(red)} + \text{NADP} \rightarrow \text{ferredoxin}_{(ox)} + \text{NADPH} \qquad (5\text{-}19)$$

This sequence is accompanied by a change in redox potential from about +0.4 volt to −0.4 volt. A schematic representation of the photosynthetic systems in the chloroplast membrane system is shown in Fig. 5-32.

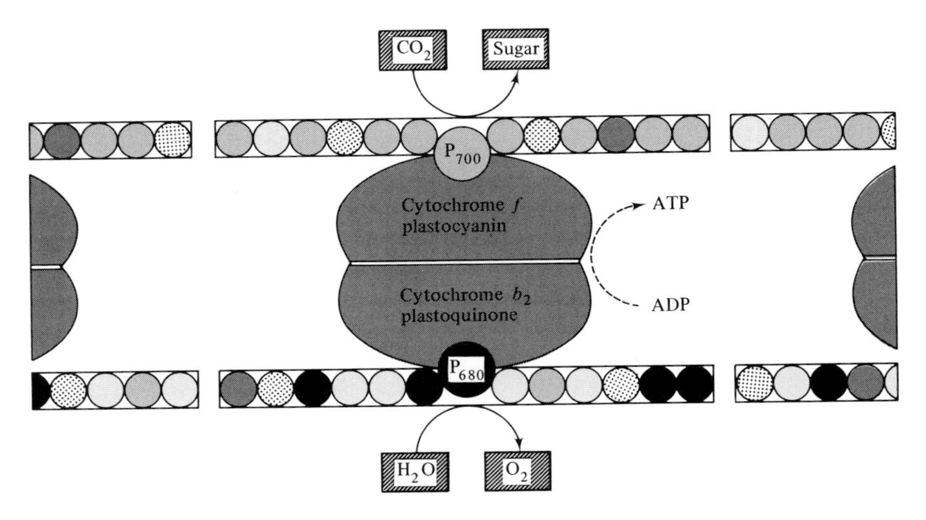

fig. 5-32. Hypothetical arrangement of pigments in a chloroplast lamella would have System I in a monomolecular layer at the top and System II at the bottom. The space between the two pigment layers might contain the compounds responsible for the transport of hydrogen atoms (or electrons). The water-to-oxygen cycle would then be linked to System II and the carbon cycle to System I. From Rabinowitch, E. I., and Govindjee. The role of chlorophyll in photosynthesis. *Sci. Am., 213,* 82 [July, 1965]. Copyright © 1965 by Scientific American. All rights reserved.)

The NADPH and ATP formed as a result of the photochemical reactions are utilized in the thermochemical reactions which assimilate carbon dioxide into carbohydrate. The pathway of the thermochemical incorporation of CO_2 was elucidated by the use of ^{14}C-labeled CO_2 by identifying the progression of label into compounds after illumination. In chloroplasts harvested 5 sec after a brief flash of illumination in the presence of ^{14}C-labeled CO_2, radiocarbon appeared in phosphoglyceric acid, alanine, aspartic acid, and malic acid. After 15 sec, the radiocarbon also appeared in ribose-5-phosphate, ribulose-5-phosphate, fructose-6-phosphate, and sucrose. At 1 min after a flash of light, the radiocarbon has labeled a variety of carbohydrate intermediates; after 5 min, the lipids and amino acids of the leaf are heavily labeled.

From experiments of this type, the pathway of CO_2 assimilation shown in Fig. 5-33 was worked out. Carbon dioxide is first incorporated into ribulose diphosphate which splits into two molecules of 3-phosphoglyceric acid. The crucial step is the next one in which the 3-phosphoglyceric acid is reduced to triose phosphate, a reaction which requires NADPH and ATP as cofactors. The triose phosphate then enters a complex pathway which resembles the alternative pathway of glycolysis described below. The photochemical and thermochemical reactions of photosynthesis thus can be summarized as follows:

$$2\,H_2O \rightarrow O_2 + 4\,e^- + 4\,H^+ \qquad (5\text{-}20)$$

$$2\,NADP + 4\,e^- + 4\,H^+ \rightarrow 2\,NADPH + 2\,H^+ \qquad (5\text{-}21)$$

$$2\,NADPH + CO_2 + 2\,H^+ \rightarrow 2\,NADP + H_2O + (CH_2O) \qquad (5\text{-}22)$$

$$H_2O + CO_2 \rightarrow (CH_2O) + O_2 \qquad (5\text{-}23)$$

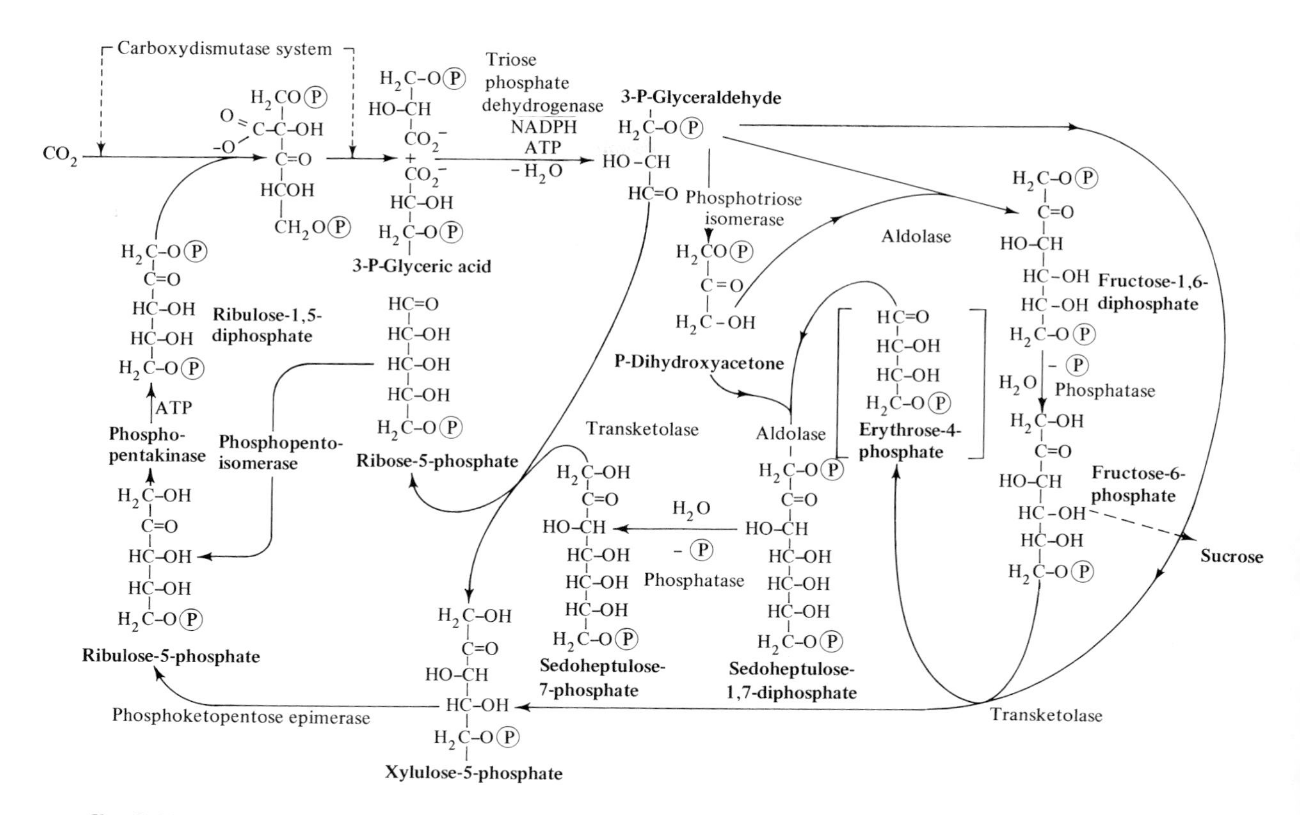

fig. 5-33. Pathways of the initial chemical reactions in photosynthesis (dark reactions). Note the similarities to the pentose shunt pathway. (From Bassham, J. A., and Calvin, M. *The Path of Carbon in Photosynthesis.* Englewood Cliffs, N.J.: Prentice-Hall, 1957, p. 57.)

nitrogen fixation

Heterotrophic organisms derive the nitrogen needed for their cellular constituents largely from amino acids in protein. Ultimately, this protein has its origin in protein synthesized by plants. While molecular nitrogen is abundantly present in the atmosphere, most plants are not capable of utilizing it in synthetic reactions, but instead depend upon the small quantities of nitrates and ammonium compounds present in the soil. A small minority of plants and certain types of microorganisms are able to assimilate molecular nitrogen as the sole source of nitrogen, and, in the last analysis, provide combined nitrogen for all other living forms. Sir Humphrey Davy was the first to suggest that plants fix nitrogen (*Elements of Agricultural Chemistry*, 1836), and two years later J. B. Boussingault showed that legumes contained more nitrogen than had been added to the soil as manure. Under withering criticism from an outstanding chemist of the day, Justus Liebig, Boussingault repeated his experiments in closed containers using sterilized soil and, of course, was unable to confirm his previous results. Actually, the importance of legumes in maintaining soil fertility was recognized in classical times, and crop rotation using legumes was well established in Greek and Roman agriculture. The nodules on the roots of legumes were well known to seventeenth-century scientists; for example, the nodules are clearly depicted in the drawings of bean plants made by Malpighi in 1675. H. Hellheigel and H. Wilfarth (1886) were the first to show that nodulated legumes were able to assimilate nitrogen and that a bacterium was associated with the nodules, while legumes grown in sterilized soil did not develop nodules and were unable to assimilate nitrogen.[35]

There are two types of organisms able to fix nitrogen: symbiotic forms and free-living microorganisms. The symbiotic forms include members of the family *Leguminosae* (peas, beans, clovers, soy beans, etc.) whose roots bear nodules, and certain nonleguminous, nodule-bearing angiosperms such as the alder, bog myrtle, and sea-buckthorn. In the legumes, the nodules contain a bacterium of the genus *Rhizobium* as a symbiont, while the nodules of the nonleguminous plants contain an actinomycete. The free-living microorganisms include certain bacteria (*Aerobacter*, *Azotobacter*, *Beijerinckia*, *Chromatium*, and *Clostridium*), certain blue-green algae (*Anabaena*, *Calothrix*, *Fischerella*, and *Nostoc*), and certain yeasts and actinomycetes (*Rhodotorula*, *Pullularia*, and *Nocardia*).

The roots of legumes appear to secrete a substance which attracts rhizobia present in the soil to the plants. The nature of the attractive substance is unknown, but biotin, amino acids, sugars, and other vitamins secreted by the roots have been implicated. Each species of legume tends to attract a specific Rhizobium. Nodule formation is initiated when the rhizobia enter the root cortex. The bacteria then elaborate a substance (which may be indoleacetic acid) which causes root-hair curling followed by the formation of a polygalacturonidase by the plant which conditions the root hair for growth of the bacteria. For a time, the bacteria multiply in the cortical cells of the root, but a point in development of the nodule is reached when the bacteria stop dividing and increase in size, forming *bacteroids* which may be 40 to 45 times as large as the original bacteria and which may cause as much as a ten-fold increase in size of the infected cell. Electron micrographs of the bacteroids show a well-developed intracellular membrane system not found in the small, rod-shaped rhizobia. High levels of nitrates, ammonia, or other nitrogen compounds in the soil inhibit nodule formation.

Many nodules have a reddish color; Kubo[36] demonstrated that this was due to the presence of hemoglobin. Except for its presence in legume root nodules and in *Neurospora* and certain other yeasts, hemoglobin is not to be found in the plant kingdom. The exact function of hemoglobin in nitrogen fixation is not known. It enhances respiration in the nodules, and there is a correlation between the amount of hemoglobin present in the nodules and the rate of nitrogen fixation.

Nodules cannot fix nitrogen when detached from the plant, and nitrogen fixation is stimulated by active photosynthesis. The bulk of the molecular nitrogen fixed by the nodules is quickly absorbed by the plant. The presence of cobalt, molybdenum, and iron is required for the development and function of nodules. A root temperature in excess of 25°C inhibits nitrogen fixation. Molecular hydrogen and carbon monoxide also inhibit nitrogen fixation. Comparative morphological studies of the free-living microorganisms that carry on nitrogen fixation suggest that they are quite primitive. The fixation process appears to be one of reduction; and respiration is not necessary for nitrogen fixation, even in aerobic bacteria such as *Azotobacter*. It is possible that nitrogen fixation developed as a metabolic process early in the history of life while the earth still had a reducing atmosphere. It has been suggested that the nitrogen-fixing organisms became well established when the atmosphere changed to an oxidizing one as the supply of combined nitrogen in the soil was depleted through the process of denitrification.

---

[35] The reader interested in the early experiments on nitrogen fixation should consult the charming paper by Wilson, P. W. *Bacteriol. Rev.*, *21*, 215 (1957).
[36] Kubo, H. *Acta Phytochim.* (*Tokyo*), *11*, 195 (1939).

The initial step in nitrogen fixation is not known. In view of the diversity of organisms that fix nitrogen, it is possible that more than one process is used. It seems more likely that nitrogen is fixed by reduction than by oxidation, probably by the formation of diimide, hydrazine, or a related substance which in turn is reduced to ammonia. When nitrogen-fixing cell-free preparations are incubated in ^{15}N-labeled molecular nitrogen, the isotropic nitrogen is detected first in ammonia, and the amount of label recovered accounts for all the nitrogen assimilated during the first minute. Nitrogen fixation is immediately inhibited when ammonia is added to nitrogen-fixing organisms or cell-free preparations; the ammonium nitrogen is utilized in preference to other nitrogen compounds or molecular nitrogen.

It appears that pyruvate is a requirement for nitrogen fixation (although α-ketobutyrate will substitute in some systems). Approximately 44 to 100 moles of pyruvate are oxidized for each mole of nitrogen assimilated, indicating that the coupling between the two processes is loose or indirect. Acetylphosphate appears to be a major product of pyruvate metabolism in many nitrogen-fixing systems. Ferredoxin, which is also involved in photochemical reactions, appears to act as an intermediate in the transport of electrons from pyruvate metabolism to nitrogen fixation. Crystalline ferredoxin

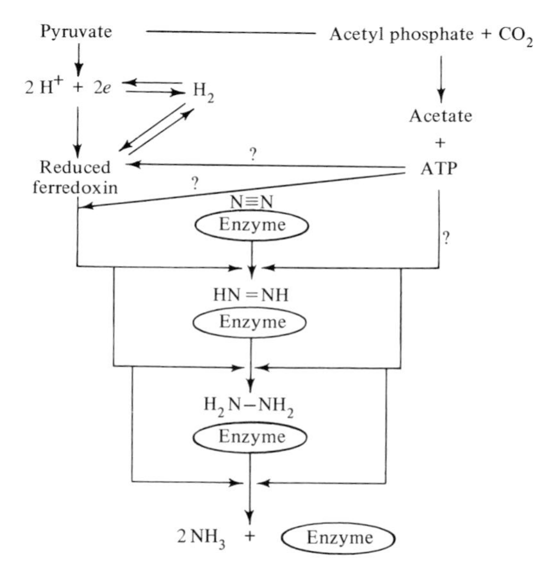

fig. 5-34. A hypothetical scheme for the reaction sequence in nitrogen fixation in leguminous root nodules. (From Burris, R. H., in Bonner, J., and Varner, J. E., eds. *Plant Biochemistry.* New York: Academic Press, 1956, p. 978. Copyright Academic Press; reprinted by permission.)

from *Clostridia* is a protein with a molecular weight of about 12,000 containing seven or eight atoms of iron per molecule. Molecular hydrogen can also act as a source of electrons for nitrogen fixation in *Clostridia* provided that ferredoxin and an energy-rich phosphate such as acetylphosphate are present. Although cobalt and molybdenum are requirements for nitrogen fixation, their place in the sequence of reactions is presently unknown. The ammonia which is formed by nitrogen fixation probably enters the ornithine cycle or combines with α-ketoglutarate to form glutamic acid.

From these intermediates, other nitrogen-containing compounds required by the plant are formed. The present view of nitrogen fixation is depicted schematically in Fig. 5-34.

the utilization of foods

The utilization of food for the production of energy to carry on the vital processes may be divided into three stages or processes:[37] digestion, fermentation, and oxidation. Most foodstuffs are macromolecules: proteins or carbohydrates. In the first stage of utilization, these macromolecules must be hydrolyzed to their constituent monomers. Although fats are not macromolecules, they too must be hydrolyzed to glycerol and fatty acids. By and large, these processes take place in the digestive tract of animals. However, the intracellular stores of glycogen, starch, or fat may also be utilized for energy; their utilization begins with intracellular hydrolysis. The amounts of energy liberated in these processes are relatively small. The free energy of hydrolysis of the peptide bond is approximately 3.0 kcal/mole; that of the glucosidic bonds of starch or glycogen is about 4.3 kcal/mole, and the free energy of hydrolysis of ester bonds is of the order of 2.5 kcal/mole. The energy liberated during these processes is not utilized except as a source of heat.

In the second stage, the small organic molecules, hexoses, amino acids, glycerol, or fatty acids, are metabolized partially to form carbon dioxide, water, and either acetyl-coenzyme A, α-ketoglutarate, or oxaloacetate. In general, these processes can occur in the absence of oxygen. One remarkable feature of catabolic metabolism is the astonishingly few chemical reactions that are needed to convert a great variety of substances into acetyl-coenzyme A, α-ketoglutarate, or oxaloacetate.

In the third stage of utilization, the closely related metabolic intermediates, acetyl-coenzyme A, α-ketoglutarate, and oxaloacetate, enter the tricarboxylic acid cycle, the common terminal pathway of oxidation for all foods. In this cycle the metabolic intermediates are oxidized to carbon dioxide and water through a series of reactions involving dicarboxylic and tricarboxylic acids as intermediates. Oxidation of these by a common pathway results in great simplicity and economy in the number of enzymes required to catalyze the respiratory sequence of reactions. In the metabolism of foodstuffs, approximately one-third of the total energy of combustion is set free in stage two, and two-thirds is set free in stage three.

Glycolysis, the anaerobic degradation of glucose to lactic acid, is depicted schematically in Fig. 5-35. The overall reaction is

$$\underset{\text{(glucose)}}{C_6H_{12}O_6} \rightarrow \underset{\text{(lactic acid)}}{2\ C_3H_6O_3} \qquad \Delta G = -52{,}000 \text{ cal/mole} \tag{5-24}$$

In this reaction no oxygen is required and there is no net oxidation nor reduction. Actually, the overall stoichiometry of the reaction as it takes place in the living cell is not that shown in eq. 5-24; rather, the process is accompanied by the phosphorylation of adenosine diphosphate to ATP by the following overall reaction:

$$\text{glucose} + 2\ \text{ADP} + 2\ P_i \rightarrow 2\ \text{lactic acid} + 2\ \text{ATP} + 2\ H_2O \qquad \Delta G = -38{,}000 \text{ cal/mole} \tag{5-25}$$

In the living cell, then, the breakdown of glucose into lactic acid is coupled to the

[37] Krebs, H. A., and Kornberg, H. L. *Ergeb. Physiol.*, *49*, 212 (1957).

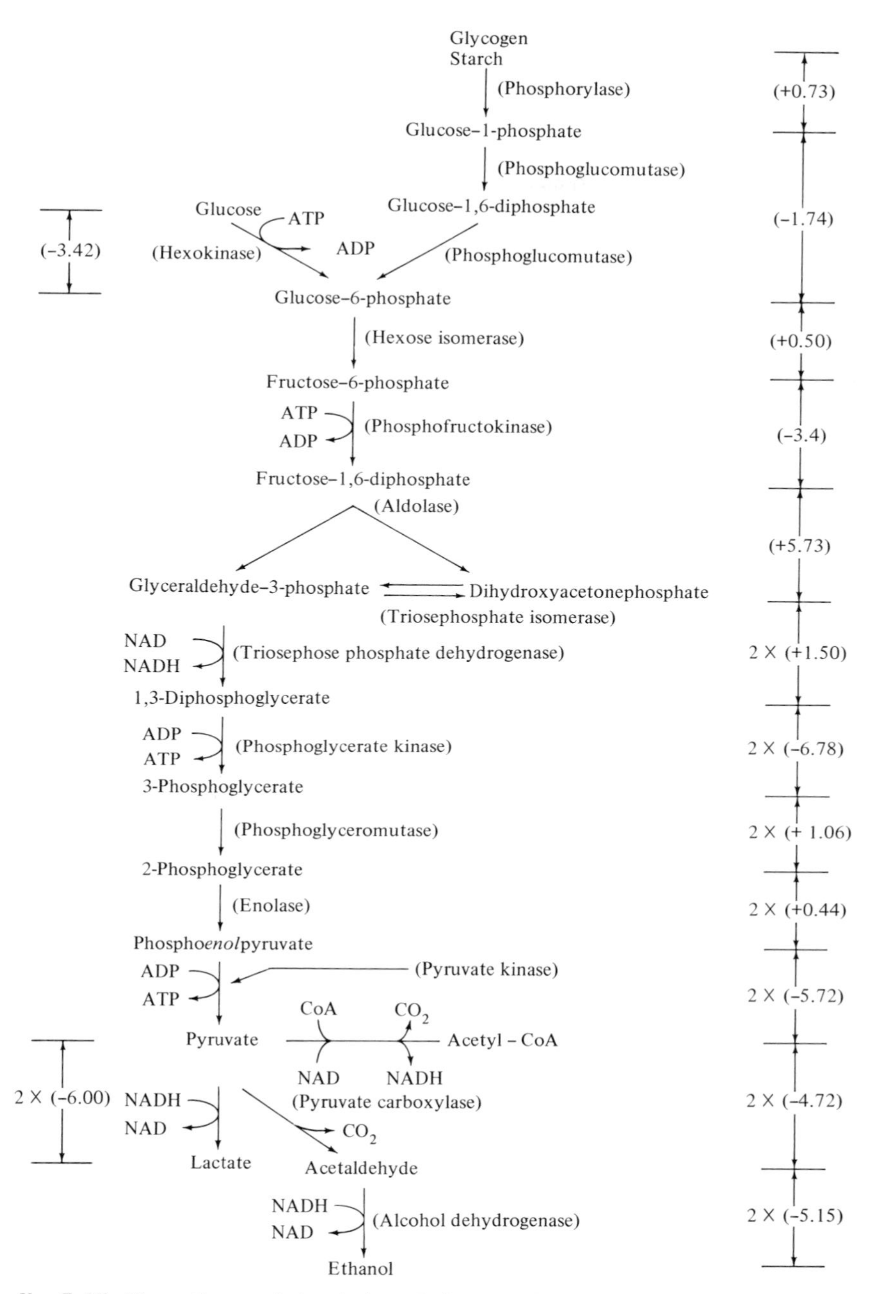

fig. 5-35. The pathway of glycolysis and glycogenolysis leading to lactic acid and ethanol. The numbers in parentheses are free energy changes ($\Delta G'$) in kcal/mole reactants at *p*H 7.0, 25°C in 0.2 atm O_2 and 0.05 atm CO_2.

formation of ATP. The difference in free energy between eqs. 5-24 and 5-25 represents energy which is conserved in ATP formation and which can be utilized for other purposes in the cellular economy. The efficiency of ATP production by glycolysis is 24,000/52,000 or 46 percent.

An examination of the energy changes in each step of the sequence of glycolysis shown

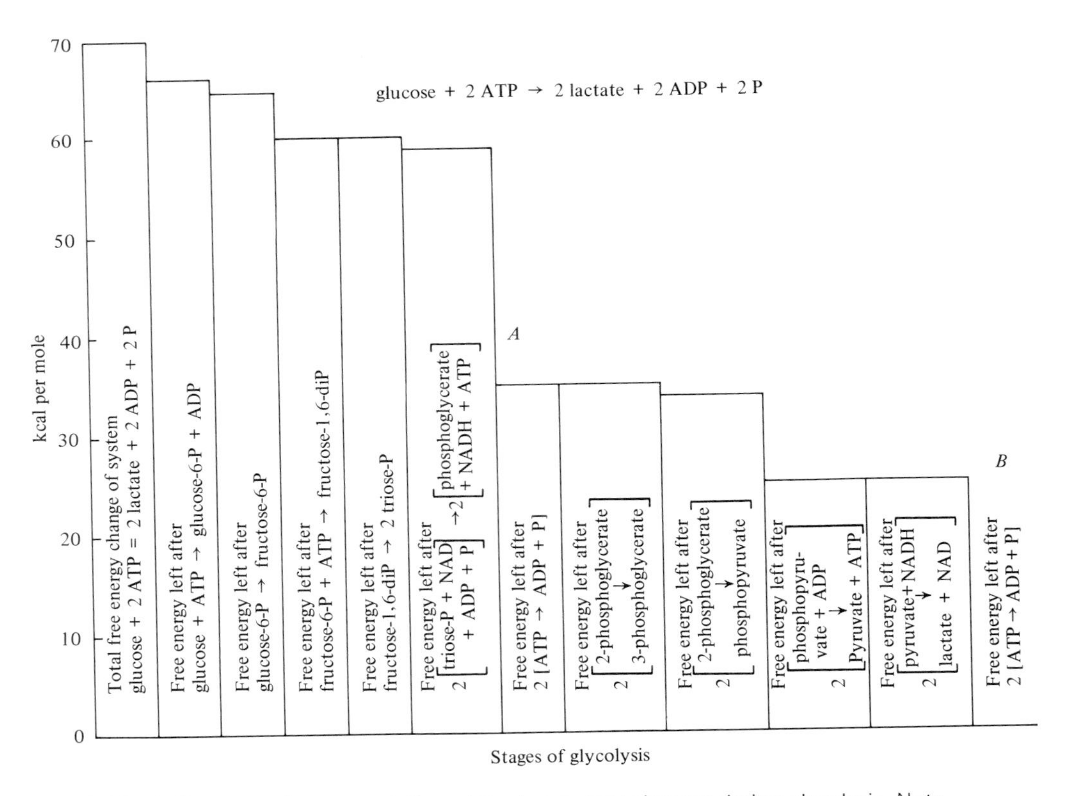

fig. 5-36. A diagrammatic representation of the free energy changes during glycolysis. Note that the major changes take place at two steps which are coupled to the synthesis of ATP. (Adapted from Krebs, H. A., and Kornberg, H. L. A survey of the energy transformation in living matter. *Ergeb. Physiol., 49,* 212–275. Berlin-Göttingen-Heidelberg: Springer [1957].)

in Fig. 5-36 reveals that there is relatively little free energy change at many steps but that a large free energy change accompanies those reactions in which ATP is formed. It should be noted that actually two molecules of ATP are needed in the initial steps of the glycolytic pathway; in these steps a high energy-rich compound is hydrolyzed while a medium energy-rich compound is formed. Four ATP molecules are liberated later in the sequence of reactions. The net production of ATP, therefore, is two molecules per molecule of glucose. In addition, the reduction of NAD is coupled to the conversion of triosephosphate to 1,3-diphosphoglycerate. Oxidized NAD is regenerated in the conversion of pyruvic acid to lactic acid.

The sequence of two reactions leading to ATP formation illustrates the general manner in which energy-conserving biological oxidation reactions take place. In the first reaction, triosephosphate is oxidized to 1,3-diphosphoglycerate, an energy-rich compound. In the second reaction of the sequence, 1,3-diphosphoglycerate, the energy-rich product of the first reaction, is hydrolyzed in a reaction coupled to the formation of ATP.

respiration

While the anaerobic hydrolysis of glucose is the only mechanism producing energy for cellular processes under specialized conditions, the bulk of energy normally results from the enzymatic oxidation by molecular oxygen of metabolic intermediates arising from glycolysis and other reactions. This process is carried on in the mitochondria and can be divided into two separate parts. In the first part, the metabolic intermediates are successively oxidized by chemical reactions to carbon dioxide and water. These reactions are coupled to the formation of reduced coenzymes. In the second part, the reduced coenzymes are oxidized and ATP is formed simultaneously by the process of oxidative phosphorylation described above.

The Krebs tricarboxylic cycle is shown schematically in Fig. 5-37. The figures in

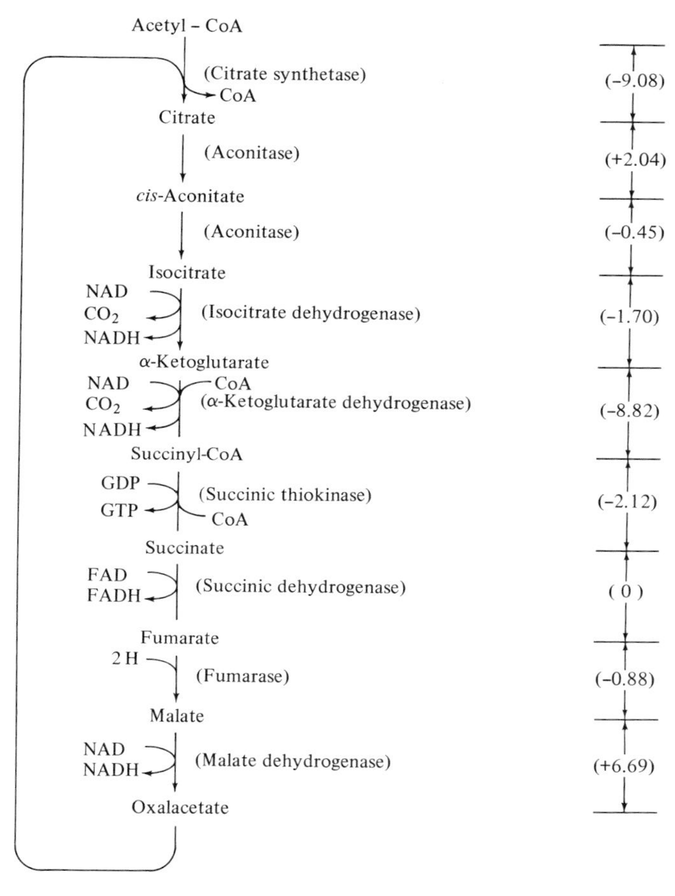

fig. 5-37. The Krebs tricarboxylic acid cycle, showing the free energy changes in kcal/mole reactants at *p*H 7.0, 25°C in 0.2 atm O_2 and 0.05 atm CO_2.

parentheses indicate the change in standard free energy for each step in the cycle. The change in free energy is relatively small for four of the eight steps. For the remaining four steps, however, there is a large free energy change. The latter reactions are coupled to the reduction of a coenzyme.

When the end products of glycolysis are to be oxidized aerobically, pyruvic acid is converted into acetyl-coenzyme A instead of into lactic acid. This reaction, which is mediated by the enzyme pyruvate dehydrogenase, requires the presence of several cofactors: magnesium ions, thiamine pyrophosphate (TPP), lipoic acid (6,8-dimercaptoöctanoic acid), and NAD. The reaction probably proceeds as outlined in Fig. 5-37 with the net reduction of a molecule of NAD and has a $\Delta G^0 = -56$ kcal/mole. The acetyl-coenzyme A formed condenses with oxaloacetic acid to form citric acid which enters the tricarboxylic acid cycle.

Similarly, the degradation of fatty acids proceeds by way of β-oxidation, a series of reactions in which successive two-carbon fragments are removed beginning at the carboxyl end of the molecule. A two-carbon fragment is split off by the sequence of reactions shown in Fig. 5-38, yielding one acetyl-coenzyme A molecule accompanied by

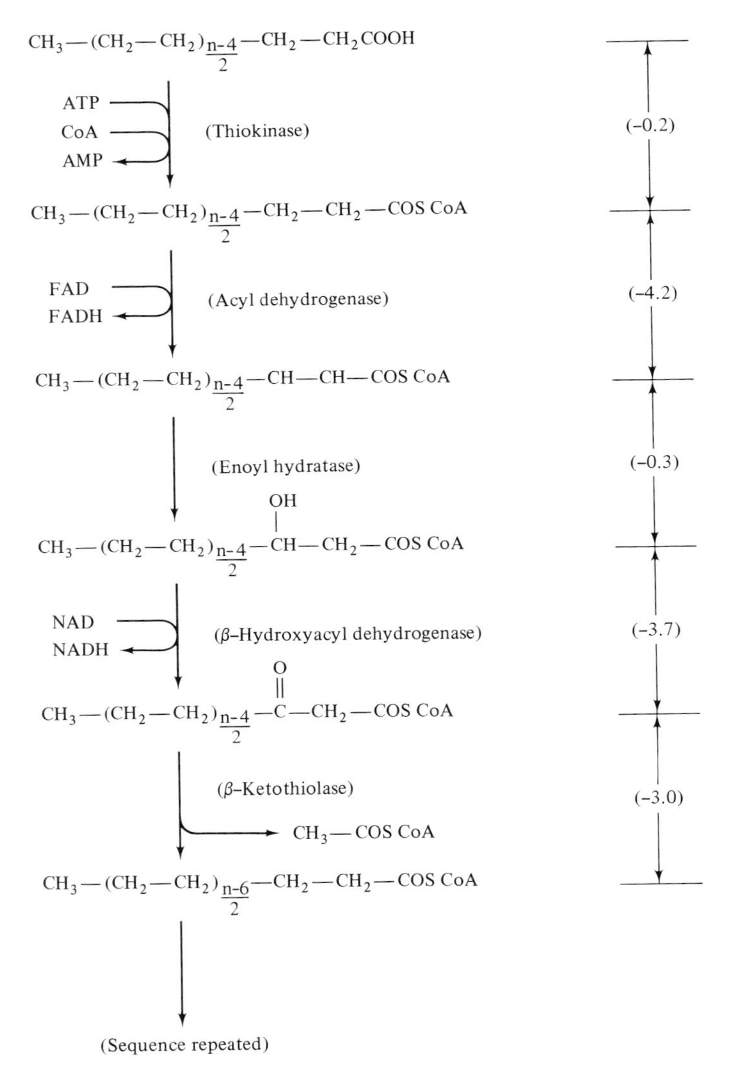

fig. 5-38. The pathway of fatty acid oxidation showing the free energy changes.

the reduction of two cytochrome *c* molecules and the formation of one molecule of NADH from NAD. The total $\Delta G^0 = -89$ kcal/mole. The acetyl-coenzyme A formed enters the tricarboxylic acid cycle. The glycerol moiety of fats is phosphorylated and then oxidized to the aldehyde, triosephosphate, which enters the glycolytic pathway leading to pyruvate and oxidation by the tricarboxylic acid cycle.

Every kind of amino acid liberated from the hydrolysis of protein has its own pathway of catabolism. In general, this sequence begins with removal of the α-amino group and is followed by degradation of the residue. In most animals, almost all amino acids undergo deamination by transfer of their amino group to α-oxoglutarate to form the corresponding α-oxoacid and glutamic acid.

$$\begin{aligned} &R{-}CHNH_2{-}COOH + HOOC{-}CH_2{-}CH_2{-}CO{-}COOH \rightarrow \\ &\qquad R{-}CO{-}COOH + HOOC{-}CH_2{-}CH_2{-}CHNH_2{-}COOH \end{aligned} \tag{5-26}$$

The α-oxoacid enters the oxidative pathway in various ways. Leucine and portions of phenylalanine and tyrosine are degraded to acetyl-coenzyme A. Glutamic acid, the prolines, histidine, and arginine are degraded to α-ketoglutaric acid. Aspartic acid and the other portions of phenylalanine and tyrosine are degraded to oxaloacetic acid. The excess glutamic acid which is formed by transamination reactions undergoes oxidative deamination

$$\begin{aligned} &HOOC{-}CH_2{-}CH_2{-}CHNH_2{-}COOH + NAD + H_2O \rightarrow \\ &\qquad HOOC{-}CH_2{-}CH_2{-}CO{-}COOH + NADH_2 + NH_4 \end{aligned} \tag{5-27}$$

yielding about $(\Delta G^0) - 45.9$ kcal/mole.

alternative pathways of glucose oxidation

While glycolysis is quantitatively the most important pathway of glucose degradation, a number of related alternate pathways of glucose catabolism exist (sometimes called the pentose shunt) not leading to the direct fission into two triose molecules, but often involving pentose phosphates as intermediates and oxidative steps requiring NADP as a coenzyme. Glucose metabolized by these alternative pathways gives rise to important intermediates, such as ribose, which are needed at times as building blocks for essential constituents in the cellular economy. In the first reaction, glucose-6-phosphate is formed, and in turn this is oxidized to gluconate-6-phosphate in a reaction accompanied by the reduction of NADP. The gluconate-6-phosphate undergoes an oxidative decarboxylation of the type shown in Fig. 5-39, yielding ribulose-5-phosphate, a reaction again accompanied by the reduction of NADP. The ribulose-5-phosphate may undergo one of two isomerizations to either ribose-5-phosphate or to xylulose-5-phosphate. A molecule of ribose-5-phosphate and one of xylulose-5-phosphate interact, in a reaction catalyzed by the enzyme transketolase which requires thiamine pyrophosphate as a cofactor, to produce a molecule of sedoheptulose-7-phosphate (a seven-carbon sugar) and a molecule of triosephosphate. These two sugars then participate in a transaldolation reaction to give a fructose-6-phosphate and a molecule of erythrose-4-phosphate (a four-carbon sugar). The erythrose-4-phosphate and another molecule of xylulose-5-phosphate also undergo a transketolation reaction to give a fructose-6-phosphate and a triosephosphate. The two molecules of fructose-6-

phosphate are isomerized to form glucose-6-phosphate which reenters the metabolic pathways for glucose while the triosephosphate formed is degraded to pyruvate and enters the tricarboxylic acid cycle.

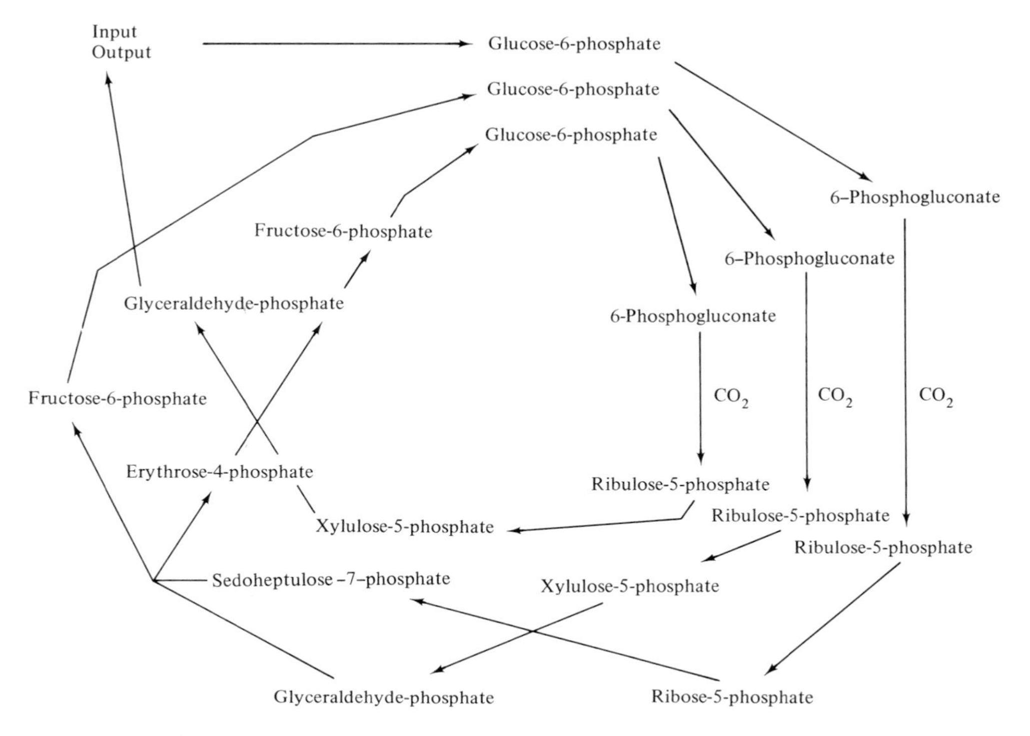

fig. 5-39. A diagram of the pentose shunt pathway.

An inspection of the alternative pathway reveals that if glucose-1-^{14}C (glucose labeled with radiocarbon only in the one-carbon atom) is metabolized, all the ^{14}C appears promptly as CO_2. On the other hand, if glucose-6-^{14}C is metabolized by the alternative pathway, the ^{14}C will not appear in CO_2 until the triosephosphate formed eventually enters the tricarboxylic acid cycle. If glucose is metabolized by the glycolytic pathway, none of the radioactivity will appear as CO_2 until the pyruvate formed enters the tricarboxylic acid cycle regardless of whether glucose-1-^{14}C or glucose-6-^{14}C is used. Thus, it is possible to estimate roughly the fraction of glucose metabolized by the glycolytic pathway and the fraction metabolized by the pentose shunt by injecting into an organism alternately small test doses of glucose-1-^{14}C and glucose-6-^{14}C and following the amount of radiocarbon in the carbon dioxide formed as a function of time. The ratio of the initial $^{14}CO_2$ formed using glucose-6-^{14}C to the initial $^{14}CO_2$ formed using glucose-1-^{14}C indicates roughly the percent of glucose metabolized by the direct Embden-Meyerhoff pathway. Evaluations of this sort, however, are only approximate at best.

A number of other alternative pathways of glucose oxidation exist, such as the one in which glucuronic acid phosphate is an intermediate. Quantitatively these other pathways are less important than the shunt pathway described above, but they lead to the formation of essential intermediates needed by the cell.

utilization of energy for synthetic reactions

Cells utilize both the metabolic intermediates formed by and the energy liberated from catabolic processes to synthesize small and large molecules needed in the cellular economy. Some substances, like ribose and glucuronic acid, are themselves intermediates in the catabolic pathways. Many other small molecules are formed from catabolic intermediates. Thus, serine is derived from 3-phosphoglycerate, alanine from pyruvate, and valine and leucine from α-acetolactate which in turn arises from pyruvate. Aspartate comes from oxaloacetate, glycerol from dihydroxyacetone phosphate, heme from δ-aminolevulinic acid which has its origin in succinate, and so on. Macromolecules are formed from activated monomers by condensation reactions which will be outlined below.

The energy required for biosynthetic reactions is obtained by the coupling of the energy-requiring biosynthetic reaction to the energy-yielding hydrolysis of ATP or another energy-rich compound. In all cases, the sum of the changes in free energy for both reactions, the biosynthetic reaction and the coupled energy-yielding reaction, is always negative. For example, the synthesis of the disaccharide sucrose from glucose and fructose is a reaction which is coupled to the hydrolysis of ATP and requires the presence of uridine diphosphate (UDP). The coupling is achieved through a sequence of reactions:

$$\mathrm{ATP + UDP \rightarrow ADP + UTP}$$
$$\mathrm{glucose + ATP \rightarrow glucose\text{-}6\text{-}phosphate + ADP}$$
$$\mathrm{glucose\text{-}6\text{-}phosphate \rightarrow glucose\text{-}1\text{-}phosphate}$$
$$\mathrm{glucose\text{-}1\text{-}phosphate + UTP \rightarrow UDP\text{-}glucose + PP_i}$$
$$\mathrm{UDP\text{-}glucose + fructose \rightarrow sucrose + UDP}$$
$$\mathrm{PP_i + H_2O \rightarrow 2\ P_i}$$

$$\mathrm{glucose + fructose + 2\ ATP + H_2O \rightarrow sucrose + 2\ ADP + 2\ P_i}$$

The energetics of this sequence of reactions is

$$\mathrm{glucose + fructose \rightarrow sucrose + H_2O} \qquad \Delta G = +5.5 \text{ kcal/mole}$$
$$\mathrm{2\ ATP + 2\ H_2O \rightarrow 2\ ADP + 2\ P_i} \qquad \Delta G = -14.0 \text{ kcal/mole}$$

$$\mathrm{glucose + fructose + 2\ ATP + H_2O \rightarrow 2ADP + 2\ P_i} \qquad \Delta G = -8.5 \text{ kcal/mole}$$

The overall reaction is driven in the direction of sucrose synthesis because of the large negative free energy change of -8.5 kcal/mole. The efficiency of the reaction sequence can be estimated roughly from the ratio $5.5/14.0 = 39$ percent. The relatively low efficiency is part of the price which is paid for a mechanism that ensures that the reaction will go nearly to completion.

The synthesis of the phospholipid, phosphatidylcholine, offers another example of the pattern of synthetic reactions which require an input of energy. The sequence of reactions is

$$\mathrm{RCOOH} + \mathrm{ATP} + \mathrm{CoA} \rightarrow \mathrm{RCO{-}CoA} + \mathrm{AMP} + \mathrm{PP_i}$$
$$\mathrm{R'COOH} + \mathrm{ATP} + \mathrm{CoA} \rightarrow \mathrm{R'CO{-}CoA} + \mathrm{AMP} + \mathrm{PP_i}$$
$$2\ \mathrm{AMP} + 2\ \mathrm{ATP} \rightarrow 4\ \mathrm{ADP}$$
$$\text{glycerol} + \mathrm{ATP} \rightarrow \text{3-phosphoglycerol} + \mathrm{ADP}$$
$$\text{3-phosphoglycerol} + \mathrm{RCO{-}CoA} \rightarrow \text{1-acyl,3-phosphoglycerol} + \mathrm{CoA}$$
$$\text{1-acyl,3-phosphoglycerol} + \mathrm{R'CO{-}CoA} \rightarrow \alpha\text{-phosphatidic acid} + \mathrm{CoA}$$
$$\alpha\text{-phosphatidic acid} + \mathrm{H_2O} \rightarrow \text{1,2-diglyceride} + \mathrm{P_i}$$
$$\mathrm{CMP} + 2\ \mathrm{ATP} \rightarrow \mathrm{CTP} + 2\ \mathrm{ADP}$$
$$\text{choline} + \mathrm{ATP} \rightarrow \text{phosphorylcholine} + \mathrm{ADP}$$
$$\text{phosphorylcholine} + \mathrm{CTP} \rightarrow \text{CDP-choline} + \mathrm{PP_i}$$
$$\text{1,2-diglyceride} + \text{CDP-choline} \rightarrow \text{phosphatidylcholine} + \mathrm{CMP}$$
$$3\ \mathrm{PP_i} + 3\ \mathrm{H_2O} \rightarrow 6\ \mathrm{P_i}$$

$$\mathrm{RCOOH} + \mathrm{R'COOH} + \text{glycerol} + \text{choline} + 8\ \mathrm{ATP} + 4\ \mathrm{H_2O} \rightarrow \text{phosphatidylcholine} + 8\ \mathrm{ADP} + 8\ \mathrm{P_i}$$

The free energy changes for all the reactions in the sequence are not known, but the hydrolysis of phosphatidylcholine into glycerol, two fatty acids, choline, and phosphate can be estimated to be about 19.0 kcal/mole. The synthesis of the phosphatidylcholine was achieved at the expense of 8 moles of ATP hydrolyzed which represents an energy input of about −56.0 kcal/mole. The net free energy change for the sequence of reactions is about −37.0 kcal/mole, and the efficiency of energy utilization for the synthetic sequence is 19.0/56.0 = 34 percent.

In general, synthetic reactions proceed by sequences of this sort which involve (1) the formation of an energy-rich (or activated) donor by an exchange reaction between the donor molecule and an energy-rich intermediate, and (2) the condensation of the energy-rich donor and an acceptor molecule with the liberation of some energy. A list of activated donors, the energy-rich intermediate required for their formation, typical acceptors, and the end products of the synthetic reactions is given in Fig. 5-40. If the activated donor and the energy-rich intermediate have approximately the same free energy of hydrolysis, then the first reaction of the sequence in which the activated donor is formed is reversible. The condensation reaction between the activated donor and the acceptor usually has a large negative free energy change and goes nearly to completion. It is usually limited by the availability of reactants.

types and kinetics of metabolic regulation

Unlike contemporary society with its planned obsolescence and its conspicuous consumption, living cells utilize foods only as they are needed for energy and to provide starting materials for synthesis. Furthermore, the multiplicity of chemical reactions which occur in the living cell are remarkably balanced. Even with greatly changing demands which result from various environmental changes, all cellular constituents are

fig. 5-40. Donors and acceptors of structural units in biological synthesis.

STRUCTURAL UNIT	DONOR	ACCEPTOR	PRODUCT
Hydrogen	e.g., NADPH	β-Oxoacyl-coenzyme A	β-Hydroxyacyl-coenzyme A
Phosphate	e.g., ATP	Glucose	Glucose-6-phosphate
	1,3-Diphosphoglycerate	ADP	ATP
Amino	e.g., Alanine	α-Oxoglutarate	Glutamate
	Glutamine (amide group)	Glucose-6-phosphate	Glucosamine-6-phosphate
Methyl	S-Adenosyl methionine	Glycocyamine	Creatine
Imino	L-Aspartate	L-Citrulline	L-Arginine
Thiol	L-Homocysteine	L-Serine	L-Cysteine
Acyl	Acetyl-coenzyme A	e.g., Oxaloacetate	Citrate
		Sulphanilamide	Acetylsulphanilamide
Aroyl	Benzoyl-coenzyme A	Glycine	Hippurate
Carbamoyl	Carbamoyl phosphate	Ornithine	Citrulline
Amidine	Arginine	Glycine	Glycocyamine
Adenosine	ATP	Methionine	S-Adenosyl methionine
Glucose	Uridine diphosphate glucose	Oligosaccharides	Polysaccharides, e.g., starch
Glucuronic acid	Uridine diphosphate glucuronic acid	Alcohol or phenol	Glucosiduronic acid
Carboxyl	Biotin-CO_2	Acetyl-coenzyme A	Malonyl-coenzyme A

produced or degraded in just the appropriate quantity so that there is neither surfeit nor lack of any given constituent. In addition, there is a remarkable adjustment between the energy-producing reactions and the biosynthetic reactions. Even though adequate substrate for the energy-producing reaction is present, only as much substrate is metabolized as energy thereby produced can be utilized. These observations reflect the presence of fine-honed intracellular regulatory systems by which the rates of intracellular reactions are governed and altered to meet the various demands upon the cell. The types of control mechanisms which govern metabolic reaction rates can be categorized as follows:

A. Control by the enzymes themselves (usually providing quick response for prompt adaptation)
   1. Control by substrate level, including competition of systems for a single metabolite
   2. Control by cofactor level, *p*H, etc.
   3. Control by obligatory coupling to a coenzyme, energy-rich intermediate, acceptor, etc.
   4. Inhibition by the product of the reaction, the product of the metabolic sequence (feedback inhibition), unrelated metabolites, ions, etc.

5. Interconversion between an active and inactive form of the enzyme, including aggregation and disaggregation of protein subunits
6. Allosteric interactions, activation or inhibition by substances which interact with the enzyme at a site different than the active site responsible for enzymatic activity

B. Control by structural factors
1. Compartmentalization and coupling
2. Control of permeability, diffusion, or transport of substrate, product, cofactor, etc.
3. Control of integrity of membranes for membrane-associated enzymes

C. Control by quantity of enzyme present (usually with a slower response; important in long-term adaptation)
1. Control by induction of synthesis
   a. By means of structural genes
   b. By means of regulatory genes
2. Control by repression of synthesis at the level of transcription
3. Regulation at the level of translation
   a. By availability of amino acids and t-RNA
   b. By availability of energy
   c. By availability of ribosomes
   d. By other environmental factors

The simplest form of regulation at the enzyme level involves *inhibitors*, substances which decrease the rate of an enzymatic reaction. Enzyme inhibition may be *reversible* or *irreversible*. In the former case, the original rate returns when the inhibitor is removed, for instance, by a specific reaction or by dialysis; in the latter case, the original activity does not return when the inhibitor is removed. Reversibility of inhibition implies that the reaction of inhibitor and enzyme is freely reversible and that a true equilibrium exists.

There are several types of reversible inhibition. *Competitive* reversible inhibition occurs when the substrate and inhibitor react with the enzyme at the same site, affecting K_M. *Noncompetitive* reversible inhibition occurs when the substrate and inhibitor react with the enzyme at different sites sufficiently far removed from each other so that the binding of substrate is not influenced by the binding of inhibitor and vice versa. Of course, various intermediate types of inhibition also occur.

In the case of fully competitive inhibition, the system can be represented by the following sequence of reactions:

$$\mathrm{E} + \mathrm{S} \rightleftharpoons \mathrm{ES} \qquad K_s = \frac{[\mathrm{E}][\mathrm{S}]}{[\mathrm{ES}]} = \frac{([\mathrm{E}_0] - [\mathrm{ES}] - [\mathrm{EI}])[\mathrm{S}]}{[\mathrm{ES}]} \tag{5-28}$$

$$\mathrm{E} + \mathrm{I} \rightleftharpoons \mathrm{EI} \qquad K_i = \frac{[\mathrm{E}][\mathrm{I}]}{[\mathrm{EI}]} = \frac{([\mathrm{E}_0] - [\mathrm{ES}] - [\mathrm{EI}])[\mathrm{I}]}{[\mathrm{EI}]} \tag{5-29}$$

$$\mathrm{ES} \rightarrow \mathrm{E} + \mathrm{P} \tag{5-30}$$

The overall velocity of the reaction will be given by

$$v = k[\mathrm{ES}] \tag{5-31}$$

Solving eqs. 5-28, 5-29, and 5-30 for v gives

$$v = \frac{k[\mathrm{E_0}]}{1 + \dfrac{K_s}{[\mathrm{S}]}\left(1 + \dfrac{[\mathrm{I}]}{K_i}\right)} = \frac{V_M}{1 + \dfrac{K_M}{[\mathrm{S}]}\left(1 + \dfrac{[\mathrm{I}]}{K_i}\right)} \tag{5-32}$$

In the case of partially competitive inhibition, the inhibitor alters the affinity of the enzyme although the substrate and inhibitor apparently combine at different sites on the enzyme. The following sequence of reactions describes this type of system.

$$E + S \rightleftharpoons ES \qquad K_s = \frac{([E_0] - [ES] - [EI] - [EIS])[S]}{[ES]} \tag{5-33}$$

$$E + I \rightleftharpoons EI \qquad K_i = \frac{([E_0] - [ES] - [EI] - [EIS])[I]}{[EI]} \tag{5-34}$$

$$EI + S \rightleftharpoons EIS \qquad K_s' = \frac{[S][EI]}{[EIS]} \tag{5-35}$$

$$ES + I \rightleftharpoons EIS \qquad K_i' = \frac{[I][ES]}{[EIS]} \tag{5-36}$$

$$ES \rightarrow E + P \tag{5-37}$$

$$EIS \rightarrow EI + P \qquad v = k([ES] + [EIS]) \tag{5-38}$$

solving eqs. 5-33 through 5-38 for v gives

$$v = \frac{K[E_0]}{1 + \dfrac{K_s}{[S]} \cdot \dfrac{\left(1 + \dfrac{[I]}{K_i}\right)}{\left(1 + \dfrac{[I]}{K_i} \cdot \dfrac{K_s}{K_s'}\right)}} = \frac{V_M}{1 + \dfrac{K_M}{[S]} \cdot \dfrac{\left(1 + \dfrac{[I]}{K_i}\right)}{\left(1 + \dfrac{[I]}{K_i} \cdot \dfrac{K_s}{K_s'}\right)}} \tag{5-39}$$

In the case of noncompetitive inhibition, the inhibitor does not affect the affinity of the enzyme for the substrate, but only the velocity with which the product is formed. For this case eqs. 5-38 and 5-39 become

$$v = k[ES] + k'[EIS] \tag{5-40}$$

$$v = \frac{\dfrac{k[E_0] + k'[E_0][I]/K_i}{1 + [I]/K_i}}{1 + K_s/[S]} \tag{5-41}$$

If the complex EIS does not dissociate to form the product, $k' = 0$, and eq. 5-41 becomes

$$v = \frac{(k[E_0]) \Big/ \left(1 + \dfrac{[I]}{K_i}\right)}{1 + K_s/[S]} \tag{5-42}$$

Many inhibitors are of the "mixed type"; they combine the attributes of both competitive and noncompetitive inhibitors. Mixed-type inhibitors affect both V_M and K_M.

allosteric interactions

If more than one molecule of substrate combines with one molecule of enzyme under conditions where the rate of binding and dissociation of substrate is rapid compared with the rate of formation of product (the assumed Michaelis-Menten conditions), the enzyme, substrate, and enzyme-substrate complexes will be virtually at equilibrium and

$$K = \frac{[E][S]^n}{[ES_n]} \tag{5-43}$$

where n is the apparent order of the reaction.[38] Assuming that the concentrations of all enzyme-substrate complexes containing fewer than n molecules of substrate are negligibly small (eq. 4-281),

$$v = K_3(ES_n) \tag{5-44}$$

Substituting $V_M = K_3[E_0]$, and $[E] = [E_0] - [ES_n]$, eq. 5-44 becomes

$$k_3[E] = V_M - v \tag{5-45}$$

Substituting eq. 5-45 into eq. 5-43 gives

$$\frac{[ES_n]}{[E]} = \frac{v}{V_M - v} = \frac{[S]^n}{K} \tag{5-46}$$

or, in the logarithmic form, the Hill equation

$$\log\left(\frac{v}{V_M - v}\right) = n \log [S] - \log K \tag{5-47}$$

Plots of $\log [v/(V_M - v)]$ *versus* $\log [S]$ should give a straight line of slope n. The value of n obtained from the experimental data will depend upon the strength of interaction between the binding sites on the enzyme molecule; it will approach the total number of binding sites if the interactions are very strong and, contrariwise, approach unity if the interactions between binding sites are weak. Most enzymes are not ideal, and the slope at the midpoint of the line ($[S]_{0.5}$) where $[v/(V_M - v)] = 1$ may be used. A characteristic of regulatory enzymes is an apparent order of kinetics greater than unity which involves multiple interacting binding sites (Fig. 5-41).

Monod, Changeux, and Jacob[39] emphasized the fact that the modulation of enzyme activity by an effector molecule could be positive as well as negative and the effector molecule frequently bore no steric similarity to the substrate molecule. Because enzymes display a very high degree of structural specificity in their interactions with low-molecular-weight compounds, it seemed very likely that the interactions of the enzyme with the modifier did not occur at the active enzymatic site. They called such interactions with modifiers *allosteric* interactions.

Allosteric modifiers which activate the enzyme are believed to act by causing a conformational change in the enzyme which increases its affinity for enzyme. Kinetic studies with some enzymes show a decrease in K_M for the substrate when the modifier is present. On the other hand, the modifier may affect the velocity with which the product is formed. In other instances, activation is thought to occur by relief of allosteric

---

[38] Hill, A. J. *Biochem. J.*, *7*, 471 (1913); Atkinson, D. E., Hathaway, J. A., and Smith, E. C. *J. Biol. Chem.*, *240*, 2682 (1965); Taketa, K., and Pogell, B. M. *J. Biol. Chem.*, *240*, 651 (1965).

[39] Monod, J., Changeux, J. P., and Jacob, F. *J. Mol. Biol.*, *6*, 306 (1963).

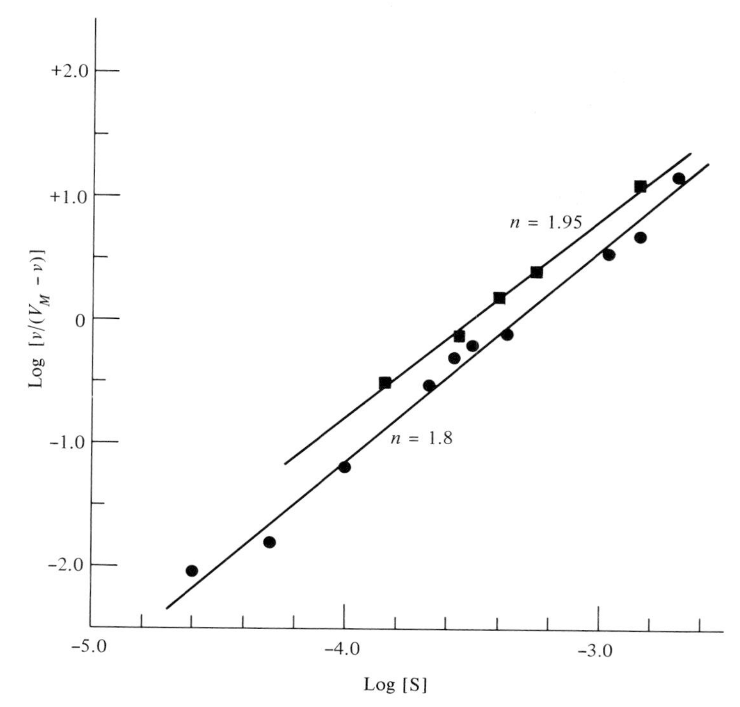

fig. 5-41. Plots of log $[v/(V_M - v)]$ *versus* log [S] according to the Hill equation: (●---●) fructose diphosphatase varying fructose-1, 6-diphosphate concentration, and (■---■) pyruvate carboxylase varying MgATP concentration. (From the data of Preiss, J., Biggs, M. L., and Greenberg, E. *J. Biol. Chem.*, *242*, 2293 [1967]; and Keech, B., and Barritt, G. J. *J. Biol. Chem.*, *242*, 1985 [1967].)

inhibition. The latter type of activation may occur either by competition between the activator and the inhibitor for the same allosteric site on the enzyme or by the activating effector's counteracting the conformational change produced by the allosteric inhibitor even though it interacts at a different site. In some instances, the modifier shows a biphasic response, activating at low concentrations and inhibiting at high concentrations.

It has been possible to modify enzymes selectively so that they are unresponsive to allosteric effectors but still retain enzymatic activity. The procedures utilized include treatment of the enzyme with organic mercurials, aging at 0°, freezing, exposure to high temperatures, high ionic strength or extremes of *p*H, or treatment with proteolytic enzymes.[40] Marked changes in the kinetics of the enzyme frequently accompany the loss of allosteric response. The loss of allosteric response without the loss of enzyme activity supports the view that different sites on the protein molecule are involved.

There is a very large number of possible combinations of modes of interaction between enzyme and modifier, particularly if there are multiple binding sites, multiple subunits, and multiple conformational forms of the protein. Nevertheless, a number of

[40] Patte, J. C., Le Bras, G., Loviny, T., and Cohen, G. N. *Biochim. Biophys. Acta*, *67*, 16 (1963); Caskey, C. T., Ashton, D. M., and Wyngaarden, J. B. *J. Biol. Chem.*, *239*, 2570 (1964); Cennamo, C., Boll, M., and Holzer, H. *Biochem. Z.*, *340*, 125 (1964); Murphy, T. A., and Wyatt, G. R. *J. Biol. Chem.*, *240*, 1500 (1965); Bauerle, R. H., Freundlich, M., Stormer, F. C., and Umbarger, H. E. *Biochim. Biophys. Acta*, *92*, 142 (1964); Taketa, K., and Pogell, B. M. *J. Biol. Chem.*, *240*, 651 (1965).

models based on simplifying assumptions have been put forward which are useful in attempting to analyze the operation of this type of metabolic control at the enzyme level. An intriguing model has been proposed by Monod, Wyman, and Changeux.[41] In this model, the enzyme can reversibly assume one of two discrete conformational states (designated R and T) which differ in their affinity for one or more ligands (R affinity greater than T). The presence of one such ligand, therefore, will tend to shift equilibrium toward the form of the enzyme to which the ligand is most avidly bound. It was also assumed in this model that allosteric enzymes consist of several subunits which are indistinguishable, and there is but one ligand-binding site per subunit. In addition, symmetry of the enzyme molecule is conserved at all times in this model; in other words, interconversion of the subunits of an enzyme molecule takes place in a concerted fashion so that all subunits in a given molecule tend to be in either the R or the T form.

While all R sites will have the same affinity for ligand and likewise for all T sites, the principle of conservation of symmetry implies that if one subunit of a protein binds one ligand molecule, the other subunits will be more likely to bind ligands in order that all subunits will convert from the R form to the T form. A cooperative effect of binding will be displayed by the system, particularly at low ligand concentrations, giving an S-shaped curve for v *versus* [S] instead of the usual hyperbolic curve.

The binding of a second ligand at a different site than that which binds the first ligand can be of two types. If the affinity of the T form is greater than that of the R form, the $R \rightleftharpoons T$ equilibrium will be shifted in favor of the T form in the presence of the second ligand. The T form, however, binds the first ligand less avidly. In this case, the second ligand acts to displace the first ligand even though it binds at a different site and can be regarded as a *negative modifier*. Contrariwise, if the affinity of the R form for a third ligand is greater, the third ligand will shift the equilibrium in favor of the R form and tend to increase the affinity of binding for the first ligand. In the latter case, the third ligand acts as a *positive modifier*.

The following equation can be derived to express the equilibrium of the system:

$$Y_s = \frac{\alpha(1+\alpha)^{n-1}}{[L(1+\beta)^n/(1+\gamma)^n] + (1+\alpha)^n} \tag{5-48}$$

where Y_s is the fraction of substrate sites to which substrate is actually bound; $L = [T]_0/[R]_0$, that is, the equilibrium constant between the R and T forms in the absence of any ligands; α, β, and γ stand for the concentrations of the first (substrate), second (negative modifier), and third (positive modifier) ligands respectively multiplied by a factor determined by their association constants to the protein; and n is the number of subunits per molecule of protein.

When the system is saturated with positive modifier, the equilibrium of the protein shifts it entirely into the R form even if substrate is absent. The cooperative interactions of substrate should disappear, and the S-shaped v-*versus*-[S] plot should become the more usual hyperbolic curve. When γ is very large, the term $[L(1+\beta)^n/(1+\gamma)^n]$ vanishes and eq. 4-43 simplifies into a form of the Michaelis equation.

$$Y_s = \frac{\alpha}{1+\alpha} \tag{5-49}$$

[41] Monod, J., Wyman, J., and Changeux, J. P. *J. Mol. Biol.*, *12*, 88 (1965).

This prediction holds for some enzymes but not for others (e.g., yeast phosphofructokinase and yeast NAD-isocitrate dehydrogenase).

Another system was analyzed by Koshland, Nemethy, and Filmer,[42] who, instead of using a single model, examined the properties of a family of models with four subunits per molecule, one binding-site subunit, and one type of ligand. It was assumed that the individual subunits could exist in one of two conformations, only one of which bound the ligand in any significant amount. The effects of different geometric arrangement of identical and nonidentical subunits, variations in the strength of interaction between subunits, and variation in the affinity for ligand were analyzed.

Four patterns of interaction were examined: tetrahedral, square, linear, and concerted. The last mode of interaction resembles the Monod-Wyman-Changeux model in the requirement that all units change conformation simultaneously. Theoretical ligand binding curves were calculated for the various models. A steepness parameter, R_s (defined as the ratio of ligand concentrations for 90 percent and 10 percent saturation, $R_s = [S]_{0.9}/[S]_{0.1}$), was introduced, as was a set of nomograms for each model relating experimental values for R_s and the ligand concentration at half-saturation $[S]_{0.5}$ to the product of the intrinsic ligand dissociation constant and the equilibrium constant for conformational change.

It was shown that the experimental hemoglobin oxygen saturation curve fits the theoretical curves for the tetrahedral or square models better than those for the linear or concerted models. The comparative approach illustrates how difficult it is to decide upon the unambiguous validity of one model from experimental saturation curves with any degree of confidence.

One of the first well-studied allosteric enzymes was aspartate transcarbamylase[43] which catalyzes the first reaction unique to pyrimidine biosynthesis, the conversion of aspartate to carbamyl aspartate. Aspartate transcarbamylase is inhibited by CTP, one of the end products of the pyridine pathway. ATP, which by itself neither inhibits nor activates the enzyme, acts to relieve the inhibition by CTP.

Aspartate transcarbamylase is a large protein sedimenting at 11.8 S_{20} which corresponds to a molecular weight of 260,000. When it is heated to 60° for 5 min and then rapidly cooled to 0°, the enzyme disaggregates into four identical subunits of molecular weight 65,000. Each subunit has a single binding site for CTP. A plot of v *versus* [S], shown in Fig. 5-42, gives a sigmoid curve rather than the usual hyperbolic curve; it resembles the oxygen saturation curve for hemoglobin. Kinetic analysis of the CTP inhibition reveals that it is partially competitive with respect to the substrate aspartate. The subunits, while enzymatically active, do not respond to inhibition by CTP. In the subunit form, the enzyme shows the usual v-*versus*-[S] plot (Fig. 5-42). Malate shows a biphasic action. At low concentrations malate activates aspartate transcarbamylase; at high concentrations, malate inhibits it.

The action of CTP is judged to occur at a regulatory site on the enzyme molecule different than the active enzymatic site because (1) CTP and aspartate differ markedly in their size, shape, and charge distribution; (2) CTP inhibition can be abolished without loss of catalytic activity; and (3) ATP, which itself does not affect the enzymatic rate, can relieve CTP inhibition, presumably by competing with CTP for binding at the regulatory site. A number of allosteric enzymes are listed in Fig. 5-43.

---

[42] Koshland, D. E., Jr., Nemethy, G., and Filmer, D. *Biochemistry*, *5*, 365 (1966).
[43] Gerhart, J. C., and Pardee, A. B. *Cold Spring Harbor Symp. Quant. Biol.*, *28*, 491 (1963).

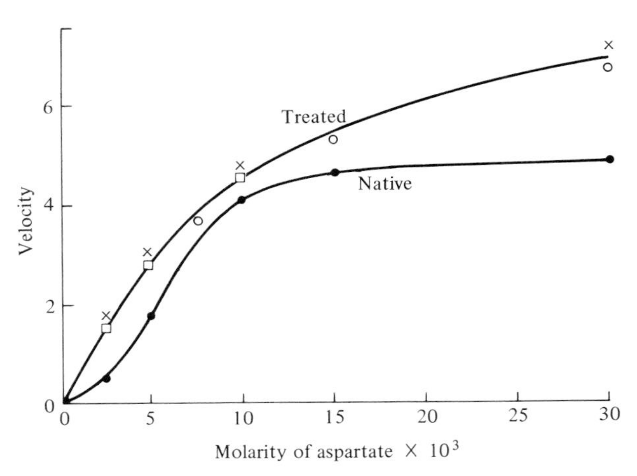

fig. 5-42. Plots of *v versus* [S] for native aspartate transcarbamylase (tetramer form) and for the enzyme treated with 10^{-6} M $Hg(NO_3)_2$ or heated at 60° for 4 min (monomer form). In addition to aspartate, the reaction mixture contained 3.6×10^{-3} M carbamyl phosphate, 2×10^{-4} M CTP, and 0.09 μg enzyme protein in 0.04 M potassium phosphate buffer, *p*H 7.0. (From Gerhart, J. C., and Pardee, A. B. *Cold Spring Harbor Symp. Quant. Biol., 28*, 494 [1963].)

fig. 5-43. Summary of properties of various allosteric systems. (From Monod, J., Wyman, J., and Changeux, J.-P. *J. Mol. Biol., 12*, 96 [1965]. Copyright Academic Press; reprinted by permission.)

ENZYME	SUBSTRATE	INHIBITOR	ACTIVATOR
Hemoglobin (vertebrates) (invertebrates)	Oxygen		
Biosynthetic L-threonine deaminase (*E. coli* K 12) and (yeast)	L-Threonine	L-Isoleucine	L-Valine
Aspartate transcarbamylase (*E. coli*)	Aspartate Carbamyl phosphate	CTP	ATP
Deoxycytidylate aminohydrolase	dCMP	dTTP	dCTP
Phosphofructokinase (guinea pig heart)	Fructose-6-phosphate ATP	ATP 5′-AMP	3′,5′-AMP
Deoxythymidine kinase (*E. coli*)	Deoxythymidine	dTTP	dCDP
NAD-isocitric dehydrogenase (*N. crassa*)	L_3-Isocitrate NAD	α-Keto-glutarate	Citrate
NAD-isocitric dehydrogenase (yeast)	L_3-Isocitrate NAD	—	5′-AMP

fig. 5-43 (*Continued*).

ENZYME	SUBSTRATE	INHIBITOR	ACTIVATOR
Homoserine dehydrogenase (*R. rubrum*)	Homoserine Aspartate semi-aldehyde NADPH-NAPH	L-Threonine	L-Isoleucine L-Methionine
L-Threonine deaminase (*C. tetanomorphum*)	L-Threonine	—	ADP
Acetolactate synthetase	Pyruvate	L-Valine	
"Threonine" aspartokinase (*E. coli*)	Aspartate	L-Threonine	
L-Glutamine-D-fructose-6-P transaminase (rat liver)	L-Glutamine D-Fructose-6-P	UDP-N acetyl-glucosamine	
Glycogen synthetase (yeast) (lamb muscle)	UDP-glucose	—	Glucose-6-P
Glutamate dehydrogenase (beef liver)	Glutamate	ATP GTP NADH Estrogens Thyroxine	ADP Leucine Methionine
Phosphorylase *b* (rabbit muscle)	Glycogen	ATP Glucose-6-P	5′-AMP Glucose-1-P
UDP-N-acetyl-glucosamine-2-epimerase (rat liver)	UDP-N-acetyl-glucosamine	CMP-N-acetyl-neuraminic acid	
Homoserine dehydrogenase (*E. coli*)	Homoserine Aspartate semialde-hyde	L-Threonine	
"Lysine"-aspartokinase (*E. coli*)	Aspartate ATP	L-Lysine	
Fructose-1-6-diphosphatase (frog muscle) (rat liver)	Fructose-1-6-diphosphate	5′-AMP	
ATP-PRPP-pyrophosphoryl-ase (*S. typhimurium*)	ATP PRPP	Histidine	
"Tyrosine" 3-deoxy-D-arabinoheptulosonic-acid-7-phosphate synthetase (*E. coli*)	Phosphoenol-pyruvate D-Erythrose-4-P	L-Tyrosine	
"Phenylalanine" 3-deoxy-D-arabinoheptulosonic-acid-7-phosphate synthetase (*E. coli*)	Phosphoenol-pyruvate D-Erythrose-4-P	L-Phenylalanine	
Acetyl-CoA carboxylase (rat adipose tissue)	Acetyl-CoA ATP, CO_2	—	Citrate

end-product inhibition

Most enzyme reactions slow down as the concentration of product increases; this phenomenon is called *product inhibition.* While the operation of enzyme-catalyzed reactions in the reverse direction may be unfavorable on energetic or rate grounds, most enzyme-catalyzed reactions, in fact, can proceed in the reverse direction. Removing this simplification from the reaction in eq. 4-250 gives

$$S + E \underset{k_2}{\overset{k_1}{\rightleftharpoons}} ES \rightleftharpoons EP \underset{k_4}{\overset{k_3}{\rightleftharpoons}} E + P \tag{5-50}$$

A set of equations analogous to eqs. 4-251 to 4-255 can be written. Under steady-state conditions when $[S] \gg [E_0]$ and $d[ES]/dt \approx d[E]/dt \approx 0$,

$$v = -\frac{d[S]}{dt} = \frac{d[P]}{dt} = \frac{(k_1 k_3[S] - k_2 k_4[P])[E_0]}{(k_2 + k_3) + k_1[S] + k_4[P]} \tag{5-51}$$

The initial velocity of the forward reaction can be obtained by setting $[P] = 0$, and, contrariwise, the initial velocity of the reverse reaction can be obtained by setting $[S] = 0$.

$$v_f = \frac{k_1 k_3[S][E_0]}{(k_2 + k_3) + k_1[S]} = \frac{V_{Mf}}{(K_{Ms}/[S]) + 1} \tag{5-52}$$

$$v_r = \frac{k_2 k_4}{(k_2 + k_3) + k_4[P]} = \frac{V_{Mr}}{(K_{Mp}/[P]) + 1} \tag{5-53}$$

At equilibrium, the velocities of the forward and reverse reactions are equal, and we can write for the equilibrium constant

$$K = \frac{k_1 k_3}{k_2 k_4} = \frac{V_{Mf} K_{Mp}}{V_{Mr} K_{Ms}} \tag{5-54}$$

which is known as the *Haldane equation.* The unidirectional quality of many enzyme-catalyzed reactions results from a large $-\Delta G^0$ (and therefore a large K_{eq}) and because frequently $K_{Ms} < K_{Mp}$. The net velocity of the reaction in the forward direction is given by

$$v = v_f - v_r = \frac{K_{Mp} V_{Mf}[S] - K_{Ms} V_{Mr}[P]}{K_{Ms} K_{Mp} + K_{Mp}[S] + K_{Ms}[P]} \tag{5-55}$$

Inspection of eq. 5-55 shows that the net velocity of the reaction will decrease as the concentration of product increases—the phenomenon of *product inhibition.* As the concentration of product increases, an increasing proportion of enzyme is immobilized as an enzyme-product complex. Product inhibition may be regarded as a special case of competitive inhibition.

A somewhat more complex feedback-control mechanism than simple inhibition of an enzyme by the product of the reaction is the inhibition of the first enzyme in a metabolic pathway by the final product formed after the last step of the reaction sequence. This phenomenon, called *end-product inhibition*, permits finer quantitative control and greater flexibility of control, particularly when an intermediate can enter several metabolic pathways. Examples of end-product inhibition are most clearly apparent in the biosynthetic pathways leading to the formation of specific amino acids and other low-molecular-weight building blocks required by cells. Most enzymes subject to feedback control catalyze physiologically irreversible reaction sequences, that is, sequences which proceed in the forward direction only.

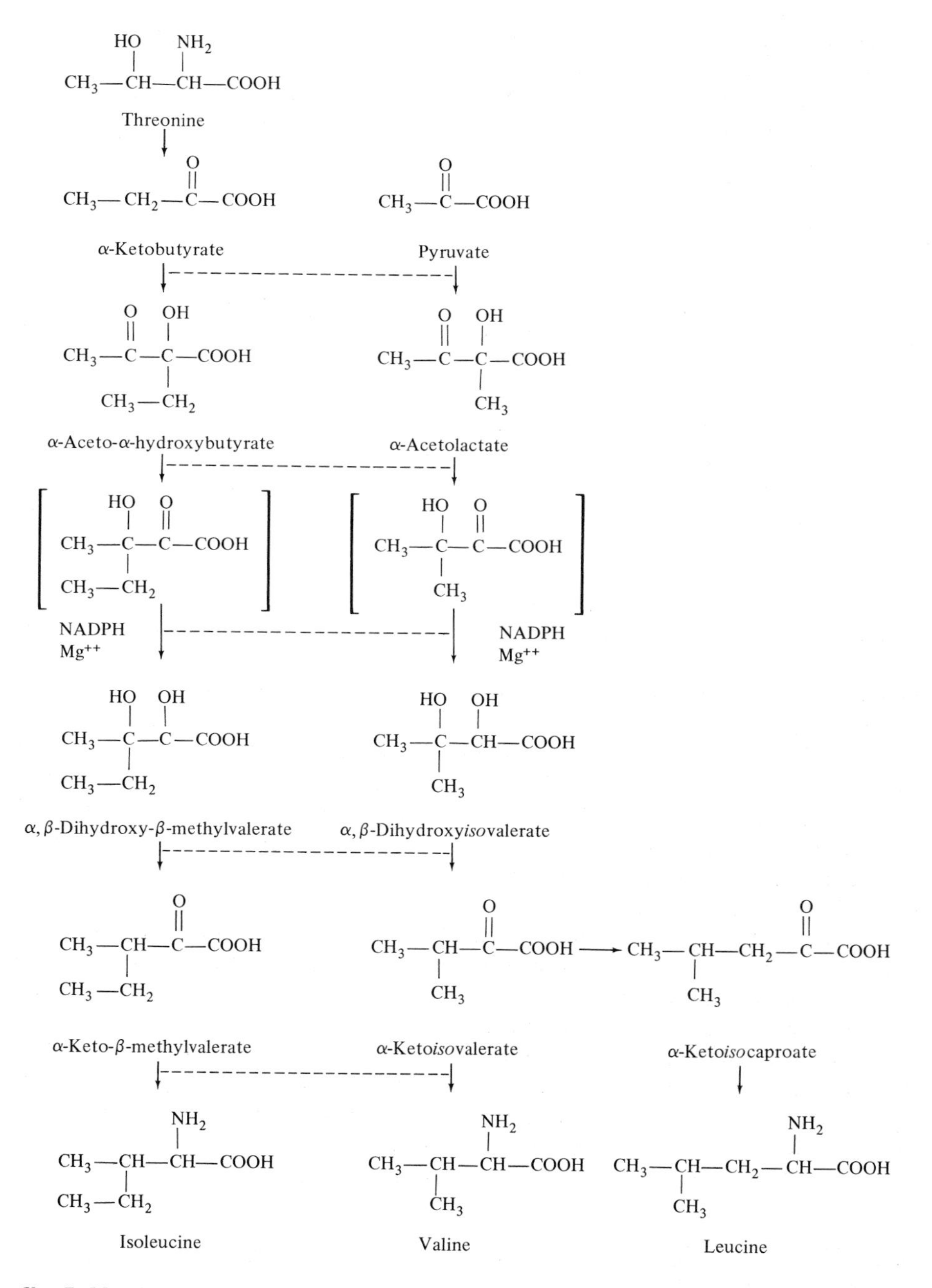

fig. 5-44. The pathways of biosynthesis of isoleucine, valine, and leucine from threonine and pyruvate. Enzymes active in both pathways are linked by dashed lines.

One of the systems displaying this type of end-product inhibition is that leading to the synthesis of isoleucine, valine, and leucine from threonine. The metabolic pathways are depicted in Fig. 5-44. The first step in the sequence of reactions leading to the biosynthesis of isoleucine is the deamination of threonine to form α-ketobutyrate. The enzyme, threonine deaminase, which catalyzes this reaction is inhibited by L-isoleucine,[44] the end product of the synthetic pathway; it is not inhibited by D-isoleucine.

The feedback loop acts to regulate the production of isoleucine, preventing its biosynthesis in excessive amounts and incidentally preventing the excessive utilization of threonine. Because control is exerted at the beginning of the biosynthetic pathway, the accumulation of intermediates is prevented. The subsequent four enzymes which mediate the conversion of α-ketobutyrate to isoleucine through α-acetohydroxybutyrate, α,β-dihydroxy-β-methylvalerate, and α-keto-β-methylvalerate, are not inhibited by isoleucine.

When *E. coli* is grown anaerobically in glucose-free nutrient broth, an adaptive L-threonine deaminase appears which enables the organisms to utilize threonine as an energy, carbon, and nitrogen source. The catabolic enzyme is quite distinct from the biosynthetic enzyme;[45] it is not inhibited by isoleucine. Thus, while the biosynthetic L-threonine deaminase is inhibited in the isoleucine-rich broth, the adaptive catabolic enzyme functions and enables the organism to grow.

Multiple enzymes for a given reaction are also found in higher organisms. For example, mammalian tissues contain two aldolases which differ in amino acid composition and which are immunologically distinct.[46] The two enzymes can be distinguished by the relative rates of hydrolysis using fructose-1,6-diphosphate and fructose-1-phosphate as substrates. Different tissues contain different relative amounts of the two enzymes. Thus, muscle contains principally the fructose-1,6-diphosphate enzyme, while liver contains principally the fructose-1-phosphate enzyme. The enzymes appear at different times in embryonic life and are resynthesized at different rates after partial hepatectomy.

Valine and leucine are synthesized from pyruvate in an analogous series of reactions, probably mediated by the same enzymes, excepting the L-threonine deaminase which is inhibited by isoleucine. The first reaction in the valine-leucine pathway, the formation of α-acetolactate from pyruvate, is inhibited by valine. Valine inhibits the formation of not only acetolactate formation but also acetohydroxybutyrate. In fact, in the K-12 strain of *E. coli*, where this feedback control is particularly marked, growth is inhibited by valine unless isoleucine is also present.

It has been shown[47] that *A. aerogenes* contains two enzymes that catalyze the condensation and decarboxylation of pyruvate to acetolactate. This conversion is a reaction not only in the biosynthesis of valine but also in the conversion of glucose to acetoin, a metabolic pathway used for energy production when bacteria are grown at an acid *p*H. Under alkaline conditions, little acetoin is formed, and only the biosynthetic enzyme which is inhibited by valine is formed. Under acid conditions of growth, when acetoin is an important product of glucose degradation, the adaptive enzyme-mediating acetolactate formation appears. The catabolic enzyme is not inhibited by valine and permits glucose metabolism in the presence of valine.

Leucine is formed by a branch of the valine biosynthetic pathway leading from

[44] Umbarger, H. E., and Brown, B. *J. Biol. Chem.*, *233*, 415 (1958).
[45] Umbarger, H. E., and Brown, B. *J. Bacteriol.*, *73*, 105 (1957); Wood, W. A., and Gunsalus, I. C. *J. Biol. Chem.*, *181*, 171 (1949).
[46] Rutter, W. J., Blostein, R. E., Woodfin, B. M., and Weber, C. S. *Advan. Enzyme Reg.*, *1*, 39 (1963).
[47] Umbarger, H. E., and Brown, B. *J. Biol. Chem.*, *233*, 1156 (1958).

α-ketoisovalerate through α-ketoisocaproate. Leucine, the end product of the branch pathway, inhibits the first enzyme after the branch point.

In addition to being a constituent amino acid of proteins, aspartic acid is an important metabolic intermediate leading to the synthesis of the pyrimidines; the amino acids methionine, threonine, and isoleucine; and also lysine and diaminopimelic acid in bacteria. These metabolic pathways are shown in Fig. 5-45. The first reaction in this

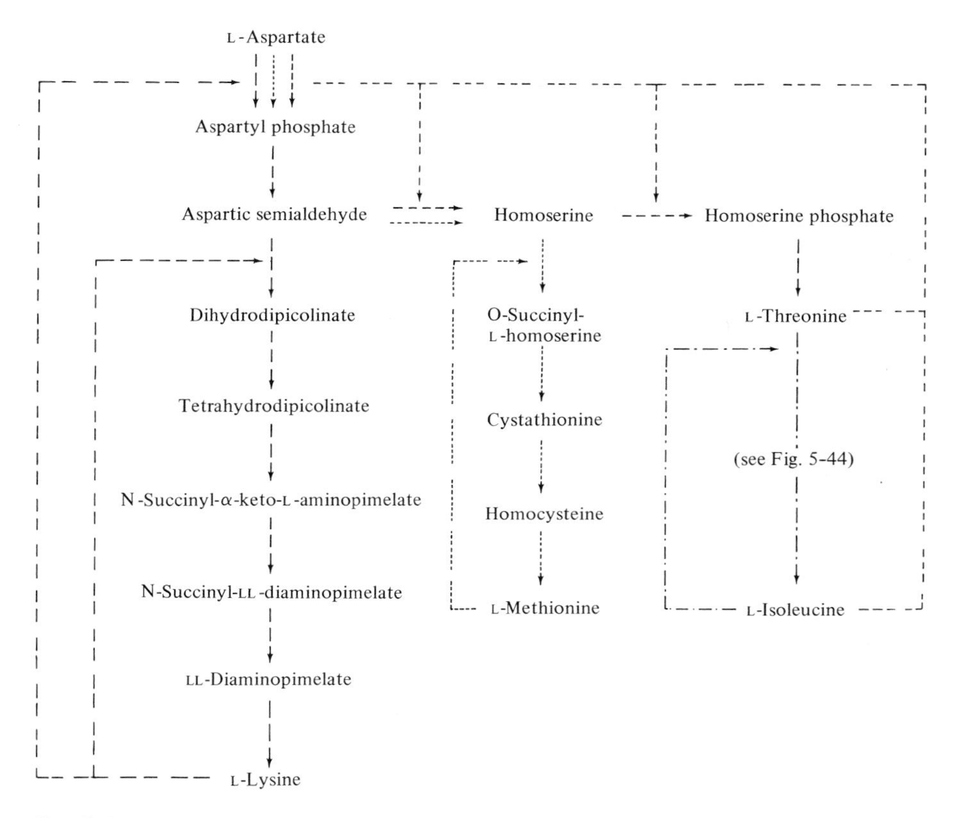

fig. 5-45. The pathways of aspartate metabolism in *E. coli* leading to the biosynthesis of diaminopimelate, lysine, methionine, and threonine, showing control by end-product inhibition.

highly complex system of pathways is the conversion of aspartate to aspartylphosphate. Three distinct aspartokinases are found in *E. coli*.[48] One aspartokinase is L-threonine. Its synthesis, and therefore the quantity present in the cell (see Chapter 6), is repressed by L-threonine and L-isoleucine. The second aspartokinase is inhibited by L-lysine, and in addition its synthesis is repressed by L-lysine. The third aspartokinase, present in smaller amounts, is specifically inhibited by homoserine, and its synthesis is repressed by methionine. End-product inhibition of the several aspartokinases is completely independent. The existence of three different aspartokinases assures properly controlled formation of the common intermediates in the metabolic sequences.

The various branches of the metabolic pathway are controlled by additional specific

[48] Stadtman, E. R., Cohen, G. N., LeBras, G., and Robichon-Szulmajster, H. *J. Biol. Chem.*, *236*, 2033 (1961).

end-product inhibition at the branch points.[49] Dihydrodipicolinic acid synthetase, the first enzyme of seven in the branch leading from aspartic semialdehyde to diaminopimelic acid and lysine, is subject to end-product inhibition by L-lysine. There are two different homoserine dehydrogenases in *E. coli.* The first, leading to the synthesis of L-threonine, is inhibited by that compound, and its synthesis is subject to multivalent repression by threonine plus isoleucine.

Chemical and genetic experiments provide convincing evidence that the threonine-inhibited homoserine dehydrogenase and the threonine-inhibited aspartokinase are, in fact, a single protein.[50] The synthesis of the second homoserine dehydrogenase is subject to repression by L-methionine. The conversion of homoserine to O-succinyl-L-homoserine, the first step in the metabolic branch leading to the synthesis of methionine is specifically inhibited by that amino acid.[51] Aspartate transcarbamylase, the first enzyme in the metabolic pathway leading to the synthesis of pyrimidines, is subject to end-product inhibition by CTP.[52] In *Neurospora crassa*, aspartate transcarbamylase is more effectively inhibited by UTP.[53] In lettuce seedlings,[54] UMP is the most potent inhibitor of aspartate transcarbamylase; and in rat liver,[55] deoxyribonucleotides are more effective than ribonucleotides as end-product inhibitors of aspartate transcarbamylase.

Glutamine occupies a key role in nitrogen metabolism. The α-amino group of glutamine contributes to the synthesis of a number of amino acids by transamination reactions with the corresponding α-keto acids. The amide nitrogen of glutamine is incorporated into at least six different compounds: tryptophane, histidine, carbamyl phosphate, glucosamine-6-phosphate, adenylic acid, and cytidylic acid.[56] Glutamine is synthesized from glutamic acid, ammonia, and ATP; the enzyme which mediates this reaction, glutamine synthetase, may be looked upon as the first enzyme in the biosynthetic pathways leading to these compounds. The divergent pathways of glutamine metabolism are depicted in Fig. 5-46.

Glutamine synthetase from *E. coli* and certain other bacteria is subject to end-product inhibition by each of the six compounds mentioned above and by glycine and alanine in addition.[57] It is of considerable interest that with nearly saturating concentrations of any one of these end-product inhibitors individually, the inhibition of glutamine synthetase is only partial. Each of these inhibitors appears to act independently of the others, and the presence of one end product does not influence the degree of inhibition by another. Consequently, when two or more end products are present together in saturating concentrations, the degree of inhibition of glutamine synthetase

---

[49] Yugari, Y., and Gilvar, C. *Biochim. Biophys. Acta, 62,* 612 (1962); Rowbury, R. J. *J. Gen. Microbiol., 37,* 171 (1964); Umbarger, H. E. *Science, 123,* 848 (1956); Patte, J. C., LeBras, G., Loviny, T., and Cohen, G. N. *Biochim. Biophys. Acta, 67,* 16 (1963); Patte, J. C., Loviny, T., and Cohen, G. N. *Biochim. Biophys. Acta, 99,* 523 (1965).
[50] Patte, J. C., Truffa-Bachi, P., and Cohen, G. N. *Biochim. Biophys. Acta, 128,* 426, 440, 450 (1966).
[51] Rowbury, R. J., and Woods, D. D. *J. Gen. Microbiol., 24,* 129 (1961).
[52] Yates, R. A., and Pardee, A. B. *J. Biol. Chem., 221,* 757 (1956).
[53] Donachie, W. D. *Biochim. Biophys. Acta, 82,* 284 (1964).
[54] Neumann, J., and Jones, M. E. *Arch. Biochem. Biophys., 104,* 438 (1964).
[55] Bresnick, E. *Biochim. Biophys. Acta, 61,* 598 (1962).
[56] Neidle, A., and Waelsch, H. *J. Biol. Chem., 234,* 586 (1959); Weiss, B., and Srinivasan, P. R. *Proc. Natl. Acad. Sci., 45,* 1491 (1959); Hurlbert, R. B., and Chakroborty, K. P. *Federation Proc., 20,* 361 (1961); Leloir, L. F., and Cardini, C. E. *Biochim. Biophys. Acta, 12,* 15 (1953); Ames, B. N., and Hartman, P. E. *Cold Spring Harbor Symp. Quant. Biol., 28,* 349 (1963); Piérard, A., and Wiame, J. M. *Biochem. Biophys. Res. Commun., 15,* 76 (1964); Cotton, R. G. H., and Gibson, F. *Biochim. Biophys. Acta, 100,* 76 (1965).
[57] Woolfolk, C. A., and Stadtman, E. R. *Biochem. Biophys. Res. Commun., 17,* 313 (1964); Hubbard, J. S., and Stadtman, E. R. *J. Bacteriol., 93,* 1045 (1967).

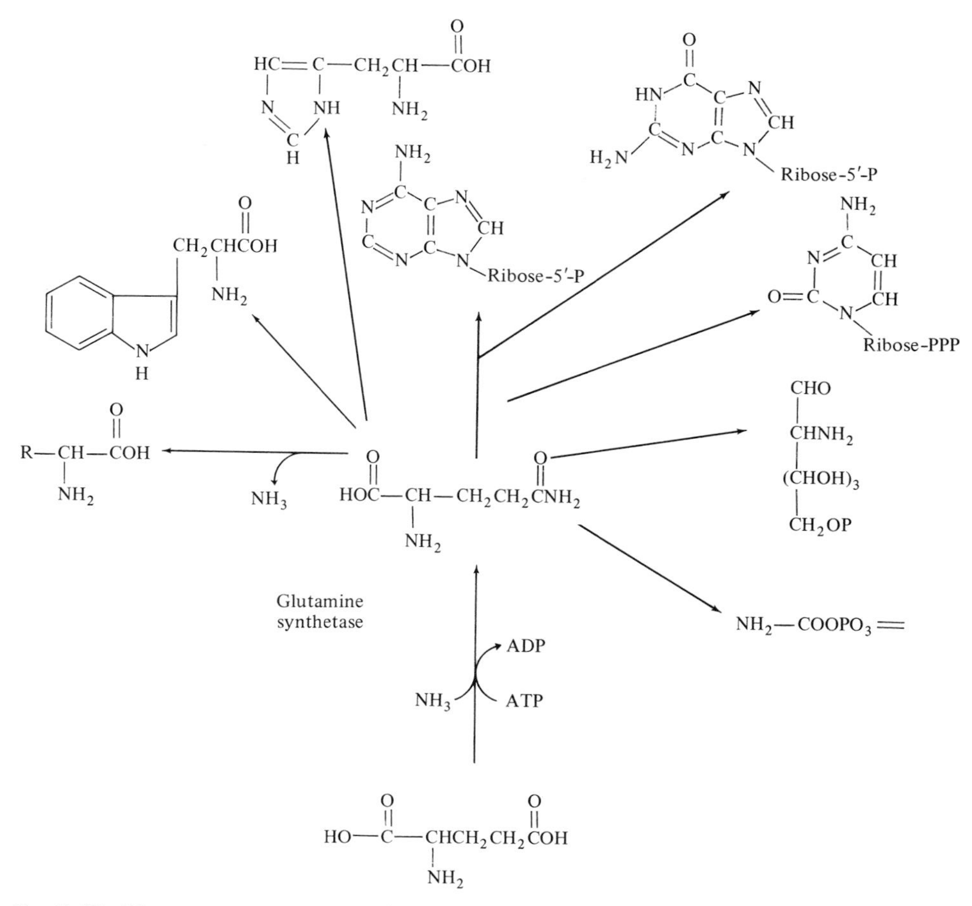

fig. 5-46. Divergent pathways of glutamine metabolism. (From Stadtman, E. R. *Advan. Enzymol., 28,* 67 [1966].)

is equal to the product of the inhibition by each compound alone. This phenomenon has been called *cumulative feedback inhibition*. It is apparent that this is a very effective mechanism for controlling the synthesis of a compound which leads to multiple end products through branched pathways.

regulation of carbohydrate metabolism

Carbohydrate metabolism may be regarded to consist of five major pathways: (1) glycolysis, the dissimilation of glucose into pyruvate or lactic acid; (2) the shunt pathway of glucose dissimilation; (3) gluconeogenesis, the formation of glucose from other metabolic intermediates; (4) glycogenolysis, the breakdown of glycogen to form glucose-1-phosphate which can be further dissimilated; and (5) glycogenesis, the synthesis of glycogen and other polysaccharides. Figure 5-47 depicts these pathways in skeleton form and shows their interrelations. The dotted lines indicate steps that appear to be under metabolic control. The enzymes catalyzing each of these critical

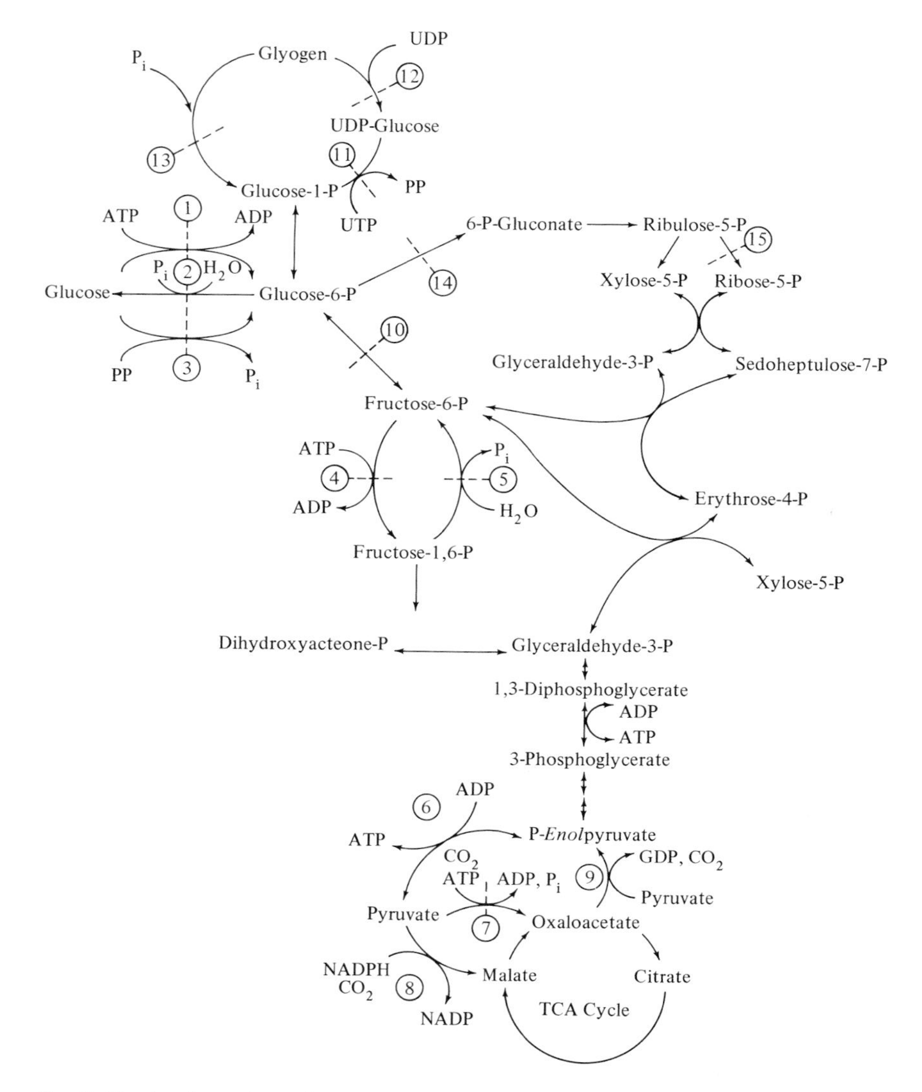

fig. 5-47. A schematic outline of carbohydrate metabolism. The dotted lines indicate steps that are subject to allosteric control. (From Stadtman, E. R. *Advan. Enzymol.*, *28*, 74 [1966].)

steps have been shown to be susceptible to inhibition or activation by various metabolites in vitro. On this basis they are judged to be subject to regulatory control.

Hexokinase, the enzyme which mediates the conversion of glucose to glucose-6-phosphate is specifically inhibited by glucose-6-phosphate. The inhibition is non-competitive with respect to substrates. The phosphate products of other sugars substituted for glucose as substrates in the hexokinase reaction are not inhibitory.[58] The end products of glycolysis, 3-phosphoglycerate, and 1,2-diphosphoglycerate also inhibit the hexokinase reaction.[59] Thus, the first step in the dissimilation of glucose

[58] Crane, R. K., and Sols, A. *J. Biol. Chem.*, *203*, 273 (1953).
[59] Dische, Z. *Bull. Soc. Biochim.*, *23*, 1140 (1940).

may serve as a physiological control point regulating its utilization. It should be noted that unlike mammalian hexokinase, yeast hexokinase does not appear to possess the allosteric binding site for glucose-6-phosphate and is relatively insensitive to direct product inhibition.

Heart hexokinase appears to exist in equilibrium between a form combined to intracellular particulates and a freely soluble form.[60] Glucose-6-phosphate appears to shift the equilibrium toward the soluble form, an effect which is related to the binding of glucose-6-phosphate at an allosteric site on the enzyme. This phenomenon may play a regulatory role by determining whether the activity of the enzyme will occur in an intracellular compartment.

Phosphofructokinase, the enzyme which catalyzes the relatively irreversible phosphorylation of fructose-6-phosphate to fructose-1,6-diphosphate, is inhibited by ATP.[61] Thus, as the intracellular level of ATP increases, it exerts feedback control on glucose entering glycolysis. In addition, phosphofructokinase is inhibited by citrate, a product of the Krebs tricarboxylic acid cycle.[62] The inhibition of mammalian phosphofructokinase by ATP and citrate may explain the well-known Pasteur effect, namely, that the rate of glycolysis increases when respiration is prevented by anaerobiosis. ATP and citrate produced by respiration may inhibit glycolysis at the phosphofructokinase stage.

The inhibition of phosphofructokinase by ATP and citrate is subject to modulation by the activating effect of 5′-AMP; or 3′,5′-cyclic-AMP, ADP, fructose-6-phosphate, and orthophosphate. Figure 5-48 illustrates the kinetics of phosphofructokinase inhibition by ATP at low and high levels of fructose-6-phosphate. At low concentrations of fructose-6-phosphate, the enzyme activity increases to a maximum at low ATP concentrations but is inhibited strongly at higher ATP levels. With high levels of fructose-6-phosphate, on the other hand, the enzyme appears to show normal substrate

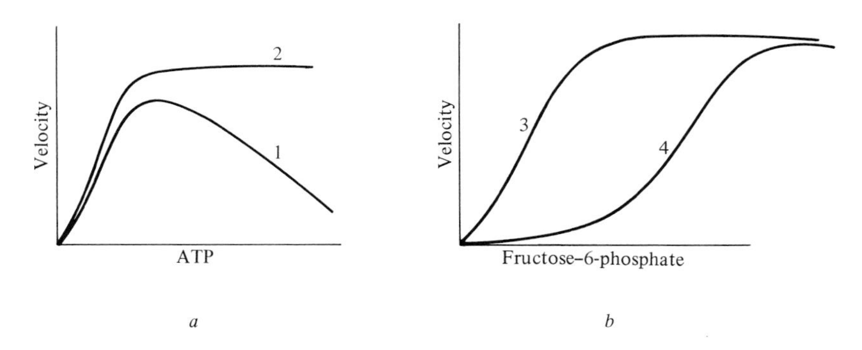

fig. 5-48. Kinetics of phosphofructokinase. (*a*) Effect of increasing ATP concentrations at low levels (curve 1) and high levels (curve 2) of fructose-6-phosphate. (*b*) Effect of increasing fructose-6-phosphate concentrations at low, noninhibitory levels of ATP (curve 3) and high inhibitory levels of ATP (curve 4). (From Stadtman, E. R. *Advan. Enzymol., 28,* 81 [1966].)

[60] Hernandez, A., and Crane, R. K. *Arch. Biochem. Biophys., 113,* 223 (1966); Green, D. E., Murer, E., Hultin, H. O., Richardson, S. H., Salmon, B., Brierley, G. P., and Baum, H. *Arch. Biochem. Biophys., 112,* 635 (1965).

[61] Mansour, T. E., and Mansour, J. M. *J. Biol. Chem., 237,* 629 (1962); Mansour, T. E., *J. Biol. Chem., 238,* 2285 (1963); Lowry, O. H., and Passonneau, J. V. *Arch. Exptl. Pathol. Pharmacol., 248,* 185 (1964).

[62] Passonneau, J. V., and Lowry, O. H. *Biochem. Biophys. Res. Commun., 13,* 372 (1963); Underwood, A. H., and Newsholme, E. A. *Biochem. J., 95,* 868 (1965).

saturation, and no inhibition is observed at high ATP levels. Nucleotide triphosphates other than ATP, such as GTP or ITP, will act as phosphate donors with yeast phosphofructokinase; however, they do not act as inhibitors of the enzyme. The data indicate that the control of phosphofructokinase occurs at an allosteric site. The possibility that the enzyme may undergo reversible aggregation and disaggregation has been suggested, but its importance in the regulation of enzyme activity is not clear.[63]

Studies in isolated perfused rat hearts[64] show that the intracellular concentrations of fructose-6-phosphate and ATP are in the range where phosphofructokinase is very sensitive to ATP inhibition; and ADP, 5′-AMP, and inorganic phosphate act physiologically to overcome the inhibition by ATP. It appears that the conversion of fructose-6-phosphate to fructose-1,6-diphosphate is frequently the most critical step controlling glycolysis in the intact cell. A high degree of sensitivity of the enzyme to changes in fructose-6-phosphate concentrations in the range found intracellularly is achieved by the cooperative interaction of at least two molecules of fructose-6-phosphate with the enzyme. This is reflected in a sigmoid response of the enzyme activity to increasing fructose-6-phosphate concentration and apparent second-order kinetics of the reaction with respect to fructose-6-phosphate.

The synthesis of glucose from pyruvate and lactate is an important physiological process which occurs principally in the liver of higher animals. Until a decade or two ago, it was believed that all enzymatic reactions are freely reversible and that glucose synthesis occurred merely by the simple reversal of the steps involved in glycolysis. However, three enzymatic steps in glycolysis—those catalyzed by the enzymes hexokinase, phosphofructokinase, and pyruvate kinase—are strongly exergonic and constitute practically insurmountable barriers to the reversal of the glycolytic pathway under physiological conditions. It was later realized that bypass reactions existed around these three strongly exergonic reactions (Fig. 5-49) which were utilized in gluconeogenesis. Each of the bypass reactions is itself strongly exergonic in the direction of gluconeogenesis. It is evident that in tissues where both glycolysis and gluconeogenesis are important physiological processes, a fine system of control is essential to direct the flow of metabolites in the direction required by any given set of physiological conditions.[65]

While pyruvate can be converted to phospho*enol*pyruvate either directly by condensation with ATP (a reaction catalyzed by pyruvate kinase) or via the formation of L-malate by condensation with CO_2 and NADPH (a reaction catalyzed by the malic enzyme), animal tissues contain such small amounts of pyruvate kinase and the malic enzyme that these pathways appear to be functionally unimportant. The major pathway for the conversion of pyruvate to phospho*enol*pyruvate in animal tissues is by condensation with ATP and CO_2 to form oxaloacetate, a reaction mediated by the enzyme pyruvate carboxylase. The enzyme contains biotin as a bound prosthetic group and requires the presence of acetyl-coenzyme A (acetyl-CoA) and magnesium ions for activity.[66]

There are three ways in which the activity of pyruvate carboxylase is regulated: (1) the enzyme is susceptible to inhibition by ADP, a product of the reaction; (2) there

---

[63] Ling, K. H., Marcus, F., and Lardy, H. A. *J. Biol. Chem.*, *240*, 1893 (1965); Mansour, T. E. *J. Biol. Chem.*, *240*, 2165 (1965).
[64] Newsholme, E. A., and Randle, P. J. *Biochem. J.*, *80*, 655 (1961); Regen, D. M., Davis, W. W., Morgan, H. E., and Park, C. R. *J. Biol. Chem.*, *239*, 43 (1964).
[65] Utter, M., and Keech, D. B. *J. Biol. Chem.*, *238*, 2603, 2609 (1963); Weber, G., Singhall, R. L., and Stamm, M. B. *Advan. Enzyme Reg.*, *2*, 1 (1964).
[66] Scrutton, M. C., Keech, D. B., and Utter, M. F. *J. Biol. Chem.*, *240*, 574 (1965).

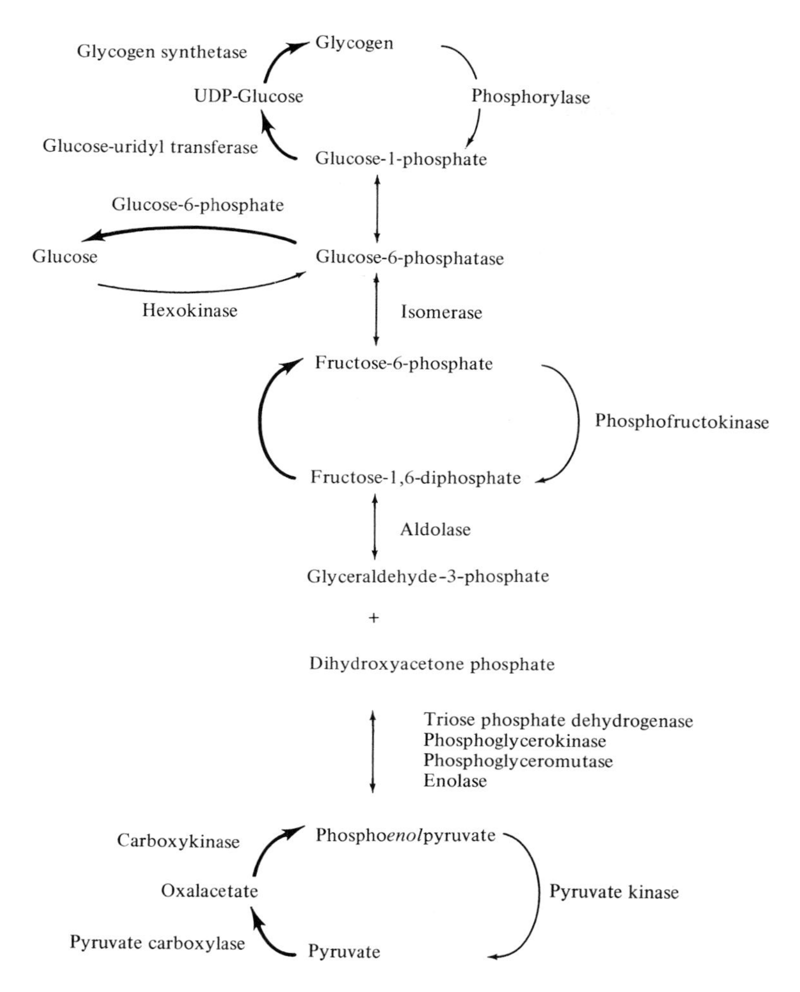

fig. 5-49. A schematic diagram showing the relation of glycogenesis and gluconeogenesis to glycogenolysis and glycolysis. The bypass reactions in gluconeogenesis and glycogenesis are shown with bold arrows.

is an absolute requirement for the presence of catalytic levels of acetyl-CoA; and (3) the enzyme is susceptible to disaggregation into subunits which are inactive. Pyruvate carboxylase is a protein which sediments at 4.8 S_{20}, which corresponds to a molecular weight of 655,000. Purified preparations of the enzyme are most stable at 24° and undergo rapid reversible inactivation at 2°, forming subunits of 7.5 *S*. The cold-induced disaggregation is prevented by the presence of acetyl-CoA. The inhibition of pyruvate carboxylase by ADP is competitive with respect to ATP.[67]

The importance of the control of pyruvate carboxylase can be appreciated by a consideration of the central position which pyruvate, acetyl-CoA, and oxaloacetate

[67] Keech, D. B., and Utter, M. F. *J. Biol. Chem.*, *238*, 2609 (1963). The sedimentation constant of a compound is often expressed in Svedberg units, *S*.

occupy in cellular metabolism (Fig. 5-50). Oxaloacetate is the intermediate in the Krebs tricarboxylic acid cycle which condenses with acetyl-CoA to form citrate. When the supply of oxaloacetate is lower than the production of acetyl-CoA from fatty acid and pyruvate oxidation, acetyl-CoA will tend to accumulate, stimulate the activity of pyruvate carboxylase, and increase the synthesis of oxaloacetate. This will lead to increased amounts of all the other intermediates in the tricarboxylic acid cycle. Citrate is a specific allosteric activator of the acetyl-CoA carboxylase. The higher levels of citrate will stimulate the conversion of acetyl-CoA to malonyl-coenzyme A, and thence to long-chain fatty acids.

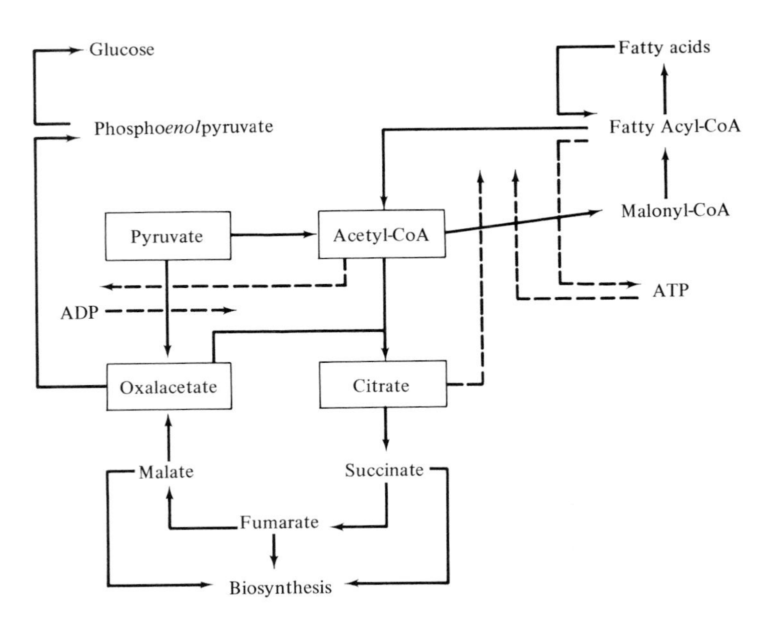

fig. 5-50. A schematic diagram showing the pivotal positions of pyruvate, oxaloacetate, and acetyl-CoA in intermediary metabolism. The broken lines indicate steps that are subject to allosteric control.

The conversion of fructose-1,6-diphosphate to fructose-6-phosphate is catalyzed by a highly specific enzyme, fructose diphosphatase, which circumvents the highly exergonic phosphofructokinase reaction.[68] This enzyme is found mainly in those tissues in which significant gluconeogenesis and glyconeogenesis take place. The mammalian enzyme is strongly inhibited by 5′-AMP and high concentrations of fructose-1,6-diphosphate, and the enzyme is reversibly activated by ADP or ATP.[69] Thus, the activators of fructose diphosphatase are the inhibitors of phosphofructokinase, and vice versa.

Liver fructose diphosphatase can be reversibly converted into an inactive state at *p*H 7.4. The conversion is not associated with demonstrable changes in the sedimentation or electrophoretic pattern, and therefore it is assumed not to involve association or disaggregation into subunits. Conversion of the inactive to the active form is

[68] Krebs, H. A. *Advan. Enzyme Reg.*, *1*, 385 (1963).
[69] Taketa, K., and Pogell, B. M. *Biochim. Biophys. Res. Commun.*, *12*, 229 (1963); Mendicino, J., and Vasarhely, F. *J. Biol. Chem.*, *238*, 3528 (1963); Underwood, A. H., and Newsholme, E. A. *Biochem. J.*, *95*, 767 (1965).

inhibited partially by fructose-1,6-diphosphate and fructose-6-phosphate and is markedly dependent on *p*H and temperature. ATP, on the other hand, induces the rapid conversion to the active form of the enzyme. The reversible changes of the enzyme which lead to the loss of activity with respect to fructose-1,6-diphosphate do not appear to affect the ability of the enzyme to hydrolyze sedoheptulose-1,7-diphosphate,[70] even though these two substrates are competitive inhibitors and appear to bind at the same catalytic site.

The inhibition of fructose diphosphatase by AMP is noncompetitive with respect to substrate, is highly specific, and is reversible. The enzyme appears to bind three moles of AMP per mole of enzyme, and the kinetic data indicate considerable cooperative interaction. Treatment of the enzyme with papain or fluorodinitrobenzene in the presence of substrate decreases its sensitivity to inhibition by AMP without appreciably altering its catalytic activity.[71]

The hydrolysis of glucose-6-phosphate is the last step in gluconeogenesis. It is obvious that the enzyme which catalyzes this step, glucose-6-phosphatase, must be under careful metabolic regulation because its activity tends to counteract that of hexokinase and glucokinase and would result in unacceptable energy losses through the cyclical phosphorylation and dephosphorylation of glucose. Glucose-6-phosphatase appears to be localized in the endoplasmic reticulum and sediments with the microsomal fraction. The enzyme has great substrate specificity, hydrolyzing only glucosamine-6-phosphate in addition to glucose-6-phosphate. However, the enzyme also catalyzes the hydrolysis of pyrophosphate and the phosphorylation of glucose by pyrophosphate.[72]

$$\begin{aligned} \text{PP} + H_2O &\rightarrow 2\ P_i \\ \text{PP} + \text{glucose} &\rightarrow \text{glucose-6-phosphate} + P_i \\ \text{glucose-6-phosphate} + H_2O &\rightarrow \text{glucose} + P_i \end{aligned} \qquad (5\text{-}56)$$

The enzyme is activated by magnesium ions and inhibited by glucose and pyrophosphate. The importance of glucose-6-phosphatase in the regulation of the glucose level in the blood is underlined by the fact that patients with hereditary glucose-6-phosphatase deficiencies have low blood glucose levels and abnormally high glycogen levels in liver and muscle.[73]

The hydrolysis of glycogen to glucose-1-phosphate is mediated by the enzyme phosphorylase which exists in two interconvertible forms, phosphorylase *a* and phosphorylase *b*.[74] The reader is referred to comprehensive reviews[75] which discuss the complex properties of the two forms of phosphorylase, the reactions which mediate their interconversion, and the regulatory factors involved (Fig. 5-51). Briefly, phosphorylase *b* can be converted into phosphorylase *a* by the phosphorylation of two serine residues of the *b* form by ATP followed by dimerization of the phosphorylated derivative. The reaction is catalyzed by a specific enzyme, phosphorylase *b* kinase. The

[70] Luppis, B., Traniello, S., Wood, W. A., and Pontremoli, S. *Biochem. Biophys. Res. Commun.*, *15*, 458 (1964).
[71] Taketa, K., and Pogell, B. M. *J. Biol. Chem.*, *240*, 651 (1965); Rosen, O. M., and Rosen, S. M. *Proc. Natl. Acad. Sci.*, *55*, 1156 (1966).
[72] Arion, W. J., and Nordlie, R. C. *J. Biol. Chem.*, *239*, 1680, 2752 (1964).
[73] Cori, G. T. *Mod. Probl. Pediat.*, *3*, 344 (1957).
[74] Cori, G. T. *J. Biol. Chem.*, *158*, 333 (1945); Fischer, E. H., and Krebs, E. G. *J. Biol. Chem.*, *216*, 121 (1955).
[75] Sutherland, E. W., and Rall, T. W. *Pharmacol. Rev.*, *12*, 265 (1960); Stetten, D., Jr., and Stetten, M. R. *Physiol. Rev.*, *40*, 505 (1960).

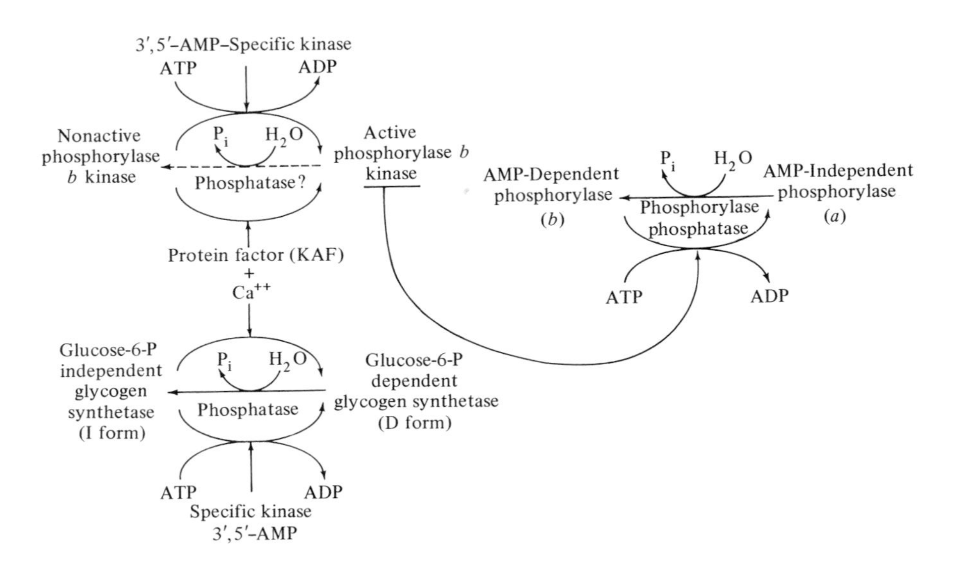

fig. 5-51. A schematic diagram depicting the interconversion of phosphorylase *a* and phosphorylase *b*, the activation of phosphorylase *b* kinase, and the interconversion of the I and D forms of glycogen synthetase. (Adapted from Krebs, E. G., and Fischer, E. H. *Advan. Enzymol., 24*, 286 [1962].)

conversion of phosphorylase *a* to phosphorylase *b* is associated with the release of orthophosphate and catalyzed by a specific enzyme, phosphorylase phosphatase:

$$2 \text{ phosphorylase } b + 4 \text{ ATP} \underset{\text{phosphorylase phosphatase}}{\overset{\text{phosphorylase } b \text{ kinase}}{\rightleftharpoons}} \text{phosphorylase } a + 4 \text{ ADP} \qquad \textit{(5-57)}$$

Considerable evidence has accumulated indicating that the stimulation of glycogenolysis which accompanies the electrical stimulation of muscle or the administration of epinephrine is followed by a marked increase in the concentration of phosphorylase *a* and a decrease in the concentration of phosphorylase *b*. Clearly, phosphorylase *a* is the more active form of the enzyme. Phosphorylase *b* has a molecular weight of 242,000 and is composed of two identical subunits with molecular weights in the neighborhood of 125,000. Phosphorylase *b* is dependent upon AMP for activity. The binding of AMP causes a decrease in the apparent K_M of the enzyme for its substrates, inorganic phosphate and glycogen, and, conversely, the binding of either substrate to the enzyme decreases the apparent K_M for AMP. The activation by AMP is not associated with any demonstrable changes in the sedimentation pattern of the enzyme and is presumed not to involve a change in the state of aggregation. While phosphorylase *a* does not have an obligatory requirement for AMP, at low levels of glycogen, inorganic phosphate, or glucose-1-phosphate, phosphorylase *a* shows activation by AMP.

The activation of phosphorylase *b* by AMP is subject to modulation by the antagonistic actions of ATP and glucose-6-phosphate which are competitive inhibitors of AMP modulation. These effects are subject to further modification by glucose-1-phosphate which binds to the enzyme and decreases the apparent K_M for AMP. Thus, glucose-1-phosphate is synergistic with AMP in its action and antagonizes the inhibitory effects of ATP and glucose-6-phosphate.

Phosphorylase *b* kinase, which catalyzes the conversion of phosphorylase *b* to phosphorylase *a*, exists in both active and nonactive forms. Conversion of nonactive phosphorylase *b* kinase to the active form can be achieved by three independent mechanisms: (1) phosphorylation with ATP in the presence of magnesium ions, (2) incubation with calcium ions in the presence of a "specific kinase activation factor," and (3) limited proteolytic digestion with trypsin. The activation by ATP is stimulated by 3′,5′-cyclic-AMP. The formation of this latter compound is stimulated by epinephrine and glucagon, thus accounting for the observed hormonal effect on the conversion of phosphorylase *b* to phosphorylase *a*. In addition, the ATP-dependent activation of phosphorylase *b* kinase is accelerated by glycogen or heparin.

It was shown by Leloir and Cardini[76] that glycogen is formed by the condensation of uridine diphosphoglucose mediated by the enzyme glycogen synthetase (Fig. 5-51). Glycogen synthetase exists in two interconvertible forms, the D form which is dependent upon glucose-6-phosphate for its activity, and the I form whose activity is independent of glucose-6-phosphate.[77] Conversion of the I form to the D form can be achieved in three ways: (1) by phosphorylation of the I form with ATP, (2) by a protein-factor activation which requires calcium ions, and (3) by treatment with proteolytic enzymes such as trypsin.[78] The phosphorylated D form of glycogen synthetase is converted to the I form by the action of a specific phosphatase. Glucose-6-phosphate greatly increases the V_M and also decreases the apparent K_M for UDP-glucose. On the other hand, glucose-6-phosphate does not influence the V_M of the I form, but it does cause some decrease in the apparent K_M for UDP-glucose. Glycogen appears to serve as a negative feedback inhibitor in the conversion of the I form to the D form, thereby regulating its own synthesis.[79]

The conversion of the I form to the D form is controlled indirectly by hormonal factors because the activity of the kinase which catalyzes the phosphorylation of the I form is dependent upon the concentration of 3′,5′-cyclic-AMP, the synthesis of which is stimulated by epinephrine. Furthermore, the calcium-dependent conversion of the I form to the D form may be modulated by fluctuations in the intracellular level of calcium ions that are associated with muscular contraction.

The regulatory reactions in the alternative (shunt) pathways of glucose metabolism have not been well studied. It is known, however, that glucose-6-phosphate dehydrogenase is inhibited by inorganic phosphate and by palmityl-coenzyme A and stearyl-coenzyme A.[80] The acyl-CoA compounds appear to be competitive inhibitors with respect to glucose-6-phosphate, but they influence both the K_M and V_M with respect to NADP. The activation of glucose-6-phosphate dehydrogenase from human erythrocytes by NADP is accompanied by increased stability to elevated temperatures and an apparent increase of the molecular weight.[81] Therefore, the possibility exists that gross conformational changes such as aggregation or disaggregation of subunits may be associated with the activation of this enzyme.

Hexose isomerase, which catalyzes the interconversion of glucose-6-phosphate and fructose-6-phosphate, is inhibited by three intermediates of the pentose phosphate

---

[76] Leloir, L. F., and Cardini, C. E. *J. Am. Chem. Soc.*, *79*, 6340 (1957).
[77] Rosell-Perez, M., Villar-Palasi, C., and Larner, J. *Biochemistry*, *1*, 763 (1962); Traut, R. R., and Lipmann, F. *J. Biol. Chem.*, *238*, 1213 (1963); Friedman, D. L., and Larner, J. *Biochemistry*, *2*, 669 (1963).
[78] Appleman, M. M., Belocopitow, E., and Torres, H. N. *Biochem. Biophys. Res. Commun.*, *14*, 550 (1964).
[79] Danforth, W. H. *J. Biol. Chem.*, *240*, 588 (1965).
[80] Theorell, H. *Biochem. Z.*, *275*, 416 (1935); Eger-Neufeldt, I., Teinzer, A., Weiss, L., and Wieland, O. *Biochem. Biophys. Res. Commun.*, *19*, 43 (1965).
[81] Kirkman, H. N., and Hendrickson, E. M. *J. Biol. Chem.*, *237*, 2371 (1962).

shunt pathway: 6-phosphogluconate, sedoheptulose-7-phosphate, and erythrose-4-phosphate.[82] Because the reaction catalyzed by hexokinase is the first divergent step which directs glucose-6-phosphate either into the glycolytic pathway or into the pentose phosphate shunt pathway, the effect of these intermediates on hexose isomerase can be regarded as a feedback mechanism enabling control of the flow of glucose-6-phosphate into the shunt pathway.

regulation of fatty acid and steroid synthesis

Neutral fat represents the major form in which food is stored in higher organisms. It is synthesized in times of plenty and degraded in times of need. The biosynthesis of fatty acids proceeds by the following sequence of reactions.[83]

$$\text{7 Acetyl-CoA} + 7\ CO_2 + \text{7 ATP} \xrightarrow{Mg^{++}} \text{7 Malonyl-CoA} + \text{7 ADP} + 7\ P_i$$

$$\text{Acetyl-CoA} + \text{7 Malonyl-CoA} + \text{14 NADPH} \longrightarrow \text{Palmityl-CoA} + \text{7 CoA} + 7\ CO_2 + \text{14 NADP} + 7\ H_2O \qquad (5\text{-}58)$$

This synthetic pathway is regulated at the first step in the sequence, namely, the carboxylation of acetyl-coenzyme A to form malonyl-coenzyme A, a reaction catalyzed by the enzyme acetyl-CoA carboxylase. Acetyl-CoA carboxylase is activated by various tri- and dicarboxylic acid intermediates of the Krebs cycle, but particularly by citrate. This activation has the physiological function of diverting acetyl-CoA away from the Krebs tricarboxylic cycle into fatty acid synthesis when the intracellular level of Krebs intermediates becomes elevated (Fig. 5-50).[84]

The activation of acetyl-CoA carboxylase by citrate occurs at 25° and is accompanied by a change in the sedimentation coefficient from about 18.8 *S* for the control enzyme to about 43 *S* for the citrate-activated enzyme. It is curious that cooling the citrate-activated enzyme from 25° to 0° results in inactivation, a process which is accompanied by a change in the sedimentation coefficient from 40–50 *S* to 17–20 *S*. The activation of the enzyme by citrate is presumed to be accompanied by an aggregation of inactive subunits.

Acetyl-CoA carboxylase is inhibited by long-chain acyl-CoA derivatives.[85] Kinetic studies have shown that the inhibition by fatty acid–CoA derivatives was competitive with respect to citrate, the positive modifier, and noncompetitive with respect to the substrate, acetyl-CoA, bicarbonate, or ATP. Free fatty acids also inhibit acetyl-CoA carboxylase in vitro,[86] but concentrations 4 to 10 times as great are required to obtain the same degree of inhibition as that produced by long-chain acyl-CoA derivatives. This system is another example of end-product inhibition.

Under conditions where fatty acid biosynthesis does not take place for long periods of time, such as during fasting, in animals fed a high fat diet, or in diabetic animals, the

[82] Kahana, S. E., Lowry, O. H., Schulz, D. W., Passonneau, J. B., and Crawford, E. J. *J. Biol. Chem.*, *235*, 2178 (1960); Grazi, E., DeFlora, A., and Pontremoli, S. *Biochem. Biophys. Res. Commun.*, *2*, 121 (1960); Venkataraman, R., and Racker, E. *J. Biol. Chem.*, *236*, 1876 (1961).
[83] Wakil, S. J. *J. Am. Chem. Soc.*, *80*, 6465 (1958); Formica, J. V., and Brady, R. O. *J. Am. Chem. Soc.*, *81*, 752 (1959); Lynen, F. *Federation Proc.*, *20*, 941 (1961).
[84] Martin, D. B., and Vagelos, P. R. *J. Biol. Chem.*, *237*, 1787 (1962), *238*, 533 (1963); Matsuhashi, M., Matsuhashi, S., and Lynen, F. *Biochem. Z.*, *340*, 263 (1964).
[85] Bortz, W. M., and Lynen, F. *Biochem. Z.*, *337*, 505 (1963).
[86] Levy, H. R. *Biochem. Biophys. Res. Commun.*, *13*, 267 (1963).

tissue levels of acetyl-CoA carboxylase are low, indicating that there may be repression in the synthesis of this enzyme.[87]

Acetyl-CoA is also the starting material which leads to the synthesis of cholesterol. Cholesterol, in turn, is utilized for the production of the various steroid hormones and bile salts. The biosynthetic pathway from acetyl-CoA to cholesterol involves the conversion of (1) acetyl-CoA to acetoacetyl-CoA, (2) acetoacetyl-CoA to β-hydroxy-β-methylglutarate, (3) β-hydroxy-β-methylglutarate to mevalonate, (4) mevalonate to squalene through a sequence of seven reactions, and (5) squalene, in turn, to cholesterol through a sequence of fifteen reactions. β-Hydroxy-β-methylglutarate is also the principal source of the ketone bodies, acetoacetate, and β-hydroxybutyrate. Cholesterol biosynthesis is controlled at the first branch step where β-hydroxy-β-methylglutarate is converted to mevalonate[88] (Fig. 5-52).

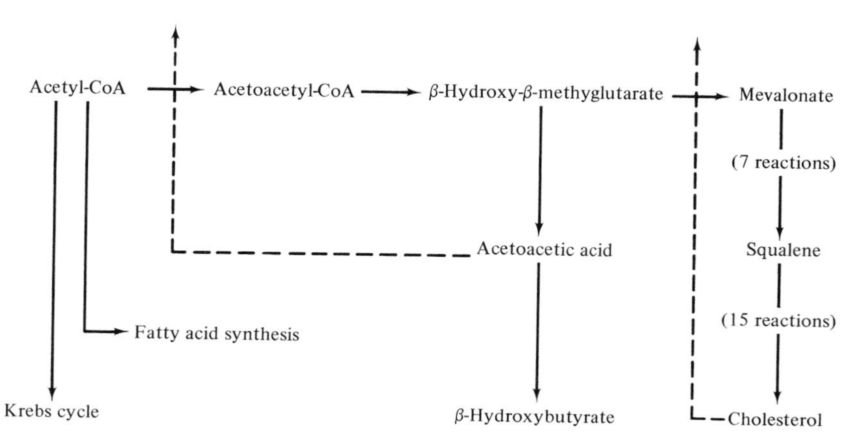

fig. 5-52. A schematic diagram of the biosynthesis of cholesterol and its regulation by end-product inhibition. (Adapted from Siperstein, M. D., and Fagan, V. M. *Advan. Enzyme Reg., 2,* 252 [1964]. Copyright Pergamon Press; reprinted by permission.)

Feeding of cholesterol does not affect the synthesis of β-hydroxy-β-methylglutarate, which may even be increased, but does significantly depress the synthesis of mevalonate. The specific inhibitor of the enzyme β-hydroxy-β-methylglutarate reductase appears to be a cholesterol-lipoprotein complex which appears within two and a half hours after the injection of cholesterol. An enzyme has been obtained from liver carcinomas which is able to catalyze the synthesis of mevalonate but does not respond to feedback inhibition by cholesterol. This observation indicates that the inhibition by cholesterol may take place at an allosteric site.

control in intact cells

Enzymatic processes within a living cell are always linked, either directly or indirectly, to very many other enzymatic processes. The substrate of one reaction is frequently the product of another reaction. In many instances there is competition between a

[87] Ganguly, J. *Biochim. Biophys. Acta, 40,* 110 (1960); Numa, S., Matsuhashi, M., and Lynen, F. *Biochem. Z., 334,* 203 (1961); Wieland, O., Neufeldt, I., Numa, S., and Lynen, F. *Biochem. Z., 336,* 455 (1963); Bortz, W., Abraham, S., and Chaikoff, I. L. *J. Biol. Chem., 238,* 1266 (1963).
[88] Siperstein, M. D., and Guest, N. J. *J. Clin. Invest., 39,* 642 (1960); Siperstein, M. D., and Fagan, V. M. *Advan. Enzyme Reg., 2,* 249 (1964).

number of enzymatic reactions for a given substrate. Similarly, common cofactors, such as NAD and NADP, are required by many enzymatic reactions. Many reactions are coupled to the oxidation of NADH, the reduction of NAD, the phosphorylation of ADP, the hydrolysis of ATP, or to the oxidation, reduction, phosphorylation, or hydrolysis of other cofactors. In many cases, a number of substrates compete for a given enzyme, as is true in the case of aldolase and transketolase.[89] On the other hand, the substrate or product of one reaction may be an inhibitor or activator for another reaction.

In a multienzyme system, the overall velocity is a function not only of the velocities of the separate enzyme reactions but also of the transit time of the various intermediates, that is, of the time required by intermediates to diffuse from one enzyme to the next in the sequence. These transit times may be as great as 10^{-2} sec. Even if all the enzymatic reactions were infinitely rapid, the overall velocity of the sequence would not be infinite, but would be the reciprocal of the product of the transit times of the various intermediates. In the case of soluble enzymes, as the concentration of an enzyme decreases (dilution), the distance between enzyme molecules increases, and the transit time becomes an increasingly important parameter in determining the overall rate of reaction. In many instances the several enzymes in a metabolic sequence are organized structurally, as they are in the sequences of oxidative phosphorylation or photosynthesis. In these instances, variations in the structural organization may play an important regulatory role in metabolism.

In addition to these considerations, interaction arising from Onsager coupling between the fluxes of various components of a metabolic system may play an important role in the system's kinetics. Two reactions catalyzed by chemically independent enzymes which, however, are geometrically constrained in a cell, will not be rate independent of each other if the product or substrate of one reaction is diffusion-coupled to the product or substrate of the other reaction. A theoretical analysis of such systems[90] indicates that a portion of the free energy of a reaction may be used for the transport of materials which are diffusion-coupled with either the substrate or the product of the reaction. A number of mechanisms come to mind by which such coupling can occur between flows of matter in cells. Two chemical species may exhibit appreciable diffusion-coupling by virtue of complex formation between the diffusing species, even though the complex may be chemically labile and difficult to isolate and purify chemically. Another type of diffusion-coupling is by electrostatic interaction.

It should be apparent from the preceding discussion of the control of metabolic pathways that multiple, interlocking control loops acting at multiple sites are present. It has been shown that two enzymes coupled by reciprocal feedback inhibition will give rise to oscillations. The levels of many intracellular metabolites oscillate continuously in the living cell. These oscillations are frequently sinusoidal, and additional continuous or damped oscillations, instead of a monatonic shift from one metabolic state to another, follow sudden environmental changes of appreciable magnitude. Many of these oscillations have a very low frequency and may represent complex error-correcting control mechanisms.

---

[89] Venkataraman, R., and Racker, E. *J. Biol. Chem.*, *236*, 1876, 1883 (1961); De La Haba, G., Leder, I. G., and Racker, E. *J. Biol. Chem.*, *214*, 409 (1955).
[90] Hearon, J. Z. *Bull. Math. Biophys.*, *12*, 135 (1950).

references

Atkinson, D. E. Biological feedback control at the molecular level. *Science, 150,* 851 (1965).

Atkinson, D. E. Regulation of enzyme activity. *Ann. Rev. Biochem., 35,* 85 (1966).

Atkinson, M. R., and Morton, R. K. Free energy and biosynthesis of phosphates, in Florkin, M., and Mason, H., eds. *Comparative Biochemistry.* New York: Academic Press, 1960, vol. 2, pp. 1–95.

Bonner, J., and Varner, J. E. *Plant Biochemistry.* New York: Academic Press, 1965.

Calvin, M., and Bassham, J. A. *The Photosynthesis of Carbon Compounds.* New York: W. A. Benjamin, 1962.

Chance, B., Estabrook, R. W., and Williamson, J. R. *Control of Energy Metabolism.* New York: Academic Press, 1965.

Clayton, R. K. *Molecular Physics in Photosynthesis.* Boston: Blaisdell, 1965.

Dixon, M., and Webb, E. C. *Enzymes,* 2nd ed. New York: Academic Press, 1964.

Gaffron, H. Energy storage: photosynthesis, in Steward, F. C., ed. *Plant Physiology.* New York: Academic Press, 1960. vol. 1B, p. 3.

Goodwin, T. *Biochemistry of Chloroplasts.* New York: Academic Press, 1966.

Grisolia, S. The catalytic environment and its biological implications. *Physiol. Rev., 44,* 657 (1964).

Huennekens, F. M., and Whiteley, H. R. Phosphoric acid anhydrides and other energy-rich compounds, in Florkin, M., and Mason, H. S., eds. *Comparative Biochemistry.* New York: Academic Press, 1960, vol. 1, pp. 107–180.

Krebs, H. A., and Kornberg, H. L. A survey of the energy transformations in living material. *Ergeb. Physiol., 49,* 212 (1957).

Lehninger, A. L. *Bioenergetics.* New York: W. A. Benjamin, 1965.

McElroy, W. D., and Glass, B., eds. *Light and Life.* Baltimore: Johns Hopkins Press, 1961.

Mahler, H. R., and Cordes, E. H. *Biological Chemistry.* New York: Harper & Row, 1966.

Mortenson, L. E., Mower, H. F., and Carnahan, J. E. Nitrogen fixation by enzyme preparations. *Bacteriol. Rev., 26,* 42 (1962).

Moyed, H. S., and Umbarger, H. E. Regulation of biosynthetic pathways. *Physiol. Rev., 42,* 444 (1962).

Pardee, A. B., and Ingraham, L. L. Free energy and entropy in metabolism, in Greenberg, D. M., ed. *Metabolic Pathways,* 2nd ed. New York: Academic Press, 1960, vol. 1, pp. 1–40.

Racker, E. *Mechanisms in Bioenergetics.* New York: Academic Press, 1965.

Stadtman, E. R. Allosteric regulation of enzyme activity. *Advan. Enzymol., 28,* 41 (1966).

Stewart, W. D. P. *Nitrogen Fixation in Plants.* London: Athlone Press, 1966.

White, A., Handler, P., and Smith, E. L. *Principles of Biochemistry,* 3rd ed. New York: McGraw-Hill, 1964.

chapter 6

protein synthesis and its regulation

overall scheme of protein synthesis

The genetic information of a cell is contained in its DNA. This information is utilized effectively and expressed, however, only when it leads to the synthesis of specific proteins by the cell. The proteins of the cell form the structural elements and, as enzymes, catalyze the large variety of chemical reactions needed for energy production and for the synthesis of substances required for viability. DNA (and RNA) cannot carry out these functions directly. In addition to encoded information for the synthesis of proteins with exactly specified structure, the genetic material contains information which permits control of the rate of synthesis of individual proteins. From an overall view, the provision of the encoded information for future generations of cells and the synthesis of protein from it proceeds in three phases: (1) faithful *replication* of DNA catalyzed by the enzyme DNA-polymerase, whereby a full complement of genetic information is provided for each daughter cell upon cell division; (2) the *transcription* of the genetic information by means of a DNA-dependent RNA-polymerase from DNA into *messenger-RNA* (m-RNA), a special form of RNA which transmits the coded information from the nucleus, the repository site of DNA, to the ribosomes, where protein synthesis occurs; and (3) the *translation* of the information encoded on

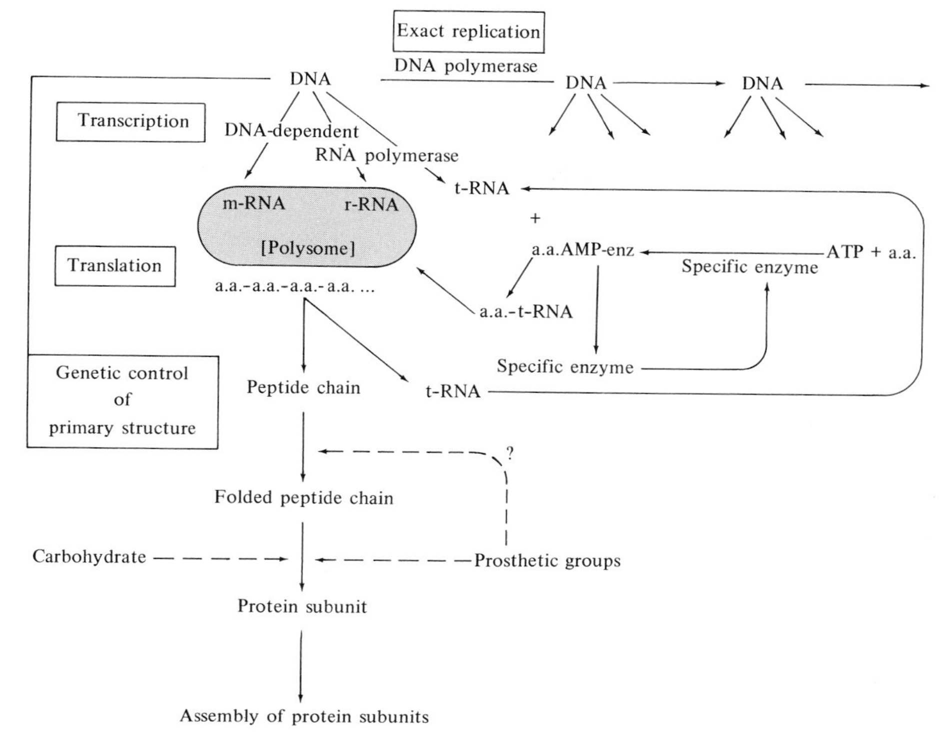

fig. 6-1. The overall scheme of DNA, RNA, and protein synthesis. (From Ingram, V. M. *The Biosynthesis of Macromolecules.* New York: W. A. Benjamin, 1965, p. 3.)

m-RNA into a newly synthesized protein molecule (Fig. 6-1). The flow of information in the living cell is primarily from DNA through RNA to protein.[1] While information does not flow in the reverse direction, there appears to be some informational feedback by means of the methylating enzymes.

Some structural features of DNA are described in Chapter 3, and the replication of DNA is discussed in Chapter 10. It has been adequately established that every gene consists of a linear sequence of nucleotides which comprises a portion of the DNA in a chromosome. A gene carries the coded information for a single polypeptide chain forming a single protein, a protein subunit, or a few closely related proteins.[2] Since there are 20 amino acids but only 4 nucleotides, a combination of nucleotides is required to specify unambiguously a given amino acid. Actually, the nucleotide code consists of sequences of three nucleotides, each of which codes for a specific amino

[1] Crick, F. H. C. *Symp. Soc. Exptl. Biol., 12,* 138 (1958). Cellular processes are sometimes said to be governed by a hierarchy of DNA, RNA, and protein.
[2] The idea (set out in a brilliant essay by Beadle, G. W., and Tatum, E. L. *Proc. Natl. Acad. Sci., 23,* 499 [1941]) that a gene, as defined operationally in genetics, corresponded to the information needed for the synthesis of a single enzyme was very influential in helping to stimulate the contemporary burst of activity and accomplishment in molecular biology. The important concept of *one gene–one enzyme* was first enunciated in the Croonian Lectures of 1908 by Archibald Garrod, *Lancet, 2,* 1, 73, 142 (1908), who recognized that alkaptonuria and other human hereditary disorders were caused by a defect in one chemical reaction. In alkaptonuria, the enzyme required for the metabolism of homogentisic acid is defective. Homogentisic acid accumulates in the tissues and is excreted in large amounts in the urine where it is oxidized to black substance.

fig. 6-2. The genetic code.

5′-OH TERMINAL BASE	SECOND NUCLEOTIDE				3′-OH TERMINAL BASE
	U	C	A	G	
U	PHE	SER	TYR	CYS	U
	PHE	SER	TYR	CYS	C
	—	SER	{Ochre / Period / Amber}	Period	A
	LEU	SER		TRP	G
C	LEU	PRO	HIS	ARG	U
	LEU	PRO	HIS	ARG	C
	LEU	PRO	GLUN	ARG	A
	LEU	PRO	GLUN	ARG	G
A	ILEU	THR	ASPN	SER	U
	ILEU	THR	ASPN	SER	C
	ILEU	THR	LYS	ARG	A
	N-Formyl-MET	THR	LYS	ARG	G
G	VAL	ALA	ASP	GLY	U
	VAL	ALA	ASP	GLY	C
	VAL	ALA	GLU	GLY	A
	VAL	ALA	GLU	GLY	G

acid. The triplet code is set out in Fig. 6-2. An inspection of the table reveals that in a number of cases more than one triplet sequence will code for a single amino acid; this is sometimes referred to as *degeneracy* in the code. Thus, an average gene contains about 1500 nucleotides which are divided into about 500 triplet frames, each coding for a specific amino acid. Faithful translation of the sequences requires that each triplet frame be read in register, starting at the 5′-end of the polynucleotide and proceeding linearly to the 3′-end. Mutations sometimes result in the deletion or insertion of a nucleotide, which thereby alters the register in which many of the frames are read. Such mutants result in the synthesis of altered proteins that usually lack functional integrity. There are also other types of mutations which result in misreading of the code.

The cell contains three types of RNA: (1) *ribosomal-RNA* (r-RNA) which accounts for three-quarters or more of the RNA content of the cell and is found in the ribosomes; (2) *soluble-RNA* (s-RNA), more often called *transfer-RNA* (t-RNA), which exists in a number of defined species, each carrying a specific amino acid, and acts to assemble them in the proper sequence as dictated by the template; and (3) *messenger-RNA* (m-RNA), defined above, the template which directs protein synthesis. It appears that DNA acts as a template for all three forms of RNA as indicated particularly by hybridization experiments which have shown that all three forms of RNA are complementary for stretches of DNA.

In *prokaryotic* (sometimes called *akaryotic*) cells, RNA is liberated into the cytoplasm directly after synthesis. On the other hand, a more complex mechanism is found in eukaryotic cells where RNA appears to be synthesized in the nucleolus from which it finds its way into the ribosomes that line the endoplasmic reticulum. While m-RNA is synthesized in the karyolymph, at the present time it appears that r-RNA precursors are only synthesized in the nucleolus, that intermediate forms of r-RNA emerge into the cytoplasm, and that *polyribosomes* (clusters of ribosomes attached to a strand of m-RNA engaged in synthesizing protein) tend to form upon the endoplasmic reticulum. When the cells of higher organisms are disrupted by homogenization, the endoplasmic reticulum is fragmented into particles which sediment in the microsome fraction upon differential centrifugation. Ribosomes can be liberated from the sediment by treatment with a detergent such as sodium deoxycholate.[3]

The ribosomes, which are the seat of protein synthesis, are particles which, when prepared from bacteria, sediment at 70 *S* in density gradient centrifugation and have an approximate molecular weight of 2.8×10^6. They consist of about 40 percent r-RNA and 60 percent basic proteins. Treatment of polyribosomes with low concentrations of RNAse yields single 70 *S* ribosomes. The various classes of RNA are identified in terms of their sedimentation constants in an ultracentrifuge. The sedimentation constants are roughly, but not exactly, proportional to the molecular weights. Intact single ribosomes are relatively resistant to RNAse. In a magnesium-free medium, ribosomes dissociate into two fragments which sediment at 30 *S* and 50 *S*; each fragment contains about 40 percent RNA[4] (Fig. 6-3). This dissociation is

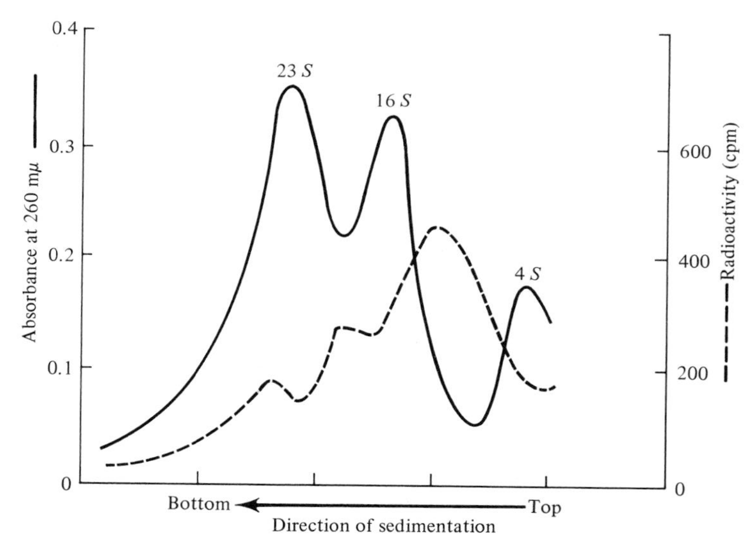

fig. 6-3. Zone sedimentation of pulse-labeled RNA from *E. coli* growing with a generation time of 80 min. Pulse labeling with ^{14}C-uracil was for 30 sec followed by phenol extraction of all RNA in the presence of the detergent sodium dodecylsulfate to inactivate ribonucleases. Zone-sedimentation analysis was carried out in a sucrose gradient of 5 to 20 percent sucrose with centrifuging for 11 hours at 4°C. The absorbency at 260 mμ represents the distribution of r-RNA (16 *S* and 23 *S*) and of t-RNA (4 *S*). The radioactivity in the broken line indicates the sedimentation profile of the pulse-labeled m-RNA fraction. (From Ingram, V. M. *The Biosynthesis of Macromolecules.* New York: W. A. Benjamin, 1965, p. 58.)

[3] Petermann, M. L., and Hamilton, M. G. *J. Biol. Chem.*, *224*, 725 (1957).
[4] Tissières, A., Watson, J. D., Schlessinger, D., and Hollingworth, B. R. *J. Mol. Biol.*, *1*, 221 (1959).

reversible, reaggregation of the particles occurring upon the addition of magnesium or polyamines such as spermine. The ribosomal protein is quite basic and contains relatively large amounts of the basic amino acids lysine and arginine.

Two types of r-RNA can be obtained from these fragments upon phenol extraction (which simultaneously denatures the ribosomal protein, cleaves it from the RNA, and renders it insoluble); these forms of r-RNA sediment at 18 *S* and 28 *S* corresponding to approximate molecular weights of 0.55×10^6 and 1.15×10^6. The base composition of r-RNA usually does not resemble the gross base composition of the cellular DNA. In solution, r-RNA shows hyperchromicity and a "melting" curve upon heating; this suggests that at least a portion of the RNA is hydrogen-bonded, possibly as hairpin loops forming two-stranded helices.[5] Of course, it is not clear that the configuration of r-RNA in solution resembles its configuration in the ribosome where it is associated with ribosomal protein. *X*-ray diffraction data of r-RNA are consistent with the presence of helical regions. The 18 *S* and 28 *S* r-RNAs have different base compositions; the G + C content of the 28 *S* species is greater than that of the 18 *S*. The 18 *S* and 28 *S* RNAs from *Drosophila* hybridize independently with DNA.

The t-RNA,[6] accounting for about 15 percent of the cellular RNA, has a molecular weight of about 25,000, sediments at 4 *S*, and is composed, therefore, of approximately 75 nucleotides. In spite of their similar size, there are many distinct species of t-RNA which can be separated from one another by countercurrent distribution or by chromatography on methylated albumin columns.[7] Each species of t-RNA combines with a specific amino acid and recognizes the triplet nucleotide sequence which codes for that amino acid. Thus, there is at least one species of t-RNA for each amino acid. For some amino acids, such as leucine, more than one species of leucine-specific t-RNA is obtained by countercurrent fractionation of a crude t-RNA mixture; each species corresponds to a different triplet sequence coding for leucine.

The specificity of t-RNA has been demonstrated by an ingenious experiment.[8] A synthetic copolymer of uridylic acid and guanylic acid present in the ratio of 4 to 1 acts as a template for the synthesis in an in-vitro system for a polypeptide rich in cysteine but with little alanine. In these experiments, ^{14}C-labeled cysteinyl-t-RNA was reduced with Raney nickel. While the cysteine moiety was reduced to alanine, the t-RNA was not affected. This resulted in the formation of a cysteinyl-t-RNA charged with ^{14}C-alanine. When this reduced t-RNA complex was used in an in-vitro protein-synthesizing system with the uridylic-acid–guanylic-acid copolymer as a template, a polypeptide rich in alanine was formed. When the reduced t-RNA complex was used in a rabbit reticulocyte system which synthesized hemoglobin, alanine was incorporated in the place of cysteine in the polypeptide that was formed.

The various species of t-RNA resemble each other in that the 3′-end always terminates in a CCA (cytidylic acid, cytidylic acid, adenylic acid) sequence and the 5′-end always terminates in guanylic acid. The amino acid is attached to the t-RNA near the 3′-end. Preliminary sequence studies indicate that the various species of t-RNA have stretches of nucleotides in which the sequence is identical. Transfer-RNA is remarkable

---

[5] Hall, B. D., and Doty, P. *J. Mol. Biol.*, *1*, 111 (1959); Schlessinger, D. *J. Mol. Biol.*, *2*, 92 (1960); Zubay, G., and Wilkins, M. H. F. *J. Mol. Biol.*, *2*, 105 (1960); Ritossa, F. M. *Natl. Cancer Inst. Monograph*, *23*, 237 (1966).

[6] Hoagland, M. B., Stephenson, M. L., Scott, J. F., Hecht, L. I., and Zamecnik, P. C. *J. Biol. Chem.*, *231*, 241 (1958).

[7] Weisblum, B., Benzer, S., and Holley, R. W. *Proc. Natl. Acad. Sci.*, *48*, 1449 (1962); Sueoka, N., and Yamane, T. *Proc. Natl. Acad. Sci.*, *48*, 1454 (1962).

[8] Chapeville, F., Lipmann, F., von Ehrenstein, G., Weisblum, B., Ray, W. J., Jr., and Benzer, S. *Proc. Natl. Acad. Sci.*, *48*, 1086 (1962); *49*, 669 (1963).

for the large content of uncommon, unusual bases including the methylated bases such as ribothymidine, methylguanosine, N,N-dimethylguanosine, methylinosine, pseudouridine, dihydrouridine, and others. There is evidence that the unusual bases are formed by modification of the common bases after the nucleotide chain is synthesized. Mammalian r-RNA also contains methylated nucleotides, mainly in the ribose moiety.[9] The conjecture has been made that the presence of the methylated nucleotides prevents t-RNA and r-RNA from acting as templates for protein synthesis.

Although t-RNA consists of a single nucleotide chain, most of the bases are hydrogen-bonded to one another in loops forming a double helix. Transfer-RNA shows considerable hypochromicity in solution which disappears upon heating and gives a melting curve similar to that of DNA.[10] At *p*H 6.7 in 0.1 M NaCl, the melting temperature of t-RNA is approximately 60°.

There must be at least four specific sites on each species of t-RNA: (1) the site which interacts with the specific triplet nucleotide sequence which codes for the specific amino acid, (2) the site at which the t-RNA attaches to the ribosome, (3) the site which interacts with the specific amino-acid–activating enzyme, and (4) the CCA site where the specific amino acid attaches. The first complete nucleotide sequence of one species of t-RNA to have been established, that of an alanine t-RNA,[11] reveals that it consists of 77 nucleotides. Of these, 9 are unusual bases. Because the unusual bases cannot participate in the hydrogen bonding which is required for base pairing, it is thought that the unusual bases are located at the specific interaction sites of t-RNA. Recently, the sequences of yeast tyrosine-t-RNA[12] and of two species of yeast serine-t-RNA have been elucidated. They, too, contain many unusual bases (Fig. 6-4).

While the precise tertiary structure of t-RNA is still unknown, Madison, Everett, and Kung proposed a probable folded structure based on forming the maximum possible number of intramolecular hydrogen bonds. The triplet of bases that interacts with m-RNA (IGC for alanine-t-RNA and GUA for tyrosine-t-RNA) appears to be in the center of the molecule. An unusual base is located immediately adjacent to the anticodon triplet, and the anticodon triplet itself contains the complementary bases which form hydrogen bonds with the coding triplet.

messenger-RNA

Messenger-RNA accounts for 5 percent or less of the total intracellular RNA and in contrast to r-RNA and t-RNA is very heterogeneous in its molecular size. Messenger-RNA labeled with radiocarbon is obtained promptly after actively growing cells are exposed briefly to ^{14}C-labeled precursors of RNA. Labeled m-RNA formed in this way shows a continuous distribution of radioactivity upon density-gradient centrifugation over a wide range of sedimentation constants corresponding to molecular weight up to 2×10^6. Obviously, the size of m-RNA molecules is related to the size of the polypeptide it codes for; there should be three times as many nucleotides in the strand of m-RNA as there are amino acids in the polypeptide. As will be pointed out below, a single m-RNA strand sometimes codes for a polypeptide chain which

[9] Brown, G. M., and Attardi, G. *Biochem. Biophys. Res. Commun.*, *20*, 298 (1965).
[10] Tissières, A. *J. Mol. Biol.*, *1*, 365 (1959).
[11] Holley, R. W., Apgar, J., Everett, G. A., Madison, J. T., Marquisee, M., Merrill, S. H., Penswick, J. R., and Zamir, A. *Science*, *147*, 1462 (1965).
[12] Madison, J. T., Everett, G. A., and Kung, H. *Science*, *153*, 531 (1966); Zachau, H. G., Düting, D., and Feldmann, H. *Angew. Chem.*, *5*, 422 (1966).

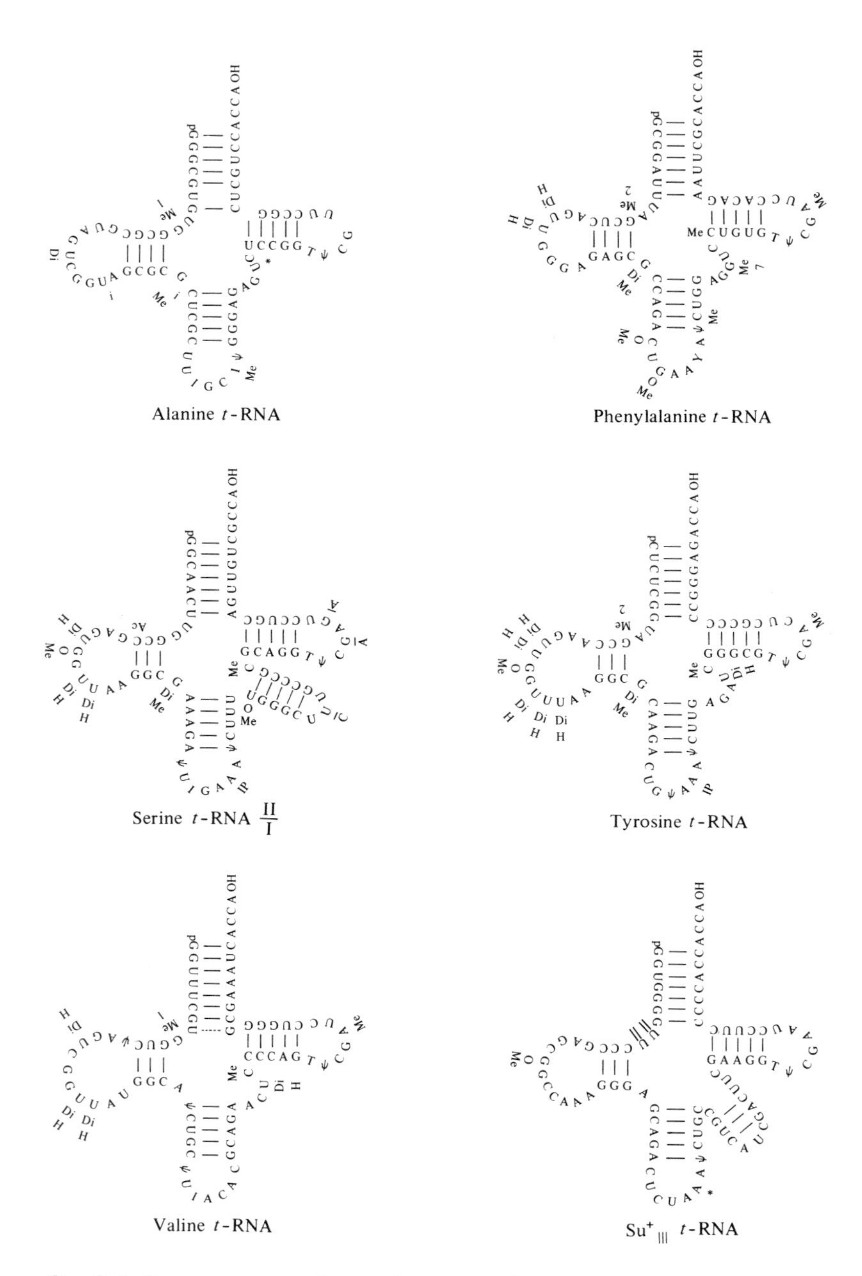

fig. 6-4. Base sequences of several yeast tyrosine t-RNAs showing the cloverleaf arrangement of folding, a scheme based on maximizing the number of hydrogen bonds in each molecule. Letters designate the base as follows: A, adenine; G, guanine; C, cytosine; U, uracil; T, ribothymidine; I, inosine; DiHU, 5, 6-dihydrouridine; ψ, pseudouridine; Ü, thiouridine; MeC, 5-methylcytidine; MeA, 1-methyladenosine; DiMeA, 6,6-dimethyladenosine; MeG, 1-methylguanosine; 2MeG, 2-methylguanosine; DiMeG, 2,2-dimethylguanosine; MeOG, 2′-O-methylguanosine; and MeI, methylinosine. (From Madison, J. T. *Ann. Rev. Biochem., 37,* 134 [1968].)

eventually becomes more than a single protein. Most m-RNAs appear to contain 900 to 1500 nucleotides which corresponds to polypeptide chains of 300 to 500 amino acids.

That base composition is complementary to that of DNA has been demonstrated by forming hybrid double helical strands of m-RNA with fragments of chromosomal DNA.[13] It has been possible by this technique to separate small amounts of m-RNA serving as templates for specific proteins. It has not been possible thus far, however, to isolate macroscopic quantities of m-RNA. The base composition of m-RNA from various organisms corresponds closely to the overall base composition of the DNA from that organism, although the range of base compositions of both DNA and m-RNA varies widely from organism to organism. Unlike t-RNA and r-RNA, m-RNA does not show any evidence of hydrogen bonding in protein-free solutions, but appears to exist only as an uncoiled, straight, single chain.

All three forms of RNA, r-RNA, t-RNA, and m-RNA, are synthesized with chromosomal DNA as the template. Although 95 percent or more of the RNA is r-RNA or t-RNA, hybridization experiments show that less than 1 percent of the DNA functions as a template for their synthesis.[14] RNA is synthesized by action of DNA-dependent RNA polymerase (Fig. 6-5). The enzyme is found in all cell fractions

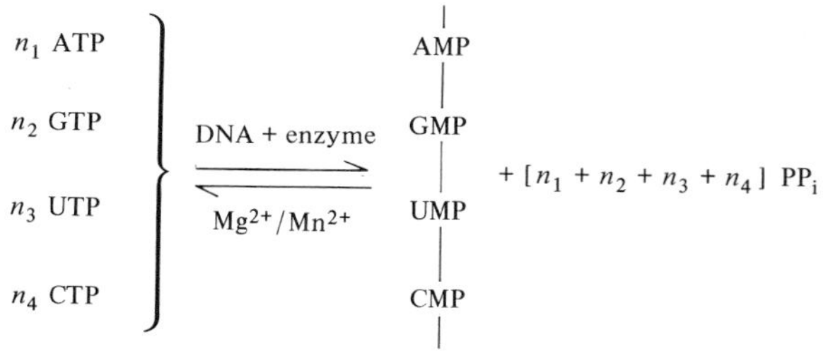

$$\left.\begin{array}{l} n_1\ \mathrm{ATP} \\ n_2\ \mathrm{GTP} \\ n_3\ \mathrm{UTP} \\ n_4\ \mathrm{CTP} \end{array}\right\} \underset{Mg^{2+}/Mn^{2+}}{\overset{\text{DNA + enzyme}}{\rightleftharpoons}} \begin{array}{c} | \\ \mathrm{AMP} \\ | \\ \mathrm{GMP} \\ | \\ \mathrm{UMP} \\ | \\ \mathrm{CMP} \\ | \end{array} + [n_1 + n_2 + n_3 + n_4]\ \mathrm{PP_i}$$

fig. 6-5. The general reaction for the formation of RNA by DNA-dependent RNA polymerase.

in prokaryotic cells, but in eukaryotic cells it is almost entirely associated with the nuclear fraction. The DNA-dependent RNA polymerase requires a divalent cation such as magnesium or manganese, DNA to serve as a template, and the simultaneous presence of the four ribonucleoside triphosphates: ATP, GTP, UTP, and CTP. If one of the nucleoside triphosphates is absent, the incorporation of all the others virtually ceases. The enzyme requires that its sulfhydryl groups be reduced for activity; because the sulfhydryl groups are easily oxidized or inactivated by heavy metals or SH-reacting compounds, in-vitro syntheses using the DNA-dependent RNA polymerase usually are carried out in the presence of mercaptoethanol or a similar compound.

If RNA is synthesized in vitro by means of the DNA-dependent RNA polymerase using DNA from various sources as the template, RNA is produced with a base composition which resembles that of the DNA. Yields of RNA about 100 times the weight of the DNA used can be obtained. Template DNA appears to be undenatured

---

[13] Hall, B. D., and Spiegelman, S. *Proc. Natl. Acad. Sci.*, *47*, 137 (1961); Bolton, E. T., and McCarthy, B. *Proc. Natl. Acad. Sci.*, *48*, 1390 (1962); Midgley, J. E. M., and McCarthy, B. J. *Biochim. Biophys. Acta*, *61*, 696 (1962); Hayashi, M., Hayashi, M. N., and Spiegelman, S. *Proc. Natl. Acad. Sci.*, *50*, 664 (1963).

[14] Yankofsky, S. A., and Spiegelman, S. *Proc. Natl. Acad. Sci.*, *48*, 1069, 1466 (1962); *49*, 538 (1963).

after use in such in-vitro syntheses. In the in-vitro syntheses, it appears that both strands of the DNA are copies; in vivo, however, it appears that only one DNA strand is copied. Double-stranded DNA appears to be required. Although single-stranded ΦX-174 DNA will act as a primer template, it is very much less active than double-stranded DNA. The complementarity of the RNA produced can be demonstrated by RNA-DNA hydribidization experiments.

The enzyme polynucleotide phosphorylase attacks m-RNA, degrading it to nucleotide fragments. In contrast, r-RNA and t-RNA are relatively resistant to degradation, possibly because they contain some secondary structure; that is, they contain stretches in the form of loops of two-stranded, hydrogen-bonded helices. Not only is m-RNA synthesized rapidly; it is also degraded rapidly, particularly in bacterial cells. In *B. subtilis*, for example, m-RNA is synthesized continuously from the nucleotide pool and degraded by a first-order reaction with a half-life of about 2 minutes. Given a half-life of this magnitude, each m-RNA molecule serves as a template for the synthesis of 15 to 20 polypeptide chains. Different species of m-RNA probably decay at somewhat different rates. When the utilization of substrate for energy is blocked by anaerobiosis or by metabolic inhibitors, m-RNA is stabilized and its half-life increased. In contrast to m-RNA, r-RNA and t-RNA are quite stable in vivo. The instability of m-RNA is not a prominent feature in the cells of higher organisms. In mammalian liver cells, for example, most of the m-RNA is quite long-lived, having a half-life of 5 days or more.

Polynucleotide phosphorylase is a ubiquitous enzyme which has been prepared in highly purified form from bacterial extracts and mammalian liver nuclei. Although the physiological function of this enzyme is primarily hydrolytic, the reverse reaction also can occur in the presence of excess ribonucleotide diphosphates, leading to the formation of polyribonucleotides. Appreciable quantities of nucleic acid are associated with crude polynucleotide phosphorylase preparations which appear to play a role in initiating the polymerization reaction. Most of this nucleic acid is removed in the process of purification, and polymerization may fail to occur with highly purified enzyme unless a nucleic acid primer is added. RNA synthesis by polynucleotide phosphorylase does not follow the sequence of a primer, and the product does not possess a specific nucleotide sequence.

It should be noted that the genetic material of certain viruses is RNA. An RNA-dependent RNA polymerase has been obtained from several bacteria and from plant sources which catalyzes the synthesis of RNA using viral RNA as the template. Analysis of the RNA synthesized by determination of nearest-neighbor frequencies indicates that there is faithful replication of the nucleotide sequence.

assembly of a polypeptide chain

Peptide synthesis requires a pool of the various t-RNAs with the proper amino acids attached to them. The amino-acyl-t-RNAs are formed by a two-stage process[15] (Fig. 6-6). Each amino acid condenses with ATP to form an amino-acyl-AMP and pyrophosphate. This reaction is catalyzed by a specific activating enzyme, amino-acyl synthetase. There is a unique amino-acyl synthetase for each species of amino acid. The amino-acyl-AMP formed by this reaction is not liberated into the medium, but

[15] Bergmann, F. H., Berg, P., and Dieckmann, M. *J. Biol. Chem.*, *236*, 1735 (1961); Loftfield, R. B., Hecht, L. I., and Eigner, E. A. *Biochim. Biophys. Acta*, *72*, 383 (1963).

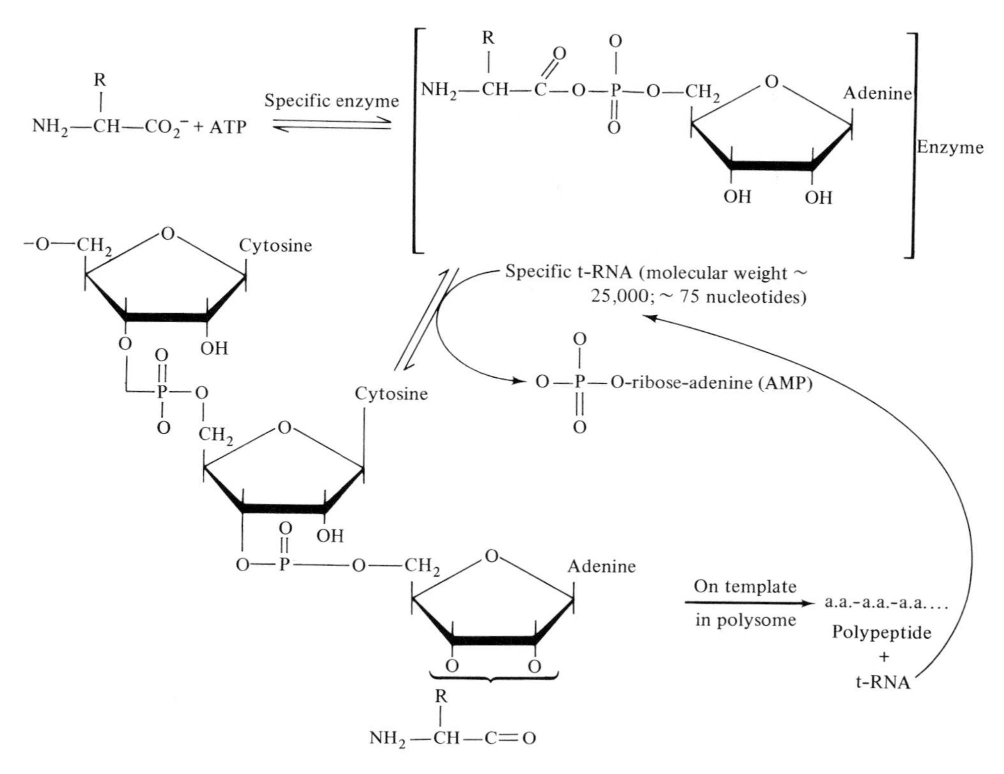

fig. 6-6. The activation of an amino acid and its attachment to t-RNA. (From Ingram, V. M. *The Biosynthesis of Macromolecules.* New York: W. A. Benjamin, 1965, p. 106.)

remains attached to the enzyme. The reaction is reversible, and an excess of pyrophosphate will cause the liberation of ATP and of the amino acid from an amino-acyl-AMP-enzyme complex. In the second stage, the amino-acyl-AMP-activating enzyme complex reacts with the specific t-RNA for that amino acid to form an amino-acyl-t-RNA accompanied by the liberation of AMP. The amino acid combines with the t-RNA by forming an ester between its carboxyl group and the 3′-hydroxyl group of the ribose at the CCA end of the nucleotide chain.[16] The sequence of reactions is highly specific, and mistakes between closely related amino acids such as leucine, isoleucine, and valine probably occur with a frequency of less than one in ten thousand. The amino-acyl-t-RNA thus formed hydrolyzes spontaneously under physiological conditions unless it is utilized. Although the spontaneous hydrolysis does not proceed rapidly, it is not possible to charge a preparation of t-RNA completely with amino acids. Instead, a steady state is reached when the rates of formation and hydrolysis balance each other. Both the amino-acyl-AMP and the amino-acyl-t-RNAs are energy-rich compounds.

While ambiguity in translation of the genetic code is difficult to evaluate in in-vivo polypeptide synthesis, ambiguity has been detected in in-vitro polypeptide synthesis, generally when the environmental conditions were severely altered. Thus, ambiguity has been found when protein synthesis was carried out at elevated temperatures[17] or

[16] Feldmann, H., and Zachau, H. G. *Biochim. Biophys. Res. Commun.*, *15*, 13 (1964).
[17] Szer, W., and Ochoa, S. *J. Mol. Biol.*, *8*, 823 (1964); Friedman, S. M., and Weinstein, I. B. *Biochim. Biophys. Acta*, *114*, 593 (1966).

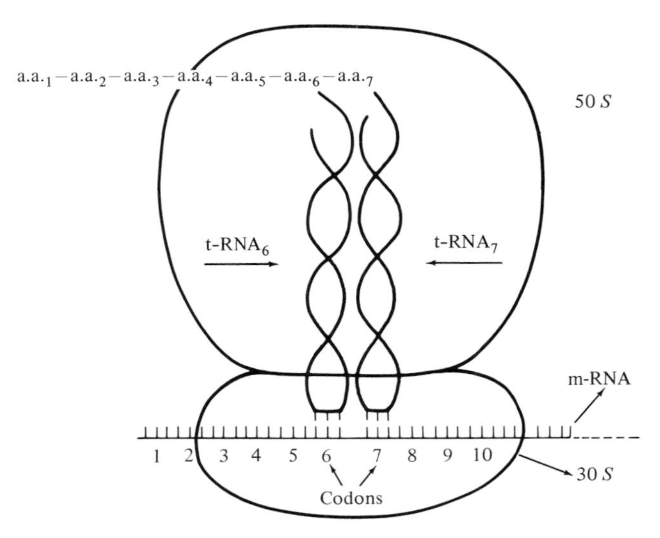

fig. 6-7. Schematic diagram of protein synthesis by the ribosome illustrating the mechanism of translation of the genetic code. (From Warner, J. R., and Soeiro, R. *New Eng. J. Med., 276,* 614 [1967].)

in the presence of organic solvents.[18] Several antibiotics, notably streptomycin, produce ambiguity in the reading of the code (see p. 324).

The actual assembly of polypeptide chains appears to occur only on the surface of ribosomes (Fig. 6-7). The ribosomes are not active in protein synthesis unless they are attached to a strand of m-RNA, and magnesium ions are required for stable attachment of ribosomes to m-RNA. Free ribosomes do not attach randomly on strands of m-RNA. Rather, there appear to be one or more specific sites on natural m-RNA strands at which free ribosomes can attach. It is thought that these sites are at or near the triplet sequence that codes for the amino-terminal amino acid of the polypeptide chain. Obviously, incomplete polypeptide chains could be synthesized if there were more than one "sticky" site for each protein coded for by a given messenger-RNA. Thus, a m-RNA strand that codes for a single protein should have but one "sticky" site, while lactose gene m-RNA which codes for three proteins might have three sites for ribosome attachment. It is of some interest that r-RNA cannot function as a messenger.

Once a ribosome becomes attached to a messenger-RNA strand, polypeptide synthesis can commence. Each mature ribosome appears to have only one site at which it can attach to a strand of m-RNA.[19] The ribosome moves along the m-RNA strand from the 5′-end toward the 3′-end, adding an amino acid to the growing polypeptide chain for every frame of three nucleotides. Charged t-RNA attaches to the 30 *S* portion of the ribosome.[20] As the ribosome moves along the m-RNA chain, successive amino-acyl-t-RNAs move into place, each amino-acyl-t-RNA corresponding to the nucleotide triplet at that point. At the other end of the amino-acyl-t-RNAs, the activated amino acid residues condense to form a polypeptide chain. The latter reaction is catalyzed by two distinct condensing enzymes. These two enzymes can be separated

[18] So, A. G., and Davie, E. W. *Biochemistry, 4,* 1973 (1965).
[19] Moore, P. B. *J. Mol. Biol., 18,* 8 (1966).
[20] Suzuka, I., Kaji, H., and Kaji, I. *Proc. Natl. Acad. Sci., 55,* 1483 (1966).

from one another by column chromatography, and both are required for protein synthesis. However, the specific way in which each of the enzymes functions is not yet known. In addition, GTP is required and utilized in peptide bond formation. The condensing enzymes possess sulfhydryl groups which must be in the reduced state for activity. In-vitro polypeptide synthesis, therefore, is carried out in the presence of mercaptoethanol or a similar compound. Thus, synthesis of the polypeptide chain proceeds as the ribosome moves down the strand of m-RNA. Incidentally, the motive force which causes the ribosome to move down the strand of m-RNA as the polypeptide chain is synthesized is a mystery. The ribosomes do not appear to possess any specificity and appear to function similarly regardless of the polypeptide chain being synthesized.

After the ribosome has moved down the m-RNA about 80 nucleotides, a second free ribosome can attach to the m-RNA strand and the synthesis of a second polypeptide chain can begin. This process is repeated so that every m-RNA strand becomes covered with ribosomes (Figs. 6-8 and 6-9). A strand of m-RNA with several ribosomes attached forms a *polyribosome* or (simply) polysome. Polyribosomes contain about 1 ribosome for every 3,000 to 4,000 molecular weight or about 25 to 30 amino acid residues of the polypeptide chain synthesized. Thus, hemoglobin subunits containing about 150 amino acids are synthesized by polysomes with 4 to 6 ribosomes,[21] while myosin subunits, with a molecular weight about 180,000, are synthesized by polysomes with about 60 ribosomes. When a ribosome comes to the 3′-end of the strand of m-RNA, it falls off and simultaneously releases the newly synthesized protein. Some idea of the rate of protein synthesis can be gleaned from pulse-labeling experiments which indicate that a hemoglobin subunit of about 150 amino acid residues is synthesized in about 7 minutes at 15° or in about 1½ minutes at 37°. Many m-RNA molecules code for more than one protein. In addition to triplet sequences that code

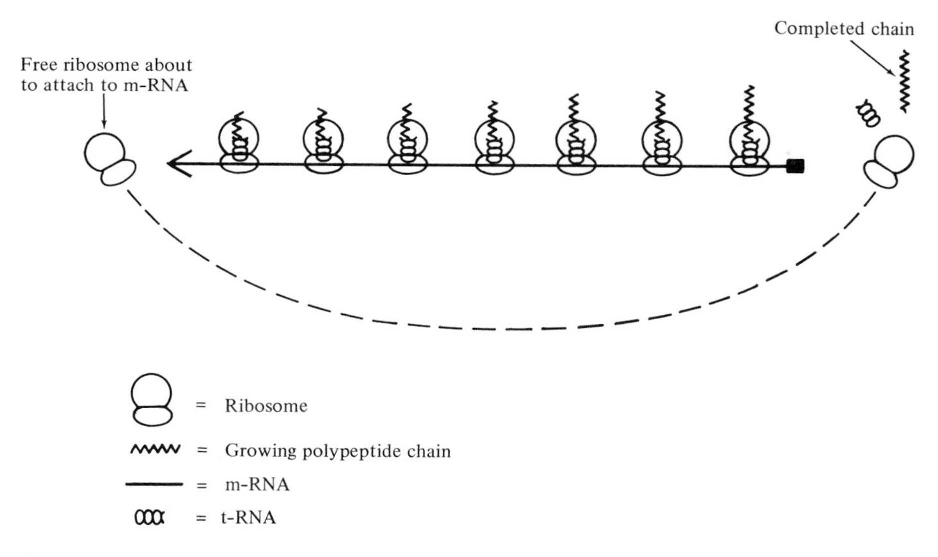

fig. 6-8. Schematic diagram of protein synthesis by a polyribosome. (From Watson, J. D. *Molecular Biology of the Gene.* New York: W. A. Benjamin, 1965, p. 332.)

[21] Warner, J. R., Knopf, P. M., and Rich, A. *Proc. Natl. Acad. Sci., 49,* 122 (1963); Heywood, S. M., Dowben, R. M., and Rich, A. *Proc. Natl. Acad. Sci., 57,* 1002 (1967).

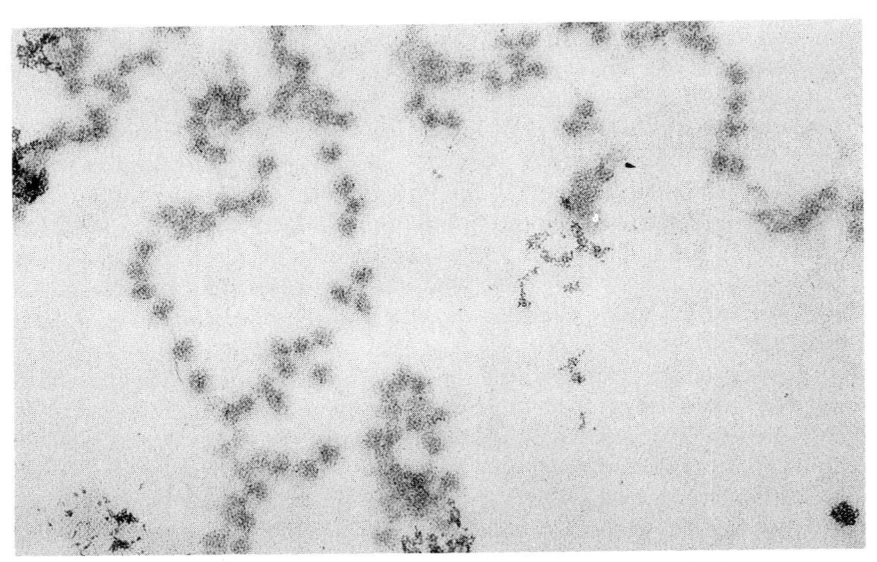

fig. 6-9. Polyribosomes from chick embryo muscle of the 15–23 unit class with which the synthesis of actin is associated. Uranyl acetate stain; magnification 123,000.

for the amino acids that make up the protein chains, the m-RNA must contain triplet sequences that act as a sort of "punctuation"—at the very least, sequences that signal the end of one protein molecule and the beginning of the next.

The synthesis of all polypeptide chains appears to commence at the amino terminal end[22] and proceed to the carboxyl terminal end. At any given time, polyribosomes will contain a family of partially synthesized polypeptide chains, ranging from nascent chains whose synthesis has barely begun to polypeptide chains whose synthesis is almost completed. If a protein-synthesizing system is exposed to a short pulse of amino acids (short compared to the time required to synthesize a complete polypeptide chain), radioactive amino acids will be incorporated for a short stretch in all chains. In the case of far advanced nascent chains, the radioactive amino acids will form the terminal sequences and the chains will be released (Fig. 6-10). Experiments of this type disclosed the label in the carboxyl terminal first with gradual increase of label backward as the time of incubation was increased. The label appeared last in the end of the polypeptide chain synthesized first, the amino terminal.

The three-dimensional structure of protein molecules appears to depend primarily upon the amino acid sequence. Some aspects of the native and denatured state of proteins were discussed in Chapter 4. It was pointed out that the native state of the protein is probably the thermodynamically most stable state under physiological conditions. In fact, a number of investigators have successfully "renatured" proteins whose tertiary structure has been altered by one or another method of denaturation.[23]

---

[22] Bishop, J., Leahy, J., and Schweet, R. *Proc. Natl. Acad. Sci.*, *46*, 1030 (1960); Yoshida, A., and Tobita, T. *Biochim. Biophys. Acta*, *37*, 513 (1960); Dintzis, H. M. *Proc. Natl. Acad. Sci.*, *47*, 247 (1961); Goldstein, A., and Brown, B. J. *Biochim. Biophys. Acta*, *53*, 438 (1961); Canfield, R. E., and Anfinsen, C. B. *Biochemistry*, *2*, 1073 (1963).

[23] Kunitz, M. *J. Gen. Physiol.*, *32*, 241 (1948); Eisenberg, M. A., and Schwert, G. W. *J. Gen. Physiol.*, *34*, 583 (1951); Levinthal, C., Signer, E. R., and Fetherolf, K. *Proc. Natl. Acad. Sci.*, *48*, 1230 (1962); Epstein, C. J., Goldberger, R. F., and Anfinsen, C. B. *Cold Spring Harbor Symp. Quant. Biol.*, *28*, 439 (1963); Stellwagen, E., and Schachman, H. K. *Biochemistry*, *1*, 1056 (1962); Imai, T., Takagi, J., and Isemura, T. *J. Biochem.* (*Tokyo*), *53*, 1 (1963).

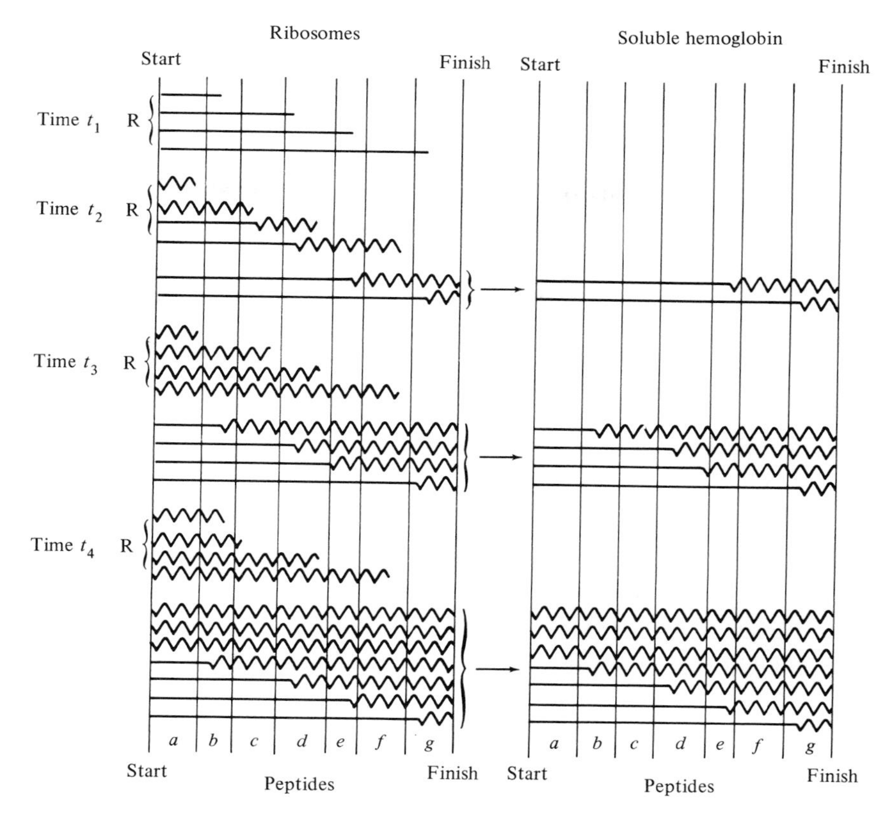

fig. 6-10. Model of sequential growth of a protein chain using hemoglobin. (From Dintzis, H. M. *Proc. Natl. Acad. Sci.*, *47*, 249 [1961].)

Denaturation, therefore, is a reversible process. While the yields have been poor, some activity of denatured soy-bean trypsin inhibitor, chymotrypsinogen, ribonuclease, alkaline phosphatase, lysozyme, and aldolase has been recovered by physical renaturation. The reason that polypeptide chains are formed in the native configuration with such readiness is that the growing polypeptide chain has an opportunity of folding into its native tertiary structure as it is formed. In addition, there may be specific enzymes that facilitate the assumption of the native configuration. It has been shown, for instance, that the renaturation of ribonuclease and lysozyme, which involves the correct formation of disulfide bonds, can be greatly accelerated by enzymes contained in liver microsomes.[24]

Waller[25] made the interesting observation that about half the proteins in *E. coli* have methionine as the amino acid at the amino end (origin) of the polypeptide chain and suggested that methionine is somehow involved in the initiation of synthesis of a polypeptide chain. It appears that the triplet sequence AUG codes for the initiation of synthesis of a polypeptide chain[26] in *E. coli*. The transfer-RNA associated with this

[24] Goldberger, R. F., Epstein, C. J., and Anfinsen, C. B. *J. Biol. Chem.*, *238*, 628 (1963); *239*, 1406 (1964).
[25] Waller, J. P. *J. Mol. Biol.*, *7*, 483 (1963).
[26] Clark, B. F. C., and Marcker, K. A. *Nature*, *207*, 1038 (1965); *J. Mol. Biol.*, *17*, 394 (1966); Capecchi, M. R. *Proc. Natl. Acad. Sci.*, *55*, 1517 (1966).

codon appears to be charged with N-formylmethionine. The function of the formyl group is not clear, but it clearly forms a peptide bond with the methionine. It may facilitate the formation of the next peptide bond in some manner. Initiation may involve the participation of some special enzymes in addition.[27] When synthetic polynucleotides which contain the AUG sequence in known positions are used as messengers, the N-formylmethionine appears to establish a register for reading the subsequent triplets.[28] After synthesis of the protein or polypeptide chain is completed, the formyl group or the whole N-formylmethionine residue is hydrolyzed off. The process of initiation of a polypeptide chain in higher animals is not known at the present time.

Ordinarily a special mechanism for chain termination may not be necessary. When the ribosomes reach the end of the strand of m-RNA and the last charged amino-acyl-t-RNA couples its amino acid to the polypeptide chain, the absence of a site for another charged t-RNA may lead to release of the polypeptide chain. Polycistronic messengers, messengers that lead to the synthesis of more than one polypeptide chain, require a special release mechanism before the end of the messenger strand is reached. Synthesis of protein in certain mutants known as amber mutants which contain nonsense triplets shows that synthesis of the growing polypeptide chain ceases where the nonsense triplet occurs and that the unfinished polypeptide chain is released.[29] These nonsense triplets (UAA, UAG, and UGA) code for a t-RNA which cannot be charged with an amino acid. Thus these triplets code for release of the polypeptide chain.

For polycistronic messengers of bacteria, initiation of the second polypeptide starts with an N-formylmethionine residue. The latter has no free amino group and cannot form a peptide bond with the preceding amino acid residue. This mechanism may also play a role in the separation of the polypeptide chain. No polycistronic messengers have yet been found in higher cells. Only trace amounts of N-formylmethionine have been found in eukaryotic cells, and this probably occurs in mitochondria.

interference with protein synthesis by antibiotics and viruses

A number of antibiotics interfere with protein synthesis, particularly in microorganisms. The effects of actinomycin D, chloramphenicol, puromycin, and streptomycin will be described briefly because they have been used widely; many other antibiotics also interfere with protein synthesis.

Actinomycin D inhibits both the replication of DNA and the transcription of RNA by inhibiting both DNA polymerase and the DNA-dependent RNA polymerase. At low levels when the inhibition is partial, replication of guanine-containing sequences is inhibited preferentially, and the antibiotic may act by binding to guanine-containing regions of DNA. RNA polymerase is more sensitive to actinomycin D than DNA polymerase; thus, at a concentration of about 1×10^{-6} M, actinomycin D reduces the RNA polymerase activity of bacterial systems to 10 percent or less of its usual activity while the DNA polymerase activity is 95 percent of normal. Except at very high con-

[27] Stanley, W. M., Jr., Salas, M., Wahba, A. J., and Ochoa, S. *Proc. Natl. Acad. Sci.*, *56*, 290 (1966).
[28] Sundararajan, T. A., and Thach, R. E. *J. Mol. Biol.*, *19*, 74 (1966).
[29] Sarabhai, A. S., Stretton, A. O. W., Brenner, S., and Bölle, A. *Nature*, *201*, 13 (1964).

centrations, actinomycin D does not interfere with translation, that is, synthesis of the polypeptide chain. Thus, actinomycin D can be used to inhibit the formation of new m-RNA without interfering with protein synthesis using already formed m-RNA as template.

Chloramphenicol interferes with protein synthesis by blocking the condensation of the amino acid residues of charged t-RNAs to form a polypeptide chain. It has also been suggested that chloramphenicol interferes with the attachment of ribosomes to m-RNA. Chloramphenicol at concentrations of 50 to 100 μg/ml results in a cessation of protein synthesis in bacterial systems at the level of translation while RNA synthesis continues unabated. In the presence of chloramphenicol, the ribosomes produced are abnormal and sometimes are called *chloramphenicol particles.* These abnormal ribosomes contain only 25 percent protein, that is, less than half the normal amount. Almost all the r-RNA synthesized is of the 16 *S* variety, less than 10 percent 23 *S* r-RNA being formed at high chloramphenicol concentrations. In the presence of chloramphenicol, the rate of decay of total m-RNA is markedly decreased.[30] The decay of specific m-RNAs for inducible enzymes such as β-galactosidase or histidase, however, does not appear to be altered.[31]

Puromycin is an antibiotic that bears some chemical structural resemblance to the amino acid end of an amino-acyl-t-RNA (Fig. 6-11). Puromycin labeled with radioactive carbon is found in the trichloracetic acid precipitable material (protein) when added to cultures of *E. coli* in concentrations sufficient to inhibit protein synthesis. When radioactive puromycin was added to a reticulocyte preparation synthesizing hemoglobin in vitro, the peptides formed contained one labeled puromycin molecule for every N-terminal valine residue. The D-amino acid analogs of puromycin are relatively ineffective in interfering with protein synthesis. Puromycin molecules appear to substitute occasionally for an amino-acyl-t-RNA with the result that the amino

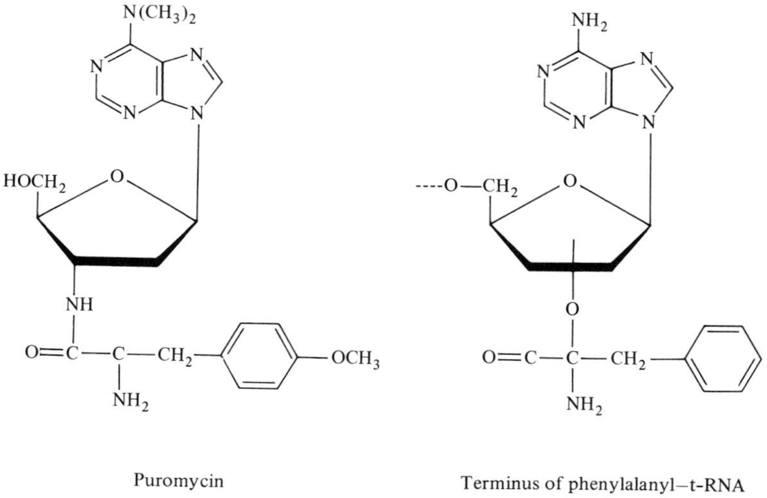

Puromycin

Terminus of phenylalanyl–t-RNA

fig. 6-11. The structures of puromycin and the terminus of phenylalanyl-t-RNA for purposes of comparison.

[30] Fan, D., Higa, A., and Levinthal, C. *J. Mol. Biol.*, *8*, 210 (1964).
[31] Hartwell, L. H., and Magasanik, B. *J. Mol. Biol.*, *7*, 401 (1963); Nakada, D., and Magasanik, B. *J. Mol. Biol.*, *8*, 105 (1964).

acid portion of a puromycin is incorporated into the growing polypeptide chain by a peptide bond. When this occurs, the peptide chain is released from the ribosome even though it has not been completely formed; the puromycin molecule forms the carboxyl terminal of the partially synthesized polypeptide.

Streptomycin appears to interfere with protein synthesis by causing misreading of the genetic code. When amino acid incorporation is studied in vitro, in the presence of polyuridylic acid as template, the amino acid phenylalanine is incorporated into the trichloracetic acid insoluble material. Using ribosomes from streptomycin-sensitive cells, in the presence of streptomycin the amino acids isoleucine, serine, and leucine are incorporated into trichloracetic acid insoluble material instead of phenylalanine. The presence of streptomycin, then, results in a misreading of the genetic code. Apparently only the two pyrimidine bases are misread. The mechanism involves the attachment of streptomycin to the 30 *S* fragment of the ribosome.[32]

Viruses are self-replicating units which consist of (1) a DNA or RNA template that contains all the information needed for replication, and (2) a coat of protein of varying complexity depending upon the individual type of virus. Viruses do not have the machinery for the replication of their polynucleotides nor for the synthesis of their coat protein, and therefore viruses are not able to reproduce themselves independently of living cells (Fig. 6-12). Often a virus infection does not appreciably disrupt the

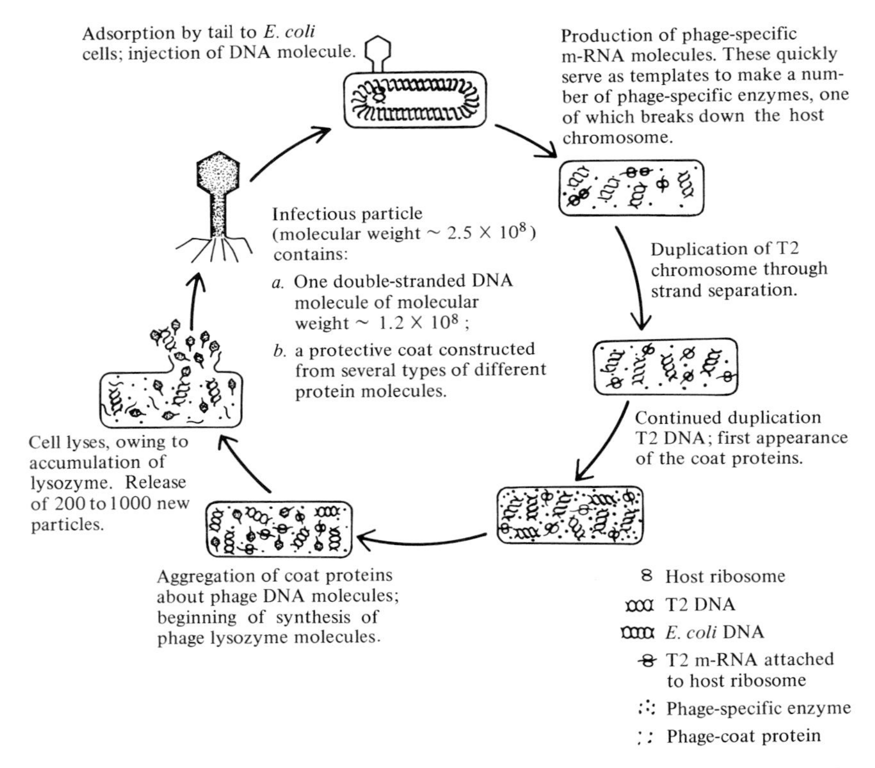

fig. 6-12. Life cycle of the DNA virus T_2 which infects *E. coli.* (From Watson, J. D. *Molecular Biology of the Gene.* New York: W. A. Benjamin, 1965, p. 352.)

[32] Gorini, L., and Kataja, E. *Proc. Natl. Acad. Sci.*, *51*, 487 (1964); Davies, J., Gilbert, W., and Gorini, L. *Proc. Natl. Acad. Sci.*, *51*, 883 (1964); Davies, J., Jones, D. S., and Khorana, H. G. *J. Mol. Biol.*, *18*, 48 (1966).

replication of the DNA nor the protein synthesis of the host cell. The viral DNA is replicated along with the DNA of the host cell. Viruses which do not interfere with the viability of the host cell, but exist in a sort of symbiotic relationship in it, are known as *temperate viruses*. On the other hand, infection with a virus frequently results in immediate cessation of the synthesis of proteins directed by the host-cell DNA and necessary for the host cell's viability.[33] The latter viruses are called *virulent*. Thus, infection of *E. coli* by T-even types of bacteriophage results in prompt cessation of the synthesis of the respiratory enzymes of the host cell,[34] and there is no subsequent net increase in RNA.[35] Cessation of synthesis of the host-cell proteins is followed by the synthesis of proteins directed by the genetic material of the virus.

Let us set out the sequence of events following infection by a virulent virus in somewhat more detail. T-even bacteriophage contains a small amount of the enzyme lysozyme which is liberated when the phage particle attaches itself to the bacterium.[36] The lysozyme digests a small part of the cell wall and causes a transient increase in cellular permeability, with leakage of some intracellular contents. In extreme instances when each host cell is infected by many virus particles simultaneously, the digestion of the cell wall may be so extensive that lysis of the host cell takes place. The synthesis of host DNA, m-RNA, r-RNA, and t-RNA ceases in infected cells.[37] While the synthesis of almost all indigenous bacterial proteins virtually ceases shortly after phage infection because there is no further synthesis of bacterial m-RNA, the production of certain proteins continues as long as functioning bacterial m-RNA remains. The mechanism of the abrupt cessation of bacterial m-RNA synthesis is not known, but a clue may lie in the abnormal leucine t-RNA found by Sueoka and Kano-Sueoka.[38] Such an abnormal t-RNA might act as a barricade to further translation and indirectly stop further m-RNA synthesis. An increased level of DNAse is found after viral infection, which results in increased bacterial DNA destruction. Viral DNA, however, is not affected, presumably because viral DNA contains methylated bases or glycosylated bases which render it resistant to hydrolysis by DNAse.

The ability to synthesize inducible enzymes such as β-galactosidase is lost very soon after viral infection.[39] RNA synthesized immediately after infection cannot form intermolecular hybrids with host-cell DNA. Although the synthesis of host-cell DNA and m-RNA ceases almost immediately after infection, there is no detectable destruction of host DNA until 10 minutes after infection.[40] This degradation of host DNA can be prevented by incubation with chloromycetin in concentrations just sufficient to block protein synthesis. In the case of phage-infected bacteria inhibited by chloromycetin, the functional integrity of the DNA 30 minutes or more after infection was demonstrated by conjugation experiments in which the DNA from the infected cells was introduced into phage-resistant F^-, lac^- cells. The recipient merozygotes could be induced for β-galactosidase. Destruction of host DNA, therefore, cannot account for the prompt cessation of DNA and m-RNA synthesis. Rather, it appears that the protein component of the phage particle may itself be responsible, or the prompt

[33] Levin, A. P., and Burton, K. *J. Gen. Microbiol.*, *25*, 307 (1961).
[34] Cohen, S. S., and Anderson, T. F. *J. Exptl. Med.*, *84*, 511 (1946).
[35] Cohen, S. S. *J. Biol. Chem.*, *174*, 281 (1948).
[36] Weidel, W., and Primosigh, J. *Z. Naturforsch.*, *12 B*, 421 (1957).
[37] Cohen, S. S. *Cold Spring Harbor Symp. Quant. Biol.*, *12*, 35 (1947); Brenner, S., Jacob, F., and Meselson, M. *Nature*, *190*, 576 (1961); Hall, B. D., and Spiegelman, S. *Proc. Natl. Acad. Sci.*, *47*, 137 (1961).
[38] Sueoka, N., and Kano-Sueoka, T. *Proc. Natl. Acad. Sci.*, *52*, 1535 (1964).
[39] Kaempfer, R. O. R., and Magasanik, B. *J. Mol. Biol.*, *27*, 453, 469, 475, 495 (1967).
[40] Okamoto, K., Sugino, Y., and Nomura, M. *J. Mol. Biol.*, *5*, 527, 535 (1962).

cessation of host-cell m-RNA synthesis may result from an alteration of the host-cell membrane as a result of viral attachment.

Shortly after phage infection the rate of total protein synthesis falls to about 70 percent of the preinfection value.[41] After a delay of a few minutes, a delay comparable to that for most inducible enzymes (see p. 327) between addition of inducer and first appearance of enzyme, a number of enzymes appear whose synthesis is directed by the genetic material of the virus itself. The following enzymes are found shortly after phage infection in bacteria: deoxycytidylate hydroxymethylase, which catalyzes the formation of deoxyhydroxymethylcytidilic acid (dHMC; the prefix "d" throughout indicates a deoxynucleotide);[42] a kinase, which catalyzes the formation of dHMC triphosphate;[43] a glucosyl transferase, which catalyzes the incorporation of glucose residues onto dHMC in intact DNA yielding glucosylated DNA;[43] deoxycytidine pyrophosphatase, which catalyzes the hydrolysis of dHMC triphosphate to dHMC and pyrophosphate;[43] deoxycytidilic deaminase, which catalyzes the conversion of dCMP to dUMP;[44] and thymidylate synthetase, which catalyzes the formation of thymidilic acid from dUMP.[42] These "early proteins" are essential for the development of virus progeny. By the twelfth minute after infection, about 60 percent of the protein being synthesized is phage protein.[45]

genetic regulation of enzyme synthesis in bacteria

The genetic material of the bacterial cells contains the information for synthesizing the very large number of enzymes which permits the bacterium to live in a wide range of environmental conditions. For example, the bacterium is capable of degrading a large variety of carbohydrates as sources of energy and as building blocks for its cellular structural components. Obviously, while the bacterium is capable of synthesing all the enzymes needed to degrade and metabolize all these sugars, it would not be economical for the cell to synthesize all enzymes all the time whether or not they are needed. Thus, bacteria growing in a medium containing glucose as the source of energy contain only trace amounts of β-galactosidase. When these organisms are transferred to a medium in which lactose is the energy source, appreciable quantities of β-galactosidase appear in these cells after a short time. In *E. coli* growing upon lactose as the sole energy source, β-galactosidase will represent about 3 percent of the intracellular protein. The thousandfold increase in β-galactosidase content upon transfer to a lactose-containing medium is the result of *de novo* synthesis and not the activation or modification of preexisting protein molecules. β-Galactosidase is antigenically distinct from all *preexisting* cell proteins,[46] and none of its sulfur nor carbon comes from preexisting protein.[47] Should these organisms be transferred instead to a medium containing histidine as the source of energy, the intracellular level of the series

[41] Hershey, A. D., Garen, A., Fraser, D. K., and Hudis, J. D. *Carnegie Inst. Wash. Year Book*, *53*, 210 (1954).
[42] Flaks, J. G., and Cohen, S. S. *J. Biol. Chem.*, *234*, 1501, 1507, 2981 (1959).
[43] Kornberg, A., Zimmerman, S. B., Kornberg, S. R., and Josse, J. *Proc. Natl. Acad. Sci.*, *45*, 772 (1959).
[44] Keck, K., Mahler, H. R., and Fraser, D. *Arch. Biochem. Biophys.*, *86*, 85 (1960).
[45] Watanabe, I. *Biochim. Biophys. Acta*, *25*, 665 (1957).
[46] Cohn, M., and Toriani, A. M. *J. Immunol.*, *69*, 471 (1952).
[47] Hogness, D. S., Cohn, M., and Monod, J. *Biochim. Biophys. Acta*, *16*, 99 (1955); Rotman, B., and Spiegelman, S. *J. Bacteriol.*, *68*, 419 (1954).

of enzymes required for the metabolism of histidine would rise from trace amounts to levels approximately 100 times greater.

It has been estimated that the chromosome of *E. coli* has encoded the information for some 2000 to 4000 different polypeptide chains. The exact number of different proteins present in a bacterium at a given time probably depends upon the environment, but a good estimate is that no more than 800 of the possible 2000 to 4000 proteins are present at any one time. The fact that certain enzymes are synthesized only in the presence of their specific substrates has been known since the turn of the century.[48] The phenomenon, first called *enzyme adaptation* by Karstrom,[49] is now known as *enzyme induction* (Fig. 6-13). Mutants of *E. coli* that have lost the ability to synthesize β-galactosidase cannot grow on lactose as the sole source of energy.

The synthesis of β-galactosidase by the bacterial cell can be induced not only by the presence of lactose in the medium but also by a large number of β-galactosides which contain an unsubstituted galactose moiety. The effectiveness of the substance as an inducer depends upon the nature of the group linked to the galactose; in general, the bulkier and more hydrophobic the group linked to the galactose, the more effective is the substance as an inducer of β-galactosidase. Substitution of sulfur for the oxygen in the galactosidic linkage gives a series of homologous compounds that are equally as effective as the oxygen compounds in inducing β-galactosidase formation but which cannot be hydrolyzed by the enzyme. Such artificial nonmetabolized inducers are extremely valuable in laboratory studies on the mechanism of induction. Only one species of β-galactosidase protein is synthesized in response to these various inducers.

While *E. coli* requires the presence of adequate amounts of β-galactosidase in order to grow in a medium containing lactose as the sole energy source, β-galactosidase alone is not sufficient. Another protein, *galactoside permease*, is required for the uptake of lactose by the bacterial cell. Galactoside permease is an inducible protein which is present only in trace amounts in the absence of lactose or a related galactoside but appears promptly in appreciable amounts after transfer of the bacteria to a medium containing lactose or a suitable inducer. The galactoside permease has not yet been isolated in pure form, although some success in partial purification has been achieved recently.[50] That the galactoside permease is a different protein than β-galactosidase is supported by studies of two classes of *E. coli* mutants. Mutants of the first class are able to accumulate and concentrate lactose within the cell but are unable to metabolize it for lack of β-galactosidase. Mutants of the other class, the so-called *cryptic* mutants, cannot accumulate lactose and do not grow in a lactose medium even though large amounts of intracellular β-galactosidase can be induced. A third protein appears to be involved in lactose metabolism, the enzyme *galactoside transacetylase*.[51] Like β-galactosidase and galactoside permease synthesis, galactoside transacetylase synthesis is induced by the presence of lactose or a related galactoside. The simultaneous induction of a group of related enzymes is a common phenomenon and is called *coordinate induction*.

It should be clearly stated that the phenomenon of induction is not an all-or-none affair but rather a graded response. Over an appreciable range of inducer concentrations, the rate of enzyme synthesis increases as the concentration of inducer increases,

[48] Duclaux, E. *Traité de Microbiologie*. Paris: Masson et Cie, 1899; Dienert, F. *Ann. Inst. Pasteur*, *14*, 139 (1900); Went, F. C. *Z. wiss. Botan.*, *36*, 611 (1901).
[49] Karstrom, H. *Ergeb. Enzymforsch.*, *7*, 350 (1938).
[50] Fox, C. F., and Kennedy, E. P. *Proc. Natl. Acad. Sci.*, *54*, 891 (1965).
[51] Zabin, I., Kepes, A., and Monod, J. *Biochem. Bipohys. Res. Commun.*, *1*, 289 (1959).

and vice versa. Thus, the cell is capable of responding to an intermediate need for an inducible enzyme by synthesizing that enzyme at a rate intermediate between the maximum and the minimum rates. In the case of enzyme systems that are induced coordinately, the graded response appears to be proportional for the various constituents of the system. While the rates of synthesis of the several enzymes in a system induced coordinately are proportional, the rates need not be identical. For instance, in the lactose system about 30 molecules of β-galactosidase are synthesized for each molecule of galactoside transacetylase.[52]

For a number of enzyme systems, the mechanism for controlling the rate of synthesis appears to operate in the opposite direction. The first system of this type, involving the enzymes required for tryptophane synthesis, was discovered in 1953.[53] The rate of synthesis of tryptophane synthetase was found to be markedly *diminished* when tryptophane itself was added to the incubation medium. This type of enzyme adaptation is called *repression*, and the low-molecular-weight compounds which mediate the regulation are called *repressors* (Fig. 6-13). The arginine system is a well-studied

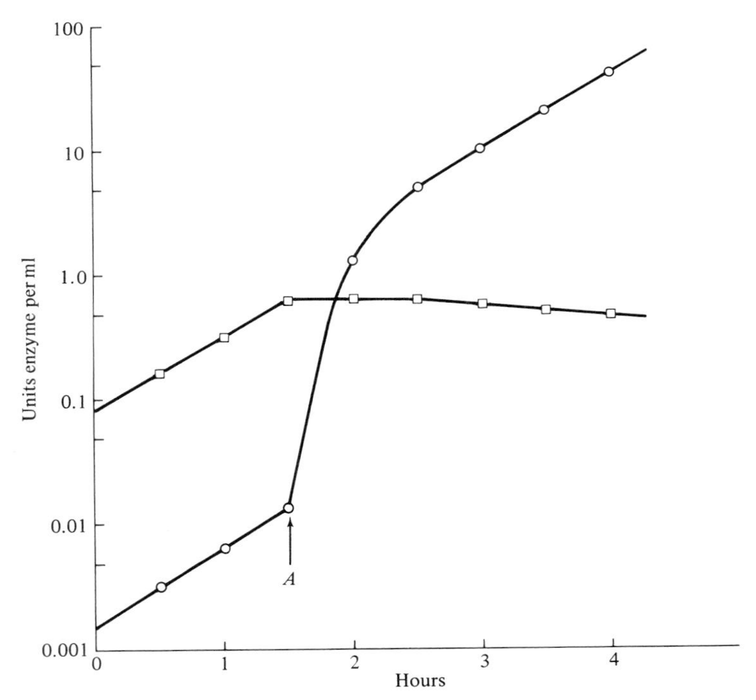

fig. 6-13. β-Galactosidase (O--- O) and arginase (□---□) activities in exponentially growing cultures of *E. coli*. The addition of *iso*-propyl-β-thiogalactoside at time *A* was followed by the *induction* of β-galactosidase, as shown by the very rapid rise in enzyme activity. A new high steady-state level of β-galactosidase per cell is reached followed by increments which reflect growth of the culture. The addition of arginine to a culture at time *A* results in *repression* of arginase activity, as shown by the leveling off of arginase activity in the culture even though the number of cells is increasing. Note the exponential scale of enzyme activity.

[52] Zabin, I. *Cold Spring Harbor Symp. Quant. Biol.*, *28*, 431 (1963).
[53] Monod, J., and Cohen-Bazire, G. *Compt. Rend.*, *236*, 530 (1953).

repressible system[54] consisting of the seven enzymes required for arginine biosynthesis. Studies in mutants of *E. coli* in which the synthesis of one of these enzymes is absent have demonstrated that the synthesis of the other six enzymes is repressed to the same extent as the wild type by the addition of arginine to the medium. Furthermore, while the arginine analog canavanine will also repress all the enzymes of the arginine system, various intermediates including ornithine and citrulline are not effective repressors. The important conclusion can be drawn from these studies that repression does not result from the accumulation of substrate or of a metabolic intermediate but only from the presence of appreciable quantities of the end product of the biosynthetic pathway.

Many inducible and repressible enzyme systems have been studied in addition to the examples given above. Other well-studied inducible systems include the galactose system,[55] the arabinose system,[56] and the histidase (catabolic) system.[57] The utilization of galactose, for instance, requires three enzymes: galactokinase, galactose transferase, and galactose epimerase. These three enzymes are induced coordinately in the presence of galactose or by gratuitous inducers such as fucose. Similarly, when *E. coli* is grown with the sugar arabinose as the sole energy and carbon source, the four enzymes required for its utilization are induced L-arabinose isomerase, L-ribulokinase, L-ribulose-5-phosphate-4-epimerase, and arabinose permease. The first three enzymes are closely linked genetically, but the last is located at a distant site on the bacterial chromosome. The utilization of histidine requires four enzymes: histidase, urocanase, and N-formiminoglutamate hydrolase. The third enzyme in the series, which catalyzes the conversion of 4-imidazolone-5-propionate to N-formiminoglutamate, has not yet been characterized. The first two enzymes, histidase and urocanase, are induced coordinately by histidine, urocanic acid, and the gratuitous inducer, imidazole-propionate. The last enzyme of the sequence, N-formiminoglutamate hydrolase, is also induced by these substances, but it is induced independently of the first two enzymes in the sequence.

Other well-studied repressible enzyme systems include the biosynthetic system leading to histidine[58] and the biosynthetic system leading to pyrimidine formation.[59] Histidine is formed by a sequence of ten reactions from phosphoribosylpyrophosphate, the starting material. The ten enzymes that catalyze these reactions are clustered in a single region of the bacterial chromosome, and they are all repressed by histidine. At least four of the enzymes have been studied quantitatively and show coordinate repression. The six enzymes involved in the synthesis of pyrimidines are repressed by uracil. Four of the enzymes, three of which arise from adjacent sites on the bacterial chromosome, are repressed in coordinate fashion. While the other two enzymes show repression, the amount of repression is not proportional to the other enzymes for intermediate concentrations of repressor.

It should be stressed that repression is a control mechanism which mediates the

[54] Vogel, H. J. *Cold Spring Harbor Symp. Quant. Biol., 26,* 163 (1961); Maas, W. K. *Cold Spring Harbor Symp. Quant. Biol., 26,* 183 (1961).
[55] Kalckar, H. M., Kurahashi, K., and Jordan, E. *Proc. Natl. Acad. Sci., 45,* 1776 (1959); Yarmolinsky, M. B., Jordan, E., and Wiesmeyer, H. *Cold Spring Harbor Symp. Quant. Biol., 26,* 217 (1961).
[56] Lee, N., and Englesberg, E. *Proc. Natl. Acad. Sci., 48,* 335 (1962); *50,* 696 (1963).
[57] Hartwell, L. H., and Magasanik, B. *J. Mol. Biol., 10,* 105 (1964); Magasanik, B., Lund, P., Neidhardt, F. C., and Schwartz, D. T. *J. Biol. Chem., 240,* 4320 (1965); Schlesinger, S., and Magasanik, B. *J. Biol. Chem., 240,* 4325, 4331 (1965).
[58] Ames, B. N., and Gary, B. *Proc. Natl. Acad. Sci., 45,* 1453 (1959); Ames, B. N., and Hartman, P. E. *Cold Spring Harbor Symp. Quant. Biol., 28,* 349 (1963).
[59] Yates, R. A., and Pardee, A. B. *J. Biol. Chem., 221,* 757 (1956); Taylor, A. L., Beckwith, J. R., Pardee, A. B., Austrian, R., and Jacob, F. *J. Mol. Biol., 8,* 771 (1964).

amount of enzyme *synthesized* and not enzyme activity. Therefore, repression is a control mechanism quite distinct from the end-product inhibition described earlier. Both induction and repression are highly specific processes responding to a few homologous compounds. In general, induction involves enzyme sequences in catabolic pathways, while repression involves enzyme sequences in anabolic (or synthetic) pathways. Inducers usually are substrates which are degraded by the cell, while repressors usually are the products of a metabolic sequence. Enzymes in a metabolic pathway may or may not be induced or repressed coordinately.

In addition to the specific repression of enzyme synthesis described above, the synthesis of many inducible enzymes in bacteria responds to a relatively nonspecific repression mechanism which appears to be mediated by the catabolic products of the compounds used as sources of energy (Fig. 6-14). This phenomenon is called appropriately *catabolite repression*.[60] For example, if *A. aerogenes* is grown in a medium containing succinate or glycerol as the energy source and an ammonium salt as the source of nitrogen, the addition of histidine to the medium will be promptly followed by the induction of the histidase sequence of enzymes. If glucose is added to the

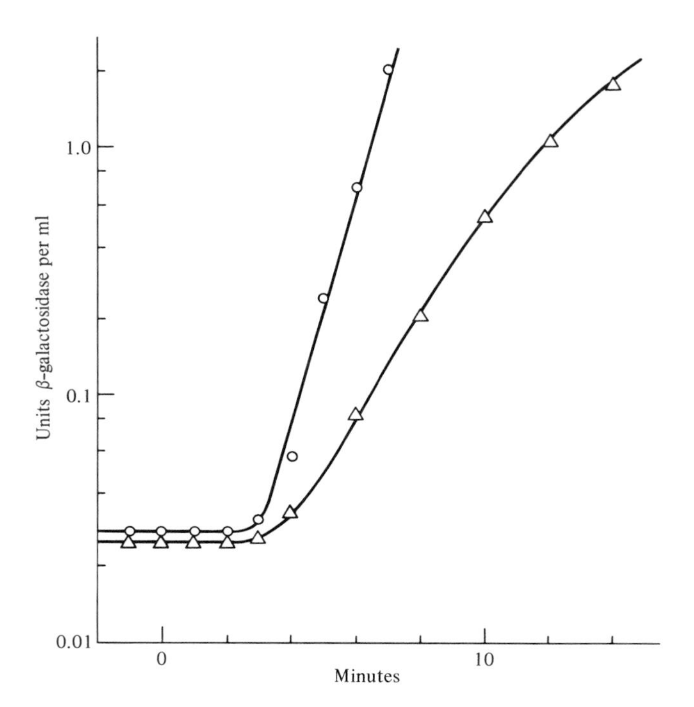

fig. 6-14. β-Galactosidase activity in exponentially growing culture of *E. coli* in minimal medium containing either glycerol (O--- O) or glucose (△---△) as the sole carbon source. A gratuitous inducer, *iso*-propyl-β-thiogalactoside, was added at time zero. After a lag of about 3 minutes, β-galactosidase appeared in rapidly increasing amounts. The rate of enzyme synthesis was greater in the glycerol-grown cells than in the glucose-grown cells even though the rate of growth was less in glycerol than in glucose.

[60] Magasanik, B. *Cold Spring Harbor Symp. Quant. Biol.*, *26*, 249 (1961).

succinate or glycerol, the subsequent addition of histidine fails to induce the histidase enzymes. Similarly, galactose fails to induce the formation of β-galactosidase in the presence of glucose. Gratuitous inducers, such as *iso*-propylthio-β-galactoside, will induce β-galactoside synthesis in the presence of glucose, but very much higher concentrations of inducer are required in its presence than in its absence. While most enzymes which respond by diminished rates of formation in the presence of glucose are inducible enzymes, not all inducible enzymes show catabolite repression. Penicillinase, nitrate reductase, and most amino acid decarboxylases are inducible enzymes which do not demonstrate catabolite repression. A common feature of enzymes whose synthesis is repressed in the presence of glucose is that they catalyze reactions which lead to products which are more readily and more rapidly formed from glucose. Probably glucose is a much more effective carbon source than other substances because it can be metabolized via the alternative pentose-shunt pathways leading to intermediates which serve as starting points for the biosynthesis of many substances required by the cell. When the supply of nitrogen-containing or sulfur-containing compounds is so small that growth is limited, the repressive effect of glucose is intensified. Under conditions where the availability of nitrogen or sulfur is growth-limiting, other energy sources, for instance glycerol, also lead to catabolite repression. Undoubtedly, catabolite repression is caused by specific compounds which are products of glucose metabolism, but at the present time these compounds have not been identified.

the operator theory of genetic regulation

In 1961, Jacob and Monod[61] put forward a theory concerning the mechanism that is involved in the genetic regulation of protein synthesis. According to their theory, the regulation of the synthesis of specific enzymes, that is, the regulation of the relative amount of synthesis of a given enzyme in terms of the total quantity of protein being synthesized, takes place largely at the level of transcription by changes in the amount of m-RNA formed. Specific m-RNA which acts as a template for the synthesis of particular proteins is formed by the replication of structural genes in the chromosome. A central feature of Jacob and Monod's model is the notion that the synthesis of m-RNA is unidirectional and that it can start only at particular sites on the strands of DNA. They use the term *operators* for these sites. Operators determine not only where the synthesis begins but also whether or not transcription occurs; they thereby regulate the synthesis of specific m-RNAs. Genetic mapping has shown that the structural genes for groups of enzymes that are coordinately induced or coordinately repressed are frequently located adjacent to one another on the chromosome. The model explains coordinate induction and coordinate repression by assuming that the transcription of the structural genes coding for such a group of enzymes is controlled by a single operator; this operator-controlled unit for transcription is termed an *operon* (Fig. 6-15). Thus, the lactose operon consists of an *operator* (o) *gene* and three structural genes coding for the coordinately inducible enzymes β-galactosidase (z gene), galactoside permease (y gene), and galactoside transacetylase (x gene). Quantitative evaluation of specific m-RNA formation by hybridization with specific DNA in the presence and

[61] Jacob, F., and Monod, J. *J. Mol. Biol.*, *3*, 318 (1961).

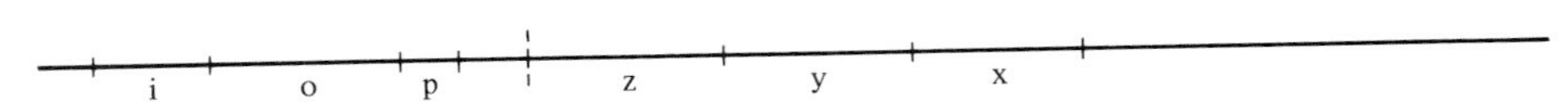

fig. 6-15. Schematic diagram of the *lac* operon containing the structural genes z for β-galactosidase, y for galactoside permease, x for transacetylase; and the operator site o, the regulator gene i, and the promoter p. It is not clear whether the promoter is a separate gene site or part of the structural gene z.

absence of inducer indicates that induction is accompanied by an increased formation of specific m-RNA.[62]

The operator model also postulates the existence of a specific *regulator* (i) *gene* which may be located at a site on the chromosome far distant from the location of the operator gene (or genes) with which it is associated. The regulator genes are thought to be responsible for the elaboration of repressor substances. In inducible systems, the repressor substance ordinarily acts on the operator gene, preventing the initiation of transcription of the structural genes. When an inducer is added, the inducer combines with the repressor elaborated by the regulatory gene to form a product which is not able to interact with the operator. The repression of the operon is lifted, and m-RNA synthesis takes place. A separate repressor gene site, different from the i-gene site, may be responsible for the effectiveness of catabolite repression.[63]

In repressible systems, the regulatory gene is supposed to elaborate a repressor precursor. The repressor precursor cannot interact with the operator gene, and the transcription of the structural genes takes place. When a repressor is added, the repressor combines with the repressor precursor elaborated by the regulatory gene to form an effective repressor substance. The latter interacts with the operator gene, blocking the initiation of transcription of the structural genes of the operon. The model supposes, then, that the exogenous inducer or repressor reacts with the repressor substance elaborated by the regulator gene. The interaction, or lack of interaction, of the repressor substance with the operator gene regulates the transcription of the structural genes and formation of the specific m-RNA. In this way, the rate of synthesis of the specific proteins is controlled.

At the present time the repressor substances are unknown, although efforts are under way to isolate them. In early experiments,[64] the regulator gene product appeared to be expressed under conditions where protein synthesis was inhibited. This led to the conjecture that the repressor substance was a ribonucleotide. Experiments with mutants in the regulator gene region have shown that the defect can be corrected by suppressor mutations;[65] this observation has led to the belief that the repressor substance is a protein. A protein has been isolated from wild-type bacteria which is not produced by organisms with a deletion in the chromosome at the site of the regulator gene.[66] Gilbert and Müller-Hill isolated a material from a "superinducible" mutant of *E. coli* which binds *iso*-propylthio-β-galactoside ($K_b \sim 1.2 \times 10^{-6}$), which is resistant to attack by DNAse or RNAse, but is degraded by pronase (a proteolytic enzyme). The presumed repressor material sediments at 7 to 8 *S* and has an approximate molecular weight of 150,000 to 200,000.

[62] Attardi, G., Naono, S., Rouviere, J., Jacob. F., and Gros, F. *Cold Spring Harbor Symp. Quant. Biol.*, *28*, 363 (1963).
[63] Loomis, W. F., Jr., and Magasanik, B. *J. Mol. Biol.*, *23*, 487 (1967).
[64] Pardee, A. B., and Prestidge, L. S. *Biochim. Biophys. Acta*, *36*, 545 (1959).
[65] Garen, A., and Garen, S. *J. Mol. Biol.*, *6*, 433 (1963).
[66] Garen, A., and Otsuji, N. *J. Mol. Biol.*, *8*, 841 (1964); Gilbert, W., and Müller-Hill, B. *Proc. Natl. Acad. Sci.*, *56*, 1891 (1966).

Classes of bacterial mutants have been described in which the regulatory mechanisms which control the rate of enzyme synthesis are awry. For example, such *constitutive mutants* of the lactose operon synthesize β-galactosidase, galactoside permease, and galactoside transacetylase at the maximal rate in the absence of an inducer. The enzymes which are formed appear to be identical to the proteins produced by inducible wild-type bacteria. Constitutive mutants may be of two types: those in which the mutation is at the operator gene, rendering it unresponsive to the repressor substance; and those with a mutation of the regulator gene, resulting in failure to elaborate an effective repressor substance. Although both types of mutants should be phenotypically similar, it is possible to distinguish the two types in several ways. For instance, genetic mapping experiments show that the defects in one group of constitutive β-galactosidase mutants are clustered at one end of the lactose operon, while the defects of other β-galactosidase constitutive mutants map at sites distant from the lactose operon. The former group are judged to be operator gene mutants, while the latter group are judged to be regulatory gene mutants. It is also possible to distinguish operator-gene and regulator-gene constitutive mutants by means of mating experiments. Merozygotes containing two strands of DNA will continue to show a constitutive phenotype if the defect is in the operator gene of one strand. On the other hand, if one strand contains a defective regulator gene, the normal regulator gene on the other strand will lead to the formation of sufficient repressor substance to overcome constitutivity. Thus, constitutive mutants in the operator region might be expected to show dominant expression of the phenotype, while mutants in the regulator gene might be expected to show recessive expression of the phenotype. Indeed, it has been possible to distinguish between two such types of constitutive mutants.[67]

Recent evidence suggests that the transcription of m-RNA begins not at the operator but at a specialized site on the DNA at or near the site at the beginning of the region where specification of the first polypeptide begins—the z gene in the case of the *lac* operon. This site is called the *promoter*.[68] In deletion mutations of the proximal portion of the z gene, the y and x genes are not expressed. If the deletion is so large that the y and x genes are connected to another functioning operon, then the y and x genes are expressed. In addition to initiating transcription, the promoter site appears to determine the maximum rate at which m-RNA can be formed.[69]

regulation of RNA synthesis in bacteria

The genetic regulatory system described above is a mechanism of prime importance in enabling the bacterium to survive and grow economically in a variety of environmental conditions. It permits the bacterium to synthesize many enzymes only when the enzymes are required. While this system serves to control the proportions of various enzymes synthesized by the cell, it does not control total protein synthesis to any appreciable degree. The overall rate of protein synthesis appears to be regulated by means of a mechanism which involves the regulation of RNA synthesis. The fraction of the total cellular synthetic processes occupied by r-RNA synthesis is determined by the overall nutritive, growth-supporting ability of the medium during balanced growth. The rate of r-RNA synthesis appears to be so regulated for a very

[67] Jacob, F., and Adelberg, E. A. *Compt. Rend.*, *249*, 189 (1959).
[68] Jacob, F., Ullman, A., and Monod, J. *Compt. Rend.*, *258*, 3125 (1964).
[69] Scaife, J., and Beckwith, J. R. *Cold Spring Harbor Symp. Quant. Biol.*, *31*, 403 (1966).

wide range of growth rates that only the number of ribosomes required are produced, and those ribosomes which are present in the cell function at this maximal rate in synthesizing protein.

The above phenomenon has been demonstrated by many careful studies. For instance, Kjeldgaard and Kurland[70] measured the total RNA, r-RNA, and t-RNA content of *S. typhimurium* at different rates of growth (Fig. 6-16). The DNA content

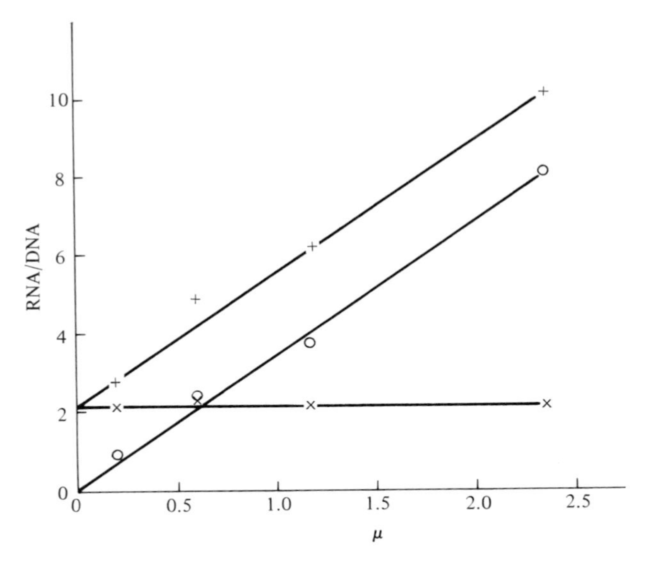

fig. 6-16. Ratios of total RNA (+), r-RNA (O), and t-RNA (X) as a function of growth rate (μ) in *S. typhimurium.* (From Kjeldgaard, N. O., and Kurland, C. G. *J. Mol. Biol., 6,* 346 [1963]. Copyright Academic Press; reprinted by permission.)

per cell was constant, as was the content of t-RNA. The content of total RNA and of r-RNA (expressed as the ratio RNA/DNA) increased linearly with the growth rate. The RNA content appeared to be determined only by the growth rate and not by the nature of the carbon source, nitrogen source, energy source, nor by the presence of growth-promoting factors such as amino acids, vitamins, or nucleic acids which determine the growth rate. In two different media that sustain the same rate of growth, the RNA content will be the same.

When a bacterial culture is shifted to a richer medium that sustains a higher rate of growth, the rate of synthesis of r-RNA and ribosomal structural protein increases almost immediately[71] (Fig. 6-17). After a lag of about 20 minutes, DNA synthesis and total protein synthesis increase to the new rate. Contrariwise, when a bacterial culture is shifted to a poorer medium in which the growth rate is slower, the rate of synthesis of r-RNA decreases almost immediately (Fig. 6-18), and the rates of DNA synthesis and total protein synthesis decrease gradually to the new lower steady-state rates. In both cases, throughout the period of adjustment as well as during balanced growth before and after the change of medium, the rate of total protein synthesis per unit mass of ribosomes is constant.

---

[70] Kjeldgaard, N. O., and Kurland, C. G. *J. Mol. Biol.*, *6*, 341 (1963).

[71] Kjeldgaard, N. O., Maaløe, O., and Schaechter, M. *J. Gen. Microbiol.*, *19*, 607 (1958); Neidhardt, F. C., and Magasanik, B. *Biochim. Biophys. Acta*, *42*, 99 (1960); Kjeldgaard, N. O., *Biochim. Biophys. Acta*, *49*, 64 (1961).

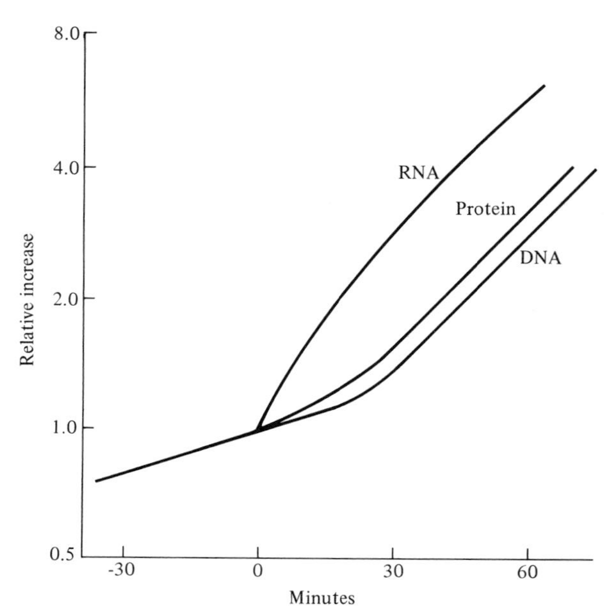

fig. 6-17. Synthesis of DNA, RNA, and protein in a bacterial culture shifted to a richer medium at zero time. The curves are idealized and the content of each component is normalized to 1.0 at zero time. (From Neidhardt, F. C. *Progr. Nucleic Acid Res., 3,* 151 [1964]. Copyright Academic Press; reprinted by permission.)

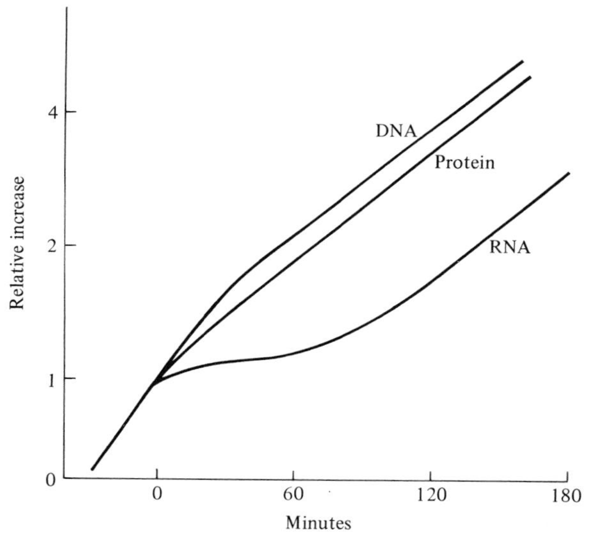

fig. 6-18. Synthesis of DNA, RNA, and protein in a bacterial culture shifted from a rich medium in which there is little or no catabolite repression to a poorer medium at zero time. The curves are idealized and the content of each component is normalized to 1.0 at zero time. (From Neidhardt, F. C. *Progr. Nucleic Acid Res., 3,* 153 [1964]. Copyright Academic Press; reprinted by permission.)

The mechanism of control which gives rise to these phenomena is not known, but it appears to function at the level of the enzymes concerned with r-RNA synthesis.[72] However, there does not appear to be any significant change in the concentrations of the enzymes involved. Rather, the intracellular levels of amino acids may mediate the regulation. When amino acid auxotrophs, mutants which are unable to synthesize an amino acid, are deprived of the required amino acid, r-RNA synthesis promptly ceases.[73] The synthesis of r-RNA is also halted abruptly by adding certain amino acid analogs to wild-type cells growing in minimal medium.[74] In these instances, the cessation of r-RNA synthesis is accompanied by a cessation in protein synthesis. On the other hand, a number of inhibitors of protein synthesis such as chloramphenicol and potassium deprivation, which act at a late stage of protein synthesis (that is, after the formation of amino-acyl-t-RNAs), block protein synthesis while permitting r-RNA synthesis to continue.[75] Furthermore, when chloramphenicol is added to amino-acid–starved cells, the inhibitory effect of amino acid starvation upon r-RNA synthesis is counteracted, and RNA synthesis resumes.

It has been suggested that uncharged t-RNAs repress RNA synthesis and that amino acids lift this repression by forming amino-acyl-t-RNAs[76] which are not able to act as repressors. In a rich medium, the t-RNA would tend to be almost fully charged with amino acids, and r-RNA synthesis would be fully depressed. Contrariwise, in a poor medium, there would be a substantial fraction of t-RNA in the uncharged form, and r-RNA synthesis would be substantially repressed. Because the absence of only one of the twenty amino acids is sufficient to cause a cessation of r-RNA synthesis in an auxotroph, it may be judged that full repression can be obtained with about 5 percent uncharged t-RNA. When the repression is lifted by chloramphenicol, the rate of r-RNA synthesis is about the same as it is in bacteria in a very rich medium.

RNA metabolism in mammalian cells

The foregoing discussion of RNA synthesis and its regulation summarizes the situation as it is now surmised to exist in bacteria, which are akaryotic organisms. The development of a nucleus and of diploid chromosomes has introduced a new order of complexity into the genetically controlled synthetic systems. Most of our knowledge about RNA metabolism in eukaryotic cells comes from studies of mammalian cells in tissue cultures. It is clear that the nucleolus is the major site of RNA synthesis.

Before examining what is known about the formation of r-RNA in mammalian cells, it should be pointed out that the ribosomes in mammalian cells resemble ribosomes in bacteria. Like bacterial ribosomes, mammalian ribosomes are composed of two subunits, a heavy one and a light one. The RNA component of the light subunits sediments at 16 *S* and appears to be indistinguishable from the RNA in the lighter

[72] Stent, G. S., and Brenner, S. *Proc. Natl. Acad. Sci.*, *47*, 2005 (1961); Morris, D. W., and DeMoss, J. A. *Proc. Natl. Acad. Sci.*, *56*, 262 (1966).
[73] Pardee, A. B., and Prestidge, L. S. *J. Bacteriol.*, *71*, 677 (1956); Schaechter, M. *Cold Spring Harbor Symp. Quant. Biol.*, *26*, 53 (1961).
[74] Gros, F., and Gros, F. *Exptl. Cell Res.*, *14*, 104 (1958); Fangman, W. L., and Neidhardt, F. C. *J. Biol. Chem.*, *239*, 1844 (1964).
[75] Aronson, A. I., and Spiegelman, S. *Biochim. Biophys. Acta*, *53*, 70 (1961); Kurland, C. G., and Maaløe, O. *J. Mol. Biol.*, *4*, 193 (1962).
[76] Stent, G. S., and Brenner, S. *Proc. Natl. Acad. Sci.*, *47*, 2005 (1961).

subunit of bacterial ribosomes. However, the heavy subunit of mammalian ribosomes contains two species of RNA, a 28 *S* RNA which corresponds to the 23 *S* RNA of bacterial ribosomes but has a molecular weight about 50 percent greater, and a unique species of RNA which sediments at 5 *S*.

It has long been known that almost all the nuclear RNA is contained within the nucleolus. Furthermore, the base composition of nucleolar RNA resembles that of r-RNA.[77] If cells are exposed for a short period of time to a radioactive precursor of RNA such as uracil, the radioactivity appears promptly in RNA, mainly in the nucleolus but also in the karyolymph. Treatment of cells with low levels of actinomycin results in inhibition of r-RNA synthesis. When the labeling experiment is repeated in actinomycin-treated cells, RNA in the karyolymph is labeled as before, but little radioactivity is found in the nucleolus.[78] Sequential analyses of RNA in nuclei after a very brief exposure to radioactive uracil indicates that the first material formed in the nucleolus is an RNA species with a sedimentation constant of 45 *S*.[79] The 45 *S* RNA appears to be cleaved quickly into 16 *S* and 32 *S* fragments[80] (Fig. 6-19). The 16 *S*

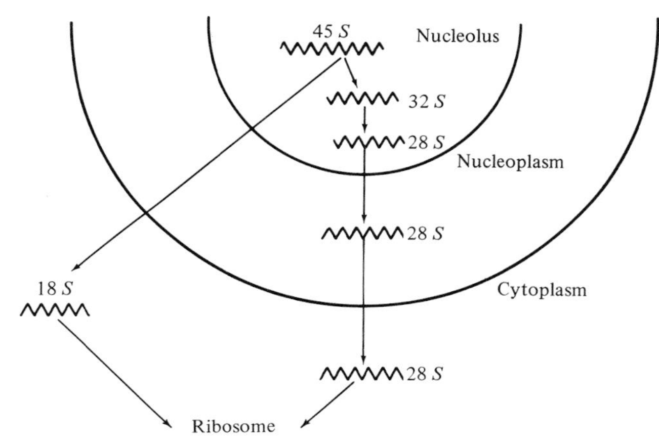

fig. 6-19. Schematic diagram of the evolution of mammalian r-RNA. (From Penman, S. *New Eng. J. Med.*, *276*, 506 [1967].)

RNA fragment finds its way into the cytoplasm rather rapidly and becomes an integral part of a ribosome.

The 32 *S* fragment is further cleaved in the nucleus, forming the 28 *S* fragment and smaller fragments of RNA. The 28 *S* fragment eventually makes its way into the cytoplasm and becomes an integral part of a ribosome. Both the 16 *S* and 28 *S* fragments have their origin in the same 45 *S* particle. However, the 16 *S* fragment makes its way into the cytoplasm rather rapidly while it takes 3 to 5 times longer for the 28 *S* fragment to reach the cytoplasm. Yet no free 16 *S* and 28 *S* fragments (that are not part of intact ribosomes) are found in the cytoplasm. The stoichiometry of the process is not understood at all, although it is known that the rates of 16 *S* production relative to 28 *S* production can be altered by various agents that interfere with RNA

[77] Edstrom, J., Grampp, W., and Schor, N. *J. Biophys. Biochem. Cytol.*, *11*, 549 (1961).
[78] Perry, R. P., Srinivasan, P. R., and Kelly, D. E. *Science*, *145*, 504 (1964).
[79] Attardi, G., Parnas, H., Hwang, M. I. H., and Attardi, B. *J. Mol. Biol.*, *20*, 145 (1966).
[80] Holtzman, E., Smith, I., and Penman, S. *J. Mol. Biol.*, *17*, 131 (1966); Greenberg, H., and Penman, S. *J. Mol. Biol.*, *21*, 527 (1966).

metabolism. The 16 *S* and 28 *S* subunits of RNA appear to enter the cytoplasm in the form of ribosomal subunits with ribosomal protein already bound. The subunits, however, may not be mature, since a lag is observed before they appear in polyribosomes actively engaged in protein synthesis. The process of maturation may involve modification of the ribosomal protein after the subunits are in the cytoplasm.[81] Very few mature ribosomes are associated with nuclei.

In the process of formation, all the methylated nucleotides present in the nuclear 45 *S* ribosomal RNA precursor are conserved and can be accounted for in the 16 *S* and 28 *S* fragments. However, a considerable quantity of the RNA in the 45 *S* precursor is lost during maturation; and its fate is unknown. The origin of the 5 *S* fragment of RNA also is not known.

Protein synthesis in mammalian cells, like that in microorganisms, occurs under the hierarchical direction of the genetic mechanism; thus the information encoded in the DNA is transcribed onto a specialized messenger RNA, which in turn carries the information to the ribosomal protein-synthesizing system. Unlike bacterial m-RNA (which has a half-life of several minutes), mammalian m-RNA is long lived.[82] There appears to be a wide range of stability of mammalian m-RNA; but even the most short-lived species in the most rapidly growing cells is orders of magnitude more persistent than bacterial m-RNA, and the more long-lived species may have stabilities comparable to that of r-RNA. It is not surprising, therefore, that it has been difficult to demonstrate induced enzyme formation in mammalian systems. What sometimes has been regarded as enzyme induction in mammalian systems appears to be substrate stabilization of labile enzymes against degradation. There is also reason to believe that regulation at the level of translation may be very important in the cells of higher organisms.

protein turnover

The foregoing discussion of genetic control of protein synthesis was developed largely from observations in bacteria. The principles that describe the observations in bacterial systems do not carry over exactly to the cells of complex organisms. Before considering the regulation of enzyme synthesis in cells of complex organisms, it is necessary to consider the phenomenon of *protein turnover*. Protein turnover implies protein degradation as well as synthesis, and the attentive reader will have observed that no mention has been made of protein degradation in bacteria. Protein degradation occupies a secondary role in bacterial metabolism, particularly in actively growing cultures. By and large, the protein composition of actively growing bacteria is determined by the synthetic processes. When a protein is no longer needed in the cellular economy, its synthesis ceases by cessation of induction or by repression. What protein is present in the cell is divided between the daughter cells upon the first cell division and diluted out further with subsequent cell divisions. Thus, if *E. coli* are grown for a short time in a medium containing a gratuitous inducer for β-galactosidase and then transferred to an inducer-free medium, further synthesis of β-galactosidase ceases in a few minutes. The total β-galactosidase present in the culture does not change as long

---

[81] Girard, M., Latham, H., Penman, S., and Darnell, J. E. *J. Mol. Biol.*, *11*, 187 (1965); Perry, R. P., and Kelly, D. E. *Biochem. Biophys. Res. Commun.*, *24*, 459 (1966).
[82] DiGirolamo, A., Henshaw, E. C., and Hiatt, H. H. *J. Mol. Biol.*, *8*, 479 (1964).

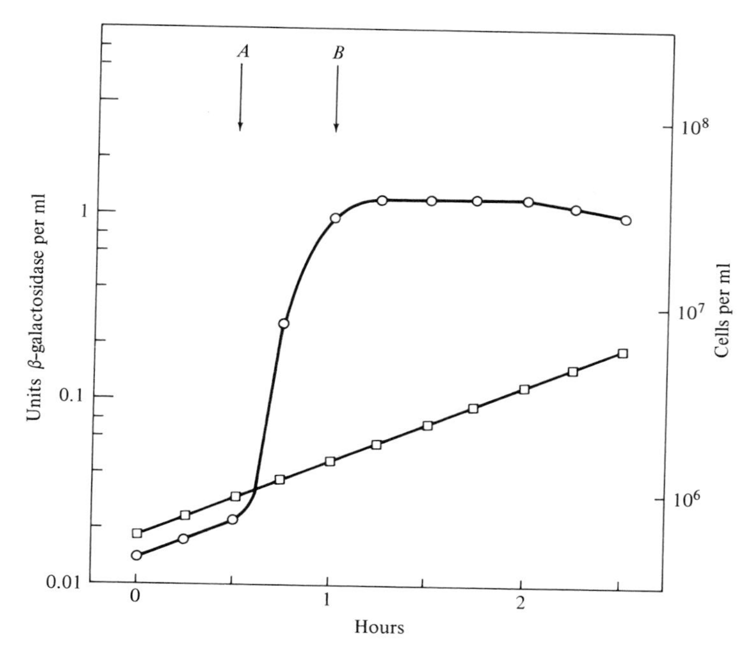

fig. 6-20. β-Galactosidase (O--- O) content of a culture of *E. coli* growing in minimal medium containing glycerol. At time *A*, a gratuitous inducer, *iso*-propyl-β-thiogalactoside, was added to the culture, resulting in prompt induction of β-galactosidase. The inducer was removed at time *B*. Although the number of cells (□---□) continued to increase exponentially, there was essentially no synthesis nor degradation of enzyme.

as it is growing actively, but the amount of β-galactosidase per cell is halved with each doubling of the culture (Fig. 6-20).

Bacteria are able, in fact, to degrade intracellular proteins. For instance, it is possible to induce β-galactosidase in a nongrowing culture of *E. coli* suspended in a nitrogen-free medium. Clearly, the nitrogen contained in the newly synthesized enzyme must come from intracellular materials, and experiments in which the intracellular proteins were prelabeled with radioisotopes indicate that the nitrogen incorporated into the newly formed enzyme arises largely from preformed protein.[83] While the rate of protein turnover in actively growing bacteria is negligible, proteins are degraded and synthesized in nongrowing bacteria. The rate of protein turnover in stationary bacterial cells can be evaluated by allowing double amino acid auxotrophs requiring, for example, leucine and arginine, to grow in ^{14}C-leucine until the intracellular proteins are labeled. The bacteria are then incubated in a medium containing a large amount of unlabeled leucine, to trap the ^{14}C-leucine liberated from the intracellular proteins, but devoid of arginine so that growth cannot take place. Protein turnover can also be evaluated by ^{18}O exchange in peptide bonds. Protein turnover in *E. coli* incubated at 37° in a medium which does not sustain growth amounts to about 5 percent per hour (Fig. 6-21). Similarly, a protein turnover of approximately 0.75 percent per hour was found in nongrowing yeast, while in actively growing yeast cells, no degradation of protein was observed. Obviously, the ability of bacteria to catabolize dispensable

[83] Mandelstam, J. *Bacteriol. Rev.*, *24*, 289 (1960).

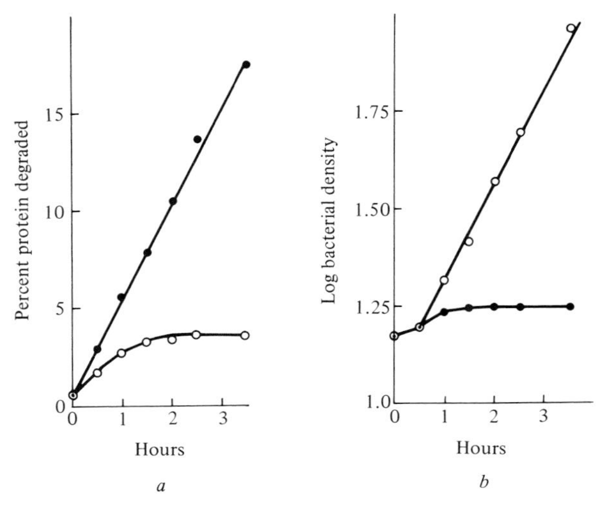

fig. 6-21. (*a*) Degradation of proteins in (O––– O) growing and (●–––●) nongrowing suspensions of *E. coli.* (*b*) Semilog plots of the bacterial density in the two suspensions. In the case of growing bacteria, most of the protein breakdown occurs in the lag before exponential growth is established. (From Mandelstam, J. *Bacteriol. Rev.*, *24*, 294 [1960].)

protein to provide building blocks for more essential protein in times of deprivation has great survival value.

One of the great adaptive advances of evolution that permitted the development of complex organisms was the segregation of reproductive function to a specialized group of cells. This permitted the bulk of cells in an organism to address themselves to other functions with the certainty that the species would be propagated. In contrast to microorganisms, higher animals carry on a variety of useful activities during long periods of their lives when cellular division is relatively insignificant.[84] Many of the somatic cells of complex organisms have lifetimes comparable to that of the whole organism. Under ordinary circumstances, rat liver cells are thought to divide about once a year;[85] and in the absence of injury, muscle cells of a mature animal divide only rarely, if at all. Yet protein turnover, as judged from experiments with labeled amino acids, is an active process in the somatic cells of higher organisms. The half-life of rat liver protein, in vivo, has been estimated to range between 2 and 8 days,[86] and the half-lives of several proteins of rabbit muscle, a peripheral tissue, have been estimated to range between 20 and 80 days.[87] The unwanted constituents of somatic cells are not diluted away by cell division, and it appears that their protein complement is being continually degraded and resynthesized.

Protein turnover appears to be of two general types. The molecules of most species of proteins are degraded in a random fashion, and their kinetics of turnover resemble the kinetics of first-order reactions such as the decay of radioactive substances. After exposure to a pulse of radioactive precursor, there is a short period of equilibration,

[84] One of my colleagues is fond of telling his students, "Bacteria are really stupid creatures. All they do in life is reproduce. Even so, they mate only rarely, and their sex life is quite uninteresting."
[85] MacDonald, R. A. *Arch. Internal Med.*, *107*, 335 (1961).
[86] Schoenheimer, R., Ratner, S., and Rittenberg, D. *J. Biol. Chem.*, *130*, 703 (1939); Korner, A., and Tarver, H. *J. Gen. Physiol.*, *41*, 219 (1957).
[87] Velick, S. F. *Biochim. Biophys. Acta*, *20*, 228 (1956).

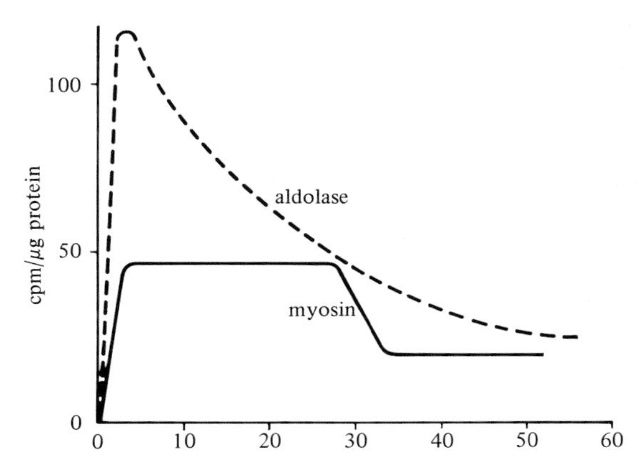

fig. 6-22. Specific radioactivity of rat muscle aldolase and myosin after the injection of ^{14}C-glycine at zero time. Aldolase shows a random turnover while myosin has a definite life time. (Drawn from the data of Dreyfus, J. C., Kruh, J., and Schapira, G. *Biochem. J., 75*, 576 [1960]; and Velick, S. F. *Biochim. Biophys. Acta, 20*, 228 [1956].)

followed by logarithmic decay of label as the protein is degraded (Fig. 6-22). On the other hand, a few species of protein appear to have a definite life span. The hemoglobin of the mammalian erythrocyte appears to have a life span of approximately 115 days,[88] and the structural proteins of the myofibril, rather than turning over randomly like the cytoplasmic proteins of muscle,[89] also appear to have a life span of defined length.

lysosomes and protein degradation

The lysosomes are a heterogeneous group of cytoplasmic organelles which contain the intracellular proteases (*cathepsins*) and other hydrolytic enzymes; the important lysosomal enzymes are listed in Fig. 6-23. The lysosomal enzymes are characterized by acid *p*H optima. They seem to be associated with the single unit membrane that forms the wall of the lysosomes or to be contained in the interior of the lysosomes. Separated in isotonic sucrose by the usual cell fractionation techniques, lysosomes are relatively

fig. 6-23. Enzymes found in lysosomes.

Acid phosphatase	Hyaluronidase
Acid proteases (cathepsins)	Acid esterases
Phosphoprotein phosphatase	Arylsulfatase
Ribonuclease	Lysozyme
Deoxyribonuclease	α-Glucosidase
β-Glucuronidase	α-Mannosidase
β-N-Acetylglucosaminidase	Collagenase
β-Galactosidase	

[88] Shemin, D., and Rittenberg, D. *J. Biol. Chem., 166*, 627 (1946).
[89] Kruh, J., Dreyfus, J. C., Schapira, G., and Gey, G. O. *J. Clin. Invest., 39*, 1180 (1960).

impermeable to the substrates upon which the lysosomal enzymes act, and the enzymes are retained by the lysosomes. Rupture of the limiting membrane by freezing and thawing, exposure to hypotonic solutions, or treatment with nonionic detergents renders the lysosomes permeable to substrates so that the latter can now be hydrolyzed, and results in leakage of the lysosomal enzymes into the medium (or cytoplasm).[90] Acidification of the suspension medium accelerates the increase in permeability of lysosomes and leakage of enzymes. Some lysosomal enzymes retain an affinity for the membrane fragments of disrupted lysosomes.[91]

The lysosomes are thought to arise between sheets of endoplasmic reticulum in cells with a rough endoplasmic reticulum, or from the vesicles of the Golgi apparatus in cells with a smooth endoplasmic reticulum.[92] The evidence for this is particularly striking in the proliferation of lysosomes in the cells of fasting animals,[93] where survival demands partial autolysis of cells to provide energy and building blocks for essential structures. On the other hand, the *storage granules* of leucocytes are lysosomes which serve as a large-scale reservoir of hydrolytic enzymes against the time when they are required. Leucocytes phagocytose bacteria or other objects by invaginations of the cell membrane to form *endocytic vacuoles.* The membrane of the storage granule merges with that of the endocytic vacuoles to form a *phagolysosome* in which the ingested material is digested.[94] Lysosomes that have carried out their digestive function, either as autolytic vacuoles or as phagolysosomes, become filled with debris and are called *residual bodies.* The residual body may move to the cell boundary, merge its membrane with the cell membrane, and discharge its contents outside the cell. Alternatively, the debris, mostly lipid in nature, may accumulate and condense into concentric lamellae giving rise to *myelin figures.*

While the presumption is made frequently that the cathepsins contained in the lysosomes are responsible for the continuous degradation of intracellular proteins, direct evidence is lacking for this mechanism under normal conditions. Both the factors which regulate the turnover of protein and the mechanism of protein turnover in ordinary cellular metabolism are not known. It is not known either whether protein molecules are degraded randomly or whether some molecules of protein are more susceptible to hydrolysis than others. From in-vitro experiments with purified proteins, it is known that native proteins are less readily hydrolyzed by proteases than denatured proteins. The presence of low-molecular-weight compounds, such as substrates for enzymes, metal ions, fatty acids, or detergents when bound by specific proteins, often retard proteolysis.[95]

The role of lysosomal enzymes in the intracellular digestion of material taken up by phagocytes is on much firmer footing.[96] As indicated above, bacteria and other material ingested by macrophages is segregated in endocytic vacuoles with which the lysosomes

---

[90] de Duve, C., Pressman, B. C., Gianetto, R., Wattiaux, R., and Appelmans, F. *Biochem. J., 60,* 604 (1955); Novikoff, A. B., Beaufay, H., and de Duve, C. *J. Biophys. Biochem. Cytol., 2,* suppl. 4, 179 (1956); Weissmann, G., and Dingle, J. *Exptl. Cell. Res., 25,* 207 (1961); Sawant, P. L., Shibko, S., Kumta, U. S., and Tappel, A. L. *Biochim. Biophys. Acta, 85,* 82 (1964).

[91] de Duve, C., in Hayashi, T., ed. *Subcellular Particles.* New York: Ronald, 1959, p. 128.

[92] Brandes, D. *J. Ultrastruct. Res., 12,* 63 (1965).

[93] Novikoff, A. B., Essner, E., and Quintana, N. *Federation Proc., 23,* 1010 (1964).

[94] Straus, W. *Exptl. Cell Res., 27,* 80 (1962); *J. Cell Biol., 21,* 295 (1964); Zucker-Franklin, D., and Hirsch, J. G. *J. Exptl. Med., 120,* 569 (1964).

[95] Linderstrøm-Lang, K. U. *Proteins and Enzymes.* Stanford, Cal.: Stanford University Press, 1952; Gorini, L., and Audrain, L. *Biochim. Biophys. Acta, 9,* 180 (1952); Azari, P. R., and Feeney, E. *J. Biol. Chem., 232,* 293 (1958); Klepper, J. A., Jr., and Cann, J. R. *Arch. Biochem. Biophys., 108,* 531 (1964); Markus, G. *Proc. Natl. Acad. Sci., 54,* 253 (1965).

[96] Cohn, Z. A., and Hirsch, J. G. *J. Exptl. Med., 112,* 983 (1960); *116,* 827 (1962); *117,* 27, 43 (1963).

coalesce. Using bacteria labeled with ^{32}P or ^{14}C, Cohn was able to show that the bacteria are taken up by macrophages within a 30-minute period. After 180 minutes, as much as 80 percent of the radioactive label was in the form of acid nonprecipitable material, indicating that extensive degradation of proteins, nucleic acids, and polysaccharides had occurred. It is of interest that the presence of immune serum retarded the digestive process. Following digestion of ingested material, the macrophages appear "degranulated" under light or electron microscopy. Because the hydrolytic enzymes are confined to the phagolysosomes, autolysis and cellular destruction of the macrophages themselves does not occur. A similar process of digestion of ingested material takes place in amoebae.[97]

Lysosomes are thought to play a role in a number of autolytic processes where invasion of the tissue by macrophages does not occur. Increased lysosomal fragility occurs in circulatory shock, whether it is caused by trauma, hemorrhage, or endotoxin.[98] Lysosomal hydrolases escape from tissues in these circumstances and have been found in increasing amounts in the blood as shock progresses. Autophagic vacuoles have been found in increased numbers in liver cells after starvation, after the administration of certain drugs known to be toxic to liver cells,[99] in various cells in vitamin A intoxication,[100] or after death.[101] On the other hand, the regression of the post-partum uterus in rats[102] or the resorption of the tail in amphibian metamorphosis[103] is accompanied by invasion of the tissue by macrophages so that a combination of autolytic and heterolytic processes appear to be involved. Although it is clear that lysosomes, which contain proteases and other hydrolytic enzymes, participate in cellular digestive processes and autolysis, the details of protein degradation and turnover in the cells of higher organisms remains to be elucidated.

regulation of tryptophane pyrrolase and tyrosine transaminase

The complexities of the regulation of the total enzyme present in tissue of higher organisms can be illustrated by two well-studied enzymes, tryptophane pyrrolase and tyrosine transaminase. Tryptophane pyrrolase is an enzyme that catalyzes the oxidation of the amino acid tryptophane to formylkynurenine by the reaction

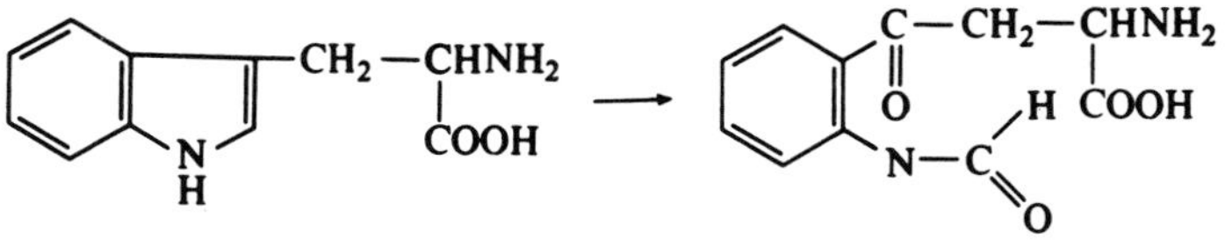

$$\text{(indole, NH)}-CH_2-CH(NH_2)-COOH \longrightarrow \text{(benzene ring)}(-C(=O)-CH_2-CH(NH_2)-COOH)(-NH-C(=O)H) \qquad (6\text{-}1)$$

[97] Straus, W. *J. Biophys. Biochem. Cytol.*, *2*, 513 (1956); *3*, 933 (1957).
[98] Janoff, A., Weissmann, G., Zweifach, B. W., and Thomas, L. *J. Exptl. Med.*, *116*, 451 (1962); Bitensky, L., Chayen, J., Cunningham, G. J., and Fine, J. *Nature*, *199*, 493 (1963); Dumont, A. E., and Weissmann, G. *Nature*, *201*, 1231 (1964).
[99] Novikoff, A. B., in de Reuck, A. V. S., and Cameron, M. P., eds. *Lysosomes*. Boston: Little, Brown, 1964, p. 36; Swift, H., and Hruban, Z. *Federation Proc.*, *23*, 1026 (1964).
[100] Dingle, J. T. *Biochem. J.*, *79*, 509 (1961); Weissmann, G., and Thomas, L. *J. Exptl. Med.*, *116*, 433 (1962); Weissmann, G., and Thomas, L. *J. Clin. Invest.*, *42*, 661 (1963).
[101] Novikoff, A. B., and Essner, E. *J. Cell Biol.*, *15*, 140 (1962).
[102] Woessner, J. F. *Biochem. J.*, *97*, 855 (1965).
[103] Weber, R., in de Reuck, A. V. S., and Cameron, M. P., eds. *Lysosomes*. Boston: Little, Brown, 1964, p. 282.

In mammals, this enzyme has been found only in the liver. Liver usually also contains appreciable quantities of the enzyme formylase, which converts formylkynurenine to kynurenine. Tryptophane pyrrolase activity is estimated by measuring the rate of formation of formylkynurenine plus kynurenine spectrophotometrically.

Tyrosine transaminase is an enzyme that catalyzes the reaction in which *p*-hydroxyphenylpyruvate and glutamate are formed from tyrosine and α-ketoglutarate:

$$HO{-}C_6H_4{-}CH_2{-}CHNH_2{-}COOH + HOOC{-}CH_2{-}CH_2{-}C{=}O{-}COOH \longrightarrow HO{-}C_6H_4{-}CH_2{-}C{=}O{-}COOH + HOOC{-}CH_2{-}CH_2{-}CHNH_2{-}COOH \tag{6-2}$$

The enzyme requires pyridoxal phosphate as a cofactor. The activity of tyrosine transaminase is usually estimated by procedures which take advantage of the strong ultraviolet absorption at 310 mμ of the complex of *p*-hydroxyphenyl*enol*pyruvate and borate.

High protein intake that provides amino acids in excess of the requirements of protein synthesis and essential metabolites may necessitate an adaptation by the organism enabling it either to utilize the excess amino acids for energy or to excrete them. Significantly higher activities of tryptophane pyrrolase[104] and tyrosine transaminase[105] are found in the livers of rats fed a high-protein diet (Fig. 6-24). The view that the increased enzyme activities measured in liver homogenates, in vitro, reflect an increase in the capacity of the animal to metabolize these amino acids under physiological conditions, in vivo, is supported by the observation that rats adapted to high-protein diets for some period of time are able to convert a large single dose of protein to ammonia more rapidly than animals that have not been adapted.[106] Not only does a high-protein diet result in severalfold increased activity of liver tryptophane pyrrolase and tyrosine transaminase, but also the feeding of the substrates themselves, tryptophane and tyrosine, results in a more rapid and greater increase in enzyme activity.[107] Furthermore, the administration of structural analogs of these amino acids also results in increased enzyme activity.[108]

The administration of cortisone, a steroid hormone elaborated by the adrenal gland, also results in a four- to ten-fold increase in tryptophane pyrrolase and tyrosine transaminase within 4 to 5 hours.[109] A general physiological effect of cortisone is an overall increase in protein catabolism. Therefore, it is not surprising that its administration is followed by an increase in two enzymes catalyzing degradative reactions of amino acids. Similar increases in tryptophane pyrrolase and tyrosine transaminase activity are observed after severe stress which results in increased endogeneous elaboration of cortisone and related hormones.[110]

Tryptophane pyrrolase and tyrosine transaminase are absent from fetal animals but appear shortly after birth. In the rat, both enzymes are absent from the liver of the

[104] Knox, W. E., and Mehler, A. W. *Science*, *113*, 237 (1951).
[105] Litwack, G., Ebert, P. S., Yankelowitz, S., and Taylor, M. W. *Enzymologia*, *20*, 183 (1959).
[106] Wergedal, J. E., Ku, Y., and Harper, A. E. *Advan. Enzyme Regul.*, *2*, 289 (1964).
[107] Civen, M., and Knox, W. E. *J. Biol. Chem.*, *235*, 1716 (1960).
[108] Lin, E. C. C., and Knox, W. E. *Biochim. Biophys. Acta*, *26*, 85 (1957).
[109] Rosen, F., and Milholland, R. J. *J. Biol. Chem.*, *238*, 3730 (1963).
[110] Rosen, F., Roberts, N. R., and Nichol, C. A. *J. Biol. Chem.*, *234*, 476 (1959).

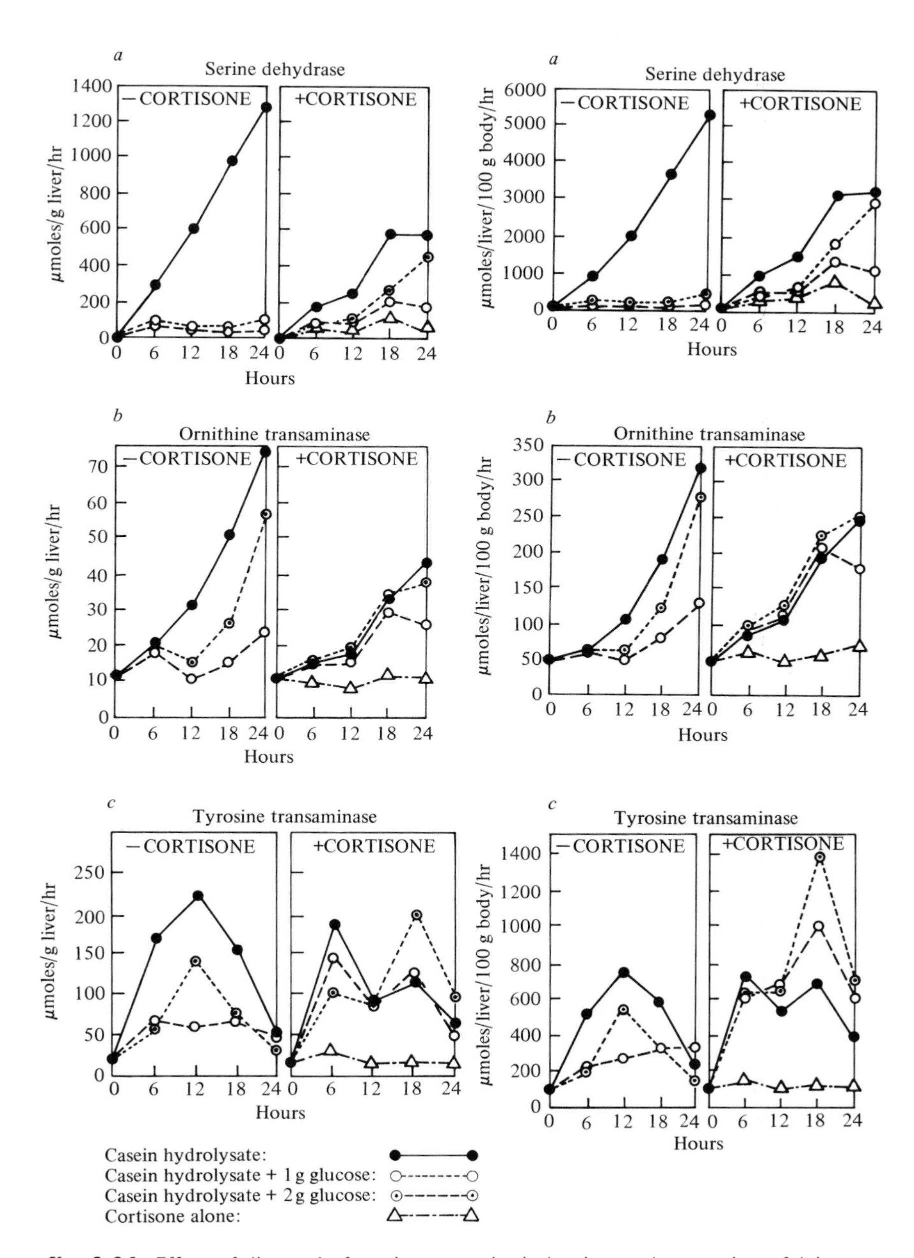

fig. 6-24. Effect of diet and of cortisone on the induction and repression of (*a*) serine dehydrase, (*b*) ornithine transaminase, and (*c*) tyrosine transaminase in rat livers. Casein hydrolysate: 1 g every 6 hours × 3. Cortisone rats were pretreated with 5 mg cortisone daily for 4 days before the experiment. (From Peraino, C., Lamar, C., Jr., and Pitot, H. C. *Advan. Enzyme Regul., 4,* 206 [1966]. Copyright Pergamon Press; reprinted by permission.)

newborn; but tyrosine transaminase reaches normal levels during the first extra-uterine day,[111] and tryptophane pyrrolase appears on about the twelfth postnatal day.[112] Prior to the appearance of enzyme activity in neonatal life, immunological tests do not reveal the presence of the enzyme[113] (Fig. 6-25). The administration of puro-

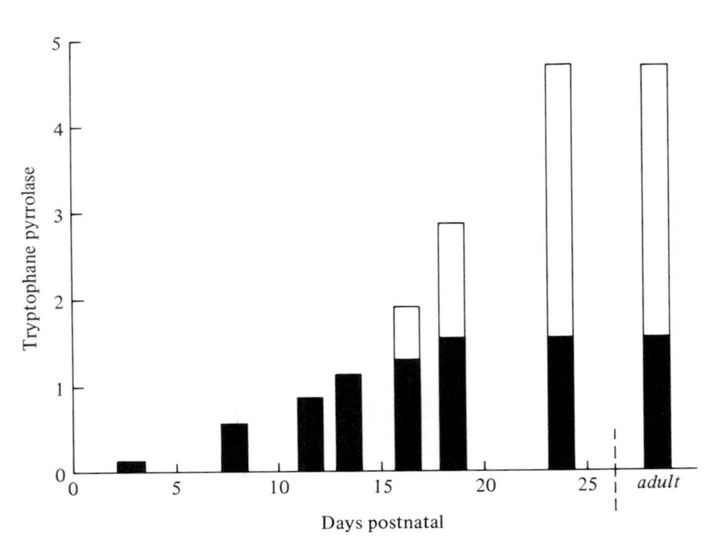

fig. 6-25. The appearance of liver tryptophane pyrrolase during postnatal development in rats. The liver homogenate was assayed without (*dark portion*) and with (*whole bars*) added boiled microsomes that provide the heme coenzyme. (From Greengard, O., and Feigelson, P. *Ann. N.Y. Acad. Sci. 111*, 230 [1963]. Copyright The New York Academy of Sciences, 1963; reprinted by permission.)

mycin, an inhibitor of protein synthesis, or of actinomycin, an inhibitor of RNA synthesis, prevents the appearance of tryptophane pyrrolase in the neonatal rat.[114] This observation suggests that the enzyme activity appears as a result of de novo synthesis rather than as a result of activating a zymogen. The mechanism which triggers the sudden appearance of these enzymes in the neonatal animal is unknown. The appearance of enzyme cannot be hastened by the feeding of substrate or by administration of cortisone. In mature rats, there is a slow but steady increase in the activities of these enzymes; the activity of tryptophane pyrrolase per gram of liver doubles in rats between when they are 38 and when they are 400 days of age. The body weights of these animals double during this period, however, and the amount of liver tryptophane pyrrolase per 100 g body weight does not change significantly.

It is necessary, of course, to determine whether the increase in enzyme activity represents an increase in enzyme protein or whether the enzyme protein remains constant and the differences in activity must be ascribed to other mechanisms. This

[111] Kretchmer, N., and McNamara, H. *J. Clin. Invest.*, *35*, 1089 (1956).
[112] Auerbach, V. H., and Waisman, H. A. *J. Biol. Chem.*, *234*, 304 (1959).
[113] Knox, W. E., Ogata, M., Hasegawa, N., and Tokuyama, K. *VI Intern. Congr. Biochem., abstr. 9–45* (1964).
[114] Nemeth, A. M., and de la Haba, G. *J. Biol. Chem.*, *237*, 1190 (1962).

can be evaluated by immunological studies, that is, by producing antibodies to the pure enzymes and using them to determine the quantity of enzyme protein present by formation of antigen-antibody complexes. Such studies indicate that the increase in activities of tryptophane pyrrolase and tyrosine transaminase reflects true increases in enzyme protein[115] (Fig. 6-26).

fig. 6-26. Immunochemical changes in the amount of tryptophane pyrrolase (TP) and tyrosine transaminase (TT). (From Knox, W. E., and Greengard, O. *Advan. Enzyme Reg., 3,* 266 [1965]. Copyright Pergamon Press; reprinted by permission.)

		INDUCED/CONTROL	
INDUCER	ENZYME	CATALTYIC ACTIVITY	ANTIGEN TITER
Hydrocortisone	TT	10.4	10.4
Cortisone	TP	4.6	5.0
Tryptophane	TP	3.6	2.8

The question that remains is whether the increase in enzyme level is the result of increased synthesis or the result of decreased degradation. Actinomycin or puromycin prevent the increase in enzyme activity which follows cortisone administration but not the increase in enzyme activity which occurs with increased levels of substrate.[116]

These data indicate that cortisone increases the level of enzymes by a mechanism which requires new RNA synthesis, presumably messenger-RNA synthesis, and protein synthesis; this implies increased *rates* of synthesis. The increased levels of enzymes associated with higher substrate levels is not mediated by this mechanism and is presumably the result of decreased degradation or inactivation. The rate of degradation of tryptophane pyrrolase was evaluated directly by administration of radioactive leucine to control rats, to rats receiving cortisone, and to rats receiving tryptophane. The animals were sacrificed at intervals after the specific radioactivity of the liver tryptophane pyrrolase had reached a plateau. The decline in radioactivity was measured in the enzyme isolated by precipitation with specific antibody. The rate of decline was the same in the control and cortisone-treated rats, but was much slower in the animals receiving substrate.[117] These data indicate that cortisone administration does not slow enzyme degradation, but substrate does.

Tryptophane pyrrolase and tyrosine transaminase catalyze the first reactions in the catabolic pathways for the amino acids tryptophane and tyrosine respectively. The physiological importance of the variations in the activities of these enzymes under various circumstances relates presumably to the control of the overall rates of degradation. For example, when the level of liver tryptophane pyrrolase was increased about

[115] Kenney, F. T. *J. Biol. Chem., 237,* 1610 (1962); Feigelson, P., and Greengard, O. *J. Biol. Chem., 237,* 3714 (1962).
[116] Greengard, O., Smith, M. A., and Acs, G. *J. Biol. Chem., 238,* 1548 (1963); Greengard, O., and Gordon, M. *J. Biol. Chem., 238,* 3708 (1963).
[117] Schimke, R. T., Sweeney, E. W., and Berlin, C. M. *Biochem. Biophys. Res. Commun., 15,* 214 (1964).

fourfold in rats by the administration of the nonmetabolizable substrate α-methyltryptophane, a much larger fraction of a test dose of radioactive tryptophane was degraded with the formation of larger amounts of $C^{14}O_2$.[118] The weight loss which these animals showed might be attributable in part to the increased degradation of tryptophane, an essential amino acid, but it may have resulted in part from other toxic effects of the tryptophane analog.

regulation of arginase activity

Arginase is a soluble cytoplasmic enzyme which catalyzes the hydrolysis of arginine to ornithine and urea—a step in the ornithine cycle (Fig. 6-27). The enzyme is found in large amounts in the livers of *ureotelic* animals which excrete urea as the principal

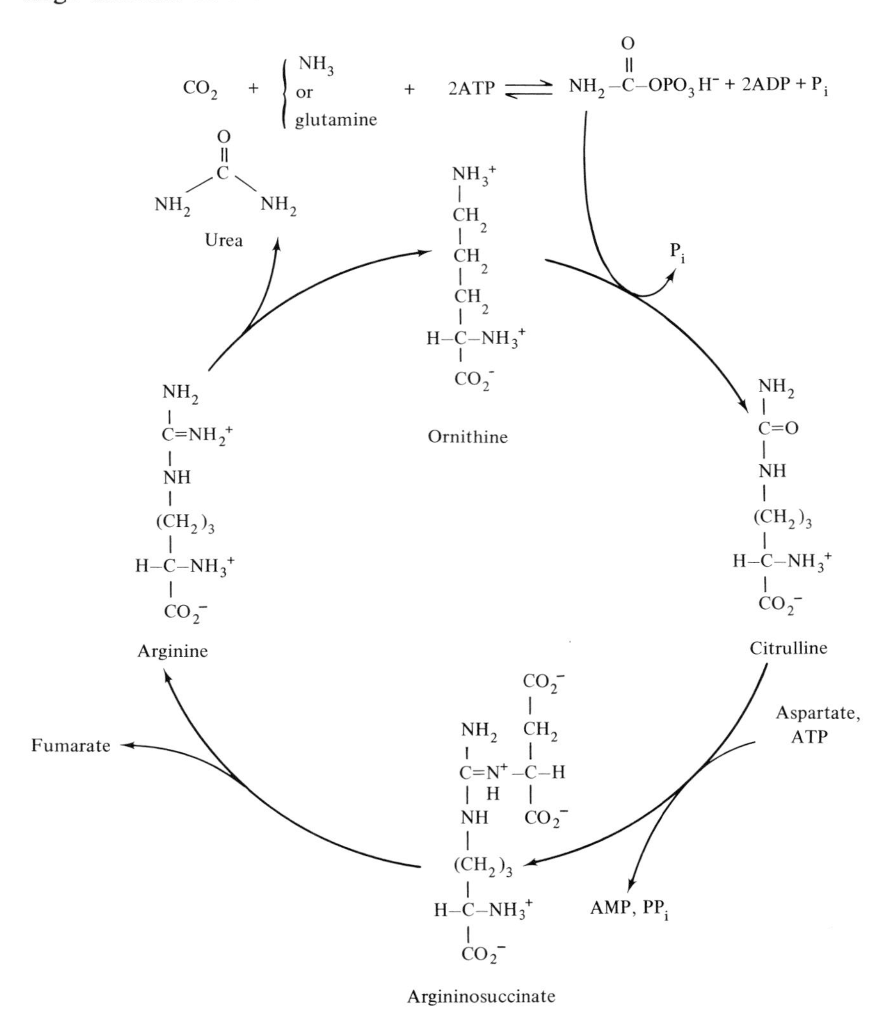

fig. 6-27. The metabolic pathway of the ornithine cycle.

[118] Moran, J. F., and Sourkes, T. L. *J. Biol. Chem.*, *238*, 3006 (1963).

end product of protein catabolism. It is found in small amounts in the livers of *uricotelic* animals which excrete uric acid or allantoin as the principal end products of protein catabolism. Arginase is involved in the degradation not just of arginine but of proteins and amino acids in general. The level of arginase varies *pari passu* with the level of urea excretion under a wide variety of physiological conditions. Urea formation, however, involves all the enzymes of the urea cycle, and in most circumstances arginine succinate synthetase appears to be rate-limiting. Arginase requires manganese as a cofactor. It and the other urea-cycle enzymes can be isolated easily; the amounts of enzymes isolated from liver parallel the activity measured enzymatically.

The ingestion of a high-protein diet more than trebles the arginase levels in rat liver[119] (Fig. 6-28). Not only arginase, but all the enzymes of the ornithine-urea cycle

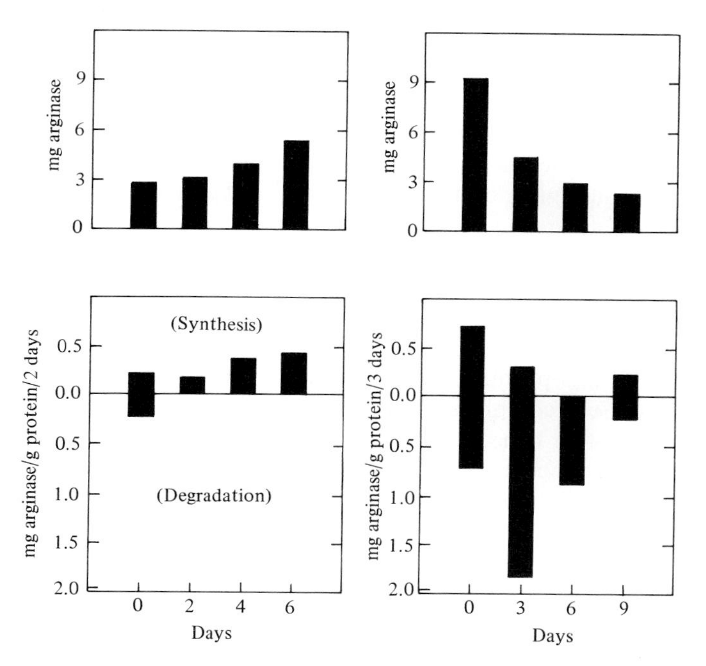

fig. 6-28. Rates of synthesis and of degradation of rat liver arginase during starvation (*left*) and after a change in diet from 70 percent casein to 8 percent casein (*right*). (From Schimke, R. T., Brown, M. G., and Smallman, E. T. *Ann. N.Y. Acad. Sci. 102*, 597 [1963]. Copyright The New York Academy of Sciences, 1963; reprinted by permission.)

are increased as a group, and the degree of increase is proportional to the protein consumed.[120] These observations are consistent with the view that the increased enzyme levels represent an adaptation to surplus protein which must be catabolized. On a protein-free diet which maintains the caloric intake with carbohydrates and fats, there is a fall in arginase levels and in urea excretion.[121] In this instance, bodily protein must be conserved while adequate calories are provided. In starved animals liver arginase and urea excretion are elevated, which is consistent with the fact that tissue protein must be degraded in order to provide energy for carrying out essential

[119] Ashida, K., and Harper, A. E. *Proc. Soc. Exptl. Biol. Med., 107*, 151 (1961).
[120] Schimke, R. T. *J. Biol. Chem., 238*, 1012 (1963).
[121] Schimke, R. T. *J. Biol. Chem., 237*, 1921 (1962).

processes to maintain viability. Feeding of arginine, ornithine, or citrulline alone to rats does not result in any elevation of arginase or any of the other urea-cycle enzymes. The addition of excess arginine to cells grown in tissue culture, however, does result in increased levels of arginase.[122] With low levels of arginine that are growth-limiting for tissue-cultured cells, the levels of the two preceding enzymes in the urea cycle, arginine succinate synthetase and arginine succinate lyase, increase two- to fivefold, presumably by the lifting of repression by arginine.

Adrenalectomy is followed by a pronounced drop in the level of liver arginase, but the drop in level of the other enzymes of the urea cycle is less great. Following adrenalectomy, then, the enzymes in the urea cycle do not change coordinately. The administration of cortisone in large doses results in elevation of all the enzymes of the urea cycle, but the change is not so dramatic as is the increase of tryptophane pyrrolase. Growth hormone depresses the level of liver arginase; this change is expected in view of the nitrogen-retaining action of growth hormone.

Changes in the levels of arginase could result from changes in the rate of synthesis, the rate of degradation, or both. Evaluation of rates of synthesis and rates of degradation show changes in both when the levels of the enzyme are increased as a result of high-protein feeding, hormone administration, or starvation.[123] The changes in the rate of degradation are appreciably greater, however, than the changes in the rate of synthesis.

The genetic regulation of protein synthesis at the level of transcription involves still another complication in the cells of higher organisms that does not exist in bacteria, namely, the entry of the inducer or repressor substance into the nucleus. Although experimental data bearing upon this problem are fragmentary, studies in eukaryotic fungi indicate that certain mutations complement each other in the diploid forms but not in heterokaryons.[124] On the other hand, a study of the repression of arylsulfatase synthesis by sulfate in the culture medium in *Aspergillus nidulans*[125] indicates that repressor formed in some nuclei fully represses all the nuclei in a multinucleate cell.

references

Cellular regulatory mechanisms. *Cold Spring Harbor Symp. Quant. Biol.*, *26*, 1–408 (1961).

Genetic code, the. *Cold Spring Harbor Symp. Quant. Biol.*, *31*, 1–748 (1966).

Ingram, V. M. *The Biosynthesis of Macromolecules.* New York: W. A. Benjamin, 1965.

Jacob, F., and Monod, J. Genetic regulatory mechanisms in the synthesis of proteins. *J. Mol. Biol.*, *3*, 318 (1961).

Maaløe, O., and Kjeldgaard, N. O. *Control of Macromolecular Synthesis.* New York: W. A. Benjamin, 1966.

Prescott, D. M. Cellular sites of RNA synthesis. *Progr. Nucleic Acid Res.*, *3*, 33 (1964).

Synthesis and structure of macromolecules. *Cold Spring Harbor Symp. Quant. Biol.*, *28*, 1–610 (1963).

Watson, J. D. *Molecular Biology of the Gene.* New York: W. A. Benjamin, 1965.

[122] Schimke, R. T. *J. Biol. Chem.*, *239*, 136 (1964).
[123] Schimke, R. T., Brown, M. B., and Smallman, E. T. *Ann. N.Y. Acad. Sci.*, *102*, 587 (1963).
[124] Roberts, C. F. *Genet. Res.*, *5*, 211 (1964).
[125] Siddiwi, O., Apte, B. N., and Pitale, M. P. *Cold Spring Harbor Symp. Quant. Biol.*, *31*, 381 (1966).

chapter 7

cell membranes

introduction

A number of vital processes (those listed in Fig. 7-1) have been thought, at one time or another, to be functions of the cell membrane. In complex organisms the cell membrane acts as a physical boundary, permitting each cell to carry out its individual vital functions and to survive in varying environments. In addition, the cell membrane facilitates the integration of functions among groups of cells and thus enables the organism to operate effectively as a unit. Yet our knowledge of the cell membrane is still fragmentary, and many uncertainties exist concerning its origin, its structure, its exact functional roles, and the mechanisms involved in fulfilling its functions.

In its most general form, the cell membrane concept is more than a century old. While Hugo von Mohl, in his *Anatomische und Physiologische Studien für Vegetarische Zellen* (1851), described plant cells as being bounded by a membrane, he actually observed the cellulose cell wall. Von Mohl observed and described plasmolysis, but it remained for Karl Wilhelm Nägeli (1817–1891) to show that the cell membrane is semipermeable and is responsible for the osmotic and related phenomena shown by living cells. Nägeli studied botany under Schleiden. With Schleiden's prodding, he undertook a thorough study of *cryptogams*, the apparently seedless and sexless algae, liverworts, and related lower plants whose mode of reproduction is so inconspicuous that they were long regarded as convincing examples of spontaneous generation.

fig. 7-1. Functions of plasma membranes.

Boundary for individual cells
Boundary for intracellular particulates
Provision of a structural framework for attachment of enzymes
Adhesion of cells
Gas exchange between interior and environment
Selective permeability and active transport of ions
Facilitated diffusion of sugars, amino acids, etc.
Selective excretion, for example, of glucuronide conjugates
Pinocytosis, phagocytosis
Secretion
Irritability and excitation
Transmission of excitation
Formation of specialized structures, for example, desmosomes, cilia
Motility
Initiation of autolysis upon cell death

Although Nägeli used the term *Zellenmembran* in his early papers, in 1855 he described the formation of a firm film when the protein-rich cell sap of an injured cell came in contact with water.[1] He called this film the *Plasmamembran* and recognized that it protected the remaining cytoplasm from the deleterious effects of the water. Nägeli found the membrane to be impermeable to naturally occurring plant pigments, which escaped, however, after a severe, penetrating injury to the cell. It is difficult to believe that Nägeli actually observed the cell membrane through the microscope; rather, he probably observed a boundary of cytoplasm and inferred the presence of a membrane from the properties of semipermeability.

It is a curious fact that after Nägeli's studies, the cell membrane was not regarded as a substantive structure with any degree of certainty until the 1920s when Robert Chambers reported his microdissection experiments in which the cell membrane was manipulated directly under the microscope by means of fine needles.[2] In the meantime, Moritz Traube, an amateur chemist, discovered the semipermeable properties of copper ferrocyanide films. These films were used by Wilhelm Pfeffer in exhaustive studies of osmotic phenomena[3] that provided much of the data used by van't Hoff in formulating his theory of solutions. Pfeffer proposed that an invisible membrane surrounded plant cells and accounted for the similarity of their osmotic behavior with that of his artificial osmometers. However, he withdrew this hypothesis in the face of insistent objections by colloid chemists of the time that plant cells failed to display true osmotic phenomena. After Pfeffer, Hamburger[4] studied osmotic phenomena in animal cells; de Vries[5] studied the phenomena extensively in plant cells; and Overton[6] measured the permeability of living cells to over 500 substances. Although the idea of a semipermeable membrane at the cell boundary is implicit in

[1] Nägeli, K., and Cramer, K. *Pflanzenphysiologische Untersuchungen*. Zürich: F. Schultess, 1855.
[2] Chambers, R. *Harvey Lectures*, *22*, 41 (1926).
[3] Pfeffer, W. *Osmotische Untersuchungen*. Leipzig: W. Engelmann, 1877.
[4] Hamburger, H. J. *Osmotischer Druck und Ionenlehre*. Wiesbaden: Bergmann, 1902.
[5] de Vries, H. *Jahrb. wiss. Botan.*, *16*, 465 (1885).
[6] Overton, E. *Vierteljahresschr. naturforsch. Ges. Zürich*, *44*, 88 (1899); Osterhout, W. J. V. *Cold Spring Harbor Symp. Quant. Biol.*, *8*, 51 (1940).

the work of these investigators, it is remarkable that none of them felt the necessity of invoking its presence as a structural entity to account for their findings.

Although the cell membrane cannot be seen through the light microscope, its presence can be inferred from microdissection observations. If a large tear is made in a naked egg by means of a microneedle, the cytoplasm flows out and the cell disintegrates. If the tear is not too large, it may be sealed off by the apparent spontaneous formation of a film across the opening. The cell will survive if the loss of cytoplasm has not been excessive. If the nucleus is well within the cell and distant from the point of injury, the healing film will form in more or less a straight line across the gap formed by the injury. When the nucleus is near the area of injury, however, the film will tend to billow out as it forms, thereby enclosing the nucleus within the cell.

Formation of the film requires the presence of calcium in the bathing medium. If an egg is injured in a calcium-free medium, healing fails to occur; this leads to complete loss of the cell contents from even a minor injury. Heilbrunn,[7] on the basis of the calcium requirement and the formation of a tough, insoluble protein for both film formation and blood clotting, proposed that the healing film was formed from a hypothetical precursor protein, *ovothrombin*, which clots in the presence of calcium ions to form the material of the healing film. It should be noted, however, that cell division can occur normally in a calcium-free medium and that the additional cell membrane which is required to cover two cells rather than one forms in the absence of calcium in the bathing medium. When first formed, the healing film differs from the intact cell membrane; if it is punctured, the new film disintegrates in a wave up to the edge of the injured region. It may be that the underlying cortical gel acts as a support for the plasma membrane, and full integrity is not restored until the underlying cortical gel is reformed.

Chambers showed that when dilute acids or dilute alkali are added to the bathing medium, neither are injurious to cells as long as the cells are covered with an intact cell membrane, even though a portion of the membrane may be a healing film formed over an area of injury. Yet when dilute acids or alkali are injected into the interior of the cell by a micropipette, they cause cell death and cytolysis. If marine eggs or protozoa are immersed in a solution of a dye such as eosin, the dye does not penetrate into the cell. On the other hand, if a droplet of dye is introduced into the interior of the cell by microinjection, the dye solution quickly diffuses to all parts of the cytoplasm but not beyond the boundary of the cell. If an egg, stained internally by means of an indicator dye such as neutral red introduced by microinjection, is placed in an isotonic ammonium chloride solution, the color of the egg becomes redder, reflecting an increase in the pH of the cytoplasm presumably resulting from penetration of ammonia into the interior of the cell.

early permeability studies

It has long been known that living cells are highly permeable to water. Sea urchin eggs swell in distilled water and shrink in salt or sucrose solutions of greater osmolarity than sea water. Similarly, mammalian erythrocytes swell when placed in hypotonic media, losing their normal discoid shape and becoming spherical; contrariwise, they shrink and become crenated when placed in hypertonic solutions (see Fig. 7-2). If erythrocytes are placed in very hypotonic solutions, they burst, losing the hemoglobin

[7] Heilbrunn, L. V. *Protoplasma*, *11*, 558 (1930).

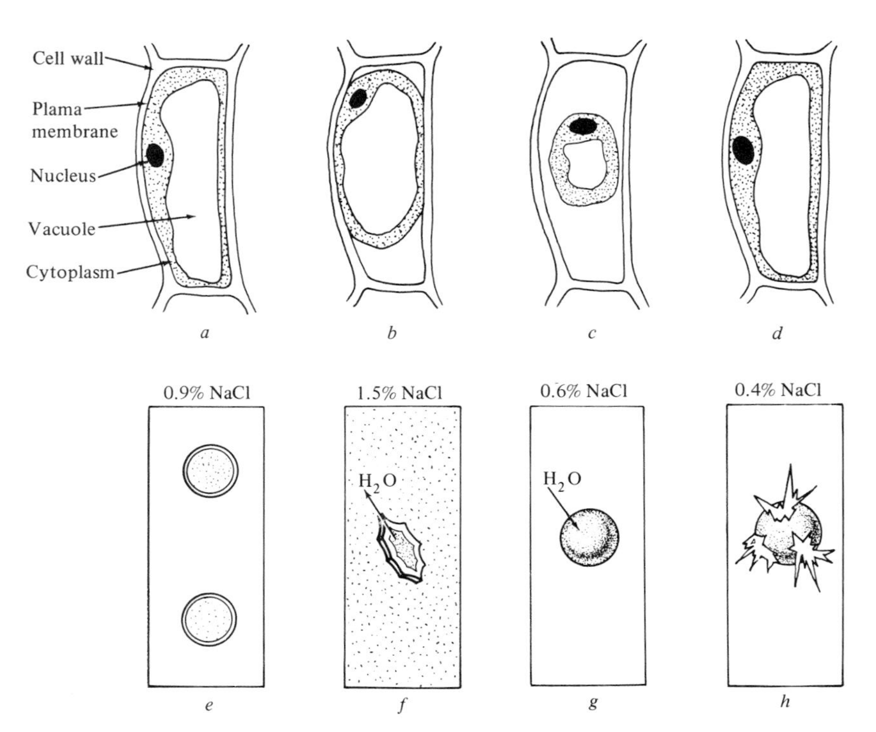

fig. 7-2. A diagrammatic representation of osmotic effects. A plant is normally expanded against its cell wall (*a*). When placed in a hypertonic solution, water leaves the vacuole and cytoplasm and the cell shrinks away from the cell wall, a phenomenon called *plasmolysis* (*b, c*). Plasmolysis is greater in highly hypertonic solutions. If the solute can penetrate the plasma membrane, *deplasmolysis* occurs after a time (*d*). Cells such as erythrocytes without a rigid cell wall (*e*) also shrink in hypertonic media (*f*). When placed in hypotonic media, such cells swell (*g*); and if the medium is sufficiently hypotonic, they may lyse (*h*).

and other intracellular constituents, and leave a ghost behind. This phenomenon is called *hemolysis*.

Plant cells are normally turgid because the protoplasts are expanded firmly against the cell walls. Plant parts, such as a leaf, possess a certain rigidity partly as a result of the collective turgor of the individual cells. If cells from a freshwater plant are placed in concentrated salt solutions, the protoplasts of each cell shrink around a vacuole which diminishes in size. This process is called *plasmolysis*. Upon changing the medium from salt solution to water, each cell regains water and the protoplast again fills the space within the cell wall completely. The rigid cell wall of plant cells mechanically limits the cell volume and prevents excessive uptake of water. If plant cells which have undergone plasmolysis are allowed to remain in hypertonic solutions, in time they return to their original volume. This phenomenon is called *deplasmolysis*; it is rapid in solutions of solutes which penetrate the cell rapidly and slow in solutions of solutes which penetrate slowly (see Fig. 7-3).

Although many substances other than water move in and out of cells in response to a concentration gradient, only a few of them, such as carbon dioxide and oxygen, have permeability coefficients as great as that of water. The rate of deplasmolysis of cells was one of the earliest and most extensively used methods for evaluating the permeability rates for many substances. Similarly, the volume of a mass of small cells such as

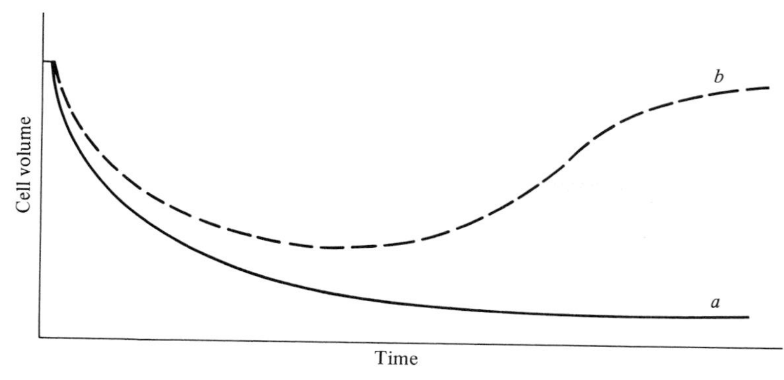

fig. 7-3. The time course of change of cell volume when cells are placed in a hypertonic medium containing (*a*) a solute which does not permeate the plasma membrane, and (*b*) a solute which permeates slowly.

erythrocytes can be determined before and after immersion in hypertonic solutions after the cells have been packed together by centrifugation.

If cells were perfect osmometers, the product of solute concentration and volume would be constant. In complex solutions with many solutes, the effective number of solute particles, expressed as the *osmolarity* of the solution, determines the osmotic behavior. Because it is frequently difficult to determine the osmolarity of a solution directly, osmolarity is often determined experimentally in terms of another colligative property of the solution such as freezing-point depression (see Chapter 4). Most cells are notoriously imperfect osmometers. For example, mammalian erythrocytes placed in *isosmolar* sucrose solution will shrink. When sodium chloride is then added to the suspension medium, the cells will swell. This phenomenon, known as *negative anomalous osmosis*, was first described by Dutrochet in 1835.

Hemolysis of erythrocytes after immersion in hypertonic solutions has also been used to evaluate permeability coefficients. At first, water leaves the cells, resulting in crenation. In time, however, solute molecules enter the cells; and as the number of osmotically active molecules within the cell increases, there is a corresponding imbibition of water. The cell membrane can stretch only to a limited extent, and eventually the cells undergo lysis. The rates of entry of solutes are reflected, therefore, in the rates of hemolysis. It should be noted that the penetration of solute molecules through the cell membranes of erythrocytes and other cells indicates that the limiting membrane is not ideally semipermeable, but, rather, is "leaky" with regard to solutes. This not only explains in part the irregular behavior in osmotic experiments but also has important implications in the analysis of transport phenomena discussed below (see p. 431).

Of course, the rates of influx of solutes can be evaluated directly by chemical means—either by analyzing the medium and determining the rate of disappearance or by analyzing the cells and determining the intracellular concentrations. Efflux rates can be determined by permitting cells to achieve equilibrium with a solution of solute, removing the cells and washing them quickly, and then measuring the rate of appearance of solute in fresh medium or of its disappearance intracellularly. In recent years, the use of radioactively labeled solutes has made this type of experiment more widely applicable, easier to perform, and more accurate. Diffusion will be considered quantitatively in more detail in Chapter 8.

Diffusion coefficients (D) have been determined by a very large number of investigators, many of whom have developed their own variations of the above-mentioned general methods. All these methods involve the determination of a rate of diffusion by use of the Fick equation (eq. 4-77). For the unidirectional case,

$$\frac{dm}{dt} = -D\mathfrak{A}\frac{\Delta c}{\Delta x} \qquad (7\text{-}1)$$

where m is the quantity of material diffusing from the more concentrated to the less concentrated medium, $\mathfrak{A}$ is the area, Δc is the concentration difference, and Δx is the thickness of the membrane.

If the influx rate of a substance is measured and the volume of the external medium is much larger than the volume of cells so that changes in the concentration of solute in the external medium can be neglected, the Fick equation is

$$D = \frac{V}{\mathfrak{A}t}\ln\frac{c_{\text{out}} - c_{\text{in}}}{c_{\text{out}} - c'_{\text{in}}} \qquad (7\text{-}2)$$

where $V/\mathfrak{A}$ is the volume-to-area ratio and depends upon the shape of the cells, and c_{in} and c'_{in} are the intracellular concentrations of solute before and after time t. In many experiments, the diffusion coefficient has been evaluated by determining the half-saturation time, that is, the time when $(c'_{\text{in}} - c_{\text{in}}) = (c_{\text{out}} - c_{\text{in}})/2$.

The first important formulation of the rules of cellular permeability was made by Overton (see footnote 6, p. 352), who found that the rates of penetration of many substances corresponded remarkably well to their partition coefficients between olive oil and water. Similar studies were carried out by Hedin and Grijns[8] using erythrocytes. Overton postulated the presence of a lipid layer on the surface of cells which acted as the main barrier to penetration. Substances with high lipid solubility could dissolve more readily in the lipid film at the cell surface, and consequently penetrate more rapidly. This theory was consistent with the electrical studies of Rudolph Höber,[9] who demonstrated that intact erythrocytes have a high electrical resistance, while the interior of the cell is a good conductor. Höber concluded that the high resistance resided in a thin film at the surface of the cells.

It was disquieting to a number of early observers that cells were quite permeable to a number of hydrophilic organic compounds, such as glycerol or urea, that were rather insoluble in lipid solvents (see Fig. 7-4). Similarly, inorganic electrolytes, which are not lipid-soluble, penetrate rather readily into living cells. On the other hand, some substances which are highly lipid-soluble, such as triethylcitrate, penetrate poorly. Such findings led Ruhland[10] to conclude that the cell membrane had pores, acting as a molecular sieve, through which many substances passed. The correlation between permeability coefficients and molecular size is particularly striking when a series of homologous compounds is examined (Fig. 7-5). To reconcile the observations that small hydrophilic molecules penetrate cells more quickly than might be expected from the lipid solubility theory and that large fat-soluble molecules penetrate more quickly than might be expected from the pore theory, Collander combined both concepts into a lipoid-filter theory.[11]

Generally, cells are less permeable to electrolytes than to nonelectrolytes of similar molecular size. Care must be taken to distinguish between permeation, pinocytosis,

[8] Grijns, G. *Pflüger's Arch. ges. Physiol.*, *63*, 86 (1896); Hedin, S. G. *Pflüger's Arch. ges. Physiol.*, *68*, 229 (1897); *70*, 525 (1898).
[9] Höber, R. *Pflüger's Arch. ges. Physiol.*, *133*, 237 (1910).
[10] Ruhland, W., and Hoffman, C. *Planta*, *1*, 1 (1925).
[11] Collander, R., and Bärlund, H. *Acta Botan. Fenn.*, *11*, 1 (1933).

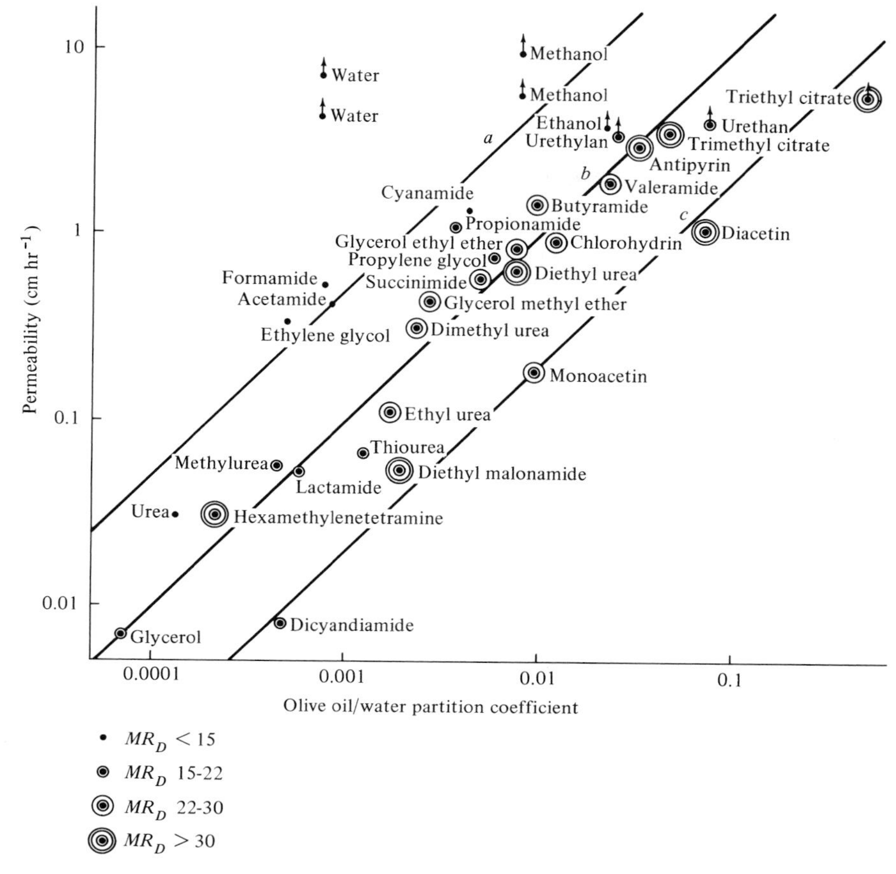

fig. 7-4. The permeability of *C. ceratophylla* cells to nonelectrolytes which vary in in molecular size and lipid solubility. MR_D is the molar refraction of the molecules, a parameter related to the molecular volume. (From Collander, R. *Physiol. Plantarum,* *2,* 300 [1949].)

and secretion. Cells are much less permeable to divalent cations and anions than to monovalent ions. In the case of weak electrolytes with acidity constants in the physiological range of pH, the nonionized form usually enters cells much more readily than the ionized form. This phenomenon is of considerable importance in the pharmaceutical industry because one of two homologous drugs will be active because it is present largely in the nonionized form and will penetrate cells, while the other will be inactive because it has a different pK_a and exists largely in the ionized form at physiological pH. A change in pH of the medium which increases the fraction of a weak electrolyte in the nonionized form increases its permeation into cells.

The rate of permeation of many cells by monovalent cations correlates with their hydrated ion diameters and can be ranked in the following series: $Cs^+ > Rb^+ > K^+ > NH_4^+ > Na^+ > Li^+ \gg$ divalent cations. A similar series is observed for anions: $SCN^- > I^- > Br^- > NO_3^- > Cl^- >$ organic anions $> F^- > SO_4^{--}$. While these orderings are found most frequently, numerous irregularities[12] have been observed for

[12] Eisenman, G., in Kleinzeller, S., and Kotyk, A., eds. *Membrane Transport and Metabolism.* New York: Academic Press, 1961, p. 163.

fig. 7-5. Permeability of *Beggiatoa mirabilis* to organic nonelectrolytes. (From Ruhland, W., and Hoffmann, C. *Planta, 1,* 1. Berlin: Springer [1925].)

SUBSTANCE	PLASMOLYSIS, THRESHOLD CONCENTRATED IN MOLES/L	MR_D	DISTRIBUTION COEFFICIENT ETHER : WATER
Urea	0.35	13.67	0.0005
Ethylenglycol	0.09	14.4	0.0068
Methylurea	0.01	18.47	0.0012
Thiourea	0.075	19.59	0.0063
Glycerol	0.009	20.63	0.0011
Ethylurethan	0.015	21.01	0.6370
Lactamide	0.007	21.13	0.0018
Malonamide	0.007	22.92	0.0003
Dimethylurea	0.005	23.43	0.0116
Butyramide	0.0125	24.11	0.0580
Erythritol	0.001	26.77	<0.0001
Succinamide	0.0015	27.54	0.0002
Arabinose	0.0008	31.40	<0.0001
Diethylurea	0.003	32.66	<0.0185
Glucose	0.00055	37.54	<0.0001
Mannitol	0.00055	39.06	<0.0001
Saccharose	0.00020	70.35	<0.0001

both cations and anions. Erythrocytes are rather unique both because of their relatively high permeability to anions and for remarkable species differences for rates of ion permeabilities.

A remarkable feature of most cells is their ability to maintain a selective intracellular ionic composition. Thus, the intracellular fluid contains much higher concentrations of K^+ and Mg^{++}, but much lower concentrations of Na^+, Ca^{++}, and Cl^- than the extracellular fluid (Fig. 7-6). Ostwald[13] called attention to the relation between the

fig. 7-6. Electrolyte concentrations (mEq/L water) and potential across cell membranes.

CELL		NA^+	K^+ (mEq/L)	CL^-	POTENTIAL
Squid axon:	Internal	50	400	40	−60 mv
	External	460	10	540	
Frog muscle:	Internal	10	130	3.0	−90 mv
	External	120	2.5	120	
Rat muscle:	Internal	16	154	4.0	−89 mv
	External	150	4.7	125	
Human erythrocyte:	Internal	17	142	72	
	External	140	4.8	115	
Ascites tumor:	Internal	54	119	61	−16 mv
	External	142	9.8	122	

[13] Ostwald, W. *Z. f. phys. Chem.*, *6*, 71 (1890).

electrical potential developed across precipitation membranes and their selective ion permeability. A similar potential develops between the normal exterior and the cut end of a nerve or muscle. Bernstein,[14] following Ostwald's analysis, correlated this "injury" potential with the distribution of potassium and chloride ions across the cell membrane. Thus, the intracellular K^+ is usually 20 to 55 times greater than the extracellular concentration. An equation was derived by Nernst[15] for the potential developed across the junction of two solutions of an electrolyte differing in concentration

$$E = \frac{RT}{Z\mathfrak{F}} \frac{u - v}{u + v} \ln \frac{c_2}{c_1} \tag{7-3}$$

where u and v are the mobilities of the cations and anions respectively. If the cation and anion differ in their mobilities, a small potential difference will develop across the membrane because of the slower diffusion of one ion species. Bernstein argued that the cell membrane was not equally permeable to all species of ions, but selectively permeable to potassium and practically impermeable to sodium and chloride. The potential difference across the cell membrane was regarded to be a limiting case of the Nernst equation.

$$E = -\frac{RT}{Z\mathfrak{F}} \ln \frac{[K^+]_{in}}{[K^+]_{out}} \tag{7-4}$$

In the 1930s it became apparent that the membrane is, in fact, permeable to chloride ions.[16] Boyle and Conway suggested that the transmembrane resting potential resulted from a Donnan equilibrium and was given by the relation

$$E = -\frac{RT}{\mathfrak{F}} \ln \frac{[K^+]_{in}}{[K^+]_{out}} = -\frac{RT}{\mathfrak{F}} \ln \frac{[Cl^-]_{out}}{[Cl^-]_{in}} \tag{7-5}$$

It was found that the injury or transmembrane potential was a logarithmic function of the external potassium concentration.

It was realized later that the membrane is permeable not only to potassium and chloride ions but also to sodium ions.[17] This discovery led to the view that there are two kinds of ion distributions across the cell membrane: an active process, leading to the extrusion of sodium ions against an electrochemical gradient, which was coupled to metabolic energy production in the cell; and the passive distribution of other ions by diffusional and electrical forces.[18] Careful measurements using microelectrodes revealed that the transmembrane potential was always less than that expected by eqs. 7-4 or 7-5. In addition, at very low external potassium concentrations, the transmembrane potential deviated appreciably from a logarithmic dependence on the $[K^+]_{out}$. Under these circumstances, the passive permeability to sodium ions was thought to influence the membrane potential significantly. It was proposed that the transmembrane potential was given by an equation derived by considering the conditions necessary for constant field strength while the distribution of charges across the membrane was permitted to vary.[19]

---

[14] Bernstein, J. *Pflüger's Arch. ges. Physiol.*, *92*, 521 (1902).
[15] Nernst, W. *Z. Physik. Chem.*, *2*, 613 (1888); Planck, M. *Ann. Physik.*, *40*, 561 (1890).
[16] Boyle, P. J., and Conway, E. J. *J. Physiol.*, *100*, 1 (1941).
[17] Steinbach, H. B. *J. Biol. Chem.*, *133*, 695 (1940); Manery, J. F., and Bale, W. F. *Am. J. Physiol.*, *132*, 215 (1941); Harris, E. J., and Burn, G. P. *Trans. Faraday Soc.*, *45*, 508 (1949).
[18] Dean, R. B. *Biol. Symp.*, *3*, 331 (1941).
[19] Goldman, D. E. *J. Gen. Physiol.*, *27*, 37 (1943); Hodgkin, A. L., and Katz, B. *J. Physiol.*, *108*, 37 (1949).

$$E = -\frac{RT}{Z\mathfrak{F}} \ln \frac{P_K[K^+]_{in} + P_{Na}[Na^+]_{in} + P_{Cl}[Cl^-]_{out}}{P_K[K^+]_{out} + P_{Na}[Na^+]_{out} + P_{Cl}[Cl^-]_{in}} \qquad (7\text{-}6)$$

where P_K, P_{Na}, and P_{Cl} are the permeability coefficients for potassium, sodium, and chloride respectively. The resting potential of squid axon can be quite accurately described by eq. 7-6 if it is assumed that $P_K : P_{Na} : P_{Cl} = 1.0 : 0.04 : 0.45$.

The view that the propagation of the nerve impulse depended upon the flow of an electric current in a cable-like structure dates to the turn of the century.[20] Bernstein (see footnote 14, p. 359) proposed that the cell membrane becomes highly permeable to ions of all species at the instant of excitation; the resting potential simultaneously falls to zero and generates an ionic current which acts to depolarize adjacent areas of the membrane. During the action potential, the transmembrane potential does not just go to zero but actually reverses polarity, and the total magnitude of the action potential may equal almost twice the resting potential.[21] It was felt that during the action potential the membrane was most permeable to sodium ions, which were predominant in determining the transmembrane potential. At the crest of the action potential, the transmembrane potential was approximately given by

$$E_{\substack{\text{action}\\\text{potential}}} = -\frac{RT}{n\mathfrak{F}} \ln \frac{[Na^+]_{in}}{[Na^+]_{out}} \qquad (7\text{-}7)$$

Recovery from excitation was held to involve a restoration of the normal ionic permeability characteristics of the membrane.

These penetrating early ideas of the permeability and electrical properties of membranes taken together with the early work on amphiphilic lipid films profoundly influenced the conception of membrane structure and function and have left their imprint on our contemporary views, which will be set out below. In recent years, however, electron microscopy and new biochemical techniques have given greater insight into the composition and structure of membranes; and formalisms based on analyses in terms of irreversible thermodynamics and electrochemistry have permitted a more precise description of transport phenomena.

surface phenomena

A fundamental property of an interface, such as that between two immiscible liquids, is that work must be performed to increase its area. Like other forms of work, this work involves the action of a force, the *surface tension*, Γ, multipied by its conjugate displacement, $d\mathfrak{A}$, the change in surface area. This set of intensive and extensive variables can be introduced into the expressions for total free energy (eqs. 4-29, *et seq.*) to account for changes in free energy originating in a change in state affecting the surface of a system. From eq. 4-45, we can write for an isothermal process

$$d\Theta = đQ - T dS + \Gamma\, d\mathfrak{A} + \sum_i \mu_i\, dn_i \qquad (7\text{-}8)$$

Any transformation which results in a lowering of the surface tension or a reduction in the surface area is exergonic; that is, $\Delta\Theta$ will be negative and will tend to occur

---

[20] Hermann, L. *Pflüger's Arch. ges. Physiol.*, *75*, 574 (1899).

[21] Curtis, H. J., and Cole, K. S. *J. Cellular Comp. Physiol.*, *19*, 135 (1942); Hodgkin, A. L., and Huxley, A. F. *Nature*, *144*, 710 (1939); Nastuk, W. L., and Hodgkin, A. L. *J. Cellular Comp. Physiol.*, *35*, 39 (1950); Huxley, A. F., and Stämpfli, R. *J. Physiol.*, *112*, 276 (1951).

spontaneously. By analogous reasoning, a modified form of the Gibbs-Duhem equation (eq. 4-50) can be written, so that for an isothermal, isobaric change of state

$$\mathfrak{A} d\Gamma + \sum_{i=1} n_i \, d\mu_i = 0 \tag{7-9}$$

If a two-component system (that is, one of solvent and solute) is examined at equilibrium between the bulk phase and the surface, the relation between the work of increasing the surface and the chemical work in transferring solute to the surface phase can be written directly as a reciprocity relation from eq. 7-8.

$$\sigma = -\left(\frac{\partial \Gamma}{\partial \mu_2}\right) = \left(\frac{\partial n_2}{\partial \mathfrak{A}}\right) \tag{7-10}$$

where σ is the *surface excess concentration* of solute and is defined by

$$\frac{d\Gamma}{d\mu_2} = \frac{n_2 - n_1 n_2^0/n_1^0}{\mathfrak{A}} \tag{7-11}$$

where n_1 and n_2 are the quantities of components 1 and 2 in the surface phase. The quantity n_2 is the number of moles of solute in the surface phase, and the term $n_1 n_2^0/n_1^0$ is the number of moles of solute associated with n_1 moles of solvent in the bulk phase.

It should be pointed out that a consequence of eq. 7-10 is that σ is an independent quantity which does not depend on n_1 (the moles of solvent segregated in the surface phase); σ depends only on the nature of the surface phase and has the dimensions of moles of solute per unit area. Substituting eq. 4-137 for μ_2 into eq. 7-10 gives

$$\sigma = -\frac{1}{RT}\left(\frac{d\Gamma}{d \ln a_2}\right) = -\frac{a_2}{RT}\left(\frac{d\Gamma}{da_2}\right) \tag{7-12}$$

Equation 7-12 is known as the *Gibbs surface isotherm*. For dilute solutions, the concentration approximates the activity, giving

$$\sigma = -\frac{c}{RT}\left(\frac{d\Gamma}{dc}\right) \tag{7-13}$$

A number of relatively insoluble substances of biological interest, including long-chain fatty acids, phospholipids, and proteins, tend to form monolayer films. Frequently these substances are amphiphilic; they possess a polar water-soluble portion and a hydrophobic water-insoluble portion. The spreading of such materials to form a monolayer and the stability of the film results from the large decrease in free energy which accompanies the great lowering of surface tension.

Surface films of poorly soluble or insoluble substances can be studied by means of a Langmuir trough, or a similar instrument, in which a film is confined to an area on the surface of solvent by movable barriers (Fig. 7-7). A barrier of length l separates the surface of solution from the surface of pure solvent. The surface tension of the solution will be less than that of pure solvent, and a counterforce F must be applied to the barrier so that the area of solution surface will not tend to expand at the expense of the surface area of pure solvent. If the barrier is allowed to move a small distance dx, $l dx = d\mathfrak{A}$, and the work performed will be given by

$$đW = (\Gamma_0 - \Gamma) l \, dx = F \, dx \tag{7-14}$$

$$\pi = F/l = (\Gamma_0 - \Gamma) = -\frac{d\Gamma}{d\bar{n}_i} \sum \bar{n}_i \approx -\frac{d\Gamma}{dc} c \tag{7-15}$$

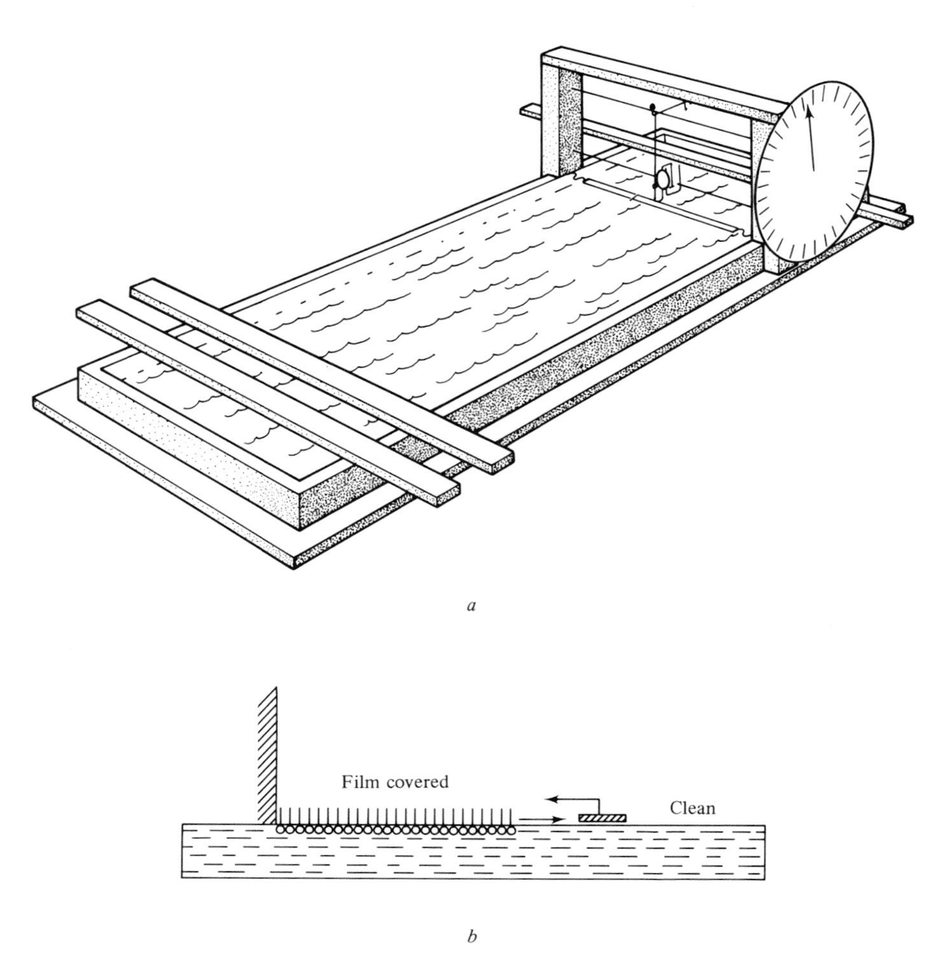

fig. 7-7. A Langmuir trough for the compression of lipid monolayers on the surface of a liquid. The film is confined to the smallest possible area by means of movable barriers. One barrier is attached to a torsion wire gauge to measure the force on the film.

where Γ_0 and Γ are the surface tensions of the pure solvent and the solution respectively and π is the surface pressure. The far right-hand terms in eq. 7-15 derive from the observation that Raoult's law (eq. 4-108) applies to the lowering of surface tension by solutes. The lowering of the surface tension is another colligative property of solutes.

Substituting eq. 7-15 into eq. 7-13 gives a relation which resembles the ideal gas law:

$$\pi = \sigma RT \qquad \textit{(7-16)}$$

Henri Devaux was the first to point out that molecules in monolayer films could exist in different states of molecular freedom that corresponded roughly to three-dimensional gases, liquids, and solids, and that changes from one state to another frequently could be brought about by changes in temperature or surface pressure. When a film is compressed in a Langmuir trough, changes in state cause a break in the pressure-*versus*-area curves. The molecules in *gaseous monolayers* lie flat and float about in the surface layer far apart enough so that there is little interaction between them. Gaseous monolayers are characterized by low surface pressure and low surface viscosities. Equation 7-16 has been used to determine the approximate molecular weights of proteins using films with low surface concentrations.[22] In gaseous monolayers, molecules occupy areas of the order of 100 to 200 Å^2. As surface concentrations increase and the area occupied by molecules begins to approach the area available, deviations from ideality are observed. A two-dimensional van der Waals equation can be written which applies in such instances

$$(\pi + a\sigma^2) = (\sigma - \sigma^0)RT \qquad (7\text{-}17)$$

where a is an interaction coefficient and σ^0 is a correction factor for the volume physically occupied by molecules in the film ($\sigma^0 = l/\mathfrak{A}^0$ where $\mathfrak{A}^0$ is the area occupied per mole).

In contrast to gaseous films, the molecules in *condensed monolayers* are arranged in the closest possible packing. In condensed films of fatty acids, alcohols, and phospholipids, the molecules stand upright with their polar ends immersed in the aqueous phase and the long hydrocarbon chains closely packed.[23] The pressure-*versus*-area plots are nearly straight and very steep, indicating low compressibility of condensed films (see Fig. 7-8). In homologous series of fatty acid monolayers, the area per molecule is about 20 Å^2, which is about equal to the cross-sectional area in bulk crystals as determined from x-ray diffraction. The area per molecule is largely independent of chain length, and optical measurements indicate that the thickness of the monolayers corresponds to fully extended chains. The pressure-area plots may be nonlinear or even show slight breaks. The transitions may reflect changes in the nature or orientation of the polar head groups such as changes in the degree of hydration, changes in the energy of hydrogen bonds between molecules or between molecules and solvent,

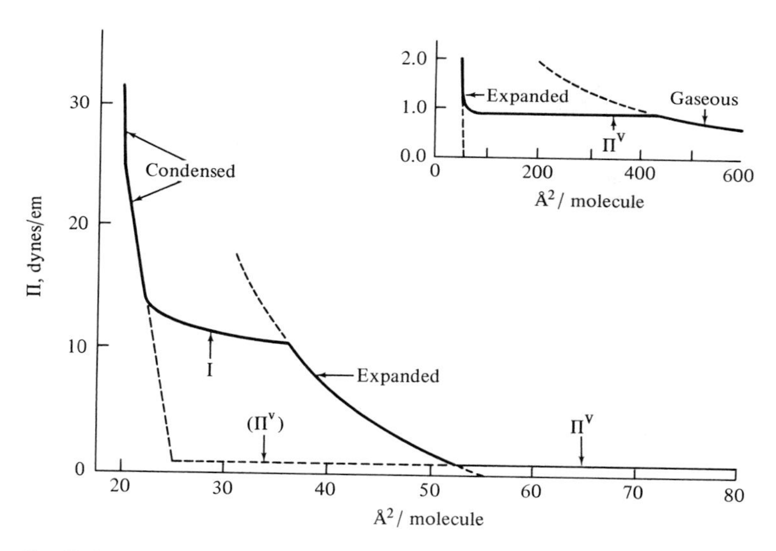

fig. 7-8. A generalized force-area curve for a long-chain amphiphilic substance obtained using a Langmuir trough, showing the various monolayer states and the transitions between them which may occur on compression. (From Gaines, G. L., Jr. *Insoluble Monolayers at Liquid-Gas Interfaces.* New York: Interscience, 1966, p. 178.)

[22] Guastalla, J. *Compt. Rend., 208,* 1078 (1939).
[23] Langmuir, I. *J. Am. Chem. Soc., 39,* 1848 (1917); Boyd, E., and Harkins, W. D. *J. Am. Chem. Soc., 61,* 1188 (1939); Ries, H. E., Jr., and Cook, H. D. *J. Colloid Sci., 9,* suppl. 1, 535 (1954); Dervichian, D. G. *J. Chem. Phys., 7,* 931 (1939).

or rearrangements of the conformation within the polar head groups.[24] Such transitions may correspond to mesomorphic liquid-crystalline states of bulk lipids.

Expanded (liquid) *monolayers* occupy an intermediate position between gaseous and condensed monolayers. The pressure-area plots of such films, although steep, show considerable curvature. Typically, the molecular area in the film is 2 to 3 times the molecular cross-sectional area; the molecular area extrapolated to $\pi = 0$ is about 40 to 55 Å^2 (Fig. 7-8). The films are coherent, even at low surface pressures; the cohesive interactions overcome the tendency of the film-forming molecules to separate. Langmuir[25] suggested that the hydrocarbon chains of the molecules in an expanded film are randomly arranged while the polar head groups are constrained to a discrete layer at the surface of the bulk solvent. The molecular mechanisms which are responsible for the lowering of surface tension and the tendency for amphiphilic lipids to localize at surfaces have been discussed briefly in Chapter 3.

artificial lipid membranes

In recent years a number of investigators have examined the properties of thin phospholipid membranes formed across the aperture of a thin diaphragm separating two chambers containing two aqueous solutions. These model systems bear considerable, though not yet clearly defined, relevance to natural membranes. Before considering the model, artificial membranes, it seems worthwhile to discuss some properties of complex phospholipids.

The acidic phospholipids bind divalent cations, particularly calcium, much more avidly than monovalent cations. The addition of calcium salts to the aqueous phase under a phospholipid monolayer in a Langmuir trough often produces marked changes in the force-area characteristics, while monovalent salts have no noticeable effect.[26] Calcium appears to cause the extrusion of water from the lipid phase of phospholipid suspensions and phospholipid membranes. While synthetic phospholipid suspensions bind K^+ and Na^+ very weakly and do not discriminate between them, phospholipids extracted from erythrocytes, brain, and other natural sources frequently contain more Na^+ than K^+, even though the potassium content in the total tissue was much higher than that of sodium.[27] The addition of calcium salts to the aqueous phase under a phospholipid monolayer results in significant changes in the surface potential and surface area while monovalent cations fail to produce these effects. Cholesterol also causes closer molecular packing in phospholipid films as reflected in the force-area characteristics.

Phospholipids swell in aqueous solutions to form myelin figures as described in Chapter 3 (Fig. 7-9). Myelin figures are concentric, multilamellar tubular or spherical structures in which bimolecular lamellae of phospholipid are separated by layers of solvent. The trapped solvent diffuses slowly out through the phospholipid layers providing a means for measuring directly the permeability of the phospholipid lamellae. Monovalent cations diffuse out quite slowly ($P \sim 10^{-12}$ cm/sec) while the permeability

---

[24] Alexander, A. E. *Proc. Roy. Soc.*, *A 179*, 470, 486 (1942); Vold, M. J. *J. Colloid Sci.*, *7*, 196 (1952); Kipling, J. J., and Norris, A. D. *J. Colloid Sci.*, *8*, 547 (1953).

[25] Langmuir, I. *J. Chem. Phys.*, *1*, 756 (1933).

[26] Woolley, D. W., and Campbell, N. K. *Biochim. Biophys. Acta*, *57*, 384 (1962); Abramson, M. B., Katzman, R., and Gregor, H. P. *J. Biol. Chem.*, *239*, 70 (1964); Joos, R. W., and Carr, C. W. *Proc. Soc. Exptl. Biol. Med.*, *124*, 1268 (1967).

[27] Kirschner, L. B. *J. Gen. Physiol.*, *42*, 231 (1958); Katzman, R., and Wilson, C. E. *J. Neurochem.*, *7*, 113 (1961).

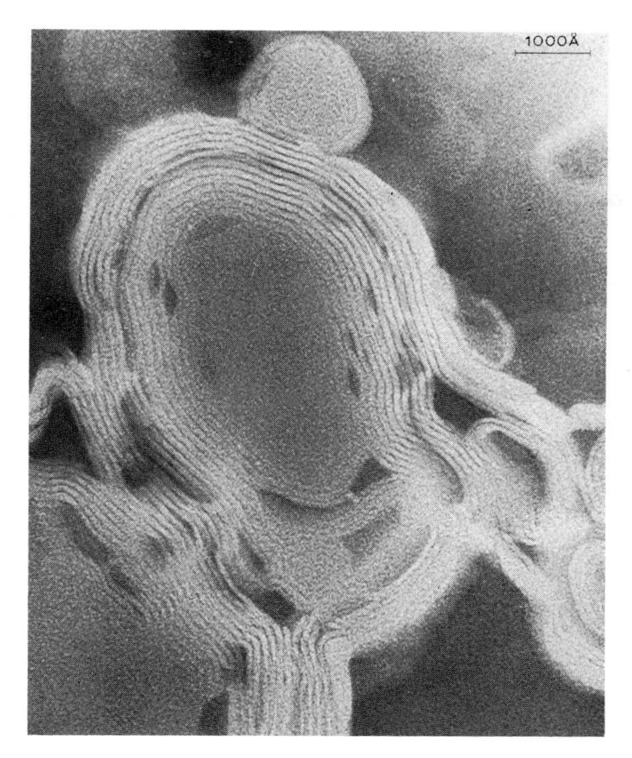

fig. 7-9. Electron micrograph of a myelin figure negatively stained with potassium phosphotungstate. Note the multilamellar structure of the fragment. (From Bangham, A. D., and Horne, R. W. *J. Mol. Biol., 8,* 662 [1964]. Copyright Academic Press; reprinted by permission.)

to anions such as chloride is about two orders of magnitude greater ($P \sim 10^{-10}$ cm/sec). The permeability to monovalent cations is lowered in the presence of calcium; calcium may also induce some Na/K discrimination.[28]

The most interesting model membrane systems utilize an apparatus, similar to that shown in Fig. 7-10, in which a droplet of a phospholipid solution in chloroform and methanol is placed in the aperture of the diaphragm separating the two aqueous solutions. The film which forms across the hole gradually becomes thinner as the solvent diffuses into the aqueous phases and flows into a thick annular ring at the edges of the hole. Finally the central portion (except for the ring at the edge of the hole) of the film thins out and appears black to reflected light. Such black films have been shown to be about 70 Å thick, the dimensions of a bimolecular leaflet of phospholipids. Complex lipids obtained from chloroform-methanol extracts of brain white matter as well as highly purified phospholipids such as phosphatidylcholine, phosphatidylethanolamine, phosphatidylinositol, and sphingomyelin have been used to prepare such artificial bilayer membranes. The presence of unsaturated fatty acid residues in the phospholipids appears to enhance the stability of the films which are

[28] Rosano, H. L., Schulman, J. H., and Weisbuch, J. B. *Ann. N.Y. Acad. Sci., 92,* 457 (1961); Bangham, A. D., Standish, M. M., and Watkins, J. C. *J. Mol. Biol., 13,* 238 (1965); Papahadjopoulos, D., and Bangham, A. D. *Biochim. Biophys. Acta, 126,* 185 (1966); Papahadjopoulos, D., and Watkins, J. C. *Biochim. Biophys. Acta, 135,* 639 (1967).

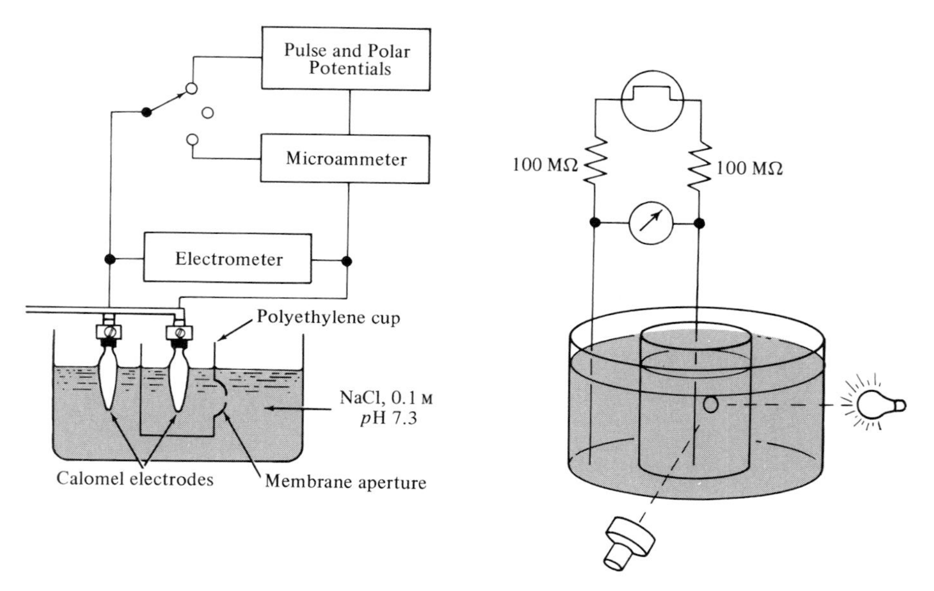

fig. 7-10. A schematic representation of the apparatus used for studying lipid bilayer films. The film is formed by painting a droplet of phospholipid solution across the aperture of the teflon cup with a fine paintbrush and letting it thin out.

formed.[29] The presence of α-tocopherol or a hydrocarbon or cholesterol also appears to be required for the formation of stable films; these compounds perhaps act to fill the spaces in the nonpolar ends of the phospholipid molecules. The films tend to form more easily at temperatures in the 20 to 37° range where the fatty acid chains possess a degree of fluidity, a condition required for the formation of liquid crystalline phases.

The electrical properties of such artificial lipid membranes can be measured by the usual electrophysiological techniques.[30] A few important characteristics are listed in Fig. 7-11. The specific resistance of these membranes is of the order of $10^8 - 10^9$ ohm · cm^2, about two orders of magnitude greater than the values obtained for natural membranes. Dividing the specific resistance by the thickness of the membranes gives a resistivity of about $10^{14} - 10^{15}$ ohm · cm, a value which corresponds to that for bulk water-saturated hydrocarbons. Nonelectrolytes permeate the bilayer membranes approximately according to the lipid partition coefficient and inversely according to molecular size. Thus the relative order of permeation, glycerol > erythritol > mannitol, is observed in both model and natural membranes.[31] The artificial membranes are highly permeable to water. In view of the high membrane resistance, this probably takes place by simple dissolution of water in the phospholipid and

[29] Mueller, P., Rudin, D. O., Tien, H. T., and Wescott, W. C. *Nature*, *194*, 979 (1962); Mueller, P., Rudin, D. O., Tien, H. T., and Wescott, W. C. *J. Phys. Chem.*, *67*, 534 (1963); Huang, C., Wheeldon, L., and Thompson, T. E. *J. Mol. Biol.*, *8*, 148 (1964); Hanai, T., and Haydon, D. A. *J. Theoret. Biol.*, *11*, 370 (1966).

[30] Hanai, T., Haydon, D. A., and Taylor, J. *Proc. Roy. Soc.*, *A 281*, 377 (1964); Hanai, T., Haydon, D.A., and Taylor, J. *J. Theoret. Biol.*, *9*, 278, 433 (1965); Maddy, A. H., Huang, C., and Thompson, T. E. *Federation Proc.*, *25*, 933 (1966); Läuger, P., Lesslauer, W., Marti, E., and Richter, J. *Biochim. Biophys. Acta*, *135*, 20 (1967).

[31] Vreeman, H. J. *Kong. Ned. Akad. Wetensch. Proc.*, *B 69*, 564 (1966); Cass, A., and Finkelstein, A. *J. Gen. Physiol.*, *50*, 1765 (1967).

fig. 7-11. Electrical properties of synthetic phospholipid membranes. (Data from Andreoli, T. *Science, 154,* 417 [1966]; Hanai, T., Haydon, D. A., and Taylor, J. *J. Theoret. Biol., 9,* 433 [1965]; Läuger, P., Lesslauer, W., Marti, E., and Richter, J. *Biochim. Biophys. Acta, 135,* 20 [1967]; Lesslauer, W., Richter, J., and Läuger, P. *Nature, 213,* 1224 [1967]; MacDonald, R. *Federation Proc., 26,* 863 [1967]; Maddy, A. H., Huang, C., and Thompson, T. E. *Federation Proc., 25,* 933 [1966]; Mueller, P., and Rudin, D. O. *Nature, 213,* 603 [1967]; Mueller, P., Rudin, D. O., Tien, H. T., and Wescott, W. C. *Recent Progr. Surface Sci., 1,* 379 [1964]; Seufert, W. D. *Nature, 207,* 174 [1965].)

LIPID	RESISTANCE ($OHM \cdot CM^2$)	CAPACITANCE ($\mu f/CM^2$)
Brain phospholipids	$10^7 - 10^8$	0.7 – 1.3
Sheep erythrocyte lipids	10^8	0.3 – 0.4
Phosphatidylcholine	$10^6 - 10^8$	0.33 – 0.38
Phosphatidylinositol	$5 - 10^7$	—
Sphingomyelin	10^6	—
Natural membranes	$10^3 - 10^5$	0.5 – 1.3

diffusion through the membrane. Some permeability coefficients for lipid bilayer membranes are given in Fig. 7-12.

The high resistivity of these membranes argues against the presence of pores and is consistent with the observation that the membranes are only very slightly permeable to both cations and anions. The addition of small amounts of the polyene antibiotics, such as the gramicidins, valinomycin, or the enniatins, results in a dramatic lowering of the resistance. These antibiotic molecules have a doughnut shape; hydrophilic residues face the hole and hydrophobic residues are oriented outward. These molecules are presumed to insert themselves into the membranes and create pores.[32]

fig. 7-12. Permeability of membranes (permeability coefficients, cm/sec). THO is tritiated water. (Data from Brinley, F. J., Jr., and Mullins, L. J. *J. Neurophysiol., 28,* 526 [1965]; Dick, D. A. T. *Cell Water.* London: Butterworth, 1966; Huang, C., and Thompson, T. E. *J. Mol. Biol., 15,* 539 [1966]; Papahadjopoulos, D., and Watkins, J. C. *Biochim. Biophys. Acta, 135,* 639 [1967]; Thompson, T. E., and Huang, C. *Ann. N.Y. Acad. Sci., 137,* 740 [1966]; Troshin, A. S. *Problems of Cell Permeability.* London: Pergamon Press, 1966; Whittam, R. *Transport and Diffusion in Red Blood Cells.* Baltimore: Williams & Wilkins, 1964.)

MEMBRANE	H_2O		K^+	NA^+	CL^-
	THO FLUX	OSMOTIC FLUX			
Phosphatidylcholine film	4.3×10^{-4}	17.3×10^{-4}	3.4×10^{-12}	—	$10^{-9} - 10^{-12}$
Human erythrocyte	41×10^{-4}	1.16×10^{-2}	2.4×10^{-10}	—	2×10^{-4}
Squid axon	—	—	5.6×10^{-7}	1.5×10^{-8}	1.0×10^{-8}
Frog sartorius	—	1.3×10^{-2}	1.6×10^{-7}	1.4×10^{-7}	9.5×10^{-8}

[32] Lev, A. A., and Buzhinski, E. P. *Tsitologiya*, *9*, 102 (1967); Mueller, P., and Rudin, D. O. *Biochem. Biophys. Res. Commun.*, *26*, 398 (1967).

Mueller, Rudin, and their collaborators[33] found that exposing bilayer membranes to a crude concentrate of the growth medium of an *Aerobacter cloacae* culture lowers the membrane resistance by three orders of magnitude, makes the membrane cation selective (that is, gives the membrane the properties of a cation exchanger), and renders the membrane "excitable." This last property is derived from the nonlinear current voltage characteristics of the membrane (see Fig. 7-13). Thus, when an increas-

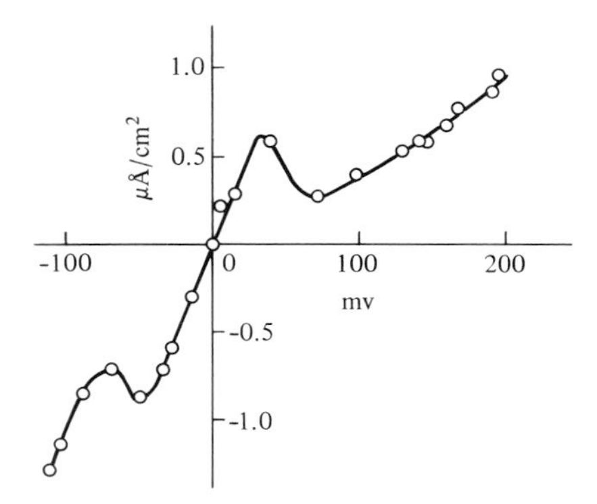

fig. 7-13. The current-voltage curve of a phospholipid bilayer rendered "excitable" by the addition of medium of a culture of *A. cloacae* grown on egg whites. (From Mueller, P., and Rudin, D. O. *J. Theoret. Biol., 4,* 272 [1963]. Copyright Academic Press; reprinted by permission.)

ing potential is applied to the membrane, there is a corresponding increase in current until a "threshold" potential is reached, whereupon the membrane undergoes a sudden spontaneous transition to a second stable resistive state with a new current value. In the presence of the bacterial excitability-inducing material, which is presumed to be a protein, the membrane displays the phenomenon of excitability shown by natural membranes. As will be discussed below, the addition of protein enhances the *semiconductor* properties of the lipid bilayer.

isolation of natural cell membranes[34]

Some of the recent developments in our concept of biological membranes have been prompted by studies of membrane constituents. To study the composition of cell membranes it is necessary to isolate reasonably pure membranes from disrupted cells in quantities sufficiently large for chemical analyses. In scrutinizing the experimental validity of isolation procedures, two crucial, but still unsettled, points should be borne in mind. First, it is not known whether the limiting surface membrane (or

[33] Mueller, P., and Rudin, D. O. *J. Theoret. Biol.*, *4*, 268 (1963); Mueller, P., Rudin, D. O., Tien, H. T., and Wescott, W. C. *Rec. Progr. Surface Sci.*, *1*, 379 (1964).
[34] This section and the following six sections were adapted from R. M. Dowben, Composition and structure of membranes, in Dowben, R. M., ed. *Biological Membranes*. Boston: Little, Brown, 1969, with permission.

plasma membrane) of the cell resembles the intracellular membranes in composition and structure or whether important differences exist between the two. Second, it is not clear whether membranes are composed of a single type of structural subunit or whether they are a mosaic of a variety of types of structural subunits.

All preparative procedures involve disruption of cells which results in at least a temporary discontinuity in the structural integrity of the membranes. In general, cellular disruption is brought about by the application of mechanical shearing forces. Curtis[35] found a remarkable drop in the surface viscosity of cells immediately after they were subjected to shearing forces. This thixotropic response reflects a decrease or loosening in the molecular packing upon the application of shearing stress. It is reasonable to assume that the molecular expansion within the membrane occurs more readily under conditions where electrostatic interactions of the membrane constituents with the solvent tend to counteract the internal cohesive forces. The most important factors which affect electrostatic interactions are low ionic strength, low concentrations of divalent cations, and high *p*H. Therefore, it is not surprising that the size and morphology of the membrane fragments depend not only on the mechanical means used to disrupt the cells but also on the composition, ionic strength, and *p*H of the suspension medium. While the cell membrane is disrupted during homogenization, electron micrographs show that the junctional specializations between cells, the tight junctions and desmosomes, remain intact.[36]

Mature mammalian erythrocytes have been the cell type most widely used as a source for membranes because they are obtained easily in suspension by venipuncture and because they lack a nucleus, intracellular organelles, and an intracellular membrane system. Membranes of erythrocytes (ghosts), with less than 2 percent hemoglobin, can be prepared by lysis in hypotonic media; they amount to 2 to 5 percent of the weight of the original cells. Control of ionic strength and *p*H is required for reproducible preparations. Lysis in 0.02 B phosphate buffer at *p*H 7.4 produces flattened ghosts of uniform appearance with about the same diameter as the intact erythrocyte[37] while lysis in media of lower ionic strength or higher *p*H may result in the formation of small fragments. During hemolysis, the membranes become transiently permeable to large molecules,[38] but they subsequently recover their relative impermeability to macromolecules and ions. The fat globules in milk are surrounded by an envelope which appears to be derived from the surface membrane of the mammary cells.[39] Preparations of milk-fat globule membranes[40] contain enzymes characteristic of other membrane preparations.

A method for the preparation of plasma membranes from liver and other solid tissues was developed by Neville[41] and later modified by Emmelot and his coworkers.[42] Plasma membranes prepared by this method appear in electron photomicrographs as sheets or as spherical vesicles with a trilaminar structure. The sheets are often still connected by desmosomes. Presumably the vesicles are formed from microvilli late in the preparative procedure. Wallach[43] has argued that the yield of membranes by

[35] Curtis, A. S. G. *Biol. Rev.*, *37*, 82 (1962).
[36] Farquhar, M. G., and Palade, G. E. *J. Cell Biol.*, *17*, 375 (1963).
[37] Dodge, J. T., Mitchell, C., and Hanahan, D. *Arch. Biochem. Biophys.*, *100*, 119 (1962).
[38] Hoffman, J. F. *J. Gen. Physiol.*, *45*, 837 (1962).
[39] Bargmann, W., and Knoop, A. *Z. Zellforsch.*, *49*, 344 (1959).
[40] Dowben, R. M., Brunner, J. R., and Philpott, D. E. *Biochim. Biophys. Acta*, *135*, 1 (1967).
[41] Neville, D. M., Jr. *J. Biophys. Biochem. Cytol.*, *8*, 413 (1960).
[42] Emmelot, P., and Bos, C. J. *Biochim. Biophys. Acta*, *58*, 374 (1962).
[43] Wallach, D. F. H. Isolation of plasma membranes of animal cells, in Davis, B. D., and Warren, L., eds. *The Specificity of Cell Surfaces*. Englewood Cliffs, N.J.: Prentice-Hall, 1967, p. 129.

this technique is low—14 percent or less of the theoretical amount calculated for liver—and that in addition to membrane fragments derived from the cell surface, membrane fragments of intracellular origin from nuclei, lysosomes, and endoplasmic reticulum are also present. Finean[44] has estimated that cell membranes prepared in this manner contain 1 to 30 percent cytoplasmic contamination.

Wallach and his coworkers[45] utilized Ehrlich ascites tumor cells or tissue-cultured cells disrupted by intracellular cavitation which follows sudden reduction in the ambient pressure. Suspensions of cells in a buffered, isotonic medium are equilibrated with an inert gas, usually nitrogen, under 50 to 75 atmospheres of pressure. After equilibration, the pressure is suddenly reduced to 1 atmosphere. This results in rupture of almost all cells without disruption of nuclei or mitochondria. The plasma membrane fragments are then purified from the microsomal fraction by centrifugation in sucrose or Ficoll density gradients containing divalent cations. In Ficoll gradients, the surface membrane fragments, identified by cell surface antigens or by the presence of sodium-potassium activated ATPase, collect in the fractions around density 1.07. Sodium-potassium activated ATPase activity is also found in the pellet which is thought to represent intracellular membranes.

Preparations of specialized membranes have been useful for certain types of studies. For example, mitochondria may be isolated in pure form by differential centrifugation of cell homogenates, and membranes may be prepared from the washed mitochondria.[46] If the mitochondria are permitted to swell in 0.02 M phosphate buffer, *p*H 7.2, containing 0.02 percent bovine serum albumin, the inner and outer membranes separate, giving a mixture of inner membrane ghosts and broken outer membrane fragments. The inner membrane and outer membrane fractions can be separated by centrifugation in a sucrose gradient.[47] The density of the inner membrane is about 1.21 while that of the outer membrane is about 1.12.

In electron micrographs, the outer membranes appear as collapsed, folded bags with a single membrane layer showing a surface ultrastructure pattern thought to

fig. 7-14. Composition of plasma membranes. (Data from O'Neill, C. H. *Exptl. Cell Res.*, *35*, 477 [1964]; Dodge, J. T., Mitchell, C. D., and Hanahan, D. J. *Arch. Biochem. Biophys.*, *100*, 119 [1963]; Emmelot, P., Bos, C. J., Benedetti, E. L., and Rümke, P. *Biochim. Biophys. Acta*, *90*, 126 [1964]; Bakerman, S., and Wasemiller, G. *Biochemistry*, *6*, 1100 [1967].)

SOURCE	ERYTHROCYTE (PERCENT)	RAT LIVER (PERCENT)	AMOEBA (PERCENT)
Lipids	37.0	39.3	32.0
Protein	51.0	56.5	42.5
Carbohydrate	10.0	4.2	14.7
RNA	1.0		1.0
Moisture			7.7

[44] Finean, J. B., Coleman, R., and Green, W. A. *Ann. N.Y. Acad. Sci.*, *137*, 414 (1966).
[45] Wallach, D. F. H., and Kamat, V. B. *Proc. Natl. Acad. Sci.*, *52*, 721 (1964).
[46] Criddle, R. S., Bock, R. M., Green, D. E., and Tisdale, H. *Biochemistry*, *1*, 827 (1962).
[47] Parsons, D. F., Williams, G. R., and Chance, B. *Ann. N.Y. Acad. Sci.*, *137*, 643 (1966).

represent patches of small particles about 45 Å in diameter. The outer membranes contain the citric acid cycle enzymes and the fatty acid oxidation enzymes.[48] The inner membranes appear as vesicles in which the cristae have been largely smoothed out, thereby permitting swelling to occur without breakage. The inner membranes contain the oligomycin-sensitive ATPase and at least some of the enzymes of oxidative phosphorylation. The outer membranes appear to be permeable to both water and sucrose, while the inner membranes are permeable to water but relatively impermeable to sucrose. Another type of specialized membrane preparation is that obtained from *Mycoplasma* (pleuropneumonia-like organisms, PPLO).[49]

The principal constituents of membranes are lipids and proteins, but smaller amounts of carbohydrate and RNA are almost always present. The gross composition of several membrane preparations is given in Fig. 7-14.

membrane lipids

Lipids account for 25 to 50 percent of the dry weight of membrane preparations. Erythrocyte ghosts, the most thoroughly studied membrane preparation, contain 95 to 100 percent of the total cellular lipids. The fact that almost all the red cell lipids can be recovered in the ghosts in spite of repeated washing means that the lipid must be firmly incorporated into the membrane. In the case of most other cells, considerable amounts of phospholipids are found in cell components other than the plasma membrane; it is not clear whether the other lipids are restricted to intracellular membranous structures or whether they also occur free.

Cholesterol, mostly free, accounts for 20 to 30 percent of the lipids extracted from the mammalian erythrocyte ghosts and other plasma membrane preparations. Bacterial and mitochondrial membranes contain little cholesterol. The phospholipids as a class account for almost all the remaining membrane lipids, but the proportion of the various phospholipids varies widely from species to species according to the tissue from which the cell membrane sample is derived and other factors such as diet. Frequently, the molar ratio of cholesterol to phospholipids approaches unity. Cholesterol and phospholipids appear to interact as judged by the fact that the mean area per molecule of mixed monolayers is less than would be expected from the composition were no interaction present (Langmuir trough experiments).

It has been shown[50] that erythrocyte cholesterol and phospholipids exchange rapidly in vivo and in vitro with serum cholesterol and serum lipoprotein lipids. The time of half exchange is approximately one hour. Turnover studies in adult rat brain using ^{32}P incorporation indicate a half-life of about 11 days for phosphoinositides, 17 days for phosphatidylethanolamine, and 40 days for the sphingophosphatides.[51] Cell membranes appear to turn over their complement of phospholipids by continual resynthesis. Erythrocyte ghosts, for example, have the capacity of incorporating ^{14}C-labeled fatty acids into phospholipids in the presence of ATP, Mg^{++}, and coenzyme A.[52]

---

[48] Green, D. E., and Perdue, J. F. *Ann. N.Y. Acad. Sci.*, *137*, 667 (1966).
[49] Razin, S. *J. Gen. Microbiol.*, *37*, 451 (1964).
[50] Hagerman, J. S., and Gould, R. G. *Proc. Soc. Exptl. Biol. Med.*, *78*, 329 (1951); Reed, C. F. *J. Clin. Invest.*, *38*, 1032 (1959).
[51] Freysz, L., Bierth, R. I., and Mandel, P. *Bull. Soc. Chim. Biol.*, *47*, 1441 (1965); Mandel, P., and Nussbaum, J. L. *J. Neurochem.*, *13*, 629 (1966).
[52] Oliveira, M. M., and Vaughan, M. *J. Lipid Res.*, *5*, 156 (1964); Mulder, E., and van Deenen, L. L. M. *Biochim. Biophys. Acta*, *106*, 106 (1965).

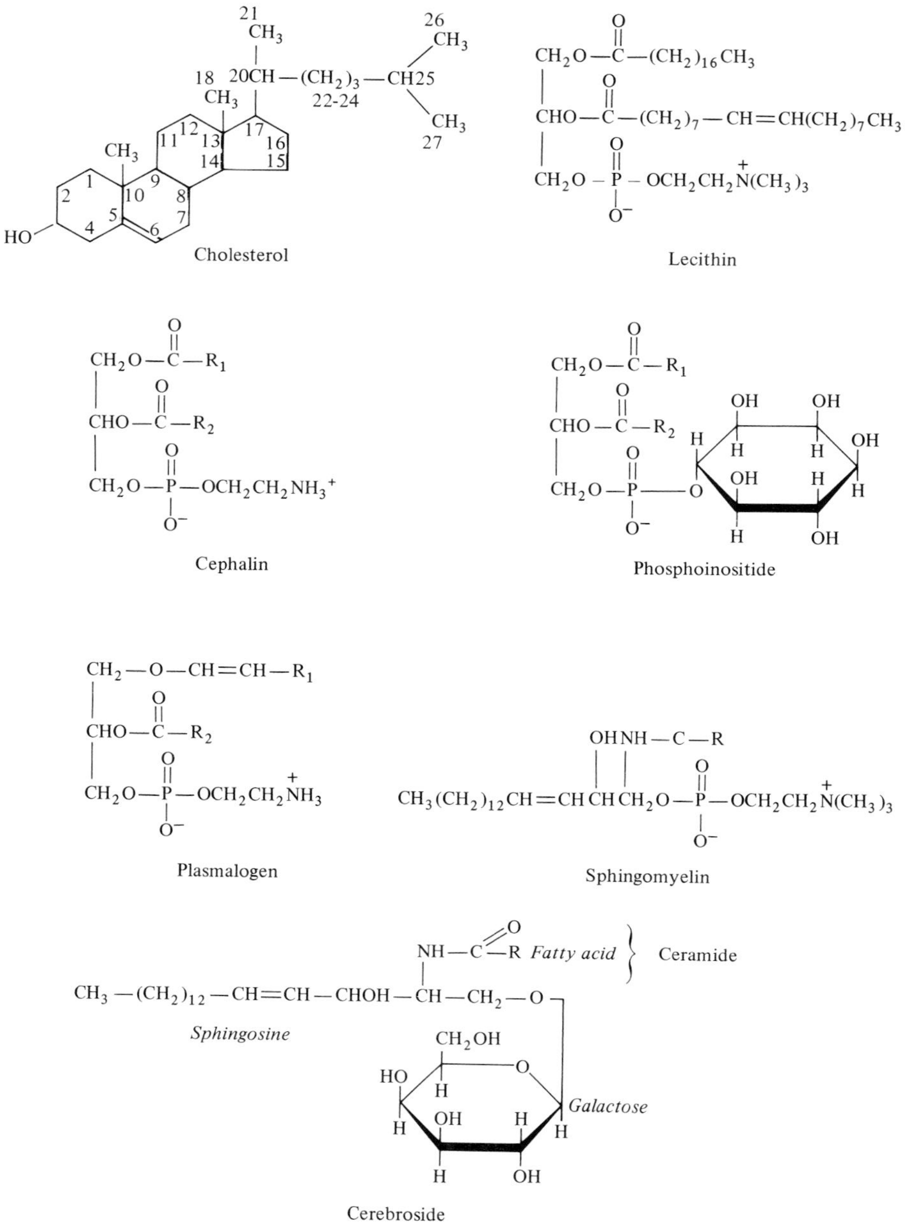

21
CH_3
18 20CH—$(CH_2)_3$—CH25
CH_3 22-24
26 CH_3
CH_3 27
CH_3
1 2 4 5 6 7 8 9 10 11 12 13 14 15 16 17
HO
Cholesterol

$CH_2O—\overset{O}{\overset{||}{C}}—(CH_2)_{16}CH_3$
$CHO—\overset{O}{\overset{||}{C}}—(CH_2)_7—CH{=}CH(CH_2)_7CH_3$
$CH_2O—\overset{O}{\overset{||}{P}}—OCH_2CH_2\overset{+}{N}(CH_3)_3$
O^-
Lecithin

$CH_2O—\overset{O}{\overset{||}{C}}—R_1$
$CHO—\overset{O}{\overset{||}{C}}—R_2$
$CH_2O—\overset{O}{\overset{||}{P}}—OCH_2CH_2NH_3^+$
O^-
Cephalin

$CH_2O—\overset{O}{\overset{||}{C}}—R_1$
$CHO—\overset{O}{\overset{||}{C}}—R_2$
$CH_2O—\overset{O}{\overset{||}{P}}—O$
O^-
OH OH H H H OH OH H H H H OH
Phosphoinositide

$CH_2—O—CH{=}CH—R_1$
$CHO—\overset{O}{\overset{||}{C}}—R_2$
$CH_2O—\overset{O}{\overset{||}{P}}—OCH_2CH_2\overset{+}{N}H_3$
O^-
Plasmalogen

OH NH—C—R
$CH_3(CH_2)_{12}CH{=}CH\,CH\,CH_2O—\overset{O}{\overset{||}{P}}—OCH_2CH_2\overset{+}{N}(CH_3)_3$
O^-
Sphingomyelin

NH—C(=O)—R *Fatty acid* } Ceramide
$CH_3—(CH_2)_{12}—CH{=}CH—CHOH—CH—CH_2—O$
Sphingosine
CH_2OH
HO H O H OH H H H OH
Galactose
Cerebroside

fig. 7-15a Structure of phospholipids.

The structure of the various phospholipids is shown in Fig. 7-15. Zwitterionic phospholipids such as phosphatidylcholine make up half, or slightly more, of the total phospholipids present in membranes from most sources.[53] The remaining phospholipids are principally sphingophospholipids, which have a net negative charge at

[53] van Deenen, L. L. M. Phospholipids and biomembranes, in Holman, R., ed. *Progress in the Chemistry of Fats and Related Lipids.* New York: Pergamon Press, 1965, vol. 8, p. 1.

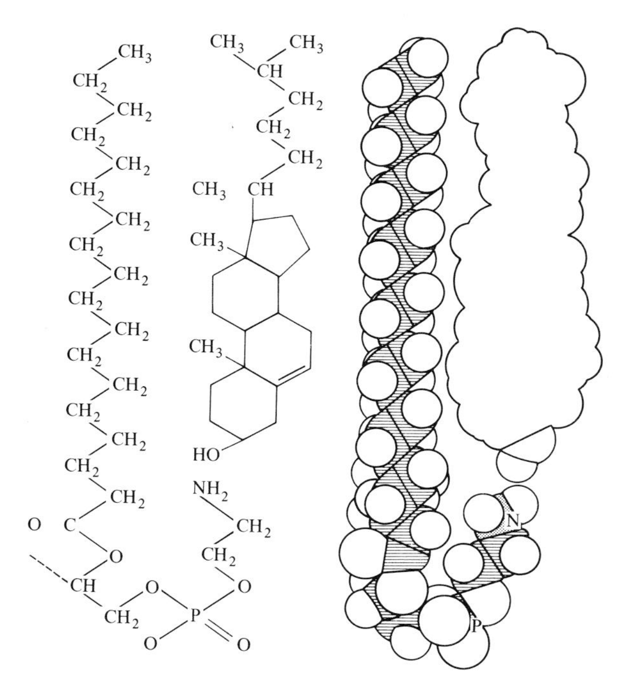

fig. 7-15b. Hypothetical conformation of a phosphatidylethanolamine molecule and a cholesterol molecule in the membrane.

physiological *p*H. The ratio between phosphatidylcholine and sphingophospholipids differs greatly from species to species and even in membrane preparations from different tissues of a given organism. The composition of lipids from erythrocyte ghosts of various mammals is depicted in Fig. 7-16.

A variety of fatty acid residues are found in the lipids which range in carbon chain

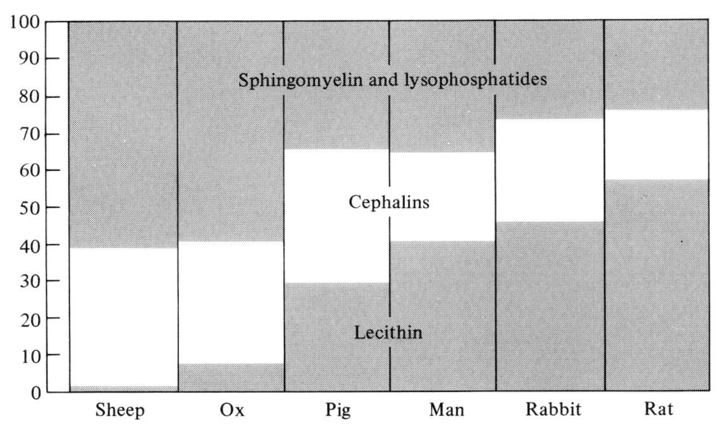

fig. 7-16. Lipid composition of erythrocyte ghosts from various mammals. (From Elbers, P. F. *Recent Progr. Surface Sci., 2*, 467 [1964]. Copyright Academic Press; reprinted by permission.)

length from 16 to 22 carbon atoms and in the degree of unsaturation from 0 to 4 double bonds. One constant finding is a relatively high proportion of unsaturated fatty acids, not infrequently amounting to 40 percent or more of the total fatty acid residues. The distribution of fatty acid residues is not fixed for any given tissue and species, but depends upon the physiological conditions of the environment, such as ambient temperature and diet. Of course, the physical characteristics of phospholipid films depend upon the nature of the fatty acid residues.

membrane proteins

Less is known about the proteins that are associated with biological membranes than is known about the lipids. Among the early studies, Jorpes[54] extracted washed erythrocyte ghosts with phosphate buffer at *p*H 5.5, then removed the lipids with an ethanol-ether mixture and obtained an insoluble protein which he called *stromatin.* Moskowitz and Calvin[55] washed freeze-dried ghosts with buffer at *p*H 9 until a colorless supernatant fraction was obtained. They called the sediment *stromin* and considered it to be the main structural framework of the membrane. After removal of the cholesterol and about half the cephalins by ether extraction, stromin appeared to consist of two components, a lipoprotein, *elinin*, which was soluble at *p*H 9, and an insoluble protein, *stromatin.* A third protein, "*s*" *protein*, could be precipitated from the elinin solution by lowering the *p*H to 6.4. The elinin fraction contained the blood-group antigens; these were absent from the "s" protein. Elinin was fibrous in character and was visualized in the electron microscope as rod-like particles 5 to 11 μ long and 0.3 to 1.3 μ wide. Sedimentation studies gave a molecular weight of 4.0×10^7. One percent solutions of elinin in water showed marked streaming birefringence, and 5 percent solutions formed a gel.

Some progress has been made toward isolating a structural protein from mitochondrial membranes solubilized by sodium deoxycholate.[56] Protein was precipitated fractionally from the solubilized mitochondrial membrane by adding increments of ammonium sulfate. The lipid moiety was removed from the precipitated lipoprotein fraction by extraction with a solution of 9 parts acetone to 1 part water. An aggregate of insoluble protein was obtained which appeared to combine stoichiometrically with phospholipid by noncovalent hydrophobic interactions. Such reconstituted lipoprotein tended to form vesicles bounded by a trilaminar unit membrane when examined in the electron microscope (see p. 380). Structural protein interacted with various cytochromes to form water-soluble adducts. After succinylation[57] the structural protein became water soluble and lost its tendency to aggregate. The monomeric species of the structural protein appeared to have a molecular weight in the neighborhood of 22,000. Similar proteins may have been prepared from liver microsomes, bovine erythrocytes, and spinach leaf chloroplasts.[58]

Solubilized lipoproteins have been isolated from erythrocyte ghosts treated with

[54] Jorpes, E. *Biochem. J.*, *26*, 1488 (1932).

[55] Moskowitz, M., and Calvin, M. *Exptl. Cell Res.*, *3*, 33 (1952).

[56] Criddle, R. S., Bock, R. M., Green, D. E., and Tisdale, H. *Biochem. Biophys. Res. Commun.*, *5*, 75, 81, 109 (1961); Criddle, R. S., Bock, R. M., Green, D. E., and Tisdale, H. *Biochemistry*, *1*, 827 (1962); Richardson, S. H., Hulton, H. O., and Fleischer, S. *Arch. Biochem. Biophys.*, *105*, 254 (1964).

[57] MacLennan, D. H., Tzagoloff, A., and Rieske, J. S. *Arch. Biochem. Biophys.*, *109*, 383 (1965).

[58] Richardson, S. H., Hulton, H. O., and Green, D. E. *Proc. Natl. Acad. Sci.*, *50*, 821 (1963).

n-butanol, sonication, detergents, or a combination of these treatments.[59] Solubilization of membrane protein by extraction of lipid with butanol indicates that nonionic, noncovalent bonds are important in maintaining the structural integrity of the membrane. In spite of considerable interest and effort, well-characterized proteins have not yet been isolated. Various fractions have been segregated which differ in their sedimentation characteristics, amino acid composition, and migration in electrophoresis. Starch-gel or acrylamide-gel electrophoresis reveals that these fractions are probably heterogeneous because they give rise to multiple bands. Similarly,[60] starch-gel electrophoresis of erythrocyte ghost protein solubilized by 8 M urea and 0.16 M mercaptoethanol after extraction of the lipids gives 10 discrete bands.

Treatment of erythrocyte ghosts with hypotonic buffers extracts aldolase, glyceraldehyde phosphate dehydrogenase, carbonic anhydrase, and adenosine deaminase without damage to the structural integrity of the ghost membrane. Further extraction of erythrocyte ghosts with hypertonic NaCl solutions (salt concentration 0.2 to 1.4 M) extracts a portion of the stromal lipids and acetylcholinesterase and other ghost proteins. Solubilization of stromal proteins by concentrated salt solutions suggests that electrostatic protein-protein interactions are also important in maintaining membrane structure.

membrane structure

Many of the contemporary ideas about the molecular structure of biological membranes can be traced to the classical experiments of Gorter and Grendel,[61] who extracted the lipid from washed erythrocytes and spread it as a monomolecular film on a Langmuir trough. At low pressure, Gorter and Grendel found that the film covered an area which was almost exactly twice the total surface area calculated for the intact red cells used in the experiment. The individual molecules were presumably packed together in the monomolecular film in the Langmuir trough with the polar, hydrophilic ends submerged in the water, and the nonpolar hydrophobic chain projecting upward into the air. Gorter and Grendel suggested that the cell membrane consisted of a bimolecular layer of lipids, the molecules standing on end and packed with the hydrophobic ends apposed at the center and the hydrophilic ends facing inward and outward. Actually, the erythrocyte surface area is probably 50 percent greater than that calculated by Gorter and Grendel.[62] It also appears that the acetone extraction used by these investigators failed to solubilize about one-third of the lipid present in the ghosts.[63] Their figures, therefore, were a happy accident; the two errors tended to offset each other.[64]

The surface tension of marine eggs and other types of cells is as low as 0.1 to 0.2 dyne/cm, a value lower than would be expected from a lipid-water interface (about 9 dynes/cm). Danielli and Harvey[65] found that the interfacial tension between oil

---

[59] Andersen, V. *Clin. Chim. Acta*, *8*, 454 (1963); Maddy, A. H. *Biochim. Biophys. Acta*, *88*, 448 (1964); Maddy, A. H. *Biochim. Biophys. Acta*, *117*, 193 (1966); Mitchell, C. D., and Hanahan, D. J. *Biochemistry*, *5*, 51 (1966); Morgan, T. E., and Hanahan, D. J. *Biochemistry*, *5*, 1050 (1966); Bakerman, S., and Wasemiller, G. *Biochemistry*, *6*, 1100 (1967).
[60] Azen, E. A., Orr, S., and Smithies, O. *J. Lab. Clin. Med.*, *65*, 440 (1965).
[61] Gorter, E., and Grendel, F. *J. Exptl. Med.*, *41*, 439 (1925).
[62] Winkler, K. C., and Bungenberg de Jong, H. G. *Arch. Neerl. Physiol.*, *25*, 431 (1940); Westerman, M. P., Pierce, L. E., and Jensen, W. N. *J. Lab. Clin. Med.*, *57*, 819 (1961).
[63] Ways, P., and Hanahan, D. J. *J. Lipid Res.*, *5*, 318 (1964).
[64] Barr, R. S., Deamer, D. W., and Cornwell, D. G. *Science*, *153*, 1010 (1966).
[65] Danielli, J. F., and Harvey, E. N. *J. Cellular Comp. Physiol.*, *5*, 483 (1935).

and water could be lowered to about 0.6 dynes/cm by adding some of the egg contents to the aqueous phase. These observations of the lowering of surface tension led Davson and Danielli[66] to postulate the presence of a protein layer attached to the polar head groups on either side of Gorter and Grendel's bimolecular lipid leaflet (Fig. 7-17). The presence of protein might also be expected to contribute to the stability and strength of the lipid film comprising the membrane.

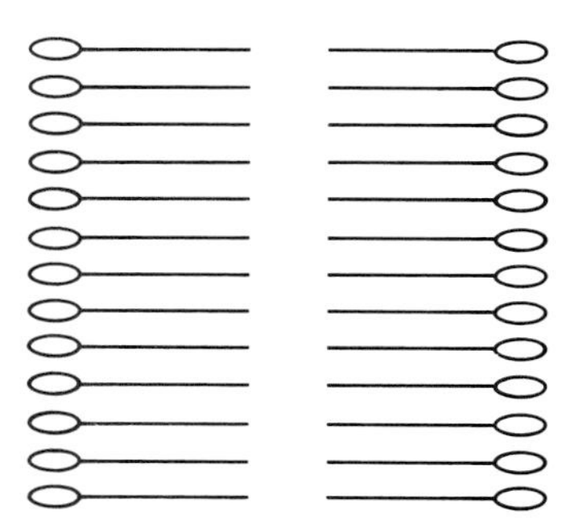

fig. 7-17. A model of the phospholipid bilayer membrane according to Gorter and Grendel.

The universality of the membrane concept depends to a considerable extent upon direct observations made with the electron microscope. The cell membrane appears as a thin band approximately 75 to 100 Å thick, consisting of two dark lines, each about 25 to 30 Å thick on either side of a light zone (Fig. 7-18). This ubiquitous, trilaminar structure, commonly referred to as the *unit membrane*, has been taken as strong support for the Davson-Danielli model. Unit membranes occur not only at the cell surface but also in the interior of cells as part of the *endoplasmic reticulum* and at the boundary of intracellular organelles.

Much of the early electron microscopic work was done on the myelin sheath which

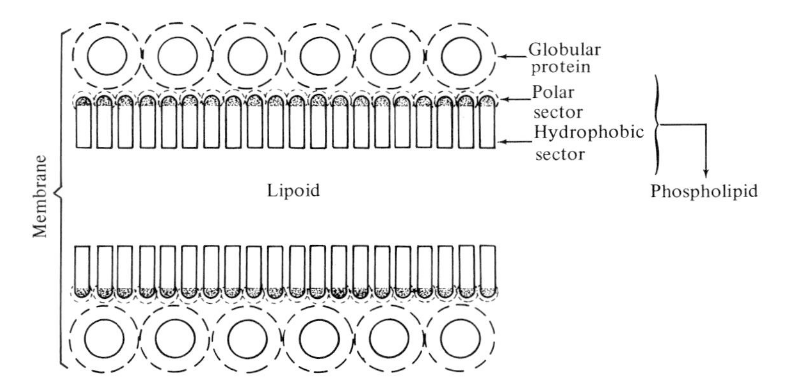

fig. 7-18. A schematic diagram of the Davson-Danielli model of membrane structure. (From Fig. 1, Danielli, J. F., and Davson, H. A. *J. Cellular Comp. Physiol., 5*, 498 [1935].)

[66] Davson, H., and Danielli, J. F. *The Permeability of Natural Membranes*, 2nd ed. London: Cambridge University Press, 1952.

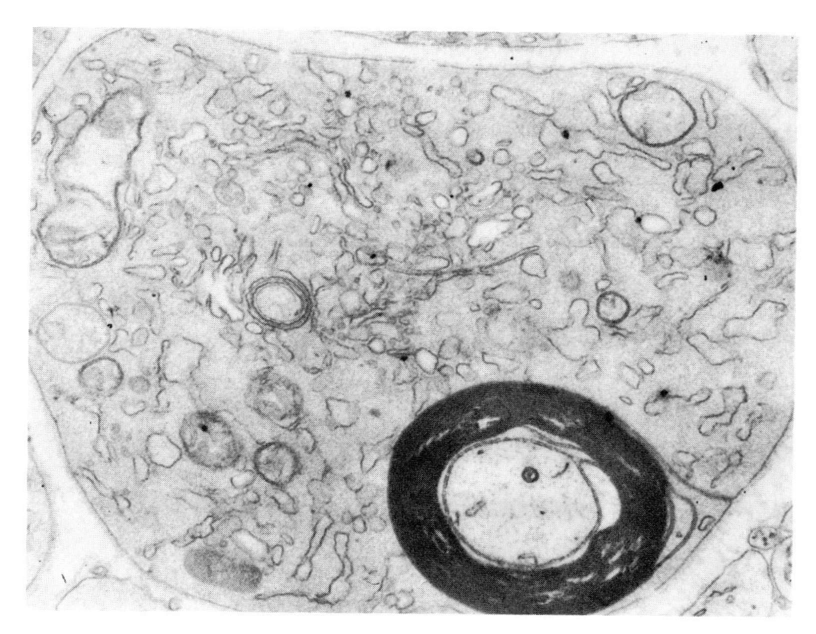

fig. 7-19. A neuron being enveloped by a Schwann cell forming the myelin sheath. Magnification 28,000. (Courtesy of Dr. J. D. Robertson.)

surrounds peripheral nerve fibers. The studies of Geren[67] have shown that myelin is laid down around a nerve fiber during embryonic development. At first the nerve axon is enveloped by a Schwann cell (Fig. 7-19). The axon is then covered by a double membrane, its own and that of the Schwann cell in which it is embedded. As development proceeds, there is rotation, either of the axon or of the Schwann cell, which results in a spiral winding of Schwann cell membranes around the axon. As the membranes wind around the axon, they come to adhere firmly to one another, obliterating the space between them.

Actually, Schmidt[68] had shown two decades before by polarization optical studies that the lipid molecules in myelin were arranged in a radial array, in alternating layers of protein and lipid, flat laminae of protein lying in a plane at right angles to stacked lipid molecules. It was deduced that the lipid-protein layers were thin compared to the wavelength of light and constituted a Wiener mixed body. The small-angle x-ray diffraction pattern showed that myelin consisted of concentric layers with a unit repeat of about 171 Å in myelin from cold-blooded animals and about 186 Å in myelin from warm-blooded animals.[69] Myelin is rich in cholesterol and has a high water content. In further x-ray diffraction studies, Finean[70] showed that there was a radial repeat of about 85.5 Å in addition to the 171 Å repeat in frog sciatic nerve. This finding gives further evidence of a double membrane layer. Upon drying, the myelin repeat, owing partly to the loss of water and partly to a rearrangement of the lipid molecules, falls from 171 Å to 146 Å.

---

[67] Geren, B. B. *Exptl. Cell Res.*, *7*, 558 (1954).
[68] Schmidt. W. J. *Die Doppelbrechung von Karyoplasma, Zytoplasma und Metaplasma*. Berlin: Borntraeger, 1937.
[69] Schmidt, F. W., Bear, R. S., and Palmer, K. J. *J. Cellular Comp. Physiol.*, *18*, 31 (1941).
[70] Finean, J. B. *Intern. Rev. Cytol.*, *12*, 303 (1961).

The electron-microscope studies of Fernández-Morán[71] and Sjöstrand[72] provided direct confirmation of the concentric laminar structure of myelin. The structure shows concentric major dense lines approximately 25 Å thick, with a center-to-center distance of 120 Å, and intervening thinner and less dense intraperiod lines. The difference between 171 Å and 120 Å was shown to result from manipulations (fixation, dehydration, and embedding) during the processing of the tissue prior to examination in the electron microscope.

It was in myelin that Robertson[73] first employed potassium permanganate fixation to show that each of the single dense lines seen upon osmium fixation could be resolved into two distinct dense lines, each about 25 Å thick, separated by a light zone of about the same thickness. Robertson believed that the membrane had structural polarity, that is, that the inside and outside surfaces were different. He conjectured that the outer surface is covered with mucoprotein while unconjugated protein covers the internal surface of the membrane (Fig. 7-20). As the Schwann cell winds around the

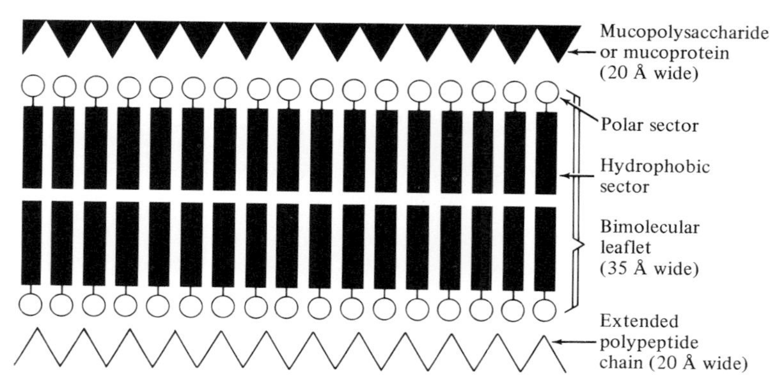

fig. 7-20. A diagrammatic representation of the unit membrane structure as proposed by Robertson. (From Robertson, J. D., in Locke, M., ed. *Cellular Membranes in Development.* New York: Academic Press, 1964, p. 13. Copyright Academic Press; reprinted by permission.)

axon, the inside surfaces of the membrane come to lie in apposition, giving rise to the major dense lines, and the outside surfaces similarly come to lie in apposition, giving rise to the intraperiod line.

Although the extensive work with myelin sheaths has been extrapolated to plasma membranes generally, it should be noted that myelin has many unique features. Myelin is poor in protein. It has a protein-to-lipid ratio of about 0.5 in contrast to other membrane preparations which have a protein-to-lipid ratio of 2 or more. In addition, the phospholipid composition of myelin differs from that of other membrane preparations.

While a trilaminar structure often can be seen after fixation and staining with osmium tetroxide alone, the trilaminar structure appears with better clarity in tissue fixed with potassium permanganate, where it is consistently and almost universally seen at cell boundaries.[74] The reactions of potassium permanganate with tissues that result in

[71] Fernández-Morán, H. *Exptl. Cell Res.*, *1*, 309 (1950).
[72] Sjöstrand, F. S. *Experientia*, *9*, 68 (1953).
[73] Robertson, J. D. *J. Biophys. Biochem. Cytol.*, *3*, 1043 (1957).
[74] Robertson, J. D. *Symp. Biochem. Soc.*, *16*, 3 (1959).

consistently clear trilaminar structures are unknown.[75] Although osmium tetroxide is known to react with proteins, its principal reaction in membranes is with the olefinic bonds in the fatty acid moieties to form an osmic acid diester of the glycol derivative.[76] Recently, these compounds have been isolated and characterized chemically in model reactions using fatty acid esters.[77] A reduction product is formed which is thought to migrate to the polar ends of the phospholipids.[78]

Bimolecular lipid leaflets formed across an aperture in a teflon diaphragm have been fixed in osmium tetroxide, and these specimens show a trilaminar structure in the electron microscope even though no protein is present.[79] The osmium is presumed to be located at the polar end groups on the outer surface of the leaflet. On the other hand, a trilaminar structure was observed in mitochondria fixed in osmium after all lipid had been removed by extraction with acetone.[80] Hollow spherules formed from proteinoid material can be stained with osmium tetroxide; these preparations show a structure like that of trilaminar unit membranes even though they contain no lipid.[81]

In addition to the uncertainties concerning the identity of the chemical groups which are responsible for the observed electron densities, the appearance of the unit membrane may reflect, in part, artifacts produced by the dehydration and extraction of the tissue with solvents during the preparation of sections for electron microscopy. In view of the ease with which artifacts can be produced and of the uncertainties of correlating electron densities with chemical structure, care should be exercised in interpreting electron micrographs; they cannot be used to verify the Davson-Danielli model.

Unit membranes show considerable variation in total thickness and in the relative thickness of the various members.[82] The cell membrane is thicker at the free surfaces of cells than when it is in contact with other cells in tissue, and it is thicker than the unit membrane of endoplasmic reticulum. To what extent these variations should be ascribed to differences in structure and to what extent they should be ascribed to artifacts of preparation is not clear.

The paucimolecular concept of membrane structure envisions the protein layers as existing in the extended or β-conformation. This arrangement tends to minimize nonpolar or hydrophobic interactions between the protein and lipid. Recent studies using infrared absorption[83] and optical rotatory dispersion[84] indicate that very little membrane protein is in the extended β-configuration. Most of it is randomly coiled and a small but significant percentage is in the α-helical form.

Several electron microscopists have observed repeating subunits in various membrane preparations, particularly in mitochondrial and chloroplast membranes.[85] The subunits appear as regular arrays of beads or transverse densities in the trilaminar

[75] Fernández-Morán, H., and Finean, J. B. *J. Biophys. Biochem. Cytol.*, *3*, 725 (1957); Korn, E. D., and Weisman, R. A. *Biochim. Biophys. Acta*, *116*, 309 (1966).
[76] Criegee, R. *Ann. Chem.*, *522*, 75 (1936).
[77] Korn, E. D., and Weisman, R. A. *Biochim. Biophys. Acta*, *116*, 309 (1966); Korn, E. D. *Biochim. Biophys. Acta*, *116*, 325 (1966); Korn, E. D. *Biochim. Biophys. Acta*, *116*, 317 (1966).
[78] Stoeckenius, W., and Mahr, S. C. *Lab. Invest.*, *14*, 1196 (1965).
[79] Henn, F. A., Decker, G. L., Greenwalt, J. W., and Thompson, T. E. *J. Mol. Biol.*, *24*, 51 (1967).
[80] Fleischer, S., Fleischer, B., and Stoeckenius, W. *Federation Proc.*, *24*, 296 (1965).
[81] Fox, S. W., Harada, K., and Kendrick, J. *Science*, *129*, 1221 (1959).
[82] Sjöstrand, F. S. *J. Ultrastruct. Res.*, *9*, 561 (1963); Yamamoto, T. *J. Cell Biol.*, *17*, 413 (1963); Elbers, *Rec. Progr. Surface Sci.*, *2*, 443 (1964).
[83] Maddy, A. H., and Malcolm, B. R. *Science*, *153*, 212 (1966).
[84] Wallach, D. F. H., and Zahler, P. H. *Proc. Natl. Acad. Sci.*, *56*, 1552 (1966).
[85] Fernández-Morán, H. *Circulation*, *26*, 1039 (1962); Fernández-Morán, H., Oda, T., Blair, P. V., and Green, D. E. *J. Cell Biol.*, *22*, 63 (1964); Stoeckenius, W. *J. Cell Biol.*, *17*, 443 (1963); Sjöstrand, F. S. *Nature*, *199*, 1262 (1963); Robertson, J. D. *J. Cell Biol.*, *19*, 201 (1963).

structure with a unit repeat of approximately 40 to 60 Å.[86] Robertson has argued that many of these subunit structures are very likely artifacts produced by examining sections which are cut slightly askew. In the case of retinal rods,[87] at least, the globular pattern in electron micrographs corresponds to a periodicity observed by low-angle x-ray diffraction.

Recently, Benedetti and Emmelot[88] examined negatively stained preparations of rat liver membranes in which the staining procedure was carried out at 37°. They observed, in addition to the 50 to 60 Å globular knobs scattered over the membrane surface, an array of hexagons and occasional pentagons spaced about 80 to 90 Å apart. The hexagonal patterns were not observed in membranes prepared at low temperatures.

Electron micrographs of mixed lipid films also show a similar hexagonal pattern of ultrastructure.[89] Evidence for a phase transition from a lamellar to a microsphere structure was obtained with model phospholipid systems examined by x-ray diffraction[90] or electron microscopy.[91] These observations bring to mind the suggestion by Hechter[92] that the membrane is composed of structural units in the form of hexagons with a few pentagons, the arrangement showing icosahedral symmetry. This type of structure would permit great flexibility.

The observation of subunits prompted Green[93] to put forward the proposal that biological membranes are always formed by the association of repeating proteolipid structural units (Fig. 7-21). According to this view, each membrane has a specific

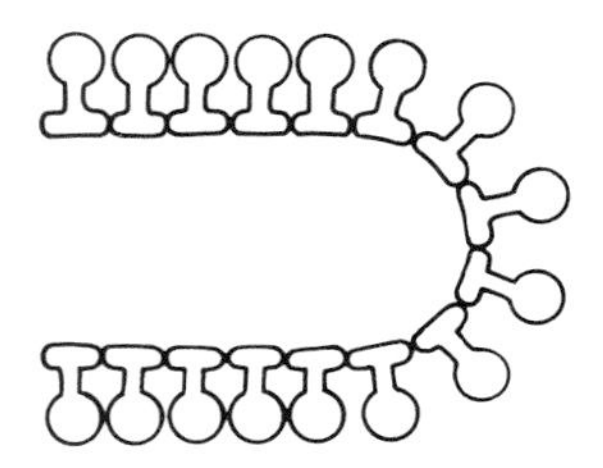

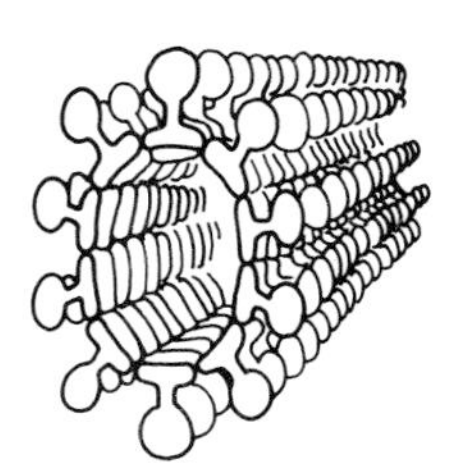

fig. 7-21. A schematic representation of Green's model of the membrane as a fused continuum of repeating particles. (From Green, D. E., and Perdue, J. F. *Proc. Natl. Acad. Sci.*, *55*, 1299 [1966].)

repeating unit which is characteristic in form, size, and composition. The repeating units always contain a membrane-forming portion; at times there may also be a detachable portion. The detachable head and stalk of the elementary particle of the inner membrane of mitochondria can be removed from the membrane-forming portion by either sonication[94] or treatment with bile salts[95] without disrupting the arrangement of the structural portion as a continuous membrane. Thus, the detachable portions are

[86] Robertson, J. D. *Ann. N.Y. Acad. Sci.*, *137*, 421 (1966).
[87] Blasie, J. K., Dewey, M. M., Blaurock, A. E., and Worthington, C. R. *J. Mol. Biol.*, *14*, 143 (1965).
[88] Benedetti, E. L., and Emmelot, P. *J. Cell Biol.*, *26*, 299 (1965).
[89] Bangham, A. D., and Horne, R. W. *Nature*, *196*, 952 (1962); Lucy, J. A., and Glauert, A. M. *J. Mol. Biol.*, *8*, 727 (1964).
[90] Luzatti, V., and Husson, F. *J. Cell Biol.*, *12*, 207 (1962).
[91] Stoeckenius, W. *J. Cell Biol.*, *12*, 221 (1962).
[92] Hechter, O. *Federation Proc.*, *24*, suppl. 15, S-91 (1965).
[93] Green, D. E., and Perdue, J. F. *Proc. Natl. Acad. Sci.*, *55*, 1295 (1966).
[94] Stasny, J. T., and Crane, F. L. *J. Cell Biol.*, *22*, 49 (1964).
[95] Kopaczyk, K., Perdue, J., and Green, D. E. *Arch. Biochem. Biophys.*, *115*, 215 (1966).

an intrinsic part of the membrane, but they are not essential to the integrity of the membrane structure. The detachable portions are thought to contain the membrane-associated enzymes. At least in mitochondria, the membrane-forming portion of the repeating unit is judged to be identical with the structural protein isolated by chemical means (see p. 374). The membrane-forming portions of the structural repeating units have an inherent tendency to form membrane-bounded vesicular structures.

A new technique has been applied recently to the study of membrane ultrastructure. The specimen to be examined is frozen rapidly in liquid freon and fractured with a microtome knife. The exposed surfaces may be "etched" by exposure to a high vacuum for a few minutes while frozen. The surfaces are then shadowed, replicated, and examined in the electron microscope. This technique tends to split membranes, thus revealing their inner aspects as well as their surfaces to examination. Small particles, about 85 Å in diameter, are seen frequently in such fractured membrane preparations, although depressions into which such particles might fit are few in number[96] (Fig. 7-22). The relative lack of "etching" in these preparations indicates that little water is

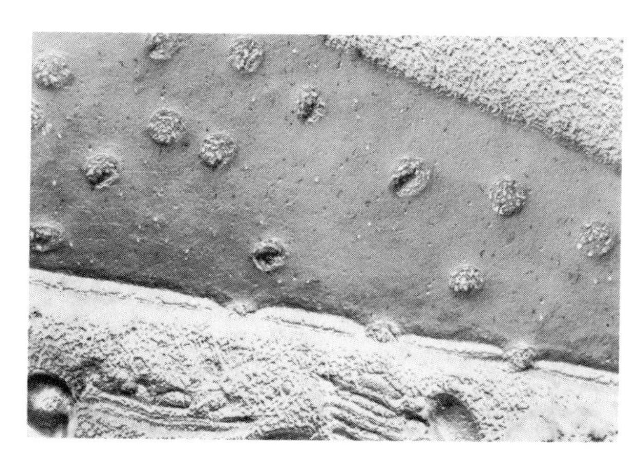

fig. 7-22. Electron micrograph of a replica of a frozen-etched fractured membrane showing vacuoles which may correspond to globular subunits. (From Branton, D. *J. Ultrastruct. Res.*, *11*, 407 [1964]. Copyright Academic Press; reprinted by permission.)

present at the exposed surfaces. These observations are consistent with the idea that it is the lipid which is exposed. The globular substructures which are revealed in this type of preparation could be structural subunits or enzymes associated with the membranes.

An emerging view of membranes is that the structural arrangement of the constituents is dynamic rather than static. The membranes are conceived to be planar aggregates of micellar subunits which are neither fixed in their physical dimensions nor collectively arranged in a fixed array.[97] Rather, the subunits are thought to undergo reversible structural changes which may possibly correspond to phase transitions. The rapid turnover of membrane constituents which has been observed can be better reconciled

[96] Branton, D. *Proc. Natl. Acad. Sci.*, *55*, 1048 (1966); Branton, D. *Exptl. Cell Res.*, *45*, 703 (1967).
[97] Kavanau, J. L. *Structure and Function in Biological Membranes*. San Francisco: Holden-Day, 1965.

with this view of the membrane than with earlier theories of its structure.[98] It may be that the membrane proteins are synthesized by polyribosomes and first form a lipid-free membrane, and that the phospholipids are subsequently synthesized *in situ*.

sodium-potassium activated ATPase

A characteristic property of many types of cells from many different organisms is the transport of sodium ions from the cytoplasm to the exterior of the cell against an electrochemical gradient, *active sodium transport* (see p. 397). Experiments on nerve[99] and on erythrocyte membranes[100] show that ATP provides the energy required to transport the sodium ions against the electrochemical gradient. ITP, GTP, and UTP cannot replace ATP as an energy source.[101] There appears to be a stoichiometry to cation transport with two K^+ ions entering for every three Na^+ transported, for example, out of the red blood cell.

Outward active transport of sodium continues, however, in the absence of potassium. This indicates that the coupling is not obligatory. Biochemists interested in transport phenomena have focused attention on an ATPase found in membrane-rich fractions of cell homogenates which requires the presence of both sodium and potassium ions for full activity.[102] While the requirement for sodium is specific, other monovalent cations can replace potassium.

The sodium-potassium activated ATPase characteristically is found in the microsomal fraction[103] of cell homogenates, in heavy microsomes,[104] in erythrocyte ghosts,[105] or in cell membranes or membrane fragments.[106] The enzyme appears to be a lipoprotein.[107] The sodium-potassium activated ATPase requires magnesium ions, and the enzyme is inhibited by calcium, fluoride,[108] and basic proteins such as protamines, histones, and polylysine.[109]

In most preparations there is a magnesium activated ATPase which is not further activated by the presence of sodium and potassium ions. A sodium-potassium activated adenylate kinase[110] and two enzymes responsible for an ADP-ATP exchange reaction[111] (one which requires only Mg^{++} ions, and the other which is activated by Na^+ and Mg^{++} ions) are also frequently present. The sodium-potassium activated ATPase can

---

[98] Omura, T., Siekevitz, P., and Palade, G. E. *J. Biol. Chem.*, *242*, 2389 (1967).
[99] Caldwell, P. C., Hodgkin, A. L., Keynes, R. D., and Shaw, T. J. *J. Physiol.*, *152*, 561 (1960).
[100] Dunham, E. T. *Physiologist*, *1*, 23 (1957); Whittam, R. *J. Physiol.*, *140*, 479 (1958).
[101] Hoffman, J. F. *Federation Proc.*, *19*, 127 (1960).
[102] Skou, J. C. *Biochim. Biophys. Acta*, *23*, 394 (1957); Skou, J. C. *Biochim. Biophys. Acta*, *42*, 6 (1960).
[103] Landon, E. J., and Norris, J. L. *Biochim. Biophys. Acta*, *71*, 266 (1963); Schwartz, A., Bachelard, H. S., and McIlwain, H. *Biochem. J.*, *84*, 626 (1962).
[104] Charnock, J. S., and Post, R. L. *Australian J. Exptl. Biol. Med. Sci.*, *41*, 547 (1963).
[105] Post, R. L., Merritt, C. R., Kinsolving, C. R., and Albright, C. D. *J. Biol. Chem.*, *235*, 1796 (1960).
[106] Wallach, D. F. H., and Ullrey, D. *Biochim. Biophys. Acta*, *88*, 620 (1964); Emmelot, P., and Bos, C. J. *Biochim. Biophys. Acta*, *120*, 369 (1966).
[107] Tanaka, R., and Strickland, K. P. *Arch. Biochem. Biophys.*, *111*, 583 (1965).
[108] Opit, L. J., Potter, H., and Charnock, J. S. *Biochim. Biophys. Acta*, *120*, 159 (1966).
[109] Yoshida, H., Fujisawa, H., and Ohi, Y. *Can. J. Biochem.*, *43*, 841 (1965); Schwartz, A. *Biochim. Biophys. Acta*, *100*, 202 (1965); Epstein, F. H., and Whittam, R. *Biochem. J.*, *99*, 232 (1966).
[110] Askari, A., and Fratantoni, J. C. *Proc. Soc. Exptl. Biol. Med.*, *116*, 751 (1964).
[111] Swanson, P. D., and Stahl, W. L. *Biochem. J.*, *99*, 396 (1966); Fahn, S., Koval, G. J., and Albers, R. W. *J. Biol. Chem.*, *24*, 1882 (1966).

be separated from other proteins and concentrated by extraction with 2 M NaI.[112] When the salt concentration is lowered to 0.6 M, the sodium-potassium activated ATPase is precipitated while most other enzymes remain in solution. Another purification method utilizes chromatography on glass beads.[113]

The sodium-potassium activated ATPase has been isolated from a large variety of tissues including erythrocyte membranes, brain, nerve, kidney, muscle, liver, intestine, electric organ, parotid gland, frog skin, ciliary body, lens, retina, thyroid, and toad bladder.[114] For a variety of tissues, the ratio of sodium flux to the amount of sodium-potassium activated ATPase is very nearly the same, although, for example, the net sodium efflux is about 25,000 times as great in the electric organ as it is in erythrocytes.[115]

It has been found from experiments using erythrocyte ghosts filled with various media by "reversible" hemolysis[116] that ATP is hydrolyzed only when it is on the inside of the membrane. The ADP liberated also remains in the interior. These experiments showed maximum ATPase activity with high intracellular sodium and high extracellular potassium concentrations. They led to the conclusion that the ATPase is oriented across the cell membrane with the sodium site facing the interior and the potassium site facing the exterior. It also has been shown that ^{22}Na is bound by microsomes, erythrocyte ghosts, and perhaps the partially purified enzyme in the presence of ATP.[117] Ouabain, a cardiac glycoside, inhibited the ATP-dependent binding of sodium ions.

Low concentrations of cardiac glycosides specifically inhibit sodium transport.[118] The cardiac glycosides inhibit the activity of the sodium-potassium activated ATPase but not the activity of the ATPase depending upon magnesium ions alone. There is a close correlation between the inhibitory potency of different glycosides on cation transport and their potency on the sodium-potassium activated ATPase.[119] In the squid axon, cardiac glycosides are effective only on the outside of the membrane.[120] In part, the inhibition by cardiac glycosides can be offset by increasing the concentration of potassium ions.[121] The erythrophleum alkaloids, which structurally are very different from the cardiac glycosides but which resemble them in pharmacological activity, also inhibit the sodium-potassium activated ATPase.[122]

In the presence of γ-^{32}P-ATP, Na^+, and Mg^{++}, the sodium-potassium activated ATPase incorporates ^{32}P into an intermediate which can be precipitated by perchloric

---

[112] Nakao, T., Tashima, Y., Nagano, K., and Nakao, M. *Biochem. Biophys. Res. Commun.*, *19*, 755 (1965); Stahl, W. L., Sattin, A., and McIlwain, H. *Biochem. J.*, *99*, 404 (1966).

[113] Schoner, W., von Ilberg, C., Kramer, R., and Seubert, W. *European J. Biochem.*, *1*, 334 (1967).

[114] Bonting, S. L., Caravaggio, L. L., and Hawkins, N. M. *Arch. Biochem. Biophys.*, *98*, 413 (1962); Bonting, S. L., Simon, K. A., and Hawkins, N. M. *Arch. Biochem. Biophys.*, *95*, 416 (1961); Skou, J. C. *Physiol. Rev.*, *45*, 596 (1965); Albers, R. W. *Ann. Rev. Biochem.*, *36*, 727 (1967).

[115] Bonting, S. L., and Caravaggio, L. L. *Arch. Biochem. Biophys.*, *101*, 37 (1963).

[116] Whittam, R. *Biochem. J.*, *84*, 110 (1962); Caldwell, P. C., Hodgkin, A. L., Keynes, R. D., and Shaw, T. J. *J. Physiol.*, *152*, 561 (1960).

[117] Järnefelt, J., and von Stendingk, L. V. *Acta Physiol. Scand.*, *57*, 328 (1963); Charnock, J. S., and Post, R. L. *Nature*, *199*, 910 (1963); Walz, F. G., Jr., and Chan, P. D. *Arch. Biochem. Biophys.*, *113*, 569 (1966).

[118] Schatzmann, J. H. *Helv. Physiol. Pharmacol. Acta.*, *11*, 346 (1953); Glynn, I. M. *J. Physiol.*, *136*, 148 (1957); Kofoed-Johnsen, V. *Acta Physiol. Scand.*, *42*, suppl. 145, 87 (1958).

[119] Dunham, E. T., and Glynn, I. M. *J. Physiol.*, *156*, 274 (1961).

[120] Caldwell, P. C., and Keynes, R. D. *J. Physiol.*, *148*, 8P (1959).

[121] Dunham, E. T., and Glynn, I. M. *J. Physiol.*, *156*, 274 (1961); Portius, H. J., and Repke, K. *Arch. Exptl. Pathol. Pharmakol.*, *243*, 335 (1962).

[122] Bonting, S. L., Hawkins, N. M., and Canady, M. R. *Biochem. Pharmacol.*, *13*, 13 (1964).

or trichloracetic acid.[123] Half-maximal phosphorylation of beef kidney sodium-potassium activated ATPase is achieved at a 1.6 mM Na^+ concentration. The sodium-dependent incorporation of ^{32}P into the ATPase is complete within a few seconds at 5°C. The bound ^{32}P is most stable at a pH of 2 to 3.[124] If a small amount of K^+ is present in addition to Na^+, ATP is hydrolyzed but the phosphorylated intermediate cannot be isolated. Exposure of the ^{32}P-labeled intermediate to methanol or ethanol results in the formation of phosphate esters of the alcohols. It is of great interest that no other cation can substitute for Na^+ in the formation of the phosphorylated intermediate. Even Li^+, which mimics Na^+ during excitation, is not able to substitute. The formation of the phosphorylated intermediate is inhibited by the presence of calcium ions but not by cardiac glycosides.[125] Upon digestion with proteolytic enzymes a phosphorylated peptide fragment with properties like those of the phosphorylated intermediate is obtained. It appears that the phosphorylated intermediate is an acyl-phosphate,[126] possibly phosphorylglutamate.

Under physiological conditions, the hydrolysis of the phosphorylated intermediate of the enzyme is markedly enhanced by the presence of K^+ ions.[127] NH_4^+, Rb^+, Cs^+, and Li^+ can replace K^+ in this reaction. These five cations can be ranked in order of activating effectiveness: $NH_4^+ > K^+ > Rb^+ > Cs^+ > Li^+$. The same order of effectiveness on increasing sodium efflux from squid axon is observed when these cations are used in the bathing solution.[128] Cardiac glycosides inhibit the phosphatase reaction by competing with potassium ions. Oligomycin inhibits the sodium-potassium activated ATPase in the phosphatase step, but other inhibitors of oxidative phosphorylation do not.[129] Particularly at low temperatures, highly purified enzyme preparations exhibit a slow sodium activated hydrolysis of ATP that does not appear to proceed through the phosphorylated intermediate stage.

In summary, the following reaction sequence can be put forward to describe this reaction:

$$\left.\begin{array}{l} E + \text{ATP} \xrightarrow[\text{Mg}^{++}]{\text{Na}^+} E \sim \text{P} + \text{ADP} \\ E \sim \text{P} \xrightarrow{\text{K}^+} E + \text{P}_i \end{array}\right\} \text{(rapid)} \qquad (7\text{-}18)$$

$$E + \text{ATP} \xrightarrow[\text{Mg}^{++}]{\text{Na}^+} E + \text{P}_i + \text{ADP} \quad \text{(slow)} \qquad (7\text{-}19)$$

[123] Albers, R. W., Fahn, S., and Covell, G. J. *Proc. Natl. Acad. Sci.*, *50*, 474 (1963); Post, R. L., Sen, A. K., and Rosenthal, A. S. *J. Biol. Chem.*, *240*, 1437 (1965).
[124] Hokin, L. E., Sastry, P. S., Galsworthy, P. R., and Yoda, A. *Proc. Natl. Acad. Sci.*, *54*, 177 (1965); Bader, H., Sen, A. K., and Post, R. L. *Biochim. Biophys. Acta*, *118*, 106 (1966).
[125] Järnefelt, J. *Biochim. Biophys. Acta*, *59*, 643 (1962); Epstein, F. H., and Whittam, R. *Biochem. J.*, *99*, 232 (1966).
[126] Post, R. L., Sen, A. K., and Rosenthal, A. S. *J. Biol. Chem.*, *240*, 1437 (1965); Nagano, K., Kanazawa, T., Mizuno, N., Tashima, Y., Nakao, T., and Nakao, M. *Biochem. Biophys. Res. Commun.*, *19*, 759 (1965); Bader, H., Sen, A. K., and Post, R. L. *Biochim. Biophys. Acta*, *118*, 106 (1966); Hokin, L. E., Sastry, P. S., Galsworthy, P. R., and Yoda, A. *Proc. Natl. Acad. Sci.*, *54*, 177 (1965); Nagano, K., Mizuno, N., Fugita, M., Tashima, Y., Nakao, T., and Nakao, M. *Biochim. Biophys. Acta*, *143*, 239 (1967); Kahlenberg, A., Galsworthy, P. R., and Hokin, L. E. *Science*, *157*, 434 (1967).
[127] Whittam, R. *Nature*, *196*, 134 (1962); Post, R. L., Sen, A. K., and Rosenthal, A. S. *J. Biol. Chem.*, *240*, 1437 (1965).
[128] Sjodin, R. A., and Beaugé, L. A. *Currents Mod. Biol.*, *1*, 105 (1967).
[129] van Groningen, H. E. M., and Slater, E. C. *Biochim. Biophys. Acta*, *73*, 527 (1963); Matsui, H., and Schwartz, A. *Biochim. Biophys. Acta*, *128*, 380 (1966).

other enzymes associated with membranes

Cell membrane preparations contain phosphatase activity which probably represents several different enzymes with different properties.[130] Most of the phosphatase activity results from an enzyme which has an optimum *p*H in the acid region and which is activated by magnesium ions and weakly inhibited by fluoride. In addition, smaller amounts of a potassium activated phosphatase with a slightly alkaline *p*H optimum and a requirement for Mg^{++} is found when *p*-nitrophenylphosphate and related substances are used as substrates. The potassium activated alkaline phosphatase is inhibited by cardiac glycosides. This enzyme activity may be carried on by a protein which is identical to the sodium-potassium activated ATPase. Membranes also contain phosphodiesterases with an alkaline *p*H optimum, particularly an enzyme which splits 2,3-diphosphoglyceric acid.[131]

The Hokins[132] have isolated two enzymes from avian salt glands, brain microsomes, erythrocyte ghosts, and other membrane preparations: diglyceride kinase, which catalyzes the formation of phosphatidic acid from α,β-diglycerides and ATP; and phosphatidic acid phosphatase, which catalyzes the hydrolysis of phosphatidic acid. The former enzyme appears to be activated by acetylcholine while the latter enzyme appears to be inhibited by cardiac glycosides. A complete cycle through both reactions during which phosphatidic acid is synthesized and broken down adds up to the net hydrolysis of ATP. In the avian salt gland, the intracellular level of these enzymes is stimulated by acetylcholine and is accompanied by the excretion of NaCl. The relationship of these enzymes to the sodium-potassium activated ATPase is unknown.

Erythrocyte ghosts and other membrane preparations contain acetylcholinesterase, a different enzyme than the pseudocholinesterase found in plasma. Acetylcholinesterase activity has been localized in the cell membrane by electron microscopic examination after histochemical staining;[133] the enzyme appears to be an integral structural component of the membrane.[134]

Erythrocyte ghosts and other membranes contain catalase, a heme-containing enzyme which both decomposes hydrogen peroxide and catalyzes the oxidation of alcohol and aldehydes.[135]

Cell membrane preparations contain enzyme systems which couple the reduction of cytochromes *c* or dyes such as methylene blue to the oxidation of NADH.[136] The NAD-diaphorase system has been found in the same deoxycholate treated submicroscopic particles isolated from brain, kidney, erythrocyte ghost, and cardiac muscle[137] that contain the sodium-potassium activated ATPase. Both the NAD-diaphorase and the cation activated ATPase are inhibited by N-ethylmaleimide, and ATP affords

[130] Davies, D. R. *Biochem. J.*, *28*, 529 (1934); Clarkson, E. M., and Maizels, M. *J. Physiol.*, *116*, 112 (1952); Herbert, E. *J. Cellular Comp. Physiol.*, *47*, 11 (1956).
[131] Rapoport, S., and Leubering, J. *J. Biol. Chem.*, *189*, 683 (1951); Emmelot, P., Bos, C. J., Benedetti, E. L., and Rümke, P. *Biochim. Biophys. Acta*, *90*, 126 (1964).
[132] Hokin, M. R., and Hokin, L. E. *J. Biol. Chem.*, *234*, 1381 (1959); Hokin, L. E., and Hokin, M. R. *J. Biol. Chem.*, *234*, 1387 (1959); Hokin, L. E., and Hokin, M. R. *Nature*, *189*, 836 (1961).
[133] Shinagawa, Y., and Ogura, M. *Kagaku* (*Tokyo*), *31*, 554 (1961).
[134] Vincent, D., Segonzak, C., and Sesque, G. *Compt. Rend. Soc. Biol.*, *155*, 662 (1961); Mitchell, C. D., Mitchell, W. B., and Hanahan, D. J. *Biochim. Biophys. Acta*, *104*, 348 (1965).
[135] Keilin, D., and Hartree, F. *Biochem. J.*, *49*, 88 (1951); Francoeur, N., and Denstedt, O. F. *Can. J. Biochem. Physiol.*, *32*, 644 (1954).
[136] Gibson, Q. H. *Biochem. J.*, *42*, 13 (1948).
[137] Skou, J. C. *Biochem. Biophys. Res. Commun.*, *10*, 79 (1963).

protection to both enzymes against the action of N-ethylmaleimide. Kamat and Wallach[138] have been able to separate the microsomal fraction into two subfractions, one rich in sodium-potassium activated ATPase and one rich in NAD-diaphorase. Because the cation activated ATPase fraction also is rich in surface antigens, these investigators thought that it might represent cell membrane fragments, while the NAD-diaphorase–rich subfraction contained little surface antigen and was thought to represent endoplasmic reticulum fragments.

Sodium-potassium activated ATPase obtained from beef heart microsomes is unaffected by aurovertin, atractyloside, dinitrophenol, or azide (inhibitors of mitochondrial ATPase and electron transport); however, it is inhibited by oligomycin, octylguanidine, and tributyltin[139] (other inhibitors of electron transport). It is not clear at the present time whether a relation exists between the electron transport NAD-diaphorase system and the cation activated ATPase. Enzymes associated with plasma membranes are listed in Fig. 7-23.

fig. 7-23. Enzymes found in cell membrane preparations.

ENZYME	RAT LIVER[a]	ERYTHROCYTE[b]	MILK FAT[c]
	(μMOLES PRODUCT/MG PROTEIN/HR)		
Na^+-K^+ activated ATPase	11.7	1.6	0.91
Alkaline phosphatase (PNPP)	1.5	1.5	0.63
K^+ activated alkaline phosphatase	1.5	—	0.63
Acid phosphatase (PNPP)	5.8	2.5	0.09
Alkaline phosphodiesterase	3.6	—	0.134
Acid phosphodiesterase	0.7	—	0.008
Glucose-6-phosphatase	1.4	0.7	0.064
NADH-cytochrome *c* reductase	7.68	1.47	0.001
Triose phosphate dehydrogenase	2.04	6.5	—
Acetylcholinesterase	—	19.06	0.17

[a] Summarized in Emmelot, P., and Benedetti, E. L., in *Carcinogenesis: A Broad Critique*. Baltimore: Williams & Wilkins, 1967, p. 512. © 1967, The Williams & Wilkins Co., Baltimore, Md. 21202. U.S.A.
[b] Summarized in Pennell, R. B., in Bishop, C., and Surgenor, D. M., eds. *The Red Blood Cell*. New York: Academic Press, 1964, p. 35. Copyright Academic Press; reprinted by permission.
[c] From Dowben, R. M., Brunner, J. R., and Philpott, D. E. *Biochim. Biophys. Acta*, *135*, 1 (1967).

Erythrocyte ghosts appear to be able to carry on the complete sequence of glycolytic reactions leading from glucose to lactic acid.[140] Schrier[141] has shown that triose phosphate dehydrogenase and phosphoglycerate kinase are particularly tightly bound to erythrocyte ghosts. He has proposed that the enzymes may be organized into a system which utilizes triose phosphate and NAD as substrates leading to 3-phosphoglyceric acid and NADH as products in a reaction which is coupled to the formation of ATP from ADP. The ATP so generated then can be used directly by the cation activated ATPase. In carefully prepared erythrocyte ghosts and yeast membranes, the

[138] Kamat, V. B., and Wallach, D. F. H. *Science*, *148*, 1343 (1965).
[139] Matsui, H., and Schwartz, A. *Biochim. Biophys. Acta*, *128*, 380 (1966).
[140] Lionetti, F., Rees, S. B., Healy, W. B., Walker, B. S., and Gibson, J. G. *J. Biol. Chem.*, *220*, 467 (1956).
[141] Schrier, S. L. *J. Clin. Invest.*, *42*, 756 (1963); Schrier, S. L. *Am. J. Physiol.*, *210*, 139 (1966).

entire complex of glycolytic enzymes is found largely associated with the membranes.[142] The loosely held enzymes of the sequence could be eluted from the membrane system and recombined by a cycle of change in *p*H.

properties of the cell surface

The surface of erythrocytes and suspensions of other cells shows the properties of a polyanion. Cell suspensions migrate toward the anode in a direct current field; this indicates that they possess a negative net surface charge. The electrophoretic mobility appears to be characteristic of all cells of a given species and is unaffected by the shape of the cells; this indicates that the density of net surface charge is constant. That the surface charge is not lost upon rupture is shown by the fact that erythrocyte ghosts migrate with the same velocity as intact cells.[143] The electrophoretic mobility is constant for a large range of salt concentrations, and the isoelectric point is quite low—in the vicinity of *p*H 2.

It appears that the negative surface charge of cells is largely due to the carboxyl group of sialic acids (N-acetylneuraminic, N-glycolylneuraminic acid, etc.),[144] which has a pK_a of about 2.5. Exposure of cells to the enzymes neuraminidase or trypsin results in cleavage of a sialomucopeptide which contains the N-acetylneuraminic acid residues. After such treatment, more that 95 percent of the sialic acid residues are removed from the cell surface and there is a marked drop in the net negative surface charge. In erythrocytes the sialic acid appears to be restricted to the plasma membrane, but in the case of other cell types, sialic acid may occur in the interior. Marcus and Salb[145] presented evidence for the presence of sialic acid in the nuclear membranes of HeLa cells and Ehrlich ascites tumor cells.

Because of the polyanionic property of cells, it is not surprising that cells interact with polycations like polylysine. Erythrocytes can be agglutinated by the addition of polylysine, and the process can be reversed by the subsequent addition of polyglutamate The amount of polylysine required to cause agglutination is 6 percent or less of the total that can be adsorbed on the surface.

Before it was established that the polyanionic character of the cell surface was due largely to sialic acid residues, it was found that the electrophoretic mobility of erythrocytes could be reduced by treatment with influenza virus.[146] Subsequently, it was shown that the viral principle responsible for this was a neuraminidase.[147] Animal viruses enter susceptible cells by attaching themselves to specific receptor sites on the cell surface. Purified receptor substance for the influenza virus has been isolated and shown to be a complex macromolecule containing sialic acid.[148] Complexes can be formed between polylysine and the virus receptor glycoprotein which frequently are insoluble.[149] Such insoluble complexes can be redissolved by adding polyaspartate.

---

[142] Green, D. E., Murer, E., Hultin, H. O., Richardson, S. H., Salmon, B., Brierley, G. P., and Baum, H. *Arch. Biochem. Biophys.*, *112*, 635 (1965).
[143] Ponder, E., and Ponder, R. V. *J. Gen. Physiol.*, *43*, 503 (1960).
[144] Gottschalk, A. *Nature*, *186*, 949 (1960); Cook, G. M. W., Heard, D. H., and Seaman, G. V. F. *Nature*, *191*, 44 (1961); Cook, G. M. W. *Nature*, *195*, 159 (1962); Eylar, E. H., Madoff, M. A., Brody, O. V., and Oncley, J. L. *J. Biol. Chem.*, *237*, 1992 (1962).
[145] Marcus, P. I., and Salb, J. N. *Virology*, *30*, 502 (1966).
[146] Hanig, M. *Proc. Soc. Exptl. Biol. Med.*, *68*, 385 (1948).
[147] Gottschalk, A. *Biochim. Biophys. Acta*, *23*, 645 (1957).
[148] Kathan, R. H., Winzler, R. J., and Johnson, C. A. *J. Exptl. Med.*, *113*, 37 (1961).
[149] Danon, D., Howe, C., and Lee, L. T. *Biochim. Biophys. Acta*, *101*, 201 (1965).

Erythrocytes have a variety of distinct antigenic groups on their surface. The division of individuals of a species into blood groups is possible because not all individuals of the species have the same complement of cell-surface antigens. The first blood-group system to be discovered,[150] the ABO system, is the most significant one in connection with the compatibility of transfused blood. Individuals are divided into four blood groups, A, B, AB, and O, according to the presence or absence of two antigens, A and B, on the erythrocyte surface. In the absence of either or both antigens, the corresponding anti-A and anti-B antibodies are found in the serum. A similar system, the MN system,[151] depends on the presence or absence of two antigens, M and N. Although the MN system is less important in connection with blood transfusion than the ABO system, it has been used extensively as a marker in genetic and anthropological studies. Another important blood-group system is the rhesus factor (Rh factor) which is genetically determined by the CDE substances.

Because the A and B, and M and N antigens are found in erythrocytes and because they are important in blood transfusions, they are called blood-group substances. However, it appears that they are present on the cell surfaces of most epithelial cells.[152] Szulman[153] examined the distribution of blood-group antigens in the tissues of fetuses. In an elegant study he showed that the distribution of A and B antigens is very widespread early in embryonic life. After the twelfth week, however, the blood-group antigens become restricted to simple or stratified confining epithelium, while epithelium which proceeds to differentiate further tends to lose these antigens. The A and B antigens, but not the M and N antigens, also are found in a water-soluble form in tissue fluids and secretions.[154]

A rather unique blood-group system is the Lewis antigen system.[155] The antigens of the Lewis system are present in the plasma and, rather than being integrated into the membrane structure, appear to be adsorbed by erythrocytes.

The purified blood-group substances are glycoproteins with molecular weights ranging from 2×10^5 to 1×10^6. Actually, the protein moiety of the molecules represents a quantitatively minor portion; it accounts for only about 15 percent of the molecular weight. The details of the molecular structures are not yet clear, but the molecules appear to consist of short oligosaccharide chains joined at intervals to a peptide backbone. The carbohydrate moiety contains five principal sugars: L-fucose, D-galactose, N-acetyl-D-glucosamine, N-acetyl-D-galactosamine, and N-acetyl-neuraminic acid. One difference observed consistently between A and B antigens is that the ratio of galactosamine to glucosamine is higher in A than in B.[156] The antigenic specificity appears to reside in the carbohydrate moiety and depends upon the nature of the sugars at the nonreducing ends of the carbohydrate chain.

In addition to the blood-group antigens, the cell membrane appears to possess a diverse constellation of antigenic determinants. One type which has received considerable attention is the histocompatibility antigens, antigens which result in host rejection responses to transplants. The *H*-2 isoantigen system produces the most intense reac-

---

[150] Landsteiner, K. *Cent. Bacteriol. Parasiten Infektionskrankheiten*, *27*, 357 (1900).
[151] Landsteiner, K., and Levine, P. *Proc. Soc. Exptl. Biol. Med.*, *24*, 600, 941 (1927).
[152] Wiener, A. S. *Blood Groups and Blood Transfusions*, 3rd ed. Springfield, Ill.: Charles C Thomas, 1943; Szulman, A. E. *J. Exptl. Med.*, *111*, 785 (1960); *115*, 977 (1962); Kosjakov, P. N., and Tribulev, G. P. *J. Immunol.*, *37*, 283 (1939).
[153] Szulman, A. E. *J. Exptl. Med.*, *119*, 503 (1964).
[154] Yamakami, K. *J. Immunol.*, *12*, 185 (1926).
[155] Mourant, A. E. *Nature*, *158*, 237 (1946); Sneath, J. S., and Sneath, P. H. A. *Nature*, *176*, 172 (1955).
[156] Rondle, C. J. M., and Morgan, W. T. J. *Biochem. J.*, *59*, xiii (1955).

tions against homotransplantation in mice. The belief that the *H*-2 system is localized in the surface membrane is supported by the fact that the entire *H*-2 activity of isoantisera can be adsorbed by suspensions of intact cells.[157] Furthermore, if cells in suspension are exposed to *H*-2 isoantiserum and then treated with fluorescein-conjugated rabbit-antimouse globulin, the fluorescent marker clearly is localized on the cell surface.[158] A comparison of the reaction of whole and disrupted cells with isoantisera indicates that 80 percent or more of the *H*-2 antigens are located on the cell surface.[159]

The cell surface also appears to possess specific antigenic sites capable of stimulating the production of specific heterologous antibodies. Such heterologous antibodies result in agglutination of cell suspensions or in cytolysis.[160] Heterologous antibodies to Ehrlich ascites tumor cells can be absorbed almost completely by suspensions of tumor cells. Reaction of disrupted cells with heterologous antibodies indicates that the antigen is found in the microsomal fraction.[161]

A number of tumor-specific transplantation antigens which can be regarded as weak histocompatibility antigens has been studied.[162] Evidence that the tumor-specific transplantation antigens are located on the cell surface includes the absorption of humoral antibodies (1) by Moloney lymphoma cells, (2) by immunofluorescence localization on the cell surface, and (3) by interference by isoantibodies with the adherence of host lymphoid cells to target cells.[163]

The reactive sulfhydryl groups on cell surfaces appear to be essential for functional integrity. The human erythrocyte contains about 4×10^{-17} moles of sulfhydryl groups per cell. Reaction of approximately 5 percent of these groups with an organic mercurial results in a marked diminution in the facilitated diffusion of glucose[164] (see Chapter 8). Cation permeability is markedly increased by reaction of the surface sulfhydryl groups with organomercurials—an effect which can be largely reversed by incubation with reduced glutathione.[165] Reaction of the surface sulfhydryl groups of erythrocytes with organomercurials results in increased fragility and when reinjected, decreased survival in vivo.[166]

Some indication of the relative importance of the protein and lipid constituents of the membrane from a functional point of view can be gleaned from studies in which the lobster giant axon was treated with a variety of enzymes.[167] Treatment with phospholipase A, phospholipase C (enzymes which split phospholipids), or digitonin (a compound which forms an insoluble complex with cholesterol) resulted in (1) a decrease in membrane resistance; (2) alterations in membrane capacitance; and (3)

---

[157] Haughton, G. *Transplantation*, *4*, 238 (1966).
[158] Möller, E. *J. Natl. Cancer Inst.*, *33*, 979 (1964).
[159] Wigzell, H. *Transplantation*, *3*, 423 (1965).
[160] Goldberg, B., and Green, H. *J. Exptl. Med.*, *109*, 505 (1959); Green, H., Barrow, P., and Goldberg, B. *J. Exptl. Med.*, *110*, 699 (1959).
[161] Vogt, P. K. *Z. Naturforsch.*, *15b*, 221 (1960); Wallach, D. F. H., and Hager, E. B. *Nature*, *196*, 1004 (1962); Kamat, V. B., and Wallach, D. F. H. *Science*, *148*, 1343 (1965).
[162] Old, L. J., and Boyse, E. A. *Ann. Rev. Med.*, *15*, 167 (1964); Klein, E., in Grabar, P., ed. *Immunopathology*. Basel: Schwabe, 1966, p. 20.
[163] Klein, G., Klein, E., and Haughton, G. *J. Natl. Cancer Inst.*, *36*, 607 (1966); Möller, E. *J. Exptl. Med.*, *122*, 11 (1965).
[164] van Steveninck, J., Weed, R. I., and Rothstein, A. *J. Gen. Physiol.*, *48*, 617 (1965).
[165] Shapiro, B., Kollman, G., and Asnen, J. *Radiation Res.*, *27*, 139 (1966).
[166] Sheets, R. F., Hamilton, H. E., and DeGowin, E. L. *Proc. Soc. Exptl. Med. Biol.*, *91*, 423 (1956); Jacob, H. S., and Jandl, J. H. *J. Clin. Invest.*, *41*, 779, 1514 (1962); Sutherland, R. M., Rothstein, A., and Weed, R. I. *J. Cellular Comp. Physiol.*, *69*, 185 (1967).
[167] Tobias, J. M. *J. Cellular Comp. Physiol.*, *46*, 183 (1955); Tobias, J. M. *J. Gen. Physiol.*, *43*, suppl. 1, 57 (1960); Narahashi, T., and Tobias, J. M. *Am. J. Physiol.*, *207*, 1441 (1964).

loss of membrane function as indicated by decreases in the membrane resting potential, magnitude of the action potential, and excitatory threshold potential. On the other hand, treatment with trypsin, chymotrypsin, or collagenase failed to alter the transmembrane resting potential or excitability even though the preparations themselves showed shortened survival. These externally applied proteases appeared to penetrate through the axonal membrane causing liquefaction of the cytoplasm. After treatment with proteases, morphological changes were observed in electron micrographs of the lobster giant axons, even though the axons functioned relatively normally. The perfusion of squid axon intracellularly with both proteases and lipases disrupts normal membrane function.[168]

bioelectric potentials

The fact that muscle gives rise to electrical potentials has been known since the time of Luigi Galvani, and the injury potentials described earlier in this chapter have been studied intensively since before the turn of the century. The introduction and widespread use of microelectrodes in the past two decades, however, has put our knowledge of bioelectric potentials on a much firmer footing. Although enameled wires ground to a fine tip had been used before 1950 in an effort to penetrate the cell membrane without injury, the technical breakthrough was the introduction of a glass micropipette whose tip was drawn out to a diameter of 0.5 μ or less and filled with 3 M KCl solution.[169] Single muscle and nerve fibers can be impaled upon such microelectrodes without apparent damage to the cell membrane, and a *transmembrane potential* can be recorded for long periods of time.

When the microelectrode is inserted into the bathing fluid surrounding a muscle or nerve, a small potential is observed which is a contact or diffusion potential. This potential is minimized by filling the capillary micropipettes with 3 M KCl. The KCl reduces the resistance of the tip and minimizes the diffusion potential because the K^+ and Cl^- ions have almost identical mobilities at this concentration.[170] No change in this very small diffusion potential is observed even as the microelectrode pushes up against the muscle or nerve fiber sufficiently to cause a visible indentation. When the microelectrode pierces the membrane, a constant potential of −50 to −90 mv is observed (a minute or two may be required for stabilization) between the indifferent electrode in the bathing medium and the interior of the cell. This constant potential is called *resting potential.* The potential change in entering the membrane occurs as the microelectrode advances less than 1 μ.

It is of considerable interest that the intracellular *milieu* is at a considerable negative potential and not almost zero with respect to the environment. Given a good muscle or nerve preparation and good microelectrode, the negative resting potential remains

---

[168] Tasaki, I., and Takenaka, T. *Proc. Natl. Acad. Sci.*, *52*, 804 (1964).

[169] Ling, G. N., and Gerard, R. W. *J. Cellular Comp. Physiol.*, *34*, 383 (1949). A diameter of less than 1.0 μ is required in order for the cell membrane to "seal in" around the microelectrode. The tips of these very fine microelectrodes frequently can become clogged, and care in the performance of experiments is required to avoid erroneous results.

[170] Most of the anionic charges, particularly in vertebrate muscle, are fixed; this results in a small chloride diffusion potential of approximately 3 mv when 3 M KCl is used to fill the electrodes. The diffusion potential has a polarity such that the measured potential is less than the actual transmembrane potential. When 0.15 M KCl is used to fill the micropipettes, a diffusion potential of approximately 18 mv results. This corresponds to the observation that the transmembrane potential is 13.6 to 17.6 mv lower when the microelectrodes used are filled with 0.15 M KCl than when they are filled with 3 M KCl.

constant for hours or days. So long as neither the fiber nor the microelectrode is damaged, a fiber will produce the same potential even if it is impaled repeatedly and in different places. Except for certain specialized areas such as synapses or motor end plates, there appears to be no potential difference within the cytoplasm. The resting potential has an almost uniform value in different cells of the same type in the same species, and the resting potential is in the same range in all excitable cells regardless of type or species.

The same muscle or nerve fiber can be impaled by a second microelectrode near the first. The second microelectrode can be connected to a square wave current generator; and a small, brief pulse of approximately 10^{-7} amp for 2 msec can be passed through it. A larger current pulse will be required in cells with a high resistance (small cells). If the electrode is connnected to the negative terminal of the pulse generator, the inside of the fiber will tend to become more negative during the pulse. Such a current pulse *stimulus*, which tends to increase the negativity of the resting potential as measured by the first microelectrode, is said to *hyperpolarize* the membrane. While the current pulse applied to the second microelectrode is a square wave, the potential pulse recorded from the first microelectrode is rounded in shape (Fig. 7-24) and lags somewhat behind the stimulus pulse. This observation reflects the fact that the membrane does not present a simple resistance to the passage of an electric current through it, but that there is an effectively large capacitance in the membrane. In invertebrate nonmyelinated nerve, the membrane capacitance is about 1 $\mu f/cm^2$, and in vertebrate myelinated

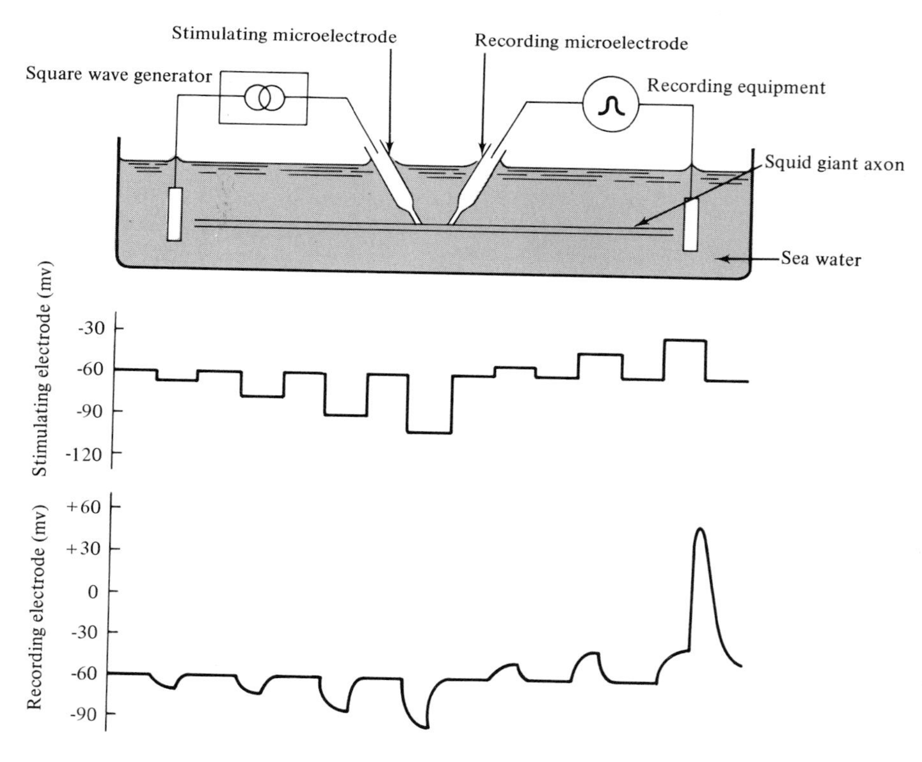

fig. 7-24. Arrangement for recording the electrotonic potential. A stimulating electrode connected to a square wave current generator and a recording microelectrode connected to a recording device are inserted side by side into an excitable fiber. The membrane capacitance results in a rounding of the square wave stimulus.

nerve it is about 5 $\mu f/cm^2$. Hyperpolarization of the membrane to 2 to 4 times the resting potential leads to electrical breakdown.

The passive potential change which is recorded in the neighborhood of a stimulus is called an *electrotonic potential.* The electrotonic potential is not propagated along the muscle or nerve fiber but is attenuated as the recording and stimulating electrodes are moved apart. A reduction of its magnitude by half is observed for about every 1 to 2 mm of separation between the recording and stimulating electrodes (depending upon the specific resistance and other variables). Muscle and nerve fibers are approximately cylindrical; their diameters are a very small fraction of their total length. The fibers may be regarded to consist of a central cylinder of cytoplasm, which is a relatively good electrical conductor, surrounded by a layer of insulation with appreciable intrinsic capacitance. Thus, the fibers can be modeled, at least for their passive properties, by electrical cables.

The electrotonic potential can be utilized to evaluate the cable properties of muscle and nerve fibers which are represented diagrammatically in Fig. 7-25. The tube of

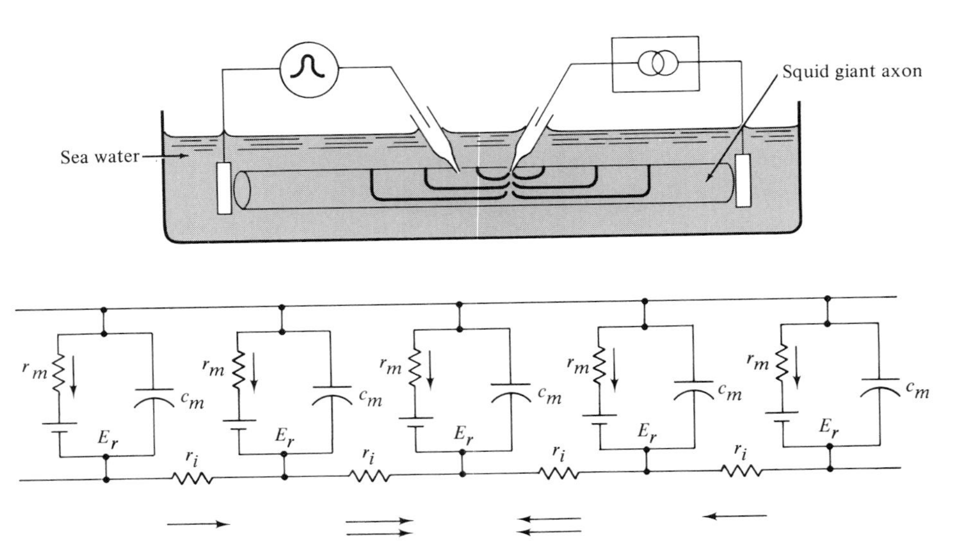

fig. 7-25. The electrotonic potential is caused by local current flows illustrated in the upper diagram. The lower diagram shows an equivalent circuit of the distributed resistance and capacitance of the membrane and the distributed resistance of the core of cytoplasm, and represents the electrical cable properties of a squid giant axon or other excitable fiber.

cytoplasm is so long compared to its diameter that its longitudinal resistance helps to determine the pattern of current flow within the fiber. The membrane is an imperfect insulator and has a leakage resistance. Also, the insulating membrane has an appreciable capacitance. The magnitude of these electrical properties can be determined by the rise time of the electrotonic potential as a function of distance from the point of stimulation.

If the polarity of the stimulus pulse is reversed (that is, if the exciting electrode is connected to the anode) and a small current pulse is passed through the electrode, the membrane potential as recorded by the first microelectrode is reduced to a less negative value. The membrane is said to be *depolarized.* For small current pulses the same local phenomena are observed as in the case of hyperpolarization, except that the polarity is reversed.

As the positive current pulses are increased in magnitude, a point of electrical instability, *threshold*, is reached when the transmembrane potential is approximately −50 mv for muscle fibers. When the threshold potential is reached, there is a sudden, spontaneous continuation of the potential change, the *action potential*, which results in complete depolarization of the membrane and actual reversal of the polarity of the transmembrane potential. At the peak of the action potential the cytoplasm is +40 to 50 mv with respect to the exterior. The peak is reached after approximately 0.5 msec and is followed by a less rapid return to the resting potential (Fig. 7-26). The spontaneous process is no longer controlled by the depolarization current; the sequence is an intrinsic property of the membrane itself. The action potential is an active response of the excitable cell *vis à vis* the passive response of the electrotonic potential.

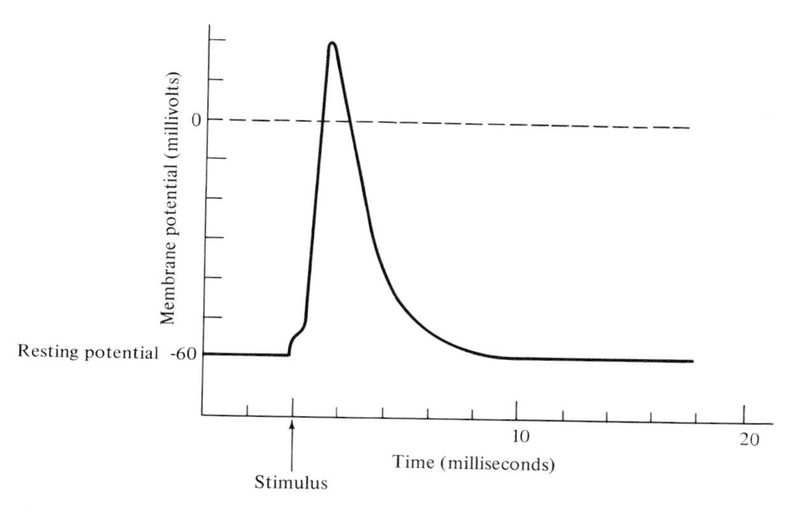

fig. 7-26. The time course of an action potential. A suprathreshold stimulus was applied at zero time.

By and large, the magnitude of the action potential is independent of the size of the stimulus as long as the latter exceeds threshold. This property of the action potential is known as the *all-or-none law*. The stimulus magnitude, however, is not entirely without effect; the time interval between the onset of the stimulus and the peak of the action potential, known as the *latent period*, decreases as the magnitude of the stimulus increases (Fig. 7-27). Immediately after an action potential, it is not possible to evoke a second action potential, no matter how strong a stimulus is applied. This period of approximately several msec is known as the *absolute refractory period*. It is followed by a longer period, known as the *relative refractory period*, during which a stronger than normal stimulus is required to produce an action potential (Fig. 7-28).

Once an action potential has been evoked, it is *propagated* or *conducted* along the length of an excitable muscle or nerve fiber. The action potential is propagated in both directions from the points of stimulus at a constant speed and uniform amplitude. The velocity of propagation, depending as it does on the membrane capacitance and linear resistance of the cytoplasm, is related to the characteristics (type) and diameter of the excitable fiber. Roughly, the velocity of the conduction varies inversely with the square root of the diameter for unmyelinated fibers.

Myelination of nerve fibers is a structural specialization of vertebrate nerve fibers

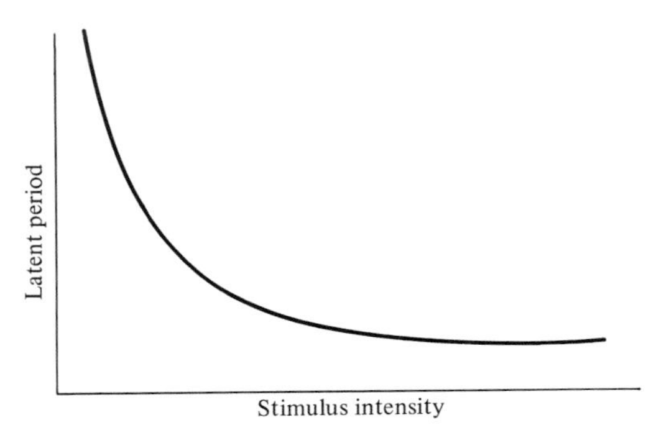

fig. 7-27. A curve showing the decrease in the latent period as the stimulus intensity is increased.

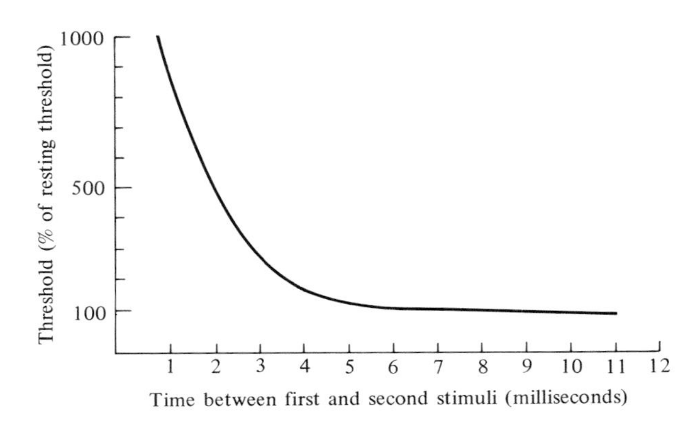

fig. 7-28. A curve showing the decrease in the refractory period as the stimulus intensity is increased.

which permits greatly increased velocity of conduction even though fiber diameter remains the same. As discussed earlier, the myelin sheath is formed from a Schwann cell which wraps itself around the nerve fiber many times. In the process all the cytoplasm of the Schwann cell is squeezed out, leaving the membranes closely opposed, thereby forming a layer approximately 170 Å thick for each rotation. With each rotation the transmembrane conductance is reduced by about one-half. Since there are usually at least 100 revolutions in a myelin sheath, the sheath forms a very effective insulator. It is approximately 2 μ thick in large nerve fibers.

Each unit of myelin sheath covers about 2 mm of axon length on the largest diameter fibers. Adjacent sheaths are separated by a gap, known as the *nodes of Ranvier*, of approximately 1 μ. The sheathed portion is called the *internode*. In the region of the internode, the effective resistance of the membrane is increased by a factor of approximately 200 and the effective capacitance is decreased, similarly, by a factor of approximately 200. In myelinated nerve the action potentials are generated only at the nodes. The propagation of the action potentials may be viewed as jumps of excitation from node to node.

The *voltage clamp technique* is a method which permits quantitative study of the properties of membranes in the region of intrinsic instability. Essentially the method consists of passing a current of such intensity that the transmembrane potential is

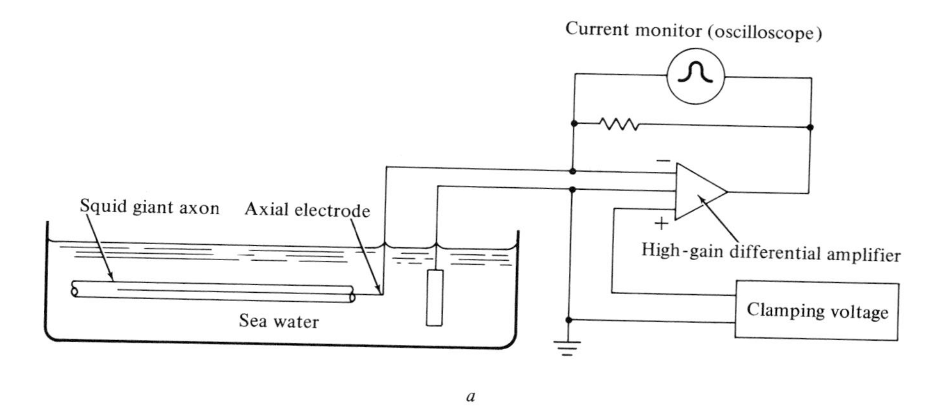

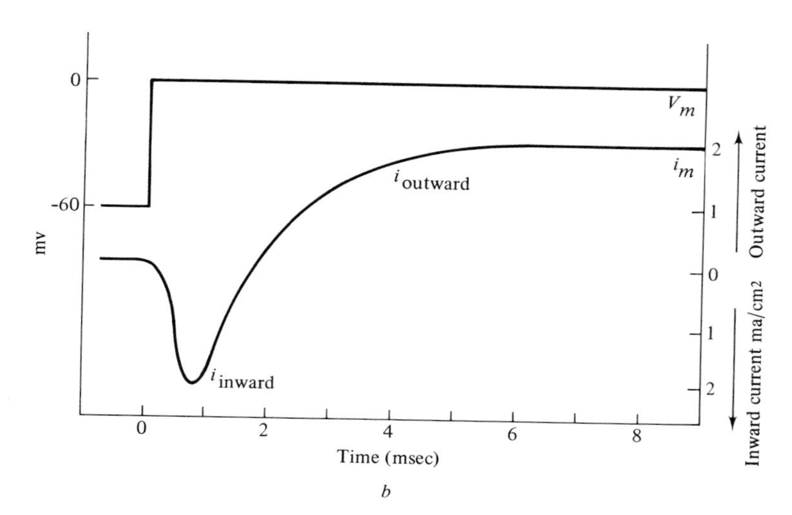

fig. 7-29. The arrangement for a voltage clamp experiment is shown in the upper part of the figure. A predetermined voltage is imposed between the axial electrode inserted into the squid giant axon and the sea water medium, and the transmembrane current flow is measured. The current flow after the sudden depolarization of the membrane to zero is shown in the lower part.

maintained at a predetermined value. The arrangement can be visualized with reference to Fig. 7-29. Two metal wires, the *internal electrodes*, are inserted into the interior of a squid giant axon to minimize the internal longitudinal resistance. One internal electrode is used to apply a potential, and the other is used for monitoring. Another electrode, the *external electrode*, is wound around the outside of the membrane. The two voltage electrodes are connected to a high gain differential amplifier and hence to a current source in such a manner that whatever current is required to maintain the transmembrane potential at the desired (constant) value is passed through the internal current electrode across the membrane.

When the membrane is suddenly depolarized, using the voltage clamp technique, by dropping from the normal resting potential, for example, to zero potential difference, the current flow which ensues can be plotted as a function of time (Fig. 7-30). As the membrane is depolarized there is an immediate surge of current which results from

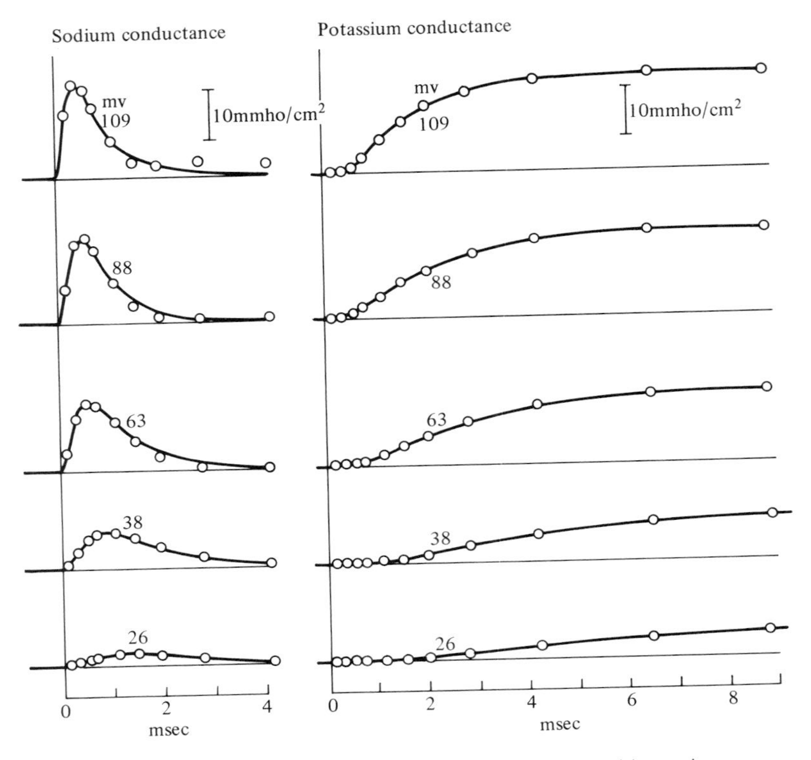

fig. 7-30. The sodium and potassium conductances caused by various displacements of the membrane potential using the voltage clamp technique. (From Hodgkin, A. L., and Huxley, A. F. *J. Physiol., 117,* 508 [1952].)

the discharge of membrane capacitance. The membrane capacitance remains completely discharged as long as the depolarization is imposed, and the subsequent current flow must be attributed to ion currents passing through the membrane. After the initial surge of current, there is a phase of inward current which reaches a peak within 1 to 2 msec. This inward current must result either from cations flowing inward or anions flowing outward from the cytoplasm. The direction of current during the second phase is opposite to that expected from a simple resistive element (from which a negative, outward current would be expected to accompany the change in membrane potential from −60 to −90 mv to 0). Finally, an outward current is observed which persists as long as the depolarized state of the membrane is maintained. The outward current obeys Ohm's law, but its magnitude is very high. This indicates that the membrane resistance has become very low.

Using radioactive tracers, Hodgkin and Huxley[171] showed that the prolonged outward current which is maintained during depolarization can be accounted for by an equivalent efflux of potassium ions from the cytoplasm. They concluded that the depolarization results in a large increase in potassium permeability. Several pieces of evidence suggest that the inward current represents mainly a flow of sodium ions. The inward current diminishes and finally disappears as the cytoplasm is made positive; the point at which no inward current is observed corresponds to the potential expected from the activities of sodium ions inside and outside of the membrane. The magnitude

[171] Hodgkin, A. L., and Huxley, A. F. *J. Physiol., 116,* 449, 473, 497 (1952).

of the inward current also can be markedly diminished by replacing the NaCl in the bathing medium with choline chloride or sucrose.

The fact that the sodium and potassium permeabilities do not increase simultaneously when the membrane is depolarized is a matter of considerable interest. It leads to the conclusion that the membrane continues to discriminate between sodium and potassium even when depolarized, and the ratio of sodium to potassium conductance is transiently reversed. The changes in sodium conductance are crucial for the action potential. During the first period, the increase in sodium conductance, leading to the spontaneous depolarization and reversal of the membrane potential, is self-reinforcing. This period is followed by an inactivation process during which the increased sodium conductance spontaneously shuts off, thereby bringing about termination of the action potential and restoration of the normal resting state and excitability of the fiber. The period during which the sodium conductance has returned to normal but the potassium conductance is still markedly increased corresponds to the refractory period. Each complete action potential sequence results in a sodium influx of approximately 3 to 4 $\times 10^{-12}$ moles/cm^2 of cell surface and an equal efflux of potassium. This amount is so small that even if the active transport of sodium has been stopped by the application of metabolic inhibitors, a squid axon is capable of generating several hundred thousand impulses.

Some of the most persuasive evidence that the electrical activity of excitable fibers resides in the cell membrane comes from the experiment of Baker, Hodgkin, and Shaw,[172] who were able to extrude the cytoplasm of a squid giant axon and fill the interior of the cylinder with an artificial salt solution. Such giant axons filled with salt solution maintained a transmembrane resting potential and were excitable. However, when a giant axon surface is damaged from either side, the results are a loss of transmembrane potential, a failure to respond to stimulation, and an inability to conduct an action potential.

active transport of sodium

The excitatory phenomena displayed by irritable cells depend upon the unequal distribution of ions across the cell membrane. It was noted above that the net movements of Na^+ ions and K^+ ions associated with a single spike are of the order of 3 to 4 $\times 10^{-12}$ moles/cm^2 in squid giant axon. Thus, a muscle or nerve fiber unable to maintain the ionic gradients would be able to sustain a very large number, perhaps 5×10^5, of depolarizations before the intracellular depletion of potassium and accumulation of sodium made further depolarization impossible in giant axons (fewer depolarizations in smaller fibers). Actually, living cells continuously utilize metabolic energy to maintain the nonequilibrium steady-state distribution of ions across the cell membrane. It was shown by Hill[173] that the heat production in a resting nerve at 20° is about 6.4×10^{-5} cal/g/sec. When the nerve is stimulated continuously at its maximum rate, the heat production is approximately doubled.

Of course, the net movement of an ion through the membrane represents the difference between the total influx of the ion and the total efflux. The use of radioactive ions such as ^{42}K and ^{24}Na has permitted the measurement of the unidirectional fluxes. The most significant result of these studies was the finding that membranes, in

[172] Baker, P. F., Hodgkin, A. L., and Shaw, T. I. *J. Physiol.*, *164*, 330, 355 (1962).
[173] Hill, A. V. *Proc. Roy. Soc.*, *B 111*, 106 (1932).

fig. 7-31. Ion fluxes in single fibers.

	FLUXES IN FROG MUSCLE FIBERS[a]		FLUXES IN GIANT AXONS[b]	
	RESTING (10^{-12} MOLE/CM^2 SEC)	STIMULATED (10^{-12} MOLE/CM^2 SEC)	RESTING (10^{-12} MOLE/CM^2 SEC)	STIMULATED (10^{-12} MOLE/CM^2 IMPULSE)
Na^+ Influx	3.5 ± 0.4	19.4 ± 1.5	32 ± 4	net entry
Na^+ Efflux	≈ 3.5	3.8 ± 1.0	39 ± 3	$3.5 - 4.5$
K^+ Influx	5.4 ± 0.8	1.8 ± 0.3	21 ± 1	net loss
K^+ Efflux	8.8 ± 1.2	11.4 ± 0.6	28 ± 5	$3.0 - 4.0$

[a] Data from Hodgkin, A. L., and Horowicz, P. *J. Physiol.*, *145*, 405 (1959).
[b] Data from Hodgkin, A. L. *Proc. Roy. Soc.*, *B 148*, 1 (1958).

fact, are quite permeable to Na^+ ions. Typical data are listed in Fig. 7-31. While it is clear that both Na^+ and K^+ ions are transferred continuously in both directions across the cell membrane, the details of the mechanism by which the individual ions penetrate the membrane are not known. The permeability of membranes to univalent cations appears to be related to the hydrated diameter of the cation and the density of fixed charges on the membrane.[174]

In the simplest possible case, it may be assumed that the individual ions move independently of each other across the cell membrane in the same way that they migrate in free solution, without the intervention of an active transport process. It is assumed also that the ionic mobility is constant at all points within the membrane and that the potential gradient across the membrane is linear. These assumptions were made in the constant field theory (see footnote 19, p. 359), which led to the following relations for the ion permeabilities.

$$P = \frac{\mathfrak{J}_{in}}{c_{out}} \left(\frac{1 - e^{-E\mathfrak{F}/RT}}{E\mathfrak{F}/RT} \right) \qquad (7\text{-}20)$$

$$P = \frac{\mathfrak{J}_{out}}{c_{in}} \left(\frac{e^{E\mathfrak{F}/RT} - 1}{E\mathfrak{F}/RT} \right) \qquad (7\text{-}21)$$

Using the flux data from frog muscle fibers gives the following permeability values.[175]

From K^+ influx: $P_{K^+} = 5.8 \times 10^{-7}$ cm/sec

From K^+ efflux: $P_{K^+} = 6.2 \times 10^{-7}$ cm/sec

From Na^+ influx: $P_{Na^+} = 7.9 \times 10^{-9}$ cm/sec

$$\frac{P_{Na^+}}{P_{K^+}} = 0.013$$

[174] Eisenman, G., Rudin, D. O., and Casby, J. U. *Science*, *126*, 831 (1957); Isard, J. O. *Nature*, *184*, 1616 (1959); Ling, G. N. *J. Gen. Physiol.*, *43*, suppl. 1, 149 (1960); Eisenman, G., in Kleinzeller, A., and Kotyk, A., eds. *Membrane Transport and Metabolism*. New York: Academic Press, 1961, p. 163.
[175] Hodgkin, A. L., and Keynes, R. D. *J. Physiol.*, *119*, 513 (1953); *128*, 28, 61 (1955); *131*, 592 (1956); Hodgkin, A. L., and Horowicz, P. *J. Physiol.*, *145*, 405 (1959); Caldwell, P. C., and Keynes, R. D. *J. Physiol.*, *154*, 177 (1960); Adrian, R. H. *J. Physiol.*, *156*, 623 (1961).

At most K^+ concentrations, the ratio of sodium to potassium permeabilities as a function of the external K^+ concentration corresponds to that expected from the transmembrane potential of single muscle fibers. At low external concentrations of K^+, however, the permeability to Na^+ ions significantly affects the transmembrane potential (Fig. 7-32).

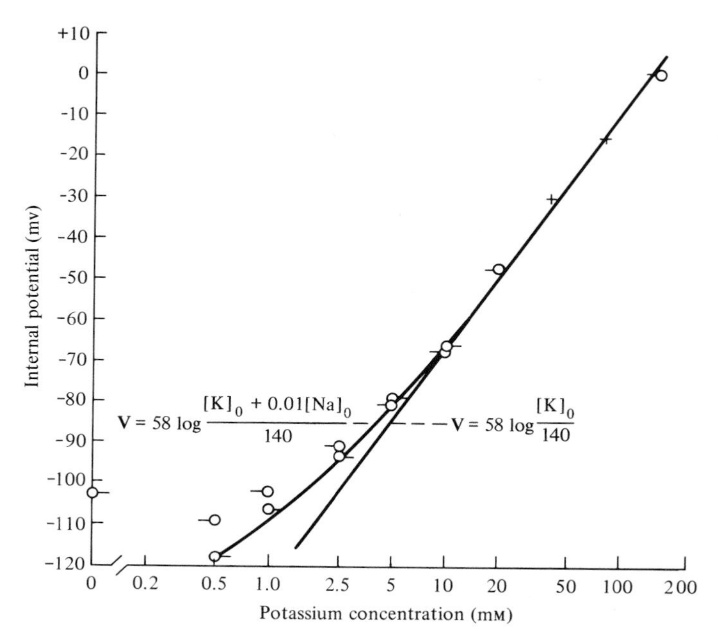

fig. 7-32. The resting transmembrane potential of single frog muscle fibers for various potassium concentrations in the external medium. At low potassium concentrations, the membrane potential is affected significantly by the permeability to sodium ions. Therefore the data are fitted better by a modified constant field equation than by a simple Nernst equation. (From Hodgkin, A. L., and Horowicz, P. *J. Physiol., 148,* 135 [1959].)

The assumptions of a constant field have been criticized as an oversimplification. Teorell[176] both has shown that the potential gradient across membranes with fixed charges is not linear and has derived flux equations for that situation. Linderholm[177] has derived sets of flux equations for a membrane having no fixed charges where the activity coefficient of the ions varies with the concentration. All these flux equations give the following common expression for the ratio of inward and outward fluxes when neither involves active transport.

$$\frac{\mathfrak{J}_{out}}{\mathfrak{J}_{in}} = \frac{c_{in}}{c_{out}} e^{(ZE\mathfrak{F}/RT)} = e^{[(E-E_S)Z\mathfrak{F}/RT]} \quad (7\text{-}22)$$

where E is the transmembrane potential and E_s is the equilibrium potential given by eq. 7-3.

In giant axons from cuttlefish poisoned with dinitrophenol (see footnote 175, p. 398),

[176] Teorell, T. *Progr. Biophys. Biophys. Chem., 3,* 305 (1953).
[177] Linderholm, H. *Acta Physiol. Scand., 27,* suppl. 97, 11 (1952).

measurements were taken of the fluxes while the external concentration of K^+ and the transmembrane potential were varied independently (the latter by the voltage clamp technique). These measurements showed that the ratio varied with the transmembrane potential as predicted by eq. 7-22 only during steady-state conditions. When the nerve fiber was gaining or losing K^+, the ratio of fluxes varied more steeply than predicted. The interactive interference between the inward and outward movement of potassium ions could be explained by either of two hypotheses. The first was that the potassium ions interacted and moved in single file through the same narrow channels in the membrane. The second was that potassium ions cross the membrane in a series of steps along a chain of negatively charged sites. Distinguishing between these hypotheses however, becomes difficult. In frog sartorius muscle, for example, chloride ions may cross the membrane by a similar single-file mechanism. Tracer flux measurements are further complicated by exchange diffusion (see Chapter 8); thus Na^+ efflux from frog sartorius muscle is reduced to approximately half when the Na^+ in the surrounding medium is replaced by Li^+ or choline ions.[178]

Efflux of Na^+ ions is rather unique in that it occurs against both concentration and electrical potential gradients. Therefore, it is an uphill process which, of necessity, is coupled to a downhill metabolic reaction. Dean (see footnote 18, p. 359) pointed out that the active extrusion of Na^+ ions would result in an electrogenic pump which would tend to make the cell interior negative. On the other hand, either an inward K^+ pump or an outward Cl^- pump would tend to make the cell interior positive. Actually, there appears to be both an active Na^+ extrusion and an active inward K^+ movement in axons, so the active movement of ions produces little change in the membrane potential. Under usual physiological circumstances, the distribution of K^+ ions is so near equilibrium that it is difficult to discern the active K^+ transport. In the absence of external K^+ ions, sodium efflux is diminished in frog muscle and mammalian erythrocytes. The active inward transport of K^+ ions is most easily demonstrated in mammalian erythrocytes[179] which contain a high concentration of intracellular Cl^- ions. The hydrolysis of ATP provides the metabolic energy for driving these processes (see footnotes 99 and 100, p. 382).

The effect of varying temperature on the rate of K^+ influx and Na^+ efflux shows a Q_{10} of about 3.5 (this indicates that they are linked to chemical reactions), while the Q_{11} for K^+ efflux and Na^+ influx are approximately 1.1 to 1.4 (this indicates that the former processes are linked to chemical reactions while the latter processes are diffusion). The magnitude of the active sodium efflux depends upon the internal Na^+ concentration and does not depend upon the membrane potential. The active and passive fluxes of sodium and potassium in frog muscle fiber are represented schematically in Fig. 7-33.

The active extrusion of Na^+ ions can be stopped by the application of dinitrophenol, azide, or cyanide to giant axons (Fig. 7-34) (see footnote 175, p. 398). Shanes and Berman[180] showed that anoxia but not iodoacetate diminishes the sodium efflux from giant axons. In vertebrate skeletal muscle or mammalian erythrocytes, glycolysis apparently suffices to maintain active transport; but in nerve, respiration is required. The influx of Na^+ ions is not affected by these metabolic inhibitors, but K^+ influx is somewhat reduced.

---

[178] Keynes, R. D., and Swan, R. C. *J. Physiol.*, *147*, 591 (1959).
[179] Post, R. L., and Jolly, P. C. *Biochim. Biophys. Acta*, *25*, 118 (1957); Maizels, M., in Kleinzeller, A., and Kotyk, A., eds. *Membrane Transport and Metabolism*. New York: Academic Press, 1961, p. 256; Whittam, R., and Ager, M. E. *Biochem. J.*, *93*, 337 (1964); *97*, 214 (1965).
[180] Shanes, A. M., and Berman, M. D. *J. Gen. Physiol.*, *39*, 279 (1956).

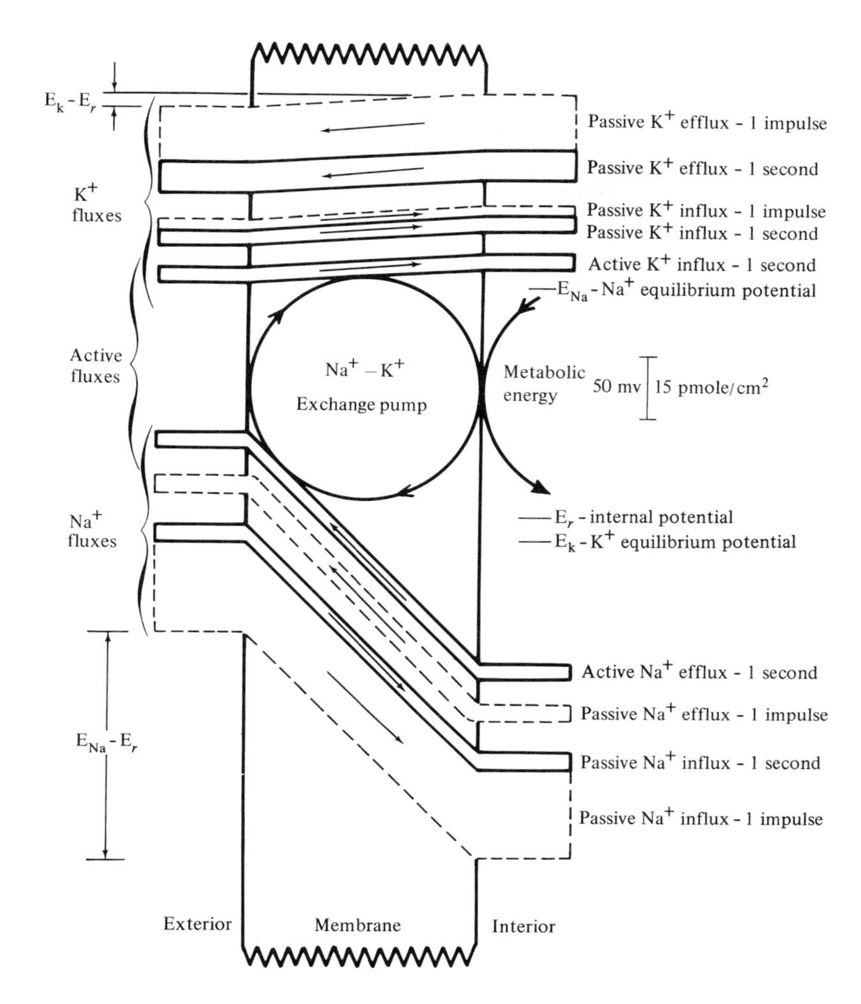

fig. 7-33. A schematic representation of the active and passive fluxes of K^+ and Na^+ ions for a frog muscle fiber and of the added fluxes accompanying a single depolarization. The width of the bars is proportional to the magnitude of the fluxes, and the vertical displacements are proportional to the changes in electrochemical potential. (From Woodbury, J. W. *Federation Proc., 22,* 33 [1963].)

Poisoning the active transport system with a metabolic inhibitor has no immediate effect on the transmembrane potential. The transmembrane potential gradually is reduced as there is a net leakage of Na^+ inward and K^+ ions outward. As long as the transmembrane potential is maintained, the membrane is excitable and the action potentials are propagated along its length. These observations indicate that the properties of excitability and conduction do not depend directly upon metabolic energy, but only upon the distribution of ions on either side of the membrane, and thus only indirectly upon active transport.

The active extrusion of Na^+ ions can be reinitiated in giant axons poisoned with metabolic inhibitors by the intracellular injection of ATP or arginine phosphate (Fig. 7-35). On the basis of experiments in which the axoplasm of giant axons was

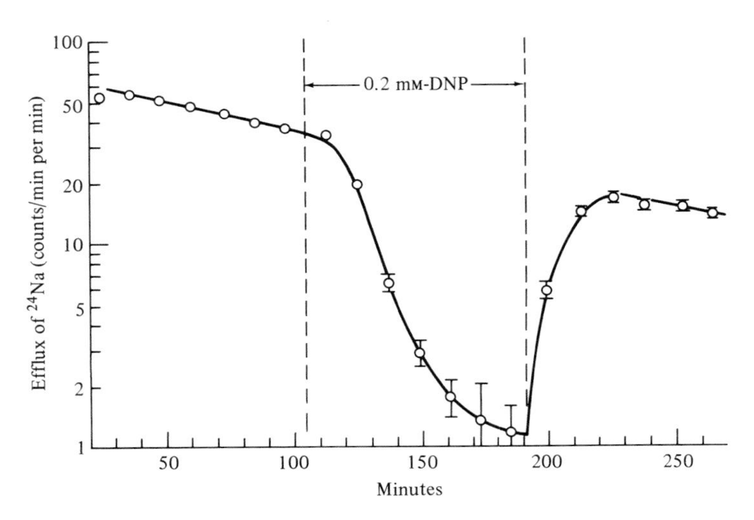

fig. 7-34. Sodium efflux from a giant axon of *Sepia*, showing its abolition upon treatment with dinitrophenol and its restoration when the drug was washed away with sea water. (From Hodgkin, A. L., and Keynes, R. D. *J. Physiol., 128*, 34 [1955].)

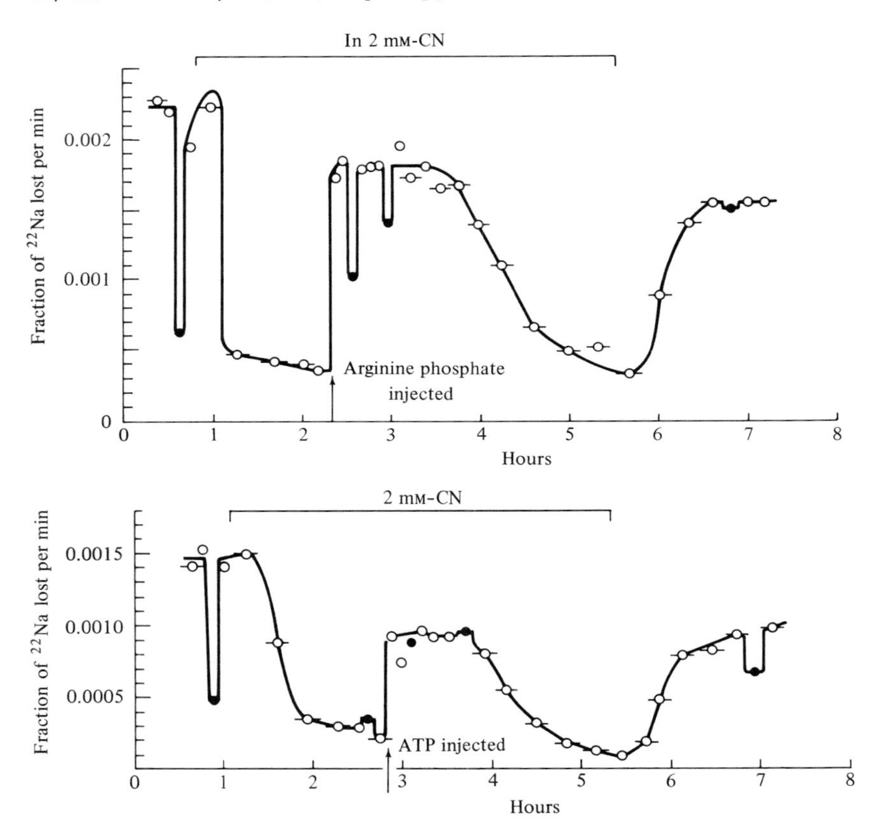

fig. 7-35. The restoration of sodium efflux in a giant axon of *Loligo* poisoned by cyanide following the intracellular injection of arginine phosphate (above) or ATP (below). (From Caldwell, P. C., Hodgkin, A. L., Keynes, R. D., and Shaw, T. I. *J. Physiol., 152*, 575, 579 [1960].)

extruded and replaced with artificial solutions, Baker and Shaw[181] concluded that approximately 3 Na^+ ions were extruded per molecule of ATP hydrolyzed. This value was obtained from two types of experiments. In the first type, it was found that the rate of formation of inorganic phosphate from ATP and arginine phosphate was approximately 28 percent less in the extruded axoplasm in the presence of cyanide than in intact cyanide-poisoned giant axons. The difference in the amount of ATP hydrolyzed was attributed to the sodium pump. A similar value was obtained by the second type of experiment: measuring the difference in the rate of inorganic phosphate appearance in cyanide-poisoned giant axons before and after inhibition of the sodium pump by ouabain.

ion transport in mitochondria

Isolated liver or kidney mitochondria maintain high intramitochondrial levels of monovalent and divalent cations which can be accumulated against an electrochemical gradient as long as oxidative phosphorylation is actively in progress.[182] The accumulation of cations by mitochondria is energy-dependent and occurs either when substrates are actively utilized in oxidative phosphorylation or when ATP is consumed. If mitochondria are incubated in the absence of substrates which support oxidative phosphorylation, the accumulated monovalent and divalent cations leak out. The extrusion of H^+ ions is associated with the accumulation of cations.

Potassium accumulated by mitochondria appears to be independent of any accumulation or extrusion of Na^+ ions.[183] β-Hydroxybutyrate is the substrate which supports K^+ uptake most effectively. Oxidative phosphorylation does not have to lead to ATP production in order to support ion transport; inhibitors of the terminal steps of oxidative phosphorylation such as oligomycin have no effect on the substrate-supported, energy-dependent ion uptake in mitochondria. Ion uptake in mitochondria supported by ATP in the absence of substrate oxidation is inhibited by oligomycin. The uptake of K^+ ions is blocked by dinitrophenol and cyanide. It is of some interest that no known mitochondrial active transport system is inhibited by ouabain or other cardiac glycosides. The rate of K^+ accumulation by mitochondria can be markedly increased by treatment with antibiotics such as valinomycin or the gramicidins[184] or by parathyroid hormone.

In addition to ion accumulation, there is K^+ exchange between the intramitochondrial and extramitochondrial pools.[185] The K^+ exchange depends upon the concentration of K^+ in the medium and is depressed by Na^+ ions in the medium. The intramitochondrial K^+ ions exist both in bound and unbound forms; while the unbound K^+ ions exchange rapidly, the bound K^+ ions do not. Organic mercurials depress

---

[181] Caldwell, P. C., Hodgkin, A. L., Keynes, R. D., and Shaw, T. I. *J. Physiol.*, *152*, 545, 561 (1960); Baker, P. F., and Shaw, T. I. *J. Physiol.*, *180*, 424 (1965).

[182] Spector, W. G. *Proc. Roy. Soc.*, *B 141*, 268 (1953); MacFarlane, M G., and Spencer, A. G. *Biochem. J.*, *54*, 569 (1953); Bartley, W., and Davies, R. E. *Biochem. J.*, *57*, 37 (1954); Lehninger, A. L. *Physiol. Rev.*, *42*, 467 (1962).

[183] Stanbury, S. W., and Mudge, G. H. *Proc. Soc. Exptl. Biol. Med.*, *82*, 675 (1953); Gamble, J. L., Jr. *J. Biol. Chem.*, *228*, 955 (1957); *Am. J. Physiol.*, *203*, 886 (1962).

[184] Moore, C., and Pressman, B. C. *Biochem. Biophys. Res. Commun.*, *15*, 562 (1964); Chapell, J. B., and Crofts, A. R. *Biochem. J.*, *95*, 393 (1965); Harris, E. J., Cockrell, R., and Pressman, B. C. *Biochem. J.*, *99*, 200 (1966).

[185] Scott, R. L., and Gamble, J. L., Jr. *J. Biol. Chem.*, *236*, 570 (1961).

the amount of K^+ ions bound by mitochondria but increase the amount of K^+ exchange.

When actively respiring mitochondria are placed in a medium containing Ca^{++} ions (or Sr^{++} or Mn^{++} ions), accumulation takes place which may result in as much as a 200-fold increase in the Ca^{++} content.[186] Mitochondria accumulate PO_4^{---} ions passively along with the Ca^{++} ions. The process of Ca^{++} uptake requires the presence of any adenine nucleotide and Mg^{++} ions, and the presence of Na^+ or K^+ ions results in further stimulation. Oxygen consumption is increased and phosphorylation is inhibited as Ca^{++} is taken up. The increase in oxygen consumption is directly related to the amount of Ca^{++} taken up. Calcium uptake is inhibited by dinitrophenol and other agents which uncouple oxidative phosphorylation.

The accumulation of Ca^{++} ions, PO_4^{---} ions, and oxygen consumption appears to follow a definite stoichiometry (Fig. 7-36). Calcium and phosphate are taken up in

fig. 7-36. Stoichiometry of ion uptake and oxidative phosphorylation in kidney mitochondria. (From Lehninger, A. L. *The Mitochondrion.* New York: W. A. Benjamin, 1964, p.168.)

SUBSTRATE	CA^{++} UPTAKE, MμATOMS	P_i UPTAKE, MμMOLES	O_2 UPTAKE, MμATOMS	ACCUMULATION RATIOS CA:O	P:O	ADP:O
β-Hydroxybutyrate	163	98	33	4.94	2.97	2.88
Succinate	292	208	109	2.70	1.91	1.91
Ascorbate	170	96	97	1.78	0.99	0.99

The test system contained the substrates shown, Mg^{++}, $Ca^{45}Cl_2$, P_i, ATP, and buffer, *p*H 7.0. Incubated 10 min at 30°. The ADP: O ratios were measured in a parallel system not containing Ca^{++}.

the ratio of 1.67, the same ratio as that with which calcium and phosphate occur in calcium hydroxyapatite. The ratio of Ca^{++} uptake to O_2 consumption depends upon whether β-hydroxybutyrate, succinate, or ascorbate is used as substrate. The ratio of calcium accumulated to oxygen consumed is 4.94, 2.70, and 1.78 respectively for these substrates. It may be concluded from these data that each of the three energy-conserving sites in the electron transport chain makes an equal contribution in supporting Ca^{++} uptake. The hydrolysis of ATP can also serve to support Ca^{++} uptake.

The active accumulation of monovalent or divalent cations by mitochondria is accompanied by the ejection of H^+ ions into the medium.[187] In the absence of permeant anions, the *molar* ratio of H^+ ions secreted to Ca^{++} ions absorbed approaches 1.0. The ratio is further increased by the presence of monovalent cations in the medium and may approach 2.0 if the extramitochondrial concentration of K^+ is high.

One hypothesis which has been proposed to explain the cation uptake by mitochondria is an extension of the traditional view of oxidative phosphorylation.[188] In

[186] Vasington, F. D., and Murphy, J. V. *J. Biol. Chem., 237*, 2670 (1962); Brierley, G. P., Murer, E., and Green, D. E. *Science, 140*, 60 (1963); Rossi, C. S., and Lehninger, A. L. *Biochem. Z., 338*, 698 (1963); *J. Biol. Chem., 239*, 3971 (1964); Chance, B. *J. Biol. Chem., 240*, 2729 (1965); Bielawski, J., and Lehninger, A. L. *J. Biol. Chem., 241*, 4316 (1966).

[187] Engstrom. G. W., and DeLuca, H. F. *Biochemistry, 3*, 379 (1964); Chappell, J. B., and Crofts, A. R. *Biochem. J., 95*, 378,387 (1965); Judah, J. D., Ahmed, K., McLean, A. E., and Christie, G. S. *Biochim. Biophys. Acta, 94*, 452 (1965).

[188] Rasmussen, H., Chance, B., and Ogata, E. *Proc. Natl. Acad. Sci., 53*, 1069 (1965); Rasmussen, H., and Ogata, E. *Biochemistry, 5*, 733 (1966).

this view, nonphosphorylated high-energy intermediates are formed at three points in the respiratory chain. These intermediates are assumed to be doubly pronated anhydride-type compounds with which cations may interact specifically within the mitochondrial membrane. During this reaction, two protons (H^+) are displaced to the exterior of the mitochondrion. A conformational change in the cation high-energy intermediate complex takes place so that upon dissociation the cations are discharged into the interior.

Mitchell[189] proposed a hypothesis to explain cation uptake based on the premise that the basic process driven by electron transport through the respiratory chain is the separation of H^+ and OH^- ions across the mitochondrial membrane, which is relatively impermeable to H^+ ions. Thus, rather than generating high-energy intermediates directly, the primary effect of carrying a pair of electrons through the respiratory chain is to produce six H^+ ions on the outer side of the membrane and to remove six H^+ ions on the inner side, as a result of the anisotropy of the electron carrier molecules in the membrane. The gradient of H^+ ions so produced is thought to be the driving force for the phosphorylation of ADP as well as for cation accumulation. While much experimental data fit one or both hypotheses, neither has been tested by crucial, definitive experiments.

composite membrane systems

Many physiological transport systems consist of two or more membranes, either in series or in parallel. The best-studied composite membrane system is that of the frog skin. The frog skin has the capacity of transporting sodium chloride from a low concentration in the outside environment to a high concentration in the interior extracellular fluid, a process which is coupled to the utilization of metabolic energy.

If a piece of frog skin is removed and placed between two compartments containing Ringer's salt solution of identical composition in an apparatus such as that shown in Fig. 7-37, a potential difference of about 50 to 100 mv develops between the inside (positive) and outside (negative) surfaces of the frog skin. There is a good correlation between the magnitude of the potential difference and the flux of NaCl transported across the frog skin. Using radioactive tracers, it can be shown[190] that the inward and outward fluxes of Cl^- ions follow eq. 7-22. This leads us to the conclusion that the migration of Cl^- ions is passive.

The presence of Na^+ or Li^+ ions in the external medium is required for generation of the potential. Using the apparatus shown in Fig. 7-37, it is possible to apply a counterpotential to that generated by the frog skin so that the net potential difference between the two sides is zero. Under these conditions the current generated by the skin is equal to the *net* inward flux of Na^+ ions and to the current of electrons required to neutralize the Na^+ ion current. Under the short-circuit conditions, the Na^+ influx amounts to approximately 105 percent of the total current while the Na^+ efflux amounts to about 5 percent of the total current. The Cl^- flux is equal in both directions under these conditions and does not contribute to the ionic current. Although K^+ ions are not transported actively by the frog skin, even in high concentrations, the presence of some K^+ ions is required for active Na^+ transport.

[189] Lundegårdh, H. *Arkiv Bot.*, *32 A*, no. 12, 1 (1945); Mitchell, P., and Moyle, J. *Nature*, *208*, 147, 1205 (1965).
[190] Koefoed-Johnsen, V., Levi, H., and Ussing, H. H. *Acta Physiol. Scand.*, *25*, 150 (1952); Ussing, H. H. *J. Gen. Physiol.*, *43*, suppl 1, 135 (1960).

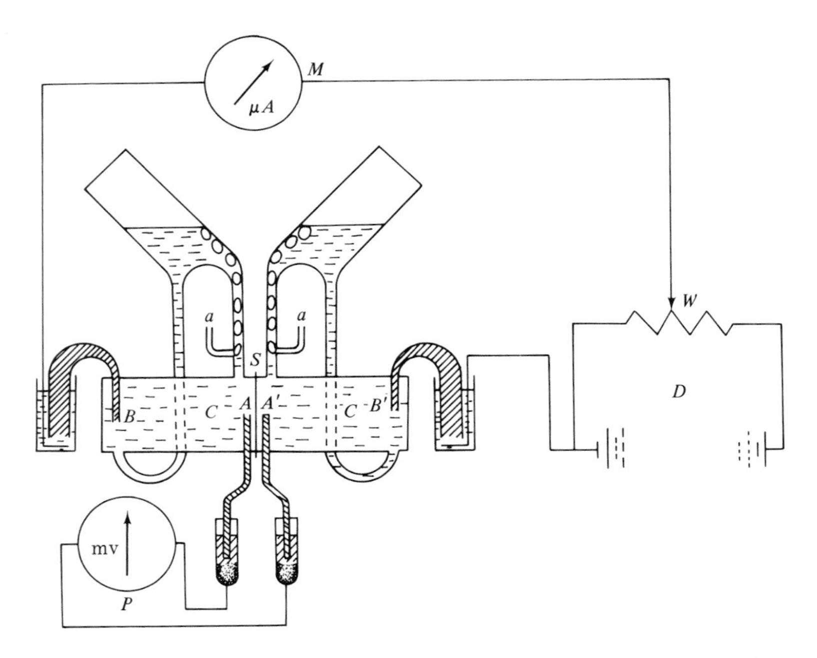

fig. 7-37. A diagram of the apparatus used for measuring ion fluxes and potential differences and currents across a frog skin. Chambers (*C*) containing Ringer's salt solution on either side of the frog skin (*S*) contain inlets for oxygen (*a*), salt bridges to calomel electrodes (*A*) for measuring the potential with a potentiometer (*P*), and salt bridges (*B*) for applying a potential from an external source (*D*) through a current meter (*M*). (From Ussing, H. H., and Zerahn, K. *Acta Physiol. Scand.*, *23*, 113 [1951].)

The fact that the inward movement of Na^+ ions was an active transport process coupled to metabolic reactions was supported by the finding that dinitrophenol, sulfonamides, or thiocyanate abolished the inward movement of Na^+ ions and the potential difference across the skin as well. Under these conditions the influx and efflux ratios for Na^+ ions obeyed eq. 7-22.[191] Oxygen consumption by frog skin was measured in the absence and presence of sodium transport;[192] a direct relation was found between the additional oxygen consumed under conditions of Na^+ ion transport and the osmotic work performed. Ouabain, a specific inhibitor of the Na-K activated ATPase, abolishes active Na^+ transport and the electrical potential difference when placed on the inner surface, but not when placed on the outer surface, of the frog skin.[193]

The frog skin consists of an ectodermal epithelium on the outside surface and a mesodermal corium on the interior side. On pushing a microelectrode from the outside surface of the skin toward the inside surface, some small negative potential is developed as the microelectrode pushes through the keratinized outer layer of epithelial cells. At a depth of about 50 μ, a positive potential of about 60 mv[194] is developed. The potential cannot be attributed to the intracellular resting potential of an epithelial

[191] Schoffeniels, E. *Arch. intern. Physiol.*, *63*, 361 (1955).

[192] Zerahn, K. *Acta Physiol. Scand.*, *36*, 300 (1956); Leaf, A., and Renshaw, A. *Biochem. J.*, *65*, 82, 90 (1957).

[193] Koefoed-Johnsen, V. *Acta Physiol. Scand.*, *42*, suppl. 145, 87 (1957).

[194] Engbaek, L., and Hoshiko, T. *Acta Physiol. Scand.*, *39*, 348 (1957); Scheer, B. T., and Mumbach, M. W. *J. Cellular Comp. Physiol.*, *55*, 259 (1960). See also Chowdhury, T. K., and Snell, F. M. *Biochim. Biophys. Acta*, *94*, 461 (1965) for somewhat different results.

cell because it disappears when the frog skin is short-circuited. Upon pushing the microelectrode through the basement membrane a further increase in potential is observed to approximately 100 mv. These two potential jumps appear to correspond in level to the two sides of the secreting epithelial cells adjacent to the basement membrane of the frog skin.

In frog skin treated with cupric salts (which virtually abolishes the permeability to Cl^- ions), the potential across the skin becomes a simple function of the potassium concentration on the inside of the skin and a simple function of the sodium concentration on the outside of the skin.[195] Thus, the inside surface of the frog skin behaves like a potassium electrode while the outside behaves like a sodium electrode. The secretory cells at the base of the epithelial layer presumably possess polarity; sodium ions enter from the outside into the cell passively and are actively extruded on the inside surface (Fig. 7-38).

The toad bladder is a composite membrane system resembling the frog skin. The toad conserves water by reabsorbing urine from its bladder, a process which is the passive consequence of the active absorption of salt. A potential difference of about

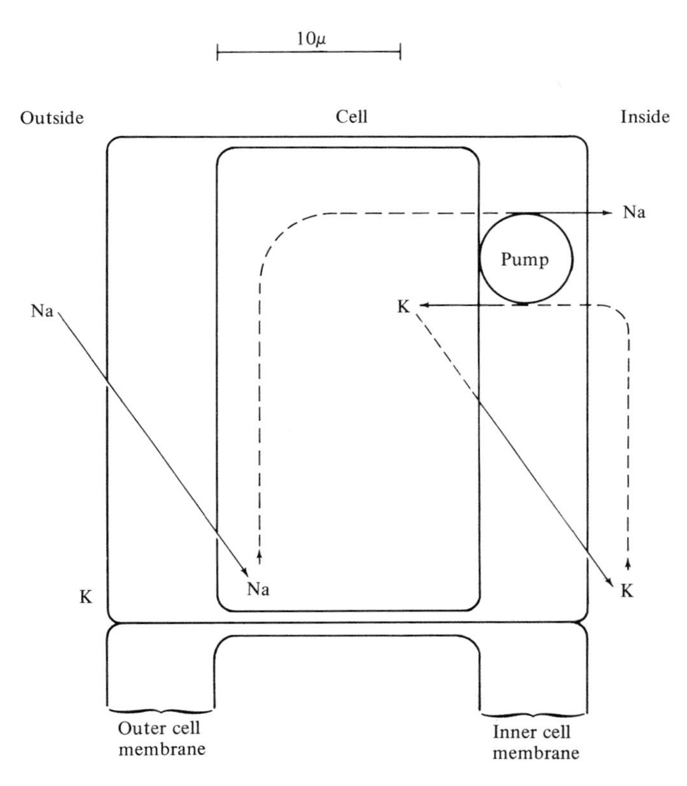

fig. 7-38. Ussing's view of the epithelial cell of the frog skin as an asymmetric system of composite membranes. The outward-facing membrane is permeable to Na^+ which enters the cell passively by flowing down an electrochemical gradient; the inward-facing membrane actively transports Na^+ out of the cell. (From Ussing, H. H. *J. Gen. Physiol., 43,* suppl. 1, 140 [1960].)

[195] Koefoed-Johnsen, V., and Ussing, H. H. *Acta Physiol. Scand.*, *42*, 298 (1958).

25 to 80 mv is generated across the toad bladder, with the inside or mucosal surface being negative and the outside or serosal surface being positive. Short-circuit experiments with isolated toad bladders indicate that the only ion actively transported is Na^+.[196] Measuring the potential with a microelectrode that was pushed gradually through the thickness of the bladder wall, it was found that the potential changed abruptly in two steps.[197] The process of Na^+ ion transport appears to resemble that in frog skin. Oxygen consumption is reduced in the absence of Na^+ ions, and the additional oxygen consumed is related to the transport of Na^+ ions.

The *parietal* or *oxyntic* cells of the vertebrate stomach present a remarkable composite membrane system which is capable of secreting an approximately 0.15 M solution of HCl into the stomach. The mammalian stomach does not secrete acid spontaneously but requires stimulation, normally by the parasympathetic nervous system or the hormone gastrin, or, experimentally by the use of drugs such as histamine or pilocarpine. The mucosa of bullfrog stomach can be stripped away from the muscle wall and mounted between two chambers containing oxygenated Ringer's salt solution. This preparation spontaneously secretes hydrochloric acid after a recovery period of about 30 minutes. The secretion of acid is inhibited reversibly by thiocyanate. It develops a potential difference of about 35 mv with the serosal surface positive to the mucosal (secretory) surface. The secretion of acid is energy-dependent; oxygen consumption varies linearly with the amount of acid secreted (Fig. 7-39).

In a short-circuited frog gastric mucosa, the net chloride flux is from the serosal to the mucosal surface and amounts to about 4.25 $\mu Eq/cm^2/hr$. The hydrogen ion secretion is 1.20 $\mu Eq/cm^2/hr$, and the short-circuit current amounts to about 3.05 $\mu Eq/cm^2/hr$. Thus, the sum of the short-circuit current and hydrogen ion secretion (serosal to mucosal) is equal to the net flux of chloride ions (mucosal to serosal), and the sum of all other net ion movements must be zero. There is a net flux of Na^+ ions from the mucosal to the serosal surface of about 0.09 $\mu Eq/cm^2/hr$ which is almost exactly offset by a net flux of K^+ ions in the opposite direction (serosal to mucosal).[198] Transport of chloride ions appears to be an active process which is inhibited, in this case, by dinitrophenol or cyanide.[199]

Studies of gastric secretion have disclosed[200] that the concentration of Cl^- in the gastric juice varies over a relatively narrow range from about 136 to 160 mEq/L. The acidity of the gastric juice, on the other hand, varies over wide limits; the difference between the H^+ ion and Cl^- ion concentrations is made up by cations which form neutral chlorides (Fig. 7-40), Na^+, or K^+. The experiments of Heinz and Durbin[201] provide evidence for the existence of a separate H^+ active transport process. These investigators replaced the Cl^- ions of Ringer's salt solution with SO_4^{--}; the mucosa is relatively impermeable to the latter ion, and its substitution resulted in the almost complete abolition of the Cl^- short-circuit current. The secretion of acid, however,

---

[196] Leaf, A., Anderson, J., and Page, L. B. *J. Gen. Physiol.*, *41*, 657 (1958); *J. Biol. Chem.*, *234*, 1625 (1959); Frazier, H. S., Dempsey, E. F., and Leaf, A. *J. Gen. Physiol.*, *45*, 529 (1962).

[197] Frazier, H. S. *J. Gen. Physiol.*, *45*, 515 (1962).

[198] Davenport, H. W., and Chavre, V. J. *Am. J. Physiol.*, *171*, 1 (1952); *174*, 203 (1953); Hogben, C. A. M. *Am. J. Physiol.*, *180*, 641 (1955); *Federation Proc.*, *24*, 1353 (1965).

[199] Crane, E. E., Davies, R. E., and Longmuir, N. M. *Biochem. J.*, *43*, 321 336 (1948); Davies, R. E., and Edelman, J. *Biochem. J.*, *50*, 190 (1951); Heinz, E., and Durbin, R. P. *J. Gen. Physiol.*, *41*, 101 (1957); *41*, 1035 (1958).

[200] Gray, J. S., Bucher, G. R., and Harman, H. H. *Am. J. Physiol.*, *132*, 504 (1941); *133*, 542 (1941); Hollander, F. *Gastroenterology*, *40*, 477 (1961).

[201] Rehm, W. S. *Gastroenterology*, *14*, 401 (1950); Heinz, E., and Durbin, R. *Biochim. Biophys. Acta*, *31*, 246 (1959).

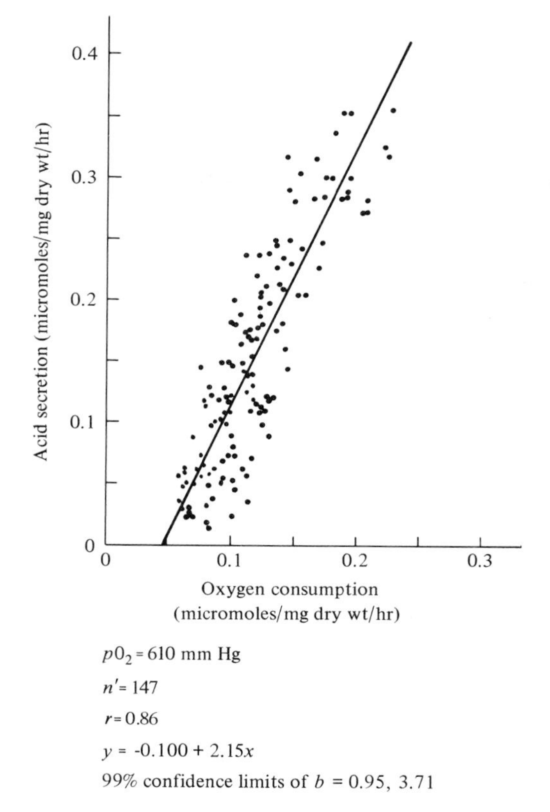

fig. 7-39. The relation of H^+ ion secretion and oxygen consumption by isolated frog gastric mucosa. (From Davenport, H. W. *Federation Proc.*, *11*, 717 [1952].)

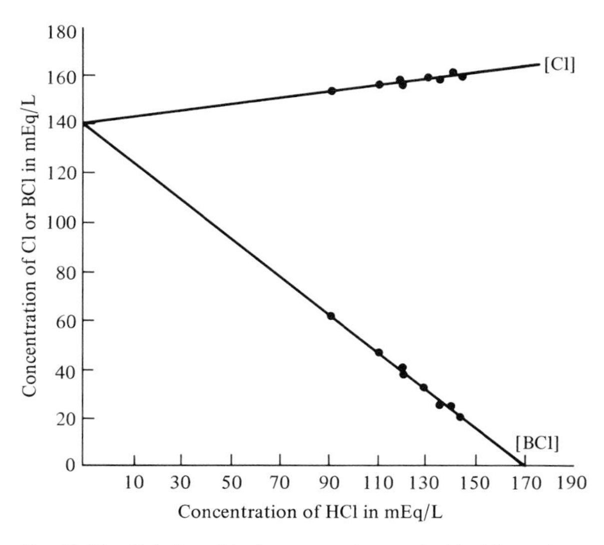

fig. 7-40. Relationship between the total chloride and neutral chloride salts (BCl)in gastric juice; as the acidity of the gastric juice increases, the concentration of neutral chloride salts decreases. (From Gray, J. S., Bucher, G. R., and Harman, H. H. *Am. J. Physiol.*, *132*, 511 [1941].)

still continued at about two-thirds its original rate. Under these circumstances a potential of opposite sign was measured. Both the acid secretion and the secondary potential could be abolished by thiocyanate.

Cells of the gastric mucosa are remarkable for their high content of the enzyme carbonic anhydrase,[202] which catalyzes the hydration of carbon dioxide to carbonic acid. Although that reaction occurs spontaneously, the nonenzymatic rate is very slow. During high rates of acid secretion, carbonic anhydrase appears to catalyze the uptake of carbon dioxide. Acid secretion can be inhibited in the intact stomach by acetazolamide, a potent inhibitor of carbonic anhydrase; however, very high concentrations of acetazolamide are required. On the other hand, the response of the isolated gastric mucosa to carbonic anhydrase inhibitors is different in several respects. Not only are very large concentrations of inhibitors required, but there is a reversible inhibition of the spontaneous transmucosal potential difference and short-circuit current. It should be noted that short-circuiting itself increases hydrogen ion secretion, and the inhibitors have little effect on the electrically short-circuited mucosa. These differences may result from the fact that the uncatalyzed hydration of carbon dioxide may be sufficient to support hydrogen transport by the isolated mucosa.

The secretion of H^+ ions may occur directly by an active process. Carbonic anhydrase would catalyze the condensation of OH^- ions left behind in the gastric epithelial cell with CO_2 produced from metabolism or derived from the circulation to form HCO_3^-.[203] On the other hand, acid formation may occur as a result of the active inward

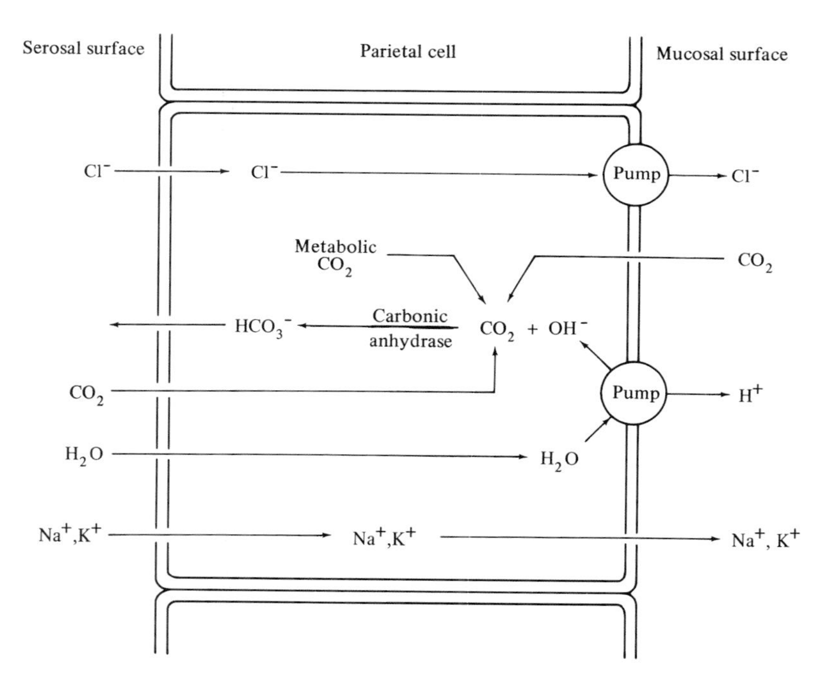

fig. 7-41. A hypothesis for the formation of HCl by the gastric mucosa.

[202] Davenport, H. W. *J. Physiol.*, *97*, 32 (1939); *Am. J. Physiol.*, *128*, 725 (1940); Janowitz, H. D., Colcher, H., and Hollander, F. *Am. J. Physiol.*, *171*, 325 (1952); Rehm, W. S., Canosa, C. A., Schlesinger, H. S., Chandler, W. K., and Dennis, W. H. *Am. J. Physiol.*, *200*, 1074 (1961); Hogben, C. A. M. *Circulation*, *26*, 1179 (1962); Byers, F. M., Jr., Jordan, P. H., Jr., and Maren, T. H. *Am. J. Physiol.*, *202*, 429 (1962).

(mucosal to serosal) transport of HCO_3^- ions. The latter hypothesis supposes that the absorption of HCO_3^- ions from the gastric fluid induces a dissociation of carbonic acid. As more HCO_3^- is absorbed, more H^+ ions are left behind in the gastric fluid; this increases the fluid's acidity. Carbonic anyhdrase on the mucosal surface of the gastric epithelial cells catalyzes the formation of more carbonic acid from water and CO_2 liberated from the metabolism of the gastric epithelium or derived from the blood stream. A model of gastric secretion is shown in Fig. 7-41.

An ATPase is present in the microsomal fraction of gastric mucosa which differs from the cation activated ATPase of most tissues in that it is not stimulated by the joint addition of Na^+ and K^+ ions, nor is it inhibited by ouabain or other cardiac glycosides.[204] Its activity is stimulated to some extent by halide ions and to a larger extent by HCO_3^- ions. The ATPase is inhibited by thiocyanate ions at levels comparable to those which inhibit acid production in the intact mucosa. Partial inhibition by thiocyanate can be overcome by raising the HCO_3^- concentration.

capillary exchange

In complex organisms the exchanges of matter between individual cells of one organ and those of another, as well as between individual cells and the external environment, are mediated by means of a circulatory system. Particularly in vertebrates, the exchange takes place through an extensive network of very fine blood vessels, the *capillaries*, which connect the arteries with the veins. The capillaries are tubules of flattened endothelial cells, about 10 μ in diameter, surrounded by a basement membrane on the exterior surface. They can be distinguished from the arterioles on one side and

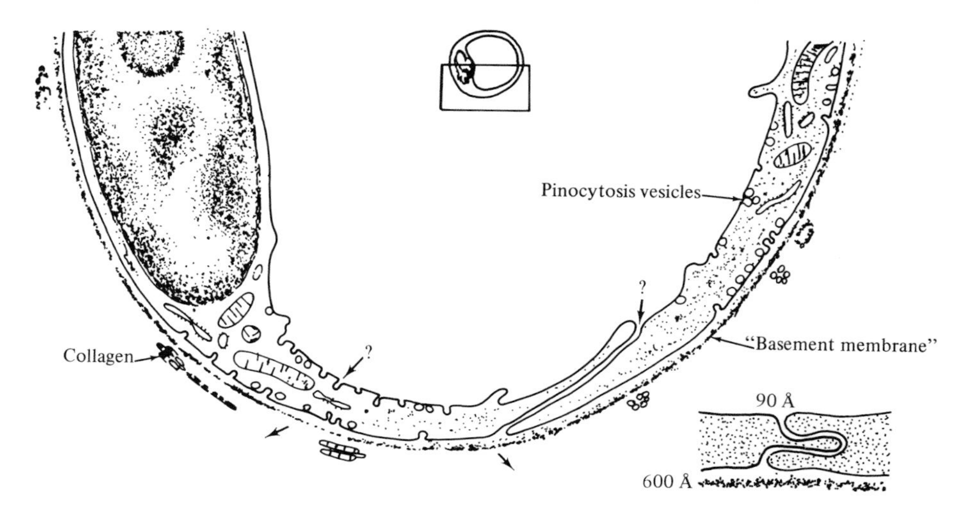

fig. 7-42. A schematic representation of a cross-sectional electron micrograph of a capillary. (From Fawcett, D. W., in Reynolds, S. R. M., and Zweifach, B. W., eds. *The Microcirculation.* Urbana, Ill.: The University of Illinois Press, 1959, p. 1.)

[203] Hogben, C. A. M. *Proc. Natl. Acad. Sci.*, *38*, 13 (1952); Rehm, W. S. *Federation Proc.*, *26*, 1303 (1967).
[204] Kasbekar, D. K., and Durbin, R. P. *Biochim. Biophys. Acta*, *105*, 472 (1965).

the venules on the other by the absence of a muscular layer. The walls of a capillary are approximately 0.2 to 0.5 μ thick and frequently consist of a single endothelial cell rolled up to form a closed channel. The junctions between the cells, as seen in electron micrographs, consist of narrow, tortuous intercellular spaces about 100 Å wide, which are filled with somewhat electron-dense material (Fig. 7-42). Just beneath the surface of the endothelial cells are numerous *pinocytic vesicles* (some of which are open to the surface while others are closed) which resemble similar structures seen in unicellular organisms.

The *extracellular* space, which is filled with the *interstitial fluid*, lies between the capillaries and the individual cells with which the capillaries exchange various materials. Thus, exchanges between the blood and the individual cells take place by way of the interstitial fluid. The volume of the extracellular space varies from organ to organ and with the physiological state of the organism, but usually it amounts to 10 to 15 percent of the volume of the organ. The interstitial fluid arises by ultrafiltration of blood plasma from the capillaries. Starling[205] was the first to point out that most of the interstitial fluid is reabsorbed into the venous end of the capillaries (Fig. 7-43). Some

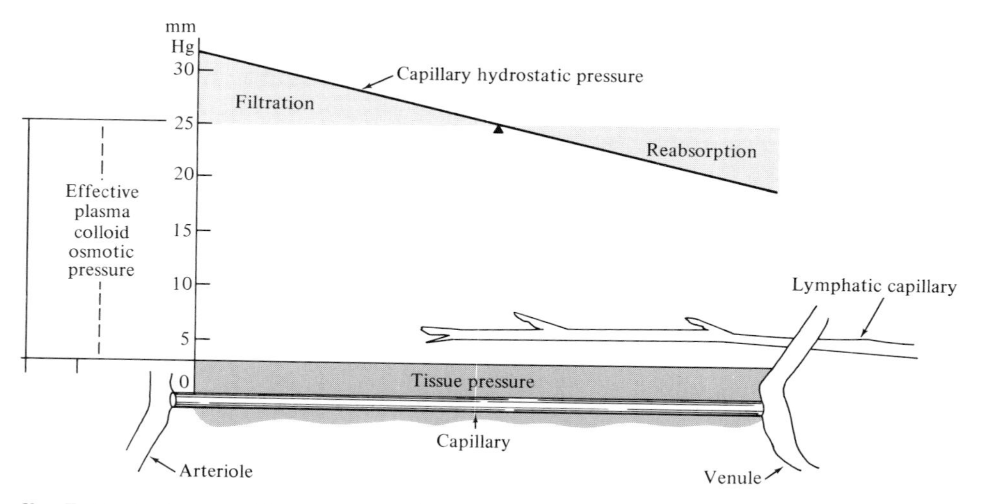

fig. 7-43. A diagram of Starling's hypothesis showing the forces leading to ultrafiltration at the arterial portion of capillaries and reabsorption at the venous portion, as well as drainage of excess interstitial fluid by the lymphatic system.

of the interestitial fluid, however, drains into the *lymphatic system*, a collection of capillaries closed at one end. The lymphatic capillaries eventually coalesce into larger vessels, the *lymphatic ducts*, which finally empty into a large vein.

The blood within the capillaries is under considerable hydrostatic pressure—approximately 32 mm Hg at the arterial end, and about 12 mm Hg at the venous end of skin capillaries in man.[206] Thus, there is also a considerable *gradient* of hydrostatic pressure over the length of the capillary. Because the capillary walls form a porous structure, there is a tendency for water and low-molecular-weight solutes to filter from the

[205] Starling, E. H. *J. Physiol.*, *19*, 312 (1896).
[206] Landis, E. M. *Physiol. Rev.*, *14*, 404 (1934); Pappenheimer, J. R. *Physiol. Rev.*, *33*, 387 (1953); Reynolds, S. R. M. and Zweifach, B. W., eds. *The Microcirculation.* Urbana, Ill.: The University of Illinois Press, 1961.

blood plasma (particularly from the arteriolar ends of the capillaries which have the greatest hydrostatic pressure) to the interstitial fluid.

Relatively large molecules such as sucrose and inulin (mol wt $\approx$ 5,000), which cannot pass through the plasma membrane of the cell, appear to pass through capillary walls with as much ease as urea and glucose. Even plasma albumin, a protein with a molecular weight of approximately 60,000, is able to penetrate the capillary membrane (although permeation is hindered). Very large protein molecules do not permeate the capillary wall. Because the capillary wall acts as a semipermeable membrane (albeit imperfect) with regard to plasma proteins, a colloid osmotic pressure difference develops between the plasma and the interstitial fluid. This pressure difference tends to cause reabsorption of intersitial fluid, particularly at the venous end.

Thus, two processes take place across the capillary wall. On the one hand, there is ultrafiltration which is driven by the hydrostatic pressure minus the tissue pressure. On the other hand, the colloid osmotic pressure tends to move water and low-molecular-weight solutes in the opposite direction from the interstitial fluid back into the capillary. At the arteriolar end of the capillary the hydrostatic pressure overcomes the colloid osmotic pressure, and the net movement is outward. At the venous end of the capillary the opposite situation obtains. Where there is venous obstruction or the venous pressure is increased, such as in cardiac failure, there is an increase in the average capillary hydrostatic pressure leading to greater exudation of fluid into the extracellular space and the accumulation of excessive interstitial fluid, or *edema.*

The effective pore radius of the aqueous channels through the capillary wall can be assessed from the hydrodynamic considerations outlined in Chapter 8. Analysis of the data in this manner yields calculated effective pore sizes with radii of 30 to 60 Å. In contrast to the situation at cell membranes, the hydrostatic pressure is important in the analysis of flow through the capillary walls.

synapses

The *synapse* was defined by Sherrington[207] as the area of functional contact between two excitable cells. The mechanisms involved in the transmission of impulses across synapses are phenomena of considerable interest to the physiologist. Synapses show great variation both in their morphology and in the mechanism of impulse transmission.

The simplest type of synaptic transmission is purely electrical. It occurs in tissues such as vertebrate heart muscle or invertebrate giant axons, which form *electrical syncytia* even though the cells may form discrete metabolic units because of barriers like the intercalated discs of heart muscle or the segmental septa of the giant axons. The electrical properties at these cell junctions are characterized by a very low cable-core resistance across the connection. Such cell junctions frequently can transmit impulses in either direction.

In the case of the giant axon which runs along each side of the abdominal cord of the crayfish and makes synapses with the segmental motor axons supplying the rapid flexor muscle of the tail, electron micrographs of the synapses show little bulbous processes of the motor axon which fit snugly into small socketlike cavities in the

[207] Sherrington, C. S., in Schaefer, E. A. S., ed. *Textbook of Physiology.* Edinburgh: Pentland, 1900, vol. 2, p. 782 ff.

surface of the giant axon.[208] The cell membranes in these ball-and-socket structures make a very close approach, and specialized tight junctions (see Chapter 2) may be seen in some places. Furshpan and Potter[209] studied the electrical conductivity of these synapses by inserting microelectrodes on both sides of the junction. They were able, by using the microelectrodes, to pass current and measure the voltage changes produced across the membranes of the presynaptic and postsynaptic cells. This synapse was found to form a good electrical conductor in the *orthodromic* direction (from presynaptic cell to postsynaptic cell) but not in the *antidromic* (reverse) direction. Thus, this type of synapse forms a rectifying element. Impulses could be transmitted from the presynaptic to the postsynaptic cell when the internal potential of the former was higher than that of the latter. The rectifying property of the synapse tends to ensure one-way transmission of impulses across the junction.

In contrast to these rather unusual types of synapses, electron micrographs of common synapses show a definite space between the presynaptic cell and the postsynaptic cell. This space amounts to 150 to 200 Å between two neurons and as much as 500 to 1000 Å in the vertebrate myoneural junction. In the myoneural junction, a basement membrane is seen in the cleft adjacent to the cell membrane of the muscle fiber.[210] Frequently the presynaptic cell ending lies in a trough of the postsynaptic cell; there are many functional folds, some 1000 Å or so wide and as long as 1 μ (Fig. 7-44). These junctional folds give rise to the appearance of *palisades*, which are described in the light microscope studies of the neuromuscular junction by Couteaux and others. In the case of myelinated fibers, the Schwann cell layer may continue to the synaptic region where it may cover the exterior portion of the presynaptic fiber; however, it does not invade the junctional cleft between the two cells.

In the common type of synapse there is an enormous attenuation of the potential generated by a depolarization of the presynaptic terminals, amounting to approximately 10^{-4} for 5μ diameter unmyelinated fibers. Because the impedance across the junction varies inversely with the square of fiber size, the electrical attenuation for large fibers is very much less; for a giant axon the attenuation may be only 0.1. Except possibly for giant axons, electronic spread of an impulse from the presynaptic to the postsynaptic fiber seems unlikely. The hypothesis that there is a nonelectrical mode of transmission here is supported by the constant finding of a *synaptic delay* of almost 1 msec in the conduction of an impulse. By and large, transmission across synapses is mediated by specific chemical compounds (secreted by the presynaptic fiber) which result in the depolarization and initiation of a propagated impulse in the postsynaptic fiber.

Belief in the chemical transmission of the impulse across the synapse is strengthened by the observation that terminal axons contain numerous synaptic vesicles[211] approximately 300 to 400 Å in diameter (Fig. 7-44). Nerve endings obtained from brain tissue

---

[208] de Lorenzo, A. J. *Biol. Bull.*, *117*, 390 (1959); Hama, K. *Anat. Rec.*, *141*, 275 (1961); *Z. Zellforsch.*, *56*, 437 (1962); Robertson, J. D. *Ann. N. Y. Acad. Sci.*, *94*, 339 (1961); Bennett, M. V. L., Aljure, E., Nakajima, Y., and Pappas, G. D. *Science*, *141*, 262 (1963).

[209] Furshpan, E. J., and Potter, D. D. *J. Physiol.*, *145*, 289, 326 (1959); Bulloch, T. H., and Hagiwara, S. *J. Gen. Physiol.*, *40*, 565 (1957); Furshpan, E. J., and Furukawa, T. J. *Neurophysiol.*, *25*, 732 (1962).

[210] Couteaux, R. *Compt. Rend. Soc. Biol.*, *138*, 976 (1944); Pease, D. C. *Anat. Rec.*, *115*, 359 (1953); de Robertis, E. *Anat. Rec.*, *121*, 284 (1955); *J. Biophys. Biochem. Cytol.*, *2*, 503 (1956); de Robertis, E., and Franchi, C. M. *J. Biophys. Biochem. Cytol.*, *2*, 307 (1956); Palay, S. L. *Exptl. Cell. Res.*, 5, suppl. 5, 275 (1958); Couteaux, R. *Exptl. Cell. Res.*, *5*, suppl. 5, 294 (1958); Gray, E. G. *J. Anat.*, *93*, 420 (1959); Birks, R., Huxley, H. E., and Katz, B. *J. Physiol.*, *150*, 134 (1960); de Robertis, E., de Iraldi, A. P., Rodriguez, G., and Gomez, C. J. *J. Biophys. Biochem. Cytol.*, *9*, 229 (1961).

[211] de Robertis, E. *Progr. Brain Res.*, *8*, 118 (1964); Whittaker, V. P. *Progr. Brain Res.*, *8*, 90 (1964).

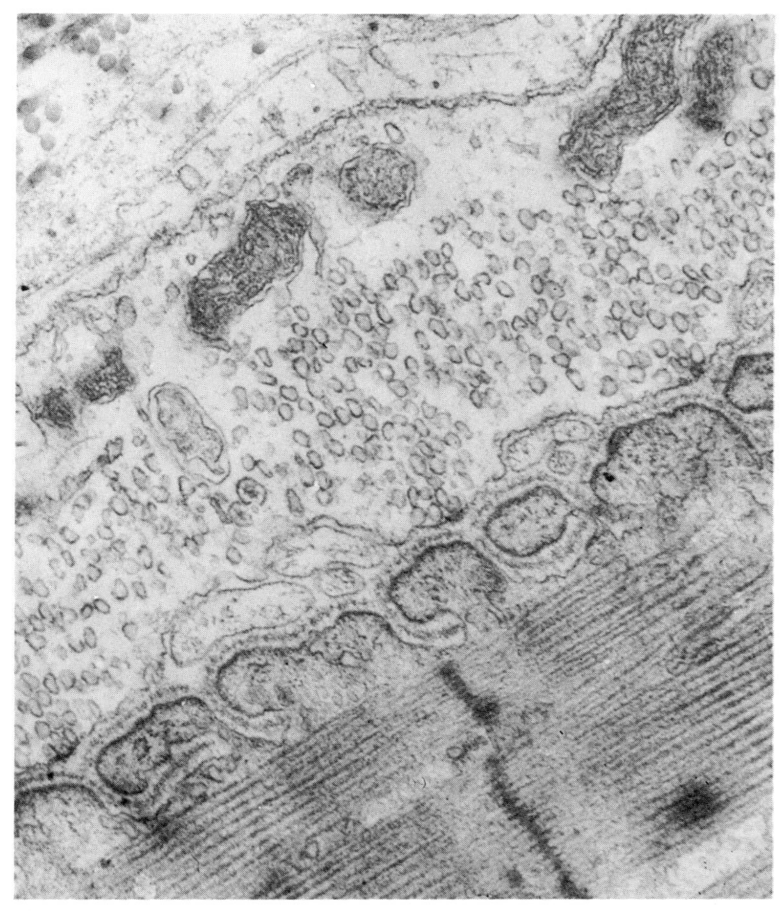

fig. 7-44. Electron micrograph of a myoneural junction showing the cleft between the presynaptic endings and the muscle fiber and the basement membrane covering the muscle cell membrane. Vesicles are seen in the presynaptic nerve endings. Osmic acid fixation and phosphotungstic acid stain: magnification 58,000. (Courtesy of Dr. B. Katz.)

may be ruptured by osmotic shock, and the vesicles from the terminals may be isolated (Fig. 7-45). Such isolated synaptic vesicles are found to contain substances which appear to be the chemical mediators of transmission in that type of synapse.

Otto Loewi was the first to demonstrate convincingly in 1921 the chemical mediation of synaptic transmission.[212] Stimulation of the vagus nerve inhibits the frequency and amplitude of contraction of the heart. Loewi stimulated the vagus nerve of the frog heart while it was being perfused with saline solution. The saline solution was then passed through a second heart. The result was inhibition of heart contraction as though the vagus nerve of the second frog were also being stimulated. The material

[212] Dixon, W. E. *Brit. Med. J.*, *ii*, 1807 (1906); Dale, H. H. *J. Physiol.*, *48*, *iii* (1914); Loewi, O. *Pflüger's Arch. ges. Physiol.*, *189*, 239 (1921); Witanowski, W. R. *Pflüger's Arch. ges. Physiol.*, *208*, 694 (1925); Loewi, O., and Navratil, E. *Pflüger's Arch. ges. Physiol.*, *214*, 678 (1926); Marnay, A., and Nachmansohn, D. *J. Physiol.*, *92*, 37 (1938); Burgen, A. S. V., Dickens, F., and Zatman, L. J. *J. Physiol.*, *109*, 10 (1949); Eccles, J. C. *Ergeb. Physiol.*, *51*, 299 (1961).

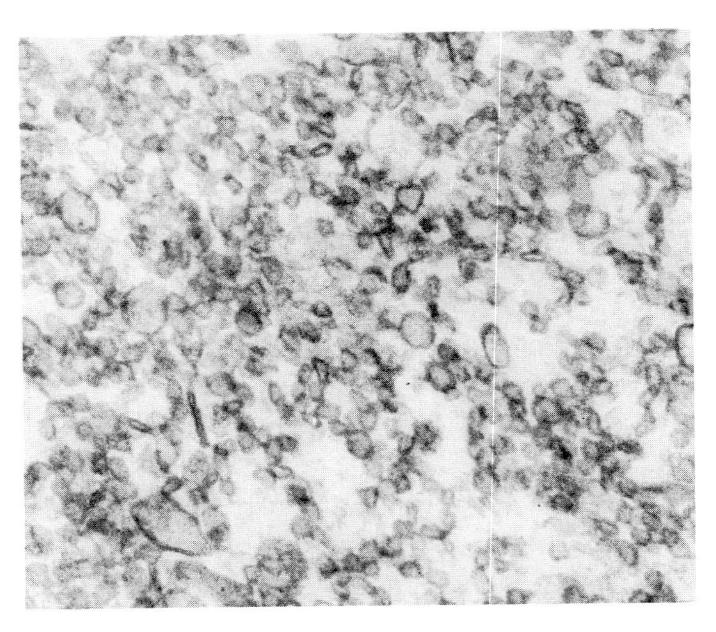

fig. 7-45. Electron micrograph of synaptic vesicles isolated from rat brain nerve endings after osmotic shock. In addition to the vesicles, membrane fragments can be seen. Osmium fixation and negative staining with phosphotungstic acid; magnification 120,000. (Courtesy of Dr. Eduardo D. P. de Robertis.)

liberated at the nerve endings of the first heart, which Loewi called *Vagusstoff*, was later identified as *acetylcholine*. While acetylcholine is an extremely potent substance, its action is short-lived because it is rapidly hydrolyzed by specific enzymes, the *cholinesterases*. Cholinesterase activity is inhibited by a number of compounds including eserine (physostigmine) prostigmine, tensilon, and the organic phosphate nerve gases. The potent pharmacological activity of the cholinesterase inhibitors results from the potentiation and increased duration of the effects of acetylcholine released during normal activity. Acetylcholine appears to act by combination with specific receptor sites on the *external surface* of the membrane; intracellular injections of acetylcholine are without effect. The cholinesterase, too, appears to be integrated into the membrane structure.

Heart muscle is also innervated by sympathetic nerve fibers which increase the frequency of contraction when stimulated. Loewi showed that stimulation of the sympathetic nerve fibers releases another chemical transmitter into the perfusing fluid which will in turn accelerate the frequency of a second heart. The experiments of Elliott and of Cannon[213] showed the close similarity between the effects of hormones secreted by the adrenal medulla and the effects of stimulating sympathetic nerves on the function of many internal organs. The substance liberated by stimulating the sympathetic nerves to the heart was identified by von Euler in 1946 as noradrenalin.[214]

The presynaptic nerve fibers contain not only acetylcholine but also the biosynthetic

[213] Elliott, T. R. *J. Physiol.*, *31*, XXP (1904); Cannon, W. B., and Rosenblueth, A. *Autonomic Neuroeffector Systems*. New York: Macmillan, 1937.
[214] von Euler, U. S. *Acta Physiol. Scand.*, *12*, 73 (1946).

enzyme,[215] *choline-acetyltransferase*, which is required for acetylcholine formation. After transection, the synaptic vesicles gradually disappear from the distal nerve endings; however, they reform just proximal to the region of the transection. This supports the view that choline-acetyltransferase and other biosynthetic enzymes are formed in the cell body and migrate down the axon.[216] The liberation of acetylcholine is greatly reduced (even though nerve impulses reach the presynaptic terminals) if the calcium concentration is lowered or the magnesium concentration is increased.[217] Botulinum toxin also inhibits the presynaptic release of acetylcholine.

The amount of acetylcholine released by stimulating a motor nerve has been estimated to be a few million molecules per impulse per end plate.[218] Similar data have been obtained for the presynaptic release of acetylcholine in sympathetic ganglia. By way of comparison, the amount of acetylcholine recovered in perfusion experiments is about 10^{-17} moles per impulse per end plate. The postsynaptic action of the chemical transmitter can be mimicked by perfusion of a muscle, for example, with a solution of acetylcholine or by applying acetylcholine directly to the motor end plate region of muscle by ionophoretic ejection from a micropipette.[219] In normal muscle, only the end plate region is sensitive to acetylcholine (see Chapter 9). Estimates from such experiments indicate that about 10^{-15} to 10^{-16} moles of acetylcholine is sufficient to excite a single muscle fiber. It is clear, then, that the postsynaptic action of the transmitter substance does not require the presence of presynaptic axon for its expression.

The sensitivity of muscle to acetylcholine can be reduced greatly by a number of quarternary ammonium compounds such as curare.[220] Curare does not affect the presynaptic release of acetylcholine greatly; its principal site of action is postsynaptic. Compounds such as curare appear to compete with acetylcholine for reaction with a specific receptor site in the postsynaptic membrane. The kinetics of inhibition can be fitted to equations of the Michaelis-Menten form.

Cholinesterase has been demonstrated histochemically and on the postsynaptic surface.[221] In their early pharmacological studies, Dale and his collaborators used the cholinesterase inhibitor eserine to facilitate the recovery of acetylcholine in perfusion experiments after nerve stimulation. Potentiation also is observed when drugs such as decamethonium or carbachol are used.[222] These substances depolarize the postsynaptic membrane, but they are not readily hydrolyzed by cholinesterase. As a result, their effect is much greater and much more prolonged than that of eserine, prostigmine, or

---

[215] Birks, R., and MacIntosh, F. C. *Brit. Med. Bull.*, *13*, 157 (1957); *Can. J. Biochem.*, *39*, 787 (1961); MacIntosh, F. C. *Can. J. Biochem.*, *37*, 343 (1959).

[216] Banister, J., and Scrase, M. *J. Physiol.*, *111*, 437 (1950); Hebb, C. O., and Waites, G. M. H. *J. Physiol.*, *132*, 667 (1956); Koenig, H. *Trans. Am. Neurol. Assoc.*, 162 (1958); Waelsch, H. *J. Nerv. Ment. Dis.*, *126*, 33 (1958).

[217] del Castillo, J., and Engbaek, L. *J. Physiol.*, *124*, 370 (1954); del Castillo, J., and Katz, B. *J. Physiol.*, *124*, 553 (1954); Brooks, V. B. *J. Physiol.*, *134*, 264 (1956); Jenkinson, D. H. *J. Physiol.*, *138*, 434 (1957).

[218] Dale, H. H., Feldberg, W., and Vogt, M. *J. Physiol.*, *86*, 353 (1936); Emmelin, N. G., and MacIntosh, F. C. *J. Physiol.*, *131*, 477 (1956); Krnjevic, K., and Mitchell, J. F. *J. Physiol.*, *155* 246 (1961).

[219] Nastuk, W. L. *Federation Proc.*, *12*, 102 (1953); del Castillo, J., and Katz, B. *J. Physiol.*, *128*, 157 (1955); Curtis, D. R., and Eccles, R. M. *J. Physiol.*, *141*, 435 (1958).

[220] Chagas, C. *Ann. N.Y. Acad. Sci.*, *81*, 345 (1959); Jenkinson, D. H. *J. Physiol.*, *152*, 309 (1960); Ehrenpreis, S. *Biochim. Biophys. Acta*, *44*, 561 (1960).

[221] Brown, G. L. *J. Physiol.*, *89*, 220 (1937); Koelle, G. B., and Friedenwald, J. S. *Proc. Soc. Exptl. Biol. Med.*, *70*, 617 (1949); Couteaux, R. *Intern. Rev. Cytol.*, *4*, 335 (1955); Barrnett, R. J. *J. Cell Biol.*, *12*, 247 (1962).

[222] Thesleff, S. *Acta Physiol. Scand.*, *34*, 218, 386 (1955); del Castillo, J., and Katz, B. *Proc. Roy. Soc.*, *B 146*, 369 (1957).

tensilon. Also, the effect of drugs like decamethonium is not increased by the use of a cholinesterase inhibitor like eserine.

Increasing the potassium in the medium causes membrane depolarization by lowering the K^+ equilibrium potential so that the transmembrane potential falls below threshold. Although choline and acetylcholine are univalent cations which resemble K^+ ions, the amount of acetylcholine liberated is not sufficient to depolarize the membrane directly by transiently lowering the potassium equilibrium potential.

quantal release of transmitter substance

At the myoneural junction, no electrical change is seen in the muscle fiber for about 0.7 msec after the nerve impulse arrives at the presynaptic terminal. After this latent period, a localized postsynaptic depolarization, the *end plate potential,* develops rapidly and within 0.5 msec reaches the threshold of excitation.[223] Increasing doses of curare produce a graded reduction in the size of the end plate potential until, finally, it cannot be detected. Similarly, the depolarization produced by the direct application of acetylcholine is also greatly diminished by the prior application of curare. The end plate potential spreads electrotonically, and its decay is governed by the cable constants of the muscle fiber. The application of cholinesterase inhibitors results in a marked prolongation of the local depolarization caused by acetylcholine.

It is known that the permeability of cell membranes to monovalent cations such as K^+ and Na^+ may be strikingly affected by quite low concentrations of heavy metal ions or certain surface active compounds. Similarly, acetylcholine appears to react with specific receptor molecules in the postsynaptic membrane to render the membrane transiently highly permeable to small cations. This effect is accompanied by a lowering of the membrane resistance and a flow of ionic current through the activated area of the membrane.

If, by using the voltage clamp technique, the transmembrane potential is varied from its resting value, the end plate current reverses at about -15 mv. This potential does not correspond to the equilibrium potential of any single one of the three principal ions. The ionic current which generates the end plate potential, therefore, must represent a combination of individual ionic currents. This problem was studied quantitatively by Takeuchi and Takeuchi[224] by experiments in which they changed the concentrations of Na^+, K^+, and Cl^- in the medium and determined the potential where the end plate current reversed direction. Their conclusion was that acetylcholine raises the membrane permeability to both Na^+ and K^+ ions about equally, while it has little effect on the permeability of the postsynaptic membrane to Cl^- ions. They also found that the increased permeability or conductance change produced by acetylcholine at the end plate was independent of the membrane potential of the muscle fiber. A given

[223] Feng, T. P., and Li, T. H. *Chinese J. Physiol., 16,* 37 (1941); Eccles, J. C., Katz, B., and Kuffler, S. W. *J. Neurophysiol., 4,* 362 (1941); *5,* 211 (1942); Fatt, P., and Katz, B. *J. Physiol., 115,* 320 (1951); Nastuk, W. L. *J. Cellular Comp. Physiol., 42,* 249 (1953); Emmelin, N. G., and MacIntosh, F. C. *J. Physiol., 131,* 477 (1956); del Castillo, J., and Katz, B. *Proc. Roy. Soc., B 146,* 339 (1957); Krnjevic, K., and Mitchell, J. F. *J. Physiol., 155,* 246 (1961); Katz, B., and Miledi, R. *Proc. Roy. Soc., B 161,* 453 (1965).

[224] Takeuchi, A., and Takeuchi, N. *J. Physiol., 154,* 52 (1960); Ito, M., Kostyuk, P. G., and Oshima, T. *J. Physiol., 164,* 150 (1962).

quantity of acetylcholine produces a local current whose intensity is proportional to (E_m − 15) mv where E_m is the resting membrane potential.

As early as 1950[225] spontaneous discharges of about 0.4 mv in amplitude resembling end plate potentials in form were observed in the region of the motor end plate in nonstimulated nerve-muscle preparations. These *miniature end plate potentials* have an average frequency of about 1 per sec. They are suppressed by curare, and their amplitude and duration are increased by cholinesterase inhibitors. Normally the miniature end plate potentials are not large enough to produce a propagated depolarization; therefore, they remain localized in the region of the end plate and do not lead to contraction of the muscle. After the application of cholinesterase inhibitors, however, they occasionally rise above the excitation threshold and lead to spontaneous twitching.

The miniature end plate potentials disappear some days after transection of the motor nerve (see Chapter 9) at about the time the presynaptic vesicles disappear. Botulinum toxin, which prevents the release of acetylcholine from the presynaptic nerve endings, also abolishes the miniature end plate potentials. Thus, it appears that nerve fibers, even at rest, intermittently liberate small quantities of acetylcholine.

The size and duration of the miniature end plate potentials are too great to be produced by one or a few molecules of acetylcholine; rather the simultaneous release of approximately 10^{-18} moles is required to produce a response of this magnitude.[226] The miniature end plate potentials appear randomly in the fibers innervated by a single axon; the end plate potentials resulting from nerve stimulation, on the other hand, are synchronized. From a variety of experiments it seems likely that, even under widely varying conditions, constant "quanta" of acetylcholine are released at irregular intervals by nerve endings. The variable factors are the frequency with which the quanta are released and the coincidence of release at a number of nerve endings.

By lowering the calcium concentration and increasing the magnesium concentration in the medium, the number of quanta of acetylcholine liberated by the depolarization at nerve endings can be reduced to a very low level.[227] The magnitude of the end plate potential evoked by nerve stimulation is reduced in discrete steps corresponding to the successive failure of individual miniature units. When the number of responding units is small, end plate potentials evoked by successive impulses show a marked random fluctuation in amplitude, and occasionally there is no response at all.

Statistical analyses of the responses under these experimental conditions were made by a number of investigators.[227] In a long recording from a single end plate using a microelectrode, it is possible to measure the amplitude of a large number of end plate potentials. The frequency of amplitudes of observed end plate potentials fits a Poisson distribution. Peak amplitudes occur at integer multiples of the amplitude of the miniature end plate potential (Fig. 7-46).

For example, Boyd and Martin[227] recorded 78 spontaneous minature end plate potentials from a single end plate. They then recorded the responses to 198 nerve stimulations repeated at intervals of several seconds. The amplitudes of all potentials were measured and represented in a histogram (Fig. 7-46). The mean size of the spontaneous potentials is 0.40 ± 0.086 mv. The amplitude of the responses to nerve stimulation fluctuated to a much greater degree. Eighteen stimulations completely

---

[225] Fatt, P., and Katz, B. *J. Physiol., 117*, 109 (1952); Liley, A. W. *J. Physiol., 132*, 650 (1956).
[226] del Castillo, J., and Katz, B. *J. Physiol., 128*, 157 (1955); Katz, B., and Thesleff, S. *J. Physiol., 137*, 267 (1957).
[227] del Castillo, J., and Katz, B. *J. Physiol., 124*, 560 (1954); Boyd, I. A., and Martin, A. R. *J. Physiol., 132*, 61, 74 (1956); Liley, A. W. *J. Physiol., 133*, 571 (1956); Katz, B., and Miledi, R. *Proc. Roy. Soc., B 161*, 496 (1965).

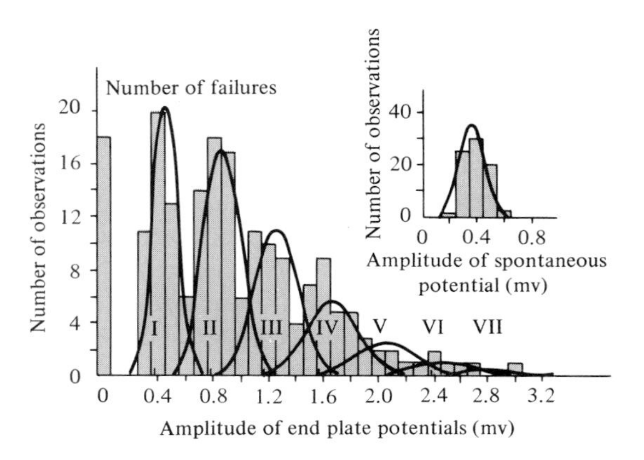

fig. 7-46. Histograms of evoked end plate potentials, and spontaneous miniature end plate potentials (inset) from a mammalian myoneural junction partially blocked by high magnesium concentration in the external medium. Peaks of the evoked end plate potentials occur at even integer multiples of the mean amplitude of the spontaneous miniature end plate potentials. A Poisson distribution was calculated for a mean value equal to the mean amplitude of the evoked potentials divided by the mean amplitude of the spontaneous potentials. Gaussian curves corresponding to the calculated numbers of each Poisson class have been plotted and superimposed on the histogram. (From Boyd, I. A., and Martin, A. R. *J. Physiol., 132,* 83, 84 [1956].)

failed to result in an end plate potential. The distribution of the remainder showed peaks at 0.4, 0.8, and 1.2 mv, while some responses were as large as 3.0 mv. The calculated response expected from a Poisson distribution, assuming a mean size of response of 0.933 mv, is also shown in the figure.

Thus, it appears that the effect of a nerve impulse at the presynaptic terminals is to produce a large increase in the rate of a secretory process that occurs spontaneously all the time. The secretion of acetylcholine can be detected by its postsynaptic effect: the appearance of end plate potentials. Depolarizing the nerve endings or increasing the potassium concentration produces a graded increase in the rate of secretion.[228] The effect of a given quantity of acetylcholine on the postsynaptic membrane is variable. For a series of end plate potentials evoked by repetitive nerve impulses, there is first a progressive increase in amplitude reaching a maximum after the sixth to tenth impulse, and then a progressive decline in amplitude.[229] The initial increase in end plate potential size is called *facilitation*, while the progressive decline is called *depression* or *Wedenski inhibition*. After a period of rest following intense nerve stimulation, a single nerve impulse may produce a very large end plate potential; this phenomenon is called *postactivity potentiation*.

[228] del Castillo, J., and Katz, B. *J. Physiol., 124,* 586 (1954); *128,* 396 (1955); Liley, A. W. *J. Physiol., 134,* 427 (1956).
[229] del Castillo, J., and Katz, B. *J. Physiol., 124,* 574 (1954); Katz, B., and Thesleff, S. *J. Physiol., 138,* 63 (1957); Araki, T., and Terzuolo, C. A. *J. Neurophysiol., 25,* 772 (1962).

synapses in the central nervous system

The synapses in the central nervous system are much more complex in their behavior than the synapses at the myoneural junction. While the myoneural junction operates simply to relay unidirectionally a nerve impulse to a muscle fiber, the presynaptic terminals of neuronal synapses in the central nervous system produce graded responses which can be summed from a number of different presynaptic nerve endings to produce integration of the various inputs. Some nerve endings produce excitatory responses while others produce inhibitory effects. Studies of various synapses indicate that the transmission probably occurs by a chemical transmitter mechanism, usually acetylcholine, although frequently other compounds mediate transmission. Postsynaptic potential changes have been found which resemble the end plate potential in muscle. Furthermore, the data support the view that nerve stimulation results in the release of excitatory and inhibitory transmitter materials in discrete quanta.[230]

Excitatory and inhibitory impulses are frequently identical and involve the same transmitter material. For example, the action of acetylcholine on the frog heart following vagus nerve stimulation is inhibitory. The antagonistic effects, then, depend upon differences in the synapses.[231] In general, acetylcholine appears to increase ionic conductance through the postsynaptic membrane. When the principal effect is an increase in Na^+ conductance, the membrane will tend to depolarize and the effect will be excitatory. On the other hand, when the principal effect is an increase in K^+ or Cl^- conductance, the transmembrane potential will tend to stabilize and the effect will be inhibitory. The depolarizing responses resemble end plate potentials and are called *excitatory postsynaptic potentials* (e.p.s.p.), while the hyperpolarizing responses are called *inhibitory postsynaptic potentials* (i.p.s.p.).

The process of integration involves the summation of subthreshold effects upon the membrane potential of the postsynaptic cell, resulting in *recruitment* or *temporal summation.* When the threshold level is exceeded, a depolarization is triggered which then is propagated along the nerve axon. In nerve cells the points of reception from various presynaptic fibers may be spatially separated by considerable distances and separated again from the point of impulse formation. On many nerve cells most of the synapses occur on the dendrites and cell body, regions of relatively low electrical excitability. Because the threshold of these regions is high, a wide range of subthreshold stimuli can be accommodated; this makes the integration of many subliminal impulses possible.

In addition to acetylcholine, glutamic acid is found in large amounts in nervous tissue and excites some neurons when applied directly to their surface,[232] particularly in invertebrate preparations. It is not clear whether glutamate acts as a transmitter

[230] Eyzaguirre, C., and Kuffler, S. W. *J. Gen. Physiol., 39,* 87 (1956); Grundfest, H. *Physiol. Rev., 37,* 337 (1957); Dudel, J., and Kuffler, S. W. *J. Physiol., 155,* 514 (1961); Eccles, J. C. *Ergeb. Physiol., 51,* 299 (1961); Katz, B., and Miledi, R. *J. Physiol., 168,* 389 (1963).

[231] Brock, L. G., Coombs, J. S., and Eccles, J. C. *J. Physiol., 117,* 431 (1952); Fatt, P., and Katz, B. *J. Physiol., 121,* 374 (1953); Coombs, J. S., Eccles, J. C., and Fatt, P. *J. Physiol., 130,* 326 (1955); Fuortes, M. G. F., Frank, K., and Becker, M. C. *J. Gen. Physiol., 40,* 735 (1957); Frank, K., and Fuortes, M. G. F. *Federation Proc., 16,* 39 (1957); Boistel, J., and Fatt, P. *J. Physiol., 144,* 176 (1958); Kuffler, S. W. *Harvey Lectures, 54,* 176 (1958); Dudel, J., and Kuffler, S. W. *J. Physiol., 155,* 543 (1961).

[232] Robbins, J. *Anat. Rec., 132,* 492 (1958); van Harreveld, A., and Mendelson, M. *J. Cellular Comp. Physiol., 54,* 85 (1959); Curtis, D. R., Phillis, J. W., and Watkins, J. C. *J. Physiol., 150,* 656 (1960); *J. Neurochem., 6,* 117 (1960).

substance in its own right or whether it modifies the postsynaptic response to acetylcholine.

Other amino acids found in the nervous system, γ-aminobutyric acid and related compounds, have been shown to cause both postsynaptic and presynaptic inhibition.[233] When applied directly to nervous tissue, these compounds cause widespread, nonspecific inhibition. They appear to increase the permeability, particularly to Cl^- ions, of both the postsynaptic and the presynaptic membranes. In this way, the potential of the postsynaptic membrane is stabilized and rendered less excitable. The presynaptic membrane appears to respond similarly, and the magnitude of the depolarization produced by an impulse is limited. As a result, fewer quanta of acetylcholine are liberated at the presynaptic nerve endings in response to an impulse.

pinocytosis

Materials penetrate the cell membrane not only as individual molecules but also by a process of imbibition in which the material is surrounded by projections of the cell membrane and taken up into the cell interior, frequently enclosed in vacuoles (Fig. 7-47). This process was first observed by Edwards (1925) in amoebae, and it was called *pinocytosis* (Gk., "cell drinking") by Lewis (1931).[234] Pinocytosis has been demonstrated in amoebae (Fig. 7-48), the tubular cells of the kidney, the epithelial cells of the intestine, leucocytes, reticulo-endothelial cells (macrophages and fibroblasts), the Kupffer (phagocytic) cells of the liver, cells lining the walls of capillaries, and some malignant cells. Pinocytosis can be followed experimentally by the use of either proteins to which flourescent dyes have been conjugated or materials labeled with radioactive tracers. Pinocytosis should be differentiated from *shagocytosis* (Gk, "cell eating"), a process in which macrophages and other cells engulf bacteria and other solid material.

Mast and Doyle and others[235] have demonstrated that cations and protein will induce pinocytosis in starved amoebae. In the case of proteins, they are effective only on the acid side of their isoelectric point. Viruses and amino acids are also effective, but neither carbohydrates nor nucleic acids induce pinocytosis. Once pinocytosis has been induced, it continues for 15 to 45 minutes in amoebae and then decreases rapidly. Leucocytes are able to continue pinocytosis for longer periods of time. Once pinocytosis stops, the cells must be thoroughly washed free of ions before it can be reinitiated. Pinocytosis appears to be an active process which results in increased oxygen consumption. The formation of pinocytotic channels is temperature-dependent and is inhibited by lack of oxygen, 2, 4-dinitrophenol, fluoroacetate, cyanide, and carbon monoxide.

It is believed that pinocytosis begins with an interaction and adhesion of the inducing material to the cell surface. The specific binding sites may be the acidic mucopolysaccharides on the cell surface. This is followed by invagination of the cell surface and

---

[233] Florey, E., and MacLennan, H. *J. Physiol.*, *130*, 446 (1955); Bazemore, A., Elliott, K. A. C., and Florey, E. *Nature*, *178*, 1052 (1956); Edwards, C., and Kuffler, S. W. *Federation Proc.*, *16*, 34 (1957); Takehashi, H., Nagashima, A., and Koshino, C. *Nature*, *182*, 1443 (1958); Florey, E. *J. Physiol.*, *156*, 1 (1961); Bindman, L. J., Lippold, O. C. J., and Redfearn, J. W. T. *J. Physiol.*, *162*, 105 (1962); Kravitz, E. A., Kuffler, S. W., and Potter, D. D. *J. Neurophysiol.*, *26*, 739 (1963).

[234] Edwards, J. G. *Biol. Bull.*, *48*, 236 (1925); Lewis, W. H. *Bull. Johns Hopkins Hosp.*, *49*, 17 (1931); Holter, H., and Holtzer, H. *Exptl. Cell Res.*, *18*, 421 (1959); Rustad, R. C. *Recent Progr. Surface Sci.*, *2*, 353 (1964).

[235] Mast, S. O., and Doyle, L. *Protoplasma*, *20*, 555 (1934); de Terra, N., and Rustad, R. C. *Exptl. Cell Res.*, *17*, 191 (1959); Holter, H. *Intern. Rev. Cytol.*, *8*, 481 (1959); Chapman-Andresen, C. *Compt. rend. Trav. Lab. Carlsberg*, *31*, 77 (1958); *33*, 73 (1962).

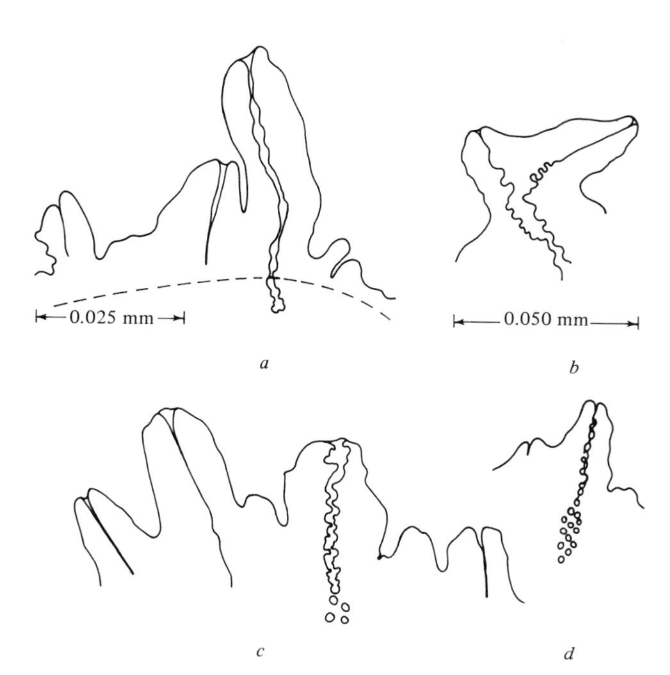

fig. 7-47. The progress of pinocytosis in *Amoeba proteus*: (*a*) the formation of channels in small pseudopods, (*b*) convoluted channels, (*c*) beginning disintegration of a channel, (*d*) advanced disintegration of a channel with droplet formation. (From Mast, S. O., and Doyle, L. *Protoplasma, 20*, 555 [1934].)

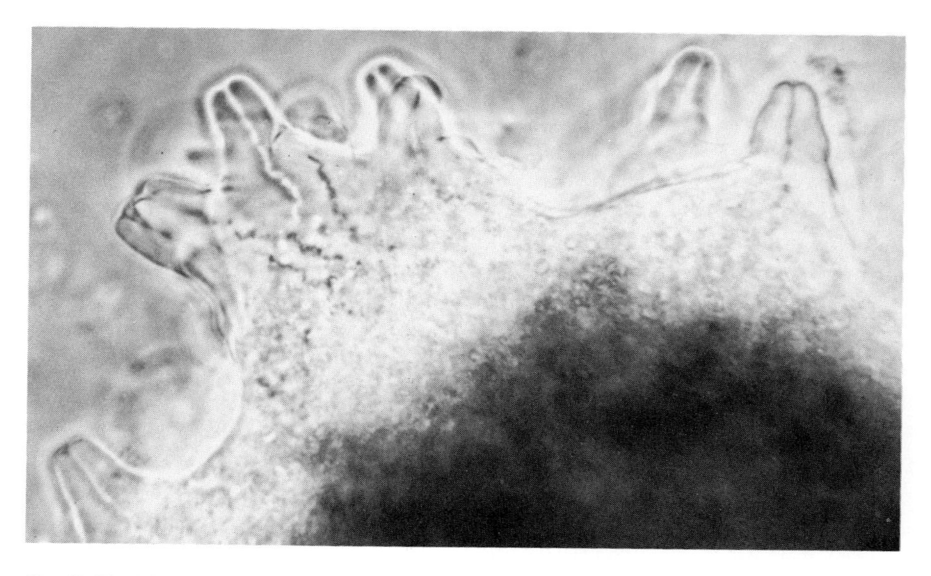

fig. 7-48. Electron micrograph showing active pinocytosis in an amoeba. (Courtesy of Dr. David Prescott.)

sometimes concomitant building up of the cytoplasm around the invagination by a sort of concentric pseudopod formation. It seems likely that the permeability of the cell membrane is increased during active pinocytosis. For example, Chapman-Andresen and Holter[235] found increased permeability to ^{14}C-labeled glucose when bovine plasma albumin was used to induce pinocytosis. If the cell membrane is, indeed, a dynamic structure continuously altering its internal organization and related to the endoplasmic reticulum, the invagination of pinocytotic vacuoles may be associated with membrane flow. Active inducers of pinocytosis may cause a decrease in the specific electrical resistance of the cell membrane of as much as 10^{-2} before pinocytotic channels appear.

When pinocytosis is induced in an amoeba, the contractile vacuole ceases to function and forms a rosette. Clear channels may be seen in the pseudopodia which pinch off to form vacuoles, the *pinosomes*. When fluorescent dyes are used as markers, they are taken up into the interior of the pinocytotic vacuoles. The density of the pinosomes separated by differential centrifugation gradually increases with time after induction of pinocytosis, indicating that the material in their interiors has been concentrated by the removal of water. This interpretation is supported by the increase in the brilliance of fluorescence within the vacuoles. Glucose labeled with ^{14}C or fluorescent-labeled protein is rapidly removed from pinosomes. Pinocytotic vacuoles finally shrink, coalesce, divide, and, like lysosomes, may end as myelin figures.

intercellular communication

Multicellular organisms possess mechanisms for integrating the activity of individual cells so that they function harmoniously with and can meet the needs of the whole organism. At the simplest level this occurs on a cell-to-cell basis. Plasmadesmata, strands of cytoplasm connecting adjacent cells in plants, were described in Chapter 2. It would be surprising if these did not serve to correlate the function of adjacent cells. Homologous mechanisms appear to exist in animal cells, particularly between adjacent epithelial cells possessing a junctional complex (Chapter 2).[236] These intercellular communications bring to mind impulse transmission in the segmental motor axon of the crayfish described on p. 413.

The cell membranes of epithelial cells usually show little or no rectification or excitation upon depolarization; the voltage current curves are fairly linear, the cell membranes behaving as simple ohmic resistors with a resistivity of about 10^5 ohms/cm^2. On the other hand, the two cell membranes in series between two adjacent epithelial cells show a combined resistivity of less than 10 ohms/cm^2. If an ionic current is passed through an epithelial cell membrane by means of a microelectrode, the transmembrane voltage decay in adjacent epithelial cells decreases with distance; but it decreases so slowly that a row of epithelial cells behaves as though their cytoplasm were a continuous core conductor bounded by an insulating sheath composed of the cell membranes exposed to the surface. Thus, the membranes that separate adjacent epithelial cells have ion permeability approximately 4 orders of magnitude greater than the nonjunctional surface membranes. The cell-coupling ratio (E_2/E_1), varies from

[236] Loewenstein, W. R., Sokolar, S., Higashino, S., Kanno, Y., and Davidson, N. *Science*, *149*, 295 (1965); Penn, R. D. *J. Cell Biol.*, *29*, 171 (1966); Loewenstein, W. R., Nakas, M., and Sokolar, S. J. *J. Gen. Physiol.*, *50*, 1865 (1967); Loewenstein, W. R., and Kanno, Y. *J. Cell Biol.*, *33*, 225 (1967); Loewenstein,W. R., and Penn, R. D. *J. Cell Biol.*, *33*, 235 (1967); Jamakosmanovic, A., and Loewenstein, W. R. *J. Cell Biol.*, *38*, 556 (1968).

0.5 to 0.9. This is the ratio of the change in the transmembrane potential of an adjacent cell to the change of transmembrane potential of a cell through which an ionic current is passed.

Not only are the intercellular membranes permeable to ions, but they are also very permeable to larger molecules. The injection of a small amount of fluorescein, a fluorescent dye with a molecular weight of 332, into the interior of one *Drosophila* salivary gland cell will diffuse in 5 to 20 minutes to all the cells in the salivary gland, even though very little dye diffuses into the bathing medium. Even molecules as large as bovine serum albumin, which has a molecular weight of 67,000, can be shown to diffuse through epithelial cell junctions.

If epithelial cells are placed in a calcium-free medium, the resistivity of the surface membrane decreases while that of the intercellular junctional membrane increases. Furthermore, if the cells are later reimmersed in a medium containing calcium, the surface membrane recovers its normal resistivity, while the high conductivity of the intercellular junctional membranes is lost. Treatment of epithelial tissue with a calcium chelating agent such as EGTA results in virtually complete interruption of intercellular communication. Intercellular communication can also be interrupted by treatment of epithelial tissue with proteolytic enzymes such as trypsin. Attempts at mechanical disruption, however, have failed; the cells disintegrate before intercellular communication is lost.

It is of immense interest that cancer cells are characterized by a lack of intercellular communication (see Chapter 2, p. 63), where the lack of junctional complexes and the defect in adhesiveness between cancer cells were described. The coupling ratio between adjacent cancer cells is almost always less than 0.02, and the resistivity of the intercellular membrane resembles that of the surface membrane.

references

Adelman, W. J., Jr., ed. Physical and mathematical approaches to the study of the electrical behavior of excitable membranes. *J. Cellular Comp. Physiol.*, *66*, suppl. 2 (1965).

Danielli, J. F., Pankhurst, K. G. A., and Riddiford, A. C., eds. *Surface Phenomena in Chemistry and Biology.* New York: Pergamon Press, 1958.

Davies, J. T., and Rideal, E. K. *Interfacial Phenomena.* New York: Academic Press, 1961.

Davis, B. D., and Warren, L., eds. *The Specificity of Cell Surfaces.* Englewood Cliffs, N.J.: Prentice-Hall, 1967.

Davson, H. *A Textbook of General Physiology*, 3rd ed. Boston: Little, Brown, 1964.

Davson, H., and Danielli, J. F. *The Permeability of Natural Membranes*, 2nd ed. London: Cambridge University Press, 1952.

Deenen, L. L. M., van. Phospholipids and biomembranes, in Holman, R. T., ed. *Progress in the Chemistry of Fats and Other Lipids.* New York: Pergamon Press, 1965, vol. 8, pp. 1–127.

Dowben, R. M., ed. *Biological Membranes.* Boston: Little, Brown, 1969.

Höber, R. *Physical Chemistry of Cells and Tissues.* New York: McGraw-Hill, 1945.

Hodgkin, A. L. *The Conduction of the Nervous Impulse.* Liverpool: Liverpool University Press, 1965.

Hodgkin, A. L. The ionic basis of electrical activity in nerve and muscle. *Biol. Rev.*, *26*, 339 (1951).

Hoffman, J. F., ed. *The Cellular Functions of Membrane Transport.* Englewood Cliffs, N.J.: Prentice-Hall, 1964.

Jacobs, M. H. Diffusion processes. *Ergeb. Biol., 12,* 1 (1935).

Katz, B. *Nerve, Muscle, and Synapse.* New York: McGraw-Hill, 1966.

Kavanau, J. L. *Structure and Function in Biological Membranes.* San Francisco: Holden-Day, 2 vols., 1965.

Kleinzeller, A., and Kotyk, A., eds. *Membrane Transport and Metabolism.* New York: Academic Press, 1961.

Korn, E. D. Structure of biological membranes. *Science, 153,* 1491 (1966).

Landis, E. M., and Pappenheimer, J. R. Exchange of substances through the capillary wall, in Hamilton, W. F., and Dow, P., eds. *Handbook of Physiology: Circulation.* Washington: American Physiological Society, 1963, vol. 2, p. 961.

Ling, G. N. *A Physical Theory of the Living State.* Boston: Blaisdell, 1962.

Lowenstein, W. R., ed. Biological membranes: Recent progress. *Ann. N.Y. Acad. Sci., 137,* 403 (1966).

Ruch, T. C., and Patton, H. D. *Physiology and Biophysics,* 19th ed. Philadelphia: Saunders, 1965.

Shanes, A. M. Electrochemical aspects of physiological and pharmacological action in excitable cells. *Pharmacol. Rev., 10,* 59, 165 (1958).

Skou, J. C. Enzymatic basis for active transport of Na and K across cell membrane. *Physiol. Rev., 45,* 596 (1965).

Stein, W. D. *The Movement of Molecules Across Cell Membranes.* New York: Academic Press, 1967.

Troshin, A. S. *Problems of Cell Permeability.* New York: Pergamon Press, 166.

Ussing, H. H. Transport of ions across cellular membranes. *Physiol. Rev., 29,* 127 (1949).

chapter 8

biophysics of transport

diffusion through membranes[1]

The principles of analyzing open systems which exchange matter and energy with the environment in terms of nonequilibrium thermodynamics were discussed in Chapter 4. Briefly, when all the forces acting on the system are constant, the processes which take place in an open system result in a net irreversible decrease in total free energy density,[2] $d\theta$, which always is a negative definite quantity and is not a conserved quantity. Time,

[1] Katchalsky, A., and Curran, P. F. *Nonequilibrium Thermodynamics in Biophysics*. Cambridge, Mass.: Harvard University Press, 1965; Eckart, C. *Phys. Rev.*, *58*, 267, 269, 924 (1940); Hearon, J. Z. *Bull. Math. Biophys.*, *12*, 135 (1950); Kirkwood, J. G., in Clark, H. T., ed. *Ion Transport Across Membranes*. New York: Academic Press, 1954, pp. 119 ff.; Kedem, O., and Katchalsky, A. *Biochim. Biophys. Acta*, *27*, 229 (1958); Scheer, B. T. *Bull. Math. Biophys.*, *20*, 231 (1958); *22*, 269 (1960); Jardetzky, O. *Bull. Math. Biophys.*, *22*, 103 (1960); Kedem, O., and Katchalsky, A. *J. Gen. Physiol.*, *45*, 143 (1961); Diamond, J. M. *J. Physiol.*, *161*, 442, 474, 503 (1962); Patlack, C. S., Goldstein, D. A., and Hoffman, J. F. *J. Theoret. Biol.*, *5*, 426 (1963); Diamond, J. M. *J. Gen. Physiol.*, *48*, 1, 15 (1964); Hill, T. L., and Kedem, O. *J. Theoret. Biol.*, *10*, 399 (1966).

[2] Nonequilibrium thermodynamics frequently is based upon an analysis of the local internal entropy production ds_i. However, ds_i *can be negative* if work is performed upon the system by the environment. In addition, the assumption of local equilibrium is required because ds_i is not an exact differential. It is preferable, therefore, to analyze open systems in terms of the total free energy density (see Chapter 4).

another quantity which is not conserved, also is introduced into the formalisms describing the system. Thus,

$$\frac{d\theta}{dt} = -T\frac{ds_i}{dt} \leq 0 \tag{8-1}$$

Near steady-state conditions, the net free energy dissipation (dissipation function), is equal to the sum of the products of all fluxes of matter or energy and their conjugate driving forces.[3]

$$\Omega = -\frac{d\theta}{dt} = \sum \mathfrak{J}_j X_j \geq 0 \tag{8-2}$$

If there is a process such that $\mathfrak{J}_j X_j < 0$, there must be a process such that $\mathfrak{J}_k X_k > 0$. It should be remembered that a chemical reaction taking place in a system represents a flux of matter, dn_j/dt, driven by its conjugate force, the *affinity* of the reaction $A = -d\theta/d\xi$ (eq. 4-57).

In Chapter 4, stationary flows (flows which do not result in a concentration change for the species), including those encountered in transport process, were noted to be linearly proportional to their conjugate forces (flows of charged solutes in magnetic fields or Coriolis flows are examples of exceptions). If more than one flow occurs in the system, any single flow may be influenced not only by its own conjugate force but also by any or all of the other forces present in the system. Assuming that each flow depends linearly on all driving forces, the flows of a volume element in any system can be described by the following set of phenomenological equations.

$$\begin{aligned}
\mathfrak{J}_1 &= L_{11}X_1 + L_{12}X_2 + L_{13}X_3 + \cdots + L_{1n}X_n \\
\mathfrak{J}_2 &= L_{21}X_1 + L_{22}X_2 + L_{23}X_3 + \cdots + L_{2n}X_n \\
\mathfrak{J}_3 &= L_{31}X_1 + L_{32}X_2 + L_{33}X_3 + \cdots + L_{3n}X_n \\
\cdots &= \cdots + \cdots + \cdots + \cdots + \cdots \\
\mathfrak{J}_n &= L_{n1}X_1 + L_{n2}X_2 + L_{n3}X_3 + \cdots + L_{nn}X_n
\end{aligned} \tag{8-3}$$

or

$$\mathfrak{J}_i = L_{ii}X_i + \sum_{j=1,\, i\neq j}^{n} L_{ij}X_j \tag{8-4}$$

where L_{ii} is the phenomenological coefficient that relates $\mathfrak{J}_i$ to its conjugate force X_i;

[3] While a detailed derivation of the flow equations is given in Chapter 4, an heuristic understanding can be gleaned from the following considerations. Let us apply the chain rule to the total free energy dissipation with respect to all extensive variables of the system

$$\frac{d\theta}{dt} = -\sum \frac{\partial\theta}{\partial Y_j}\cdot\frac{\partial Y_j}{\partial t} \tag{8-2a}$$

It is seen, however, that a velocity of flow is the rate of change of an extensive variable

$$\mathfrak{J}_j = \frac{\partial Y_j}{\partial t} \tag{8-2b}$$

and the driving force for the flow is

$$X_j = \frac{\partial\theta}{\partial Y_j} \tag{8-2c}$$

and L_{ij} are the phenomenological *cross coefficients* which reflect the extent to which the flow $\mathfrak{J}_i$ is influenced by the other, nonconjugated forces X_j in the system. Onsager showed that the matrix of the linear coefficients is symmetrical

$$L_{ij} = L_{ji} \tag{4-100}$$

The description of transport processes in a system of n components requires knowledge of only $n(n+1)/2$ coefficients rather than of all n^2 coefficients.

A number of mechanisms come to mind whereby flows of matter may be coupled. Two chemical species may interact electrostatically or as a result of the formation of a complex. Interactions may arise as a result of frictional coupling between moving particles, for example, as in the coupling of flow between solute and solvent. The flows of matter in chemical reactions may be coupled if a substrate or product of one reaction is the substrate or product of another reaction.

Sometimes it is desirable to express the forces as linear functions of the flows by a set of equations.

$$X_i = \mathfrak{R}_{ii}\mathfrak{J}_i + \sum_{j=1,\, i\neq j}^{n} \mathfrak{R}_{ij}\mathfrak{J}_j \tag{8-5}$$

The *resistance coefficients* $\mathfrak{R}_{ij}$ also obey Onsager's law ($\mathfrak{R}_{ij} = \mathfrak{R}_{ji}$); they may be evaluated by the relationship

$$\mathfrak{R}_{ij} = \frac{|L|_{ij}}{|L|} \tag{8-6}$$

where $|L|$ is the determinant of the matrix of the coefficients L_{ij}, and $|L|_{ij}$ is the cofactor of the determinant corresponding to the term L_{ij}.

Consider an idealized system consisting of a membrane of thickness Δx, under isothermal steady-state conditions between gradient-free solutions on either side of the membrane. Let us assume that all flows take place in the x direction so that scalar quantities can be used to represent the components of flows and forces in the x direction. The problem also could be treated in terms of three-dimensional vectors, but the treatment is more complex and the results are not more useful. For stationary flows of matter near the steady state, the driving force becomes the difference in the electrochemical potential across the membrane, $X_i = \Delta\mu_i$. Thus,

$$-\left(\frac{d\theta}{dt}\right)_{\substack{\text{stationary}\\ \text{flows}}} = \sum \mathfrak{J}_i \, \Delta\mu_i \tag{8-7}$$

It is assumed that the electrochemical potentials at the surfaces of the membrane are the same as those of the corresponding solutions. Furthermore, since forces in the real world do not become infinite, the electrochemical potential must be continuous across a phase boundary (although no restriction is placed on the continuity of its derivative).

The linear flow equations can be written immediately as

$$\mathfrak{J}_i = L_{ii}\,\Delta\mu_i + \sum_j L_{ij}\,\Delta\mu_j \qquad (j\neq i) \tag{8-8}$$

The parameters in this set of equations do not correspond to easily measured quantities; however, by appropriate transformations, sets of equations retaining Onsager symmetry can be derived which relate flows to directly measurable variables. Consider a ternary solution of a salt in water (eq. 4-218) where

$$\Delta\mu_i = \bar{V}_i \, \Delta P + RT \, \Delta \ln c_i + Z_i \mathfrak{F} \, \Delta\psi \tag{8-9}$$

where $\bar{V}_i$ is the partial molal volume, Z_i is the charge of the ith substance, and P is the hydrostatic pressure. The forces which cause the movement of substances through a membrane are listed in Fig. 8-1.

fig. 8-1. Principal driving forces of transport through membranes.

	FORCE			
	HYDROSTATIC	OSMOTIC	ELECTRIC	METABOLIC
Origin of the force:	Hydrostatic pressure gradient	Chemical potential (concentration or activity gradient)	Electric potential gradient	Affinity gradient
Formalism:	$\bar{V}_i \Delta P$	$RT \Delta c_i$	$Z_i \Delta\psi$	$m_{ij} \Delta\xi_j$

For a binary solution of a nonelectrolyte, the differences in electrochemical potentials across the membrane for water and for the solute are given by

$$\Delta\mu_w = \bar{V}_w \, \Delta P + RT \, \Delta \ln c_w \approx \bar{V}_w \, \Delta P - \frac{RT \, \Delta c_s}{c_w} = \bar{V}_w \, \Delta P - \frac{\Delta\Pi}{c_w} \tag{8-10}$$

$$\Delta\mu_s = \bar{V}_s \, \Delta P + RT \, \Delta \ln c_s = \bar{V}_s \, \Delta P + \frac{RT \, \Delta c_s}{c_s} = \bar{V}_s \, \Delta P + \frac{\Delta\Pi}{c_s} \tag{8-11}$$

where $\Delta\Pi$ is the difference in osmotic pressure across the membrane. Let us denote the flow conjugated to ΔP as $\mathfrak{J}_V$, the volume flow,[4] and the flow conjugated to $\Delta\Pi$ as $\mathfrak{J}_D$, the diffusion flow. The phenomenological equations for $\mathfrak{J}_V$ and $\mathfrak{J}_D$ are

$$\mathfrak{J}_V = L_P \, \Delta P + L_{PD} \, \Delta\Pi \tag{8-12}$$

$$\mathfrak{J}_D = L_{DP} \, \Delta P + L_D \, \Delta\Pi \tag{8-13}$$

L_P is the mechanical coefficient of filtration and represents the volume flow per unit-pressure difference when the concentrations of solute on both sides of the membrane are equal ($\Delta\Pi = 0$). The coefficient L_D represents the exchange flow when the hydrostatic pressure is equal on both sides of the membrane. Thus, L_D is a diffusion coefficient.

The cross coefficient L_{DP} is the ultrafiltration coefficient which describes the difference between solute and solvent flows for unit hydrostatic pressure in a selective membrane ($\Delta\Pi = 0$, $\mathfrak{J}_D = L_{DP} \Delta P$). In analogous fashion, the cross coefficient L_{DP} describes the osmotic volume flow when solutions of different concentrations are found on either

[4] Volume flow $\mathfrak{J}_V$ is related to solvent flow $\mathfrak{J}_{\text{solv}}$ in the following manner:

$$\mathfrak{J}_V = \bar{V}_{\text{solv}} \mathfrak{J}_{\text{solv}} + \sum \bar{V}_i \mathfrak{J}_i \approx \mathfrak{J}_{\text{solv}} \tag{8-11a}$$

where $\bar{V}$ is the partial molal volume of solvent or the ith solute. For dilute solutions such as those usually of concern to biologists, the contribution of solutes to volume flow often is negligible because volume flow and solvent flow are approximately equal.

side of the membrane ($\Delta P = 0$, $\mathfrak{J}_V = L_{PD}\ \Delta\Pi$). Onsager's law states that $L_{DP} = L_{PD}$. Three coefficients are required to describe the system; numerous attempts of physiologists to describe the permeation of a nonelectrolyte solution through a membrane in terms of only two coefficients, one for filtration and one for osmotic flow, have been inadequate. The cross coefficient is a function of the selectivity of the membrane and is related to Staverman's *reflection coefficient*,[5] which may be defined as

$$\sigma = -\frac{L_{PD}}{L_P} \tag{8-14}$$

For an ideally semipermeable membrane, at the steady-state conditions when $\mathfrak{J}_V = 0$, $\Delta P = \Delta\Pi$, and $L_P = -L_{PD}$. For a very leaky membrane which is equally permeable to solute and solvent, neither osmotic flow nor ultrafiltration takes place, and $L_{PD} = 0$. Hence, in general

$$0 \leq \sigma \leq 1 \tag{8-15}$$

The effective osmotic pressure required to keep $\mathfrak{J}_V = 0$ across a permeable membrane is $\Delta\Pi_{\text{eff}} = \sigma RT\ \Delta c$.

The phenomenological equations (eqs. 8-12 and 8-13) can be rewritten in a form using frequently measured coefficients:

$$\mathfrak{J}_V = L_P(\Delta P - \sigma\ \Delta\Pi) \tag{8-16}$$

$$\mathfrak{J}_s = c_s(1 - \sigma)\mathfrak{J}_V + \omega\ \Delta\Pi \tag{8-17}$$

where

$$\omega = \frac{c_s(L_P L_D - L_{PD}^2)}{L_P} = \left(\frac{\mathfrak{J}_s}{\Delta\Pi}\right)_{\mathfrak{J}_V = 0} \tag{8-18}$$

that is, ω is the *solute mobility coefficient* in the membrane at zero volume flow; ω expresses the permeability of the solute.

As stated above, a set of linear force equations can be written for any set of linear flow equations. The force equations are sums of products of flows and their frictional (resistive) coefficients. For an aqueous solution of a single nonelectrolyte,

$$X_s = \mathfrak{R}_s \mathfrak{J}_s + \mathfrak{R}_{sw} \mathfrak{J}_w \tag{8-19}$$

$$X_w = \mathfrak{R}_{ws} \mathfrak{J}_s + \mathfrak{R}_w \mathfrak{J}_w \tag{8-20}$$

These equations apply at a given point x in the membrane. The frictional force of a steady flow can be expressed as the product of a frictional coefficient and relative velocity ($f_{ij}[\mathfrak{v}_i - \mathfrak{v}_j]$). Thus

$$X_s = f_{sw}(\mathfrak{v}_s - \mathfrak{v}_w) + f_{sm}(\mathfrak{v}_s - \mathfrak{v}_m) \tag{8-21}$$

If the membrane is not movable, $\mathfrak{v}_m = 0$, and

$$X_s = (f_{sw} + f_{sm})\mathfrak{v}_s - f_{sw}\,\mathfrak{v}_w \tag{8-22}$$

$$X_w = -f_{ws}\,\mathfrak{v}_s + (f_{ws} + f_{wm})\mathfrak{v}_w \tag{8-23}$$

It should be noted that the frictional coefficients and the resistive coefficients are different.

[5] Staverman, A. J. *Rec. Trav. Chim.*, *70*, 344 (1951).

Assuming (1) that the electrochemical potentials at the two surfaces of the membrane are the same as in the bulk of the corresponding solutions, (2) that the magnitudes of the flows are steady and independent of x, and (3) that equilibrium between driving and frictional forces exists at all points in the membrane, it is possible to integrate eqs. 8-19 and 8-20 [6] across the thickness of the membrane Δx. First let us express the velocities in terms of flows using $\mathfrak{J}_i = c_i \boldsymbol{v}_i$; the membrane is taken as the reference for all flows ($\boldsymbol{v}_m = 0$).

$$X_s = \frac{(f_{sw} + f_{sm})}{c_{s(x)}} \mathfrak{J}_s - \frac{f_{sw}}{c_{w(x)}} \mathfrak{J}_w \tag{8-24}$$

$$X_w = -\frac{f_{ws}}{c_{s(x)}} \mathfrak{J}_s + \frac{(f_{ws} + f_{wm})}{c_{w(x)}} \mathfrak{J}_w \tag{8-25}$$

Because the local concentrations within the membrane $c_{s(x)}$ and $c_{w(x)}$ are unknown and not amenable to measurement experimentally, distribution coefficients must be used to relate them to known external concentrations. For a homogeneous membrane, the distribution coefficients used are

$$K_w = \frac{c_{w(x)}}{c_w} \qquad K_s = \frac{c_{s(x)}}{c'_{s(x)}} \tag{8-26}$$

where $c_{w(x)}$ is the concentration of water in the membrane, c_w is the concentration of water in the medium, $c_{s(x)}$ is the concentration of solute in the membrane, and $c'_{s(x)}$ is the concentration of solute in an equivalent aqueous phase. Integrating over the membrane thickness,

$$\int_{-\Delta x/2}^{+\Delta x/2} -\frac{d\Pi}{dx}\, dx = \frac{(f_{sw} + f_{sm})}{K_s} \mathfrak{J}_s \int_{-\Delta x/2}^{+\Delta x/2} dx \tag{8-27}$$

which gives

$$(\Delta\Pi)_{\mathfrak{J}_w = 0} = \frac{(f_{sw} + f_{sm})\,\Delta x}{K_s} \mathfrak{J}_s \tag{8-28}$$

In terms of frictional coefficients, the permeability coefficient ω is given by

$$\omega = \left(\frac{\mathfrak{J}_s}{\Delta\Pi}\right)_{\mathfrak{J}_v = 0} \approx \left(\frac{\mathfrak{J}_s}{\Delta\Pi}\right)_{\mathfrak{J}_w = 0} = \frac{K_s}{(f_{sw} + f_{sm})\,\Delta x} \tag{8-29}$$

while, in the terms of the simple Fick law of diffusion (eq. 7-1), the definition of the permeability coefficient used by early physiologists is

$$\omega = \frac{\mathfrak{J}_s}{\Delta\Pi_s} = \frac{\varphi_w}{f^0_{sw}\,\Delta x} \tag{8-30}$$

where φ_w is the volume fraction of water in the membrane, and f^0_{sw} is the frictional coefficient of free diffusion of the solute in bulk solution.

Examination and comparison of eqs. 8-29 and 8-30 reveal three relations of interest.

---

[6] Kirkwood, J. G., in Clarke, H. T., ed. *Ion Transport Across Membranes*. New York: Academic Press, 1954, p. 119; Teorell, T. *Discussions Faraday Soc.*, *21*, 9 (1956); Spiegler, K. S. *Trans. Faraday Soc.*, *54*, 1409 (1958); Katchalsky, A., and Curran, P. F. *Nonequilibrium Thermodynamics in Biophysics*. Cambridge, Mass.: Harvard University Press, 1965, p. 126.

Both analyses indicate that the mobility coefficient is inversely proportional to membrane thickness. In the contemporary view, ω is inversely proportional not only to the frictional coefficient of diffusion but also to a frictional coefficient which represents the hydrodynamic interaction between solute and membrane. For small solute molecules in highly hydrated membranes, $(f_{sw} + f_{sm})$ is not appreciably greater than f_{sw}^0. On the other hand, as the size of the solute molecules increases and approaches the size of the membrane pores, the value of f_{sm} rises steeply, as it does when there is an interaction between the solute and the membrane. Also, in the case of lipophilic substances, f_{sm} may be larger than f_{sw}. Lastly, when the solute is not soluble in the membrane, the distribution coefficient K_s is proportional to the volume fraction of water in the membrane φ_w. K_s will be high, however, for materials which actually dissolve to an appreciable extent in the membrane matrix. The dependence of the permeability coefficient on K_s describes the phenomenon of its dependence on the lipoid solubility of the solute which concerned Overton, Osterhout, and others.[7] In many cases of lipoid-soluble materials, K_s will be very high; and in spite of a concomitant increase in f_{sm}, a high value of ω will result. Ideally the frictional coefficients are independent of solute concentration and ω is a constant describing the mobility of a solute in the membrane.

An expression for the reflection coefficient in terms of the frictional coefficients can also be derived from eqs. 8-24 and 8-25:

$$\sigma = 1 - \frac{\omega \overline{V}_s}{L_P} - \frac{K_s f_{sw}}{\varphi_w (f_{sw} + f_{sm})} = 1 - \frac{\omega \overline{V}_s}{L_P} - \frac{\omega f_{sw} \Delta x}{\varphi_w} \tag{8-31}$$

Equation 8-31 shows that for an ideally semipermeable membrane which is completely impermeable to solute, $\omega = 0$ and $\sigma = 1$, while for a coarse, completely nonselective membrane, $\sigma = 0$. In some cases, ω may be so large that $\sigma < 0$. When σ is negative, at zero volume flow, $\Delta P = \sigma \Delta \Pi$; and a negative pressure must be applied if a steady state is to be maintained. This phenomenon is called *negative anomalous osmosis* and occurs frequently in the case of charged membranes separating solutions of electrolytes where ω increases as the concentration is increased, or in the case of solutes which are very soluble in the membrane.

evaluation of the phenomenological coefficients

In the case of living membranes, it usually is not possible to measure L_P directly, that is, by measuring the rate of change of volume of a cell subjected to a difference in hydrostatic pressure. Instead, a volume flow is produced using a solute to which the membrane is completely impermeable to create an osmotic gradient across the membrane. Under these conditions $\sigma = 1$ and $L_P = -L_{PD}$. The concentrations of solute are manipulated to provide the required osmotic gradients. It should be noted that volume flow acts to diminish the osmotic gradient, and suitable corrections must be made.[8] The cell volume may be assessed by direct microscopic measurement,[9] by measurement

[7] Overton, E. *Vierteljahresschr. naturforsch. Ges. Zürich*, *44*, 88 (1899); Osterhout, W. J. V. *Cold Spring Harbor Symp. Quant. Biol.*, *8*, 51 (1940).
[8] Jacobs, M. H., in Barron, E. S. G., ed. *Modern Trends in Physiology and Biochemistry*. New York: Academic Press, 1952, p. 149; LeFevre, P. G. *J. Gen. Physiol.*, *47*, 585 (1964).
[9] Dick, D. A. T. *Intern. Rev. Cytol.*, *8*, 387 (1959); Stadelmann, E. J. *Protoplasma*, *57*, 660 (1963); *59*, 14 (1964).

of the volume of a known number of packed cells,[10] by measurement of the light scattering of a suspension of cells,[11] or by using a thin epithelium to form the boundary of a closed compartment and then measuring the movement of the epithelium as the compartment volume changes.[12]

The reflection coefficient σ can be measured under conditions where there is no volume flow across the cell membrane. Goldstein and Solomon[13] suspended cells in various solutions and determined the concentration of solute required in the bathing medium c_s for zero initial volume flow (that is, no volume change of the cells). Under these conditions, $c_i = \sigma c_s$, where c_i is the effective intracellular osmolarity. The quantity c_i was determined independently by using a solute which was known not to penetrate the membrane ($\sigma = 1$). This method has been used subsequently by other investigators.[14]

As was indicated earlier in this chapter, permeability coefficients have usually been determined by measuring the volume changes which occur as a result of osmotic entry of water into cells as solute enters. Such measurements may be inaccurate because solute may enter not only by diffusional flow but also by drag by solvent molecules. In addition, the effective osmotic pressure of a solute is given by

$$\Delta\Pi_{\text{eff}} = \sigma RT \, \Delta c \qquad \textbf{(8-32)}$$

Most earlier determinations failed to take the reflection coefficient into account. The effect of volume flow on the classical permeability coefficient, which may be defined as $P_s = \mathfrak{J}_s/\Delta c_s$, is given by eqs. 8-16 and 8-17. The solute permeability coefficient ω is best determined under conditions of zero volume flow. Under these conditions the classical coefficient $(P_s)_{\mathfrak{J}_V=0} = \omega RT$. The best methods involve either the use of isotopically labeled compounds under conditions of solute equilibrium across the membrane or extrapolation of data obtained with volume flow, back to zero volume flow. With the use of tracer solute, special apparatus may be required when the exchange rates are very rapid.[15] Some determinations of ω, σ, and L_P are given in Fig. 8-2.

If the three phenomenological coefficients ω, σ, and L_P have been measured and the parameters K_s, φ_w, and Δx are known, the three frictional coefficients f_{sw}, f_{sm}, and f_{wm} can be determined by solving a set of simultaneous equations. Ginzburg and Katchalsky[16] have calculated the frictional coefficients for two synthetic membranes; their data are summarized in Fig. 8-3. Both membranes used were highly hydrated and yielded the expected results, $f_{sw} > f_{sm} \gg f_{wm}$. Such a relation would not be anticipated for some biological materials and living membranes.

It has been thought that many substances diffuse through aqueous channels or *pores* in the membrane. Such pores should not be regarded as straight cylinders perpendicular to the surface of the membrane, but rather as irregular, twisted tubules with an

[10] Hempling, H. G. *J. Gen. Physiol.*, *44*, 365 (1960).
[11] Ørskov, S. L. *Biochem. Z.*, *279*, 241 (1935); Widdas, W. F. *J. Physiol.*, *120*, 20P (1953); Sidel, V. W., and Solomon, A. K. *J. Gen. Physiol.*, *41*, 243 (1957).
[12] Leaf, A., and Hays, R. M. *J. Gen. Physiol.*, *45*, 921 (1962); Diamond, J. M. *J. Gen. Physiol.*, *48*, 1 (1964).
[13] Goldstein, D. A., and Solomon, A. K. *J. Gen. Physiol.*, *44*, 1 (1960).
[14] Curran, P. F., in Wasserman, R. H., ed. *The Transfer of Calcium and Strontium Across Biological Membranes*. New York: Academic Press, 1963, p. 3; Dainty, J., and Ginzburg, B. Z. *Biochim. Biophys. Acta*, *79*, 129 (1964).
[15] Keynes, R. D. *J. Physiol.*, *114*, 119 (1951); Paganelli, C. V., and Solomon, A. K. *J. Gen. Physiol.*, *41*, 259 (1957); Lacko, L., and Burger, M. *Nature*, *191*, 881 (1961).
[16] Ginzburg, B. Z., and Katchalsky, A. *J. Gen. Physiol.*, *47*, 403 (1963).

fig. 8-2. Properties of membranes. (From Katchalsky, A., and Curran, P. *Nonequilibrium Thermodynamics in Biophysics.* Cambridge, Mass,: Harvard University Press, 1965, p. 123.)

MEMBRANE	SOLUTE	SOLUTE PERMEABILITY, ω $\left(10^{-15}\frac{\text{MOLE}}{\text{DYNE SEC}}\right)$	REFLECTION COEFFICIENT, σ	FILTRATION COEFFICIENT L_p $\left(10^{-11}\frac{\text{CM}^3}{\text{DYNE SEC}}\right)$
Toad skin	Acetamine	0.0041	0.89	0.4
	Thiourea	0.00057	0.98	
Nitella translucens	Methanol	11	0.50	1.1
	Ethanol	11	0.44	
	Isopropanol	7	0.40	
	Urea	0.008	1	
Human red blood cell	Urea	17	0.62	0.92
	Ethylene glycol	8	0.63	
	Malonamide	0.04	0.83	
	Methanol	122	—	
Visking dialysis tubing	Urea	20.8	0.013	3.2
	Glucose	7.2	0.123	
	Sucrose	3.9	0.163	
Dupont "wet gel"	Urea	31.6	0.0016	9.7
	Glucose	12.2	0.024	
	Sucrose	7.7	0.036	

fig. 8-3. Frictional coefficients for cellulose membranes. (From Ginzburg, B. Z., and Katchalsky, A. *J. Gen. Physiol.*, *47*, 415 [1963].)

MEMBRANE	SOLUTE[a]	f_{sw} $\left(10^{16}\frac{\text{DYNE SEC}}{\text{MOLE CM}}\right)$	f_{sm} $\left(10^{16}\frac{\text{DYNE SEC}}{\text{MOLE CM}}\right)$	f_{wm} $\left(10^{13}\frac{\text{DYNE SEC}}{\text{MOLE CM}}\right)$
Visking dialysis tubing	Urea	0.66	0.065	8.30
	Glucose	1.89	0.23	8.52
	Sucrose	3.25	0.65	8.55
Dupont "wet gel"	Urea	0.28	0.0046	1.68
	Glucose	0.78	0.030	1.71
	Sucrose	1.12	0.066	1.72

[a] Solute concentrations: urea, 0.5 M; glucose, 0.050 M, sucrose, 0.025 M.

effective length l greater than the thickness of the membrane. Mackay and Meares[17] suggested the use of a tortuosity factor ϑ to characterize the pores such that[18]

$$\vartheta = \frac{\Delta x}{l} \tag{8-33}$$

[17] Mackay, D., and Meares, P. *Trans. Faraday Soc.*, *55*, 1221 (1959).
[18] Bjerrum, N., and Manegold, E. *Kolloid-Z.*, *43*, 5 (1927) showed that $\vartheta = 1/3$ for an assembly of tubules oriented in a completely random fashion with respect to the membrane surface. In actuality, the aqueous channels occupy an intermediate orientation between absolutely perpendicular to the surface and completely random, and $1 > \vartheta > 1/3$.

If it is assumed that the frictional coefficient between solute molecules and water within the aqueous channels is the same as it is in the bulk solution, then the overall frictional coefficient in the membrane will be given by

$$f_{sw} = f^0_{sw}/\vartheta \tag{8-34}$$

Similarly, the effective fraction of membrane area available for solvent flow will be given by

$$\mathfrak{A}_w = \vartheta \varphi_w \tag{8-35}$$

If the solute flows only through an assembly of capillaries in the membrane filled with solution under conditions where no volume flow occurs, the flow of solute will be given by

$$(\mathfrak{J}_s)_{\mathfrak{J}_V=0} = \mathfrak{A}_s D \frac{\Delta c_s}{\Delta x} = \mathfrak{A}_s \frac{RT\,\Delta c_s}{f^0_{sw}\,\Delta x} \tag{8-36}$$

where $\mathfrak{A}_s$ is defined as the effective fraction of membrane area available for solute flow, and D is the coefficient of free diffusion of solute in bulk solution and is equal to $D = RT/f^0_{sw}$.

Substituting eqs. 8-34 and 8-35 into eq. 8-36 gives

$$(\mathfrak{J}_s)_{\mathfrak{J}_V=0} = \frac{\mathfrak{A}_s \varphi_w \,\Delta\Pi}{\mathfrak{A}_w f_{sw}\,\Delta x} \tag{8-37}$$

Rearranging eq. 8-37 and substituting eq. 8-29 into it gives

$$\frac{\mathfrak{A}_s}{\mathfrak{A}_w} = \frac{K_s f_{sw}}{\varphi_w(f_{sw} + f_{sm})} \tag{8-38}$$

Substituting eq. 8-38 into eq. 8-31 and rearranging gives

$$\frac{\mathfrak{A}_s}{\mathfrak{A}_w} = 1 - \sigma - \frac{\omega \bar{V}_s}{L_P} \tag{8-39}$$

It should be noted again that $\mathfrak{A}_s$ and $\mathfrak{A}_w$ in eq. 8-39 represent diffusion areas only, and they are not related directly to the effective ultrafiltration areas.[19] Whenever eq. 8-39 applies, it is a safe presumption that solute flow as well as solvent flow takes place only through a system of capillary channels in the membrane. On the other hand, if solute and solvent flow through different channels (such as when there is dissolution of solute in the membrane while solvent moves through capillary channels), there is no interaction between solute and solvent molecules in the membrane, $f_{sw} = 0$, and eq. 8-31 becomes

$$\sigma = 1 - \frac{\omega \bar{V}_s}{L_P} \tag{8-40}$$

When solute and solvent flow entirely through an assembly of capillary channels, a

[19] It can be shown that when solute diffuses through the same channels as solvent,

$$\left(\frac{\Delta P}{\Delta\Pi}\right)_{\mathfrak{J}_w=0} = \left(\frac{\Delta P}{\Delta\Pi}\right)_{\mathfrak{J}_V=0} - \frac{\omega \bar{V}_s}{L_P} \tag{8-39a}$$

In most systems of interest to the biologist, the difference between $\mathfrak{J}_w$ and $\mathfrak{J}_V$ is small, and the correction term $\omega \bar{V}_s/L_P$ is also very small and can frequently be neglected.

hydrodynamic analysis may be applied to evaluate the equivalent pore size of the channels.[20] The reflection coefficient can be determined for a series of molecules differing in molecular size, and the results can be used to assess the effective pore diameter. A family of curves showing $1 - \sigma$ as a function of the radius of the probing molecule is depicted in Fig. 8-4a. The values of $1 - \sigma$ for nine substances in the erythrocyte best fit the curve for a pore radius of 4.2 Å (Fig. 8-4b).

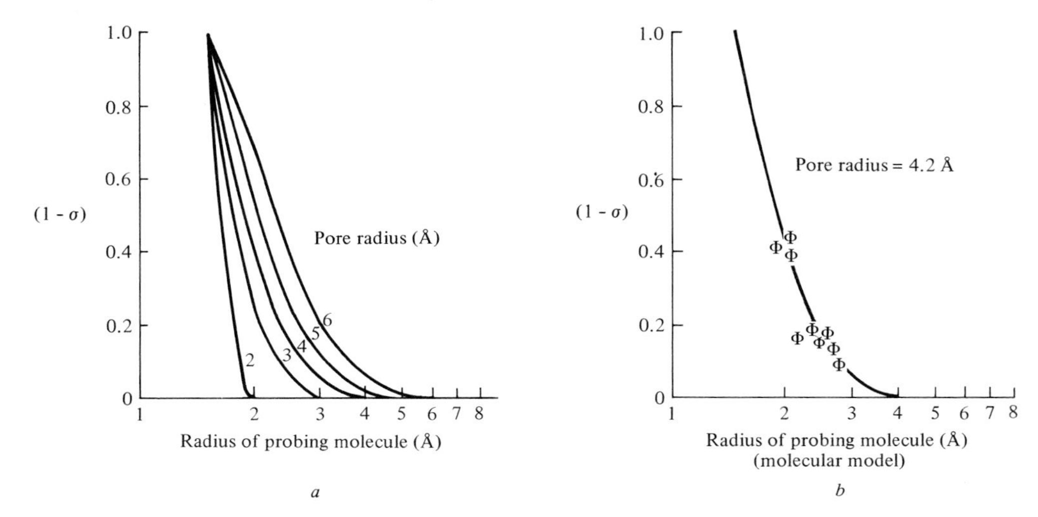

fig. 8-4. (*a*) A family of theoretical plots of $1 - \sigma$ *versus* the radius of the probing molecule for various effective pore radii. (*b*) The experimental values of $1 - \sigma$ for nine different substances in the erythrocyte. The data best fit the curve for an effective pore radius of 4.2 Å. (From Goldstein, D. A., and Solomon, A. K. *J. Gen. Physiol., 44,* 10 [1960].)

When solute molecules are larger than solvent molecules, the apparent area available for solute flow $\mathfrak{A}_s$ is smaller than the apparent area available for solvent flow $\mathfrak{A}_w$ because (1) the stomata of the pores present greater hindrance to the entrance of solute molecules, and (2) the solute molecules encounter increased frictional resistance as they pass through the capillary channels.[21] The first effect results from the requirement that a solute molecule must pass through the opening of a pore without striking the edge in order to enter the capillary channel. In effect, the solute molecules are required to pass through an opening of radius $(r - a)$, where r is the radius of the pore and a is the radius of the solute molecule. In terms of the effective fractional areas for solute and solvent flow, the following expression will describe this effect:

$$\frac{\mathfrak{A}_s}{\mathfrak{A}_w} \propto \left(1 - \frac{a}{r}\right)^2 \tag{8-41}$$

The Faxen equation can be used to describe the second effect, that is, the reduced effective area for solute flow resulting from the increased resistance encountered by the

[20] Goldstein, D. A., and Solomon, A. K. *J. Gen. Physiol., 44*, 1 (1960); Durbin, R. P. *J. Gen. Physiol., 44*, 315 (1960).
[21] Faxen, H. *Arch. Mat. Astron. Fysik., 17*, no. 27 (1922); Ferry, J. D. *J. Gen. Physiol., 20*, 95 (1936); Renkin, E. M. *J. Gen. Physiol., 38*, 225 (1954); Peterson, C. M., and Livingston, E. M. *J. Appl. Polymer Sci., 8*, 1429 (1964).

solute molecules in the capillary channels:

$$\frac{\mathfrak{A}_s}{\mathfrak{A}_w} \propto 1 - 2.104\left(\frac{a}{r}\right) + 2.09\left(\frac{a}{r}\right)^3 - 0.95\left(\frac{a}{r}\right)^5 \tag{8-42}$$

Combining eqs. 8-41 and 8-42 gives an expression which takes both effects into account.

$$\frac{\mathfrak{A}_s}{\mathfrak{A}_w} = \left[1 - \frac{a}{r}\right]^2 \left[1 - 2.104\left(\frac{a}{r}\right) + 2.09\left(\frac{a}{r}\right)^3 - 0.95\left(\frac{a}{r}\right)^5\right] \tag{8-43}$$

The radius of small solute molecules can be estimated by calculating the radius of a sphere of equal weight and density using the expression

$$a = \sqrt[3]{3M/4\pi\rho N} \tag{8-44}$$

where M is the gram molecular weight, ρ is the density of the solute, and N is Avogadro's number. For solute molecules much larger than those of the solvent, the molecular radius can be estimated from the Stokes-Einstein equation

$$a = RT/6\pi\eta DN \tag{8-45}$$

where η is the viscosity of the solvent and D is the diffusion coefficient of the solute in solvent. The Stokes-Einstein equation can be applied, if a correction is used,[22] when the solute and solvent molecules are comparable in size.

$$a' = 1.5\left(\frac{a}{b} + \frac{b}{a+b}\right)a \tag{8-46}$$

where a and b are the radii of solute and solvent molecules respectively.

Assuming that transport across a membrane takes place through an assembly of capillary channels, the *effective pore radius* has been estimated from the following analyses of the solvent flow (Fig. 8-5). During volume flow of solution through the tubules in response to (1) a hydrodynamic pressure difference, (2) an osmotic pressure difference, or (3) a combination of these forces, *if* Poisseuille's Law for laminar flow will hold,[23] from eq. 8-12 and Poisseuille's Law, the following expression can be written:

$$\mathfrak{J}_V = L_P(\Delta P - \sigma\,\Delta\Pi) = \frac{n\pi r^4}{8\eta\bar{V}\,\Delta x/\vartheta}(\Delta P - \sigma\,\Delta\Pi) \tag{8-47}$$

where n is the number of channels, r is their radius, η is the viscosity of the solution, Δx is the thickness of the membrane, ϑ is the tortuosity factor, ΔP is the hydrostatic pressure difference, and $\Delta\Pi$ is the osmotic pressure difference. Under conditions where $\mathfrak{J}_V = 0$, the self-diffusion of solvent can be ascertained using isotopically labeled solvent. Self-diffusion of solvent should follow the Fick equation:

$$\mathfrak{J}'_D = \frac{D}{RT}\frac{n\pi r^2}{\Delta x/\vartheta}(\Delta P - \sigma\,\Delta\Pi) \tag{8-48}$$

[22] Gierer, A., and Wirtz, K. *Z. Naturforsch.*, *8A*, 532 (1953).
[23] Pappenheimer, J. R., Renkin, E. M., and Borrero, L. M. *Am. J. Physiol.*, *167*, 13 (1951); Pappenheimer, J. R. *Physiol. Rev.*, *33*, 387 (1953); Koefoed-Johnsen, V., and Ussing, H. H. *Acta Physiol. Scand.*, *28*, 60 (1953); Renkin, E. M. *J. Gen. Physiol.*, *38*, 225 (1954); Robbins, E., and Mauro, A. *J. Gen. Physiol.*, *43*, 523 (1960); Goldstein, D. A., and Solomon, A. K. *J. Gen. Physiol.*, *44*, 1 (1960).

fig. 8-5. Measured values of the reflection coefficient for various solutes and the calculated values for the equivalent pore radius using eq. 8-47.
(Data from Goldstein, D. A., and Solomon, A. K. *J. Gen. Physiol.*, *44*, 11 [1960]; Whittembury, G., Sugino, N., and Solomon, A. K. *Nature*, *187*, 699 [1960]; Villegas, R., and Barnola, F. V. *J. Gen. Physiol.*, *44*, 963 [1961]; Zadunaisky, J. A., Parisi, M. N., and Montoreano, R. *Nature*, *200*, 365 [1963].)

CELL TYPE	SOLUTE	σ	EQUIVALENT PORE RADIUS (r) (Å)
Human erythrocyte	Glycerol	0.88	4.2
	Propylene glycol	0.85	
	Thiourea	0.85	
	Methylurea	0.80	
	Propionamide	0.80	
	Urea	0.62	
	Acetamine	0.58	
Frog muscle fibers	Mannitol	1.00	4.0
	Sucrose	1.00	
	Glycerol	0.86	
	Urea	0.82	
	Formamide	0.65	
Squid axon	Glycerol	0.96	4.25
	Ethylene glycol	0.72	
	Urea	0.70	
	Ethanol	0.63	
	Formamide	0.44	
Necturus kidney	Sucrose	1.00	5.6
	Erythritol	0.89	
	Glycerol	0.77	
	Urea	0.52	

Combining eqs. 8-47 and 8-48 gives

$$r^2 = \frac{8\eta D\overline{V}}{RT}\frac{\mathfrak{J}_V}{\mathfrak{J}'_D} \tag{8-49}$$

Some data of this type culled from the literature are listed in Fig. 8-6.

fig. 8-6. Some values for the filtration coefficient, the self-diffusion coefficient, and the calculated pore radius. (Data from Prescott, D. M., and Zeuthen, E. *Acta Physiol. Scand.*, *28*, 77 [1953]; Sidel, V. W., and Solomon, A. K. *J. Gen. Physiol.*, *41*, 243 [1957]; Paganelli, C. V., and Solomon, A. K. *J. Gen. Physiol.*, *41*, 259 [1957]; Hayes, R. M., and Leaf, A. *J. Gen. Physiol.*, *45*, 905 [1962]; Hanai, T., Haydon, D. A., and Taylor, J. *J. Gen. Physiol.*, *48*, suppl. 1, 59 [1965].)

CELL TYPE	L_P $\left(\frac{\text{CM}}{\text{SEC}} \times 10^{-4}\right)$	P_w $\left(\frac{\text{CM}}{\text{SEC}} \times 10^{-4}\right)$	$\frac{L_P}{P_w}$	PORE RADIUS (Å)
Amoeba	0.37	0.23	1.61	2.1
Frog oöcyte	1.30	0.75	1.74	2.8
Human RBC	127	53	2.4	3.5
Toad bladder	4.1	0.95	4.3	8.5
Phospholipid bilayer	8.3	2.3	3.6	5.0

The foregoing analyses have all assumed (as, in fact, have the majority of physiologists who have measured permeability coefficients) that the bulk solutions on either side of the membrane are well stirred and that the concentration of solute in the bulk solutions is always everywhere uniform. For many membrane systems, there may be a layer of unstirred solution immediately adjacent to the membrane. Therefore, as a solute permeates through the membrane, a concentration gradient of solute in the bulk solution near the membrane is established. The changes in the local concentration of solute at the membrane surface result in a steady diminution of solute flow through the membrane with time.[24] These effects are much greater for very rapidly permeating solutes than for solutes which diffuse more slowly through the membrane.

The actual concentration distribution near the membrane can be calculated from the following differential equation:

$$\text{div}\,\nabla(Dc) = \frac{\partial c}{\partial t} \tag{8-50}$$

Explicit solutions for this equation are known for the semi-infinite case (two semi-infinite compartments connected by a small aperture in an otherwise impermeable diaphragm), and the special case of diffusion into a sphere under conditions where a mechanism exists for maintaining the concentration of solute within the sphere

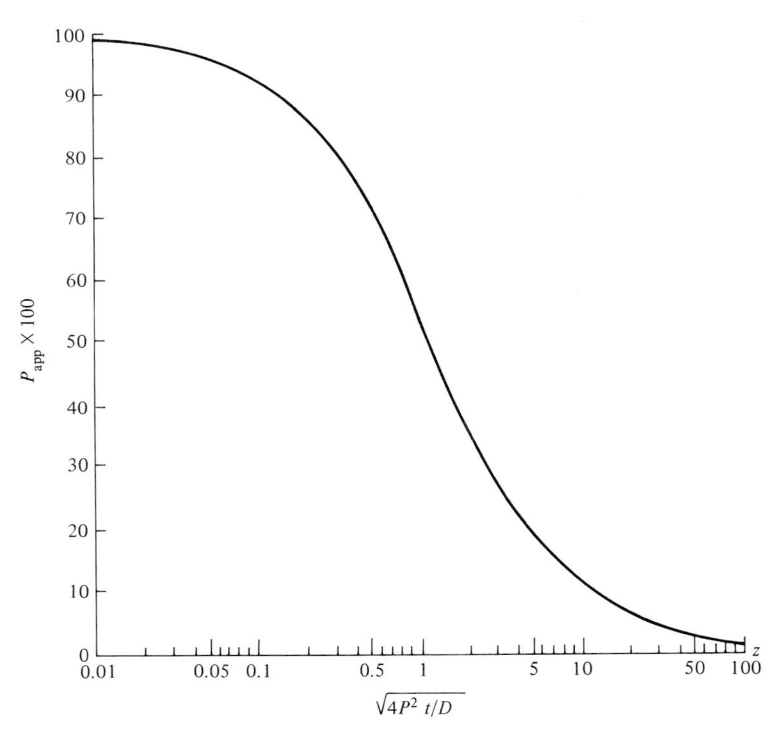

fig. 8-7. The approximate calculated function of the ratio of the apparent permeability coefficient P_{app} to the true permeability coefficient P *versus* $\sqrt{4P^2t/D}$. (From Vreeman, H. J. *Proc. Koninkl. Ned. Akad. Wetenschap.*, *69 B*, 558 [1966].)

[24] Vreeman, H. J. *Proc. Koninkl. Nederl. Akad. Wetenschap.*, *69B*, 555, 564 (1966).

constant. For other cases of interest to the physiologist, numerical solutions using a computer should be possible.

Vreeman[24] evaluated the semi-infinite case. In Fig. 8-7, the ratio of the apparent permeability coefficient P_{app} (between the bulk solutions) to the true permeability coefficient (at the membrane interfaces) is plotted as a function of $\sqrt{4P^2t/D}$. In the case of water (D_2O or THO permeation experiments) with a permeability coefficient of about 10^{-4} cm sec^{-1} for many membranes and a diffusion coefficient of 2.5×10^{-5} cm^2 sec^{-1}, at 2 sec the apparent permeability coefficient is already 10 percent less than the true permeability coefficient. The apparent permeability coefficient will decrease with time and with increasing membrane area if diffusion in the bulk solutions is appreciable.

For many solutes of interest to the biologist $P < 10^{-5}$ cm sec^{-1}; for such substances $P_{app} \approx P$. However, for rapidly permeating substances such as water, methanol, ethanol, or urea, the true permeability coefficient may be considerably greater than the apparent permeability coefficient. For very large values of $\sqrt{4P^2t/D}$, diffusion in the bulk solutions rather than permeation through the membrane becomes the rate-determining factor. If the permeability coefficient is measured under conditions where volume flow is permitted, the flow of solvent will tend to overcome the depletion of solute in the bulk solution immediately adjacent to the membrane. This may explain why the permeability coefficient obtained from measurements of net flow at several solute concentration differences and extrapolated back to $\Delta c \rightarrow 0$ gives higher values, particularly for highly permeable solutes, than the "self-diffusion" permeability coefficient determined using labeled solutes under conditions of zero volume flow.

Finally, there is no necessity that the permeability be constant in living cells. In fact, permeability may change with variations in the environment; and regulation of cell function, for example, by hormones, may be mediated by changes in permeability.

role of the bulk intracellular phase

The bulk intracellular phase may profoundly influence permeability measurements when whole cells are used. Some mechanisms by which this can happen are set out below.

It is usually tacitly assumed that the solute under investigation does not enter into metabolic reactions within the cell nor is it a product of metabolism. Frequently this assumption is not justified. Glucose, ethanol, and glycerol, for example, are actively metabolized by many cells. Human erythrocytes are especially suitable for studies of glucose permeability by accumulation because the rate of glucose penetration is high while its rate of utilization is low. On the other hand, in pig erythrocytes, the rate of permeation of glucose is so low that it may limit the rate of glucose utilization.

As stated above, it is usually assumed that the penetrating solute diffuses very rapidly within the cell interior compared to its rate of diffusion across the cell membrane; thus its concentration in the interior of the cell is essentially uniform at all times. This assumption fails for very rapidly permeating substances such as water, urea, and ethanol. Also, the time required for intracellular equilibration obviously will be greater in larger cells where it is more likely that a significant concentration gradient will be generated. Dick[25] has pointed out that the computed permeability constant for water increases as the cell size decreases and consequently as the surface-to-volume ratio increases (Fig. 8-8). Other studies[26] have shown that intracellular diffusion may

fig. 8-8. Surface-to-volume ratio and mean permeability constant for different groups of cells. (From Dick, D. A. T. *Intern. Rev. Cytol., 8,* 387 [1959]. Copyright Academic Press; reprinted by permission.)

CELL TYPE	SURFACE-TO-VOLUME RATIO	MEAN PERMEABILITY CONSTANT (CM/SEC $\times 10^{-4}$)
Amphibian and fish eggs	0.005	1.1
Amoeba	0.039	0.565
Marine invertebrate eggs	0.064	6.05
Seaweed eggs	0.086	3.4
Freshwater Peritricha	0.23	3.4
Mammalian leucocytes	0.74	12.8
Avian fibroblasts	0.96	30.8
Mammalian erythrocytes	1.84	79

be rate-limiting and that permeation has the kinetics of bulk diffusion. If the intracellular concentration gradients are sufficiently large, they may lead to additional errors if osmotic swelling is measured.

The binding of a solute to intracellular macromolecules or organelles may markedly affect the actual concentration in solution at the cell membrane and, consequently, the transmembrane flux which is observed. While it is well known that lipid-soluble substances are often avidly absorbed by proteins, the effect of binding of nonelectrolyte solutes by intracellular proteins on the apparent permeability coefficient has received little attention. On the other hand, the intracellular binding of ions is well known. In a typical early experiment, Ernst and Fricker[27] found that most of the potassium contained in ground muscle was leached by distilled water only with difficulty.

A number of investigators[28] have brought forward evidence that at least a portion of the intracellular potassium is not osmotically active or, on the basis of kinetic studies using radioactive ions, that a portion of the intracellular potassium is sequestered or that multiple intracellular pools exist. In the unfertilized sea urchin egg, only 15 percent of the intracellular potassium is readily exchangeable; after fertilization, 85 percent is readily exchangeable.[29] Ling[30] has compiled the evidence that at least some of the intracellular potassium exists as ion pairs with protein. He proposes that this mechanism may play an important role in potassium accumulation by living cells. The intracellular potassium in muscle has been localized by the formation of an insoluble

[25] Dick, D. A. T. *Exptl. Cell Res., 17,* 5 (1959); *J. Theoret. Biol., 7,* 504 (1964).
[26] Løvtrup, S. *J. Theoret. Biol., 5,* 341 (1963); Ling, G. N., Ochsenfeld, M. M., and Karreman, G. *J. Gen. Physiol., 50,* 1807 (1967).
[27] Ernst, E., and Fricker, J. *Pflüger's Arch. ges. Physiol., 234,* 399 (1934).
[28] Steinbach, H. B. *J. Cellular Comp. Physiol., 24,* 291 (1944); Harris, E. J. *J. Physiol., 117,* 278 (1952); *120,* 246 (1953); Simon, S. E., Shaw, F. H., Bennett, S., and Muller, M. *J. Gen. Physiol., 40,* 753 (1957); Simon, S. E., Johnstone, B. M., Shankly, K. H., and Shaw, F. H. *J. Gen. Physiol., 43,* 81 (1959); Troshin, A. S. *Problems of Cell Permeability.* New York: Pergamon Press, 1966.
[29] Tyler, A., and Monroy, A. *J. Exptl. Zool., 142,* 675 (1959).
[30] Ling, G. N. *Physical Theory of the Living State.* Boston: Blaisdell, 1962.

complex with sodium tetraphenylborate and found to reside largely in the A bands and Z lines while the I bands were relatively potassium-poor.[31]

Recent experiments[32] with cation-sensitive electrodes which permit direct estimation of the potassium activity coefficient have shown that the activity coefficient of intracellular potassium is not low: about 1 in barnacle muscle, 0.77 in frog sartorius muscle, and 0.61 in squid axon. It is possible, of course, to observe high activity coefficients for potassium even though appreciable quantities of potassium are bound if some of the intracellular water is sequestered and not available as solvent for potassium.

In the case of sodium, studies with cation-sensitive electrodes reveal a much lower activity coefficient than in comparable bulk aqueous solutions.[32] These findings are supported by nuclear magnetic resonance studies[33] which indicate that much of the intracellular sodium is held by strong secondary forces. Exchange studies using radioactive sodium[34] also indicate intracellular binding of sodium. Recently in electron micrographs of the frog sartorius muscle, sodium has been localized in the transverse tubules of the sarcoplasmic reticulum after formation of an insoluble electron-dense complex with potassium pyroantimonate.[35] There is also considerable evidence for the binding of sodium within nuclei.[36]

Compartmentalization by intracellular organelles is also important. The localization of sodium by the transverse tubules in muscle and its accumulation in nuclei has been mentioned. Calcium is taken up by the sarcoplasmic reticulum of muscle by an active process coupled to ATP hydrolysis. (Because of the importance of calcium sequestration by the sarcoplasmic reticulum in relaxation of skeletal muscle, it will be discussed in detail in Chapter 9.) Potassium and other ions appear to be sequestered in mitochondria[37] where their concentrations may differ from that in the cytoplasm as a whole. In fresh mitochondria, most of the potassium and an equivalent quantity of phosphate are tightly bound but are released when the mitochondria deteriorate after prolonged incubation. Sulphate also appears to be actively accumulated by mitochondria.[38] Clearly the intracellular distribution of many solutes is not uniform, but the information currently available is meager.

transport of salt through charged membranes

In the consideration of the transport of an aqueous solution of a single neutral electrolyte salt through a charged membrane, an additional flow, the electric current, I,

[31] Nesterov, V. P., and Tigyi-Sebes, A. *Acta Physiol. Acad. Sci. Hung.*, *28*, 97 (1965.
[32] Hinke, J. A. M. *J. Physiol.*, *156*, 314 (1961); Lev, A. A. *Nature*, *201*, 1132 (1964); McLaughlin, S. G. A., and Hinke, J. A. M. *Can. J. Physiol. Pharm.*, *44*, 837 (1966).
[33] Cope, F. W. *J. Gen. Physiol.*, *50*, 1353 (1967); Rotunno, C. A., Kowalewski, V., and Cereijido, M. *Biochim. Biophys. Acta*, *135*, 170 (1967).
[34] Burnstock, G., Dewhurst, D. J., and Simon, S. E. *J. Physiol.*, *167*, 210 (1963); *J. Cellular Comp. Physiol.*, *63*, 77 (1964); Dick, D. A. T., and Lea, E. J. A. *J. Physiol.*, *174*, 55 (1964).
[35] Zadunaisky, J. A. *J. Cell Biol.*, *31*, C 11 (1966).
[36] Abelson, P. H., and Duryee, W. R. *Biol. Bull.*, *96*, 205 (1949); Langendorf, H., Siebert, G., Lorenz, I., Hannover, R., and Beyer, R. *Biochem. Z.*, *335*, 273 (1961); Naora, H., Naora, H., Izawa, M., Allfrey, V. G., and Mirsky, A. E. *Proc. Natl. Acad. Sci.*, *48*, 853 (1962); Langendorf, H., Siebert, G., and Nitz-Litzow, D. *Nature*, *204*, 888 (1964).
[37] Bartley, W., and Davies, R. E. *Biochem. J.*, *57*, 37 (1954); Amoore, J. E., and Bartley, W. *Biochem. J.*, *69*, 223 (1958); Gamble, J. L., Jr. *Am. J. Physiol.*, *203*, 886 (1962); Gamble, J. L., Jr., and Hess, R. C., Jr., *Am. J. Physiol.*, *210*, 765 (1966).
[38] Deyrup, I. J. *J. Gen. Physiol.*, *41*, 49 (1957); Davies, R. E., Delluva, A. M., Deyrup, I. J., and Winters, R. W., in Kleinzeller, A., and Kotyk, A., eds. *Membrane Transport and Metabolism*. New York: Academic Press, 1961, p. 285.

and its conjugate driving force, the gradient of electrical potential ($\boldsymbol{E} = -\text{grad}\ \psi$), must be considered. The dissipation function (eq. 8-2) becomes[39]

$$\Omega = \mathfrak{J}_V\, \Delta P + \mathfrak{J}_D\, \Delta \Pi + I\boldsymbol{E} \tag{8-51}$$

A set of phenomenological equations relating the three flows and the three forces can be written

$$\mathfrak{J}_V = L_P\, \Delta P + L_{PD}\, \Delta \Pi + L_{PE}\, \boldsymbol{E} \tag{8-52}$$

$$\mathfrak{J}_D = L_{DP}\, \Delta P + L_D\, \Delta \Pi + L_{sE}\, \boldsymbol{E} \tag{8-53}$$

$$I = L_{EP}\, \Delta P + L_{Es}\, \Delta \Pi + L_E\, \boldsymbol{E} \tag{8-54}$$

This set of equations has six independent phenomenological coefficients. Therefore, it is necessary to introduce three coefficients in addition to the filtration coefficient L_P, the solute permeability coefficient ω, and the reflection coefficient σ. The new coefficients are obtained under conditions where there is no solute concentration difference and no volume flow. The *specific conductance* κ is given by

$$\kappa = \left(\frac{I}{\boldsymbol{E}}\right)_{\Delta\Pi = 0,\ \mathfrak{J}_V = 0} \tag{8-55}$$

The *transport number* (Hittorf) of the ion which does not interact with the reversible electrodes used to study the system is given by

$$t_i = \nu_i Z_i \mathfrak{F} \left(\frac{\mathfrak{J}_s}{I}\right)_{\Delta\Pi = 0,\ \mathfrak{J}_V = 0} = -\nu_i Z_i \mathfrak{F} \left(\frac{E}{\Delta\Pi / c_s}\right)_{\mathfrak{J}_V = 0,\ I = 0} \tag{8-56}$$

where E is the potential gradient. The third new phenomenological coefficient can be the *electrosmotic pressure* P_E, the pressure developed per unit potential difference under conditions where there is no volume flow.

$$P_E = \left(\frac{\Delta P}{\boldsymbol{E}}\right)_{\Delta\Pi = 0,\ \mathfrak{J}_V = 0} \tag{8-57}$$

Using these new phenomenological coefficients (which can be determined experimentally), the set of flow equations can be rewritten as

$$\mathfrak{J}_V = L_P\, \Delta P - \sigma L_P\, \Delta \Pi - (P_E L_P / \kappa) I \tag{8-58}$$

$$\mathfrak{J}_s = c_s(1 - \sigma)\mathfrak{J}_V + \omega\, \Delta\Pi + (t_\pm / \nu_\pm Z_\pm \mathfrak{F}) I \tag{8-59}$$

$$I = -P_E \mathfrak{J}_V + \frac{\kappa t_\pm}{\nu_\pm Z \mathfrak{F}} \frac{\Delta \Pi}{c_s} + \kappa E \tag{8-60}$$

Under some experimental conditions it is easier to determine a set of different phenomenological coefficients by keeping the hydrostatic pressure on either side of the membrane equal and letting the volume flow reach a steady state, that is to say, under

[39] Kedem, O., and Katchalsky, A. *J. Gen. Physiol.*, *45*, 143 (1961); *Trans. Faraday Soc.*, *59*, 1918 (1963); Schlögl, R. *Stofftransport durch Membranen.* Darmstadt: Theodor Steinkopff, Verlagsbuchhandlung, 1964; Caplan, S. R., and Mikulecky, C. D., in Marinsky, J. A., ed. *Ion Exchange.* New York: Marcel Dekker, 1966, p. 1.

conditions where $\Delta P = 0$ rather than $\mathfrak{J}_V = 0$. The electrical coefficients in this situation are (1) the practical conductance κ',

$$\kappa' = \left(\frac{I}{E}\right)_{\Delta\Pi=0,\ \Delta P=0} \tag{8-61}$$

(2) the *transference number* t'_i,

$$t'_i = \nu_i Z_i \mathfrak{F}\left(\frac{\mathfrak{J}_s}{I}\right)_{\Delta\Pi=0,\ \Delta P=0} = -\nu_i Z_i \mathfrak{F}\left(\frac{E}{\Delta\Pi/c_s}\right)_{[\Delta P-\Delta\Pi]=0,\ I=0} \tag{8-62}$$

and (3) the *coefficient of electrosmotic flow* β, the volume flow of solution through the membrane per unit current when both the hydrostatic pressure gradient and the osmotic gradient are zero,

$$\beta = \left(\frac{\mathfrak{J}_V}{I}\right)_{\Delta\Pi=0,\ \Delta P=0} \tag{8-63}$$

The set of flow equations using these latter three phenomenological coefficients are

$$\mathfrak{J}_V = L_P\,\Delta P - \sigma L_P\,\Delta\Pi + \beta I \tag{8-64}$$

$$\mathfrak{J}_s = c_s(1-\sigma)\mathfrak{J}_V + \omega'\,\Delta\Pi + (t'_\pm/\nu_\pm Z\mathfrak{F})I \tag{8-65}$$

$$I = \kappa'\beta\,\Delta P + \kappa'\left(\frac{t'_\pm}{\nu_\pm Z\mathfrak{F}} - \beta\right)\Delta\Pi + \kappa' E \tag{8-66}$$

where ω' is the solute permeability coefficient in the absence of a hydrostatic pressure gradient:

$$\omega' = \left(\frac{\mathfrak{J}_s}{\Delta\Pi}\right)_{\Delta P=0,\ I=0} \tag{8-67}$$

In the simplest case, where no current flows, the sets of flow equations (eqs. 8-58, 8-59, and 8-60; or eqs. 8-64, 8-65, and 8-66) reduce to eqs. 8-12 and 8-13, and the three coefficients L_P, ω, and σ are sufficient to describe the system.

For some purposes, it is more convenient to rewrite eqs. 8-64, 8-65, and 8-66 in terms of volume flow, solute flow, and membrane potential.

$$\mathfrak{J}_V = L_P(\Delta P - \Delta\Pi) + c_s(1-\sigma)L_P\left(\frac{\Delta\Pi}{c_s}\right) + \beta I \tag{8-68}$$

$$\mathfrak{J}_s = c_s(1-\sigma)L_P(\Delta P - \Delta\Pi) + c_s\,\omega'\left(\frac{\Delta\Pi}{c_s}\right) + (t'_\pm/\nu_\pm Z\mathfrak{F})I \tag{8-69}$$

$$E = -\beta(\Delta P - \Delta\Pi) - (t'_\pm/\nu_\pm Z\mathfrak{F})\left(\frac{\Delta\Pi}{c_s}\right) + \frac{I}{\kappa'} \tag{8-70}$$

When the phenomenological flow equations are transposed into force equations, however, six frictional coefficients $f_{(+)w}$, $f_{(-)w}$, $f_{(+)(-)}$, $f_{(+)m}$, $f_{(-)m}$, and f_{wm} must be taken into account. Let us consider the transport of a uni-univalent salt through a membrane of high charge density W. If c_1 is the concentration of counterions (ions of charge opposite in sign to that of the net charge on the membrane) and c_2 is the concentration of co-ions, under conditions of electroneutrality at any point in the membrane

$$c_1 = W + c_2 \tag{8-71}$$

In many cases the charge density is much greater than the salt concentration ($W \gg c_s$). Neglecting f_{12}, the frictional coefficient between the two ions, equations analogous to eqs. 8-25 and 8-26 can be written:

$$X_1 = -\frac{d\mu_1}{dx} = \frac{(f_{1w} + f_{1m})}{c_1}\mathfrak{J}_1 - \frac{f_{1w}}{c_w}\mathfrak{J}_w \tag{8-72}$$

$$X_2 = -\frac{d\mu_2}{dx} = \frac{(f_{2w} + f_{2m})}{c_2}\mathfrak{J}_2 - \frac{f_{2w}}{c_w}\mathfrak{J}_w \tag{8-73}$$

If no electrical potential is applied across the membrane, the flow of both ion species is equal, and electroneutrality is preserved ($\mathfrak{J}_1 = \mathfrak{J}_2 = \mathfrak{J}_s$). The force acting on the salt as a whole is

$$X_s = -\frac{d\mu_s}{dx} = -\frac{d\mu_1}{dx} - \frac{d\mu_2}{dx} \tag{8-74}$$

Equations 8-72 and 8-73 can be summed to give

$$X_s = \left(\frac{[f_{1w} + f_{1m}]}{c_1} + \frac{[f_{2w} + f_{2m}]}{c_2}\right)\mathfrak{J}_s - \frac{(f_{1w} + f_{2w})}{c_w}\mathfrak{J}_w \tag{8-75}$$

If the term $(f_{1w} + f_{1m})$ approximates $(f_{2w} + f_{2m})$ in magnitude, the first term on the right-hand side of eq. 8-75 can be neglected because $c_1 \gg c_2$. In the case where $\mathfrak{J}_w \approx \mathfrak{J}_V \approx 0$, eq. 8-75 simplifies to

$$-\frac{d\mu_s}{dx} = \frac{(f_{2w} + f_{2m})}{c_s}\mathfrak{J}_s \tag{8-76}$$

which can be integrated across the thickness of membrane to give

$$K_s\,\Delta\Pi = \mathfrak{J}_s(f_{2w} + f_{2m})\,\Delta x \tag{8-77}$$

Using developments similar to those used in the case of a nonelectrolyte, the following expressions can be derived.

$$\omega = \left(\frac{\mathfrak{J}_s}{\Delta\Pi}\right)_{\mathfrak{J}_V = 0} = \frac{K_s}{(f_{2w} + f_{2m})\,\Delta x} \tag{8 78}$$

$$\sigma = 1 - \frac{\omega \bar{V}_s}{L_P} - \frac{K_s}{\varphi_w}\left(\frac{f_{1w} + f_{2w}}{f_{2w} + f_{2m}}\right) = 1 - \frac{\omega \bar{V}_s}{L_P} - \frac{\omega f_{sw}\,\Delta x}{\varphi_w} \tag{8-79}$$

where $f_{sw} = f_{1w} + f_{2w}$.

If it is assumed, in addition to the foregoing simplifications, that the membrane is highly hydrated and that the solutes pass through channels filled with solvent (water), the frictional coefficients between solute and water in the aqueous channels in the membrane and in the bulk solution will be approximately equal ($f_{sw} \approx f^0_{sw}$). Some further simplifications can be made. Because $c_1 \approx W \gg c_s \approx c_2$, that is, the co-ion concentration is small compared to the fixed charges in the membrane, most of the frictional interactions of the co-ion in the aqueous channels will be mainly with water and $f_{2w} \gg f_{2m}$. The distribution coefficient K_s may be evaluated in terms of the requirements for a Donnan equilibrium (eq. 4-236). The concentration of the ions in the membrane will be c_1/φ_m and c_2/φ_m, where φ_m is the volume fraction of water in the membrane. The Donnan requirement that the activity of the salt in the aqueous channels is equal to the activity of the salt in an equivalent solution is satisfied when

$$(c_s')^2 = \frac{c_1}{\varphi_w} \cdot \frac{c_2}{\varphi_w} = \frac{(c_s + W)c_s}{\varphi_w^2} \tag{8-80}$$

Because the solute is composed of an anion and a cation, the distribution coefficient is given by

$$K_s = \left(\frac{c_{s(x)}}{c_s'}\right)^2 \approx \frac{c_s \varphi_w^2}{c_s + W} \approx \frac{c_s \varphi_w^2}{W} \tag{8-81}$$

From eq. 8-81, an alternate expression for the solute permeability coefficient can be derived

$$\omega = \frac{\bar{c}_s \varphi_w^2 \vartheta}{f_{2w} W \,\Delta x} \tag{8-82}$$

where $\bar{c}_s$ is the average salt concentration and ϑ is the *tortuosity* factor of Mackay and Mears (see footnote 17, p. 435). Let $f_{1w} = f^0_{1w}/\vartheta$ and $f_{2w} = f^0_{2w}/\vartheta$, and assume that the membrane consists of a loose network of aqueous channels. The friction encountered by the co-ion will be mainly with water so that $f_{2m} \ll f_{2w}$. Substituting these relations and eq. 8-82 into eq. 8-79,

$$\sigma = 1 - \frac{\omega \overline{V}_s}{L_P} - \frac{\bar{c}_s \varphi_w}{W}\left(\frac{f^0_{1w} + f^0_{2w}}{f^0_{2w}}\right) \tag{8-83}$$

But the frictional coefficients of ions in solution are proportional to the reciprocals of the ionic mobilities; thus

$$t_1^0 = \frac{u_1^0}{u_1^0 + u_2^0} = \frac{1/f^0_{1w}}{(1/f^0_{1w}) + (1/f^0_{2w})} = \frac{f^0_{2w}}{f^0_{1w} + f^0_{2w}} \tag{8-84}$$

Substituting eq. 8-84 into eq. 8-83 gives

$$\sigma = 1 - \frac{\omega \overline{V}_s}{L_P} - \frac{\bar{c}_s \varphi_w}{W t_1^0} \tag{8-85}$$

In a membrane where flow of both solvent and solute take place through a system of microscopic channels, the term $\omega \overline{V}_s/L_P$ is usually negligibly small.

It is evident from eqs. 8-82 and 8-85 that, in the case of electrolytes, both ω and σ vary widely with the average salt concentration. In nonelectrolytes, on the other hand, K_s is relatively independent of concentration. Particularly when t_1^0 is small, σ decreases rapidly as $\bar{c}_s$ increases and may become negative, leading to *negative anomalous osmosis.* When σ is negative, a hydrostatic pressure must be applied to prevent backward volume flow. Negative anomalous osmosis is particularly prominent when the counterion is multivalent (t^0 is very small).[40]

From similar considerations, the following expressions can be derived:

$$L_P = \frac{r^2 \varphi_w}{8\eta} \frac{\vartheta}{\Delta x} \tag{8-86}$$

$$\kappa = \frac{\mathfrak{F}^2 W}{f^0_{1w}} \frac{\vartheta}{\Delta x} \tag{8-87}$$

$$\beta = \frac{r^2 f^0_{1w}}{8\eta \mathfrak{F}} \tag{8-88}$$

$$t_2 = \left(\frac{c_s \varphi_w}{W}\right) \frac{f_{1w}}{f_{2w}} \tag{8-89}$$

$$t_1 = 1 - \left(\frac{c_s \varphi_w}{W}\right)^2 \cdot \frac{f_{1w}}{f_{2w}} \tag{8-90}$$

The foregoing considerations are useful in exploring the models proposed by Meyer and Sievers, by Teorell, and by Conti and Eisenman.[41] Before continuing the analytical discussion, however, let us explore some nonlinear transport processes and the qualitative aspects of coupling.

facilitated diffusion

A number of substances such as glucose, certain amino acids, and vitamins permeate cell membranes at a much faster rate than would be expected from their molecular size or lipoid solubility. Their penetration through the membrane appears to be mediated by a structural constituent of the membrane itself. This type of transport is called *facilitated diffusion.*[42] Facilitated diffusion has the following characteristics:

1. The rate of permeation is highly stereospecific. Isomers and optical enantiomorphs are likely to diffuse at markedly different rates.
2. The rate of permeation is not directly proportional to concentration of solute and, except at very low concentrations, does not follow Fick's law. Rather, the rate of permeation appears to reach a limiting or saturation value as the concentration of solute is increased.
3. The rate of permeation may be markedly reduced by the presence of structurally similar solutes. The latter appear to compete with the permeant for participation in the facilitated diffusion process.
4. Facilitated diffusion is driven by an existing electrochemical gradient and does not

[40] Schlögl, R. *Z. phys. Chem.*, *3*, 73 (1955); Grim, E., and Sollner, K. *J. Gen. Physiol.*, *40*, 887 (1957).
[41] Meyer, K. H., and Sievers, J. F. *Helv. Chim. Acta*, *19*, 649, (1936); Teorell, T. *Progr. Biophys. Biophys. Chem.*, *3*, 305 (1953); Conti, F., and Eisenman, G. *Biophys. J.*, *5*, 511 (1965).
[42] Bowyer, F. *Intern. Rev. Cytol.*, *6*, 469 (1957); Wilbrandt, W., and Rosenberg, T. *Pharmacol. Rev.*, *13*, 109 (1961); Stein, W. D. *Recent Progr. Surface Sci.*, *1*, 300 (1964).

require the input of energy beyond that required to generate the electrochemical gradient. Facilitated diffusion may occur against an electrochemical gradient by coupling to another transport process.
5. The rate of penetration may be markedly reduced by substances which are generally regarded to be inhibitors of enzyme reactions. Various facilitated diffusion systems will be "poisoned" by different substances.
6. The unidirectional flux of solute as measured by the use of radioactive tracer may be much larger than the rate of net diffusion of solute.
7. Facilitated diffusion frequently shows the high temperature coefficients characteristic of chemical reactions ($Q_{10} \approx 3$).

It has been found experimentally that the net flow of a solute which permeates by facilitated diffusion can be described by an expression similar to the Michaelis-Menten equation for the velocity of an enzyme-catalyzed reaction

$$\mathfrak{J}_s = \frac{c_s V_M}{k_M + c_s} \tag{8-91}$$

where c_s is the concentration of solute and V_M and k_M are constants which depend upon the number of cells, the cell type, and the solute. The term V_M is equivalent to the maximal flow of the solute that can occur, while k_M is the solute concentration at which the flow is one-half V_M. Thus, these constants are analogous to the Michaelis constants.

Facilitated diffusion generally is regarded to take place as a result of the interaction between the solute and a constituent of the membrane. The solute permeates the membrane in combination with a specific *carrier* (Fig. 8-9). When not combined with

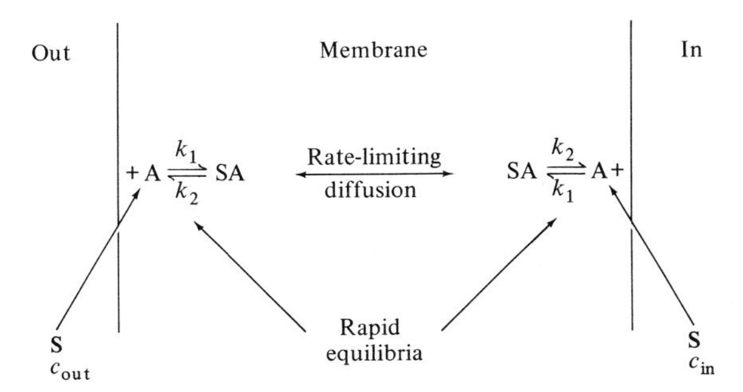

fig. 8-9. A diagram illustrating the hypothetical carrier mechanism for facilitated diffusion. The solute combines with a carrier at the membrane interface. The reaction leading to the formation of a complex is judged to be rapid compared to the rate of diffusion of the complex across the membrane.

this carrier, the solute permeates at a very slow rate. Whether the carrier-solute complex actually moves with the membrane or whether the carrier is stationary is not clear, but the exact nature of the carrier does not alter the analysis of the phenomenon. Actually, any mechanism (for example, stereospecific channels) that can be saturated by solute will show the kinetics of facilitated diffusion, and the concept of a carrier must be interpreted in the very broadest sense.

The best evidence for an actual carrier comes from studies of facilitated diffusion in bacteria,[43] where the transport systems are inducible. Thus, the genes controlling the formation of the permease system for β-galactosides in *E. coli* reside in the *lac* operon and are induced coordinately with β-galactosidase and galactoside transacetylase by lactose and certain nonmetabolized analogs such as *o*-nitrophenyl-β-D-thiogalactoside. After incubation with these inducers, the amount of carrier for galactosides is increased. Furthermore, mutant strains are well known with a defect in the galactoside permease system resulting in poor uptake of galactosides. Upon genetic mapping, the defects are localized in the y region of the *lac* operon. Fox and Kennedy[44] have isolated the product of the y gene, a membrane-bound lipoprotein with a high affinity for galactosides which is inactivated by sulfhydryl reagents.

In bacteria, proteins which appear to be constituents of the membrane and which specifically bind sulfate[45] or leucine[46] have been identified. In mammals, the absorption of calcium from the intestine appears to be mediated by a specific carrier. A calcium-binding protein which requires vitamin D has been isolated recently[47] from the mucosa of chicken intestine.

Frequently, the net flow is the difference between an inward and an outward flux which are themselves much greater than the net flow of solute. Assuming that V_M and k_M are the same for the unidirectional fluxes in both directions,

$$\mathfrak{J}_s = \mathfrak{J}_{\text{in}} - \mathfrak{J}_{\text{out}} = \frac{c_{\text{out}} V_M}{k_M + c_{\text{out}}} - \frac{c_{\text{in}} V_M}{k_M + c_{\text{in}}} \tag{8-92}$$

$$= \frac{(c_{\text{out}} - c_{\text{in}}) k_M V_M}{(k_M + c_{\text{out}})(k_M + c_{\text{in}})} \tag{8-93}$$

where c_{out} and c_{in} are the concentrations of solute on the outside and inside of the membrane respectively. If both c_{out} and c_{in} are small compared to k_M, eq. 8-93 becomes $\mathfrak{J}_s = (c_{\text{out}} - c_{\text{in}})V_M/k_M$, an expression which has the form of the Fick equation.

A curious phenomenon results from the fact that the unidirectional fluxes are greater than the net flux. Consider an aliquot of cells that have been immersed in a medium containing glucose until equilibrium has been reached. Upon transfer to a glucose-free medium, an efflux of glucose from the cells will occur. If, however, the second medium contains galactose, a sugar which diffuses by combination with the same carrier as glucose, the efflux of glucose will be even higher than in the glucose-free medium. Furthermore, careful measurements show that the extra efflux of glucose from cells placed in the galactose-containing medium is exactly equal to the influx of galactose into the cells (Fig. 8-10). There appears to be a stoichiometric exchange of galactose for glucose. This phenomenon is called *competitive exchange diffusion.*

Counterflow is a similar phenomenon. Glucose and the nonmetabolized sugar 3-O-methyl-D-glucose compete for the same carrier for diffusion into cells. If glucose is present together with 3-O-methyl-D-glucose, less of the latter is taken up by the cells. If, after a period of incubation in a medium containing 3-O-methyl-D-glucose alone, glucose is added, there is an actual efflux of 3-O-methyl-D-glucose into the incubation

[43] Cohen, G. N., and Monod, J. *Bacteriol. Rev., 21,* 169 (1957); Koch, A. L. *Biochim. Biophys. Acta, 79,* 177 (1964).
[44] Fox, C. F., and Kennedy, E. P. *Proc. Natl. Acad. Sci., 54,* 891 (1965); *57,* 698 (1967).
[45] Pardee, A. B. *J. Biol. Chem., 241,* 5886 (1966).
[46] Piperno, J. R., and Oxender, D. L. *J. Biol. Chem., 241,* 5732 (1966).
[47] Wasserman, R. H., and Taylor, A. N. *Science, 152,* 791 (1966).

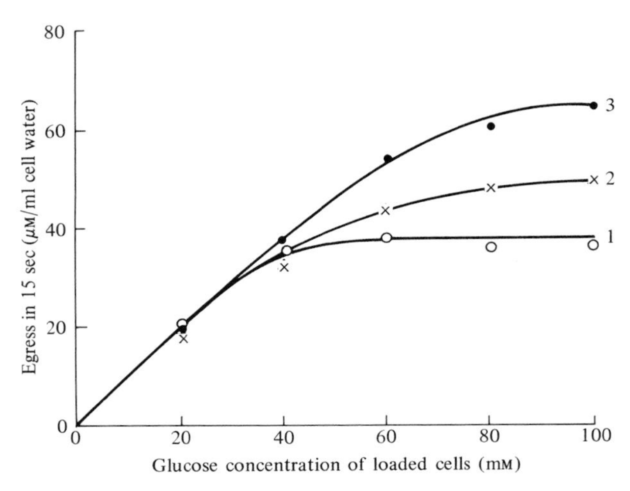

fig. 8-10. An experiment illustrating exchange diffusion. Human erythrocytes were equilibrated with ^{14}C-glucose solutions of various concentrations. The efflux of the labeled glucose was measured 15 sec after transfer of the cells into saline (curve 1), into equimolar unlabeled glucose (curve 2), or into 200 mM unlabeled galactose (curve 3). (From Levine, M., Oxender, D. L., and Stein, W. D. *Biochim. Biophys. Acta, 109,* 155 [1965].)

mixture against the existing concentration gradient. A lower level of 3-O-methyl-D-glucose is reached which corresponds to that which would have been expected were the 3-O-methyl-D-glucose and glucose present together during the entire course of the incubation (Fig. 8-11). The difference in free energy required for the efflux of the 3-O-methyl-D-glucose against its concentration gradient comes from the coupling of its efflux to the influx of glucose.

Exchange diffusion and counterflow require that the inward and outward fluxes do not interfere with one another. This condition can be satisfied either by a mobile carrier or by a system of unidirectional channels with some channels for entry and some for exit. The solute levels on at least one side of the membrane must be high compared to k_M.

The great specificity of facilitated diffusion systems can be illustrated by the permeation of monosaccharides. For a number of technical reasons, most studies of the uptake of simple sugars have utilized the human erythrocyte. The primate erythrocyte, in contrast to the red cells of rodents, carnivores, ungulates, and other mammals, is relatively permeable to glucose.[48] Yet the utilization of glucose by the primate erythrocyte is relatively low. In muscle, glucose utilization is so great that glucose transport may be rate-limiting; and there is an additional complication because glucose uptake in muscle is markedly accelerated by insulin.

The entry of sugars is measured by changes in light scattering which result from

[48] Kozawa, S. *Biochem. Z., 60,* 231 (1914); Wilbrandt, W. *Pflüger's Arch. ges. Physiol., 241,* 302 (1938); Laris, P. C. *J. Cellular Comp. Physiol., 51,* 273 (1958). Widdas, W. F. *J. Physiol., 127,* 318 (1955) discovered that red cells from the blood of fetal pigs, rabbits, guinea pigs, sheep, and deer are about as permeable to glucose as are human erythrocytes. The change from high to low permeability occurs at birth or in the neonatal period.

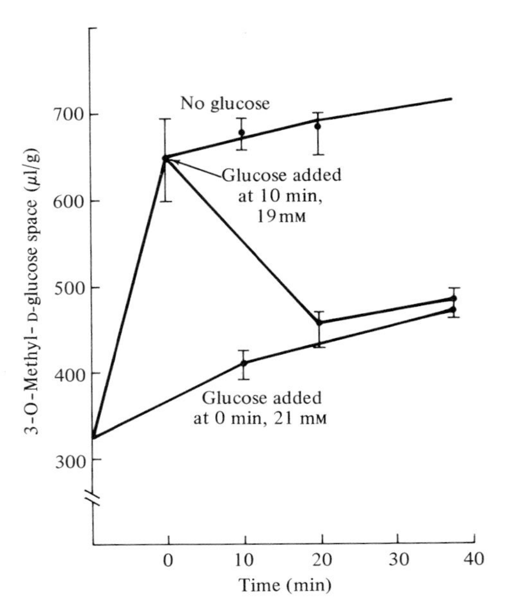

fig. 8-11. An experiment illustrating countertransport. Hearts were perfused with 0.75 mM 3-O-methylglucose (upper curve) and the uptake determined. Less 3-O-methylglucose was taken up when 21 mM glucose was added at zero time (lower curve). When 19 mM glucose was added at 10 min, the amount of 3-O-methylglucose taken up fell from the value of 3-O-methylglucose alone to that of 3-O-methylglucose plus glucose (middle curve). (From Morgan, H. E., Regen, D. M., and Park, C. R. *J. Biol. Chem.*, *239*, 370 [1964].)

volume changes of suspended red cells.[49] Another direct method utilizes the time required for a given fraction of the erythrocytes to swell and hemolyze after being placed in a sugar solution.[50] The extent of hemolysis can be followed spectrophotometrically, and the decrease in absorbance can be recorded as hemolysis progresses. Lastly, the sugar content of red cells can be determined chemically: the quantity of sugar taken up from the medium can be determined chemically by difference; or, when labeled sugars are used, the red cells can be assayed for radioactivity (see footnote 48, p. 451).

While D-glucose and D-galactose are taken up, L-glucose and L-galactose are not. Erythrocytes are also permeable to a number of sugars related to D-glucose. Among the permeable hexoses, the relative rates of penetration are D-mannose > D-galactose > D-glucose > L-sorbose > D-fructose (see footnote 48). D-Xylose and L-arabinose penetrate readily while their enantiomorphs do not.[51] On the other hand, a number of compounds related to glucose such as methylglucose and mannitol do not penetrate erythrocytes.

---

[49] Ørskov, S. L. *Biochem. Z.*, *279*, 241, 250 (1935).
[50] Parpart, A. K. *J. Cellular Comp. Physiol.*, *7*, 153 (1935); Wilbrandt, W. *Pflüger's Arch. ges. Physiol.*, *241*, 289 (1938); *250*, 569 (1948); *Arch. Exptl. Pathol. Pharmakol.*, *212*, 9 (1950).
[51] Hillman, R. S., Landau, B. R., and Ashmore, J. *Am. J. Physiol.*, *196*, 1277 (1959); LeFevre, P. G., and McGinnis, G. F. *J. Gen. Physiol.*, *44*, 87 (1960).

It appears that the mechanism for sugar entry is shared by the various sugars that penetrate the cell. Thus, the total uptake of glucose, arabinose, and xylose in a mixture of the three sugars is the same as the uptake of any single sugar from a solution of that sugar of the same concentration as the total in the mixture.[52] While each sugar which penetrates the cell interferes with the uptake of every other penetrating sugar, there are differences in the degree of interference (Fig. 8-12). Competition between sugars for

fig. 8-12. Mutual inhibition in penetration of sugars into the human erythrocyte. (From LeFevre, P. G. *Symp. Soc. Exptl. Biol., 8,* 123 [1954]. Copyright Academic Press; reprinted by permission.)

INHIBITING SUGAR	INHIBITION OF PENETRATION OF:						
	D-GLUCOSE	MANNOSE	GALACTOSE	XYLOSE	ARABINOSE	SORBOSE	L-GLUCOSE
D-Glucose	—	+++	+++	+++	+++	++++	++++
Mannose	+++	—	+++	++	++	++++	++++
Galactose	++	++	—	+	++	+++	++++
Xylose	++	++	++	—	+	++	+++
Arabinose	++	++	++	+	—	++	+++
Sorbose	0	0	0	0	0	—	+++
L-Glucose	0	0	0	0	0	0	—

entry frequently is not reciprocal; for example, sorbose and fructose are inhibited from entering the cell in the presence of glucose, but the uptake of glucose is not prevented by fructose or sorbose.

In solution, free sugars are present largely in the form of pyranose (6-membered) rings composed of one oxygen atom and five carbon atoms. The valence angle at the oxygen atom is approximately the same as the tetrahedral angle at the carbon atoms, and the C-O bond length is only slightly less than the C-C bond length. The sugar pyranose rings, therefore, bear a marked resemblance to the cyclohexane ring and exist in two specific strainless conformations, frequently designated as the "chair" and "boat" conformations because of the obvious analogies in form. In the case of the sugars, the ring atoms are not entirely equivalent; this leads to six distinct kinds of boat configurations and two kinds of chair shapes. The six boat forms are readily interconvertible and may be considered as a single conformational form. The chair conformations, on the other hand, are relatively rigid. Large deformation of the valence angle is required to twist a molecule from one chair form to any other conformation.[53]

For most sugars the chair conformations are much more favored at ordinary temperatures than the boat forms. The two possible chair conformations are shown in Fig. 8-13. Because of the tetrahedral bond angles at each carbon atom on the ring, one free substituent extends approximately in the plane of the ring while the other free substituent extends approximately perpendicular to the ring. The first substituent is called the *equatorial group* while the latter is called the *axial* substituent. Of the two possible chair conformations, the one which tends to have most of the bulky substituents in the equatorial position is favored. It has been shown[54] that the *C*1 chair form

[52] Wilbrandt, W. *Helv. Physiol. Pharmacol. Acta, 5,* 64 (1947); LeFevre, P. G., and Davies, R. I. *J. Gen. Physiol., 34,* 515 (1951).
[53] Hazebroek, P., and Oosterhoff, L. J. *Discussions Faraday Soc., 10,* 87 (1951); Reeves, R. E. *J. Am. Chem. Soc., 72,* 1499 (1950); *Ann. Rev. Biochem., 27,* 15 (1958).
[54] LeFevre, P. G., and Marshall, J. K. *J. Biol. Chem., 234,* 3022 (1959); LeFevre, P. G. *Pharmacol. Rev., 13,* 39 (1961).

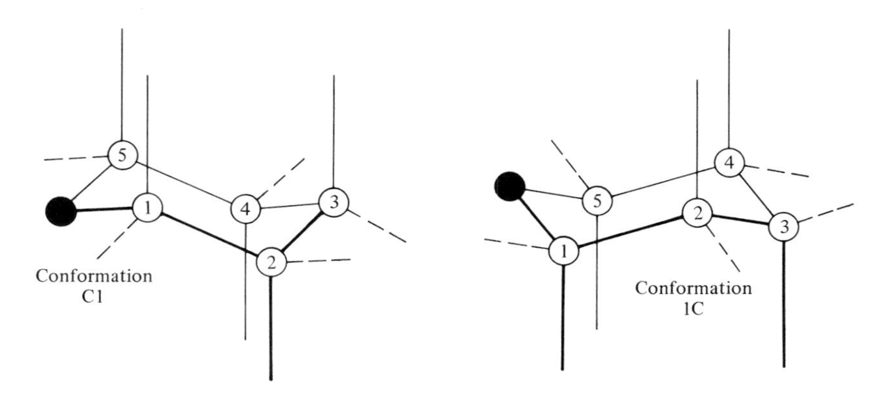

fig. 8-13. A diagram of the two chair conformations of the pyranose ring of simple sugars. The filled circle represents the oxygen atom while the numbered circles represent the corresponding carbon atoms. The side of the ring facing the observer is heavier, equatorial bonds are shown by broken lines, and axial bonds are depicted by vertical solid lines. (From LeFevre, P. G., and Marshall, J. K. *Am. J. Physiol., 194,* 335 [1958].)

is the preferred structure for the sugars which permeate the human erythrocyte. The sequence of affinity for the transport carrier as judged by the value for k_M parallels the tendency to assume the *C*1 conformation (Fig. 8-14)—the order of affinity being 2-deoxy-D-glucose > D-glucose > D-mannose > D-galactose > D-xylose > L-arabinose > D ribose. Sugars which tend to assume the 1*C* conformation (L-glucose, L-galactose, L-xylose, L-rhamnose, L-fucose, and D-arabinose) penetrate very poorly.

The glucose transport system is inhibited by a number of substances. Phlorizin and its aglycone, phloretin, and stilbestrol behave as reversible competitive inhibitors.[55] In the process, they appear to be adsorbed on the cell membrane. The sulfhydryl reagents *p*-chloromercuribenzoate, mercury, and gold act as nonpenetrating, noncompetitive inhibitors of glucose uptake. It is of some interest that concentrations of iodoacetate which cause a cessation of glycolysis do not inhibit glucose uptake. Another inhibitor of glycolysis, fluoride, also fails to affect glucose uptake. The nonpenetrating disaccharide sugars also act as competitive, reversible inhibitors of glucose transport.[56]

There appear to be at least three facilitated diffusion systems for amino acids:[57] one for the permeation of L-glycine and related amino acids, one for L-methionine and related amino acids, and one for L-valine and related amino acids. The presence of active metabolism to maintain the high intracellular sodium concentration is necessary for amino acid uptake against a concentration gradient. The uptake of amino acids frequently has been studied using nonmetabolized amino acid analogs such as amino-*iso*-butyric acid.

---

[55] LeFevre, P. G. *J. Gen. Physiol., 31,* 505 (1948); Rosenberg, T., and Wilbrandt, W. *Helv. Physiol. Pharmacol. Acta, 15,* 168 (1957); Christensen, H. N., and Jones, J. C. *J. Biol. Chem., 236,* 76 (1961).
[56] Lacko, L., and Burger, M. *Biochem. J., 83,* 622 (1962).
[57] Oxender, D. L., and Christensen, H. N. *J. Biol. Chem., 234,* 2321 (1959); *238,* 3686 (1963); Quastel, J. H. *Brit. Med. Bull., 21,* 49 (1965); Johnstone, R. M., and Scholefield, P. G. *J. Biol. Chem., 236,* 1419 (1961); *Biochim. Biophys. Acta, 94,* 130 (1965); Begin, N., and Scholefield, P. G. *J. Biol. Chem., 240,* 332 (1965); *Biochim. Biophys. Acta, 104,* 566 (1965); Oxender, D. L. *J. Biol. Chem., 240,* 2976 (1965); Vidaver, G. A., Romain, L. F., and Haurowitz, F. *Arch. Biochem. Biophys., 107,* 82 (1964).

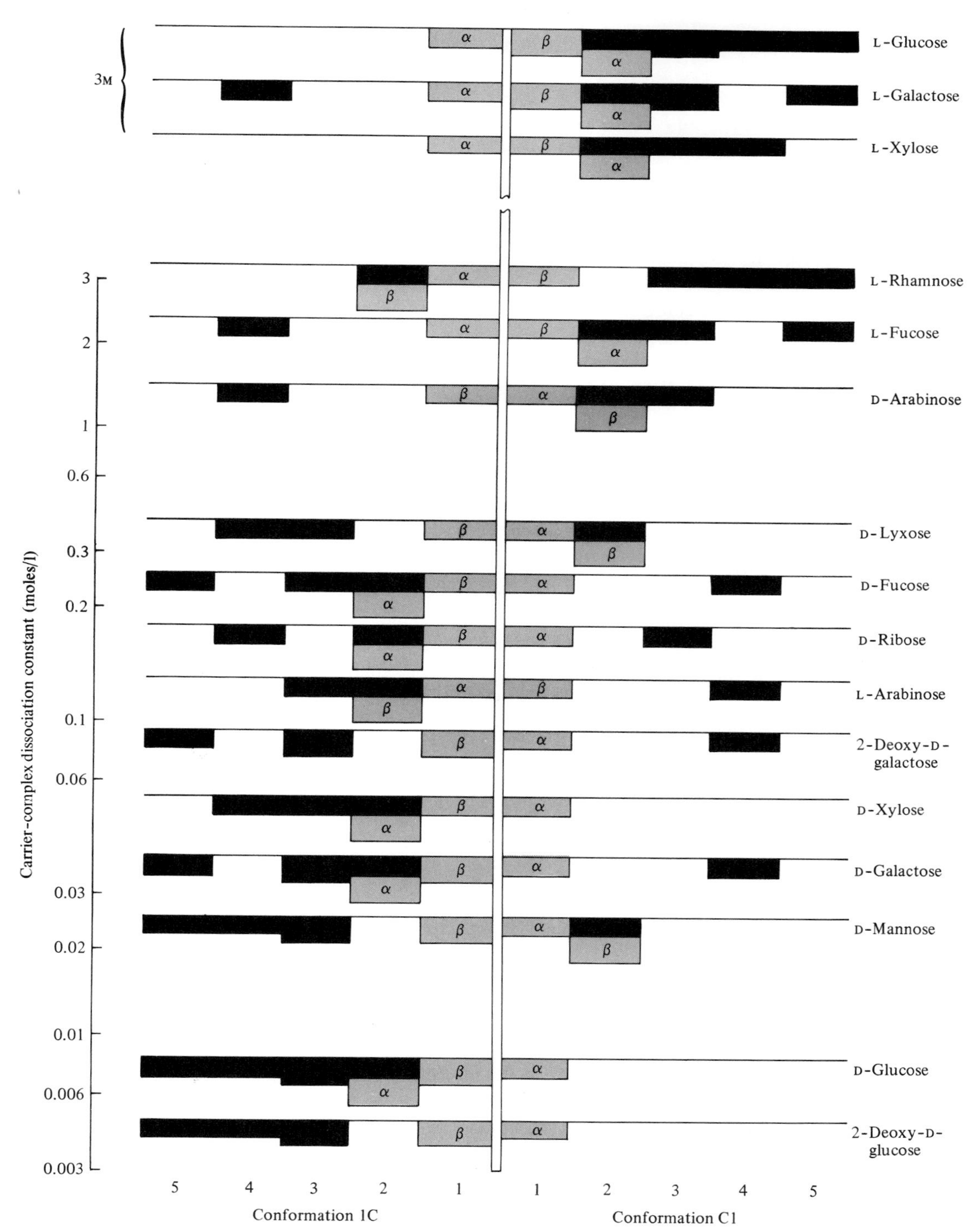

fig. 8-14. Conformational stability of some sugars compared to their affinity for the human erythrocyte transport system. Shaded regions represent weighted instability factors; sugars will tend to assume the conformation with the least instability (that is, lack of shaded areas). (From LeFevre, P. G. *Pharmacol. Rev., 13,* 48 [1961]. Copyright 1961, The Williams & Wilkins Co., Baltimore, Md. 21202, U.S.A.)

In dealing with the various flows and forces, it is important to remember the Curie-Prigogine principle (discussed in Chapter 4), which states that in an isotropic system the various vector flows of matter and electric currents can interact with each other, and coupling can occur between various chemical reactions which are scalar flows. Coupling between chemical reactions (scalars) and diffusional flows (vectors) cannot occur in isotropic systems. In an anisotropic system, however, coupling between vector and scalar flows can occur. The fact that chemical reactions are coupled to mass transport processes is a powerful argument in favor of the existence of a substantive structure at the cell boundary.[58] Whether or not the anisotropy of function in the cell membrane corresponds to the structures seen in electron micrographs is not known at the present time.

In an anisotropic membrane the flows due to the various forces can be written as[59]

$$\mathbf{X}_i = \mathfrak{R}_{ii}\mathfrak{J}_i + \sum_{j,\, j\neq i} \mathfrak{R}_{ij}\mathfrak{J}_j + \boldsymbol{\mathfrak{R}}_{ir}\mathfrak{J}_r \tag{8-94}$$

$$A_r = \sum_i \boldsymbol{\mathfrak{R}}_{ri}\mathfrak{J}_i + \mathfrak{R}_{rr}\mathfrak{J}_r \tag{8-95}$$

where $\mathbf{X}_i$ are the vector forces driving the vector flows; $\mathfrak{J}_i$ are the vector flows (diffusional flows, electric currents, etc.); and A_r is the affinity of a chemical reaction, a scalar force driving the scalar flow represented by the rate of advancement of the reaction, $\mathfrak{J}_r = d\xi/dt$. It should be noted that the coupling coefficients between vector forces and vector flows, $\mathfrak{R}_{ii}$ and $\mathfrak{R}_{ij}$, are scalar quantities (whose values depend upon the frictional coefficients and concentration of the solute), as are the coupling coefficients $\mathfrak{R}_{rr}$ between the scalar force A_r driving the scalar flow of the chemical reaction $\mathfrak{J}_i$. However, the cross-coupling coefficients $\boldsymbol{\mathfrak{R}}_{ir}$ relating the vector flows to the scalar chemical reaction must be vector quantities.

Equation 8-94 can be rearranged to yield

$$\mathfrak{J}_i = -\frac{\Delta\mu_i}{\mathfrak{R}_{ii}} - \sum \frac{\mathfrak{R}_{ij}}{\mathfrak{R}_{ii}}\mathfrak{J}_{ij} - \frac{\boldsymbol{\mathfrak{R}}_{ir}}{\mathfrak{R}_{ii}}\mathfrak{J}_r \tag{8-96}$$

where the force driving the transport of a chemical species has been identified as the difference in electrochemical potential. Equation 8-96 serves to segregate the various contributions to a flow of matter: the first term on the right-hand side of the equation represents the contribution to a flow that results from the difference in electrochemical potential of the substance across the membrane; the middle term represents the cross contributions resulting from interactions with other flows across the membrane; and the far right-hand term represents the contribution resulting from coupling to a chemical reaction. By analogy, flows of matter across a membrane can be divided into three categories: flows that depend primarily upon their conjugate driving force, flows that are coupled to the flows of other materials, and flows that derive the driving force from coupling to metabolic reactions.

---

[58] Kedem, O., in Kleinzeller, A., and Kotyk, A., eds., *Membrane Transport and Metabolism*. New York: Academic Press, 1961, p. 87; Jardetzky, O., and Snell, F. M. *Proc. Natl. Acad. Sci.*, *46*, 616 (1960); Moszynski, J. R., Hoshiko, T., and Lindley, B. D. *Biochim. Biophys. Acta*, *75*, 447 (1963); Vaidhyanathan, V. S. *J. Theoret. Biol.*, *9*, 489 (1965).

[59] Kedem, O., in Kleinzeller, A., and Kotyk, A., eds. *Membrane Transport and Metabolism*. New York: Academic Press, 1961, p. 87.

Onsager reciprocity is based on the assumption of microscopic reversibility and holds only near equilibrium. The coupling of ATP hydrolysis to active sodium transport occurs far from equilibrium, and in this process, Onsager reciprocity may not apply to the cross coefficients. If Onsager reciprocity did hold, reversal of active transport would be expected to result in resynthesis of ATP. Resynthesis of ATP has not been unequivocally demonstrated, although lowering the electrochemical gradient results in a sparing of ATP.

The movement of chloride ions across the isolated frog skin or mammalian intestine[60] (described in Chapter 7) is an example of a species of matter whose transport depends solely upon the difference in the electrochemical potential for Cl^- across the membrane. Furthermore, because the unidirectional fluxes of Cl^- ions conform to eq. 7-22, one can conclude that the movement of Cl^- ions is indistinguishable kinetically from simple diffusion. It should be noted that in many cases facilitated diffusion, which apparently depends upon a carrier substance within the membrane, may also depend primarily upon the conjugate driving force of that species. In such cases, the unidirectional fluxes may not satisfy eq. 7-22 but will satisfy the relation $\mathfrak{J}_i = -\Delta\mu_i/\mathfrak{R}_{ii}$.

On the other hand, Na^+ ions are transported against an electrochemical gradient by coupling to the hydrolysis of ATP—that is, by active transport. The magnitude of the coupling coefficient can be evaluated under conditions where no net flow of Na^+ ions occurs when active transport just offsets the effect of the electrochemical gradient.

$$(\Delta\mu_{\text{Na}})_{\mathfrak{J}=0} = RT \ln \frac{c'_{\text{Na}}}{c''_{\text{Na}}} + \mathfrak{F}\Delta\psi = \mathfrak{R}_{\text{Na}-r}\mathfrak{J}_r \tag{8-97}$$

For the flow of Na^+ ions and Cl^- ions across frog skins, eq. 8-96 becomes

$$\mathfrak{J}_{\text{Na}} = -\frac{\Delta\mu_{\text{Na}}}{\mathfrak{R}_{\text{Na}}} - \frac{\mathfrak{R}_{\text{Na}-r}}{\mathfrak{R}_{\text{Na}}}\mathfrak{J}_r \qquad \mathfrak{J}_{\text{Cl}} = -\frac{\Delta\mu_{\text{Cl}}}{\mathfrak{R}_{\text{Cl}}} \tag{8-98}$$

The coupling of volume flow to the passive diffusion of solute has been discussed above. Volume flow can be coupled to the active transport of solute in an analogous manner. For example, it has long been known[61] that an isolated piece of small intestine separating two solutions of identical composition will transport water from the mucosal surface to the serosal surface even against a hydrostatic pressure difference. A similar net transport of water in the fish gall bladder was studied by Diamond,[62] who showed the dependence of this process upon active metabolism. Water transport does not appear to be directly linked to a metabolic chemical reaction; instead, it appears to depend in an obligatory fashion upon the active transport of Na^+ ions.[63] Thus, the active transport of Na^+ ions against an electrochemical gradient results from coupling to metabolic chemical reactions; in turn, the net transport of water is coupled to solute transport. Studies by Diamond indicate clearly that the NaCl solution transported by the gall bladder is isotonic with the solution bathing the mucosal surface for a wide range of compositions and osmolarities obtained either by varying the NaCl concentration or by the addition of nonpermeant solutes.

---

[60] Ussing, H. H., Kruhoffer, P., Thaysen, J. H., and Thorn, N. A. *The Alkali Metal Ions in Biology.* Berlin: Springer, 1960; Clarkson, T. W., and Toole, S. R. *Am. J. Physiol., 206,* 658 (1964); Schultz, S. G., Zalusky, R., and Gass, A. E., Jr. *J. Gen. Physiol., 48,* 375 (1964).
[61] Reid, E. W. *Brit. Med. J., 1,* 1133 (1892); Parsons, D. S., and Wingate, D. L. *Biochim. Biophys. Acta, 46,* 170 (1961).
[62] Diamond, J. M. *J. Physiol., 161,* 503 (1962).
[63] Curran, P. F., and Solomon, A. K. *J. Gen. Physiol., 41,* 143 (1957); Curran, P. F. *J. Gen. Physiol., 43,* 1137 (1960); Diamond, J. M. *J. Gen. Physiol., 48,* 1, 15 (1964).

A model system which accounts for water transport against an osmotic pressure gradient has been developed by Curran and his collaborators[64] and analyzed by Patlak and his coworkers.[65] The model system involves two membranes arranged in series as illustrated diagrammatically in Fig. 8-15. The membrane separating compartments A and B, membrane α, has a high reflection coefficient, while the membrane

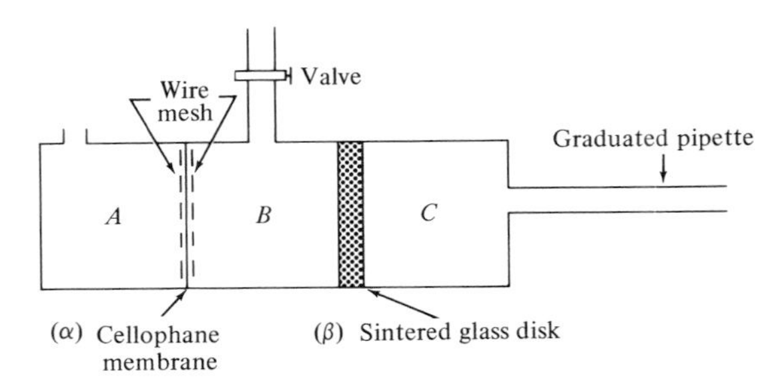

fig. 8-15. A model system showing the transport of water against a concentration gradient. The solutions in compartments *A* and *C* are dilute while the solution in compartment *B* is concentrated. The volume of compartment *B* is fixed by closing the valve. The reflection coefficient of membrane α is greater than that of membrane β. Water flows from compartment *A* to compartment *C* against an osmotic pressure gradient. (Adapted from Curran, P. F., and McIntosh, J. R. *Nature, 193*, 347 [1962].)

separating compartments B and C, membrane β, has a low reflection coefficient ($\sigma^{\alpha} \gg \sigma^{\beta}$). The effective osmotic pressure difference across membrane α is given by

$$\Delta\Pi^{\alpha} = \sigma^{\alpha}RT(c_s^B - c_s^A) \tag{8-99}$$

where c_s^B and c_s^A are the concentrations of the solute in compartments B and A respectively.

If the concentration of solute in compartment B is greater than that in compartment A, a net flow of solution will occur from compartment A to compartment B which will follow the relation

$$\mathfrak{J}_V^{\alpha} = L_P^{\alpha}\sigma^{\alpha}RT(c_s^B - c_s^A) \tag{8-100}$$

Because the reflection coefficient of membrane β is much less than that of membrane α, the osmotically induced volume flow from compartment C to compartment B will be small compared to that induced across membrane α. If the volume of compartment B is fixed and not permitted to expand, the flow of solution from compartment A into compartment B will result in an increased hydrostatic pressure in the latter. This, in turn, will produce a flow of solution from compartment B across the more permeable membrane β to compartment C.

In the simplest case, the volume flows across membrane α and membrane β are

[64] Curran, P. F., and McIntosh, J. R. *Nature, 193*, 347 (1962); Ogilvie, J. T., McIntosh, J. R., and Curran, P. F. *Biochim. Biophys. Acta, 66*, 441 (1963).
[65] Patlak, C. S., Goldstein, D. A., and Hoffman, J. F. *J. Theoret. Biol., 5*, 426 (1963).

given by

$$\mathfrak{J}_V^\alpha = L_P^\alpha[(P^A - P^B) + \sigma^\alpha RT(c_s^B - c_s^A)] \quad (8\text{-}101)$$

$$\mathfrak{J}_V^\beta = L_P^\beta[(P^B - P^C) + \sigma^\beta RT(c_s^C - c_s^B)] \quad (8\text{-}102)$$

where P^A, P^B, and P^C denote the hydrostatic pressures in each of the compartments. When the steady-state condition is achieved, $\mathfrak{J}_V^\alpha = \mathfrak{J}_V^\beta = \mathfrak{J}_V$. If the additional assumption is made that compartments A and C are open to the atmosphere so that $P^A = P^C$, the following expression can be obtained for the overall volume flow of solution:

$$\mathfrak{J}_V = L_P RT[\sigma^\alpha(c_s^B - c_s^A) + \sigma^\beta(c_s^C - c_s^B)] \quad (8\text{-}103)$$

where L_P is the overall filtration coefficient for the series membrane system and is given by $L_P = L_P^\alpha L_P^\beta/(L_P^\alpha + L_P^\beta)$. If the concentrations of solute are approximately equal in compartments A and C, eq. 8-103 reduces to

$$\mathfrak{J}_V = L_P RT(\sigma^\alpha - \sigma^\alpha)(c_s^B - c_s^A) \quad (8\text{-}104)$$

This analysis is substantiated by the experimental observation that solution does flow from compartment A to compartment C when the solutions in compartment A and compartment C are identical if $\sigma^\alpha > \sigma^\beta$ and the concentration of solute in compartment B is greater than that in compartment A. Furthermore, volume flow can take place from compartment A to compartment C even when $c_s^A > c_s^C$ (that is, against an osmotic gradient) provided that the concentration in compartment B is sufficiently high and the reflection coefficient of membrane α is much greater than that of membrane β. Some experimental data obtained with this system are listed in Fig. 8-16.

fig. 8-16. Volume flow in a series-membrane system. (Data from Curran, P. F., and McIntosh, J. R. *Nature, 193,* 347 [1962].)

SUCROSE CONCENTRATION (MOLE/L) IN COMPARTMENT			
A	*B*	*C*	VOLUME CHANGE IN *C* (μL/MIN)
	(1) *Compartment A Variable*		
0.1	0.5	0.02	7.6
0.2	0.5	0.02	5.3
0.3	0.5	0.02	3.6
0.5	0.5	0.03	0.0
0.7	0.5	0.02	−3.5
	(2) *Compartment C Variable*		
0.1	0.5	0.0	8.0
0.1	0.5	0.1	8.4
0.1	0.5	0.5	7.8

The apparatus depicted in Fig. 8-15 was used. The concentration of sucrose solutions added to compartments A, B, and C are indicated in the table. In the first set of experiments, compartment C initially contained distilled water, and the value recorded for C is the concentration at the end of the experiment. In the second set, the values recorded are the initial values. A positive value for the volume change in column 4 indicates net water movement from A to C.

In the foregoing discussion, it has been assumed that the osmotic gradient between compartments A and B has been established *de novo*. In biological systems, however, the concentration gradient of solute may arise as the result of active transport coupled to metabolic chemical reactions. Thus the active volume flow of solution may be coupled to active transport. A number of such examples in biological systems are known, for example, the volume flow of solutions out of the proximal tubule of the kidney. In this case, the basement membrane surrounding the tubular epithelial cells appears to form a compartment between it and the cell membrane (like compartment B of the model) whose volume cannot expand. Active transport of salt into the labyrinth formed between the tubular cell membrane and the basement membrane results in an increase in hydrostatic pressure in this compartment.[66]

Solvent drag is the converse situation to that described above. In solvent drag, solvent flow may result in the net movement of a solute, sometimes against an electrochemical gradient.[67] Solute flow resulting from solvent drag can be quantified by the following expression, which is a restatement of eq. 8-17.

$$\mathfrak{J}_s = \bar{c}_s(1 - \sigma)\mathfrak{J}_V + \omega RT\,\Delta c_s \qquad \textbf{(8-105)}$$

where $\bar{c}_s$ is the average concentration of solute in the membrane and ω is the solute permeability coefficient.

The transport of matter by facilitated diffusion can also occur against an electrochemical gradient by coupling to the downhill diffusion of another solute species. Thus, various sugars and inositols,[68] α-oxoglutarate,[69] various amino acids,[70] sulfate ions,[71] choline,[72] and *p*-aminohippurate[73] can be accumulated by cells against an electrochemical potential gradient provided that there is simultaneous downhill transport of Na^+ ions into the cells.

For many systems, the requirement for Na^+ ions is apparently specific; Na^+ cannot be replaced by Li^+, Mg^{++}, or choline ions.[74] In the case of the intestine, transmural transport of sugars and amino acids requires the presence of Na^+ on the mucosal side. Of course, the Na^+ ions which are accumulated intracellularly are pumped out by the active transport system for sodium. The abolition of active sodium transport by the cardiac glycosides or metabolic inhibitors results in decreased transport of sugars and amino acids which can be transported against a concentration gradient, but it does not interfere with the facilitated diffusion of substances which cannot be transported

---

[66] Pitts, R. J. *Physiology of the Kidney and Body Fluids*, 2nd ed. Chicago: The Year Book Medical Publishers, Inc., 1968, p. 105.
[67] Fisher, R. B. *J. Physiol.*, *130*, 655 (1955); Andersen, B., and Ussing, H. H. *Acta Physiol. Scand.*, *39*, 228 (1957); Leaf, A., and Hays, R. M. *J. Gen. Physiol.*, *45*, 921 (1962); Hakim, A. A., and Lifson, N. *Am. J. Physiol.*, *206*, 1315 (1964); *211*, 1137 (1966).
[68] Crane, R. K. *Physiol. Rev.*, *40*, 789 (1960); Csaky, T. Z. *Am. J. Physiol.*, *201*, 999 (1961); Hauser, G. *Biochem. Biophys. Res. Commun.*, *19*, 696 (1965).
[69] Willis, J. S. *Biochim. Biophys. Acta*, *102*, 609 (1965).
[70] Christensen, H. N., Riggs, T. R., Fischer, H., and Palatine, I. M. *J. Biol. Chem.*, *198*, 1, 17 (1952); Christensen, H. N., Riggs, T. R., and Ray, N. E. *J. Biol. Chem.*, *194*, 41 (1952); Rosenberg, I. H., Coleman, A. L., and Rosenberg, L. E. *Biochim. Biophys. Acta*, *102*, 161 (1965); Wheeler, K. P., and Christensen, H. N. *J. Biol. Chem.*, *242*, 1450 (1967).
[71] Anast, C., Kennedy, R., Volk, G., and Adamson, L. *J. Lab. Clin. Med.*, *65*, 903 (1965).
[72] Sung, C. P., and Johnstone, R. M. *Can. J. Biochem.*, *43*, 1111 (1965).
[73] Schultz, S. G., Fuisz, R. E., and Curran, P. F. *J. Gen. Physiol.*, *49*, 849 (1966).
[74] Csaky, T. Z., and Thale, M. *J. Physiol.*, *151*, 59 (1960); Csaky, T. Z., and Zollicoffer, L. *Am. J. Physiol.*, *198*, 1056 (1960).

uphill.[75] Uphill exchange diffusion, however, does not appear to require the simultaneous movement of Na^+ ions and is not affected by metabolic inhibitors.[76]

It was explained previously (see p. 449) that the kinetics of facilitated diffusion are consistent with the view that transport of such material is mediated by distinct membrane components with which complexes are formed, analogous to enzyme substrate complexes. Crane[77] proposed that facilitated diffusion systems requiring Na^+ ions are analogous to bisubstrate systems and transport is mediated by the formation of a ternary complex of membrane component, substrate, and Na^+ ions (Fig. 8-17). This

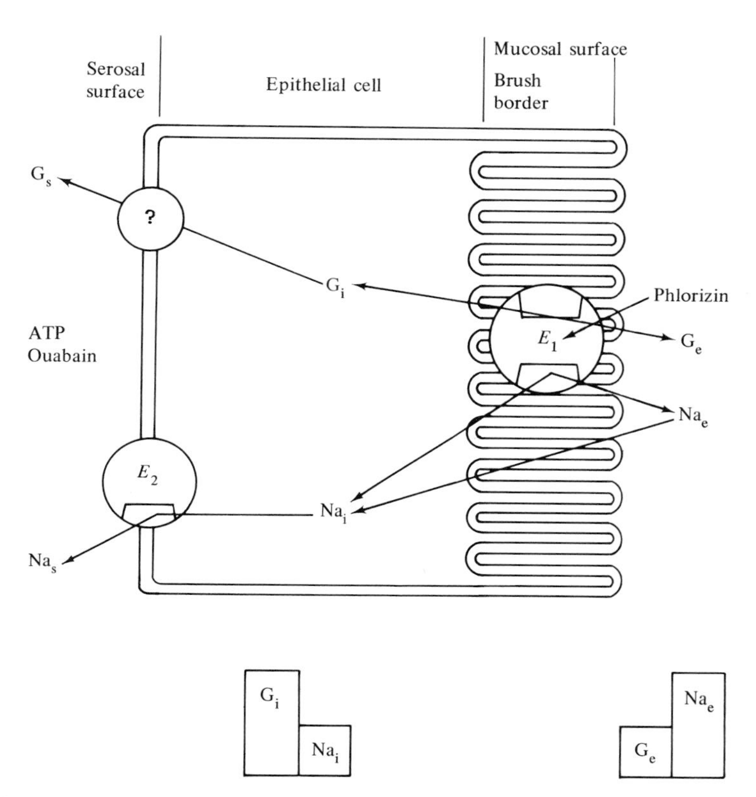

fig. 8-17. A schematic diagram of the cotransport model proposed by Crane (Crane, R. K., *Federation Proc., 24,* 1000 [1965]) for the interdependent transport of sodium and glucose in the intestine. E_1 is a membrane component which accounts for the facilitated diffusion system requiring both sodium and glucose. This system is sensitive to inhibition by phlorizin. E_2 is the system which carries on active sodium transport coupled to ATP hydrolysis and is sensitive to inhibition by cardiac glycosides. The height of the blocks at the bottom of the figure represents the steady-state levels of glucose and sodium intracellularly and at the exterior mucosal surface.

[75] Csaky, T. Z., Hartzog, H. G., and Fernald, G. W. *Am. J. Physiol., 200,* 459 (1961); Crane, R. K., Miller, D., and Bihler, I., in Kleinzeller, A., and Kotyk, A., eds. *Membrane Transport and Metabolism.* New York: Academic Press, 1961, p. 439; Lyon, I., and Crane, R. K. *Biochim. Biophys. Acta, 112,* 278, (1966); *126,* 146 (1966); *135,* 61 (1967).
[76] Jacquez, J. A., and Sherman, J. H. *Biochim. Biophys. Acta, 109,* 128 (1965); Johnstone, R. M., and Scholefield, P. G. *Biochim. Biophys. Acta, 94,* 130 (1965).
[77] Crane, R. K. *Federation Proc., 24,* 1000 (1965).

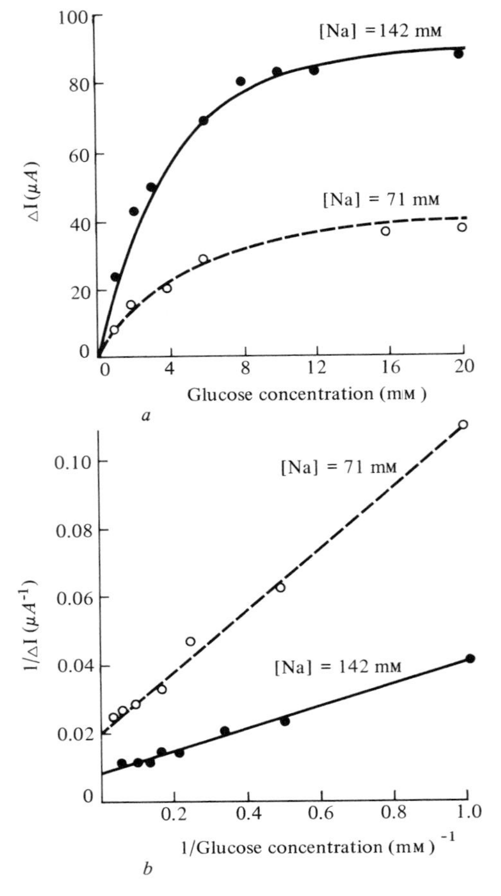

fig. 8-18. The increase in short-circuit current across an isolated strip of rabbit ileum at various concentrations of glucose: (*a*) plotted directly, and (*b*) plotted as reciprocals. (From Schultz, S. G., and Zalusky, R. *J. Gen. Physiol.*, *47*, 1050 [1946].)

view is supported by the observations that sugars and amino acids are absorbed by segments of small intestine *pari passu* with the rate of Na^+ ion absorption[78] (Fig. 8-18). Nonmetabolized sugars, such as 3-O-methylglucose, and nonmetabolized amino acids, such as γ-aminobutyric acid, also increase the rate of Na^+ ion absorption by the intestine.

In terms of a model,[79] the substrate (a sugar or amino acid molecule) S combines with a membrane component to form a complex with a dissociation constant K_1. The complex XA may cross the membrane, or it may combine with a Na^+ ion to form the ternary complex XANa. The ternary complex has a dissociation constant K_2. If the rates at which (1) the membrane component X, (2) the binary complex with substrate, and (3) the ternary complex cross the membrane are rate-limiting and equal for all

[78] Schultz, S. G., and Zalusky, R. *J. Gen. Physiol.*, *47*, 567, 1043 (1964); *Nature*, *205*, 292 (1965).
[79] Curran, P. F., Schultz, S. G., Chez, R. A., and Fuisz, R. E. *J. Gen. Physiol.*, *50*, 1261 (1967).

three forms, the unidirectional flux of substrate is given by

$$\mathfrak{J}_s^{in} = \frac{\mathfrak{J}_{S_M}[S]_{out}}{\dfrac{K_1K_2}{K_2 + [Na]_{out}} + [S]_{out}} \tag{8-106}$$

where $[S]_{out}$ is the substrate concentration on the outer surface, $[Na]_{out}$ is the sodium concentration on the outer surface, and $\mathfrak{J}_{s_M}$ is the maximum influx for substrate. Similarly, the efflux is given by

$$\mathfrak{J}_s^{out} = \frac{\mathfrak{J}_{S_M}[S]_{in}}{\dfrac{K_3K_4}{K_4 + [Na]_{in}} + [S]_{in}} \tag{8-107}$$

where K_3 and K_4 are the dissociation constants in the outward direction for the binary complex and ternary complex respectively. If the system is symmetrical, $K_1 = K_3$ and $K_2 = K_4$, and the net flux of substrate across the membrane is given by

$$\mathfrak{J}_S = \mathfrak{J}_{S_M}\left[\frac{[S]_{out}}{\dfrac{K_1K_2}{K_2 + [Na]_{out}} + [S]_{out}} - \frac{[S]_{in}}{\dfrac{K_1K_2}{K_2 + [Na]_{in}} + [S]_{in}}\right] \tag{8-108}$$

Because the intracellular Na^+ concentration is much lower than the concentration in the medium ($[Na]_{in} \ll [Na]_{out}$), a net influx of substrate will occur even when $[S]_{in} > [S]_{out}$. In the presence of metabolic inhibitors or cardiac glycosides (which inhibit active sodium transport), the sodium concentrations intracellularly and extracellularly tend to equilibrate, the asymmetry in the system is diminished, and the ability of the system to move a substrate against a concentration gradient is lost. The conditions under which the accumulation of substrate against a concentration gradient can occur spontaneously must follow the net free energy dissipation in eq. 8-2, which in this case is given by

$$\frac{d\theta}{dt} = \mathfrak{J}_S\,\Delta\mu_S + \mathfrak{J}_{Na}\,\Delta\mu_{Na} < 0$$

$$= \mathfrak{J}_S RT \ln\frac{[S]_{in}}{[S]_{out}} + \mathfrak{J}_{Na}\left(RT \ln\frac{[Na]_{in}}{[Na]_{out}} + \mathfrak{F}\,\Delta\psi\right) < 0 \tag{8-109}$$

regulation of cell volume

It is well known that the volume of animal cells that are metabolically active remains constant for long periods ot time. This is true in spite of the fact that animal cells are bounded only by a membrane approximately 100 Å thick with little mechanical strength. Because they lack a rigid cell wall, animal cells swell or shrink rapidly when placed in hypotonic or hypertonic solutions, until the gradient of water activity between the cytoplasm and extracellular fluid is dissipated (usually in a matter of seconds). Measurement of the pressure in the interior of individual cells[80] indicates that this is 2 to 3 mm H_2O higher than in the surrounding medium. This difference in pressure across the cell membrane corresponds to a total solute concentration approximately 0.2 mOsm/L greater intracellularly than in the surrounding medium. Plant cells and most bacteria, unlike animal cells, have rigid cell walls that can resist very large pressure differences.

Measurement of the freezing-point depression of cytoplasm from various cells[81] indicates that the activity of water is virtually the same in both the intracellular and the extracellular phases. Even though the interior of animal cells contains large numbers of macromolecules to which the plasma membrane is impermeable, the ions to which the cell membrane is permeable are not at a Donnan equilibrium. Were animal cells at a Donnan equilibrium, the osmolarity of the intracellular phase would be expected to exceed that of the medium by 25 to 30 mOsm/L, which would correspond to the pressure difference of several thousand mm H_2O.[82]

Animal cells maintain their volume by the outward transport of water coupled to the active outward transport of Na^+ ions in the manner described above. Treatment of cells with ultraviolet light, antibodies, and a variety of lysins increases the passive leakage of the plasma membrane to cations.[83] Particularly under conditions when active transport is abolished, such as after the application of cardiac glycosides, the

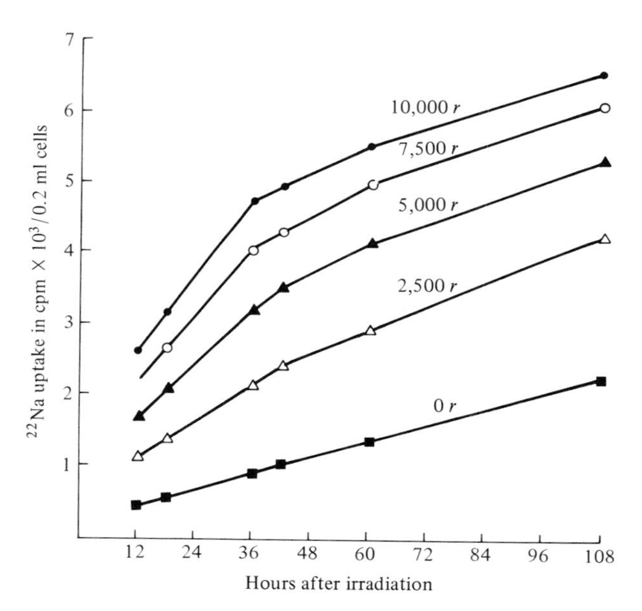

fig. 8-19. The increased sodium uptake of erythrocytes after exposure to *x*-irradiation. (From Shapiro, B., Kollmann, G., and Asnen, J. *Radiation Res., 27,* 144 [1966]. Copyright Academic Press; reprinted by permission.)

[80] Cole, K. S. *J. Cellular Comp. Physiol., 1,* 1 (1932); Rand, R. P., and Burton, A. C. *Biophys. J., 4,* 115 (1964).
[81] Conway, E. J., and McCormack, J. I. *J. Physiol., 120,* 1 (1953); Appelboom, J. W. T., Brodsky, W. A., Tuttle, W. S., and Diamond, I. *J. Gen. Physiol., 41,* 1153 (1958).
[82] Ponder, E. *J. Gen. Physiol., 32,* 53 (1948); Cook, J. S. *J. Cellular Comp. Physiol., 47,* 55 (1956).
[83] Mudge, G. H. *Am. J. Physiol., 165,* 113 (1951); Deyrup, I. *J. Gen. Physiol., 36,* 739 (1953); Leaf, A. *Biochem. J., 62,* 241 (1956); Robinson, J. R. *Physiol. Rev., 40,* 112 (1960).

gradual accumulation of cations within the cells results in swelling (Fig. 8-19). Similarly, the inhibition of active transport by metabolic poisons and by cold also results in swelling.[84] When chilled cells are warmed to 37°, active metabolism increases and water extrusion follows the increase in active efflux of sodium.

The interplay of the various factors involved in the maintenance of cell volume was demonstrated in a series of elegant studies by Tosteson and Hoffman.[85] Certain strains of sheep are a genetic variant characterized by a low level, approximately one-tenth of normal, of the Na-K activated ATPase in the erythrocyte. This defect is expressed by a lower concentration of intracellular potassium in the red cells of these sheep than in the red cells of normal sheep. Swelling in both types of erythrocytes can be induced by blocking active sodium transport with cardiac glycosides. The low capacity for active sodium transport in the erythrocytes from the genetically variant sheep is offset to a large degree by lower passive permeability to cations in these cells.

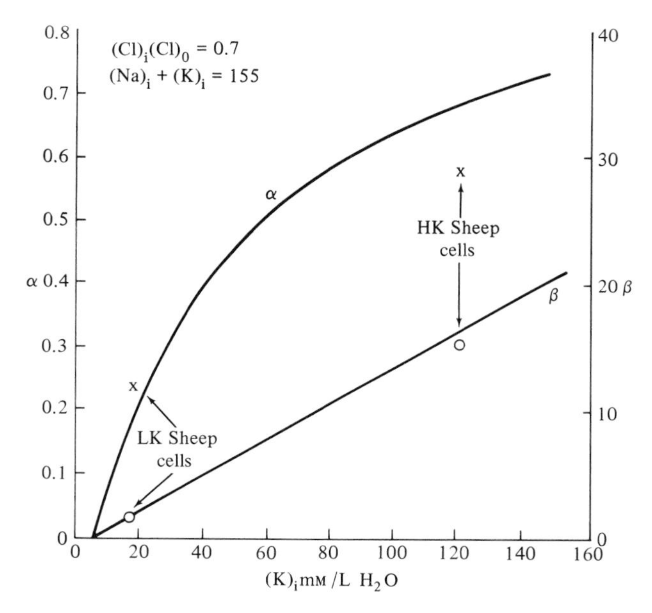

fig. 8-20. Potassium concentration and membrane transport properties in the red blood cells of sheep. The lines are calculated from the steady-state equations, while the points represent experimentally measured values of α and β. (From Tosteson, D. C., and Hoffman, J. F. *J. Gen. Physiol.*, *44*, 178 [1960].)

Figure 8-20 depicts α, the ratio of the rate coefficient for inward movement of Na^+ ions by diffusion to the rate coefficient for inward movement of K^+ ions by diffusion, and β, the ratio of the active inward transport of K^+ ions to the influx of K^+ ions by diffusion. The parameter α is approximately 0.6 for the normal high-potassium cells; their rate of swelling is approximately equal when they are suspended in a medium containing NaCl or in a medium containing KCl (the active transport of sodium

[84] Post, R. L., and Jolly, P. C. *Biochim. Biophys. Acta*, *25*, 118 (1957).
[85] Tosteson, D. C., and Hoffman, J. F. *J. Gen. Physiol.*, *44*, 169 (1960).

blocked with cardiac glycosides). For the variant low-potassium cells, α is approximately 0.2, which is to say that they are leakier to K^+ ions than to Na^+ ions. For these cells the rate of swelling in a medium containing KCl is much greater than in the NaCl medium (Fig. 8-21).

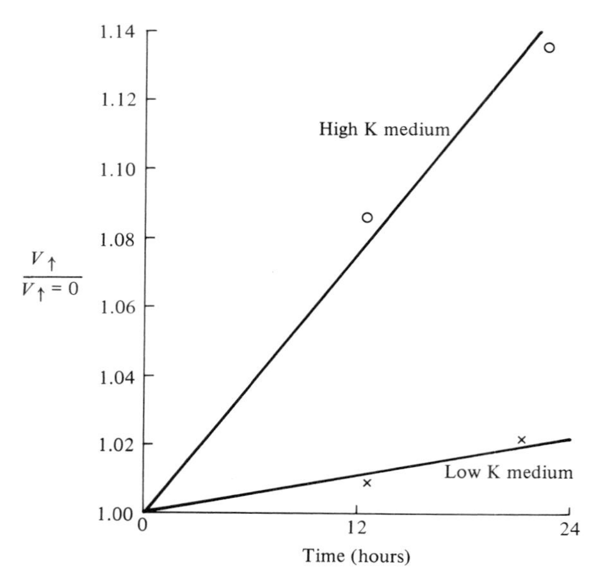

fig. 8-21. Effect of cation composition of medium on rate of swelling of LK sheep red blood cells with Na-K pump blocked by strophanthidin. Cells in buffered NaCl and KCl. For details, see text. (From Tosteson, D. C., and Hoffman, J. F. *J. Gen. Physiol.*, *44*, 188 [1960].)

In the case of normal cells, upon cessation of active sodium transport, K^+ ions and Na^+ ions diffuse down their electrochemical gradients across the membrane. Their movement is reciprocal so that the net transport of total cations and the associated movement of water across the membrane is small. The cell volume will begin to rise only after a large interchange of Na^+ and K^+ ions has occurred.

excretion by the vertebrate kidney

In vertebrate organisms, the constant composition of the *milieu intérieur*, the blood and extracellular fluid, is maintained principally by the kidney. The kidney acts to maintain a constant osmolarity, constant concentrations of the principal cations, and a constant *p*H; and to excrete a number of products of metabolism such as urea. In the resting animal, as much as 20 to 25 percent of the cardiac output flows through the kidneys. Thus, the kidneys are able to adjust rapidly the composition of the blood and interstitial fluid.

The kidney is composed of a large number of identical units called *nephrons* (Fig. 8-22). Each nephron can be divided into two parts: the *glomerulus* and the *tubule*. The glomerulus consists of a dilated sac, *Bowman's capsule*, which surrounds a

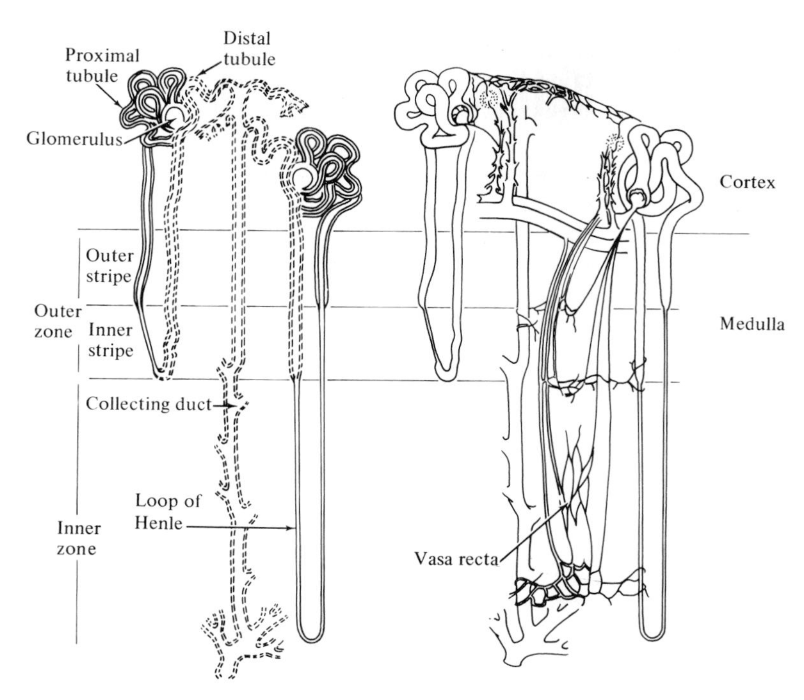

fig. 8-22. Schematic diagram of vascular pattern and two nephrons, one with a short and the other with a long loop, in the rat kidney. Only a few of the long loops reach the tip of the papilla in the rat, and the great majority of the long loops are intermediate in length between the two shown. Approximately 70 percent of the nephrons in the rat have short loops and extend only to the boundary of the inner and outer zones of the medulla. (Adapted from Moffat, D. B., and Fourman, J. *J. Anat., 97*, 545 [1963], reprinted by permission of the publisher, Cambridge University Press; and Gottschalk, C. W. *Am. J. Med., 36*, 673 [1964].

network of capillaries, the *glomerular tuft*. The capillaries of the glomerular tuft are supplied by an *afferent arteriole* and drain into an *efferent arteriole*, which has a diameter about one-fifth that of the afferent arteriole. Bowman's capsule connects with the tubule through a short neck. In birds and mammals, the tubule is divided into three parts: the *proximal tubule*, the *loop of Henle*, and the *distal tubule*. The mammalian kidney is divided into an outer layer, the *cortex*, and an inner portion, the *medulla*. The glomeruli and the convoluted portions of the proximal tubules are located in the cortex. The straight portion of the proximal tubule and the loop of Henle extend through the medulla toward the base of the kidney, reverse at a hairpin turn, and lead back to the cortex where the convoluted portion of the distal tubule is located. The output of the distal tubules enters into a collecting duct system which ultimately leads to the pelvis of the kidney and the ureter. The efferent arterioles from the glomeruli break up into capillary systems which surround the tubules, from which the blood collects in the renal vein. The *functional* unit of excretion is the entire nephron together with the associated blood vessels.

An ultrafiltrate of blood plasma is formed in the glomeruli. The driving force for the filtration process is the glomerular capillary pressure which is kept at a high level both because the glomerular capillary network is located within the arterial system and because the efferent arteriole has a much smaller diameter than the afferent arteriole.

As long as the blood pressure is maintained at normal levels, the glomerular capillary pressure far exceeds the counteracting force caused by the colloid osmotic pressure of the plasma proteins and the resistance to the flow of fluid through the tubular system.

Micropuncture studies,[86] in which micropipettes were inserted into Bowman's capsule, demonstrated that the concentration of low-molecular-weight solutes in the glomerular fluid was equal to their concentration in plasma. The limiting size of molecules that can be filtered by the glomerular membrane and pass into the glomerular fluid have molecular weights in the neighborhood of 10,000 to 40,000;[87] this suggests that the largest pores in the glomerular membrane have radii in the neighborhood of 50 Å.

The quantification of the primary filtration process is basic to all studies of renal function. Usually this is done in terms of the amount of blood *cleared* of a low-molecular-weight solute. The quantity of plasma cleared per minute by glomerular filtration, $\boldsymbol{P}$, is given by

$$\boldsymbol{P} = \boldsymbol{UV}/\boldsymbol{B} \tag{8-110}$$

where $\boldsymbol{U}$ is the concentration of solute in the urine, $\boldsymbol{V}$ is the volume of urine formed per minute, and $\boldsymbol{B}$ is the concentration of the solute in plasma. Of course, only low-molecular-weight solutes that are neither reabsorbed nor excreted by the tubules can be used to evaluate glomerular filtration. Creatinine (a normal constituent of plasma), inulin (a polysaccharide of medium molecular weight), sorbitol, mannitol, and thiosulphate are examples of such solutes.

The *filtration fraction*, the actual fraction of plasma passing through the kidneys that is filtered and appears in the glomerular fluid, can be measured by injecting a solute such as inulin and measuring its concentration simultaneously in samples from the renal artery and the renal vein. In man, the filtration fraction using inulin is approximately 0.20; using creatinine, it is approximately 0.26.[88]

The human kidney produces about 100 liters of glomerular filtrate in a 24-hour period, yet during water deprivation less than 1 liter of urine is excreted. Under such conditions more than 99 percent of the glomerular filtrate is reabsorbed in the tubules. Furthermore, normal urine does not contain glucose, amino acids, or other metabolites found in the blood. Approximately 85 percent of the glomerular filtrate is reabsorbed in the proximal tubule. Here there is active transport of sodium across the epithelial cells of the tubule from the lumen to the interstitial fluid. The tubule epithelial cells appear to be able to transport Na^+ against a gradient of 57 mEq/L or less. As outlined above, this is accompanied by an isosmotic reabsorption of water.

Associated with the active sodium transport across the tubular wall is a potential difference of about 20 mv (with the lumen negative to the interstitial fluid). The intracellular potential of the epithelial cells is approximately 53 mv, negative with respect to

[86] Richards, A. N. *Proc. Roy. Soc.*, *B 126*, 398 (1938); Smith, H. W. *The Kidney. Structure and Function in Health and Disease.* Fair Lawn, N.J.: Oxford University Press, 1951; Walker, A. M., Bott, P. A., Oliver, J., and MacDowell, M. C. *Am. J. Physiol.*, *134*, 562 580 (1941); Bott, P. A. *Am. J. Physiol.*, *203*, 662 (1962); Windhager, E. E., and Giebisch, G. *Am. J. Physiol.*, *200*, 581 (1961).

[87] Wallenius, G. *Acta. Soc. Med. Upsala.*, *59*, suppl. 4 (1954); Giebisch, G., Lauson, H. D., and Pitts, R. F. *Am. J. Physiol.*, *178*, 168 (1954); Oken, D. E., and Solomon, A. K. *J. Clin. Invest.*, *39*, 1015 (1960).

[88] Pitts, R. J. *Physiology of the Kidney and Body Fluids*, 2nd ed. Chicago: The Year Book Medical Publishers, Inc., 1968, p. 146.

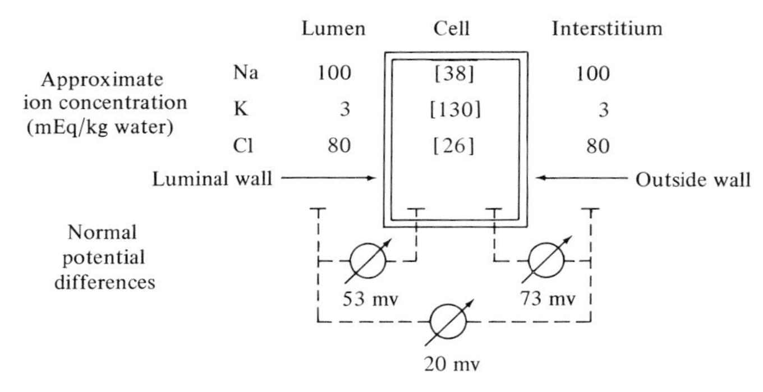

fig. 8-23. Schematic drawing showing the various electrical potential differences measurable in the proximal tubule. It can be seen that the normal transcellular electrical potential difference is 20 mv (lumen negative); the transcellular (outside wall) electrical potential difference is 73 mv (cell negative). So the electrical potential difference across the luminal wall is 53 mv (cell negative). (From Whittembury, G., and Windhager, E. E. *J. Gen. Physiol., 44,* 679 [1961].)

the lumen, or 73 mv, negative with respect to the interstitial fluid (Fig. 8-23). Giebisch[89] accounted for the difference in potential at the two faces of the epithelial cell by assuming that the relative permeability coefficients for Na^+ and K^+ ions were different; that is, the lumenal base of the epithelial cell was regarded to be more permeable to Na^+ ions than the interstitial surface. An idea of the reabsorption of glomerular filtrate in various parts of the tubular system can be gleaned from Fig. 8-24, where the

fig. 8-24. Average values of the fluid-to-plasma concentration ratios (***F/P***) for total osmolarity, inulin, and urea. (From Lassiter, W. E., Gottschalk, C. W., and Mylle, W. M. *Am. J. Physiol., 200,* 1145 [1961].)

SOURCE	OSMOLARITY (*F/P*)	INULIN (*F/P*)	UREA (*F/P*)	UREA RATIO/INULIN RATIO
Early proximal	1.0	1.0	1.0	1.0
Late proximal	1.0	3.0	1.5	0.5
Early distal	0.7	6.9	7.7	1.1
Late distal	1.0	14.9	10.5	0.7
Ureteral urine	6.4	690	90	0.13

The value of the ratio, urea ratio/inulin ratio, is a measure of the fraction of the filtered urea absorbed; the fact that this becomes 1.1 in the early distal tubule indicates that there has been a gain of urea following the loss in the proximal tubule.

osmolarity of the urine and the ratio of urea (which is subject to passive reabsorption) to inulin (which is not reabsorbed in the tubular system) is listed for various parts of the tubular system.

[89] Solomon, S. *J. Cellular Comp. Physiol., 49,* 351 (1957); Giebisch, G. *Circulation, 21,* 879 (1960); Eigler, F. W. *Am. J. Physiol., 201,* 157 (1961); Whittembury, G., Sugino, N., and Solomon, A. K. *J. Gen. Physiol., 44,* 689 (1961); Bank, N. *Am. J. Physiol., 203,* 577 (1962).

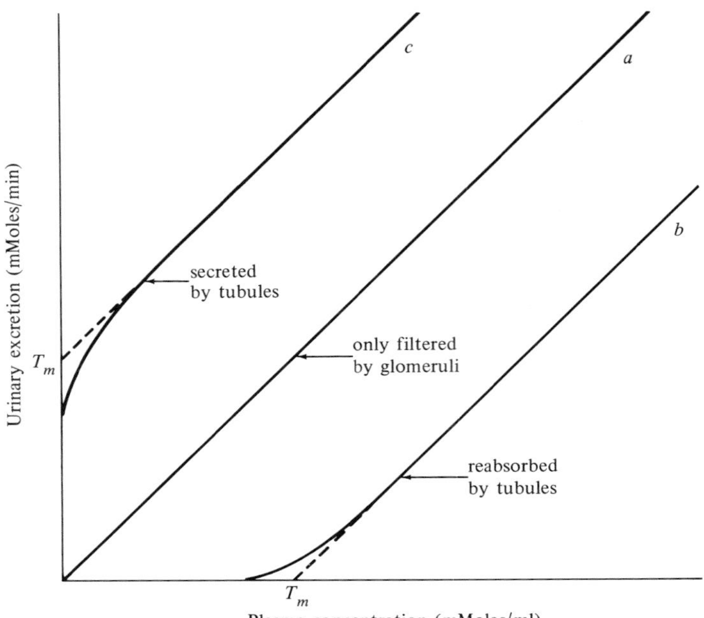

fig. 8-25. Excretion in the urine as a function of plasma concentration for three types of substances: (*a*) inulin, an example of a substance which is only filtered by the glomeruli and neither reabsorbed nor excreted by the tubules; (*b*) glucose, an example of a substance which is reabsorbed by the tubules; and (*c*) *p*-aminohippurate, an example of a substance which is excreted by the renal tubules.

Glucose, amino acids, and other metabolites are reabsorbed against a concentration gradient by facilitated diffusion coupled to other transport processes. For many of these substances there appears to be an upper limit to the amount of substance that may be reabsorbed; the rate depends upon its concentration in the plasma. Thus, at low plasma concentrations of sugar, no glucose appears in the urine; that is, all the glucose present in the glomerular filtrate is reabsorbed. At approximately 200 mg per 100 mL plasma glucose, the maximum capacity of the tubules to reabsorb glucose is reached. When the plasma concentration is greater than this amount, the amount of glucose reabsorbed is constant but the excess is excreted in the urine. The *maximal reabsorptive capacity*, T_M, appears to have a characteristic value for each substance reabsorbed by the kidney. When a mixture of sugars is presented to the tubules, the total amount of sugar reabsorbed remains the same but the presence of one sugar decreases the reabsorptive capacity of the others. It appears, therefore, that the tubular reabsorptive mechanism for sugars involves a single carrier.[90] Ultimately, the reabsorp-

[90] Cross, R. J., and Taggart, J. V. *Am. J. Physiol.*, *161*, 181 (1950); Forster, R. P., and Taggart, J. V. *J. Cellular Comp. Physiol.*, *36*, 251 (1950); Forster, R. P., and Copenhaver, J. H. *Am. J. Physiol.*, *186*, 167 (1956); Kleinzeller, A., and Cort, J. H. *Biochem. J.*, *67*, 15 (1957); Milne, M. D., Scribner, B. H., and Crawford, M. A. *Am. J. Med.*, *24*, 709 (1958); Forster, R. P., and Hong, S. K. *J. Cellular Comp. Physiol.*, *51*, 259 (1958); Gutman, A. B., Yii, T. F., and Berger, L. *J. Clin. Invest.*, *38*, 1778 (1959); Cade, J. R.,Shalhoub. R. J., Canessa-Fischer, M., and Pitts, R. F. *Am. J. Physiol.*, *200*, 373 (1961); Essig, A. *Am. J. Physiol.*, *201*, 303 (1961); Despopoulos, A. *Am. J. Physiol.*, *197*, 1107 (1959); *200*, 163 (1961); Despopolous, A., and Callahan, P. X. *Am. J. Physiol.*, *203*, 19 (1962); Strickler, J. C., and Kessler, R. H. *J. Clin. Invest.*, *40*, 311 (1961); Burg, M. B., and Orloff, J. *Am. J. Physiol.*, *202*, 565 (1962); *203*, 327 (1962).

tive mechanisms are coupled to active transport; thus the inhibition of active transport by metabolic inhibitors or cardiac glycosides leads to decreased tubular reabsorption.

A number of materials are cleared by the kidney considerably faster than are inulin and creatinine. This indicates that, in addition to glomerular filtration, these substances are secreted by the tubules into the urine. A variety of materials conjugated to glucuronic acid or organic sulfates and a number of foreign substances such as phenosulfophthalein (phenol red), *p*-aminohippuric acid, penicillin, and iodopyracet belong to this category of materials. At low plasma concentrations almost all these substances entering through the renal artery may be cleared by secretion. As the concentration of such substances in the plasma increases, increased amounts are secreted by the tubules into the urine until the *maximal secretory capacity*, T_M, is reached. At plasma concentrations in excess of the T_M, the increased quantities found in the urine are due entirely to filtration. The rate of excretion of the three classes of substances, (*a*) materials which are neither reabsorbed nor secreted by the tubules, (*b*) materials which are reabsorbed by the tubules, and (*c*) materials which are secreted by the tubules as a function of plasma concentration, is depicted in Fig. 8-25. When the kidney is presented with a mixture of substances that are secreted by the tubules, competitive inhibition of secretion frequently is found. The distal tubules are the site of the major portion of tubular secretion.

countercurrent concentration of urine

Birds and mammals are able to excrete a markedly hyperosmolar urine during water deprivation: as concentrated as 1000 to 1400 mOsm in man, 1800 to 2300 mOsm in the dog, and up to 5000 mOsm in the desert rat. Only animals with a well-developed loop of Henle are able to excrete hyperosmolar urine, and it has been known since the studies of Peter[91] in 1909 that a correlation exists between the length of the loop of Henle and the maximum urine concentration which various species can achieve. At about the same time Hirokawa[92] found that the osmotic pressure of the fluid in the kidney cortex was quite constant and was independent of the osmolarity of the excreted urine, while the osmotic pressure of the fluids in the renal medulla were extremely variable, were always higher than the osmotic pressure in the cortex, and fluctuated *pari passu* with the osmolarity of the excreted urine. These studies were extended and substantiated by careful cryoscopic data obtained in kidney slices by Wirz and his colleagues.[93] Kuhn[94] originated the concept that urine was concentrated in the loop of Henle by a countercurrent multiplier mechanism.

When a solution flows in opposite directions in two parallel tubes separated by a semipermeable membrane and connected by a hairpin turn, a small difference in the concentration of constituents at any given point is multiplied continuously along the

---

[91] Peter, K. *Untersuchungen über Bau und Entwicklung der Niere*. Jena: G. Fischer, 1909; Sperber, I. *Zool. Bidrag Uppsala*, *22*, 249 (1944); by way of contrast, the osmolarity of plasma is about 300 mOsm.

[92] Hirokawa, W. *Beitr. chem. Physiol. Path.*, *11*, 458 (1908).

[93] Wirz, H., Hargitay, B., and Kuhn, W. *Helv. Physiol. Pharmocol. Acta*, *9*, 196 (1951).

[94] Kuhn, W., and Ryffel, K. *Z. physiol. Chem.*, *276*, 145 (1942); Hargitay, B., and Kuhn, W. *Z. Elektrochem.*, *55*, 539 (1951); Malvin, R. L., Wilde, W. S., and Sullivan, L. P. *Am. J. Physiol.*, *194*, 135 (1958); *195*, 549 (1958); Bergmann, F., and Dikstein, S. *J. Physiol.*, *145*, 14 (1959); Abbrecht, P. H., and Malvin, R. L. *Am. J. Physiol.*, *199*, 919 (1960); Gottschalk, C. W. *Am. J. Med.*, *36*, 670 (1964); Berliner, R. W., Levinsky, N. G., Davidson, D. G., and Eden, M. *Am. J. Med.*, *24*, 730 (1958).

length of the tubes by the imposition of a difference in electrochemical potential of a constituent of the solution between the two tubes. The system is presented schematically in Fig. 8-26. Its operation depends upon the active transport of sodium from the ascending limb of the loop to the descending limb. Because sodium salts are secreted into the fluid of the descending limb, the concentration of sodium in the fluid rises progressively as it approaches the turn at the tip. After passing the turn, the fluid is diluted progressively as it flows up the ascending limb by the continual removal of Na^+ ions.

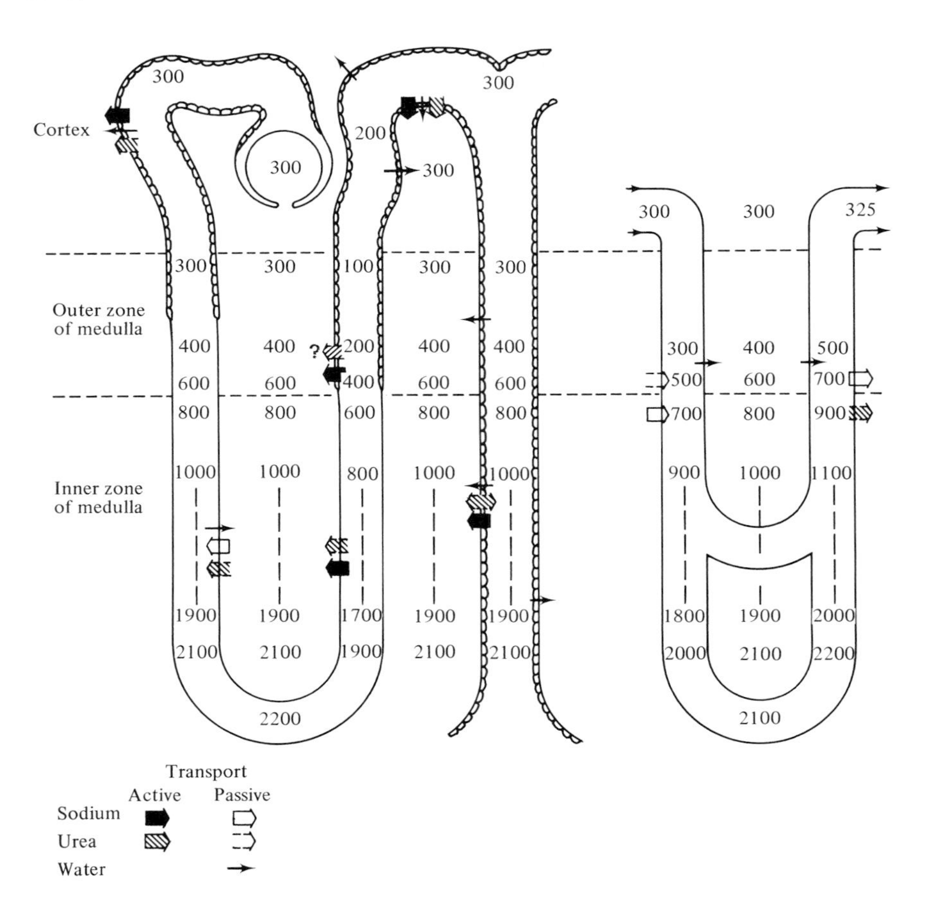

fig. 8-26. Diagram depicting the countercurrent mechanism as it is believed to operate in a nephron with a long loop and in the vasa recta. The numbers represent hypothetical osmorality values. No quantitative significance is to be attached to the number of arrows, and only net movements are indicated. As is the case with the vascular loops, all loops of Henle do not reach the tip of the papilla, and hence the fluid in them does not become as concentrated as that of the final urine but only as concentrated as the medullary interstitial fluid at the same level. (From Gottschalk, C. W., and Mylle, W. M. *Am. J. Physiol., 196*, 935 [1959].)

The effective operation of the countercurrent mechanism requires that the loop of Henle, particularly the ascending limb, be relatively impermeable to water.

Of course, there is a continuous recirculation of sodium salts through the loop. In spite of the fact that Na^+ ions are not transported across a steep gradient at any point, the fluid at the turn of the loop may become markedly hyperosmolar. The effect is described by the relation

$$c_x = \frac{c_0}{1 - \dfrac{L_P(\Delta P - \Delta\Pi)}{au_0}x} \tag{8-111}$$

where c_x is the concentration of the solution at the point x, c_0 is the concentration of the solution entering the countercurrent multiplier loop, a is the diameter of the tubes, u_0 is the linear velocity of the fluid entering the system, L_P is the filtration coefficient of the membrane, ΔP is the difference in hydrostatic pressure between the limbs of the loop, and $\Delta\Pi$ is the difference in osmotic pressure between the limbs of the loop.

It will be appreciated that the osmotic gradient rises hyperbolically as one moves down the limbs toward the turn (Fig. 8-27). The total longitudinal osmotic gradient

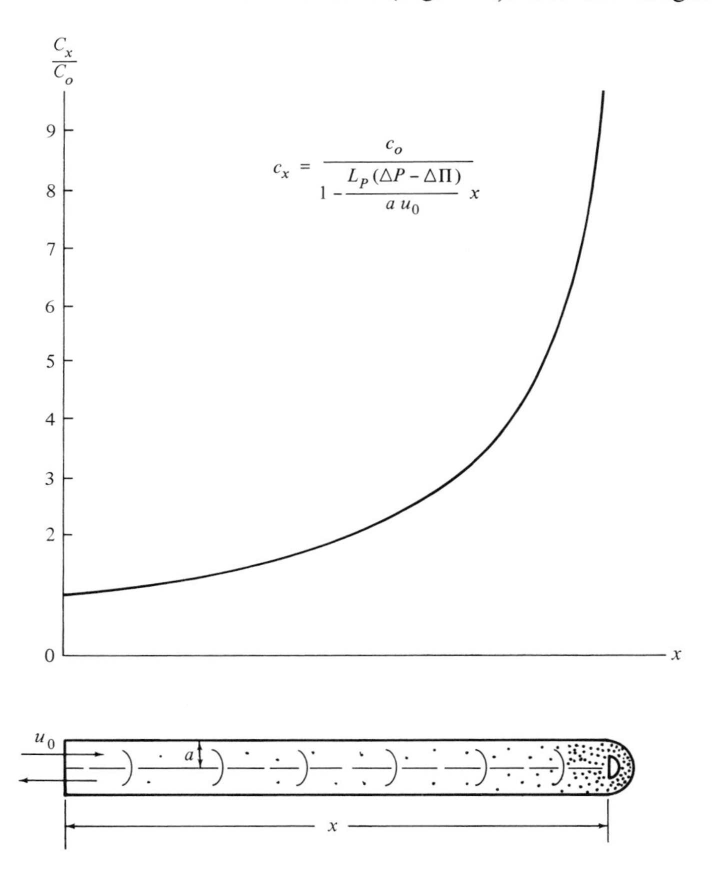

fig. 8-27. The concentration increase in a countercurrent multiplier system *versus* the distance along the tubes. (Adapted from Hargitay, B., and Kuhn, W. *Z. Elektrochem.*, *55*, 543 [1951].)

along the loop of Henle can amount to 700 to 800 mOsm in the human kidney, while in the kidney of rodents it may be as large as 3000 mOsm. Yet at any point along the longitudinal axis the difference in osmotic pressure between the two limbs amounts to not more than 0 to 15 mOsm. Because the gradients at any point along the longitudinal axis are small, the energy required for active sodium transport to operate the countercurrent system is small. The human kidney reabsorbs about 25,000 mEq Na^+ every 24 hours.

The hyperosmolarity of the interstitial fluid in the renal medulla promotes the effective operation of the countercurrent multiplier system, since it obviates the necessity for intimate contact between adjacent limbs of the loop of Henle, and between the loop of Henle, the collecting ducts, and the *vasa recta* (the capillary network which surrounds the loop of Henle). The vasa recta function as countercurrent exchangers, helping to maintain the hyperosmolarity of the interstitial fluid in the medulla.

The fluid which leaves the loop of Henle and enters the distal tubule should be somewhat hyposmolar. This was found, in fact, upon measuring the osmolarity of fluid removed from the distal tubules by micropuncture.[95] The somewhat hyposmolar fluid which enters the distal tubules becomes isosmotic by the time it reaches the collecting ducts. The collecting ducts extend parallel to the limbs of the loop of Henle through the renal medulla in the direction of increasing osmolarity of the interstitial fluid. The collecting ducts are permeable to water, and more permeable to urea than to salt. Thus, there is an outward flow of water from the fluid in the collecting duct and an inward flow of urea, which tends to equilibrate the osmolarity of the urine in the collecting ducts with the hyperosmolarity of the medullary interstitial fluid. The degree of water permeability of the collecting ducts is affected by antidiuretic hormone which provides a means for controlling the osmolarity of the urine and thus the water content of the entire organism.

The countercurrent mechanism for the production of hyperosmolar urine by the kidneys of higher vertebrates represents a remarkable integration of a few fundamental transport processes by a specialized structural arrangement. The important features of the mechanism are that (1) the loop of Henle is involved in the process by providing the appropriate structural relation, (2) the mechanism operates by virtue of active sodium transport, without the necessity of invoking the active transport of water—a process which is hard to reconcile with many observations, (3) the diffusion of water and urea is passive, and (4) a countercurrent exchange system exists with the vasa recta.

membrane potentials[96]

The conductance g_j and the resistance $\mathfrak{R}_j$ of any ionic species which is transported through a membrane may be defined as

$$g_j = \frac{I_j}{\Psi - E_j} = \frac{1}{\mathfrak{R}_j} \tag{8-112}$$

where Ψ is the voltage difference between the solutions on either side of the membrane, I_j is that portion of the membrane current carried by the jth ion species, and E_j is the electrochemical equilibrium potential of the jth species. Because Ψ does not depend on any particular ion species, eq. 8-112 can be summed for all species, giving

$$\Psi = \frac{\Sigma I_j - \Sigma g_j E_j}{\Sigma g_j} \tag{8-113}$$

[95] Gottschalk, C. W., and Mylle, W. M. *Am. J. Physiol., 196*, 927 (1959); Lassiter, W. E., Gottschalk C. W., and Mylle, W. M. *Am. J. Physiol., 200*, 1139 (1961).
[96] This development is based upon that of Kornacker, K., in Dowben, R. M., ed. *Biological Membranes.* Boston: Little, Brown, 1969.

Equation 8-113 takes into account the experimental observation that the conductance of an ion species does not become infinite when the transmembrane potential is zero.

For functioning biological membranes, ion species that are actively transported do not follow eq. 8-112. For example, the net sodium current through nerve membranes at rest is zero, even though the membrane potential differs from the sodium equilibrium potential by more than 0.1 v. The sodium conductance, as measured by the fluxes of radioactive sodium, amounts to about 1 μamp/cm^2. Equation 8-112 can be modified to take these observations into consideration by introducing the *active transport current.* Letting $\mathfrak{J}_j$ represent the electrogenic effects of the active transport of the *j*th ion species, we can write

$$g_j = \frac{I_j - \mathfrak{J}_j}{\Psi - E_j} \tag{8-114}$$

The effects of all ion species can be summed to give

$$\Psi = \frac{\Sigma I_j - \Sigma \mathfrak{J}_j + \Sigma g_j E_j}{\Sigma g_j} \tag{8-115}$$

The circuit diagram which is described by eqs. 8-114 and 8-115 is depicted in Fig. 8-28. Implicit in eq. 8-114 is the fact that the product $g_j \mathfrak{R}_j$ differs from unity.

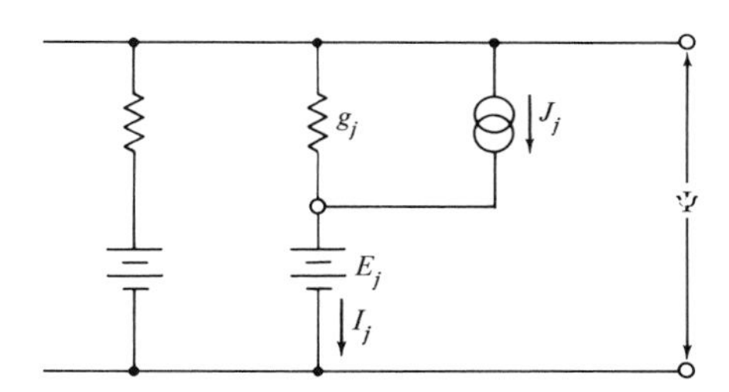

fig. 8-28. The equivalent circuit model for the electrical properties of a biological membrane in which active transport is regarded to be a constant current source.

It is well known that biological membranes have semiconductor properties; they act as rectifiers of ionic currents, offering more resistance to the passage of current in one direction than in the opposite direction. The voltage-current curve of a semiconductor is depicted in Fig. 8-29*a*. If the circuit includes a constant voltage source which "biases" the inflection point where the change in resistance occurs, the voltage-current curve has the form shown in Fig. 8-29*b*. If a constant current source is included in the circuit instead, the voltage-current curve has the form shown in Fig. 8-29*c*. In fact, the voltage-current curves of biological membranes have the form shown in Fig. 8-29*d*. This indicates that the ionic gradients across a membrane produce an effect which is intermediate between a constant current source and a constant voltage source. In terms of a constant voltage source, the electrogenic effects of active transport can be accounted for in an equation analogous to eq. 8-114.

$$\mathfrak{R}_j = \frac{\Psi - E_j - \varphi_j}{I_j} \tag{8-116}$$

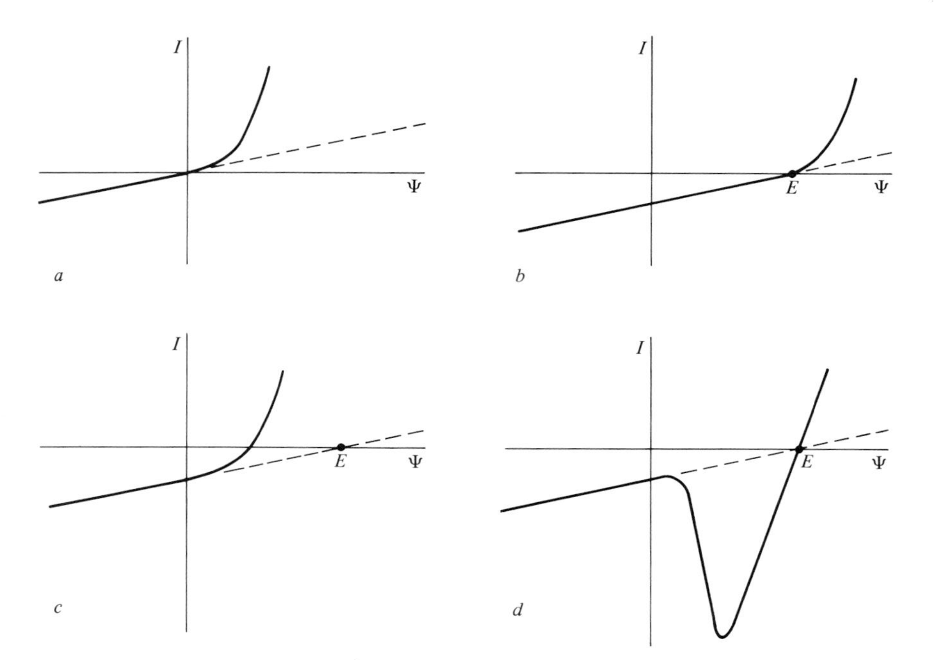

fig. 8-29. Voltage-current curves for a simple rectifying membrane with different electrical sources. The dotted line shows the curve obtained when the rectifying element is replaced with a phased resistance: (*a*) no electrical source, (*b*) a constant voltage source, (*c*) a constant current source, and (*d*) an ionic concentration gradient.

where φ_j is the active transport voltage for the *j*th species. Summing over all charged ion species,

$$\Psi = \frac{\Sigma I_i + \Sigma(\varphi_j/\mathfrak{R}_j) + \Sigma(E_j/\mathfrak{R}_j)}{\Sigma(1/\mathfrak{R}_j)} \tag{8-117}$$

Let us evaluate a tiny area of membrane which contains but a single active transport channel. Over a period of time, the potential difference across such a tiny area of membrane will fluctuate from an average value as individual ions are actively transported through the channel. The instantaneous quantities vary because of local high-frequency thermal and chemical noise. Ordinarily, fluctuations in the instantaneous values of the membrane potential and transmembrane current are averaged out because a large area of membrane is examined and because the measuring instruments themselves have a large time constant. Such fluctuations from the mean electrochemical potential will be given by

$$e_j = (\psi - E_j) - (\overline{\psi} - \overline{E_j}) \tag{8-118}$$

where ψ and E_j represent the instantaneous transmembrane potential and equilibrium potential respectively, while the quantity $(\overline{\psi} - \overline{E_j})$ represents the average value obtained over a time considerably greater than the time constant of the resting membrane.

Equations 8-112 and 8-118 can be combined to give

$$I_j = g_j(\overline{\psi} - \overline{E_j}) + e_j g_j \tag{8-119}$$

The net transmembrane current can be obtained by averaging the instantaneous current given by eq. 8-119:

$$\overline{I}_j = \overline{g}_j(\overline{\psi} - \overline{E}_j) + \overline{e_j g_j} \tag{8-120}$$

which may be rearranged in the form

$$\overline{g_j} = \frac{\overline{I}_j - \overline{e_j g_j}}{\overline{\psi} - \overline{E}_j} \tag{8-121}$$

A comparison of eqs. 8-121 and 8-114 reveals that the active transport current can be identified as

$$\mathfrak{I}_j = \overline{e_j g_j} \tag{8-122}$$

Similarly, the average voltage produced by the fluctuation in the instantaneous electric current across a tiny patch of membrane can be identified in terms of another cross correlation as

$$\varphi_j = \overline{\mathfrak{R}_j i_j} \tag{8-123}$$

where i_j is the instantaneous transmembrane current of the jth species. It can be shown that the equivalent voltage source and current source terms of active transport are related by the expressions

$$\varphi_j = \overline{\mathfrak{R}}_j \mathfrak{I}_j + (1 - \overline{\mathfrak{R}}_j \overline{g}_j)(\overline{\psi} - \overline{E}_j) \tag{8-124}$$

$$\mathfrak{I}_j = -\overline{g}_j \varphi_j + (1 - \overline{\mathfrak{R}}_j \overline{g}_j)\overline{i}_j \tag{8-125}$$

The product of the instantaneous values g_j and $\mathfrak{R}_j$ is one. If one of these variables increases, the other decreases, and vice versa. The cross correlation $(\overline{\mathfrak{R}_j g_j} - \overline{\mathfrak{R}}_j \overline{g}_j)$ equals zero if and only if g_j is perfectly constant with time. If g_j were constant, however, then $\mathfrak{I}_j$ in eq. 8-122 would vanish. Therefore, for ion species that are actively transported, the quantity $(1 - \overline{\mathfrak{R}}_j \overline{g}_j) = (\overline{\mathfrak{R}_j g_j} - \overline{\mathfrak{R}}_j \overline{g}_j)$ must be negative definite and not zero. Furthermore, the equivalent source terms $\mathfrak{I}_j$ and φ_j do not follow Ohm's law.

During excitation, the capacitance across the membrane becomes important. If the voltage-current relation in the membrane does not change with time and there is no leakage path for current around the membrane, the sum of the current generated in the membrane and the current passing through the capacitative elements is zero $(I_m + I_c = 0)$. Furthermore,

$$\frac{d\Psi}{dt} = \frac{I_c}{C} = -\frac{I_m}{C} \tag{8-126}$$

where C is the capacitance. Multiplying eq. 8-126 by $(dI_m/d\Psi)$ gives

$$\frac{dI_m}{dt} = -\frac{I_m}{C}\left(\frac{dI_m}{d\Psi}\right) \tag{8-127}$$

In order for the membrane to be spontaneously unstable,

$$(dI_m/d\Psi) = \Sigma(dI_j/d\Psi) < 0 \tag{8-128}$$

so that the value of I_m will increase continually with time. In any real membrane $(dI_m/d\Psi)$ eventually must become positive because I_m cannot become infinite. The quantity $(dI_j/d\Psi)$ can be obtained by differentiating eq. 8-112.

$$\frac{dI_j}{d\Psi} = (\Psi - E_j)\frac{dg_j}{d\Psi} + g_j \tag{8-129}$$

In order for $(dI_m/d\Psi)$ to be negative, $(dI_j/d\Psi)$ must be negative for at least one species of ion, or

$$(E_j - \Psi)\frac{dg_j}{d\Psi} > g_j \tag{8-130}$$

It should be noted that g_j is always positive definite. From eq. 8-130 it is evident that negative values of $(dI_j/d\Psi)$ occur only when the quantities $(E_j - \Psi)$ and $(dg_j/d\Psi)$ have the same sign. For a simple rectifier, $(dg_j/d\Psi)$ does not change sign. Therefore, negative values of $(dI_j/d\Psi)$ occur only at values of the transmembrane potential on one side of the equilibrium potential for that ion; for positive $(dg_j/d\Psi)$, $\Psi < E_j$, and vice versa.

The unstable excitatory state of the membrane must be returned to its original resting state. Resetting of the system can occur because the voltage-current characteristics of the system may undergo a change during excitation or because there may exist near the new resting point where $I_m' = 0$, a second region where $(dI_m/d\Psi)$ is negative.

These quantitative considerations do not explain the molecular mechanism of active transport or excitation. While the mechanism of active transport is unknown, several possibilities come to mind. One possibility is that a carrier[97] exists in the membrane which binds Na^+ in the presence of ATP on the internal surface of the membrane. At the external surface where no ATP is present, Na^+ is released and K^+ is bound. Another possibility is that the Na-K activated ATPase exerts the sort of specificity upon the products of a reaction which enzymes are known to possess for the recognition of reactants. In this hypothetical mechanism, the energy released from ATP hydrolysis would not be distributed randomly to the reactant molecules; instead the sodium ions would have a greater kinetic energy while the vector resultant of the kinetic energies of the other products would satisfy the requirements of conservation of momentum. Thus, the Na^+ ions might acquire sufficient kinetic energy to penetrate the barrier of the electrochemical gradient.[98] The elucidation of the molecular mechanism of active transport and of excitation is a topic of primary interest to cell physiologists.

Hodgkin-Huxley equations

Hodgkin and Huxley proposed a set of differential equations[99] which, although it does not distinguish between mechanisms of ionic transport or excitation, nevertheless does describe the characteristics of excitable cells. The derivation of these equations starts from the *cable equation* which describes the longitudinal current in a coaxial cable. Let us assume that a nerve axon or muscle fiber resembles a coaxial cable (see Chapter 7) and that (1) the fiber does not branch, (2) the electrical properties of the membrane are uniform over its entire surface, (3) the electrical resistance of the extracellular fluid is very low and can be neglected and as a result the extracellular fluid is isopotential, and (4) the electrical resistance of the intracellular fluid is very low and can be neglected and consequently all current flow is either along the axis of the cylinder of cytoplasm or

[97] Shaw, T. I. *J. Physiol.*, *129*, 464 (1955); Glynn, I. M. *Progr. Biophys. Biophys. Chem.*, *8*, 241 (1957).
[98] Schmitt, O. H., in First Josiah Macy, Jr. Foundation Conference on Metabolic Interrelations.
[99] Hodgkins, A. L., and Huxley, A. F. *J. Physiol.*, *117*, 500 (1952); Huxley, A. F. *Ann. N.Y. Acad. Sci.*, *81*, 221 (1959); Stämpfli, R. *Ann. Rev. Physiol.*, *25*, 493 (1963); Noble, D. *Physiol. Rev.*, *46*, 1 (1966).

through the membrane. From Ohm's law, the longitudinal current I_L is given by

$$I_L = \frac{1}{\mathfrak{R}_{ax}} \frac{\partial \Psi}{\partial y} \tag{8-131}$$

where $\mathfrak{R}_{ax}$ is the resistance of the cytoplasm per unit length of fiber, Ψ is the transmembrane potential, and y is the distance along the fiber. Differentiating eq. 8-131 gives

$$I_m = \frac{\partial I_L}{\partial y} = \frac{1}{\mathfrak{R}_{ax}} \frac{\partial^2 \Psi}{\partial y^2} = C \frac{\partial \Psi}{\partial t} + \sum I_j \tag{8-132}$$

an expression for the membrane current I_m. The membrane current, it will be remembered, has two types of components: current through the capacitative elements $\left(C \frac{\partial \Psi}{\partial t}\right)$ and ionic currents (ΣI_j).

In evaluating the ionic components of the membrane current, Hodgkin and Huxley made some additional assumptions: (1) the active transport processes are not electrogenic or the current produced by active transport is negligibly small, (2) the ionic current carried by ion species other than K^+ and Na^+ can be neglected, and (3) the ion currents depend only upon their respective electrochemical gradients and their conductance through (the ease with which they cross) the membrane. In view of the preceding discussions, these assumptions are an oversimplification because (1) active transport is frequently electrogenic, (2) the ion current carried by species other than K^+ and Na^+ may be important at times, and (3) the electrical properties of the membrane may not be independent of metabolic reactions. Making these three assumptions, however,

$$\frac{1}{\mathfrak{R}_{ax}} \frac{\partial^2 \Psi}{\partial y^2} = C \frac{\partial \Psi}{\partial t} + g_{K^+}(\Psi - E_{K^+}) + g_{Na^+}(\Psi - E_{Na^+}) \tag{8-133}$$

where E_{K^+} and E_{N^+} are the electrochemical equilibrium potentials for K^+ and Na^+ respectively.

The equilibrium potentials, of course, are given by

$$E_{K^+} = \frac{RT}{\mathfrak{F}} \ln \frac{[K]_o}{[K]_i} \tag{8-134}$$

$$E_{Na^+} = \frac{RT}{\mathfrak{F}} \ln \frac{[Na]_o}{[Na]_i} \tag{8-135}$$

In the resting fiber, the transmembrane potential is constant through time and over the entire fiber, and the terms $(\partial^2\Psi/\partial y^2)$ and $(\partial\Psi/\partial t)$ are zero. Thus

$$g_{K^+}(\Psi - E_{K^+}) = -g_{Na^+}(\Psi - E_{Na^+}) \tag{8-136}$$

and

$$\Psi = \left(\frac{g_{Na^+}}{g_{Na^+} + g_{K^+}}\right) E_{Na^+} + \left(\frac{g_{K^+}}{g_{Na^+} + g_{K^+}}\right) E_{K^+} \tag{8-137}$$

While the ionic currents are nonlinear functions of the membrane potentials when steady-state conditions are reached, *instantaneously* the ionic conductances are almost constant. The term *delayed rectification* frequently is used in describing the properties of excitable membranes to emphasize that the conductance changes take a few milliseconds to develop. Hodgkin and Huxley[100] evaluated the ionic conductance changes by use of the voltage clamp technique (see Chapter 7) which permits measurements of the total ion current as a function of time after predetermined stepwise changes in the membrane potential. The total ion current was separated into sodium and nonsodium (mostly potassium) components by measuring the current in the presence and absence of Na^+ ions in the external medium.

In the case of the K^+ ion current, the potassium conductance increased as the amount the membrane depolarization was increased. In addition, the *rate* of the conductance change also increased as the membrane was depolarized to a greater extent; that is, a larger depolarization produces a larger and faster increase in K^+ conductance than does a smaller depolarization. The simplest interpretation of these findings is that the K^+ conductance depends upon the state or conformation of some charged groups or molecules in the membrane; the conformation of this membrane constituency in turn is a function of the membrane potential. If there are two possible states of these groups or molecules, α and β, and the transformation from one state to the other is a first-order process, then

$$dn/dt = \alpha_n(1 - n) - \beta_n n \tag{8-138}$$

where n is the fraction of groups in state α, α_n is the rate constant for conversion from the β-state to the α-state, and β_n is the rate constant for the reverse reaction. If changes in the state of charged groups take place, α_n and β_n will be voltage-dependent.

If the capacity of the membrane to permit the movement of K^+ ions were simply proportional to the number of groups in the α-state, a step change in the voltage would be followed by an exponential change in the K^+ conductance to the new steady-state value. In fact, however, the changes in K^+ conductance are sigmoid rather than exponential. This can be accounted for by assuming that each membrane site of K^+ transport involves several charged groups all of which must be in the α-state for the site to be permeable. Then

$$g_{K^+} = g^*_{K^+} n^\gamma \tag{8-139}$$

where $g^*_{K^+}$ is the maximum K^+ conductance and γ is the number of charged groups involved at each site. Hodgkin and Huxley found that $\gamma = 4$ gave the best fit for their data from squid axon (although other values for γ have been obtained using other preparations).

The initial changes in the Na^+ conductance resemble those in the K^+ conductance except that the rate of conductance change is about one order of magnitude greater for Na^+ than for K^+. As a result, after depolarization of the membrane, the rise in Na^+ conductance becomes well established before there is an appreciable rise in K^+ conductance. A set of equations analogous to eqs. 8-138 and 8-139 can be written describing the initial changes in Na^+ conductance.

$$dm/dt = \alpha_m(1 - m) - \beta_m m \tag{8-140}$$

$$g_{Na^+} = g^*_{Na^+} m^\delta \tag{8-141}$$

[100] Hodgkin, A. L., Huxley, A. F., and Katz, B. *Arch. Sci. Physiol.*, *3*, 129 (1949); *J. Physiol.*, *116*, 403, 424, 449, 473, 497 (1952); *121*, 403 (1953).

where m, α_m, and β_m are the sodium terms analogous to n, α_n, and β_n; g_{Na}^* is the maximum Na^+ conductance; and δ is empirically determined to be 3.

A crucial difference between the Na^+ and K^+ conductances is that the increase in g_{Na^+} following a depolarization is not maintained. Moreover, the value of g_{Na}^* depends upon the initial value of the transmembrane potential. Hodgkin and Huxley accounted for these two findings by supposing that a reaction occurred in the membrane which is opposite in its voltage dependence to the reactions of eqs. 8-140 and 8-141. This opposite reaction can be described by the relation

$$dh/dt = \alpha_h(1 - h) - \beta_h h \tag{8-142}$$

The overall description of the change in Na^+ conductance is given by

$$g_{Na^+} = g_{Na^+}^* m^3 h \tag{8-143}$$

Equations 8-139 and 8-143 can be substituted into eq. 8-133 to give

$$\frac{1}{\mathfrak{R}_{ax}} \frac{\partial^2 \Psi}{\partial y^2} = C \frac{\partial \Psi}{\partial t} + g_{K^+}^* n^4(\Psi - E_{K^+}) + g_{Na^+}^* m^3 h(\Psi - E_{Na^+}) \tag{8-144}$$

The values of the rate constants can be determined empirically. For squid axon, they are

$$\alpha_n = \frac{0.01(\Delta\Psi + 10)}{e^{(\Delta\Psi + 10)/10} - 1} \qquad \beta_n = 0.125\, e^{\Delta\Psi/80}$$

$$\alpha_m = \frac{0.1(\Delta\Psi + 25)}{e^{(\Delta\Psi + 25)/10} - 1} \qquad \beta_m = 4\, e^{\Delta\Psi/18}$$

$$\alpha_h = 0.07\, e^{\Delta\Psi/20} \qquad \beta_h = \frac{1}{e^{(\Delta\Psi + 30)/10} + 1}$$

where $\Delta\Psi$ is the change in membrane potential.

The propagated action potential can be obtained by solving the cable equations for a wave propagating at a constant velocity θ. At a given point in the fiber,

$$\frac{1}{R_{ax}\theta^2} \frac{\partial^2 \Psi}{\partial t^2} = C \frac{\partial \Psi}{\partial t} + \sum I_j \tag{8-145}$$

When the constants derived from voltage clamp experiments (such as those listed above for squid axon) are used, the Hodgkin-Huxley equations describe the action potential in form, amplitude, and duration. They also predict many other properties such as the threshold, refractory period, and the strength-latency relation.

references

Davson, H. *A Textbook of General Physiology*, 3rd ed. Boston: Little, Brown, 1964.

Davson, H., and Danielli, J. F. *The Permeability of Natural Membranes*, 2nd ed. London: Cambridge University Press, 1952.

Dowben, R. M., ed. *Biological Membranes*. Boston: Little, Brown, 1969.

Katchalsky, A., and Curran, P. F. *Nonequilibrium Thermodynamics in Biophysics*. Cambridge, Mass.: Harvard University Press, 1965.

Lakshminarayanaiah, N. Transport phenomena in artificial membranes. *Chem. Rev.*, *65*, 491 (1965).

Ling, G. N. *Physical Theory of the Living State*. Boston: Blaisdell, 1962.

Loewenstein, W. R., ed. Biological membranes: Recent progress. *Ann. N.Y. Acad. Sci., 137*, 403 (1966).

Mullins, L. J., ed. Newer properties of perfused squid axons. *J. Gen. Physiol., 48*, suppl. 1 (1965).

Ruch, T. C., and Patton, H. D. *Physiology and Biophysics*, 19th ed. Philadelphia: Saunders, 1965.

Schlögl, R. *Stofftransport durch Membranen*. Darmstadt: Theodor Steinkopff, Verlagsbuchhandlung, 1964.

Shanes, A. M. Electrochemical aspects of physiological and pharmacological action in excitable cells. *Pharmacol. Rev., 10*, 165 (1958).

Teorell, T. Transport processes and electrical phenomena in ionic membranes. *Progr. Biophys. Biophys. Chem., 3*, 305 (1953).

Ussing, H. H. Transport of ions across cellular membranes. *Physiol. Rev., 29*, 127 (1949).

chapter 9
contractility

structure of muscle

Movement appears to be a fundamental property of living systems. Locomotion as well as streaming within the cytoplasm is observed even in unicellular organisms. It is curious that we have much less of an understanding of the primitive, undifferentiated motile systems such as those in leucocytes or *Protozoa* than we have of the most highly developed contractile system, skeletal muscle. The contraction of muscles was a phenomenon that aroused the curiosity of ancient physicians. Erasistratus, an Alexandrian physician of the third century B.C., thought that muscular contraction occurred as the result of *pneuma,* or air, entering a muscle from its blood vessels and causing it to swell. When a muscle was filled with pneuma, its breadth was supposed to have increased while its length diminished, resulting in contraction.

Galen appreciated that the ability of a muscle to contract depended upon its nerve supply. He showed that cutting of the motor nerve is followed by paralysis of the muscle, and that cutting a section of the spinal cord paralyzes all the muscles of the body supplied by nerves arising below the point of transection. He even realized that mere injury or compression of the motor nerve may result in its loss of function. Galen put forward the theory that the nervous system controlled muscle function by regulating the passage of *animal spirits* down the nerve trunks. This view persisted even as late as the seventeenth century, when Franciscus Sylvius said, "And the contraction of a muscle is nothing else than a distention of its fibers, swollen with Animal Spirit, and hence it shortens."[1]

Jan Swammerdam carried out a series of experiments (while he was a student in the University at Leyden between 1661 and 1665) which showed that muscles did not swell during contraction and that, in fact, there was a slight reduction in their volume.[2] William Croone[3] introduced a new view of muscular contraction by proposing that contraction occurred in muscle as a result of a fermentative interaction between the juice of the nerves and the blood in muscle. Croone thought that the fermentative process resulted in a change in the shape of many microscopic internal fibers which had been observed previously by van Leeuwenhoek.

Giovanni Borelli[4] made an extensive analysis of the mechanics of muscular contraction, examining in detail the origin and insertion of muscles, the movements they cause at joints, the tension which they must develop in order to overcome a given mechanical resistance, and other mechanical properties. In the course of these studies, he discovered reciprocal innervation and control by opposing muscles and made some interesting observations on muscle tone.

Skeletal muscle is so named because it is closely associated with the parts of the skeleton and its contraction results in voluntary motion. Skeletal muscle is frequently called *striated muscle* because of the alternate light and dark crossbands which are observed in the microscope. The individual cells, *muscle fibers*, consist of elongated cylinders of varying length, 50 to 200 μ in diameter, which contain multiple nuclei. Each muscle fiber is surrounded by a thin membrane known as the *sarcolemma*. Within the muscle fiber are bundles of numerous parallel *myofibrils* 1 to 3 μ in diameter which run the length of the muscle fiber. The myofibrils contain the contractile elements, and they are aligned so that the cross striations are in register. Between the myofibrils and the sarcolemma is cytoplasm, or *sarcoplasm*, which contains the multiple nuclei, mitochondria (*sarcosomes*), and other intracellular organelles. A number of muscle fibers are collected into a bundle, called a *fasciculus*, which is surrounded by a covering of connective tissue called the *endomysium*. A muscle consists of a number of fasciculi enclosed in a heavy external sheath of connective tissue called the *perimysium* (Fig. 9-1).

The basic facts about the cross striations in skeletal muscle were discovered during the nineteenth century by light microscopy. Sir William Bowman[5] suggested that the cross striations resulted from bands of material with different refractive indices, a view which has been subsequently confirmed by microscopic phase contrast and interference methods. It was shown by Brücke[6] that the band of high refractive index is birefringent; that is, the refractive index of this band is slightly higher when viewed in a direction parallel to the length of the fiber than it is when the optical axis is perpendicular. This band, therefore, is anistropic and is called the *A band*, while the band of lower refractive index is optically isotropic and is called the *I band*. In unstained specimens of muscle, the cross striations are best seen with the microscope adjusted slightly below the level of perfect focus (*tiefe Einstellung*) with the condenser stopped down, or in a phase contrast microscope; then the A bands and Z lines (see below) appear darker than the I bands.

---

[1] Sylvius, F. *Opera Medica*. Cologne: D. Elsevirium, 1680.
[2] These experiments were published posthumously in Swammerdam's *Biblia Naturae*. Leyden: I. Severinum, 1737.
[3] Croone, W. *De Ratione Motus Musculorem*. London: J. Hayes, 1664.
[4] Borelli, G. A. *De Motu Animalium*. Rome: A. Bernabo, 1680.
[5] Bowman, W. *Phil. Trans.*, *130*, 457 (1840).
[6] Brücke, E. *Denkschr. Akad. wiss. Wien*, *15*, 69 (1858).

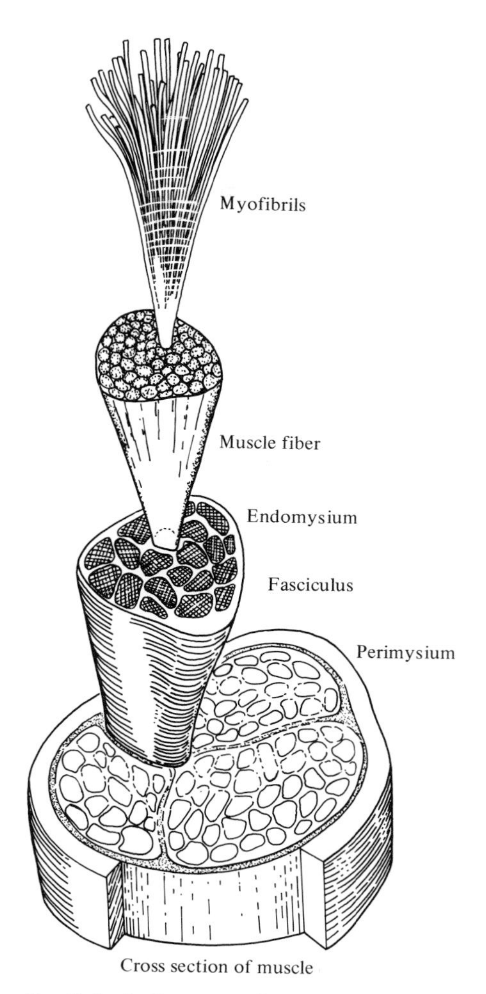

fig. 9-1. A diagrammatic representation of a cross section of muscle showing its gross organization.

Each I band is bisected by a dark, narrow line, the *Z line*, which appears to be attached to the sarcolemma.[7] Engelmann[8] described the *H zone*, a region of relatively lower refractive index in the center of the A band which is somewhat better defined in stretched than in contracted muscle fibers. The H zone is sometimes bisected by the *M line*. In the latter part of the nineteenth century, microscopists observed that in contracted muscle the A band remained about the same size but the I band became considerably thinner. The contractile unit from one Z line to the next is called a *sarcomere*; it varies in length from 1.5 to 3.0 μ (Fig. 9-2).

The nerve supply to a skeletal muscle consists of a number of fibers which enter the muscle and divide. Each nerve fiber finally divides and ends on a number of muscle fibers. The nerve fibers end in a specialization of the muscle fiber called the *motor end plate*, in which there is a large area of contact between the nerve axon and the

[7] Dobie, W. M. *Ann. Mag. Nat. Hist.*, *3*, 109 (1849).
[8] Engelmann, T. W. *Pflüger's Arch. ges. Physiol.*, *7*, 33 (1873).

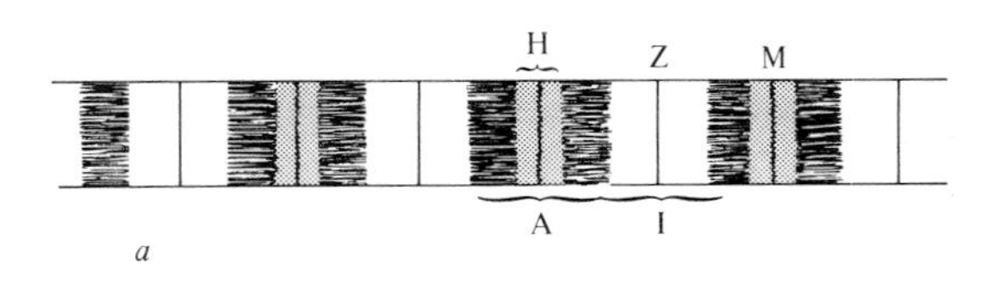

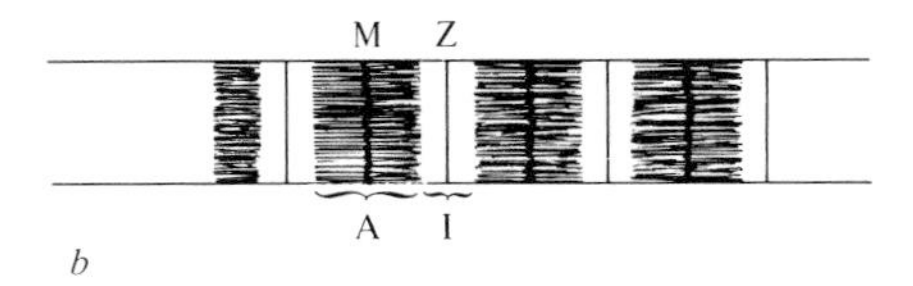

fig. 9-2. A diagrammatic representation of the microscopic appearance of a myofibril (*a*) in the relaxed state, and (*b*) in the contracted state. A sarcomere extends from one Z line to the next and is divided into an A (anisotropic) band and an I (isotropic) band. The Z line transects the I band, and the H zone in the center of the A band is transected by the M line. Upon contraction, the I band shortens and the H zone may disappear.

muscle-fiber membrane. It is clear, however, that the nerve axon and muscle cell are distinct from each other at all points. Each motor nerve fiber and the muscle fibers which it innervates constitute a *motor unit* (Fig. 9-3). Some muscle fibers are innervated by more than a single motor nerve fiber.

The connective tissue which envelops a muscle extends continuously at either end into *tendons*, by means of which muscles are attached to bones. The attachment of a muscle toward the center of a body is called its *origin*, while the distal attachment is known as its *insertion*. Often the connective tissue surrounding a muscle is quite dense and contains a matrix of elastic fibers constituting a *fascia*.

By and large, the number of muscle fibers does not increase after birth. The increase in size of the muscle during growth, or as a result of exercise and training, is due to an increase in the diameter of the individual muscle fibers rather than to an increase in

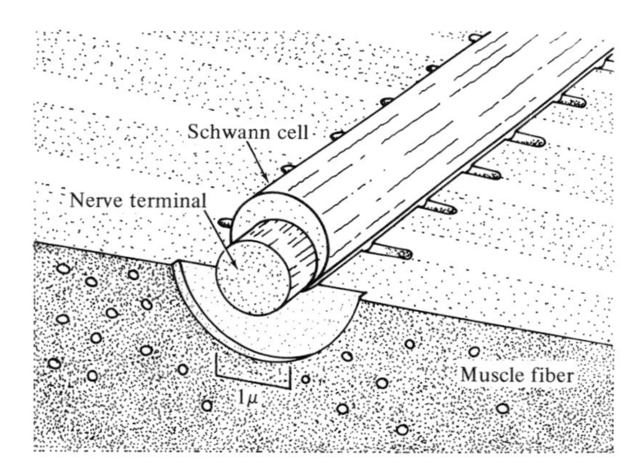

fig. 9-3. A diagrammatic representation of the myoneural junction. (Modified from Birks, R., Huxley, H. E., and Katz, B. *J. Physiol., 150,* 136 [1960].)

their number. Furthermore, the capacity of a muscle to regenerate is slight. While an injured muscle fiber can repair itself, a gross injury to muscle results in its replacement by connective tissue and fat. The gross composition and some physical properties of skeletal muscle are shown in Fig. 9-4.

Smooth muscle does not exhibit cross striations when examined under the microscope. Usually it is not associated with the skeleton, but rather is found in the visceral organs, the walls of the alimentary tract, the arteries and veins, and the ducts of various glands. An isolated smooth muscle cell tends to be spindle-shaped, usually with a

fig. 9-4. Chemical composition of muscle. (From Davson, H., and Eggleton, M. G., eds. *Principles of Human Physiology,* 13th ed. Philadelphia: Lea & Febiger, 1962, London: J. & A. Churchill, p. 799. By permission of J. & A. Churchill, London.)

COMPONENT	MAMMAL	FROG	INVERTEBRATE (MARINE)	NOTES
Water, percent	74–84	79–82	78–84	Man; lobster
Protein, percent	18.5	17–20	14–20	Man; lobster
Glycogen, percent	1.3–2.2	—	2.6–4.2	Man; oyster
Creatine, mg/100 g	440	400	—	Man
ATP, mg/100 g	330	250	—	Rat
Carnosine, mg/100 g	50–250	250	—	Various
Anserine, mg/100 g	90–500	—	—	Various
Lactate, mg/100 g	20	—	—	Man
PO_4, mg/100 g	150–200	120–170	—	Man
Magnesium, mg/100 g	18.4–21.5	24	—	Man
Calcium, mg/100 g	6.5–7.4	16	—	Man
Sodium, mmole/kg	44.5	24	54	Much Na in interspaces; Man; squid
Potassium, mmole/kg	63	85	114	Man; squid
Sodium in mmole/kg body fluid	147	104	350	Man; squid
Potassium in mmole/kg body fluid	6	3	16	Man; squid
Bicarbonate, mg/100 g	98	30	—	Man
Chloride, mg/100 g	45–110	45	—	Man

PHYSICAL PROPERTIES OF MUSCLE[a]

1. Density, 1.062 g/ml
2. Diffusion constant of oxygen, 0.14 ml/min for 1 cm² area, 1μ thickness, 1 atm pressure difference, 20°C
3. Thermal conductivity 1.18×10^{-3} cal/min for 1 cm² area, 1 cm thickness, 1°C temp difference
4. Volume coefficient of thermal expansion, 0.16×10^{-3} ml/ml °C (unloaded, resting)
5. Linear coefficient of thermal expansion $(-0.1 \text{ to } +0.6) \times 10^{-3}$ cm/cm °C depending on initial length
6. Thermal capacity per gram, 0.88 cal/°C

[a] Measured on frog's skeletal muscle; the values for other types of muscle probably are not greatly different.

single oval nucleus in its center. The individual cells are held together by means of connective tissue. Smooth muscle is innervated by the autonomic nervous system and is not subject to direct voluntary control. It is therefore frequently called *involuntary muscle*. Cardiac muscle is composed of branched cells showing cross striations. The cells are arranged in an end-to-end fashion, and they are separated by specialized junctions, the *intercalated discs*. Depolarizations of the sarcolemma are conducted across the intercalated discs, making the heart a functional syncytium.

mechanics of muscle contraction

The contractile unit of muscle may be regarded as a tension generator associated with two elastic components, one parallel to and one in series with the contractile units. Resting muscle is elastic; it develops tension if it is stretched. Like most biological materials, however, resting muscle does not obey Hooke's law. There is little inherent elasticity at very short lengths. When a muscle is greatly stretched, it becomes less extensible and the tension increases up to the point at which rupture of the muscle fibers occurs. Resting muscle displays rubbery thermoelastic properties, shortening when warmed and elongating when cooled.[9] Upon stimulation, the muscle rapidly becomes rigid and not easily stretched, even before shortening begins.

The process which begins with the stimulation of a motor nerve and ends with the contraction of the muscle fiber which is innervated can be divided into a number of distinct processes. (1) Stimulation of the motor nerve involves a depolarization which is conducted to the termination of the axon at the motor end plate. (2) At the axon terminal the depolarization causes the liberation of a chemical transmitter substance, acetylcholine. (3) The acetylcholine produces a greater-than-threshold depolarization of the muscle fiber at the motor end plate and initiates a propagated action potential along the muscle fiber sarcolemma. (4) The depolarization of the muscle membrane induces contraction of the muscle fiber; this process is called *excitation-contraction coupling* and should be distinguished from (5) the actual production of tension by the contractile units which may occur without shortening.

It will be helpful at this point to examine the temporal relation between the depolarization of the muscle cell membrane and the development of tension during a single twitch. In most muscle fibers the action potential reaches its maximum magnitude in approximately 1.5 msec after the stimulus is applied. There is then a gradual return to the resting transmembrane potential which is completed approximately 4 to 5 msec after the stimulus. On the other hand the tension developed by the muscle fiber does not begin to rise during the *latent period* which lasts until 3 to 5 msec after the stimulus. Tension develops slowly to a peak at about 50 msec. The tension then declines very slowly, reaching the initial or resting tension at approximately 150 to 180 msec after stimulation (Fig. 9-5). Tension development is accompanied by an increase in the opacity of a muscle.

The development of tension is characteristic of the contractile element. Tension is developed whether or not shortening is permitted. The tension produced by the whole muscle results from a summation of the effects of twitches produced by the individual muscle fibers transmitted to the connective tissue and tendons of the muscle. Immediately after the action potential there is a latent period during which a second stimulus is ineffective. If the second stimulus occurs after recovery from the latent

[9] Hill, A. V. *Proc. Roy. Soc.*, *B 139*, 464 (1952).

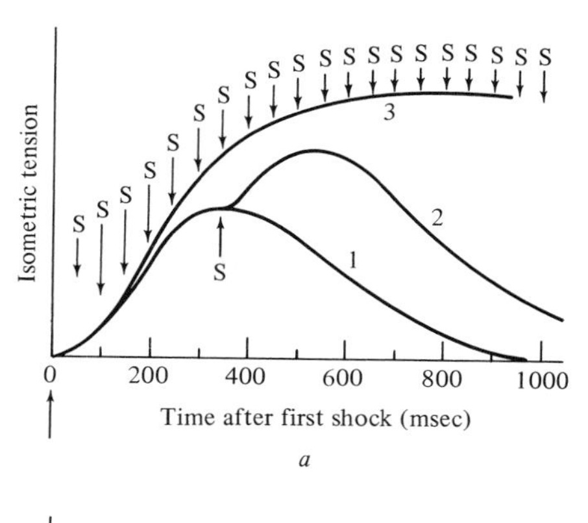

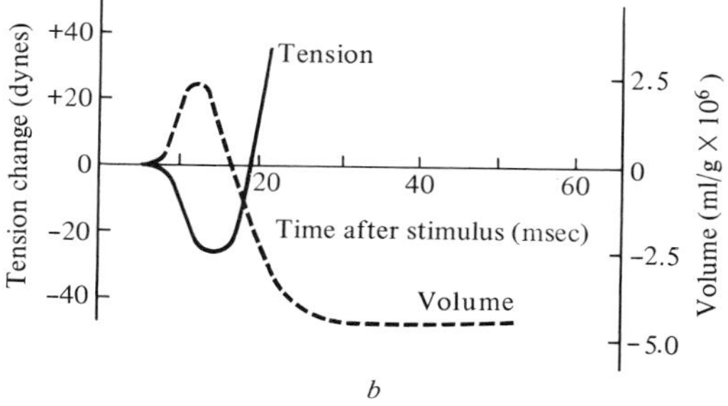

fig. 9-5. A diagram illustrating the time course of tension development and of volume change in muscle during a single twitch: (*a*) the time course of isometric contractions of a frog sartorius muscle at 0° showing (1) a single twitch following a single stimulus, (2) the summation of two twitches, and (3) a tetanus following repeated stimuli; and (*b*) early tension change recorded at high sensitivity showing the initial fall in tension and the volume change. (Adapted from Abbott, B. C., and Ritchie, J. M. *J. Physiol. 107*, 6P [1948]; Abbott, B. C., and Baskin, R. G. *J. Physiol., 161*, 384 [1962].)

period but before tension has disappeared, the tension produced by the second twitch will be added onto that remaining from the first. If the stimulus is repeated regularly at a high frequency (20 to 120 per sec), individual responses cannot be detected. Rather, the muscle shows a maintained contraction with constant tension, a *tetanus*.

In experimental work, muscle may be stimulated in a device which prevents it from shortening. The tension developed in such an *isometric* contraction can be measured by means of a strain gauge. In an *isotonic* contraction, a muscle is permitted to shorten freely while lifting a predetermined constant load.

At the end of the latent period just before the onset of the tension increase, the tension in a stimulated muscle drops for a very brief period.[10] This phenomenon, known as *latency-relaxation*, lasts about 1.5 msec and is particularly well demonstrated during the isometric contraction using a rather rigid measuring system. Latency-relaxation is thought to reflect some molecular rearrangement prior to the onset of active contraction. It is accompanied by a slight increase in muscle volume amounting to perhaps 2.5×10^{-6} cc/g muscle. The increase in tension during the

[10] Abbott, B. C., and Ritchie, J. M. *J. Physiol., 113*, 330 (1951).

active contraction is slightly preceded by a *decrease* in muscle volume which reaches a minimum at 30 to 50 msec after stimulation and amounts to 2 to 6 × 10^{-5} cc/g muscle.[11] The volume changes during isometric contractions are dependent upon muscle length. The initial volume increase becomes more pronounced as muscle length is decreased, while the diminution in volume during tension development is greatest at the muscle rest length and diminishes at longer or shorter initial lengths. At lower temperatures, the rate of volume recovery is slowed.

The tension which is developed during tetanic stimulation depends upon whether the muscle is maintained at its rest length (the length the muscle has at rest in the body), whether it is stretched, or whether it is permitted to contract. The tension developed by a muscle may be plotted as a function of its length at the height of contraction (Fig. 9-6), taking the rest length of the muscle to be 100 percent. It is seen that the

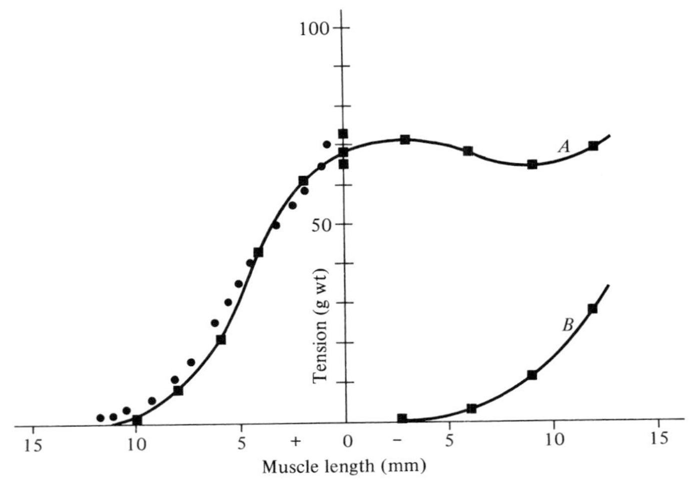

fig. 9-6. The length-tension curve for a muscle stimulated tetanically (curve *A*), and the stress-strain curve for a resting muscle (curve *B*). (Modified from Wilkie, D. R. *Brit. Med. Bull., 12,* 178 [1956].)

maximum tension is developed at approximately the rest length of the muscle. Shortening the length of the muscle surgically in a growing animal leads to a corresponding shift in its length-tension curve after a few weeks so that the optimal length for maximum tension development corresponds to its resting length again. The stretch-strain curve of resting muscle depends upon the amount of connective tissue in the particular muscle.

The connective tissue and other inert structural components endow muscle with elastic properties. The important elastic properties can be described by assuming that an expanding elastic element is arranged in series with the contractile element. The series elastic element acts to smooth the development of tension when the contractile element is activated. The tension developed within the contractile element in a single twitch appears to be the same as the tension developed in a tetanus. The series elastic element, however, is not fully extended by a single twitch. The series elastic element extends about 10 to 15 percent of the initial muscle length during the development of

[11] Ernst, E. *Pflüger's Arch. ges. Physiol., 209,* 613 (1925); Meyerhof, O., and Hartmann, H. *Pflüger's Arch. ges. Physiol., 234,* 722 (1934); Abbott, B. C., and Baskin, R. J. *J. Physiol., 161,* 379 (1962); Baskin, R. J., and Paolini, P. J. *J. Gen. Physiol., 49,* 387 (1966).

tension in an isometric tetanus. A virtual elastic element parallel to the contractile element and the series elastic element also is present; this parallel elastic element is almost completely relaxed when the muscle is not stretched beyond its rest length. The parallel elastic element shows rubberlike thermoelasticity; that is, a relaxed muscle cools slightly when it is passively stretched beyond its rest length.

The stress-strain curve of the series elastic component can be evaluated by stimulating a muscle by a single shock while various-sized weights are attached to it. At first the muscle is prevented from shortening by a mechanical stop which forces it to develop tension isometrically. At a predetermined interval after the shock, an interval which can be varied, the stop is removed and the muscle is permitted to shorten. At first there is a sudden shortening which depends upon the difference between the isometric tension developed in the muscle at the moment of release and the weight load on the lever after release.

A series of stress-strain curves obtained by use of different loads and by variation of the time of release after the stimulus is depicted in Fig. 9-7. That all the curves are

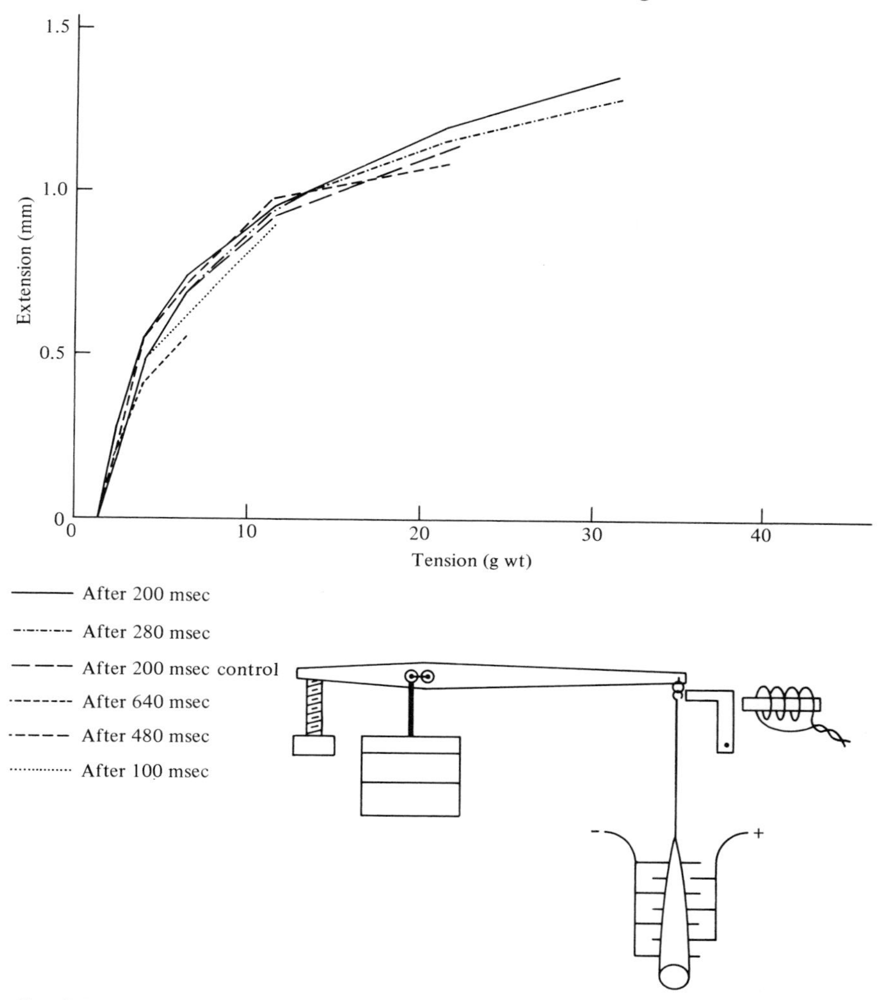

fig. 9-7. The stress-strain curves of the series elastic component of muscle at various times after a single stimulus. The experimental arrangement is shown below. (From Wilkie, D. R. *Brit. Med. Bull.*, *12*, 178, 179 [1956].)

superimposed one on another indicates that the series elastic component is inert and is not altered by activation of the contractile unit. While the stress-strain curve of resting muscle appears to depend largely upon the amount of connective tissue in a particular muscle, some of the elasticity may be a property of the submicroscopic filaments of the myofibril. The series elastic component, damping out rapid changes in tension, has an important effect on the mechanical properties of the whole muscle.

A series of shortening curves developed by a muscle against various loads is depicted in Fig. 9-8. Three changes are apparent as the load is increased: (1) the latent period

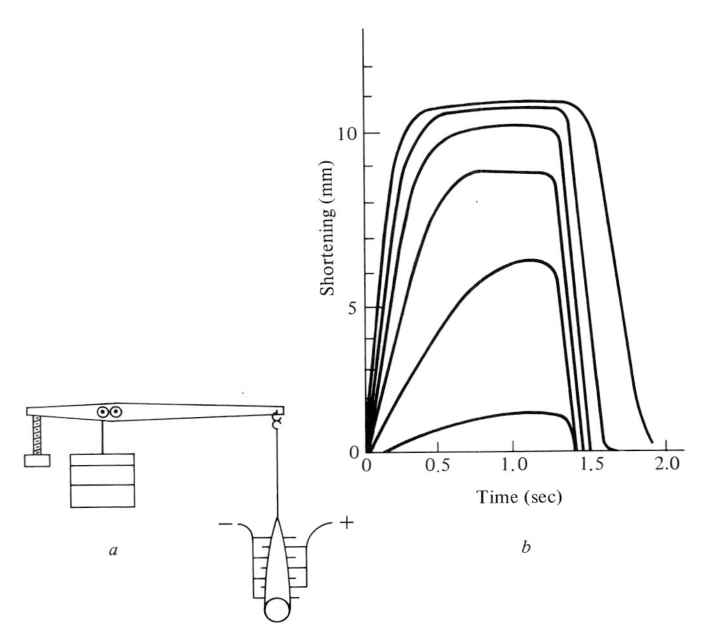

fig. 9-8. The shortening during isotonic contraction of a frog sartorius muscle at 0° (tetanus). The curves were obtained using weights of (from top to bottom) 1.0, 2.5, 5.0, 10.0, 20.0, and 30.0 g. (From Wilkie, D. R. *Brit. Med. Bull.*, *12*, 179 [1956].)

becomes lengthened, (2) the maximum amount of shortening diminishes, and (3) the initial velocity of shortening diminishes. The latent period is the time required by a muscle to develop a tension equal to its load at its starting length. The greater the load, the longer the latent period.

A curve of the type shown in Fig. 9-9 is obtained if the initial velocity of shortening is plotted against the isotonic force. The general shape of the force-velocity curve is the same for many muscles from various species. The maximum isometric tension is about the same, 1 to 2 kg/cm^2. However, the velocity of initial shortening varies widely between the quick striated muscles and the very slow smooth muscles. The force-velocity curve for an isotonic contraction can be described by the Hill equation[12]

$$\frac{dl}{dt} = \frac{(F_0 - F)b}{(F + a)} \tag{9-1}$$

where F is the tension, F_0 is the maximum isometric tension which the muscle is able

[12] Hill, A. V. *Proc. Roy. Soc.*, *B 126*, 136 (1938).

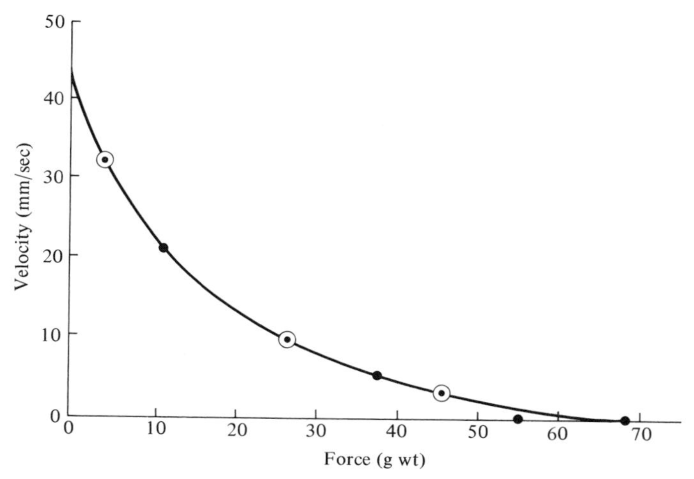

fig. 9-9. Force-velocity curve of tetanized frog sartorius muscle at 0°. The small circles represent experimental points, and the large circles represent points used to calculate the theoretical curve from Hill's equation. (From Wilkie, D. R. *Brit. Med. Bull.*, *12*, 179 [1956].)

to develop, dl/dt is the velocity of contraction, and a and b are constants. The constant b depends upon the intrinsic speed of the muscle and is about one-fourth the maximum speed of shortening under zero load.

Because F_0 appears as a constant in eq. 9-1, the relation holds only in the neighborhood of the flat top of the length-tension curve (Fig. 9-6). However, F_0 can be made to vary as an experimentally determined function of the length using the length-tension curve

$$F_0 = f_2(l) \qquad \textit{(9-2)}$$

Substituting eq. 9-2 into eq. 9-1 gives[13]

$$\frac{dl}{dt} = \frac{[f_2(l) - F]b}{(F + a)} \qquad \textit{(9-3)}$$

an expression which fits the full range of shortening with acceptable accuracy.

For isotonic contractions discussed above, the effect of the series elastic component has been eliminated. For nonisotonic contractions, the stress-strain function, determined experimentally by use of the stress-strain curve (Fig. 9-7) must be incorporated into eq. 9-1.

$$\frac{dl}{dt} + \frac{df_1(F)}{dt} = \frac{(F_0 - F)b}{(F + a)} \qquad \textit{(9-4)}$$

For an isometric contraction, $dl/dt = 0$ and the rate of shortening of the contractile mechanism is equal to the rate of lengthening of the series elastic component.[14]

$$\frac{df_1(F)}{dt} = \frac{(F_0 - F)b}{(F + a)} \qquad \textit{(9-5)}$$

[13] Abbott, B. C., and Wilkie, D. R. *J. Physiol.*, *120*, 214 (1953).
[14] Wilkie, D. R. *J. Physiol.*, *110*, 249 (1950).

Under optimal conditions, the mechanical efficiency of contracting muscle may be as high as 25 percent. In a constant environment, the basal metabolic processes in resting muscle result in a low, uniform rate of heat production. In frog sartorius muscle at 20°, the heat generated at rest amounts to 1.7 to 2.4×10^{-3} cal/g min. Assuming that the rate of heat production in resting human muscle is approximately the same as in frog muscle and that the temperature coefficient is also the same (about 2.5 per 10°C), the 30 kg of muscle in an average 70 kg man should produce about 300 cal/min.[15] This is equivalent to an oxygen consumption of about 60 ml/min, a substantial fraction of the total oxygen consumption during basal conditions. Under anaerobic conditions, an isolated muscle produces only about half as much heat as it does in the presence of oxygen. Lactic acid and other products of anaerobic metabolism accumulate in the muscle. Upon readmitting oxygen to the system, the metabolic intermediates are oxidized. During oxidation, excess heat is liberated which corresponds to the deficit accumulated during anaerobiosis. Raising the potassium concentration in the medium and stretching the muscle both result in increased heat production at rest.[16]

The contraction of muscle is accompanied by the production of additional heat over the resting heat production. After a stimulus, heat is generated even before shortening can be detected. Under aerobic conditions, the heat produced by contraction, whether it is a single twitch or a tetanus, can be divided into two phases, the *initial heat* and the *heat of recovery* or delayed heat.[17] With a tetanic stimulation the heat production rises rapidly, reaching a value of approximately 1.22 cal/g min. Upon the cessation of the tetanus, heat production falls rapidly to approximately 1 percent of the initial rate. The excess heat production during recovery, however, is so prolonged that the total heat of recovery approximately equals the initial heat. When contraction occurs under anaerobic conditions, the initial heat is practically the same as under aerobic conditions, while the recovery heat is almost zero. If oxygen is readmitted to the system, there is an excess heat production which is approximately equal to that expected of the aerobic recovery heat.

It has been shown by Hill[18] that the energy transfers during a single muscle twitch can be described by the relation

$$U = A + a\,dl + W \qquad (9\text{-}6)$$

where U is the total energy; A is the heat of activation, that is, the heat produced by the activation of the contractile unit; $a\,dl$ is the heat of shortening where dl is the amount of shortening and a is a constant; and W is the mechanical work. In a tetanus the heat of activation due to successive stimuli are summed and become the heat of maintenance. It is quite remarkable that when the load against which a muscle shortens is increased, exactly the amount of extra energy required to lift the heavier load is generated,[19] while the heat of shortening is influenced only to a slight degree by the magnitude of the load. The constant a has the dimensions of a force and in many

[15] Hill, A. V. *Proc. Roy. Soc.*, *B 126*, 136 (1938).
[16] Feng, T. P. *Proc. Roy. Soc.*, *B 108*, 522 (1931); Solandt, D. Y. *J. Physiol.*, *86*, 162 (1936); Hill, A. V., and Howarth, V. *Proc. Roy. Soc.*, *B 147*, 21 (1957).
[17] Hill, A. V. *Proc. Roy. Soc.*, *B 136*, 220 (1949); *B 137*, 40 (1950).
[18] Hill, A. V. *Proc. Roy. Soc.*, *B 136*, 220 (1949); *B 137*, 40 (1950).
[19] Fenn, W. O. *J. Physiol.*, *58*, 175 (1923); *58*, 373 (1924).

different types of muscles has the value of about 400 g/cm^2.[20] The constant a is identical to that appearing in eq. 9-1 for the velocity of shortening. The heat production of a muscle maintained in a steady isometric contraction is equal to the product ab (after an initial transient).[21] The heat of activation precedes the onset of tension; it is independent of the muscle length and temperature and amounts to 1.2 mcal/g. When an actively contracting muscle is stretched forcibly (by applying a force greater than the maximum tension, F_0), the heat output is reduced; but it is never abolished entirely.

biochemistry of energy production and utilization

The elucidation of the chemical reactions leading to the production of energy utilized in muscular contraction began with the demonstration by Fletcher and Hopkins[22] which showed that lactic acid accumulated in muscle during fatiguing exercise or in rigor. Parnas and Wagner later showed that the lactic acid was derived from the glycogen in muscle. The extensive studies of Otto Meyerhof[23] demonstrated that the lactic acid formed in muscle during anaerobic contraction was proportional to the work performed by the muscle. The conversion of glycogen to lactic acid, an exergonic reaction, was found to yield 16.2 kcal/mole; this reaction could very well provide the energy for muscular contraction.

As mentioned above, experiments on isolated muscle showed that the initial heat of contraction occurred immediately and had the same magnitude whether the muscle contracted aerobically or in the absence of oxygen. The idea that the immediate chemical reactions involved in the contraction of muscle are not oxidative received further support from the studies of D. K. Hill[24] who demonstrated that for very brief contractions in the presence of oxygen, increased oxygen consumption starts only after the contraction is terminated. Lundsgaard[25] found that muscle poisoned with iodoacetate (which inhibits glycolysis and prevents lactic acid formation) was able to contract. Furthermore, he showed that the work performed by such muscle was proportional to the breakdown of phosphorylcreatine, a substance which had been discovered independently by Eggleton and Eggleton, and by Fiske and Subbarow.[26] Lundsgaard suggested that phosphorylcreatine supplies energy for contraction not only in iodoacetate-poisoned muscle but in normal muscle as well, and that the catabolism of carbohydrates supplied the energy required for its resynthesis.

Nachmansohn[27] made a careful comparison between the work performed by a muscle and phosphorylcreatine disappearance and found that during a succession of contractions the rate of disappearance was much greater in the early contractions

---

[20] Abbott, B. C. *J. Physiol.*, *112*, 438 (1951); Abbott, B. C., and Lowy, J. *J. Physiol.*, *130*, 25P (1955).
[21] Hill, A. V. *Proc. Roy. Soc.*, *B 127*, 434 (1939); *B 148*, 397 (1958); *B 159*, 297 (1964); Gibbs, C. L., Ricchuiti, N. V., and Mommaerts, W. F. H. M. *J. Gen. Physiol.*, *49*, 517 (1966).
[22] Fletcher, W. M., and Hopkins, F. G. *J. Physiol.*, *35*, 247 (1907); Parnas, J., and Wagner, R. *Biochem. Z.*, *61*, 387 (1914).
[23] Meyerhof, O. *Pflüger's Arch. ges. Physiol.*, *182*, 233 (1920); *191*, 128 (1921); Meier, R., and Meyerhof, O. *Biochem. Z.*, *150*, 233 (1924).
[24] Hill, D. K. *J. Physiol.*, *98*, 207 (1940).
[25] Lundsgaard, E. *Biochem. Z.*, *217*, 162, (1930); *227*, 51 (1930); *233*, 322 (1931). At a concentration of 0.5 μM, iodoacetate inhibits phosphoglyceraldehyde dehydrogenase completely within 30 min but does not inhibit creatine phosphokinase; Meyerhof, O., and Kiessling, W. *Biochem. Z.*, *264*, 40 (1933); Carlson, F. D., and Siger, A. *J. Gen. Physiol.*, *43*, 301 (1959).
[26] Eggleton, P., and Eggleton, G. P. *Biochem. J.*, *21*, 190 (1927); *J. Physiol.*, *63*, 155 (1927); Fiske, C. H., and Subbarow, Y. *Science*, *65*, 401 (1927); *J. Biol. Chem.*, *81*, 629 (1929).
[27] Nachmansohn, D. *Biochem. Z.*, *196*, 73 (1928); *208*, 357 (1929).

than in the later ones. It was also shown that most of the lactic acid production in a nitrogen atmosphere occurred after a tetanus[28] and that the delayed production of lactic acid was coupled to the resynthesis of phosphorylcreatine.

It is of interest that phosphagens other than phosphorylcreatine are found in muscle of various species. While phosphorylcreatine is found in all vertebrate muscle and in some invertebrate muscle, phosphorylarginine is characteristic of most arthropod muscle and annelids contain phosphorylglycocyamine and phosphoryltaurocyamine.

Adenosine triphosphate (ATP) was discovered in muscle independently by Lohmann, and by Fiske and Subbarow.[29] An appreciation of the interrelationship between phosphorylcreatine and ATP came from further experiments of Lohmann[30] who demonstrated the transphosphorylation reaction between phosphorylcreatine and ADP on the one hand and creatine and ATP on the other—a reaction mediated by the enzyme creatine phosphokinase.

$$\mathrm{PC + ADP} \underset{}{\overset{\text{creatine phosphokinase}}{\rightleftharpoons}} \mathrm{C + ATP}$$

$$\mathrm{ATP} \longrightarrow \mathrm{ADP} + P_i$$

Lohmann found that dialyzed muscle extracts would hydrolyze phosphorylcreatine only if adenine nucleotides were added. The ATP content of iodoacetate-poisoned muscle fell only when it was completely fatigued, that is, after the phosphorylcreatine had been exhausted. The role of ATP as the immediate energy source for muscular contraction received further support from the finding that the major portion of the ATPase activity in muscle was associated with the myosin fraction,[31] and that structural changes were induced in actomyosin by ATP (see p. 505).

Many attempts have been made to determine experimentally the material which is the immediate energy source for muscular contraction. Such studies have encountered enormous technical difficulties, such as overcoming variations between pairs of muscle so that an experimentally contracted muscle can be compared to a noncontracted control, finding a means of rapidly and precisely stimulating the experimental muscle and a means of rapidly and completely freezing the muscle to prevent either further breakdown of compounds or resynthesis through metabolism, and finding the chemical methods for the accurate determination of the labile high-energy intermediates. Because of the slow rate of penetration into muscle and the segregation of organic phosphates into functional compartments, studies of inorganic phosphate (P_i) turnover using ^{32}P have failed to give any decisive results.[32]

In frog *sartorius* muscles in which glycolysis has been inhibited with iodoacetic acid and respiration has been inhibited by anaerobiosis, the amount of creatine and inorganic phosphate liberated after a series of isometric twitches is proportional to the number of twitches. At 0°, the amount of phosphorylcreatine split per twitch in a

[28] Lehnartz, E. *Klin. Wochschr.*, *10*, 27 (1931); Meyerhof, O. *Klin. Wochschr.*, *10*, 214 (1931).
[29] Lohmann, K. *Naturwiss.*, *17*, 624 (1929); *Biochem. Z.*, *233*, 460 (1931); Fiske, C. H., and Subbarow, Y. *Science*, *70*, 381 (1929).
[30] Lohmann, K. *Biochem. Z.*, *271*, 278 (1934).
[31] Engelhardt, W. A., and Ljubimova, M. N. *Nature*, *144*, 668 (1939).
[32] Carlson, F. D. *Progr. Biophys. Biophys. Chem.*, *13*, 261 (1963).
[33] Munch-Petersen, A. *Acta Physiol. Scand.*, *29*, 202 (1953); Fleckenstein, A., Janke, J., Lechnor, T., and Bauer, T. *Pflüger's Arch. ges. Physiol.*, *259*, 246 (1954); Lange, G. *Biochem. Z.*, *326*, 172, 369 (1955); Fleckenstein, A., Janke, J., and Davies, R. E. *Arch. exptl. Parthol. Pharmakol.*, *228*, 596 (1956); Fleckenstein, A., Gerlach, E., Janke, J., and Marimier, P. *Pflüger's Arch. ges. Physiol.*, *271*, 75 (1960); Carlson, F. D., and Siger, A. *J. Gen. Physiol.*, *43*, 301 (1959); Cain, D. F., and Davies, R. E. *Biochem. Biophys. Res. Commun.*, *8*, 361 (1962).

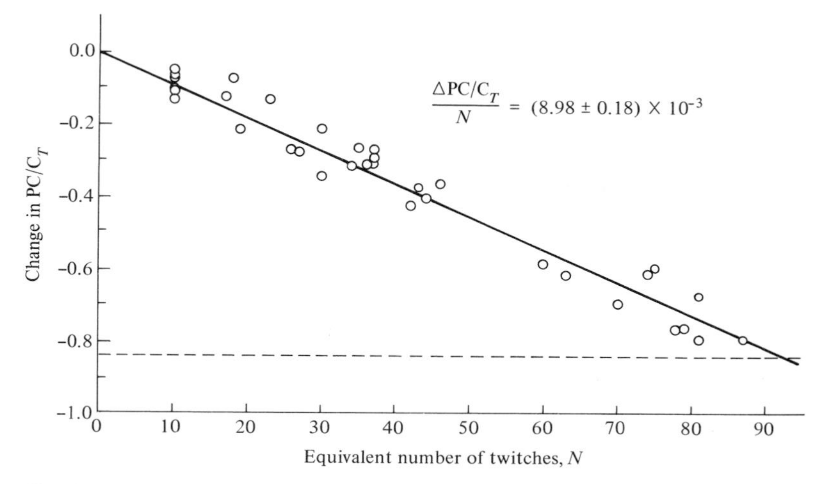

fig. 9-10. A plot of the change in phosphorylcreatine content of muscle for an increasing number of twitches. The best fit regression line determined by the method of least squares passes through the region and has a slope of $8.98 \pm 0.18 \times 10^{-3}$ mole/twitch. (From Carlson, F. D., and Siger, A. *J. Gen. Physiol., 44,* 41 [1960].)

series is about 0.3 μmole/g muscle.[33] In the *rectus abdominus* of the frog performing 125 g · cm work at 0° without inhibition of glycolysis or respiration, about 0.5 μmole/g inorganic phosphate is produced per twitch *in a series of twitches.* Muscle contains about 22 to 28 μmole/g phosphorylcreatine and 1.5 to 2.5 μmole/g ATP. The increase in ADP per twitch amounts to about 0.06 μmole/g, a quantity too small to account for the energy of a twitch (Fig. 9-10). There appears to be no variation in the concentration of other phosphorylated intermediates such as phospho*enol*pyruvate during single twitches, nor does 1,3-diphosphoglycerate appear to be a direct energy source. The amount of phosphorylcreatine hydrolyzed during muscular contraction depends upon the work done rather than upon the amount of shortening[34] (there is a discrepancy between the breakdown of phosphorylcreatine and the heat of shortening).

Definitive studies showing that ATP is the immediate energy source for muscular contraction were performed in muscles treated with 1-fluoro-2,4-dinitrobenzene under conditions where respiration, glycolysis, *and* creatine phosphokinase were inhibited. Frog *sartorius* muscle treated in this manner contracts for about 40 min at 0°.[35] Very little, if any, ATP or phosphorylcreatine is hydrolyzed during the activation of the contractile unit, and there does not appear to be a coincident metabolic equivalent of the heat of activation. The hydrolysis of ATP *during a single twitch* in unloaded muscles at 0° amounts to approximately 0.08 μmole/g. Assuming 100 percent efficiency of ATP hydrolysis producing an enthalpy change of -10 kcal/mole, about 0.15 μmole/g ATP would be required to account for the heat of shortening. It is more likely that the ATP hydrolysis observed is linked to the reaccumulation of calcium by the sarcoplasmic reticulum during relaxation (see p. 515). The heat of shortening, therefore, may arise from an entropic change which accompanies the conformational changes in the contractile proteins during shortening.

[34] Carlson, F. D., Hardy, D. J., and Wilkie, D. R. *J. Gen. Physiol., 46,* 851 (1963); Mommaerts, W. F. H. M., Seraydarian, K., and Maréchal, G. *Biochim. Biophys. Acta, 57,* 1 (1962).
[35] Infante, A. A., and Davies, R. E. *Biochem. Biophys. Res. Commun., 9,* 410 (1962); *J. Biol. Chem., 240,* 3996 (1965).

The amount of ATP hydrolyzed is related to the quantity of work performed. ATP is hydrolyzed during a single isotonic contraction as well as during a series of twitches. In unpoisoned muscle, the resynthesis of ATP from phosphorylcreatine presumably occurs with such rapidity that phosphorylcreatine rather than ATP hydrolysis is observed. When the reservoir of energy-rich phosphorylcreatine is depleted, ATP levels finally diminish as ATP is irreversibly hydrolyzed, and finally the contracture of rigor ensues.

It is surprising that under resting conditions in the intact animal, fat provides the principal source of energy for skeletal muscle.[36] By canulating the artery and deep vein to the forearm, it is possible to measure the arteriovenous differences of various substances. The blood flow to the forearm also can be measured, and from these data the uptake or output of various substances can be calculated. Skeletal muscle makes up about two-thirds of the bulk of the forearm, and about 85 percent of the blood to the forearm perfuses skeletal muscle. Measurements show that at rest the respiratory quotient (R.Q.) is 0.76. Only about 16 percent of the oxygen uptake of resting muscle can be attributed to the metabolism of glucose. The remainder represents the oxidation of a substance with a very low R.Q., probably free fatty acids. Resting muscle produces lactate which represents about 45 percent of the glucose utilized. Similarly, heart muscle cells in tissue culture utilize mainly fat as an energy source.

myofibrillar proteins

More than a century ago Kühne[37] soaked muscle in a solution of 10 percent sodium chloride, thereby extracting most of the protein constituents. A fractionation of muscle proteins was carried out by Danilewsky[38] who obtained three fractions: proteins soluble in water; proteins extracted by low-ionic-strength solutions; and myosin, which was extracted by 6 to 12 percent ammonium chloride. Actin was actually extracted from muscle in 1887 by Halliburton.

The sarcoplasmic proteins, which are extracted with water or neutral salt solutions of less than 0.15 M concentration, give solutions of low viscosity containing myoglobin and a large number of enzymes, including those of the glycolytic system and various transaminases and phosphokinases. The sarcoplasmic proteins, which comprise about 30 percent of the total protein, do not appear to contribute to the structural organization of muscle, and the characteristic morphological features remain after their removal. When homogenized muscle is extracted in this manner, the sarcosomes and microsomes are also removed; they can be separated from the soluble proteins by centrifugation.

Neutral salts of a concentration greater than 0.5 M are required for the extraction of the myofibrillar proteins, which comprise about 55 percent of the total muscle proteins. Removal of the myofibrillar proteins is accompanied by the disorganization and disappearance of the myofilaments. Danilewsky (see footnote 38) observed that the extraction of the myosin fraction was accompanied by the disappearance of light birefringence in the A bands. The extracts of myofibrillar proteins have a high viscosity,

---

[36] Andres, R., Cader, G., and Zierler, K. L. *J. Clin. Invest.*, *35*, 671 (1956); Zierler, K. L., and Andres, R. *J. Clin. Invest. 35*, 991 (1956); Baltzan, M. A., Andres, R., Cader, G., and Zierler, K. L. *J. Clin. Invest.*, *41*, 116 (1962); Fujimoto, A., and Harary, I. *Biochim. Biophys. Acta*, *86*, 74 (1964).
[37] Kühne, W. *Arch. Anat. Physiol. wiss. Med.*, 748 (1859).
[38] Danilewsky, A. *Z. Phys. Chem.*, *5*, 162, 349 (1881); *7*, 124 (1882); Halliburton, W. D. *J. Physiol.*, *8*, 133 (1887); Finck, H. *Science*, *160*, 332 (1968).

indicative of the fibrous nature of the proteins. Three major constituents, *myosin, actin,* and *tropomyosin,* and several minor proteins can be isolated from the extract of myofibrillar proteins. In the catch muscles of molluscs and annelids, there is an additional major myofibrillar protein, *paramyosin.* After prolonged extraction with strong salt solutions, a residue of the *stromal proteins* remains.

Myosin is prepared by extracting coarsely minced muscle with 0.5 M KC1 solutions buffered with potassium phosphate at *p*H 6.5 for short periods of time, 20 minutes or less. The myosin can be precipitated from such an extract by dilution with water until the salt concentration is 0.04 M. Most of the sarcoplasmic proteins remain in solution. Any actomyosin complex present in the precipitate can be centrifuged out after dissolving the actin-free myosin in 0.28 M KC1.[39] As a result of the marked asymmetry of the molecules, myosin solutions are very viscous. The viscosity of an actin-free myosin solution is not lowered by the addition of ATP or pyrophosphate. At high rates of shear, myosin solutions exhibit double refraction of flow, a property which is increased when small amounts of actin are present as an impurity.

fig. 9-11. Some physical constants of the contractile proteins. (Data from Bailey, K., Gutfreund, H., and Ogston, A. G. *Biochem. J., 43,* 279 [1948]; Snellman, O., and Erdös, T. *Biochim. Biophys. Acta, 2,* 650, 660 [1948]; Portzehl, H., Schramm, G., and Weber, H. H. *Z. Naturforsch., 5b,* 61 [1950]; Tsao, T. C., Bailey, K., and Adair, G. S. *Biochem. J., 49,* 27 [1951]; Szent-Györgyi, A. G. *Arch. Biochem. Biophys., 42,* 305 [1953]; Parish, R. G., and Mommaerts, W. F. H. M. *J. Biol. Chem., 209,* 901 [1954]; Laki, K., and Carroll, W. R. *Nature, 193,* 269 [1955]; Kominz, D. R., Saad, F., Gladner, J. A., and Laki, K. *Arch. Biochem. Biophys., 70,* 16 [1957]; Kay, C. M. *Biochim. Biophys. Acta, 27,* 469 [1958]; Johnson, P., and Rowe, A. J. *Biochem. J., 79,* 524 [1960]; Lowey, S., and Cohen, C. *J. Mol. Biol., 4,* 293 [1962]; Adelstein, R. S., Godfrey, J. E., and Kielley, W. W. *Biochem. Biophys. Res. Commun., 12,* 34 [1963]; Gellert, M. F., and Englander, S. W. *Biochemistry, 2,* 39 [1963]; Lewis, M. S., Maruyama, K., Carroll, W. R., Kominz, D. R., and Laki, K. *Biochemistry, 1,* 987 [1963]; Lowey, S., Kucera, J., and Holtzer, A. *J. Mol. Biol., 7,* 234 [1963]; Grant, R. J., Cohen, L. B., Clark, E. E., and Hayashi, T. *Biochem. Biophys. Res. Commun., 16,* 314 [1964]; Mueller, H. *J. Biol. Chem., 239,* 797 [1964]; *240,* 3816 [1965]; Young, D. M., Himmelfarb, S., and Harrington, W. F. *J. Biol. Chem., 239,* 2822 [1964]; *240,* 2428 [1965]; Cohen, L. B. *Arch. Biochem. Biophys., 117,* 289 [1966]; Mueller, H. *J. Biol. Chem., 240,* 3816 [1966]; Rice, R. V., Brady, A. C., Depue, R. H., and Kelly, R. E. *Biochem. Z., 345,* 370 [1966]; Tonomura, Y., Appel, P., and Morales, M. *Biochemistry, 5,* 515 [1966].)

PROTEIN	$S^0_{20} \times 10^{13}$	$D^0_{20} \times 10^7$	INTRINSIC VISCOSITY cc/g	MOLECULAR WEIGHT	LENGTH (Å)	WIDTH (Å)
Myosin	6.25	1.05	234	4.8×10^5	1550	20 (tail) 50 (head)
Heavy meromyosin	7.2	2.9	8	3.5×10^5	220	50
Light meromyosin	3.0	3.8	100	1.3×10^5	1220	20
G-Actin	3.3	2.5	3.5	4.8×10^4	55	55
F-Actin	>50			$>2.5 \times 10^6$	>6000	85
Tropomyosin	2.6	2.4	52	5.4×10^4	400	15
Paramyosin	3.0	2.21	256	2.2×10^5	1330	20

[39] Straub, F. B. *Stud. Inst. med. Chem. Univ. Szeged., 2,* 3 (1942); *3,* 23 (1943); Guba, F., and Straub, F. B. *Stud. Inst. med. Chem. Univ. Szeged., 3,* 46 (1943); Szent-Györgyi, A. *Stud. Inst. med. Chem. Univ. Szeged., 3,* 76 (1943); Portzehl, H., Schramm, G., and Weber, H. H. *Z. Naturforsch., 5,* 61 (1950); Tonomura, Y., Appel, P., and Morales, M. *Biochemistry, 5,* 515 (1966).

Because of the ease with which myosin is denatured at room temperature, at surfaces, and in the presence of minute traces of heavy metals, and because of its great tendency to aggregate, there have been great difficulties in determining its physical properties. The myosin molecule is very asymmetric, as its intrinsic viscosity of 2.34 dl/g indicates. The molecular weight is approximately 500,000. On the basis of physical measurements, the myosin molecule is approximately 20 Å in diameter and approximately 1600 Å long. These physical data, with references to original articles, are summarized in Fig. 9-11. Treatment of myosin with 5 M guanidine hydrochloride or 12 M urea results in its dissociation into two identical subunits[40] with a molecular weight of 200,000 to 260,000. The subunits are tightly bound together in the tail region in a double-stranded coil; in the globular head region, however, binding between the subunits is relatively weak. Myosin has ATPase activity and a capacity to form a specific complex with actin.

Very brief digestion of myosin with proteolytic enzymes such as trypsin or chymotrypsin, under conditions where proteolysis is limited, appears to cleave the molecule into two large subfragments called *heavy meromyosin* and *light meromyosin*. Heavy meromyosin has a molecular weight of approximately 350,000. It is soluble in water but possesses the ATPase activity and actin-combining capacity of myosin. Light meromyosin, on the other hand, which has a molecular weight of approximately 130,000, retains the solubility properties of myosin, but lacks both enzymatic activity and the capacity to combine with actin. On the basis of optical rotatory dispersion measurements, about 55 percent of the amino acid residues of myosin are involved in α-helical structures. Almost all the amino acid residues in light meromyosin participate in α-helical structures, while heavy meromyosin has a much lower helicity than myosin.[41]

Electron microscopic studies[42] show that the myosin molecule is a rodlike molecule approximately 1550 Å in length and, over most of its extent, approximately 20 Å in diameter. It has a head approximately 210 Å long and 50 Å in diameter. The appearance of heavy meromyosin and light meromyosin molecules in electron micrographs indicates that they represent the head and tail portions respectively of the myosin molecule. An electron micrograph of myosin molecules is shown in Fig. 9-12, and a diagrammatic representation of the structure of myosin is shown in Fig. 9-13.

When a solution of myosin is diluted so that the salt concentration is lowered to the point where precipitation begins, the myosin molecules aggregate into fibers 0.2 to 12 μ long.[43] The first two myosin molecules tend to lie with their tails side by side and their heads pointing in opposite directions. Additional myosin molecules add to the aggregate, and the aggregate grows in both directions (Fig. 9-14). The myosin molecules appear to be arranged in a staggered fashion with the globular heads projecting from the central core. The fibers formed by aggregation of myosin molecules from solution bear a structural resemblance to the thick filaments of the A bands described below.

---

[40] Kielley, W. W., and Harrington, W. F. *Biochim. Biophys. Acta*, *41*, 401 (1960); Dreizen, P., Hartshorne, D. J., and Stracher, A. *J. Biol. Chem.*, *241*, 443 (1966); Openheimer, H., Barany, K., Hamoir, G., and Fenton, J. *Arch. Biochem. Biophys.*, *115*, 233 (1966); Slayter, H. S., and Lowey, S. *Proc. Natl. Acad. Sci.*, *58*, 1611 (1967). There has been some uncertainty as to whether myosin molecules consist of 2 or 3 subunits; the evidence appears to favor 2 subunits.

[41] Cohen, C., and Szent-Györgyi, A. G. *J. Am. Chem. Soc.*, *79*, 248 (1957); Schechter, E., and Blout, E. R. *Proc. Natl. Acad. Sci.*, *51*, 695 (1964).

[42] Huxley, H. E. *J. Mol. Biol.*, *7*, 281 (1963); Zobel, C. R., and Carlson, F. D. *J. Mol. Biol.*, *7*, 78 (1963); Rice, R. V., Brady, A. C., Depue, R. H., and Kelly, R. E. *Biochem. Z.*, *345*, 370 (1966).

[43] Jakus, M. A., and Hall, C. E. *J. Biol. Chem.*, *167*, 705 (1947); Huxley, H. E. *J. Mol. Biol.*, *7*, 281 (1963).

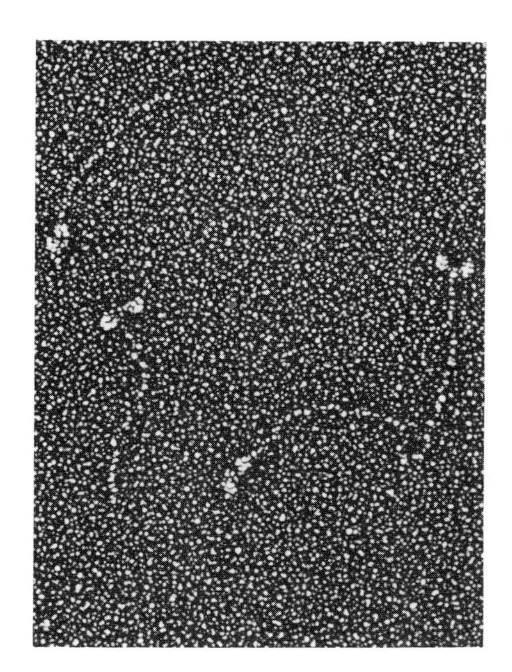

fig. 9-12. Electron micrograph of myosin molecules shadow cast with platinum, showing the separated subunits in some of the heads of the molecule. Magnification 175,000. (Courtesy of Dr. Henry S. Slayter.)

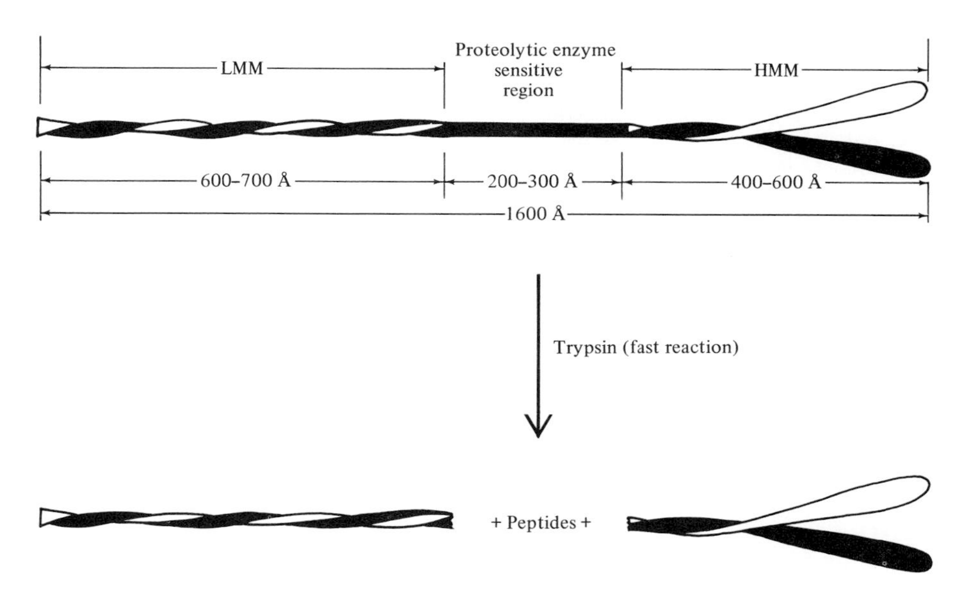

fig. 9-13. A schematic diagram of the myosin molecule showing that it is composed of two identical subunits. Partial proteolysis with trypsin cleaves both subunits just behind the head into a heavy meromyosin portion (HMM) and a light meromyosin portion (LMM), each containing parts of the two original subunits.

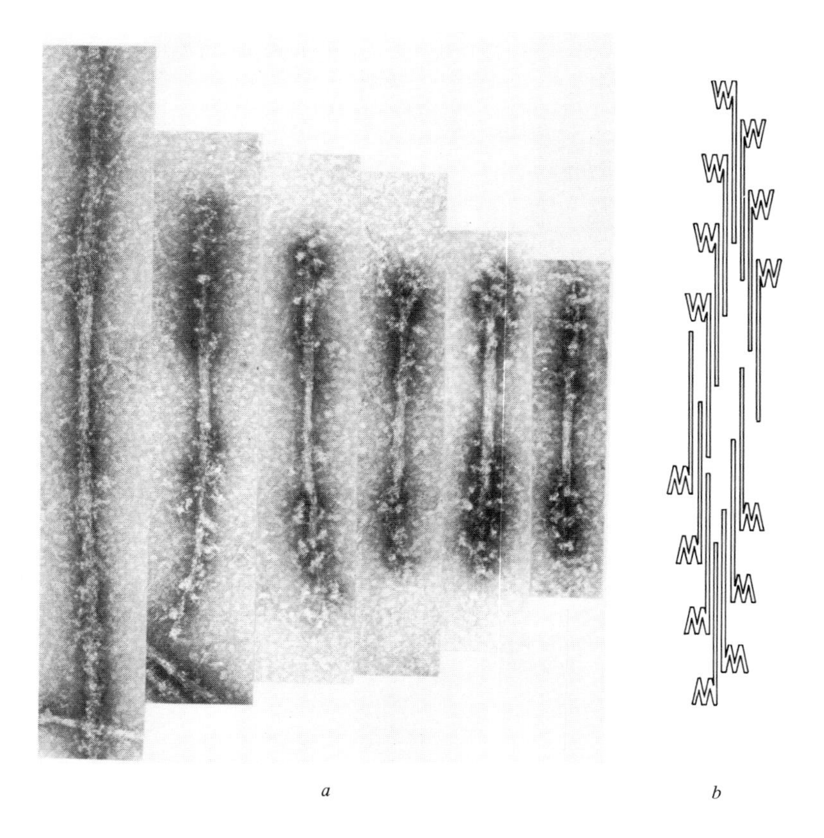

a *b*

fig. 9-14. (*a*) An electron micrograph of aggregations of several myosin molecules negatively stained with phosphotungstic acid. They appear as a thick strand with projections near the ends and a thinner region in the middle. Magnification 86,000. (*b*) A diagram showing the arrangement of myosin molecules in the aggregate. The head of the molecule is represented by a zig-zag line; the tail is represented by a straight line. The tails are oriented toward the center while the heads project at opposite ends. (Electron micrograph courtesy of Dr. Hugh E. Huxley.)

For the preparation of actin, myosin is extracted first from minced muscle. The muscle residue is washed to remove the salt ions and is dehydrated by extraction with *n*-butanol and acetone. The residual myosin is denatured by the dehydration process.[44] Actin may then be extracted from the acetone dried powder by water or, better still, by a very dilute buffered solution of ATP and a reducing agent such as ascorbic acid or mercaptoethanol. In contrast to the other contractile proteins, actin dissociates into monomers in the *absence* of ions and aggregates in the presence of neutral salts. When first extracted from the acetone dry powder, the solution is watery and exists in the monomeric or globular form, called *G-actin*. Upon the addition of KCl, especially if traces of Mg^{++} are present, aggregation into the fibrous form, called *F-actin*, occurs.

[44] Straub, F. B. *Stud. Inst. med. Chem. Univ. Szeged.*, *2*, 3 (1942); *3*, 23 (1943).

The most recent careful measurements indicate that the molecular weight of G-actin is approximately 48,000.[45] Measurements of the intrinsic viscosity of carefully prepared G-actin are in the neighborhood of 3.5 cc/g, indicating that this protein is almost spherical in shape. Each actin monomer molecule contains a tightly bound molecule of ATP and a tightly bound Ca^{++} ion. Generally the presence of both bound nucleotide and bound calcium on G-actin is necessary for its polymerization into F-actin. Removal of the bound nucleotide or bound calcium leads to a form of G-actin which is very labile and easily denatured. Denatured G-actin cannot be polymerized. Under conditions where the G-actin is not denatured, nucleotideless G-actin can polymerize to form F-actin strands. Actin (and perhaps some of the other muscle proteins) contains 3-methylhistidine, an unusual amino acid, as part of the polypeptide chain.[46]

The polymerization reaction is accompanied by the stoichiometric conversion of the bound ATP to bound ADP with the liberation of inorganic phosphate.[47] The depolymerization of F-actin can be brought about in the absence of neutral salt if ATP is present; it is accompanied by a rephosphorylation of the bound ADP to form bound ATP. The integrity of some SH groups on G-actin is necessary for polymerization. During the process of polymerization some of the sulfhydryl groups on G-actin become masked; there is no formation of disulfide bridges, however, since upon depolymerization the sulfhydryl groups become unmasked again.

The formation of F-actin fibers begins by a process of nucleation which requires the aggregation of at least three G-actin monomers. Polymerization proceeds by the lengthwise addition of G-actin monomers resulting in the formation of a right-handed, double-stranded, helical chain with a pitch of about 700 Å and 13 monomers per

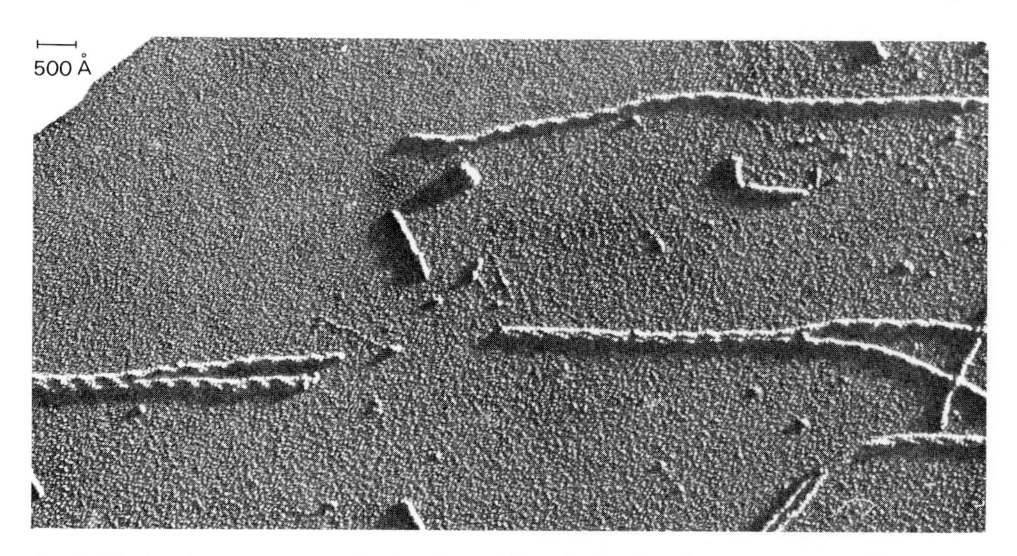

fig. 9-15. An electron micrograph of replicas of F-actin showing the arrangement of the globular monomers in a two-stranded right-handed helix. Magnification 100,000. (Courtesy of Dr. Robert V. Rice.)

[45] Adelstein, R. S., Godfrey, J. E., and Kielley, W. W. *Biochem. Biophys. Res. Commun.*, *12*, 34 (1963).
[46] Johnson, P., Harris, C. I., and Perry, S. V. *Biochem. J.*, *105*, 361 (1967).
[47] Straub, F. B., and Feuer, G. *Biochim. Biophys. Acta*, *4*, 455 (1950); Laki, K., Bowen, W. J., and Clark, A. J. *J. Gen. Physiol.*, *33*, 437 (1950); Maruyama, K., and Gergely, J. *Biochem. Biophys. Res. Commun.*, *6*, 245 (1961); Martonosi, A., and Gouvea, M. A. *J. Biol. Chem.*, *236*, 1345 (1961); Barany, M., Nagy, B., Finkelman, F., and Chrambach, A. *J. Biol. Chem.*, *236*, 2917 (1961).

strand per turn. Two types of intermolecular bonds appear to be involved in the formation of F-actin. Replicas of F-actin are shown in Fig. 9-15.

Tropomyosin constitutes about 5 percent of the myofibrillar proteins. It is best extracted from alcohol and ether-dried minced muscle by 1 M KCl, and it can be purified by repeated isoelectric precipitations and ammonium sulfate fractionations.[48] In the absence of neutral salts, tropomyosin polymerizes to form a nonthixotropic gel. Tropomyosin is largely in the form of an α-helix as judged by optical rotatory dispersion measurements. The molecules aggregate into a twin-stranded, right-handed helical fiber, but the aggregation is reversed by the addition of neutral salts. The molecular weight of the tropomyosin monomer is approximately 54,000. Its intrinsic viscosity is about 52 cc/g, which gives a calculated length-to-width ratio of about 25. Recently, tropomyosin has been prepared in the presence of dithiothreitol, which prevents oxidation of the sulfhydryl groups; such tropomyosin renders reconstituted actomyosin sensitive to superprecipitation in the presence of calcium.[49] The properties of tropomyosin are markedly altered by the presence of a minor protein troponin (see p. 507). Antibody studies show tropomyosin to be located in the thin filaments. In vitro, tropomyosin forms structures which resemble the Z lines in their appearance in the electron microscope.[50]

Paramyosin is a major protein component of certain specialized muscles in molluscs and annelids, the *catch muscles*, which have the unique ability to maintain tension for prolonged periods of time with very low concomitant metabolic activity. Minced muscles dried with ethanol and ether are extracted with concentrated neutral salt solutions.[51] Paramyosin precipitates when the salt concentration is lowered below 0.3 M in slightly acidic solutions, less than *p*H 6.5. The molecular weight of paramyosin is approximately 220,000, and the molecule probably contains two identical subunits. The intrinsic viscosity is approximately 200 cc/g, which indicates a very pronounced asymmetry of the molecules. Paramyosin has no ATPase activity and does not interact with actin.

Amino acid analyses of the contractile proteins show a high concentration of bifunctional amino acids. There are relatively more anionic groups than cationic groups; this accounts for the low isoelectric points of these proteins. Several minor structural proteins have been isolated which appear to have a regulatory function in contraction; these will be discussed below.

interactions of myofibrillar proteins

In concentrated salt solutions, greater than 0.3 M, myosin and actin interact to form a viscous complex, actomyosin. The relative viscosity of the complex is very much greater than the sum of the relative viscosities of its constituent proteins measured separately. Upon mixing myosin and actin under these conditions, there is also a marked increase in light scattering. While the stoichiometry of the interaction is not sharp, the optimum combining ratio is approximately four parts myosin to one part

[48] Bailey, K. *Biochem. J.*, *43*, 271 (1948).
[49] Mueller, H. *Biochem. Z.*, *345*, 300 (1966).
[50] Knappeis, G. G., and Carlsen, F. *J. Cell Biol.*, *13*, 323 (1962).
[51] Bailey, K. *Pubbl. Staz. Zool. Napoli*, *29*, 96 (1957); Laki, K. *Arch. Biochem. Biophys.*, *67*, 240 (1957).

actin by weight[52] as determined by superprecipitation, light scattering, and ultracentrifugation experiments.

The addition of ATP results in a dissociation of the actomyosin complex in concentrated salt solutions, as reflected in a marked drop in viscosity, a marked drop in light scattering of the solution, and a marked decrease in light birefringence. After the ATP is hydrolyzed, the viscosity increases to its former value. The process can be repeated by subsequent additions of ATP. The hydrolysis of ATP is not required for this effect because inorganic pyrophosphate causes the same changes, particularly if traces of magnesium ions are present.

In dilute salt solutions, less than 0.3 M KCl, the actomyosin complex is insoluble. The addition of small amounts of ATP, to a final concentration of 1 mM or less, results in *syneresis*, a marked contraction of the actomyosin gel with the extrusion of water. Hydrolysis of ATP is essential for the phenomenon of syneresis. It occurs to a lesser extent with other triphosphate nucleotides, but not with inorganic pyrophosphate. Superprecipitation of an actomyosin gel is illustrated in Fig. 9-16. Blocking a sufficient number of sulfhydryl groups to inhibit ATPase activity also abolishes syneresis.

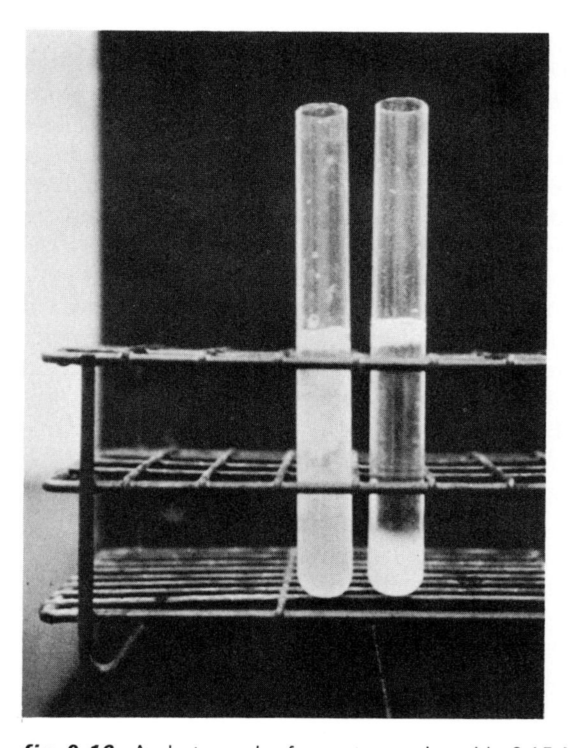

fig. 9-16. A photograph of an actomyosin gel in 0.15 M KCl before and 20 min after the addition of 2 mM final concentration ATP.

---

[52] Spicer, S. S., and Gergely, J. *J. Biol. Chem.*, *188*, 179 (1951); Gergely, J., and Kohler, H., in Kumagai, H., ed. *Conference on the Chemistry of Muscular Contraction*. Tokyo: Igaku Shoin, 1957, p. 14; Tonomura, Y., Tokura, S., and Sekiya, K. *J. Biol. Chem.*, *237*, 1074 (1962); Nanninga, L. B. *Biochim. Biophys. Acta*, *82*, 507 (1964). Many of the properties of actomyosin described in this section were first reported by Albert Szent-Györgyi; see the references at the end of Chapter 9.

Threads of actomyosin may be obtained by squirting an actomyosin solution in 0.3 M KCl through a fine orifice into a solution of low ionic strength, such as 0.05 M KCl. With the addition of ATP, such threads shorten to between one-third and one-quarter their original length. The shortening of precipitated actomyosin threads, however, is unlike the contraction of muscle; it is isodimensional, representing syneresis with squeezing out of large amounts of water with a marked increase in the protein concentration of the threads. This phenomenon is called *supercontraction.*

The ATPase activity of myosin has been a topic of great investigative interest since its discovery by Engelhardt and Ljubimova.[53] The ATPase activity of pure myosin is activated by low (millimolar) concentrations of Ca^{++} and is inhibited by Mg^{++}; it may also be stimulated by higher concentrations of K^+ in the absence of Ca^{++} ions. Other purine trinucleotides can replace ATP. The sulfhydryl groups of myosin are necessary for its ATPase activity. Curiously, however, when ATP is used as substrate in the presence of Ca^{++} ions, reaction of the first few sulfhydryl groups per molecule of myosin results in an activation of the ATPase activity until approximately four sulfhydryl groups per myosin molecule are blocked. The activation by SH reagents is not observed when inosine triphosphate is used as substrate, nor is it observed for the K^+ activated ATPase activity. Further reactions of the sulfhydryl groups result in a precipitous loss of ATPase activity.

In contrast to the ATPase activity of pure myosin, the ATPase activity of the actomyosin complex is *stimulated* by the presence of Mg^{++}, particularly at low ionic strength. The ATPase activity of the actomyosin complex is much greater in dilute salt solutions where the complex exists as a gel than in more concentrated salt solutions where the complex is dissolved. The Mg^{++} activated ATPase of actomyosin gels has severalfold greater activity than does the Ca^{++} activated ATPase of the myosin component alone. The actomyosin system is very complex and is affected by the presence or absence of the minor proteins described below.

Actin and heavy meromyosin also form a complex. The actin–heavy meromyosin complex has solubility properties similar to those of F-actin, while its ATPase activity resembles that of the actomyosin complex. Even under conditions where viscosity and light-scattering measurements indicate dissociation of the actin–heavy meromyosin complex, the complex is still strongly activated by Mg^{++}. The actin–heavy meromyosin complex, however, does not superprecipitate.

Weber and her coworkers demonstrated that Ca^{++} was necessary for superprecipitation of native actomyosin, that is, actomyosin extracted directly from minced muscle as the complex.[54] Treatment of natural actomyosin (containing tropomyosin) with EDTA, a chelating agent which complexes almost all Ca^{++} ions, abolishes superprecipitation. Addition of Ca^{++} ions to a final concentration of 0.3 to 1.5 μM restores the capacity of the actomyosin to supercontract upon the addition of ATP. It should be noted that this concentration of Ca^{++} is about 1/1000 that required for half-maximal activation of myosin ATPase activity or half-inhibition of the Mg^{++} activated ATPase of actomyosin. Reconstituted actomyosin prepared from *highly purified* myosin and actin does not superprecipitate, even upon the addition of Ca^{++}.

It appears that the ATPase activity and actin-combining capacity occur at different sites on the myosin molecule. The evidence in favor of this view is, briefly, as follows.

[53] Engelhardt, B. A., and Ljubimova, M. N. *Nature*, *144*, 668 (1939); Ljubimova, M. N., and Engelhardt, B. A. *Biokhimiya*, *4*, 735 (1939).
[54] Weber, A., and Winicur, S. *J. Biol. Chem.*, *236*, 3198 (1961); Weber, A., and Herz, R. *J. Biol. Chem.*, *238*, 599 (1963); Weber, A., Herz, R., and Reiss, I. *Federation Proc.*, *23*, 896 (1964).

Treatment of actomyosin with high concentrations of iodoacetamide abolishes the enzymatic activity but not the actin-combining capacity of myosin.[55] Similarly, treatment of heavy meromyosin with phenylmercuriacetate destroys the ATPase activity but not the capacity to combine with actin.[56] The sulfhydryl groups protected when myosin is treated with *bis*-β-carboxyethyldisulfide in the presence of ATP are different from those protected when myosin is treated in the presence of actin.[57]

Actin and tropomyosin associate to form mixed aggregates. The fibers which are formed by the mixture of these two proteins, in contrast to pure F-actin fibers, show a periodicity of 406 Å. Several minor structural proteins have been isolated which appear to modify the contractile process. β-Actinin can be prepared from KI extracts of muscle by precipitation with low concentrations of ammonium sulfate. In the presence of about one-tenth weight β-actinin, G-actin polymerizes to form filaments about 1 μ in length, the approximate length of actin filaments *in situ*; in the absence of β-actinin, the fibers formed are 10 to 12 μ long.[58] Another protein, α-actinin, accelerates the polymerization of actin, promotes the formation of actin gels, and enhances the superprecipitation of reconstituted actomyosin.[59] The actinins do not interact with myosin nor do they modify the ATPase activity of myosin or reconstituted actomyosin.

Another minor protein, troponin, has been isolated from the supernatant fraction during the isoelectric precipitation of tropomyosin. Troponin combines with tropomyosin which in turn forms a complex with actin.[60] Immunochemical studies have shown that troponin is distributed at about 400-Å intervals along the whole of the thin filament. This corresponds to the length of tropomyosin molecules, and it appears that troponin molecules join two adjacent molecules of tropomyosin. Tropomyosin containing troponin restores the normal reactivity of reconstituted actomyosin toward Ca^{++} ions and calcium-chelating agents. Tropinin itself has a very high affinity for Ca^{++}; the affinity constant is approximately 1.8×10^{-6}.

ultrastructure of striated muscle

Ultrastructure studies of striated muscle by electron microscopy reveal that the myofibril is made up of many small, parallel fibers[61] (Fig. 9-17). Thick filaments with a diameter of about 110 to 150 Å, arranged in a simple hexagonal fashion about 450 Å apart, extend from one edge to the other of the dense, birefringent A band. Thin filaments, with a diameter of about 40 to 60 Å, are located in a regular manner between the thick filaments, so that each thick filament is surrounded by six thin filaments. The thin filaments appear to be connected to the Z line, from which they extend through the I band and into the A band as far as the boundary of the H zone. Cross-sectional

[55] Barany, M., and Barany, K. *Biochim. Biophys. Acta*, *35*, 293 (1959).
[56] Perry, S. V., and Cotterill, J. *Biochem. J.*, *92*, 603 (1964).
[57] Stracher, A. *J. Biol. Chem.*, *239*, 1118 (1964).
[58] Maruyama, K. *Biochim. Biophys. Acta*, *94*, 208 (1965); Hama, H., Maruyama, K., and Noda, H. *Biochim. Biophys. Acta*, *102*, 249 (1965); Maruyama, K. *Biochim. Biophys. Acta*, *126*, 389 (1966).
[59] Ebashi, S., Maruyama, K., and Ebashi, F. *J. Biochem.* (*Tokyo*), *58*, 7, 13, 20 (1965); Seraydarian, K., Briskey, E. J., and Mommaerts, W. F. H. M. *Biochim. Biophys. Acta*, *133*, 399, 412, 424 (1967).
[60] Ebashi, S. *Nature*, *200*, 1010 (1963); Ebashi, S., and Ebashi, F. *J. Biochem.* (*Tokyo*), *55*, 604 (1964); Maruyama, K. *Biochim. Biophys. Acta*, *94*, 208 (1965); *126*, 389 (1966); Ohtsuki, I., Masaki, T., Nonomura, Y., and Ebashi, S. *J. Biochem. (Tokyo)*, *61*, 817 (1967).
[61] Hall, C. E., Jakus, M. A., and Schmitt, F. O. *Biol. Bull.*, *90*, 32 (1946); Draper, M. H., and Hodge, A. J. *Australian J. Exptl. Biol. Med. Sci.*, *27*, 465 (1949); Huxley, H. E. *Biochim. Biophys. Acta*, *12 A*, 387 (1953); Huxley, H. E. *J. Biophys. Biochem. Cytol.*, *3*, 631 (1957).

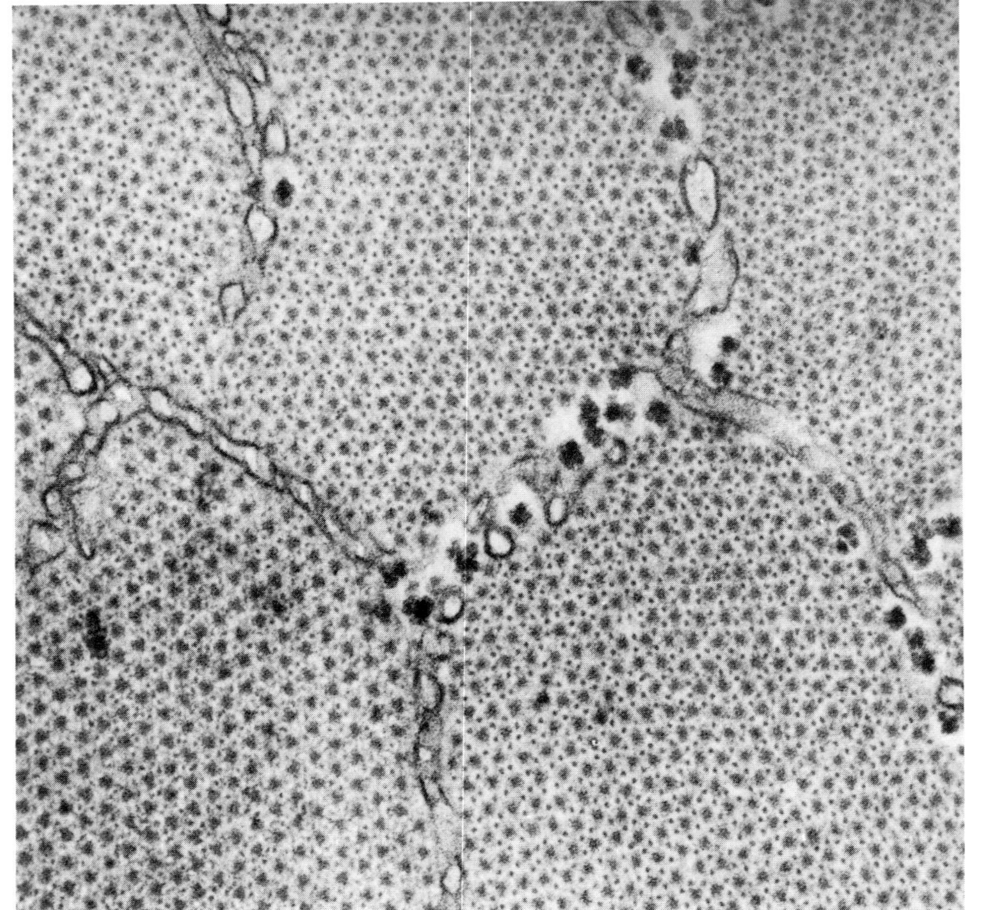

b

fig. 9-17. Electron micrographs of rabbit muscle cut (*a*) longitudinally and (*b*) in cross section. In the longitudinal sections the dense A bands bisected by the H zones with a central M line can be seen, contrasted to the lighter I bands which are bisected by dark Z lines. The cross section taken from the region of an A band shows the thick filaments surrounded by thin filaments. (Courtesy of Dr. Hugh E. Huxley.)

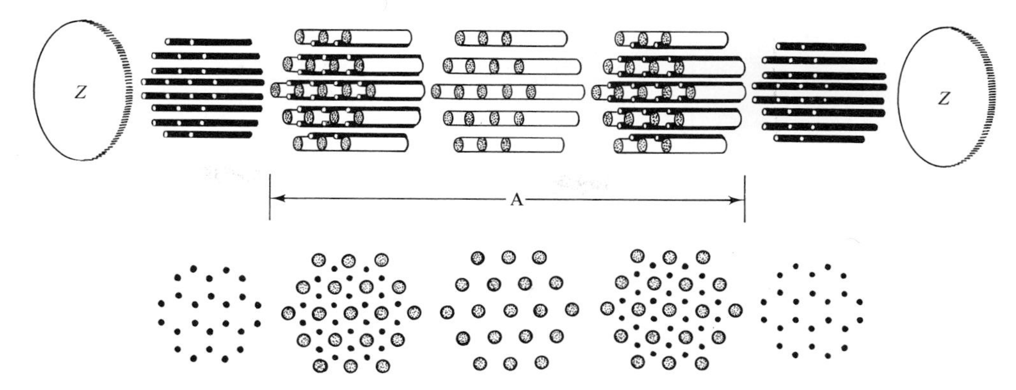

fig. 9-18. A schematic representation of the filament arrangement in skeletal muscle. The thin filaments composed of actin extend from the Z lines through the I band and into the A band as far as the H zone. The thick filaments composed of myosin extend from one edge of the A band to the other. (Adapted from Huxley, H. E. *J. Biophys. Biochem. Cytol.*, *3*, 633 [1957].)

electron micrographs of muscle show a variety of patterns, depending upon the position of the section through the sarcomere. Thus, sections through the H zone show only thick filaments, sections through the I band show only thin filaments, and sections through the dense portion of the A band show both thick and thin filaments (Fig. 9-18).

The two kinds of filaments appear to be joined by a system of cross bridges which extend from the thick filaments toward the thin filaments. Each thick filament appears to have two projections in opposite directions approximately once every 140 Å along the length of the filament. The direction of succeeding projections is rotated 120° around the filament axis. A thick filament thus appears to be joined to one of the six adjacent thin filaments by a cross bridge at 430-Å intervals. The projections appear to correspond to the globular heads of myosin molecules in synthetic myosin fibers.[62]

Treatment of myofibrils with hypertonic KCl solution selectively extracts myosin. Electron micrographs of such myofibrils show that the thick fibers from the A band have been selectively removed, leaving thin fibers stretching from the Z line to the edge of the H zone.[63] Extraction of the thick filaments, however, does not result in a collapse of thin filaments. The H zone itself now has a very low density. Muscle fibers from which the thick filaments have been extracted may be stretched without rupturing the myofibrils; stretching leads to an increase in width of the H zone.

Further treatment of such KCl-extracted myofibrils with 0.6 M KI results in extraction of actin.[64] Such myofibrils lose all the filaments and leave behind only the Z lines. It appears that the thick filaments which make up the A band are composed of myosin, while the thin filaments are composed of actin. The observed ratio of myosin to actin of approximately three to one agrees with the ratio of volumes calculated for the two types of filament (Fig. 9-19).

The localization of the contractile proteins within the sarcomere has also been studied by the use of fluorescent labeled antibodies to the purified proteins. Antibodies prepared against myosin are found to deposit within the A band region, while anti-

[62] Huxley, H. E. *J. Mol. Biol.*, *7*, 281 (1963); Pepe, F. A. *J. Mol. Biol.*, *27*, 203, 227 (1967).
[63] Hasselbach, W. *Z. Naturforsch.*, *8 B*, 449 (1953); Hanson, J., and Huxley, H. E. *Nature*, *172*, 530 (1953).
[64] Hanson, J., and Huxley, H. E. *Symp. Soc. Exptl. Biol.*, *9*, 228 (1955).

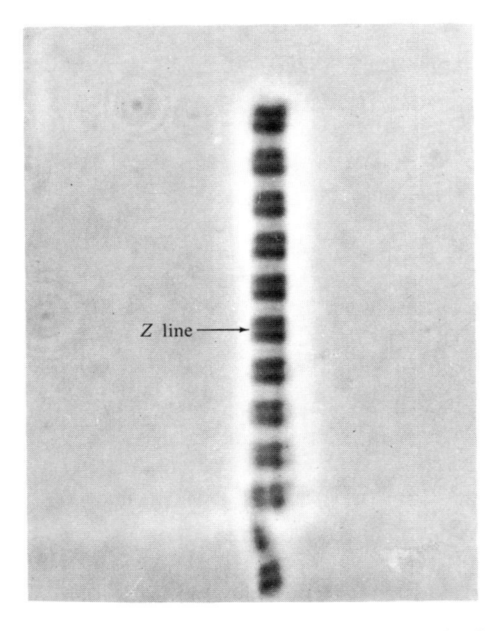

fig. 9-19. Phase contrast photomicrograph of a glycerinated myofibril after extraction with 0.6 M KCl. The high concentration salt solution extracts the myosin which is found in the thick filaments of the A bands. (Courtesy of Dr. Andrew G. Szent-Györgyi.)

bodies prepared against actin deposit in the I band and in the distal portion of the A band. Antibodies prepared against tropomyosin appear to deposit more or less evenly throughout the sarcomere.

The development of this highly organized architectural pattern has been followed in the chick embryo skeletal muscle.[65] The thin filaments appear first in 9 to 10 day old embryos—about the time of appearance of 15 to 25–unit polyribosomes with which actin biosynthesis is associated. The thick filaments begin to appear at about 12 days and show a rapid increase in number; and, at about the same time, the very large polyribosomes of 55 to 70 units associated with myosin biosynthesis appear. At first the thin filaments and thick filaments are scattered free in the muscle fiber without evidence of any pattern of organization, but then the thick and thin filaments associate in a hexagonal array. At about 16 days the Z lines appear. The 4 to 8–unit polysomes with which tropomyosin is associated appear at 14 to 18 days.

It has been shown that the width of the A band remains approximately constant regardless of whether a muscle fiber is relaxed, contracted, or stretched.[66] On the

[65] Allen, E. R., and Pepe, F. A. *Am. J. Anat.*, *116*, 115 (1965); Dessovky, D. A., and Hibbs, R. G. *Am. J. Anat.*, *116*, 523 (1965); Obinata, T., Yamamoto, M., and Maruyama, K. *Develop. Biol.*, *14*, 192 (1966); Fischman, D. A. *J. Cell Biol.*, *32*, 557 (1967); Heywood, S. M., and Rich, A. *Proc. Natl. Acad. Sci.*, *59*, 590 (1968).

[66] Krause, W. *Die motorischen Endplatten der quergestreiften Muskelfasern.* Hanover: Hahn, 1869, p. 172; Dempsey, E. W., Wislocki, G. B., and Singer, M. *Anat. Record*, *96*, 221 (1946); Hoffmann-Berling, H., and Kausche, G. A. *Z. Naturforsch.*, *5 B*, 139 (1950); Huxley, A. F., and Niedergerke, R. *Nature*, *173*, 971 (1954); Huxley, H. E., and Hanson, J. *Nature*, *173*, 973 (1954); Harman, J. W. *Federation Proc.*, *13*, 430 (1954); Hanson, J., and Huxley, H. E. *Symp. Soc. Exptl. Biol.*, *9*, 228 (1955).

other hand, the width of the I band becomes smaller during contraction of the muscle fiber and wider upon its stretching. While the H zone is wide in relaxed muscle, it narrows upon contraction and may even disappear entirely. Thus, it may be presumed that the length of the thin filaments remains constant, because the width of the I band and of the H zone increase or decrease *pari passu*. When a muscle is made to contract markedly, the thin filaments may actually cross the M line and interdigitate (Fig. 9-20). Upon very great shortening the A bands reach the Z line and the ends of the thick filaments fold over upon themselves, giving rise to the *contraction bands* at the Z lines. These observations have led to the sliding filament hypothesis which was proposed independently by Huxley and Hanson, and by Huxley and Niedergerke.[67]

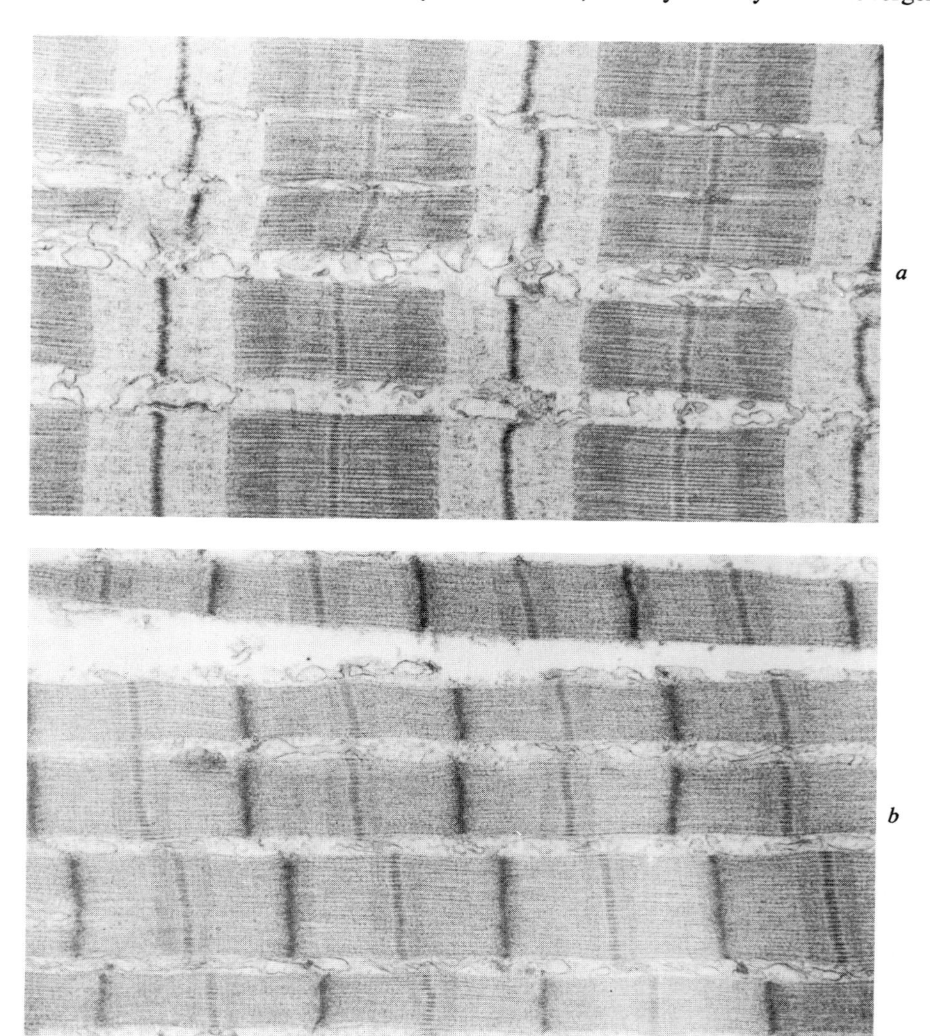

fig. 9-20. Electron micrographs of (*a*) relaxed and (*b*) contracted muscle. In the contracted muscle the thick and thin filaments overlap to a greater extent, leading to a shortening of the I band. (Courtesy of Dr. Hugh E. Huxley.)

[67] Huxley, A. F., and Niedergerke, R. *Nature*, *173*, 971 (1954); Huxley, H. E., and Hanson, J. *Nature*, *173*, 973 (1954); Huxley, H. E. *J. Biophys. Biochem. Cytol.*, *3*, 631 (1957).

According to this theory, all changes in sarcomere length result from motion of the two types of filaments relative to one another. The tension produced thus should decrease as a muscle is stretched because the region of overlap is decreased, and zero tension should be produced at the point where the fibers are stretched beyond any overlap. Qualitatively, this has been found to be true in frog muscle.

Muscle has a well-developed endoplasmic reticulum, an extensive membranous system within the cytoplasm which in muscle is often called the *sarcoplasmic reticulum*. The membranes form a network of tubules around each myofibril. The sarcoplasmic reticulum differs from the endoplasmic reticulum of other cells in that it possesses certain characteristic features which are repeated in the same relative positions in every sarcomere. A characteristic *triad* structure is formed by the lateral cisternae of the sarcoplasmic reticulum on either side of central or *transverse tubules* which cross the myofibril. The dilated lateral cysternae are formed by anastomoses of numerous finger-like connecting tubules (Fig. 9-21) of the sarcoplasmic reticulum.

Some, but not all, of the elements of the sarcoplasmic reticulum appear to be connected to the plasma membrane of the muscle cell. The central element of the triad of vertebrate muscle, the transverse tubule, appears to be connected to the muscle fiber surface.[68] Ferritin (about 110 Å in diameter) placed in a solution bathing a frog sartorius muscle was shown to enter the transverse tubules but not any other part of the muscle cell.[69] Ferritin molecules were not found within the lateral cisternae. In general, the surface area of the transverse tubular system of a muscle fiber is approximately four times as great as the surface area of the plasma membrane. The reticular triad appears to bear a fixed position in the sarcomere of a given species, but the position varies according to the species. In most mammals the triad is centered near the junction of the I and A bands, while in frogs it coincides with the Z line.

excitation contraction coupling

The process by which a depolarization of the sarcolemma leads to contraction has been a topic of experimental interest.

It does not seem likely that the longitudinal currents generated by the propagation of the action potential play a direct role in triggering the contractile mechanism. It is well known that immersing a muscle fiber in a KCl solution results in contraction even though the surface membrane is depolarized uniformly and internal currents are not generated.[70] Furthermore, Watanabe[71] was unable to induce contraction by passing current pulses several times greater in magnitude than the action potential current between two microelectrodes inserted into the sarcoplasm. Contraction is probably triggered by inwardly directed electrotonic currents.

The relationship between the magnitude of membrane depolarization and the development of tension was studied by Hodgkin and Horowicz,[72] who submerged single frog skeletal muscle fibers in solutions containing increasing concentrations of

[68] Franzini-Armstrong, C., and Porter, K. R. *J. Cell Biol.*, *22*, 675 (1964).
[69] Huxley, H. E. *Nature*, *202*, 1067 (1964).
[70] Kuffler, S. W. *J. Neurophysiol.*, *9*, 367 (1946).
[71] Watanabe, A. *Japan. J. Physiol.*, *8*, 123 (1958).
[72] Hodgkin, A. L., and Horowicz, P. *J. Physiol.*, *153*, 386, 404 (1960).

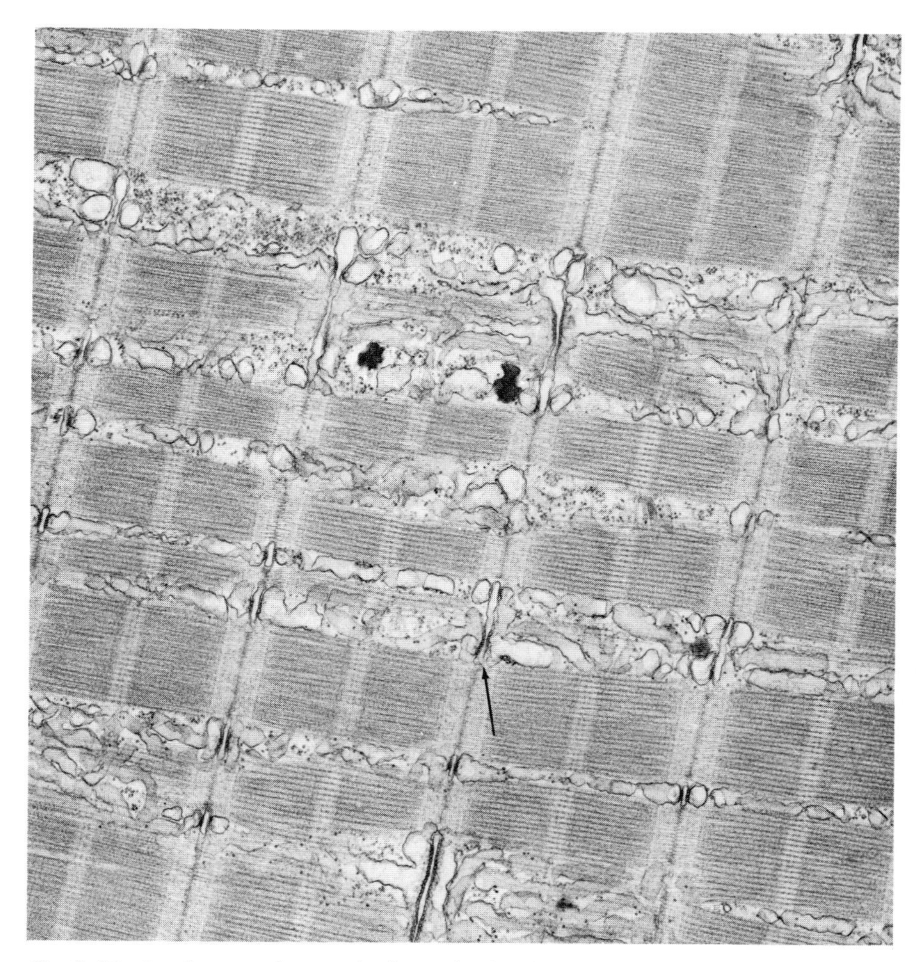

fig. 9-21. An electron micrograph of muscle showing the sarcoplasmic reticulum. The triad complex (arrow) is located at the level of the Z lines. Magnification 21,000. (Courtesy of Dr. Keith R. Porter.)

K^+ ions. They found that tension output begins to appear only when the membrane is depolarized to a value of -50 mv (this value may be regarded as a *mechanical threshold*). As the membrane is depolarized to a greater extent, the tension rises steeply and then levels off to maximal tension production at a membrane potential of approximately -20 mv. During the course of an ordinary action potential, the membrane is depolarized to a value greater than -50 mv for approximately 1.5 msec. Sandow[73] has called this time interval the *mechanically effective period.*

On the basis of quick stretch experiments, Hill[74] concluded that muscle fibers become fully active long before a substance can diffuse from the surface to the central part of the muscle cell. It should be noted that the rate of conduction of an action potential is much greater than are rates of diffusion. Hill's experiments suggested that an action potential activated the entire cross section of a muscle fiber 100 μ in diameter long before the twitch tension reached peak value.

---

[73] Sandow, A., Taylor, S. R., and Preiser, H. *Federation Proc.*, *24*, 1116 (1965).
[74] Hill, A. V. *Proc. Roy. Soc.*, *B 136*, 399 (1949).

The first suggestion that the transverse tubules might play a role in excitation contraction coupling came from a fascinating series of experiments by A. F. Huxley, R. E. Taylor, and R. W. Straub[75] in which areas only a few microns in length on the surfaces of single myofibrils were depolarized. Highly localized contraction of the myofibril was observed when certain regions were depolarized. These reactive spots were localized precisely in relation to the sarcomere, but their location in muscle differed in different species of animals. Thus, in frogs, depolarization occurred at the Z line, while in crabs and mammals muscle fiber contraction occurred near the ends of the A band. The reactive locations which responded to depolarization by local contraction corresponded to the location of the triads, and thus to the location of the transverse tubules. The transverse tubules, it will be recalled, appear to be connected directly to the plasma membrane. The development of the transverse tubular system appears to be extensive in muscles which contract very rapidly, while in slow muscles the development of the transverse tubular system is minimal.

It is unlikely that the tubular membrane system generates an action potential. The local stimulation experiments of Huxley and his collaborators displayed only local contraction rather than the contraction of the entire myofibril which would have been expected if an impulse propagated itself along the myofibril. It appears, then, that during the depolarization of the plasma membrane surrounding the muscle fiber, there is a flow of positive current from the sarcoplasm through the tubular membrane, and along the lumen of the tubular membrane system back to the outside membrane. The bulk of this electrotonic flow of outward current appears, on the basis of indirect evidence, to be carried by potassium ions that move from the sarcoplasm or from the lateral cisternae into the transverse tubular system.[76]

There is strong evidence that the final steps in activation of the contractile process involve an increase in the concentration of Ca^{++} ions in the region of the myofilaments in the interior of the muscle fiber. Ringer[77] observed long ago that the frog heart stops beating when immersed in calcium-free media. Yet while contraction is abolished, hearts develop a normal action potential in the absence of calcium. In skeletal muscle, however, neither contraction nor an action potential takes place in the absence of Ca^{++} ions.[78]

The first direct evidence that calcium ions might be involved in activation of the contractile process in skeletal muscle came from the experiments of Heilbrunn and Wiercinski,[79] in which it was demonstrated that the injection of calcium chloride solution into the interior of a muscle fiber by means of a micropipette was followed by contraction, while injection of solutions of sodium, potassium, or magnesium salts had no effect, even when considerably higher concentrations were injected.

Another experiment which added to the evidence that calcium was involved in contraction was the demonstration that the application of calcium directly to a muscle fiber from which the sarcolemma had been removed resulted in a contractile response when the muscle was at rest length.[80] However, if the muscle fiber had been stretched beforehand so that the sarcomere length was greater than the sum of the lengths of

---

[75] Huxley, A. F., and Straub, R. W. *J. Physiol.*, *143*, 40P (1958); Huxley, A. F., and Taylor, R. E. *Nature*, *176*, 1068 (1955); *J. Physiol.*, *144*, 426 (1958).
[76] Adrian, R. H., and Freygang, W. H. *J. Physiol.*, *163*, 61 (1962); Freygang, W. H., Goldstein, D. A., and Hellam, D. C. *J. Gen. Physiol.*, *47*, 929 (1964); *48*, 235 (1964).
[77] Ringer, S. *J. Physiol.*, *4*, 29 (1883); Mines, G. R. *J. Physiol.*, *46*, 188 (1913).
[78] Edman, K. A. P., and Grieve, D. W. *Experientia*, *19*, 40 (1963).
[79] Heilbrunn, L. V., and Wiercinski, F. J. *J. Cellular Comp. Physiol.*, *29*, 15 (1947).
[80] Podolsky, R. J. *J. Physiol.*, *170*, 110 (1964).

the thin filaments and thick filaments, that is to say, so that there was no area of overlap between thin and thick filaments, then the application of calcium failed to produce a contractile response.

The hypothesis that calcium ions move from the lateral cisternae of the sarcoplasmic reticulum to the A band region of the myofibril receives support from autoradiographic studies of skeletal muscle fixed during relaxation and comparable preparations fixed during contraction.[81] A large amount of calcium (which does not participate in excitation) is bound to actin; an alternative hypothesis of activation proposes that some of the calcium bound to the other proteins of the actomyosin system is liberated in the ionic form upon excitation.[82]

relaxing system

While depolarization of the sarcolemma initiates a series of events leading to contraction, repolarization of the cell membranes does not initiate relaxation. It was known from the work of Marsh and Bendall[83] that a system existed in muscle which was capable of inhibiting or reversing syneresis of actomyosin fibers, suppressing ATPase activity and superprecipitation of actomyosin gels, and initiating the relaxation of contracted glycerinated muscle fibers. It was then shown that the relaxing system is present in the microsomal fraction of muscle, and that it is derived mainly from the membrane of the sarcoplasmic reticulum.[84]

The sarcomplasmic reticulum, in the form of microsomal vesicles or *grana*, is able to accumulate Ca^{++} ions from the external medium against very high electrochemical gradients.[85] Upon perfusion with sodium oxalate solutions, the calcium within the microsomal vesicles can be quantified by precipitation as calcium oxalate.[86] The calcium pumping mechanism is coupled to the hydrolysis of ATP. When microsomal vesicles are added to various actomyosin systems, they can reduce the free Ca^{++} concentration to 0.02 μM or less, thereby causing the actomyosin to dissociate and the system to exhibit typical relaxation phenomenona.[87] Ca^{++} accumulated by the vesicles leaks out again if the supply of ATP is blocked or if the pumping mechanism is inhibited—for example, with salyrgan.

Perfusion by Costantin and his collaborators of single, denuded frog muscle fibers with sodium oxalate showed deposits of calcium oxalate only in the lateral sacs of the sarcoplasmic reticulum.[88] The studies were important because they demonstrated that the calcium-pumping property of fragmented sarcoplasmic reticulum in the form of microsomal vesicles also operates in the fully organized reticulum of intact muscle fibers.

The fact that calcium uptake appears to be localized mainly in the lateral sacs of the triad is significant because of the proximity of these structures to the transverse

---

[81] Winegrad, S. *J. Gen. Physiol.*, *48*, 455, 997 (1965).
[82] Weber, A., Herz, R., and Reiss, I. *Proc. Roy. Soc.*, *B 160*, 489 (1964).
[83] Marsh, B. B. *Biochim. Biophys. Acta*, *9*, 247 (1952); Bendall, J. R. *J. Physiol.*, *121*, 232 (1953).
[84] Portzehl, H. *Biochim. Biophys. Acta*, *26*, 373 (1957); Nagai, T., Makinose, M., and Hasselbach, W. *Biochim. Biophys. Acta*, *43*, 223 (1960); Muscatello, U., Andersson-Cedergren, E., and Azzone, G. F. *Biochim. Biophys. Acta*, *63*, 55 (1962).
[85] Hasselbach, W., and Makinose, M. *Biochem. Z.*, *333*, 518 (1961); Ebashi, S., and Lipmann, F. *J. Cell Biol.*, *14*, 389 (1962).
[86] Hasselbach, W. *Federation Proc.*, *23*, 909 (1964).
[87] Weber, A., Herz, R., and Reiss, I. *J. Gen. Physiol.*, *46*, 679 (1963).
[88] Costantin, L. L., Franzini-Armstrong, C., and Podolsky, R. J. *Science*, *147*, 158 (1965); *Federation Proc.*, *24*, 1141 (1965).

tubules. It is possible that calcium is released from the lateral cisternae during excitation. This hypothesis receives support from Winegrad's autoradiographic studies (see footnote 81, p. 515) which show calcium to be localized principally in the area of the lateral sacs of the triad in relaxed frog skeletal muscle fibers, while in contracted fibers, calcium is also found in the region of overlap of thick and thin filaments in the A band. Winegrad's findings substantiate earlier studies which indicated that the calcium in relaxed muscle was almost entirely bound to intracellular particulate structures, while in highly exercised muscle, free calcium was found in the cytoplasm[89]

The studies of Podolsky and Costantin[90] in isolated frog skeletal muscle indicate that the sarcoplasmic reticulum accumulates calcium ions as a first-order reaction with a rate constant of approximately 36 sec^{-1} at room temperature. This result may be contrasted with the studies of Hodgkin and Horowicz[91] on the kinetics of potassium contractures in frog skeletal muscle, which led them to presume that depolarization releases an activator which is destroyed by a first-order reaction with a rate constant of about 30 sec^{-1}.

The results are typical of several experiments supporting the idea that the mechanical response of muscle results from the introduction of Ca^{++} into the myofibrils and that relaxation results from its removal. The time course of Ca^{++} removal from the free cytoplasm corresponds approximately to the rate of relaxation of muscle. A number of substances, including the anions NO_3^- and I^-, the divalent cations Zn^{++} and UO_2^{++}, and caffeine, are known to potentiate contraction by skeletal muscle.[92] The divalent cations apparently prolong the repolarization phase of the muscle action potential, thereby prolonging the mechanically effective period. On the other hand, the nitrate and iodide anions and caffeine appear to act by inhibiting the calcium pump,[93] thereby prolonging and potentiating the single twitch. In addition, caffeine causes the direct release of Ca^{++} ions into the myoplasm. Evidence is accumulating that the heat of activation corresponds to the pumping of Ca^{++} ions.

It has been tacitly assumed in the foregoing discussion that relaxation is a passive process and that muscle elongation takes place as a result of elastic forces, both internal and external. While this can be visualized in whole muscle *in situ*, particularly where there is a balance between opposing muscles, it is difficult to visualize sarcomere lengthening in isolated myofibrils only as a result of elastic forces. Gross differences in the characteristics of relaxation of whole muscle and single muscle fibers have been described (see footnote 18, p. 494). Nevertheless, sarcomere lengthening does occur in isolated muscle fibers and tissue-cultured muscle cells during relaxation; thus an intrafibrillar force may result in elongation by means of an active process.

atrophy of muscle

During development in the embryo, muscle and nerve cells differentiate independently. The differentiation of myoblasts, the development of the myotube, and the formation

[89] Weise, E. *Arch. exptl. Pathol. Pharmakol.*, *176*, 367 (1934); Woodward, A. A. *Biol. Bull.*, *97*, 264 (1949); Cosmos, E. *Am. J. Physiol.*, *195*, 705 (1958); Shanes, A. M., and Bianchi, C. P. *J. Gen. Physiol.*, *43*, 481 (1960).

[90] Podolsky, R. J., and Costantin, L. L. *Federation Proc.*, *23*, 933 (1964).

[91] Hodgkin, A. L., and Horowicz, P. *J. Physiol.*, *153*, 386 (1960).

[92] Sandow, A., and Isaacson, A. *Biochem. Biophys. Res. Commun.*, *2*, 455 (1960); Isaacson, A., and Sandow, A. *J. Gen. Physiol.*, *46*, 655 (1963); Mashima, H., and Washio, H. *Japan. J. Physiol.*, *14*, 538 (1964); Axelsson, J., and Thesleff, S. *Acta Physiol. Scand.*, *44*, 55 (1958); Herz, R., and Weber, A. *Federation Proc.*, *24*, 208 (1965).

[93] Sandow, A. *Arch. Phys. Med. Rehabil.*, *45*, 62 (1964); Weber, A., and Herz, R. *J. Gen. Physiol.*, *52*, 750, 760 (1968).

of myofibrils all proceed without the influence of nerve fibers. Only the differentiation of the motor end plate requires innervation by a motor nerve fiber. The capacity of a muscle to grow and differentiate continues for a time,[94] in spite of denervation, but in the fully developed animal, denervation is followed by changes in structure and function called *atrophy* which are reversed upon reinnervation by a motor nerve. It appears that sensory or sympathetic nerve fibers are not able to exert such a trophic influence upon skeletal muscle. Atrophy consists of two classes of changes in the muscle: (1) loss of bulk, changes in composition and morphological changes, and (2) changes in the irritability and electrical properties of muscle. The former class of changes is also seen in the atrophy which accompanies prolonged disuse or immobilization of a muscle, and this class of changes can be lessened in denervated muscle by direct electrical stimulation or passive exercise. The changes in the irritability of muscle are seen only after denervation and are not ameliorated by passive exercise.

The loss of bulk which accompanies atrophy is most easily followed by measuring the diameters of the muscle fibers.[95] In the rat, for example, 70 to 85 percent of the fiber diameter is lost by the end of the first month after denervation. After denervation in the rabbit, 30 percent of the fiber diameter is lost by the end of the first month, 60 percent by the end of the second month, and 70 percent by the end of the eighth month. The decrease in fiber diameter, which is a better index of functioning muscle mass, decreases more rapidly than the muscle weight. Muscle weight decreases to about 20 percent of the original weight over a period of a few months after denervation and remains rather constant thereafter. The changes in bulk are greater in muscle which has *hypertrophied* beforehand because of exercise.[96]

A number of morphological changes accompany the process of atrophy.[97] In man, 1 to 2 months after denervation, an increased number of nuclei are found. The nuclei tend to be located in the center of the fibers or in clumps instead of just under the sarcolemma as in normal muscle fibers. The nuclei contain an increased number of nucleoli. After about 4 months, there is an increased variation and overall marked diminution in the diameters of muscle fibers. After 1 to 3 years, the muscle fibers have lost their cross striations and the nuclei are hyperchromatic and pyncnotic. The muscle has been invaded and partially replaced by connective tissue, and there is some replacement by fat.

The interpretation of the changes in composition of muscle after denervation depends upon whether whole muscle or noncollagenous protein is used as the reference base. There is a slight increase in the amount of intracellular water shortly after denervation.[98] In denervated muscle, the concentrations of sodium and chloride ions increase, while the concentration of potassium ions remains about constant when noncollagenous nitrogen (or dried, fat-free muscle) is used as the reference base. On the other hand, in the whole muscle, the content of sodium and chloride ions remains about constant while that of potassium diminishes after denervation. These data are interpreted as an indication that the extracellular space (which contains most of the sodium and chloride ions) remains relatively the same, while the functioning muscle

---

[94] Hamburger, V. *Physiol. Zool.*, *12*, 268 (1939); Zelena, J., in Gutmann, E., ed. *The Denervated Muscle.* Prague: Czechoslovak Academy of Sciences, 1962, p. 103.
[95] Gutmann, E. *J. Neurophysiol.*, *11*, 279 (1948).
[96] An orthopedic surgeon will make a very tight cast around the limb of an athlete who has broken a bone, knowing that the cast will be loose after a few days because of muscle atrophy.
[97] Tower, S. S. *Physiol. Rev.*, *19*, 1 (1939); Bowden, R. E. M., and Gutmann, E. *Brain*, *67*, 273 (1944).
[98] Hines, H. M., and Knowlton, G. C. *Am. J. Physiol.*, *104*, 379 (1933); *120*, 719 (1937); Eichelberger, L., Akeson, W. H., and Roma, M. *Am. J. Physiol.*, *185*, 287 (1956); *J. Appl. Physiol.*, *12*, 42 (1958); Drahota, Z. *Physiol. Bohemoslov.*, *8*, 102 (1959); *9*, 1, 240 (1960).

mass (where most of the potassium is located) decreases after denervation. Similarly, the total amount of DNA in a muscle remains approximately constant after denervation while the concentration compared to noncollagenous nitrogen increases. The RNA and protein content in whole muscle and their concentrations compared to noncollagenous nitrogen diminish after denervation.[99] *Pari passu*, there is an increase in the intracellular proteolytic enzymes in muscle and a decrease in glycogen synthesis.

Many of the prominent findings in denervated muscle are related to the general increase in irritability.[100] Observations of these phenomena are more than a century old. The most spectacular finding is the nonsynchronized spontaneous contractions of individual muscle fibers occurring at irregular intervals, called *fibrillation*. There is a variable lag between denervation and the onset of fibrillation amounting to about 2 days in the rat, 5 days in the rabbit, 9 to 14 days in man, and 40 to 60 days in frogs. Fibrillation continues for a variable period of time, usually several months. The transmembrane potential of muscle oscillates, particularly at the end plate. Here the oscillations are particularly frequent and large, and constitute the *end plate potentials*. Following denervation there is a decrease in the transmembrane potential of about 15 mv as well as a lowering of electrical threshold. Gradually and after several days, the end plate potentials actually result in a propagated depolarization of the muscle membrane. Thus, fibrillation appears to begin at the end plates, and then is propagated in both directions along the muscle fiber. The velocity of conduction of fibrillary potentials is substantially less than the rate of conduction of a normal propagated depolarization after stimulation of the motor nerve.[101]

Embryonic muscle is sensitive to depolarization by acetylcholine over its entire surface. After innervation, sensitivity of acetylcholine becomes restricted to the region of the motor end plate, while the remainder of the sarcolemma is unresponsive. Shortly after denervation, the muscle fiber again develops an increased response and sensitivity to acetylcholine over its entire surface.[102] Accompanying this change is a lowered efflux of K^+ ions. It has been suggested that the terminals of the motor nerve continuously liberate subthreshold quantities of acetylcholine and that the spontaneous, nonsynchronous liberation of these subthreshold quanta of acetylcholine give rise to the end plate potentials.

It is curious that neither the increased sensitivity to acetylcholine nor the fibrillation occurs with the atrophy of disuse.[103] After reinnervation, the muscle increases in weight, the increased sensitivity to acetylcholine and the fibrillation disappears, and the electrical time constants of the strength-duration curve and of accommodation return to normal before neuromuscular transmission is recovered.[104] It also has been shown that novocaine block of neuromuscular transmission fails to produce the changes in composition characteristic of denervated muscle.[105] These observations

---

[99] Fischer, E., and Ramsey, V. W. *Am. J. Physiol.*, *145*, 571 (1946); Zak, R., and Gutmann, E. *Nature*, *185*, 766 (1960); *Physiol. Bohemoslov.*, *10*, 493, 501 (1961); Kohn, R. R. *Am. J. Pàthol.*, *45*, 435 (1964).
[100] Erb, W. *Dtsch. Arch. klin. Med.*, *4*, 242 (1868); Young, J. Z. *Physiol. Rev.*, *22*, 318 (1942); Gutmann, E., and Young, J. Z. *J. Anat.*, *78*, 15 (1944); Denny-Brown, D., and Pennybacker, J. B. *Brain*, *61*, 311 (1938).
[101] Jarcho, L. W., Berman, B., Dowben, R. M., and Lilienthal, J. L. *Am. J. Physiol.*, *178*, 129 (1954); Li, C. L., Shy, G. M., and Wells, J. *J. Physiol.*, *135*, 522 (1957).
[102] Fatt, P., and Katz, B. *J. Physiol.*, *117*, 109 (1952); Axelsson, J., and Thesleff, S. *J. Physiol.*, *147*, 178 (1959); Miledi, R. *J. Physiol.*, *151*, 1 (1960); *154*, 190 (1960); Lüllman, H. *Arch. exptl. Pathol. Pharmakol.*, *240*, 351 (1961).
[103] Eccles, J. C. *Med. J. Australia*, *2*, 160 (1941); John, T. R., and Thesleff, S. *Acta Physiol. Scand.*, *51*, 136 (1961).
[104] Gutmann, E. *J. Neurol. Neurosurg. Psychiat.*, *5*, 81 (1942); Desmedt, E. J. *Arch. intern. Physiol.*, *58*, 23, 125 (1950); *Am. J. Phys. Med.*, *38*, 248 (1959).
[105] Gutmann, E., and Zak, R. *Physiol. Bohemoslov.*, *10*, 493, 501 (1961).

have led to the view that the motor nerve, in addition to its role in neuromuscular transmission, exerts a trophic influence upon the skeletal muscle which it has innervated; however, the mechanism by which this trophic influence takes place is still unknown.

When skeletal muscle is made to contract considerably in excess of normal use (as in athletic training), it usually *hypertrophies*, that is, increases in size and weight, and is capable of increased performance. It has been shown[106] that exercise increases and disuse decreases the proportion of myofibrillar (contractile) proteins in muscle. Although some increase in creatine kinase, ATPase, and other enzyme activity probably occurs upon exercise, it is still not clear whether exercise induces changes in the enzyme content or chemical composition of muscle.[107] The situation is complicated by the fact that a number of muscle enzymes such as lactate dehydrogenase, creatine kinase, and aldolase leak into the circulation in high amounts after exercise.[108]

red and white muscles

There are two types of skeletal muscle which differ in color and so frequently are called red skeletal muscle and white skeletal muscle.[109] Some muscles contain both red and white muscle fibers. The red muscle fibers are rich in sarcosomes, and therefore, contain relatively large amounts of the respiratory enzymes, while the white muscles contain relatively large amounts of phosphorylase and the glycolytic enzymes

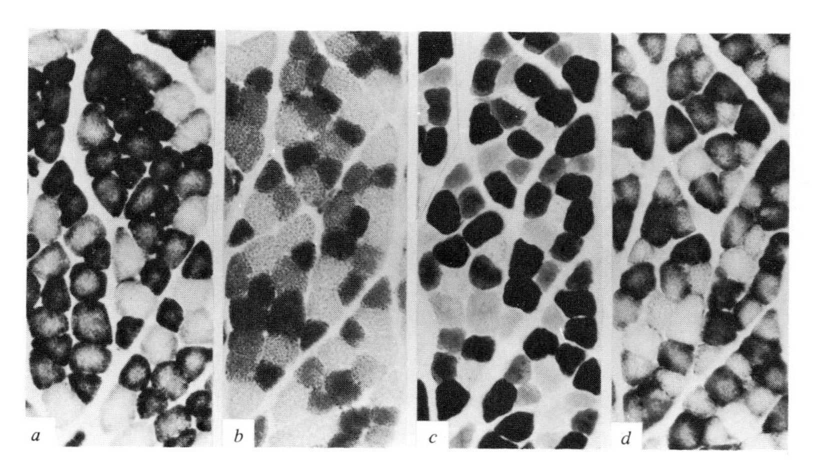

fig. 9-22. Histochemical stains of serial cross sections of a muscle fasciculus from rat plantaris muscle which contains both red and white muscle fibers. (*a*) Stained for succinic dehydrogenase, and (*b*) stained for esterase, both of which stain the white muscle fibers. (*c*) Stained for phosphorylase, and (*d*) stained for α-glycerophosphate dehydrogenase, both of which stain the red muscle fibers. (Courtesy of Dr. F. C. A. Romanul.)

---

[106] Helander, E. A. S. *Biochem. J.*, *78*, 478 (1961).
[107] Yakovlev, N. N., Krasnova, A. F., and Chagovets, N. R., in Gutmann, E., and Hnik, P., eds. *Effects of Use and Disuse on Neuromuscular Functions*. Prague: Czechoslovak Acad. Sci., 1963, p. 461; Hearn, G. R., and Wainio, W. W. *Am. J. Physiol.*, *185*, 348 (1956); *190*, 206 (1957); Kendrick-Jones, J., and Perry, S. V. *Nature*, *208*, 1068 (1965).
[108] Altland, P. D., and Highman, B. *Am. J. Physiol.*, *201*, 393 (1961); *205*, 162 (1963); *207*, 467 (1964).
[109] Ranvier, L. *Compt. Rend.*, *77*, 1030 (1873); Graf, W. *Anat. Anz.*, *95*, 65 (1944); Needham, D. M. *Physiol. Rev.*, *6*, 1 (1926).

(Fig. 9-22). Red muscle fibers derive energy predominantly from respiration, while in white muscle fibers, glycolysis and lactic acid production is more prominent.

Red and white muscle fibers are sometimes called slow and fast muscle fibers, respectively. Slow muscle fibers respond to a stimulus with a slow, sustained contraction, while fast muscle fibers react with a rapid twitch.[110] The slow fibers respond to the application of acetylcholine with local, nonpropagated, graded, long-lasting contractions, while fast muscle fibers either respond with a propagated depolarization resulting in a twitch, or (to smaller amounts of acetylcholine) do not respond at all.[111] Slow and fast muscle fibers have a different type of innervation. The fast fibers are innervated by larger nerve fibers which terminate in plaquelike motor end plates, while the slow fibers are innervated by finer nerve fibers which terminate in grapelike clusters on the muscle fiber.[112] A single muscle fiber never has both types of innervation. The motor end plates of both types of fibers contain both true acetylcholinesterase and pseudocholinesterase, but the proportion of pseudocholinesterase is much higher in the slow muscle fibers innervated by the grapelike clusters of nerve endings.

The ATPase activity of myosin isolated from fast muscles is greater than that isolated from slow muscles.[113] This and other differences in the physical properties of the proteins probably result from differences in the structures of the two proteins. The myosin ATPase activity is related to the speed of contraction—an observation that may have an important place in understanding the molecular mechanism of muscle contraction.

The characteristics of muscle fibers appear to depend to a large degree upon the motor nerve. If the motor nerves to red and white (or slow and fast) muscle fibers are sectioned and crossed so that, upon regeneration of the distal portion of the motor nerve, the coarse nerve fibers will innervate the former slow muscle and the fine nerve fibers will innervate the former fast muscle, the muscles will reverse their characteristics. Thus the muscle now innervated by the slow motor nerve will become a slow muscle and the muscle now innervated by the fast motor nerve will become a fast muscle; both the speeds of contraction and the enzyme profiles of the muscles will reverse.[114]

models of muscle contraction

The simplest model which undergoes shortening and develops tension upon the addition of ATP is the oriented actomyosin thread.[115] A concentrated solution of

[110] Kuffler, S. W. *J. Neurophysiol.*, *9*, 367 (1946); Kuffler, S. W., and Vaughan Williams, E. M. *J. Physiol.*, *121*, 289 (1953).

[111] Riesser, O., and Richter, F. *Pflüger's Arch. ges. Physiol.*, *207*, 287 (1925); Tasaki, I., and Mizutani, K. *Japan. J. Med. Sci. Biol.*, *10*, 237 (1945).

[112] Häggqvist, G. *Acta Med. Scand.*, *104*, 8 (1940); *Z. Zellforsch. Mikroskop. Anat. Abt. Histochem.*, *50*, 588 (1959); *Acta Physiol. Scand.*, *48*, 63 (1960); Krüger, P. *Acta Anat. (Basel)*, *40*, 186 (1960); Hess, A. *J. Physiol.*, *157*, 221 (1961).

[113] Barany, M., Barany, K., Reckard, T. and Volpe, A. *Arch. Biochem. Biophys.*, *109*, 185 (1965); Sreter, F. A., Seidel, J. C., and Gergely, J. *J. Biol. Chem.*, *241*, 5772 (1966); Seidel, J. C. *J. Biol. Chem.*, *242*, 5623 (1967).

[114] Buller, A. J., Eccles, J. C., and Eccles, R. M. *J. Physiol.*, *150*, 417 (1960); Drahota, Z., and Gutmann, E. *Physiol. Bohemoslov.*, *12*, 339 (1963); Romanul, F. C. A., and van der Meulen, J. P. *Nature*, *212*, 1369 (1966); D'Agostino, A. N., Ziter, A., Rallison, M. L., and Bray, P. F. *Arch. Neurol.*, *17*, 388 (1967); Gutmann, E., and Hanzlíková, V. *Physiol. Bohemoslov.*, *16*, 244 (1967).

[115] Weber, H. H. *Ergeb. Physiol. Biol. Chem. Exptl. Pharmakol.*, *36*, 109 (1934); Szent-Györgyi, A. *Chemistry of Muscular Contraction*. New York: Academic Press, 1951; Portzehl, H., and Weber, H. H. *Z. Naturforsch.*, *5 B*, 123 (1950); *6 B*, 355 (1951); *7 B*, 1 (1952); *Z. Elektrochem.*, *55*, 511 (1951); Hayashi, T. *J. Gen. Physiol.*, *36*, 139 (1952).

actomyosin, prepared by the prolonged extraction of muscle with 0.6 M KCl and purified by repeated precipitation and dissolution with changes in salt concentration, is extruded through a small orifice into distilled water. A thread is formed in which the long actomyosin molecules tend to be oriented in the direction of the fiber axis. Similarly, actomyosin can be spread as a monolayer and compressed into a thread. Upon the addition to the medium of Mg^{++} ions and ATP, such threads will contract anisodiametrically while ATP is being hydrolyzed, and will develop a maximum tension of about 300 g/cm^2 (compared to about 4 kg/cm^2 for muscle itself). While the actomyosin thread may have relevance to smooth muscle, it does not appear to explain the interdigitation of the filaments in striated muscle.

A somewhat more complex but experimentally more useful model is the glycerinated muscle fiber.[116] When rabbit psoas muscle (or another muscle with parallel fibers) is extracted with 50 percent glycerol at 0° for 24 hours, most of the sarcoplasmic proteins and low-molecular-weight compounds, including ATP, go into solution. The contractile proteins remain and retain their striated appearance when examined microscopically. Such glycerol-extracted muscle fibers can be stored in 50 percent glycerol at −20° for many weeks. When washed in buffer, they contract upon the addition of Mg^{++} ions and ATP, and develop a maximum tension approximately the same as that of muscle itself. The velocity of shortening of glycerol-extracted muscle, however, is much less than that of normal muscle stimulated electrically. Glycerinated muscle fibers can lift a load and perform work with a maximum efficiency 25 to 40 percent in terms of the ATP hydrolyzed. Glycerinated muscle fibers show changes in birefringence upon contraction which resemble the changes of normal muscle.

When the ATP is consumed by these model systems, the muscles do not relax; rather they resemble muscle in rigor and require a force to extend them about one order of magnitude greater than the force required to extend normal muscle. Before all the ATP is hydrolyzed, glycerinated muscle fibers may be stretched with a lesser force than is required for muscle in rigor but greater than that required to extend normal muscle. Thus, ATP not only causes contraction but also exerts a plasticizing action on muscle. This plasticizing action can be clearly demonstrated in glycerol-extracted muscle fibers which have been treated with a sulfhydryl reagent such as salyrgan.[117] The ATPase activity is abolished by these reagents and the fiber no longer contracts; however, it becomes more easily extended upon the addition of ATP. Pyrophosphate and pyrophosphates other than ATP and ITP do not cause contraction but exert a plasticizing action upon glycerinated muscle fibers. The presence of Mg^{++} ions appears to be necessary for this effect.[118]

The interaction of actomyosin and ATP can be studied in the structureless gel formed by lowering the salt concentration of actomyosin solutions. This gel shows superprecipitation upon the addition of ATP in the presence of Mg^{++} ions. The process can be followed by a number of physical techniques such as light scattering.

---

[116] Szent-Györgyi, A. *Chemistry of Muscular Contraction*. New York: Academic Press, 1951; Varga, L. *Enzymologia*, *14*, 196, 392 (1950); Weber, A. *Biochim. Biophys. Acta*, *7*, 214, 339 (1951); Ulbrecht, G., and Ulbrecht, M. *Biochim. Biophys. Acta*, *11*, 138 (1953); *13*, 319, 564 (1954).

[117] Portzehl, H. *Z. Naturforsch.*, *7 B*, 1 (1952); Bozler, E. *Am. J. Physiol.*, *167*, 276 (1951); *168*, 760 (1952).

[118] The "relaxing factor," that is, the process of relaxation described above (the uptake of Ca^{++} ions by the sarcoplasmic reticulum coupled to the hydrolysis of ATP), was discovered using glycerinated muscle fibers. Marsh, B. B. *Nature*, *167*, 1065 (1951); Bendall, J. R. *Proc. Roy. Soc.*, *B 142*, 409 (1954); *J. Physiol.*, *121*, 232 (1953); Nagai, T., Makinose, M., and Hasselbach, W. *Biochim. Biophys. Acta*, *43*, 223 (1960).

A large number of models have been proposed to account for the mechanism of muscle contraction.[119] The theories have attempted to satisfy the following properties of muscle: (1) shortening occurs as the result of a sliding of the thin filaments between the thick filaments; (2) muscle is activated by the release of calcium from the vessels of the sarcoplasmic reticulum, and the calcium is removed by the action of the relaxing-factor system during relaxation; (3) the maximum tension developed in a tetanus depends on the length of the muscle, and if the muscle is stretched beyond a certain point, the tension developed is zero; (4) the force developed decreases with the increasing velocity of shortening, that is, the rate of work production decreases with the speed of contraction, (5) the energy used during contraction increases with the amount of work done (the Fenn effect); (6) the heat of shortening is independent of the speed of contraction; and (7) ATP is hydrolyzed during the contraction of muscle (Fig. 9-23). While none of the proposed mechanisms is entirely satisfactory, two are worthy of consideration in some detail.

A. F. Huxley[120] proposed a theory based on intermittent links between the thin and thick filaments in the region of overlap. The theory is best explained with reference to Fig. 9-24, which shows a thick myosin filament, with sites capable of interacting with actin, located on a flexible projection (which may be the head of the myosin molecule). Some movement of the myosin heads may result from thermal agitation. Huxley supposed that the reaction between the movable myosin site and a fixed site on the actin filament occurs spontaneously. He presumed that the formation of a link favors a conformational change in the flexible portion of the myosin molecule and thus gives rise to a shortening and movement of the movable site *M* toward the fixed site *A*, resulting in a small amount of shortening. He conjectured that the links were broken by a reaction in which ATP was hydrolyzed with the formation of a phosphorylated intermediate and thereby permitted the breaking of the link between the myosin and the actin.

It was assumed that the chances of sliding backward were greater if the tension on the muscle was large than if the tension was small; this accounted for the Fenn effect. Similarly, rapid shortening was thought to occur under conditions where less force is exerted; while if greater force was exerted, the tendency to slide back was greater and the velocity of contraction was less.

The tension developed is clearly determined by the relative number of links formed at different points in the range of oscillation of all *M* groups capable of forming a link with an *A* group. The energy released will be the sum of (1) the mechanical work, (2) a simple function of the distance moved by a given link and the elastic constant of the series elastic elements, and (3) the heat produced during the ATP hydrolysis when the links are broken. A mathematical formulation on these assumptions allowed Huxley to derive a force-velocity relationship similar to that of Hill.

A molecular model proposed by R. E. Davies[121] assumes the sliding filament mechanism of shortening. This model is based upon a conjectured interaction between,

---

[119] Astbury, W. T. *Proc. Roy. Soc.*, *B 134*, 303 (1947); Riseman, J., and Kirkwood, J. G. *J. Am. Chem. Soc.*, *70*, 2820 (1948); Polissar, M. J. *Am. J. Physiol.*, *168*, 766, 782, 793, 805 (1952); Wilkie, D. R. *Progr. Biophys. Biophys. Chem.*, *4*, 288 (1954); Goodall, M. C. *Yale J. Biol. Med.*, *30*, 224 (1957); Spencer, M., and Worthington, C. R. *Nature*, *187*, 388 (1960); Arnold, W. *J. Theoret. Biol.*, *1*, 404 (1961); Podolsky, R. J. *Federation Proc.*, *21*, 964 (1962).

[120] Huxley, A. F. *Progr. Biophys. Biophys. Chem.*, *7*, 255 (1957).

[121] Davies, R. E. *Nature*, *199*, 1068 (1963).

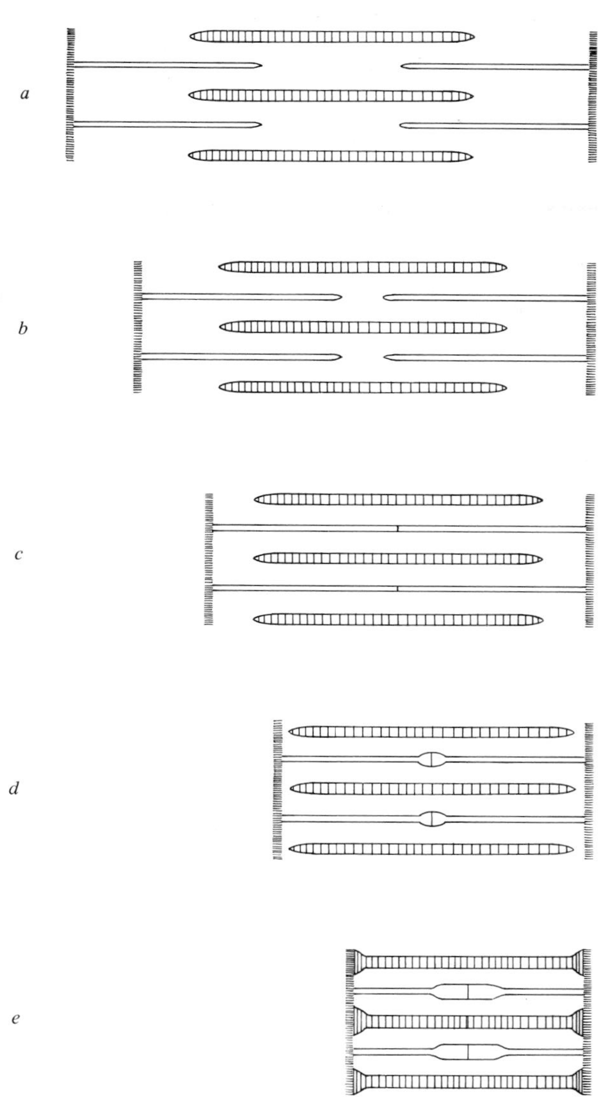

fig. 9-23. Change in length of the muscle changes the arrangement of the filaments. In *a* the muscle is stretched; in *b* it is at its resting length; in *c, d,* and *e* it is contracted. In *c* the thin filaments meet; in *d* and *e* they crumple. In *e* the thick filaments also meet adjacent thick filaments (not shown) and crumple. The crumpling gives rise to new band patterns. Adapted from Huxley. H. E. *Sci. Am., 199,* 76 [November, 1958.])

on one hand, the bound ADP of the *F*-actin thin filaments and, on the other hand, a postulated series of flexible polypeptides in the H-meromyosin head of the myosin molecules composing the thick filaments. In this theory there is a cycle of (1) formation of the link, (2) development of tension, (3) contraction of the flexible polypeptide at the point of the link, (4) breakage of the link, and (5) reextension and formation of the link at the next actin site (Fig. 9-25).

Quantitative considerations require that the movement of about 100 Å occurs with

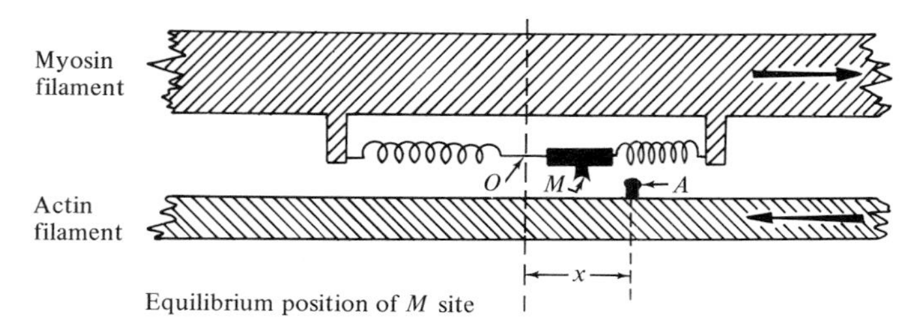

fig. 9-24. Diagram illustrating the mechanism by which it is assumed that tension is generated. The part of a fibril that is shown is in the right-hand half of an A band, so that the actin filament is attached to a Z line which is outside and to the right of the picture. The arrows give the direction of the relative motion between the filaments when the muscle shortens. (From Huxley, A. F. *Progr. Biophys. Biophys. Chem.*, *7*, 281 [1957]. Reprinted by permission of Pergamon Press, Ltd.)

each cycle. During each cycle the flexible polypeptide end of the H-meromyosin goes from an α-helical conformation to an extended form and back again. An ATP molecule is thought to be required for the transformation from helix to extended form. The hydrogen bonds and hydrophobic interactions which occur when the extended polypeptide re-forms into the α-helix release energy which is for the contractile process. Thus, if an activated muscle is stretched, hydrogen bonds and hydrophobic interactions would break, causing transient heat uptake and a reduction in the amount of ATP which would be split. However, the process would not lead to a resynthesis of ATP.

In the model, it is envisioned that Ca^{++} ions released from the transverse tubules of the sarcoplasmic reticulum diffuse to the contractile proteins and participate in links between the ATP bound to the F-actin filaments and an ATP residue thought to be bound to the end of the symmetrically extended polypeptide portion of an H-meromyosin molecule. When the calcium link is formed, the residual charge on the bound ATP is neutralized and the polypeptide spontaneously twists and contracts to form an α-helix. The percent work on troponin, however, makes a simple Ca^{++} link improbable. The actin filament then moves with respect to the myosin filament, bringing the ATP into the region of the H-meromyosin ATPase. The terminal phosphate of the ATP is hydrolyzed, thus breaking the link of the myosin with the actin filament. Tension in the muscle is maintained at all times because the cycle is not synchronized in all of the cross bridges, and some of them will be linked at all times.

The cycle is completed when the ADP is rephosphorylated to ATP by exchange or transphosphorylation with soluble ATP or by transphosphorylation with phosphorylcreatine (a reaction catalyzed by creatine phosphotransferase). Upon rephosphorylation to ATP, hydrogen bonds are broken in the flexible portion of the polypeptide chain, and the configuration changes from an α-helix to the extended form. This is thought to be an electrostatic effect between the ionized ATP and a postulated fixed negative charge on the heavy meromyosin. The ATP will now compete again for calcium, and the whole cycle will be repeated. The active state of contraction is terminated when the relaxing system in the sarcotubular membranes has removed the calcium ions from the sarcoplasm by active transport.

This model leads to the force-velocity relationship of Hill, the reduction of Hill's constant a at low loads and high velocities, and other changes. While these models are interesting conjectures, the mechanism of muscular contraction must still be regarded as an unsolved mystery.

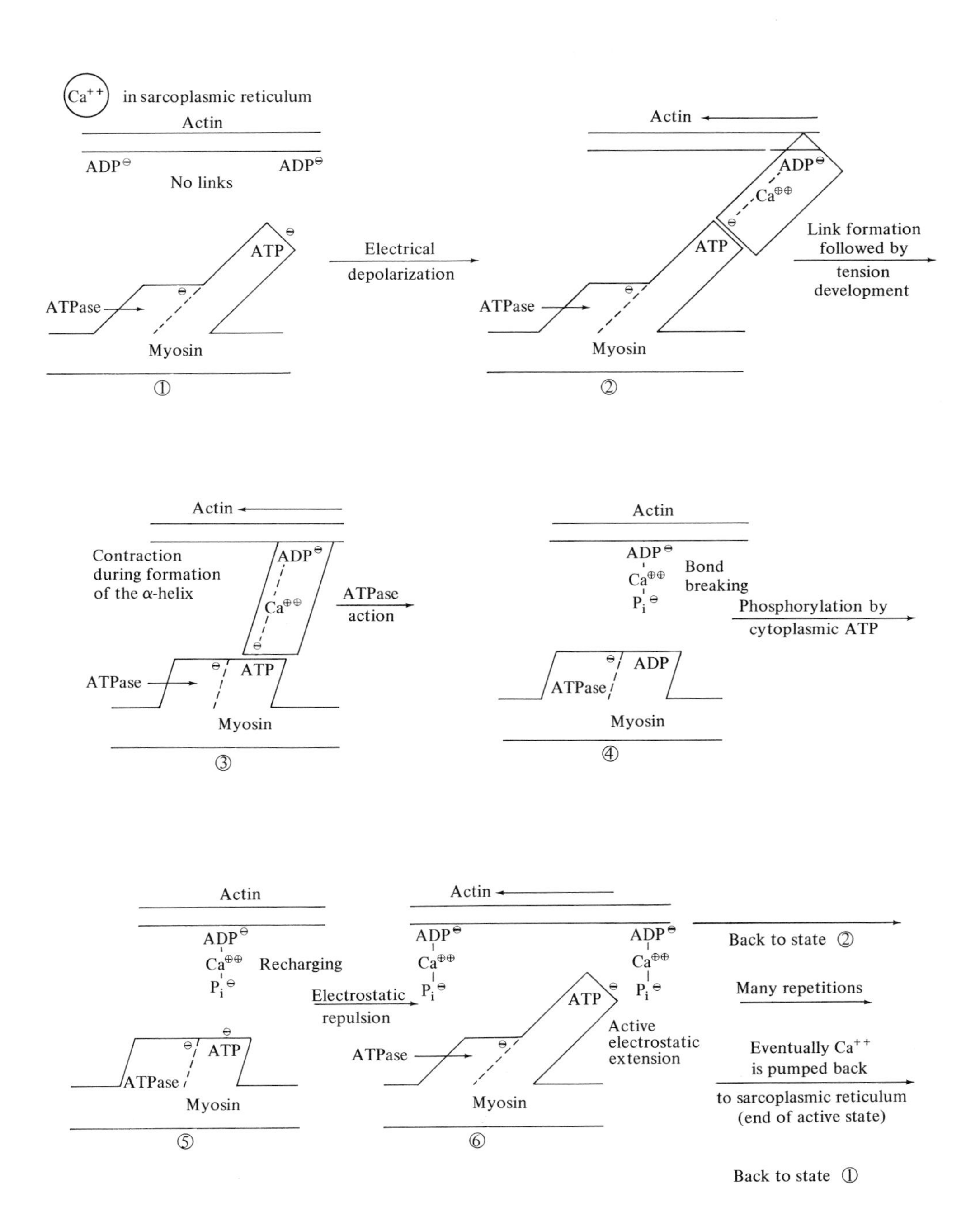

fig. 9-25. Calcium-dependent contraction during α-helix formation in the head of a myosin molecule followed by ATP-dependent extension of the cross-bridges, according to the Davies model. (From Davies, R. E. *Nature, 199,* 1069 [1963].)

cilia and flagella

Cilia and flagella are motile, hairlike appendages which project from the free surfaces of cells. The *shaft*, as the external part of the flagellum organelle is called, varies greatly in length, from 2 μ to as much as 3 mm. The diameter of various flagella, however, is remarkably uniform, about 0.2 μ. At the base of the shaft, frequently in a depression of the cell membrane, is the *basal body* or *kinetosome* to which the shaft is attached. The basal body is a cylindrical structure about 0.15 μ in diameter and 0.5 μ long. Its inner end is usually open to the cell interior, and often it is connected by fine fibrils to various structures within the cytoplasm.

The ultrastructure of basal bodies and flagella has been described in Chapter 2. These organelles, regardless of the species of origin, appear to possess a uniform internal structure consisting of a ring of nine fibers surrounding two central fibers. This nine-plus-two unit structure is called the *axoneme*. The fibers, which are about 240 Å in diameter, usually consist of two or three tubular fibrils with a dense exterior and a more electron-lucent core. The wall of the basal body is made up of nine triplets of fibrils joined by interfibrillar linkages. The fibrillar triplets are lined up so that, when the structure is viewed from the base outward, they project outward at an angle in a clockwise direction (Fig. 9-26). In many basal bodies, an array of thin radial fibrils is present which joins the triplets to a central cylinder like spokes in a wheel. The outwardmost subfibril of the triplet terminates at about the level of the cell membrane where the basal body is closed by a plate of dense material, the *transverse plate*.

The shaft of the flagellum is a continuation of the fibrillar structure of the basal body into the shaft of the flagellum where it is enclosed by an extension of the cell membrane. Beyond the transition region at the level of the cell membrane, two single fibrils appear in the center of the flagellum in addition to the ring of nine double fibrils. In some instances, the central pair of fibers has been found to originate in a small, convex axial granule or *axosome*, while in other instances it appears to originate from the transverse plate. The fibrils extend continuously along the length of the flagellum without twisting or spiraling. Toward the end of the flagellum they terminate at somewhat different levels; this produces a taper. Usually the peripheral ring of fibers is longer than the central pair. The outer fibers are connected to the central fibers by radial spokes that extend from the central sheath to the innermost fibril of each outer fiber.

The walls of the tubular fibrils are sometimes seen to be composed of 10 to 14 longitudinal *protofilaments* 45 to 50 Å in diameter. The protofilaments have the appearance of a row of heads about 48 Å in diameter; this suggests that they are linear aggregates of globular protein subunits.

Most flagella exhibit undulatory movement. Usually the wave begins at the base and proceeds to the tip. The stroke consists of a propagation of a region of circular arc in sort of an uncoiling whiplike motion. However, some organisms are able to reverse the direction of the beat, and thereby reverse the direction of their movement. Some flagella themselves bear hairlike appendages, *mastigonemes*. In such organisms, the beating flagella propel the organism in the same direction as the beat. Naked flagella, in contrast, propel the organism in a direction opposite to that of the beat.

The majority of cilia and a few flagella move in a *tonsate* or oarlike manner. Each complete stroke can be divided into two parts, an *effective stroke*, during which the shaft is stiff and rotates about its base, and a *recovery stroke*, in which the shaft appears flexible (Fig. 9-27). When many cilia are present on the surface of the cell

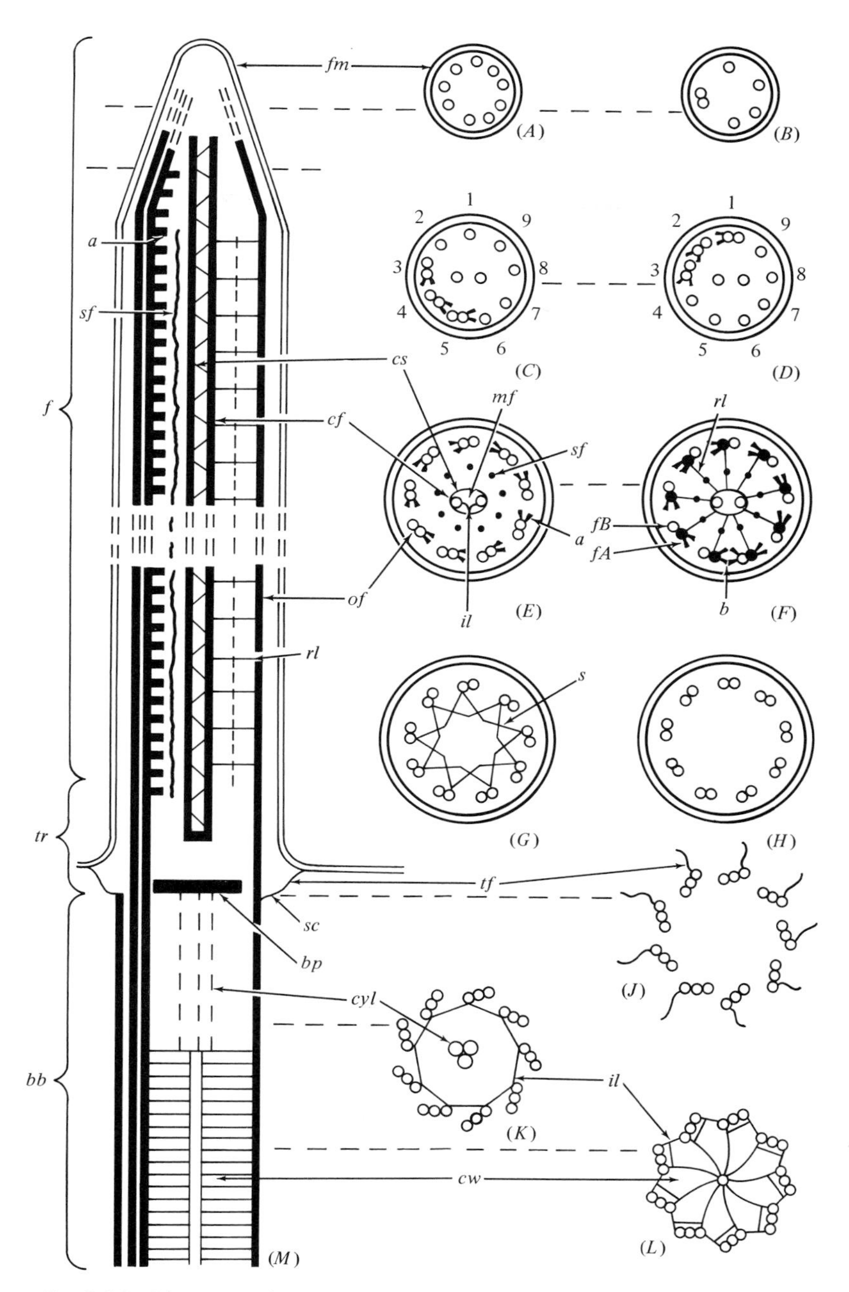

fig. 9-26. Diagrammatic representation of flagellar ultrastructure. *A* through *L* are transverse sections at the levels indicated on the longitudinal section, *M*. *A* and *B* are simplified fibrils at the tips. *C* and *D* are the order in which the peripheral fibrils terminate. *E* and *F* are alternative interpretations of the flagellar shaft structure. *G, H,* and *J* are structural details of the transition region. *K* and *L* are structural details of the basal body. In *M,* for the sake of clarity, the peripheral fibrils on the left of the diagram have been turned and separated. The two halves of the diagram have been used to demonstrate alternative interpretations of electron micrographs. *Key to abbreviations: a,* arms; *b,* bridge; *bb,* basal body; *bp,* basal plate; *cf,* central fibril; *cs,* central sheath; *cyl,* cylinders; *cw,* cartwheel structure; *f,* flagellar shaft; *fA,* subfibril A; *fB,* subfibril B; *fm,* flagellar membrane; *il,* interfibrillar link; *mf,* midfibril; *of,* outer fibril; *rl,* radial link; *s,* stellate pattern; *sc,* distal end of subfibril C; *sf,* secondary fibril; *tf,* transitional fibril; *tr,* transition region. (From Holwill, M. E. M. *Physiol. Rev., 46,* 698 [1966].)

closely adjacent to one another, there is usually a large degree of coordination between their movements. The cilia do not beat synchronously, but rather appear to produce a progressive wave (*metachronal wave*) by beating in succession. The mechanism responsible for this syncronization is not known.

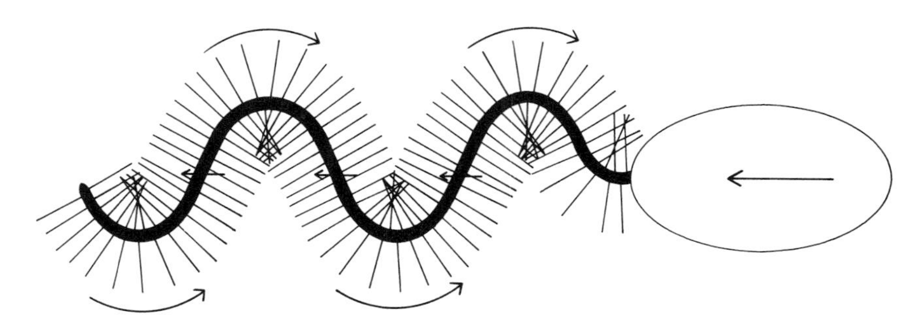

fig. 9-27. Diagram illustrating the beating of a flagellum. The mastigonemes are assumed to remain at 90 degrees to the surface of the flagellum. A wave moving in the direction of the arrows on the axis of the wave will cause the mastigonemes to move in the direction indicated by the peripheral arrows. If the organism is free to move, it will do so in the direction of the arrow within the oval representing the body. (From Jahn, T. L., Landman, M. D., and Fonseca, J. R. *J. Protozool., 11,* 294 [1964].)

The rate of beating increases as the temperature is increased with a Q_{10} in the range of 2 to 2.5. The rate of beating can be fitted to an Arrhenius plot. It is well known that an increase in the viscosity of the medium slows the rate of beating. The amplitude and wavelength of flagellar undulation also decrease in viscous fluids.

Repeated observations indicate that the amplitude of a wave does not decrease as it passes along the shaft of the flagellum. Such observations indicate that the flagellum contains a series of contractile units distributed along its length, presumably in the outer fibrils. In addition to its having contractile units, the shaft must also contain a structure, presumably the central fibrils, which resists compression. According to the theories of Machin and Brokaw,[122] the contractile units of the flagellum are activated when the shaft is physically deformed. This may occur by local passive propagation of event just ahead of a region of activation or perhaps by the diffusion of a stimulating chemical compound.[123]

Satir[124] proposed a sliding filament mechanism for flagellar contraction similar to that operating in striated muscle. The evidence for his theory comes from electron micrographs of cilia fixed in various stages of metachronal waves. At rest, it was shown that the peripheral fibrils terminated at approximately equal length from the tip of the flagellar shaft. Assuming that the lateral fibrils remain stationary, Satir was able to show that the order in which filaments terminate at the ciliary tip at various stages of a tonsate stroke is consistent with a sliding filament mechanism.

[122] Machin, K. E. *J. Exptl. Biol., 35,* 796 (1958); *Proc. Roy. Soc., B 158,* 88 (1963); Brokaw, C. J. *Nature, 209,* 161 (1966).
[123] Grigg, G. W., and Hodge, A. J. *Australian J. Sci. Res., B 2,* 271 (1949); Bradfield, J. R. G. *Symp. Soc. Exptl. Biol., 9,* 306 (1955).
[124] Satir, P., and Satir, B. *J. Theoret. Biol., 7,* 123 (1964); *J. Cell Biol., 26,* 805 (1965).

It is known that the ciliary shaft contains an adenosine triphosphatase[125] and that ATP provides the energy for ciliary motility.[126] It is not surprising that proteins resembling myosin and actin should have been sought in cilia, nor that they have, in fact, been found there.

Cilia from the protozoan *Tetrahymena* can be isolated by suspending a culture in a solution containing 9 percent ethanol, 2.5 mM EDTA, and tris buffer at *p*H 8.2.[127] The addition of 12 mM $CaCl_2$ causes immediate detachment of the cilia. Examination of such isolated cilia by electron microscopy shows that the procedure causes little distortion of their structures. The membrane may be removed by extraction with digitonin, leaving a preparation of pure axonemes. Dialysis of the membrane-free shaft against EDTA at low ionic strength solubilizes approximately one-third of the axonemal proteins. Examination by electron microscopy of the insoluble residue shows that it consists largely of the outer fibers; the central fibers, arms of the outer fibers, and radial fibers have been extracted.

Essentially all the ATPase activity is found in the solubilized fraction of the axonemal proteins. Upon analysis in an analytical ultracentrifuge, it is found that the solubilized fraction contains three principal constituents which are designated by their sedimentation constants as 4 *S*, 14 *S*, and 30 *S*. These constituents have been separated in the zonal ultracentrifuge. The slow constituent which sediments at 4 *S* has no ATPase activity, while the other two major constituents contain a Mg^{++} activated ATPase. The two heavier sedimenting peaks appear to represent a single protein which has been named *dynein*; the 30 *S* peak probably represents an aggregated form of the 14 *S* protein. Both the 14 *S* and 30 *S* forms break down in alkaline solution to form a single peak sedimenting at about 10 *S*.

The addition of 14 *S* or 30 *S* dynein to a suspension of outer fibers in the presence of magnesium ions results in a recombination of the dynein with the insoluble axonemal proteins. Thirty *S* dynein appears to recombine more readily than 14 *S* dynein. Electron photomicrographs of the preparation before and after the combination show that the 30 *S* dynein restores arms to many of the outer fibers. It seems probable, therefore, that the arms of the outer fibers consist of 30 *S* dynein. Dynein has approximately the same molecular weight as myosin; but unlike the highly asymmetric myosin molecule, the dynein monomer is nearly globular. Shadow casting 14 *S* dynein shows globular particles whose heights are 70 to 100 Å and whose widths range from 90 to 140 Å.[128]

A protein which resembles actin extracted from skeletal muscle[129] has been extracted from an acetone powder of the outer fibers (which are the main components of the insoluble pellet described above). This ciliary protein has a molecular weight of about 55,000. When it is reduced and alkylated with iodoacetate, it migrates as a single band on acrylamide gel with about the same electrophoretic mobility as actin from muscle.

---

[125] Tibbs, J. *Biochim. Biophys. Acta*, *33* 220 (1959); Brokaw, C. J. *Exptl. Cell Res.*, *22*, 151 (1961); Burnasheva, S. A., Yefremenko, N. V., and Lubimova, M. N. *Biokhimiya*, *28*, 547 (1963).

[126] Hoffmann-Berling, H. *Biochim. Biophys. Acta*, *16*, 146 (1955); Brokaw, C. J. *Exptl. Cell Res.*, *22*, 151 (1961).

[127] Watson, M. R., and Hopkins, J. M. *Exptl. Cell Res.*, *28*, 280 (1962); Gibbons, I. R. *Arch. Biol. (Liège)*, *76*, 317 (1965).

[128] Gibbons, I. R. *J. Cell Biol.*, *26*, 707 (1965); Gibbons, I. R., and Rowe, A. J. *Science*, *149*, 424 (1965); Gibbons, I. R. *J. Biol. Chem.*, *241*, 5590 (1966).

[129] Stevens, R. E., Renaud, F. L., and Gibbons, I. R. *Science*, *156*, 1606 (1967); Renaud, F. L., Rowe, A. J., and Gibbons, I. R. *J. Cell Biol.*, *36*, 79 (1968).

The amino acid composition of the ciliary protein also resembles that of actin. Unlike muscle actin, however, the bound nucleotide appears to be GTP rather than ATP.

bacterial flagella

Bacterial flagella are unlike the flagella of eukaryotic cells. Bacterial flagella are 100 to 350 Å in diameter and lack the 9-plus-2 fiber structure. They consist almost entirely of protein in globular subunits approximately 45 Å in diameter, aggregated end-to-end to form two or three long fibrils helically intertwined. The flagellum penetrates through the bacterial cell membrane and is attached to a granule or blepharoplast in the cell wall.

Bacterial flagella appear to be composed of a single species of protein, *flagellin*, which has a monomer molecular weight of approximately 20,000.[130] Flagellin resembles muscle actin in many of its properties. The subunits tend to dimerize, forming a material which sediments at about 2.5 *S* in the ultracentrifuge. Monomers of flagellar protein do not polymerize unless fragments of flagella, such as those obtained by sonication, are added to provide nucleation[131] centers for propagation of the strands (Fig. 9-28).

The formation of normal or curly flagella appears to be an inherent property of the protein produced by a given strain of bacteria. Flagellin obtained from normal flagella and reconstituted by fragments from normal flagella produces reconstituted flagella of the normal type. Flagella reconstituted from curly flagellin and curly fragments become curly. In cross-polymerization experiments, it was observed that flagellar fragments forced flagellin molecules to take the same structure as the fragments in the reconstitution process, even if the molecules originally came from the other type of flagella.

sensory receptors

Many sensory receptors contain a cilium which displays a ring of nine fibrils. Usually the central two fibrils are either very short or entirely missing from receptor organelles. In the hair plate mechanoreceptors of insects,[132] for example, the distal nerve end terminates in a cilium which possesses a basal body and extends from the nerve to the terminal segment of the receptor hair. The distal nerve processes end in ciliary structures lacking central filaments. Frequently the number of microtubules increases distally, and they may come to be bound in an electron-dense material. In all receptors of this type, the terminal segments end within special caps or tubes which lend themselves to transmitting mechanical disturbances rather precisely to the specialized terminal cilium (Fig. 9-29).

Similarly, the sensory cells (hair cells) of the inner ear are mechanoreceptors bearing fine hairs which project into the vestibular part of the labyrinth. Each vestibular sensory cell possesses a *cuticular plate* located immediately beneath the plasma membrane. A bundle of regularly arranged *stereocilia* protrude from the cuticular plate through the surface of the cell. Nearby is a basal body from which a long *kinocilium*

---

[130] Kobayashi, T., Rinker, J. N., and Koffler, H. *Arch. Biochem. Biophys.*, *84*, 342 (1959).
[131] Asakura, S., Eguchi, G., and Iino, T. *J. Mol. Biol.*, *10*, 42 (1964); *16*, 302 (1966).
[132] Gray, E. G. *Phil. Trans. Roy. Soc.* (*London*), *B 243*, 75 (1960); Whitear, M. *Phil. Trans. Roy. Soc.* (*London*), *B 245*, 291 (1962); *B 248*, 437 (1965); Thurm, U. *Science*, *145*, 1063 (1964).

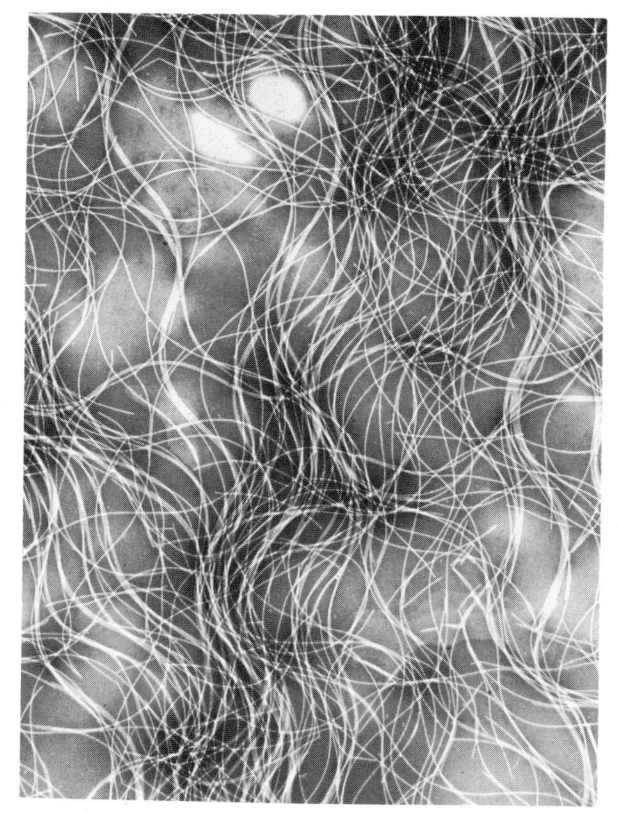

fig. 9-28. An electron micrograph of bacterial flagellin reconstituted from *Salmonella flagella* showing the arrangement of the monomers in a two-stranded, right-handed helix. Phosphotungstate negative staining; magnification 15,000. (Courtesy of Dr. Fumio Oosawa and Dr. T. Iino.)

projects from the cell surface.[133] Thus these sensory cells contain two types of cilia. The core of the kinocilium contains two central fibers surrounded by a ring of nine peripheral double filaments. The stereocilia, on the other hand, contain dense fibrillar material without the characteristic organizational structure. The embryonic sensory cells of the organ of Corti (basilar cells in the cochlea) also contain a kinocilium. In the sensory cells of the fully developed mammalian organ of Corti, however, the kinocilium has disappeared and only the basal body remains. The olfactory receptor cells are also provided with one or more motile flagella.[134]

The cilium may legitimately be considered to be the sensory organelle of the receptor cell that makes contact with the environment. Yet some mechanoreceptors, such as the Pacinian corpuscles, vertebrate muscle spindle cells, and certain stretch receptors in arthropods clearly lack any structure resembling a cilium.

The visual receptor cells, whether rods or cones, consist of two portions, an *inner*

---

[133] Flock, Å., and Duvall, A. J. *J. Cell Biol.*, *25*, 1 (1965); Duvall, A. J., Flock, Å., and Wersäll, J. *J. Cell Biol.*, *24*, 497 (1966).
[134] Slifer, E. H. *Intern. Rev. Cytol.*, *11*, 125 (1961).

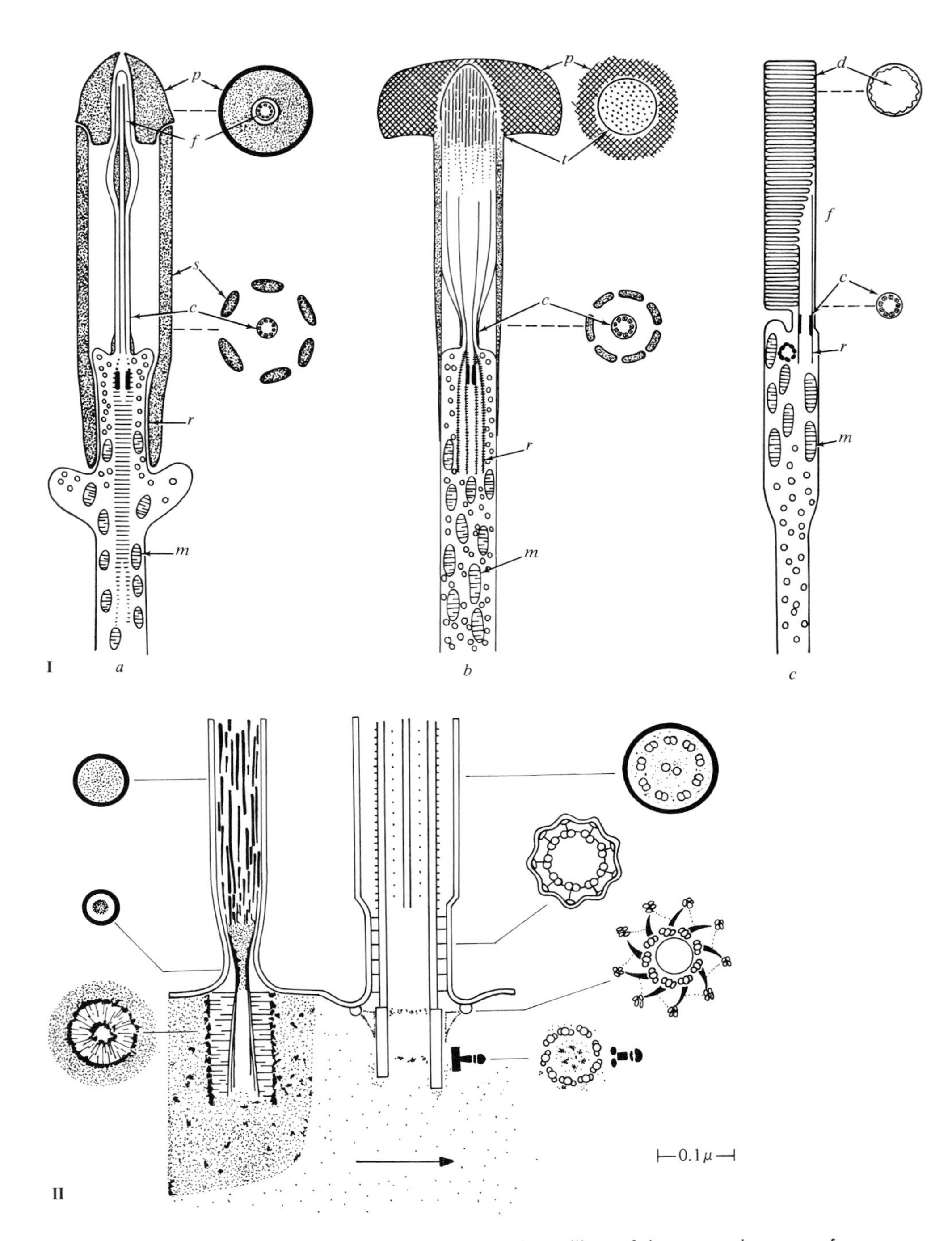

fig. 9-29. **I**. Schematic diagrams of (*a*) a chordotonal sensillum of the tympanic organ of *Locusta,* (*b*) a hair plate or campaniform sensillum of the honey bee, and (*c*) a rod of the vertebrate retina. *Key to abbreviations: c,* ciliary structure; *d,* membrane disc; *f,* ciliary filament; *m,* mitochondrion; *p,* cap; *r,* root structure; *s,* scolopale rod; *t,* tubule. (From Gray, E. G. *Phil. Trans. Roy. Soc., B 243,* 79-81, [1960]. Reprinted with permission of the Royal Society.)
II. Schematic drawing showing the ultrastructure of the stereocilium with its rootlet and the kinocilium and its basal body. The arrow indicates the direction of excitatory stimulation. (From Flock, Å. *Acta Oto-Laryngol. Suppl., 199,* 19 [1965].

segment and an *outer segment*. A thin structure which resembles a cilium connects the two segments.[135] Like the cilia in other sensory receptors, it contains nine pairs of double filaments arranged in a circle but it lacks the central pair. The cilium originates from a basal body in the inner segment of the retinal cell, and a second basal body is usually found nearby oriented at right angles to the first. From this second basal body a fiber frequently is seen to extend deep into the inner segment. The outer segments of visual receptor cells appear to be cilial derivatives. The outer segments consist of

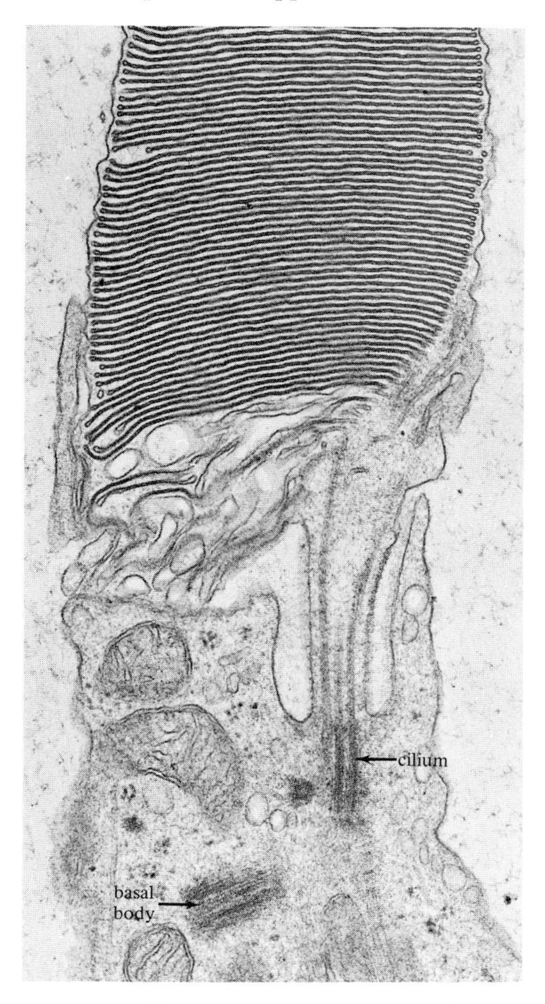

fig. 9-30. An electron micrograph of a retinal cone cell showing the stack of flattened membranous discs in the outer segment, the thin process containing the cilium which connects the outer and the inner segments, and the basal body and rootlet of the cilium within the inner segment. (Courtesy of Dr. Toichiro Kuwabara.)

[135] DeRobertis, E. *J. Biophys. Biochem. Cytol.*, *2*, 319 (1956); Tokuyasu, K., and Yamada, E. *J. Biophys. Biochem. Cytol.*, *6*, 225 (1959).

many layers of transverse membrane-limited discs enclosing a less dense inner space.[136] A typical outer segment may contain as many as 1000 such discs. The discs are derived from the plasma membrane of the outer segment (Fig. 9-30).

In primitive organisms the cilia or flagella may serve both for locomotion and as a sensory receptor. The green alga *Euglena* possesses two cilia, one of which has a lateral swelling, the *paraflagellar body*, at the base of the flagellum adjacent to the *eye spot*. The paraflagellar swelling is enclosed by the flagellar membrane and fits into the concavities of the eye spot. The eye spot itself is a curved plate of lipid material containing a red pigment *astaxanthin*.[137] The paraflagellar swelling has long been considered to be a photoreceptor; mutants of *Euglena* which lack the paraflagellar swelling are nonphototactic.

Photoreceptors are found to be increasingly complex and more highly differentiated as one ascends the phylogenetic tree.[138] With the division of labor in metazoans, the

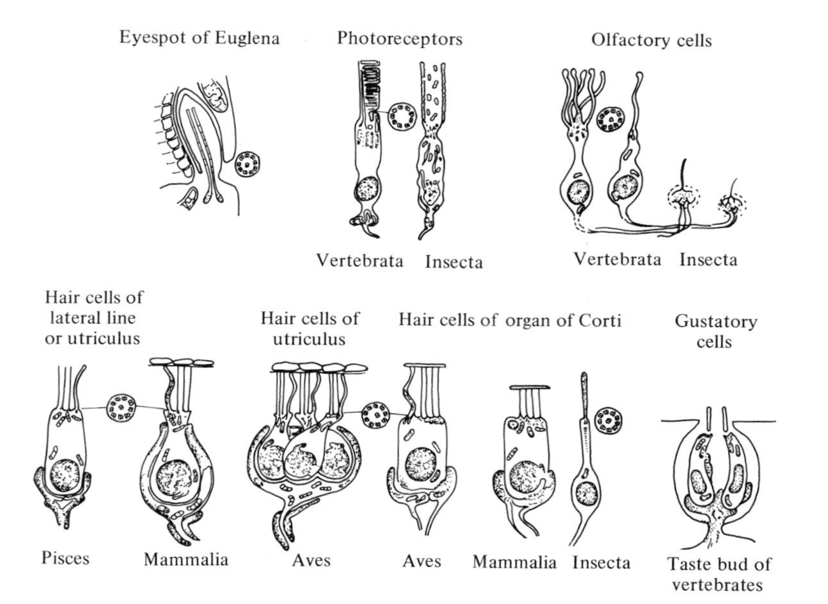

fig. 9-31. Diagram of the evolution of the structural organization of sensory receptor cells. As a rule, the main perceptive unit in all the receptors is represented by a motile "antenna," provided with nine peripheral and two central fibrils. (From Vinnikov, J. A. *Cold Spring Harbor Symp. Quant. Biol., 30,* 294 [1965].)

task of photoreception seems restricted to cells in certain strategically located regions of the ectoderm which are invaginated, forming *ocelli* or eye cups. Light-sensitive cilia project into the cavity of the ocellus from the distal ends of the cells lining it, and nerve fibers extend from the basal end of these cells, connecting the ocellus to neural ganglia (which first appear in these animals). In still more complex organisms, either outward or inward foldings of the ciliary membranes appear to have evolved, result-

[136] Sjöstrand, F. S. *J. Cellular Comp. Physiol., 42,* 15 (1953).
[137] Gibbs, S. B. *J. Ultrastruct. Res., 4,* 127 (1960); Leedale, G. F., Meeuse, B. J. D., and Pringsheim, E. G. *Arch. Mikrobiol., 50,* 68 (1965).
[138] Eakin, R. M. *Cold Spring Harbor Symp. Quant. Biol., 30,* 363 (1965).

ing in an increase in the membranous surfaces available for conversion of light into electrical impulses (Fig. 9-31).

Although vitamin A is characteristically associated with photoreceptors, it is interesting to note that many other cells provided with hairs or flagella contain vitamin A or related compounds. Differentiation into a ciliary cell may be induced by exposure of squamous cornified epidermis to vitamin A. Contrariwise, vitamin A deficiency induces the reverse transformation.[139]

protoplasmic streaming and saltatory particle movement

The simplest and most general form of cellular motility is the constant churning or flowing motion of the cytoplasm. This motion is called *protoplasmic streaming*, and it is found to a greater or lesser degree in all cell types. In most cells, there appears to be a layer of cytoplasm of variable thickness immediately beneath the cell membrane, the *cortical gel*, which behaves as though it were a rather rigid gel. The bulk of the central cytoplasm or *endoplasmic material*, in contrast, appears to be quite fluid and in constant motion. In cells which are not likely actually to move, such as plant cells with a rigid cell wall, the endoplasmic material tends to circulate in a constant direction within the cell around the central tonoplast, carrying suspended particles and intracellular organelles along with it. This type of protoplasmic streaming is called *cyclosis*. Occasionally, however, the movement of the endoplasmic material becomes quite turbulent as shown by the agitation of suspended particles.

In cells that are free to move, protoplasmic streaming gives rise to *amoeboid movement*. The endoplasmic material appears to move forward at the advancing pole of the cell in a fountain-like pattern of flow and is transformed into a cuff of stiff cortical gel. The reverse process appears to take place at the receding pole of the cell where the cortical gel undergoes liquefaction and enters the forward-moving stream of endoplasmic material. In these transformations, the cytoplasm behaves as though it were a thixotropic gel. Hydrating agents such as potassium thiocyanate tend to cause a liquefaction of the gel while dehydrating agents like sodium sulfate induce gel formation. Amoeboid movement frequently gives rise to one or more projections or *pseudopodia* which are thrust forward and adhere to the surface on which the cell is moving. Pseudopod formation sometimes gives the cell the appearance of stepping or crawling across the surface. The organization of the cytoplasmic flow can be easily observed in cells with amoeboid movement by watching the movement of particles suspended in the endoplasmic material. While there is no motion of the cell without protoplasmic streaming, streaming may occur without translocation of the cell if it is not attached or if pseudopodia are thrown out in opposite directions.

In the slime molds, protoplasmic streaming is somewhat more complex. The slime molds are true syncytia consisting of large masses of cytoplasm containing many nuclei which are not separated from one another by cell membranes. Protoplasmic streaming in these molds resembles that seen in amoebae, but many channels of cytoplasmic flow oriented in different directions are found within the mass of protoplasm. The rate of flow in slime molds may be very rapid, as great as 1.35 mm/sec, and it characteristically oscillates, rhythmically alternating direction.

Protoplasmic streaming in slime molds has been studied by means of an ingenious

---

[139] Jackson, S. F., and Fell, H. B. *Develop. Biol.*, 7, 394 (1963).

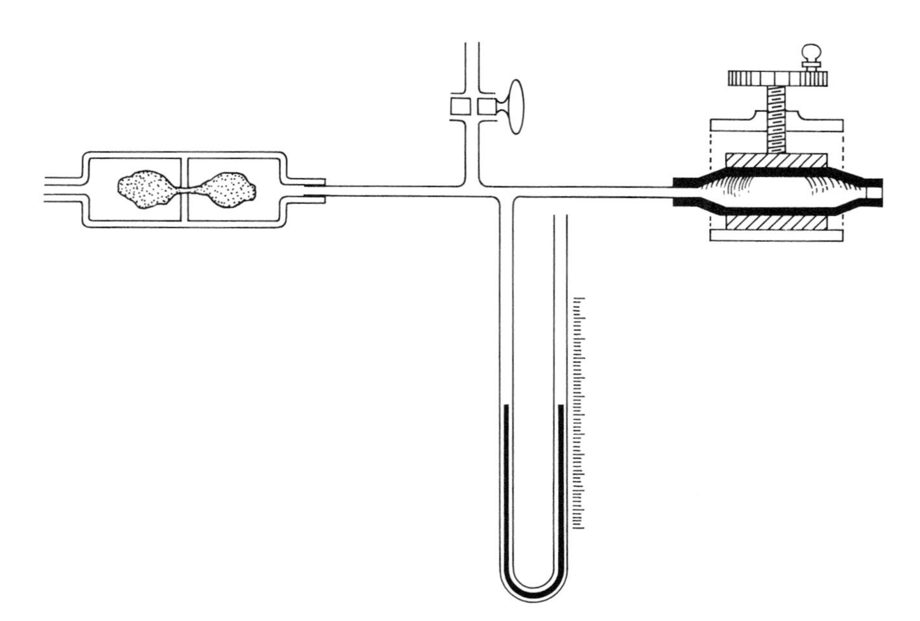

fig. 9-32. A diagram of the apparatus developed by Kamiya for the study of protoplasmic streaming using the slime mold *Plasmodium*. The slime mold is suspended between two compartments by a thin connecting strand. A rubber bulb which can be precisely compressed controls the pressure which is measured with a mercury manometer. The flow of streaming can be quantified with this apparatus. (From Kamiya, N., in Seifritz, W., ed. *Structure of Protoplasm.* Ames, Iowa: Iowa State College Press, 1942, p. 199, © 1942 by Iowa State College Press, reprinted by permission; and Kamiya, N. *Protoplasmatologia, 8,* 3a, 41 [1959].)

arrangement devised by Kamiya[140] (Fig. 9-32). A mass of slime mold is separated into two portions each housed in a separate container. A very thin strand of protoplasm connects the two masses, so thin that at any moment the streaming within it consists of a single channel and occurs only in one direction. Like the streaming in bulk slime mold, however, the direction of flow in the connecting strand of cytoplasm oscillates back and forth. The streaming may be halted by the application of an external pressure to the chambers in a direction opposite to the direction of flow. External pressures of about 15 cm water are required to cause a cessation of flow at the peaks of the cycle. In addition, oxygen can be excluded from the apparatus and the effects of various substances on protoplasmic streaming can be studied.

Saltatory particle streaming is a phenomenon related to protoplasmic streaming. In a variety of cells, intracellular particles can be observed to undergo saltatory or jumping movements which are much greater in magnitude and more rapid than movements that can be attributed to Brownian motion. Typically, particles at rest or involved in local Brownian motion suddenly move in one direction at velocities of 0.5 to 6 μ/sec over trajectories as long as 30 μ. Sometimes a single particle or several in a cluster of particles will suddenly move while the other particles remain stationary. Contrariwise, a group of particles covering a distance of as much as several microns will suddenly move in unison in the same direction with the same velocity. As a rule, the velocity of movement and the distances traversed do not depend upon the particle

[140] Kamiya, N., in Seifritz, W., ed. *Structure of Protoplasm*. Ames, Iowa: The Iowa State University Press, 1942, p. 199; *Protoplasmatologia*, *8*, 3a, 41 (1959).

size. The activity of saltatory particle movement frequently varies during the cell cycle; it tends to increase during the prophase of mitosis and continue at an active level through most of mitosis.

Electron micrographs of systems displaying protoplasmic streaming have revealed the presence of fibrillar material of two types. In many instances microtubules have been found showing orientation and a specific pattern of organization such as the double spiral of microtubules in the axopods of heliozoans.[141] The microtubules themselves are about 200 Å in diameter and appear to consist of 12 to 14 filaments arranged in a cylindrical array. The filaments are made up of rows of globular subunits about 35 Å in diameter. The other type of fibrillar material consists of bundles of microfilaments about 60 to 80 Å in diameter which form an interlacing network, particularly in the cortical gel, but are usually oriented sufficiently to produce optical birefringence. Saltation is frequently observed in systems where microtubules are found and is absent in systems containing microfilaments.[142]

Protoplasmic streaming is increased in many systems during anaerobiosis or upon the addition of potassium cyanide, a poison of respiration. Active glycolysis is necessary for protoplasmic streaming; the streaming ceases when glycolysis is inhibited by such substances as iodoacetic acid or fluoride. The microinjection of ATP results in an increase in cytoplasmic flow, while AMP and ADP are without effect. Glycerinated amoebae and glycerinated slime mold contract upon the addition of ATP,[143] indicating that ATP produced by glycolysis is the proximate energy source for protoplasmic streaming.

Three types of mechanisms have been proposed to explain protoplasmic streaming and amoeboid motion (Fig. 9-33). The first type of theory holds that the force which results in motion resides at the interface between the cortical gel layer and the endoplasmic material.[144] The sliding of the endoplasmic material along the cortical gel may be regarded as analogous to the sliding of the thick and thin filaments in skeletal muscle resulting from the interaction of hypothetical myosinlike and actinlike proteins. Alternatively, a surface tension change might occur at the interface as a result of a chemical reaction which is propagated in a wavelike fashion. Kamiya and Kuroda brought forward evidence that the viscosity at the cortical gel–endoplasmic material interface is lower than the viscosity within the endoplasmic sol itself.

A second type of theory explaining the mechanism of protoplasmic streaming and pseudopod formation holds that the active process at the receding end of the cell is accompanied by a transformation of the cortical gel into the sol of the endoplasmic material.[145] At the tail of the organism, the cortical gel is thought to contract by a process which utilizes energy made available by the hydrolysis of ATP. During the process of contraction, protein molecules are thought to undergo a conformational change from an extended form to a compact form. Water is squeezed out of the gel during this synersis; thus a hydrostatic pressure is created which propels the endoplasmic sol forward toward the tip of the cell. The contracted protein molecules

[141] Watters, C. Ph. D. thesis, Princeton University, 1965; Ledbetter. M. C. and Porter, K. R. *J. Cell Biol.*, *19*, 239 (1963); du Praw, E. J. *Develop. Biol.*, *12*, 53 (1965).
[142] Wohlfarth-Botterman, K. E. *Intern. Rev. Cytol.*, *16*, 61 (1964); Nagai, R., and Rebhun, L. I. *J. Ultrastruct. Res.*, *14*, 571 (1966).
[143] Kamiya, N., and Kuroda, K. *Proc. Japan Acad.*, *41*, 837 (1965); Nachmias, V. T. *J. Cell Biol.*, *23*, 183 (1964).
[144] Loewy, A. G. *Proc. Am. Phil. Soc.*, *93*, 326 (1949); Jarosch, R. *Phyton* (*Buenos Aires*), *6*, 87 (1956); Kamiya, N., and Kuroda, K. *Protoplasma*, *46*, 423 (1956); *50*, 144 (1958).
[145] Mast, S. O. *J. Morphol. Physiol.*, *41*, 347 (1925); de Bruyn, P. P. H. *Quart. Rev. Biol.*, *22*, 1 (1947); Goldacre, R. J., and Lorch, I. J. *Nature*, *166*, 497 (1950).

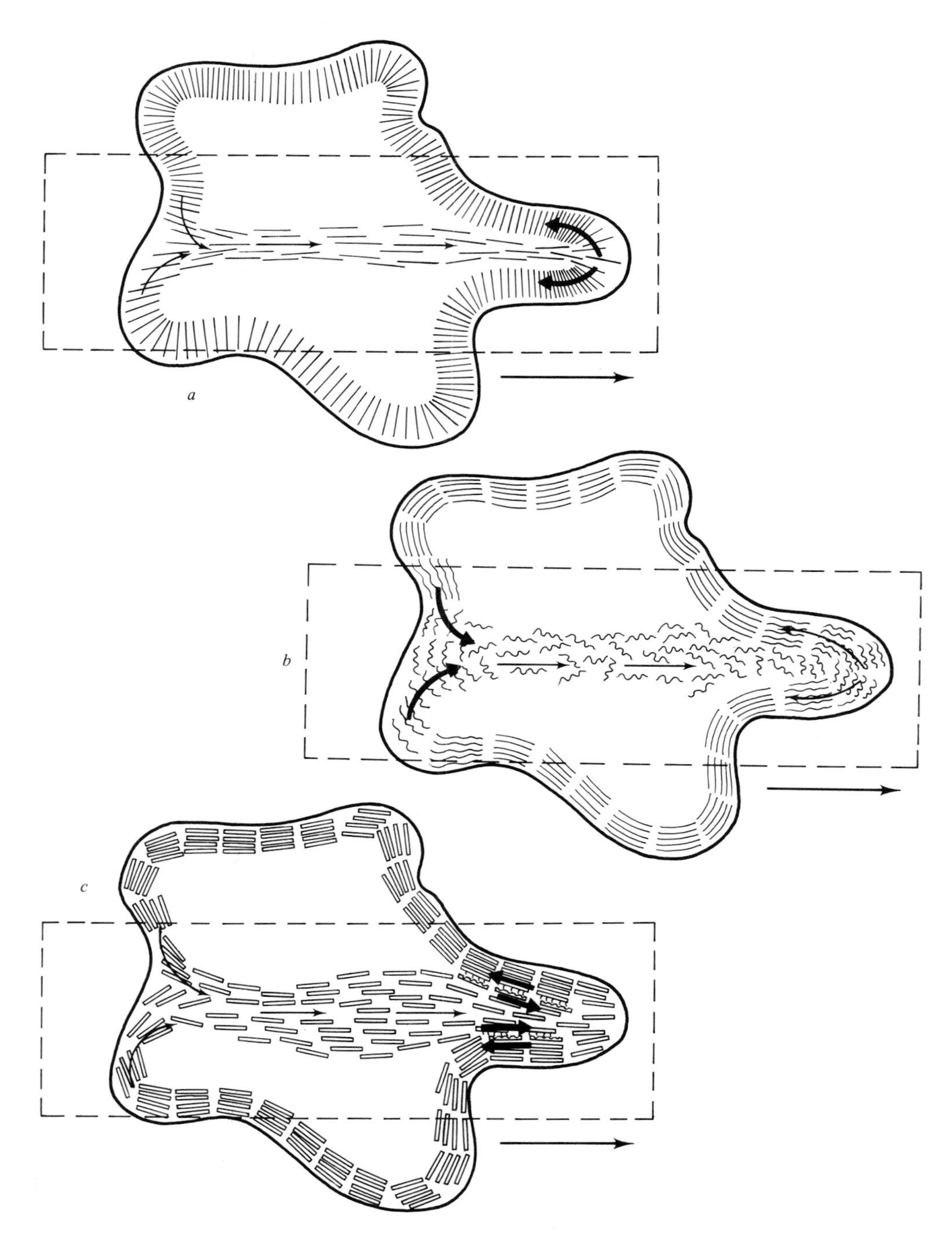

fig. 9-33. The three theories of amoeboid movement are depicted in this diagram. (*a*) The theory held by Robert D. Allen and others proposes that cortical gel is formed at the head of a pseudopod from the more liquid endoplasm. Shortly after the cortical gel is formed it contracts, providing the force for movement. As cortical gel is formed, the endoplasm is pulled forward, resulting in cytoplasmic streaming. (*b*) According to the theory held by R. J. Goldacre and others, the cortical gel contracts at the tail, liquefies into endoplasm, and is projected forward. The forward movement of the endoplasm through the tube of cortical gel is seen as cytoplasmic streaming and results in forward movement of the pseudopod. (*c*) The third theory holds that the force which results in movement occurs at the interface between the endoplasm and the cortical gel. At the forward end of the pseudopod, endoplasm is converted to cortical gel. At the tail the reverse process takes place.

dissolve in the material of the sol and are carried forward with it toward the tip, where molecular relaxation occurs with reformation of the gel material.

This theory receives support from the fact that the dye, neutral red, when taken up by amoebae is transported in the cortical gel, presumably by adsorption on unfolded protein molecules, to the tail end where it accumulates. Neutral red accumulation in the tail end occurs if, and only if, active cytoplasmic streaming is taking place. Furthermore, the injection of ATP into cells induces a liquefaction of the gel which resembles the spontaneous transformation at the tail end of cells. The injection of ATP at the forward end of cells produces liquefaction at that point, followed by the formation of a tail-like structure and protoplasmic streaming away from the point of injection.

The third theory, proposed by Allen,[146] envisions contraction occurring at the forward end of the cell; in this process, the core of endoplasmic material shortens as it thickens to form the outer tube of cortical gel. The cross-sectional area of the tube of cortical gel is always greater than the cross-sectional area of the core of endoplasmic material. This process pulls more endoplasmic material forward. The endoplasmic material appears to stream forward at several times the velocity with which the cortical layer moves backward. Allen feels that the hyaline cap at the forward tip of a cell is formed by fluid expressed by syneresis accompanying the contraction of the gel at the forward end. The primitive motile systems are very poorly understood, and they represent a fruitful area for research.

A contractile protein has been isolated in crude form from slime mold[147] which bears a general resemblance to muscle actomyosin. This protein dissolves in strong salt solutions but forms a gel when the salt concentration is lowered. Upon adding ATP, supercontraction of the gel takes place and water is extruded. The protein is an ATPase. Recently, a protein has been isolated in pure form from slime mold which closely resembles muscle actin in its amino acid composition and physical properties.[148] Like muscle actin, the protein from slime mold undergoes a G-F transformation upon the addition of salt. It combines with muscle myosin to form a mixed actomyosin which (1) shows a drop in viscosity upon the addition of ATP when dissolved in strong salt solutions, (2) shows supercontraction of the gel in weak salt solutions upon the addition of ATP, and (3) induces activation of the myosin ATPase by Mg^{++} ions. It is attractive to suppose that this actomyosinlike protein in slime mold is responsible for the motile force which drives the endoplasmic streaming.

references

Allen, R. D., and Kamiya, N., eds. *Primitive Motile Systems in Cell Biology.* New York: Academic Press, 1964.

Bourne, G. H., ed. *Structure and Function of Muscle.* New York: Academic Press, 3 vols., 1960.

Davson, H., and Eggleton, M. G. *Starling's Principles of Human Physiology.* Philadelphia: Lea & Febiger, 1962.

Dubuisson, M. *Muscular Contraction.* Springfield, Ill.: Charles C Thomas, 1954.

Ebashi, S., Oosawa, F., Sekine, T., and Tonomura, Y. *Molecular Biology of Muscular Contraction.* Amsterdam: Elsevier, 1965.

[146] Allen, R. D., Cooledge, J. W., and Hall, P. J. *Nature*, *187*, 896 (1960); Griffin, J. L., and Allen, R. D. *Exptl. Cell Res.*, *20*, 619 (1960); Allen, R. D. *Exptl. Cell Res. Suppl.*, *8*, 17 (1961).

[147] Loewy, A. G. *J. Cellular Comp. Physiol.*, *40*, 127 (1952); Ts'o, P. O. P., Bonner, J., Eggman, L., and Vinograd, J. *J. Gen. Physiol.*, *39*, 325, 801 (1956); Nakajima, H. *Protoplasma*, *52*, 413 (1960).

[148] Hatano, S., and Oosawa, F. *J. Cellular Physiol.*, *68*, 197 (1966); *Biochim. Biophys. Acta*, *127*, 488 (1966); *140*, 109 (1967).

Gergely, J., ed. *Biochemistry of Muscle Contraction,* Retina Foundation, Monographs and Conferences, vol 2. Boston: Little, Brown, 1964.
Gergely, J. Contractile proteins. *Ann. Rev. Biochem., 35,* 691 (1966).
Gutmann, E., ed. *The Denervated Muscle.* Prague: Czechoslovak Academy of Sciences, 1962.
Holwill, M. E. J. Physical aspects of flagellar movement. *Physiol. Rev., 46,* 696 (1966).
Huxley, H. E., in Brachet, J., and Mirsky, A. E., ed. *The Cell.* New York: Academic Press, 1961, vol. 4, p. 365.
Mommaerts, W. F. H. M. *Muscular Contraction.* New York: Interscience, 1950.
Perry, S. V. The structure and interactions of myosin. *Progr. Biophys. Mol. Biol., 17,* 325 (1967).
Ruch, T. C., and Patton, H. D. *Physiology and Biophysics,* nineteenth ed. Philadelphia: Saunders, 1965.
Sensory receptors. *Cold Spring Harbor Symp. Quant. Biol., 30,* 1 (1965).
Stracher, A., ed. *The Contractile Process.* Boston: Little, Brown, 1967.
Szent-Györgyi, A. *Chemical Physiology of Contraction in Body and Heart Muscle.* New York: Academic Press, 1953.
Szent-Györgyi, A. *Chemistry of Muscular Contraction.* New York: Academic Press, 1951.

chapter 10

cell division

introduction

Even after it was well established that living organisms are composed of cells, the origin of new cells remained a matter of conjecture. Trembley[1] was probably the first person to observe cell division in the protozoa *Epistylis* and *Stentor* as well as in the freshwater diatom *Synedra*. Spallanzani[2] observed cell division in protists (Fig. 10-1) and cleavage in toad eggs, and the Danish biologist Müller[3] described cell division in a desmid in the 1780s. There then intervened a long period of time during which two erroneous theories of the origin of cells were held.

Exogeny, the first of these theories, held that cells were formed freely within an amorphous extracellular *blastema*, either by partitioning, by vacuolation, or from granules. Among others, Schwann[4] championed the theory of exogeny. He regarded the nucleolus to be the first object to appear in an area of previously homogeneous

---

[1] Trembley, A. *Phil. Trans. Roy. Soc. (London)*, *43*, 169 (1746); *44*, 627 (1748).
[2] Spallanzani, L. *Opuscules de Physique, Animale et Vegetale*. Modena: Societa Typografica, 1777.
[3] Müller, O. F. *Animalcula infusoria fluviatilia et marina*. Hanniae: Mölleri, 1786.
[4] Schwann, T. *Mikrosklopische Untersuchungen über die Übereinstimmung in der Struktur und dem Wachstum der Thiere und Pflanzen*. Berlin, 1839.

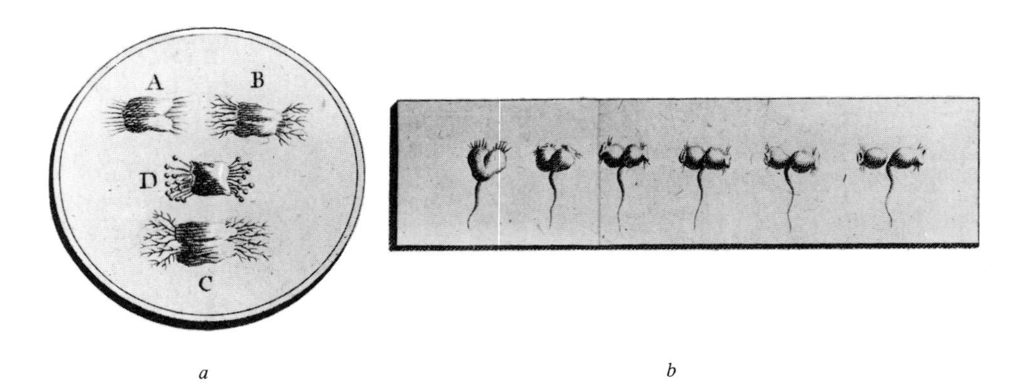

a *b*

fig. 10-1. Sketches showing cell division in ciliated protists from Spallanzani, L. *Opuscules de Physique, Animale et Vegetale.* Modena: Societa Typografica, 1777. (Courtesy of the Library of Congress.)

blastema. Granules then were supposed to appear around the nucleolus; these condensed later into a nucleus with a distinct boundary. After the nucleus grew and reached a critical size, another substance derived from the blastema was deposited around the nucleus to form the cytoplasm; the outer surface of this formed the future cell wall. Belief in the origin of cells by exogeny was widely held until the middle of the nineteenth century.

Perhaps even more widely accepted was the theory of *endogeny*, which held that a new cell developed within an older one. Treviranus[5] thought that cell multiplication took place in certain algae by endogeny, starting with intracellular granules. It is remarkable that F. V. Raspail, who discovered that the granules contained starch by means of the iodine test, held the view (from his studies on the germination of cereals) that these intracellular granules enlarged, eventually bursting and giving rise to a collection of daughter cells.

The writings of Schleiden,[6] which strongly influenced scientific opinion in the mid-nineteenth century, supported the endogenous origin of new cells. In part, Schleiden's misinterpretation of the origin of cells may have resulted from his choosing the endosperm for his studies. The endosperm in certain plants develops first as a syncytium, and subsequently divides into individual cells. Schleiden believed that the nucleus formed by condensation of a granular coagulum around the nucleolus. He called the nucleus the *cytoblast* because he thought that it gave rise to the whole cell. It is partly owing to the strength of his writings that Kölliker[7] and others who studied cleavage in early development and observed cellular aggregates by 2's, 4's, 8's, 16's, etc., did not stumble upon the fact that cell division takes place by cleavage.

The early cytologists may have been led astray because they concentrated their attention on the cell wall. The cell was not thought to divide if the cell wall did not divide, regardless of what happened to the intracellular organelles. General appreciation of the process of cell division followed the description in the 1830s of the formation of a partition across the cell with subsequent division into two cells, in *Protozoa*

[5] Treviranus, L. C. *Vom inwendingen Bau der Gewächse und von der Saftbewegung in demselben.* Göttingen: Dietrich, 1806.
[6] Schleiden, M. J. *Arch. Anat. Physiol. wissen. Med.*, 137 (1838); *Contributions to Phytogenesis (1838)*, trans. by Smith, H. London: Sydenham Society, 1847.
[7] Kölliker, A. *Entwickelungsgeschichte der Cephalopoden.* Zürich: Meyer und Zeller, 1844.

by Morren[8] and by Ehrenberg,[9] in filamentous algae by von Mohl,[10] and in the cleavage of animal eggs by Prévost and Dumas[11] and by Bergmann.[12] In 1852 Remak[13] collected all the available evidence and put forward the general theory that cells multiplied by cleavage (cytokinesis). He realized that the central feature of cell division involved the protoplasm and not the cell walls or vitelline membrane.

The mistaken idea that *nuclei* originate exogenously was supported mainly by Schleiden (see footnote 6), although a number of scientists thought that nuclei might arise without any relation to preexisting nuclei. Kölliker was the major proponent of the erroneous idea that new nuclei originate endogenously within preexisting nuclei. Although a number of mid-nineteenth century biologists saw chromosomes and the spindle of the mitotic apparatus, they failed to focus their attention on these structures, and instead described simple division of nuclei.

Hofmeister,[14] using the staminal hair cells of *Tradescantia* as a system for study, discovered that the nuclear membrane disappeared before cell division began, but that the nuclear contents remained visible. Hofmeister was an amateur biologist who began his career in business with his father, a publisher and bookseller in Leipzig. At the age of nineteen he read Schleiden's magnum opus, *Principles of Scientific Botany*, and was so influenced by this work that he embarked on studies of the microscopic structure of plants in his leisure hours. Hofmeister observed that, between the disappearance of the nuclear membrane and cell division, the nuclear material separated into two masses, and a membrane formed around each so that two daughter nuclei were produced. The disappearance of the nucleus and the reappearance of two nuclei just before cell division was also described by K. B. Reichert. The asters in sea urchin eggs were seen by A. Derbes in 1847, and A. Krohn described the whole astral configuration with the double system of diverging spindles in 1852.

A few years later, the French protozoologist E. G. Balbiani (1825–1899) studied conjugation in the ciliated Protozoa. His paper of 1861 shows in great detail much of the complex cycle of events which occurs in these organisms. Balbiani, however, believed that the Protozoa were complete animals, which, like larger, multicellular animals, contained intestines and reproductive organs. For him, the macronucleus was the ovary and the micronucleus was the testicle. The spindle fibers and chromosomes in metaphase were identified as a bundle of spermatozoa.

To reiterate, Schleiden believed that a nucleolus appeared without any relation to a preexisting nucleus, and that the nucleus or cytoblast was formed around the nucleolus by the deposition of a granular coagulum. This cytoblast then produced the cell around itself. Remak, in a series of studies in the 1840s, decided that nuclear material persisted from one cell generation to the next and that division of both the nucleus and the cell was "centrifugal"—nucleolus, nucleus, cytoplasm, and cell membrane dividing in turn.

Hofmeister, realizing that most contemporary cytologists were neglecting the importance of the nucleus, concluded that when the nuclear membrane disappeared,

---

[8] Morren, C. F. A. *Ann. Sci. natur.*, *20*, 404 (1850).
[9] Ehrenberg, C. G. *Organization, Systematik und geographisches Verhältnis der Infusionsthierchen.* Berlin: Akademie du Wissenschaft, 1830; *Die Infusionsthierchen als vollkommene Organismen.* Leipzig: Voss, 1838.
[10] von Mohl, H. *Allgem. bot. Z.*, *1*, 17 (1837).
[11] Prévost, J. L., and Dumas, J. B. A. *Ann. Sci. natur.*, *2*, 100 (1824).
[12] Bergmann, C. *Arch. Anat. Physiol. wissen. med.*, 89 (1841); 92 (1842).
[13] Remak, R. *Arch. pathol. Anat. Physiol.*, *4*, 375 (1852); *Üntersuchungen über die Entwickelung der Wirbelthiere.* Berlin: Reimer, 1855.
[14] Hofmeister, W. *Botan. Zeitschrift*, *6*, 425, 649 (1848).

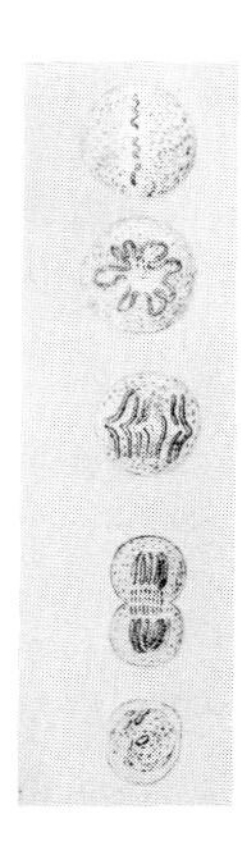

fig. 10-2. An illustration showing the stages of mitosis during the first cleavage of an egg of *Mesostomum*, from Schneider, A. *Ber. Oberhess. ges. Natur- Heilk. Geissen, Naturw-Abt., 14,* 69 (1873). (Courtesy of the Library of Congress.)

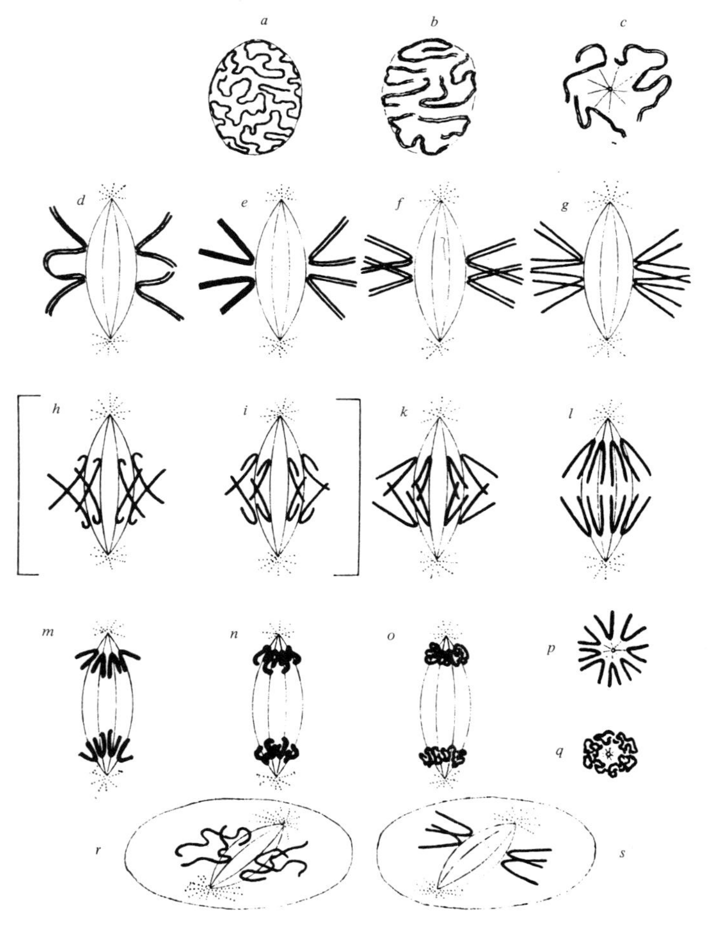

fig. 10-3. A diagram of the stages of mitosis showing the characteristic number of chromosomes and the longitudinal splitting, from Flemming, W. *Zellsubstanz, Kern und Zelltheilung.* Leipzig: Vogel, 1882. (Courtesy of the National Library of Medicine.)

its contents formed numerous small collections (which undoubtedly were chromosomes). It is noteworthy that the number of coagula in Hofmeister's drawings coincides fairly accurately with chromosome counts obtained in these species by later biologists. For example, 54 bodies, presumably chromosome pairs, can be found in a figure of metaphase of *Psilodum*; contemporary chromosome counts are 52 in this species.

Chromosomes were clearly visualized and described by Schneider[15] (Fig. 10-2). Schneider described the sequence of stages in mitosis and noticed that one-half of the chromosomes went to one pole and the other half to the other pole. During the 1870s, chromosomes, the spindles, and the sequence of stages in mitosis were described by a number of biologists. The state of knowledge in the middle of that decade, including detailed descriptions of metaphase and anaphase, was summarized by E. Strasburger in his book, *Über Zellbilgung und Zelltheilung* (1875). Flemming[16] observed and described the formation of the spindle in the cytoplasm prior to the disappearance of the nuclear membrane (prophase) and described the longitudinal splitting of chromosomes as well. Following the longitudinal splitting of the chromosomes, Flemming observed that one part migrated to each daughter nucleus (Fig. 10-3).

mitosis

At this point, it seems appropriate to describe the sequence of events observed in the division of somatic cells. During the interval between cell divisions, *interphase*, little structural change can be observed, but several noteworthy processes do take place. Early in interphase (at the end of the previous cell division) the *centrioles* or basal bodies divide, forming a pair of new centrioles whose axes are at right angles. It is a curious fact that the daughter centriole appears at right angles to the parent. The DNA is replicated and the basic nuclear proteins, histones, are synthesized. At the end of interphase the proteins which later will be found in the spindle of the mitotic apparatus are synthesized, as are the energy-rich compounds required to drive the process of mitosis.

Thus, interphase can be divided into three periods: (1) the *postmitotic gap phase* (G_1), which follows the end of one cell division, and during which there is no DNA synthesis, although RNA and protein are synthesized; (2) the DNA synthetic phase (S), during which the purine and pyrimidine nucleotides are incorporated into nuclear DNA; and (3) the *premitotic gap phase* (G_2), when again RNA and protein synthesis continues, but DNA synthesis has ceased. The second gap phase is in turn followed by mitosis. The lengths of the S phase, G_2 phase, and mitosis are approximately proportional. The length of the G_1 phase is more variable than that of the other phases; cells undergoing frequent cell division have a shorter G_1 phase than those cells which divide infrequently. Thus, a cell that has entered into the S phase and begun the replication of DNA usually has committed itself to cell division. The G_1 period can be terminated dramatically and cell division can be initiated by various stimuli, such as by phytohemagglutinin in lymphocytes and other cells. During interphase the nucleolus usually is quite distinct, but the karyolymph is granular and amorphous, and distinct chromosomes cannot be discerned. The events during the various phases of the cell cycle are summarized in Fig. 10-4.

[15] Schneider, A. *Ber. Oberhess. ges. Natur- Heilk. Giessen, Naturw-Abt., 14*, 69 (1873).
[16] Flemming, W. *Zellsubstanz, Kern und Zelltheilung*. Leipzig: Vogel, 1882.

fig. 10-4. Biochemical changes reported in models of stimulated DNA synthesis. (From Baserga, R. *Cell and Tissue Kinetics, 1*, 179 [1968].)

EARLY PREREPLICATIVE PERIOD	LATE PREREPLICATIVE PERIOD	ONSET OF DNA SYNTHESIS
Increase in total RNA synthesis	Increased RNA synthesis	Increased activity of:
Increase in nucleolar RNA synthesis	Increased RNA polymerase activity	Thymidine kinase
Increase in 28 *S* r-RNA synthesis	Increased r-RNA synthesis	Thymidylic kinase
Increase in RNA polymerase activity	Sensitive to Dactinomycin	DNA polymerase
Appearance of new RNA species	Increased activity of uridine and cytidine kinases	Deoxycytidylate-deaminase
Sensitive to Dactinomycin (low doses)	Increased protein synthesis	Thymidylate synthetase
Decrease in RNA content per cell	Sensitive to puromycin	
Increase in histone acetylation	Increased glycogen concentration	
Increase in phosphoprotein turnover	Increased glutathione concentration	
Increased protein synthesis	Decreased response to induction of tryptophane pyrrolase	
Increased amino acid pool size	Increased synthesis of mitochondrial DNA	
Increased spermidine synthesis		
Increased glycogen synthetase activation		
Sensitive to puromycin and other inhibitors of protein synthesis		

The sequence of cell division is depicted in Fig. 10-5. Mitosis begins with *prophase*, during which the chromosomes appear as distinct organelles. They divide longitudinally into identical halves, the *chromatids*. At the same time, the two centrioles separate and migrate to opposite sides of the nucleus. The *spindle* begins to form between the centrioles at about the time that the nuclear membrane begins to disappear. It should be noted, however, that in many *Protozoa* and some other animal cells the nuclear membrane persists throughout mitosis.

During *metaphase*, the spindle system of fibers or microtubules becomes well developed. There are two sets of fibers: one set extends from one pole to the other, and the other set extends from either pole to the chromosomes at the equator of the spindle. The fibers are attached to the chromosomes at the *centromeres*; the centromeres form a circle at the equator. Usually all the chromosomes lie in the metaphase plate at the equator. Occasionally, however, only the centromeres are aligned in the

fig. 10-5. Mitosis in the whitefish blastula. (*a*) Prophase showing the chromosomes as delicate filaments; (*b*) late prophase showing the condensation of the chromosomes with variation in thickness and density of the chromatin; (*c*) metaphase showing the chromosomes in the equatorial plate and the formation of the mitotic apparatus (spindle and asters); (*d*) the beginning migration of the daughter chromosomes toward the poles; (*e*) anaphase: the daughter chromosomes have migrated toward the poles; (*f*) telophase: the daughter chromosomes have collected in the region of the poles, and there is beginning indentation of the cytoplasm; (*g*) late telophase: the spindle is disappearing and cell division is almost completed; and (*h*) early interphase showing the reformation of nuclei and the uncoiling of the chromosomes. (Courtesy of Dr. A. G. McLeod, The Upjohn Company, Kalamazoo, Mich.)

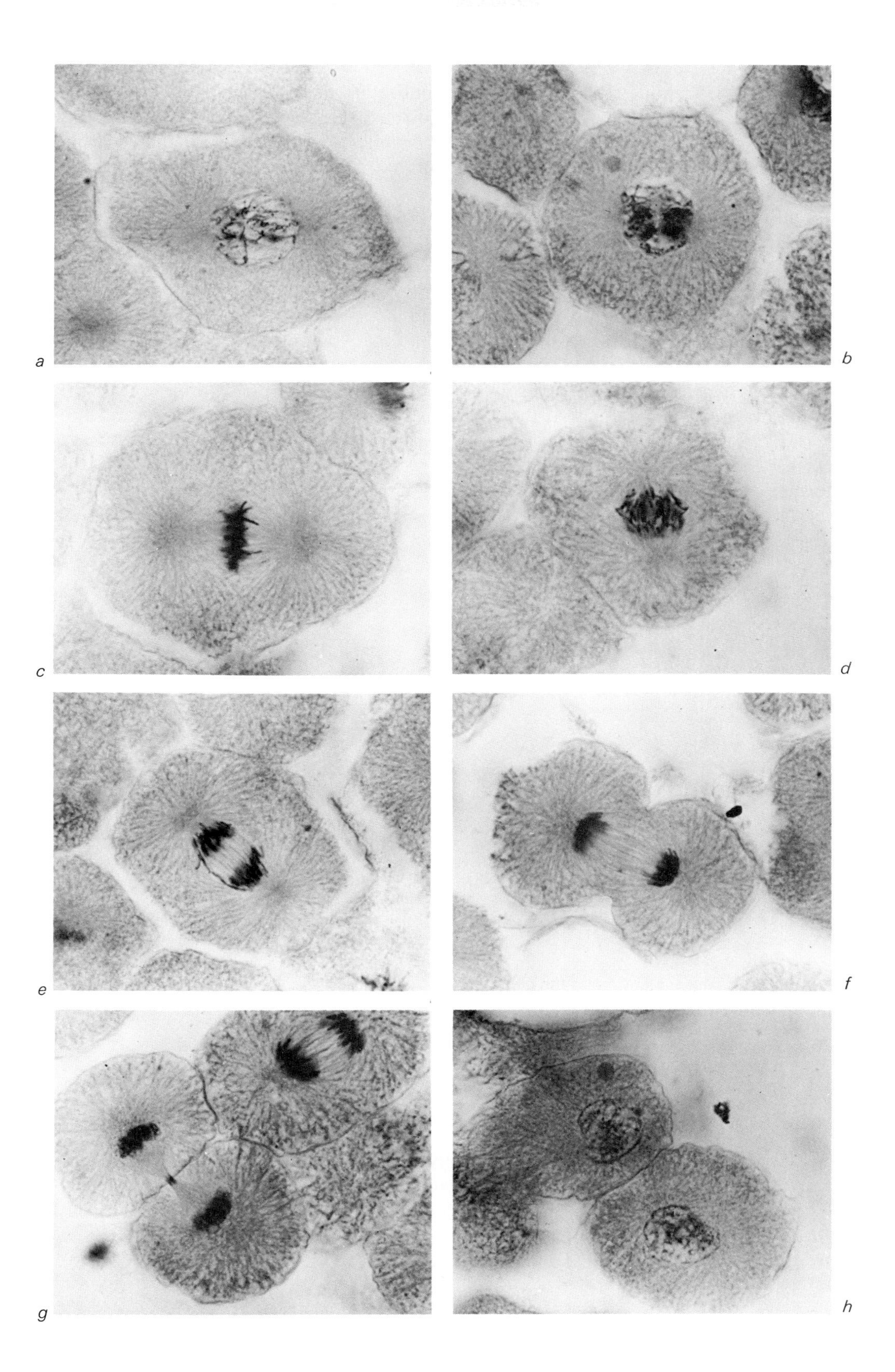

547 cell division

equatorial plane while the arms of the chromosomes dangle toward the poles. It is rare that no equatorial alignment of chromosomes is found. Usually distinct asters are found at the mitotic pole; in many higher plants, however, no differentiated structures can be identified at the poles. RNA synthesis comes to a halt during metaphase and anaphase.[17]

During *anaphase*, the centromeres of the chromosomes split, and the chromatids migrate to opposite poles. Usually the fibers appear to shorten, thus dragging the chromatids toward the poles by their attachment at the centromere. Occasionally, however, the chromatids appear to move with the arms preceding the centromere. In certain insects, each chromosome appears to move within a distinct spindle element of its own. All chromosomes move toward the poles simultaneously, except for the sex-determining chromosome, which frequently is tardy.

During *telophase*, the chromosomes revert to their interphase appearance, the nuclear membrane is reformed, the nucleolus reappears, the spindle disappears, and *cytokinesis* (the division of the cytoplasm with formation of two daughter cells) occurs. Of course, nuclear division may take place without cytokinesis, leading to the formation of syncytia. Frequently, the syncytium later partitions itself into cells by furrowing and laying down membranes between the nuclei. The time course of cell division is illustrated in Fig. 10-6.

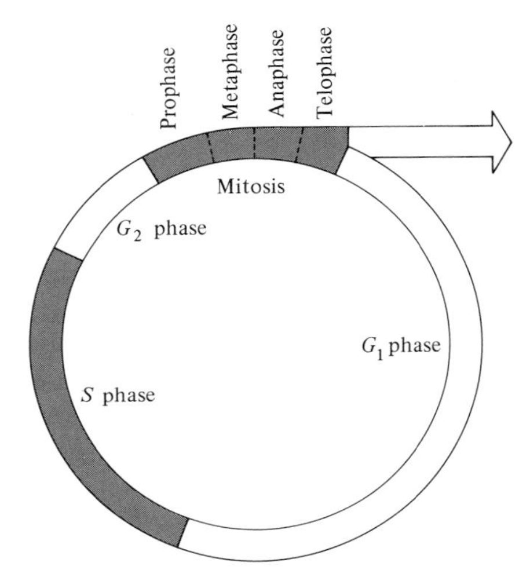

fig. 10-6. A diagram illustrating the time sequence of stages in the cell cycle and mitosis.

DNA and its replication

Most of the cellular DNA, nucleotide polymers which contain the genetic information transmitted from one generation to succeeding ones, is located in the nucleus. The chemical composition and physical properties of DNA were discussed briefly in Chapter 3. The genetic information is encoded in the structure of the DNA in terms of sequences of triplets along the linear polymer (see Chapter 6, pp. 308–310).

[17] Prescott, D. M. *Progr. Nucleic Acid Res.*, *3*, 33 (1964).

The linear polymers of DNA exist as a double-stranded helix in which a purine base is coupled to a complementary pyrimidine base in the opposite strand[18] by hydrogen bonds (Fig. 10-7). Thus, the ratio of adenine to thymine or of guanine to cytosine (sets of complementary base pairs) is almost exactly unity,[19] while the ratio of A + T to G + C varies from about 0.1 to 10.

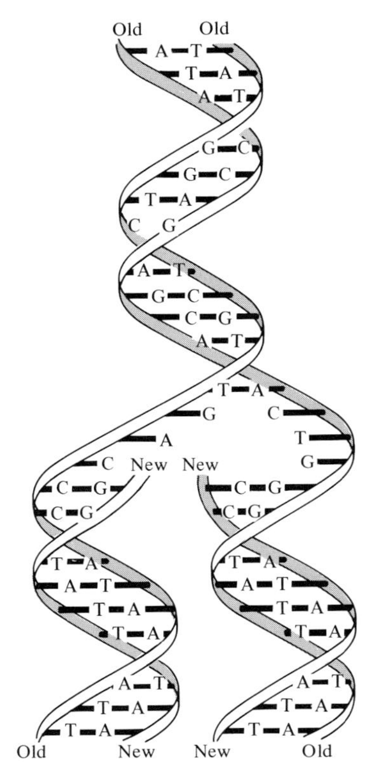

fig. 10-7. A schematic representation of the replication of DNA. (From Watson, J. D. *Molecular Biology of the Gene.* New York: W. A. Benjamin, 1965, p. 267.)

In addition to the four common bases, a number of unusual bases are found in DNA. Thus, DNA of animal origin contains trace amounts of 5-methylcytosine, while larger amounts of this base are found in DNA of plant origin.[20] Similarly, 6-methyladenine is found in DNA from bacteria and viruses.[21] Some of the cytosine in the DNA of T-even bacteria phages of *E. coli* is replaced by hydroxymethylcytosine, to which glucose is linked instead of deoxyribose.[22] In some viral DNAs, the rare base 5-hydroxymethyluracil substitutes for thymine.[23]

---

[18] Watson, J. D., and Crick, F. H. C. *Nature*, *171*, 737, 964 (1953).
[19] Chargaff, E., and Davidson, J. N., eds. *The Nucleic Acids*. New York: Academic Press, 1955, vol. 1, p. 307.
[20] Wyatt, G. R. *Nature*, *166*, 237 (1950); *Biochem. J.*, *48*, 581 (1951).
[21] Dunn, D. B., and Smith, J. D. *Biochem. J.*, *68*, 627 (1958).
[22] Wyatt, G. R., and Cohen, S. S. *Biochem. J.*, *55*, 774 (1953); Lehman, I. R., and Pratt, E. A. *J. Biol. Chem.*, *235*, 3254 (1960).
[23] Kallen, R. G., Simon, M., and Marmur, J. *J. Mol. Biol.*, *5*, 248 (1962); Roscoe, D. H., and Tucker, R. G. *Biochem. Biophys. Res. Commun.*, *16*, 106 (1964).

DNA varies from relatively small molecules with a molecular weight of 3×10^6 and a length of 1.6 μ in viruses to perhaps as much as 1 to 5×10^{12} molecular weight and 1 to 2.5 m in higher animals and plants.

The extremely long, thin molecules of DNA are easily broken by shearing forces. Very careful studies have demonstrated that the DNA molecule of *E. coli* and of the virus ϕX-174 is circular in shape[24] (Fig. 10-8). While it is risky to reason teleologically,

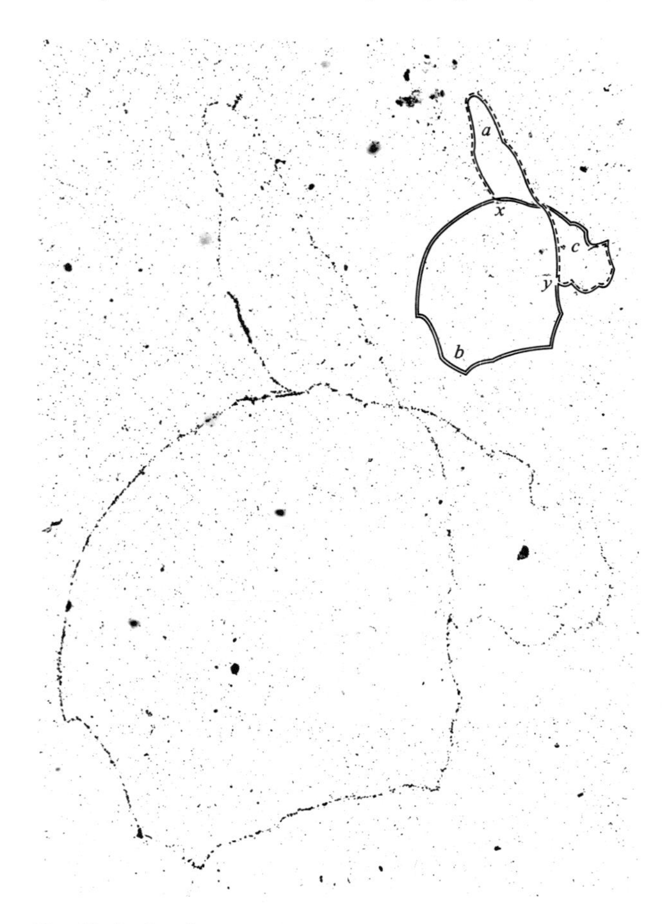

fig. 10-8. An electron micrograph of the circular chromosome of *E. coli* undergoing replication. The starting point of replication is labeled *x*, and the growing point of active replication is labeled *y*. The original double strand is in loop *b*, while the daughter loops *a* and *c* each contain one of the original DNA strands. (From Cairns, J. *Cold Spring Harbor Symp. Quant. Biol., 28*, 43 [1963].)

it is attractive to suppose that the circularity of DNA helps to prevent unwanted replication.

An interesting consequence of the Watson-Crick model for DNA structure was that it suggested a mechanism for the faithful replication of DNA molecules. It is

[24] Cairns, J. *Cold Spring Harbor Symp. Quant. Biol.*, *28*, 43 (1963); Josse, J., and Eigner, J. *Ann. Rev. Biochem.*, *35*, 789 (1966).

obvious that a high accuracy of replication is required for the preservation of the encoded information to the progeny of a cell. Replication involves the separation of the DNA strands and the synthesis of a complementary copy of new DNA on each of the two parent strands. This process gives rise to two pairs of DNA molecules of which half is derived from the parent DNA molecule and the other half is newly synthesized. If the base pairing is accurate during the course of synthesis, the two new sets of DNA molecules are exact replicas of the original pair.

Three possible types of DNA replication can be envisioned (Fig. 10-9). In the

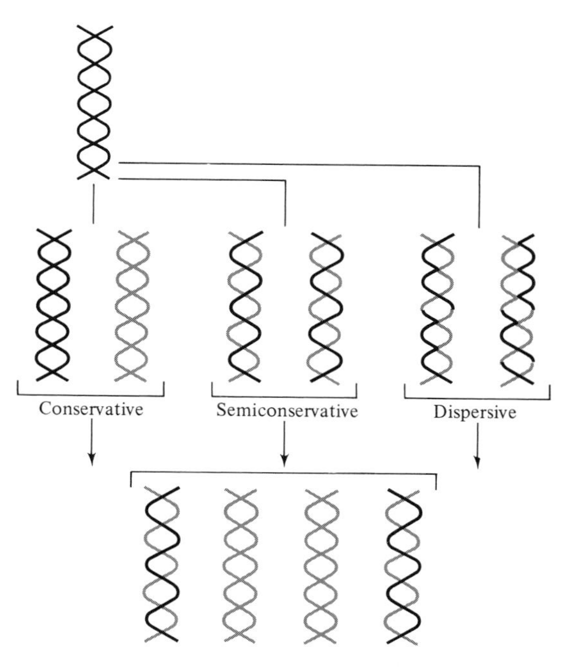

fig. 10-9. A diagram illustrating three possible modes of DNA replication.

conservative mode, the two strands of parent DNA remain together after replication, and the replicated DNA is entirely synthesized. This conservative mode of replication requires that the parental strands undergo transient separation and reassociation as new DNA is synthesized. In the *semiconservative mode*, the two strands of parental DNA separate from each other, and each strand serves as a template for the synthesis of a new complementary strand. Thus, each molecule of progeny DNA consists of one parental strand and one strand of newly synthesized DNA. Lastly, it is conceivable that the DNA molecules are fragmented during the process of replication and that the fragments appear in the daughter strands of DNA in a random fashion. This last mode of replication is called the *dispersive mode*. In the case of circular DNA, replication requires a swiveling as the complementary strands separate prior to replication (Fig. 10-10).

There is no compelling evidence to support either the conservative or the dispersive mode of DNA replication. There is, however, considerable support for the semiconservative mode of replication. In the Meselson-Stahl experiment,[25] *E. coli* were

[25] Meselson, M., and Stahl, F. W. *Proc. Natl. Acad. Sci.*, *44*, 671 (1958).

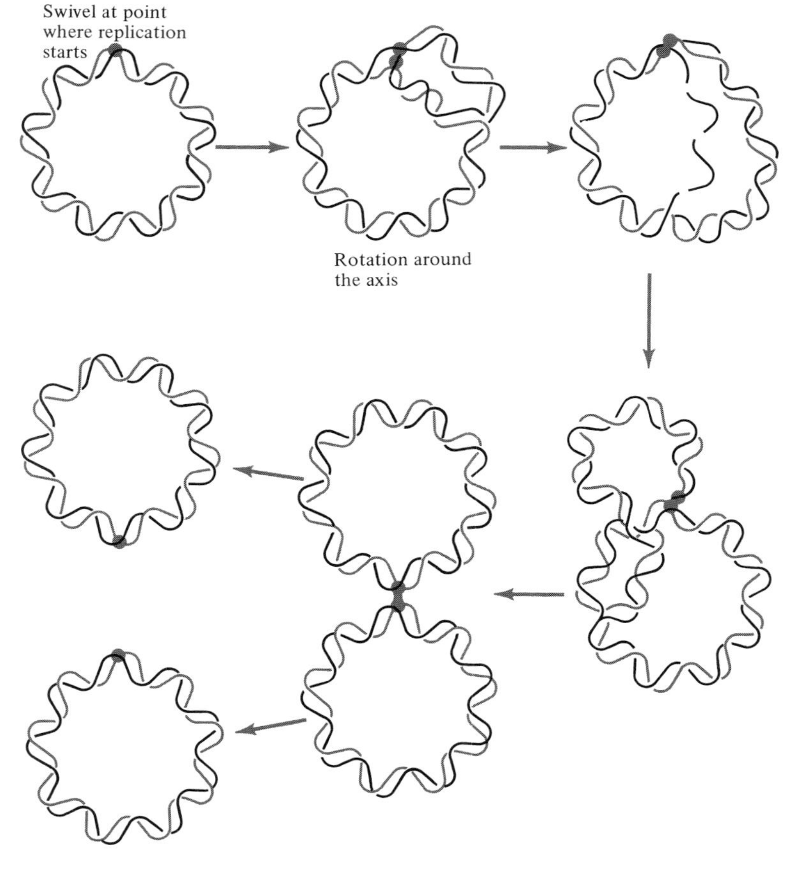

fig. 10-10. A diagram illustrating a plausible model for the replication of a circular DNA molecule. Replication begins at a fixed point and always proceeds in the same direction. Because the complementary strands of DNA are twisted in a double helix, the parent helix must rotate as the strands separate. (Adapted from Cairns, J. *Cold Spring Harbor Symp. Quant. Biol.*, *28*, 43 [1963].)

grown in a medium containing heavy nitrogen ($^{15}NH_3$) as the sole nitrogen source. Thus, the DNA molecules in these organisms contained ^{15}N and had a slightly higher density than DNA molecules from cells grown in ordinary medium. The buoyant density of DNA can be determined by centrifugation in a cesium chloride gradient. By such centrifugation it was determined that the density of ^{15}N DNA was 1.725 and that of ^{14}N DNA was 1.709.

After the bacteria were grown in heavy nitrogen, they were transferred to new medium containing $^{14}NH_3$. Organisms were removed at various intervals of time, the DNA isolated, and its buoyant density determined. At zero time, only a single band of DNA was obtained corresponding to ^{15}N DNA. After a short period of growth, the DNA isolated contained a band corresponding in density to a hybrid DNA molecule composed of half heavy nitrogen and half ^{14}N. At the end of one generation, all the DNA corresponded to the hybrid form. At the end of two generations, two bands of DNA were found corresponding to hybrid DNA and a lighter band was found corresponding to ordinary DNA. The possibility that these results might be consistent with the conservative mode of replication was ruled out by denaturing the hybrid DNA and showing that it was composed of two strands. Upon sedimentation after strand separation, two separate bands of different density were formed, so that one strand of the hybrid DNA contained only ^{15}N bases while the other contained only ^{14}N bases (Fig. 10-11).

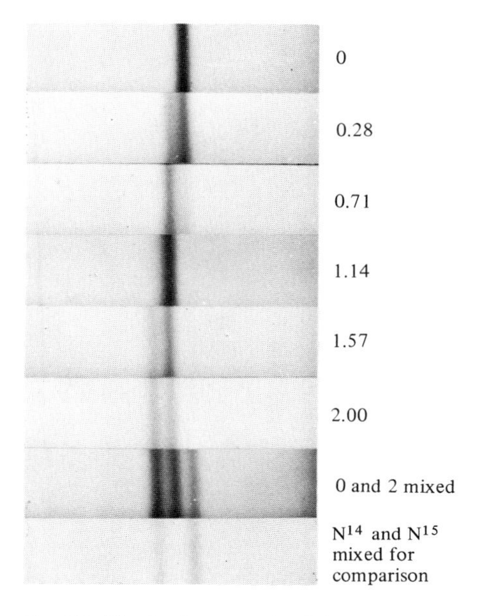

fig. 10-11. A photograph of the sedimentation patterns of *E. coli* DNA. The bacteria were grown in $^{15}NH_3$-containing medium and then transferred to $^{14}NH_3$-containing medium. The bands are formed by DNA's of different densities. The density increases from left to right. (Courtesy of Dr. Matthew Meselson.)

The synthesis of new DNA is mediated by the enzyme *DNA polymerase*.[26] DNA from any source, and even synthetic deoxyribonucleotides can serve as a template or *primer* for the synthesis of new DNA. In addition to a primer, the enzyme requires the presence of all four deoxyribonucleoside triphosphates, dATP, dGTP, dTTP, and dCTP. When the DNA polymerase is highly purified, natural DNA, either native or denatured, is less effective as a primer than either DNA partially digested by pancreatic DNAse or synthetic deoxyribonucleotides. It is thought that the poor ability of highly purified DNA polymerase to replicate native DNA results from the removal of nucleases in the purification process.[27] Highly purified DNA polymerase contains an exonuclease which appears to be an intrinsic part of the enzyme. Attempts to separate

---

[26] Kornberg, A., ed. *Enzymatic Synthesis of DNA*. New York: Wiley, 1961.
[27] Richardson, C. C., Schildkraut, C. L., Aposhian, H. V., and Kornberg, A. *J. Biol. Chem.*, *239*, 222 (1964).

the polymerase from the exonuclease activity or selectively to inactivate either of the two activities have failed.[28]

Under optimal conditions, twenty times as much DNA can be synthesized as was originally present as primer (Figs. 10-12 and 10-13). If an inadequate amount of one

fig. 10-12. A comparison of the base composition of enzymatically synthesized DNA and their DNA templates. (From Watson, J. D. *Molecular Biology of the Gene.* New York: W. A. Benjamin, 1965, p. 269.)

SOURCE OF DNA TEMPLATE	BASE COMPOSITION OF THE ENZYMATIC PRODUCT				$\frac{A+T}{G+C}$ IN PRODUCT	$\frac{A+T}{G+C}$ IN TEMPLATE
	ADENINE	THYMINE	GUANINE	CYTOSINE		
Micrococcus lysodeiticus (a bacterium)	0.15	0.15	0.35	0.35	0.41	0.39
Aerobacter aerogenes (a bacterium)	0.22	0.22	0.28	0.28	0.80	0.82
Escherichia coli	0.25	0.25	0.25	0.25	1.00	0.97
Calf thymus	0.29	0.28	0.21	0.22	1.32	1.35
Phage T2	0.32	0.32	0.18	0.18	1.78	1.84

fig. 10-13. Physical properties of enzymatically synthesized DNA. (From Lehman, I. R., Zimmerman, S. B., Adler, J., Bessman, M. S., Simms, E. S., and Kornberg, A. *Proc. Natl. Acad. Sci., 44,* 1191 [1958].)

PROPERTY	PRIMER	PRODUCT	PRIMER[a]	PRODUCT
Sedimentation coefficient	25	20–25	20	14
Intrinsic viscosity $(g/100\ ml)^{-1}$	40–50	15–45	<1	<1
Molecular weight	8×10^6	$4–6 \times 10^6$		

[a] Heated at 100°C for 15 min.

of the triphosphates is present, synthesis proceeds until that triphosphate is exhausted. Enzymatically synthesized DNA shows the same frequency of dinucleotide (nearest neighbor) sequences as the template used as primer.[29] The newly synthesized molecules of DNA have a molecular weight of 10^6 or more and approach the molecular weight of the primer.

histones

The histones are a group of low-molecular-weight basic proteins, rich in the amino acids lysine and arginine, which are tightly complexed to the nuclear DNA of eukaryotic cells. The histones can be dissociated from the DNA at low *p*H and high salt

[28] Lehman, I. R., and Richardson, C. C. *J. Biol. Chem.*, *239*, 233 (1964).
[29] Josse, J., Kaiser, A. D., and Kornberg, A. *J. Biol. Chem.*, *236*, 864 (1961).

concentration; they tend to aggregate at *p*H above 4.5. As prepared from isolated nuclei, the histones are exceedingly heterogeneous. They may be separated into a number of fractions by chromatography on anion exchange resins; the fractions vary in the content of lysine and arginine from *lysine-rich* to *arginine-rich* fractions.[30] The interaction between the histones and DNA is largely electrostatic and takes place between the free basic groups of the former and the acidic phosphate residues of the latter. The histones have molecular weights in the range 10,000 to 18,000. In addition to histones, nuclei contain neutral proteins.

Optical rotatory dispersion, hydrogen-deuterium exchange, and *x*-ray diffraction studies indicate that histones have a high content of α-helix; two-thirds or more of the amino acid residues are in helical portions.[31] The helical structure of the histones appears to be maintained and stabilized when they are associated with DNA.

A DNA molecule forms two helical grooves with an angle of pitch approximating 30 degrees. The larger groove is about 18 Å across and can accommodate a helical protein molecule. Molecules with molecular weights in the range 7,000 to 18,000 would occupy only one or two turns of the DNA helix. Thus, they would cover a length of polynucleotides that would code for from 3 to 10 amino acids (Fig. 10-14).

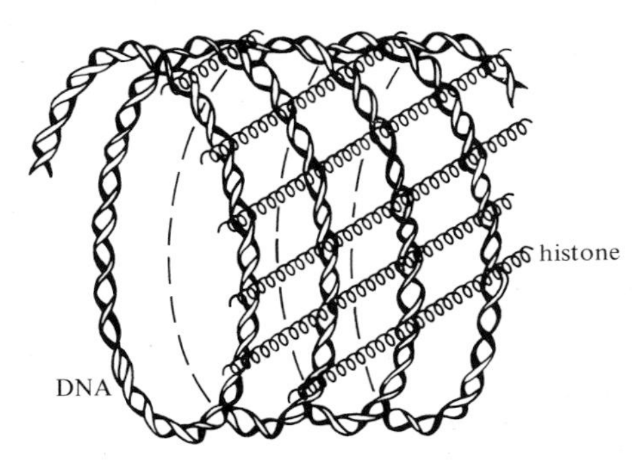

fig. 10-14. A diagrammatic representation of one possible arrangement of histone molecules which form bridges across turns of DNA supercoils. The histones may regulate transcription and replication by changing the characteristics of the bridges. (From Zubay, G., in Bonner, J., and Ts'o, P., eds. *The Nucleohistones.* San Francisco: Holden-Day, 1964, p. 102.)

While the molecules of DNA are metabolically stable and are conserved in viable cells (one-half of the DNA molecules of a parent cell goes to each daughter cell), the histone molecules are degraded and resynthesized but the rate is low compared to other nuclear proteins. A burst of histone synthesis occurs during the *S* phase when DNA is replicated.[32] The histones are thought to have a regulatory function in

[30] Phillips, D. M. P., and Simson, P. *Biochem. J.*, *82*, 236 (1962); *87*, 258 (1963); Hnilica, L., Johns, E. W., and Butler, J. A. V. *Biochem. J.*, *82*, 15, 123 (1962); Rasmussen, P. S., Murray, K., and Luck, J. M. *Biochemistry*, *1*, 79 (1962); Murray, K. *Biochemistry*, *3*, 10 (1964).
[31] Zubay, G., and Doty, P. *J. Mol. Biol.*, *1*, 1 (1959); Bradbury, E. M., Price, W. C., Wilkinson, G. R., and Zubay, G. *J. Mol. Biol.*, *4*, 50 (1962); Zubay, G., and Wilkins, M. H. F. *J. Mol. Biol.*, *4*, 444 (1962); Bradbury, E. M., and Crane-Robinson, C., in Bonner, J., and Ts'o, P., eds. *The Nucleohistones.* San Francisco: Holden-Day, 1964, p. 117.
[32] Borun, T. W., Scharff, M. D., and Robbins, E. *Proc. Natl. Acad. Sci.*, *58*, 1977 (1967).

transcription. Allfrey and Mirsky showed that the addition of arginine-rich histones to lampbrush chromosomes induced a retraction of the DNA loops. Owing to complex formation with template DNA, histones appear to inhibit transcription by RNA polymerase. The inhibition of DNA and RNA synthesis by histones seems to relate to the elevation of the melting temperature of the complexes. Furthermore, the nearest neighbor base composition of the RNA synthesized is altered by the presence of histones. Huang and Bonner[33] found that native nucleohistones from pea buds contained RNA covalently linked to the protein. After splitting the RNA in acid medium, a molecule containing approximately 40 residues was obtained which had an unusual base composition far different from that of other classes of RNA. The RNA-histone complex contained 8 percent RNA and 92 percent protein by weight. The mechanism of regulation of gene function by histones remains obscure.

chromosome structure

While the chromosomes are present at all times in the nucleus of eukaryotic cells, they cannot be discerned as separate structural elements during interphase. During mitosis, however, the chromatin assumes a compact arrangement and individual chromosomes can be seen. Chromosomes are most easily visualized and identified

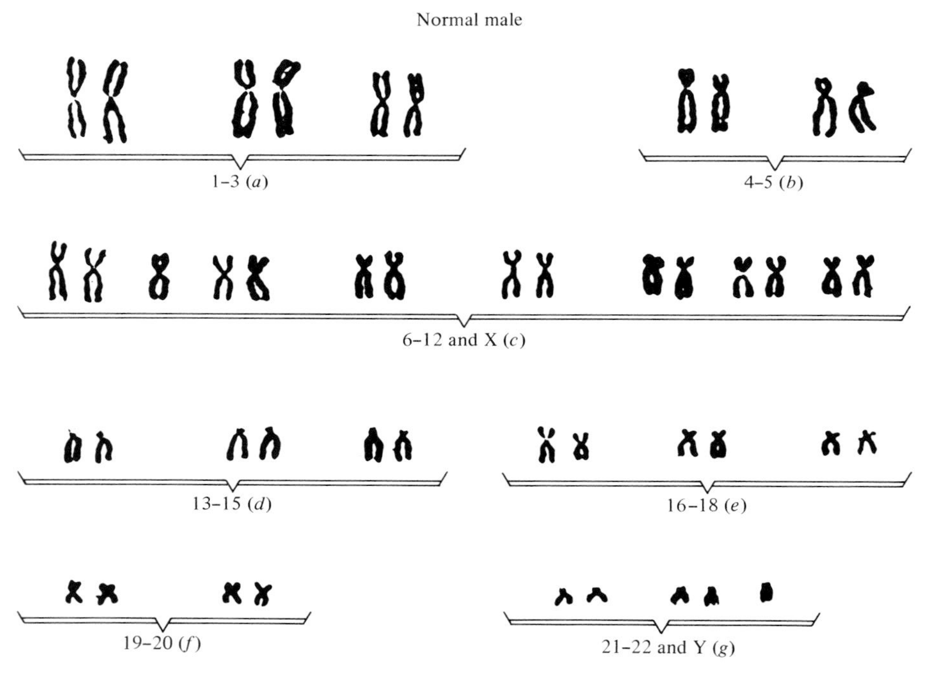

fig. 10-15. A karyotype from a leucocyte of a normal human male arrested in metaphase by colchicine. The chromosomes have been arranged into groups according to length, and into subgroups according to the position of the centromere.

---

[33] Huang, R. C., and Bonner, J. *Proc. Natl. Acad. Sci.*, *48*, 1216 (1962); *J. Mol. Biol.*, *6*, 169 (1963); Allfrey, V. G., and Mirsky, A. E. *Proc. Natl, Acad. Sci.*, *48*, 1590 (1962); Hurwitz, J., Evans, A., Babinet, C., and Skalka, A. *Cold Spring Harbor Symp. Quant. Biol.*, *28*, 59 (1963); Huang, R. C., Bonner, J., and Murray, K. *J. Mol. Biol.*, *8*, 54 (1964).

in photomicrographs of cells taken during metaphase. Cells may be arrested at metaphase by applying colchicine or the periwinkle alkaloids to them. Every somatic cell of higher organisms possesses a characteristic number of chromosomes. The individual chromosomes may be identified on the basis of their length and the relative position of the centromere. The 46 chromosomes from a normal human male are shown in Fig. 10-15; such a portrait of the chromosome complement of a cell is called a *karyotype*.

The X and Y sex chromosomes usually are distinguishable from the somatic chromosomes both on morphological grounds and because they tend to divide slightly later than the somatic chromosomes. In most species the male is characterized by an X and a Y chromosome and the female by two X chromosomes. However, in certain insects the male is XO and the female is XX, while in certain birds and Lepidoptera the male is XY while the female is XO. It is believed that only one X chromosome is functionally active in an interphase cell. If the cell contains more than one X chromosome, all but one of these condense into small, discrete masses called *Barr bodies* (named after their discoverer). The Barr body is characteristically located at the periphery of the nucleus and stains densely with chromatin stains (Fig. 10-16). The cells of a normal

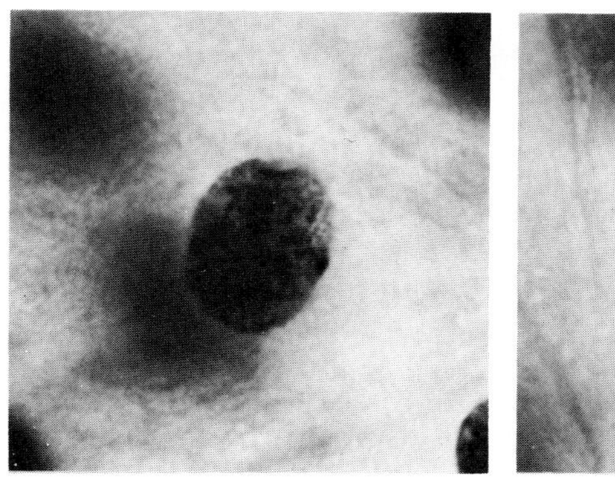

a

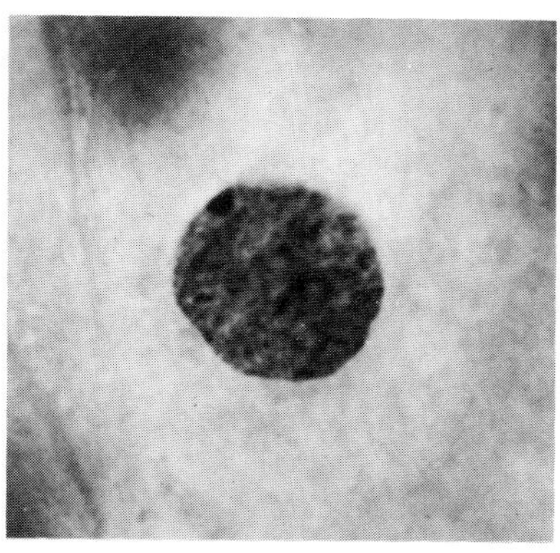

b

fig. 10-16. (*a*) A cell from the buccal epithelium of a normal female (XX) showing a single Barr body. (*b*) A cell from the buccal epithelium of a female with three X chromosomes showing two Barr bodies. (Courtesy of Dr. Park Gerald.)

male, which contain but one X chromosome, will not exhibit Barr bodies, while the cells of a normal female, which each have two X chromosomes, will have one Barr body each. In rare individuals with more than two X chromosomes, some cells will be found with several Barr bodies. The maximum number of Barr bodies in any cell will always be one less than the number of X chromosomes present.

In the light microscope the centromere appears to be a darkly staining granule surrounded by a relatively clear region, but no characteristic ultrastructure has been observed in the electron microscope. The centromere represents the *primary constriction* which divides each chromosome into two arms. Spindle fibers connect the centromere to the poles of the spindle; these fibers help to orient the chromosomes at metaphase and provide a means of segregation into the daughter nuclei during anaphase. The chromosomes of mutants lacking a centromere do not orient properly during cell division and are left stranded as the other chromosomes move to the poles.

What makes the centromere so distinctive a structural and functional component of the chromosome or what establishes its precise location is unknown at the present time.

The *chromomeres* are localized thickenings or enlargements which occur in characteristic positions on given chromosomes. They may be seen particularly well during the early stages of meiosis. The consistent, distinctive pattern of chromomeres typical of a given chromosome in a given cell type of a given species has led to the suggestion that they have functional significance. The hypothesis favored at the present time is that the chromomeres are localized regions of tight spirals representing genetic foci which are shielded from activity.

Even during interphase, chromosomes vary in their staining properties according to their cell types. The older light microscopists referred to the darkly staining regions in the nucleus as *heterochromatin*; the lightly staining regions were called *euchromatin*. The current view holds that the variation of staining properties results from differences in the tightness of coiling. Frequently, the heterochromatic region becomes very lightly stained during interphase; the tight coiling of the euchromatic regions is surpassed by some formerly heterochromatic regions during this stage in the cell cycle.

The salivary glands of certain insects contain chromosomes which may be 200 times the length and many times wider than the typical chromosomes found at metaphase in other cells. It is thought that these chromosomes have undergone repeated replication such as occurs during mitosis but that the products have remained together. This phenomenon is called *polyteny*. Hundreds of alternating dark and light bands, in patterns which are exactly reproduced in particular chromosomes of a given species (Fig. 10-17), may be observed along the length of polytene chromosomes. The giant chromosomes in the salivary gland frequently undergo *synapsis*, a process by which the two homologous chromosomes fuse (synapsis occurs frequently during meiosis; see p. 565). When synaptic pairing occurs, the cells of the salivary gland appear to have only half the normal complement of chromosomes. The giant salivary gland chromosomes have been used extensively in genetic mapping studies.

Reconciling the Watson-Crick model of the DNA molecule with chromosome structure poses some problems. A double-stranded molecule of DNA from mammalian sources is approximately 2 $m\mu$ wide and 0.5 to 4.0 μ long. Average mammalian metaphase chromosomes, on the other hand, are approximately 500 $m\mu$ wide and 2 to 10 μ long. Thus, an average chromosome is about three orders of magnitude larger than the average DNA molecule. The largest chromosome in man, for example, contains approximately 0.6×10^{-12} g of DNA; this is equivalent to 10^5 molecules of DNA with a molecular weight of 3,000,000 at one extreme, or a single DNA molecule with a molecular weight of about 10^{12} on the other. If each chromosome contains more than one DNA molecule, there must be a definite mechanism to keep these molecules from becoming tangled during the replication and segregation of chromosomes.

The mode of replication and segregation of genetic material in chromosomes has been studied by means of tritium (^{3}H)-labeled thymidine,[34] a deoxynucleotide which is incorporated exclusively in DNA. After a brief exposure to tritiated thymidine, during which this precursor is incorporated into the DNA, cells are arrested in metaphase by colchicine. The distribution of radioactivity in individual chromosomes is then determined from autoradiographs. In such experiments, the radio-

[34] Taylor, J. H., Woods, P. S., and Hughes, W. L. *Proc. Natl. Acad. Sci.*, *43*, 122 (1957); Lima-de-Faria, A. *Progr. Biophys. Biophys. Chem.*, *12*, 282 (1962).

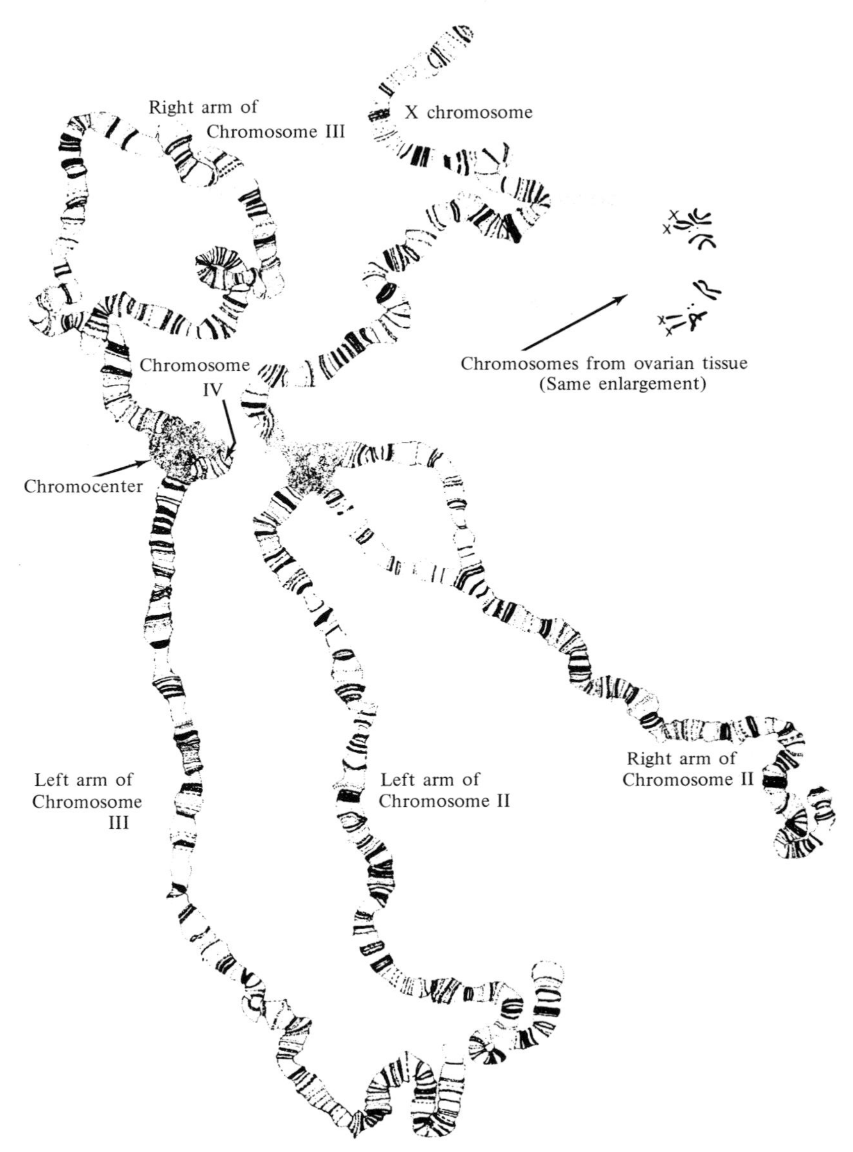

fig. 10-17. A drawing of the giant chromosomes from the salivary gland cells of the female larva of the fruit fly, *Drosophila melanogaster*, showing the banding patterns. A portion of the right arm of Chromosome II has not undergone synapsis, but the remainder of the chromosomes are paired. (From Painter, T. S. *J. Heredity*, *25*, 466 [1934].)

activity has been found to be distributed randomly in the metaphase chromosomes of the first mitotic division following exposure to the labeled precursor. If the cells are permitted to complete one division after exposure to tritiated thymidine and are arrested during the second metaphase, autoradiographs reveal that one chromatid is labeled while its fellow is not. Thus, it appears that chromosomes replicate by a semi-conservative pattern similar to that which characterizes DNA replication.

In view of the tritiated thymidine experiments, it is of interest that studies of Fuelgen-stained, trypsin-treated metaphase chromosomes show that the DNA is

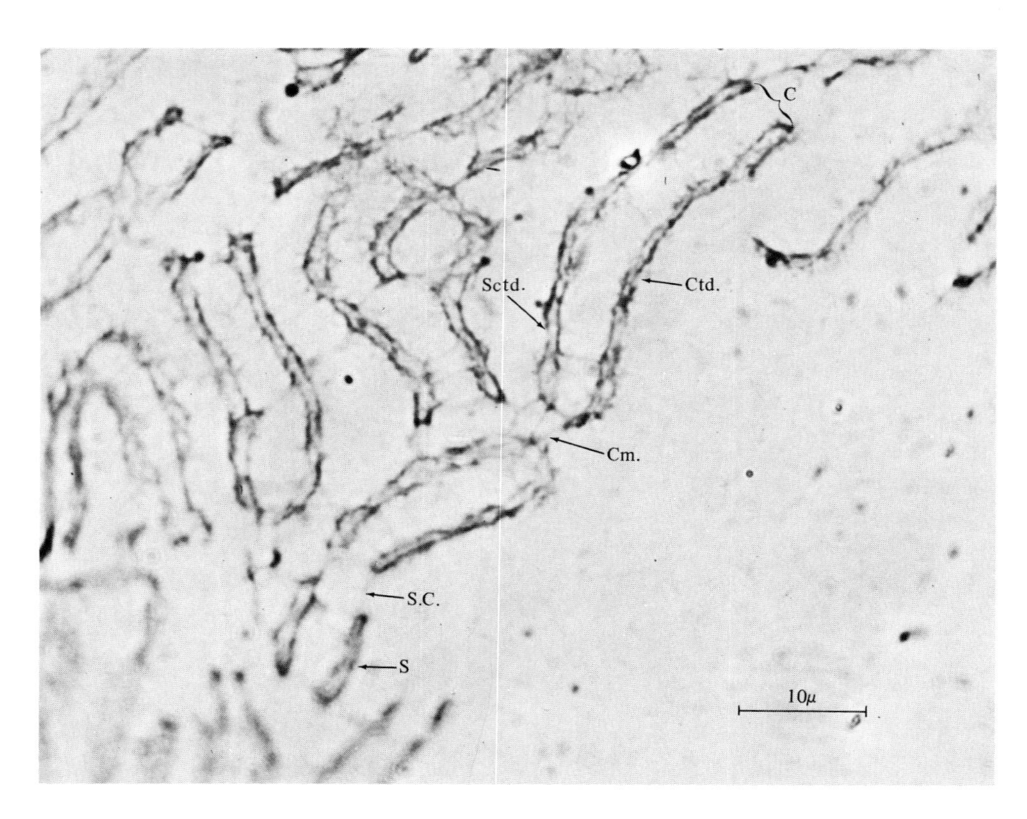

fig. 10-18. The long (M) chromosome of *Vicia faba*, which has been isolated from cells in metaphase, air-dried, and relaxed by the enzymatic action of trypsin. *Key to abbreviations: C*, chromosome; *Ctd.*, chromatid; *Sctd.*, subchromatid; *Cm.*, centromere; *S.C.*, secondary or nucleolar constriction; *S*, satellite. (From Trosko, J. E., and Wolff, S. *J. Cell Biol.*, *26*, 130 [1965].)

condensed in two strands (Fig. 10-18). The multiple strands of DNA in the chromosome appear to be compacted in a regular fashion; they can be loosened by treatment with ammonia, hot water, or potassium cyanide. Such studies reveal at least two orders of coiling[35] (Fig. 10-19).

Lampbrush chromosomes usually are found in animal cells which are about to undergo the reduction division to form ova (egg cells). They frequently are found in the ova of animals in which the egg contains large quantities of yolk, and their unusual physical appearance may be related functionally to the synthesis of yolk. The appearance of the lampbrush chromosomes is thought to result from the lateral extension of the DNA into loops (Fig. 10-20). The appearance of the lampbrush chromosomes is distinctive and characteristic for the individual chromosomes of a given species.

A technique has been reported for the isolation of large quantities of metaphase chromosomes.[36] Studies using large quantities of isolated chromosomes may supply answers to many questions concerning chromosome composition and structure.

[35] Ris, H., in McElroy, W., and Glass, B., eds. *Chemical Basis of Heredity*. Baltimore: Johns Hopkins Press, 1957, p. 23; Kaufmann, B. P., Gay, H., and McDonald, M. R. *Intern. Rev. Cytol.*, *9*, 77 (1960).
[36] Salzman, N. P., Moore, D. E., and Mendelsohn, J. *Proc. Natl. Acad. Sci.*, *56*, 1449 (1966).

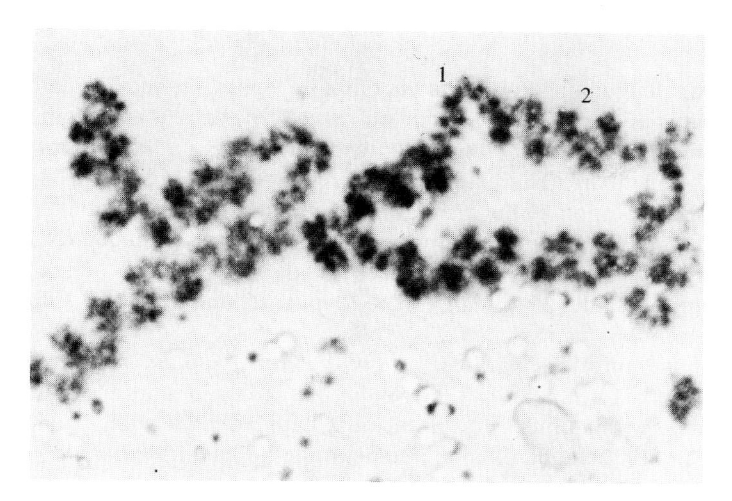

fig. 10-19. A photomicrograph of an anaphase II chromosome from a microsporocyte of *Lilium longiflorum* partially uncoiled by treatment with KCN. Two orders of coiling are shown, the minor spiral at 1, and the major spiral at 2. Magnification 35,000. (Courtesy of Dr. J. Herbert Taylor.)

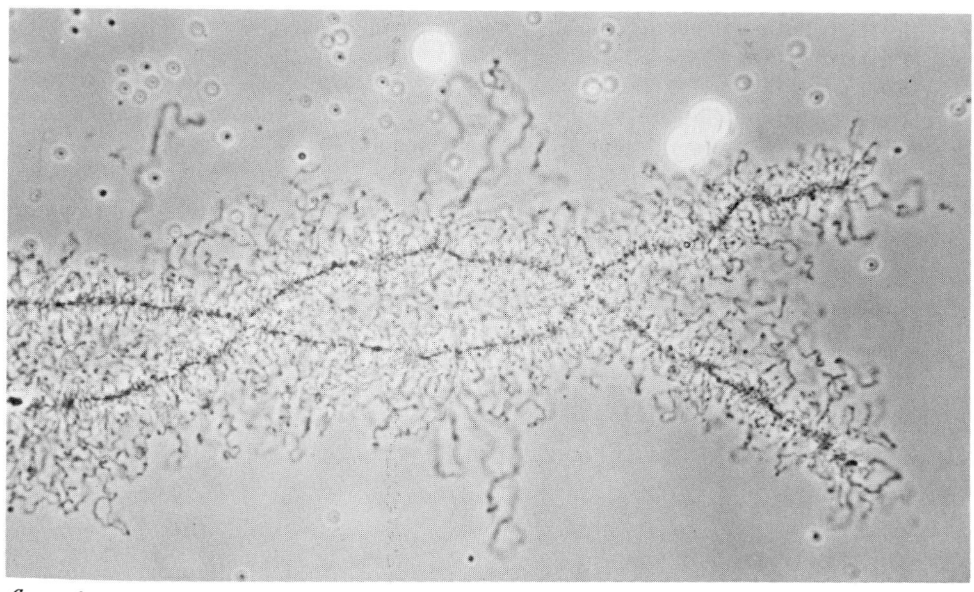

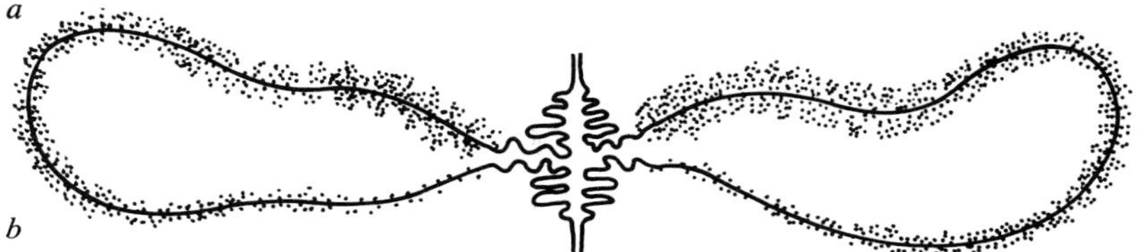

fig. 10-20. (*a*) A phase contrast micrograph of a portion of a giant lampbrush chromosome from a developing oöcyte of the newt, *Triturus*. (*b*) A diagram of one loop. The uneven thickness is thought to result from differences in the rate of RNA and protein synthesis. The loop is thought to represent a projection of the linear structure of the chromatid. (Courtesy of Dr. Joseph Gall.)

mitotic apparatus

The information which is available concerning the chemical composition and formation of the mitotic apparatus is very sketchy, even more sketchy than the current information concerning the organization of the chromosomes. The spindle is composed of positively birefringent fibers. The property of birefringence can be utilized to observe the formation and evolution of the spindle with a polarizing microscope.[37] It appears quite suddenly and disappears equally quickly. The spindle moves the chromosomes toward the poles. The early microdissection studies showed that the mitotic apparatus was a tough structure which could be pushed about within the dividing cell.

Electron micrographs of the mitotic apparatus[38] show that the spindle consists of microtubules 150 to 250 Å in diameter with an electron-opaque cortex and a much less dense center. The spindle microtubules consist of fibrils approximately 35 Å in diameter which appear to be long chains of monomer granules. The surfaces of the spindle microtubules are studded with particles which resemble ribosomes.

Mazia[39] was able to isolate the mitotic apparatus by the use of sulfhydryl compounds which appear to stabilize the spindle fibers. The mitotic apparatus then can be separated by cell fractionation techniques[40] (using differential centrifugation—see Chapter 2). The spindle accounts for about 10 percent of the total protein content of the sea urchin egg. Most of the protein of the spindle can be dissolved in alkaline thioglycolate, but a considerable residue remains. About 2 to 6 percent of the spindle is composed of RNA;[41] the RNA does not appear to sediment like native ribosomal-RNA, but it may represent r-RNA which has been altered by the isolation technique.

It would be attractive to suppose that the spindles were composed of a contractile protein. In fact, a contractile protein has been isolated by extraction with high concentrations of KCl.[42] This protein contracts upon the addition of heavy metal ions or upon oxidation of the sulfhydryl groups to disulfide groups. The contraction can be reversed by the addition of reducing agents such as ascorbic acid or mercaptoethanol. It is interesting to note that mitosis can be inhibited by the use of mercaptoethanol.[43] While the mitotic apparatus appears to have a somewhat higher ATPase activity than the whole cytoplasm,[44] the isolated mitotic apparatus does not exhibit prominent ATPase activity nor does it respond to the addition of exogenous ATP.

The protein which makes up the spindle microtubules appears to be synthesized prior to the beginning of mitosis. From about 30 minutes before the start of mitosis, the addition of puromycin, actinomycin, or chloramphenicol does not inhibit fiber

---

[37] Inoue, S., and Sato, H. *J. Gen. Physiol.*, *50*, suppl. no. 6, part 2, p. 259 (1967).
[38] Mazia, D., Mitchison, J., Medina, H., and Harris, P. *J. Biophys. Biochem. Cytol.*, *10*, 467 (1961); Harris, P. *J. Cell Biol.*, *14*, 475 (1962); Kane, R. *J. Cell Biol.*, *12*, 47 (1962); *15*, 279 (1962); Barnicot, N. *J. Cell Sci.*, *1*, 217 (1966); Rebhun, L., and Sander, G. *J. Cell Biol.*, *34*, 859 (1967); Roth, L. *J. Cell Biol.*, *34*, 47 (1967).
[39] Mazia, D., and Dan, K. *Proc. Natl. Acad. Sci.*, *38*, 826 (1952); *Symp. Soc. Exptl. Biol.*, *9*, 335 (1955).
[40] Mazia, D., Chaffee, R. R., and Iverson, R. M. *Proc. Natl. Acad. Sci.*, *47*, 788 (1961); Kane, R. *J. Cell Biol.*, *12*, 47 (1962); *15*, 279 (1962).
[41] Mazia, D. *Symp. Soc. Exptl. Biol.*, *9*, 335 (1955); Zimmerman, A. M. *Exptl. Cell Res.*, *20*, 529 (1960); Sakai, H. *Biochim. Biophys. Acta*, *112*, 132 (1966).
[42] Sakai, H. *J. Gen. Physiol.*, *45*, 411, 427 (1962).
[43] Mazia, D., and Zimmerman, A. M. *Exptl. Cell Res.*, *15*, 138 (1958).
[44] Mazia, D., Chaffee, R. R., and Iverson, R. M. *Proc. Natl. Acad. Sci.*, *47*, 788 (1961); Miki, T. *Exptl. Cell Res.*, *29*, 92 (1963).

formation.[45] Nevertheless, no protein with the antigenic properties of spindle protein has been found in the interphase cell by immunological techniques. The major protein component (comprising about 70 percent of the total spindle protein) has a molecular weight of 34,000 and contains two SH-groups. Its amino acid composition bears some resemblance to the composition of flagellin or actin. This protein is about the size which corresponds to the individual granules comprising the fibrils of the spindle microtubules.

If tissue-cultured amniotic cells are grown in a medium containing *p*-fluorophenylalanine (an analog of the amino acid phenylalanine), mitosis is prolonged.[46] The daughter cells also show prolonged mitosis. Kinetic studies have shown that a specific protein is synthesized in the G_2 phase which is required for mitosis and which is conserved. It is not known whether or not this protein is a nuclear protein or part of the mitotic apparatus.

The formation of spindle fibers is inhibited by low temperatures and by externally applied pressure; either low temperature or pressure may actually result in the disappearance of spindle birefringence. Yet the fibers reappear spontaneously when the preparation is warmed or when the pressure is released. The process of formation appears to be a polymerization of monomers involving disulfide linkages, a process which has a high enthalpy and a high entropy increase, as shown by van't Hoff plots. Heavy water[47] tends to stabilize the formation of spindle fibers; this stabilization is further increased by the application of high pressure.[48] The reversible formation and disappearance of the spindle is thought to represent a polymerization and depolymerization of a monomer protein molecule involving a sulfhydryl-disulfide equilibrium. The reversible contraction and elongation of the polymer may involve the formation of a complex with Ca^{++} or other divalent cations also involving the sulfhydryl-disulfide equilibrium. The immediate source of energy for driving the process of mitosis is not known. Recently it has been possible to separate and purify SH-containing proteins by chromatography on thiolated or mercurated Sephadex.[49] The use of such techniques may lead to the isolation of larger quantities of pure spindle protein for more definitive studies.

meiosis

Bisexual reproduction in higher organisms ensures the continuity of, and increases the possibilities for, recombination of inherited traits within the species. Bisexual reproduction involves two complementary processes: *meiosis*, the production of haploid *gametes* (which contain half the characteristic number of chromosomes) by a set of reduction divisions of the reproductive cell; and *fertilization* (syngamy), the fusion of two haploid gametes of different sex to form a diploid cell.

Typically, the cells of higher organisms are diploid; that is, they contain sets of chromosome pairs. The homologous chromosomes constituting a pair are morphologically identical and genetically similar. Occasionally, tetraploid cells containing four

[45] Inoué, S., Sato, H., and Ascher, M. *Biol. Bull.*, *129*, 409 (1965).
[46] Sisken, J. E., and Wilkes, E. *J. Cell Biol.*, *34*, 97 (1967).
[47] Mazia, D., and Dan, K. *Proc. Natl. Acad. Sci.*, *38*, 826 (1952); Gross, P. R., and Spindel, W. *Science*, *131*, 37 (1960); *Ann. N.Y. Acad. Sci.*, *90*, 500 (1960).
[48] Marsland, D., and Zimmerman, A. M. *Exptl. Cell Res.*, *38*, 306 (1965).
[49] Jellum, E., and Eldjarn, L. *Biochim. Biophys. Acta*, *100*, 144 (1965).

chromosomes of each type—or cells of even higher ploidy can be found. The DNA content of cells is proportional to their ploidy, diploid cells containing twice as much DNA as haploid cells, tetraploid cells containing twice as much DNA as diploid cells, and so on. The amount of DNA per cell is largely independent of the size of the cell.

There are exceptions to the usual pattern of bisexual reproduction. The vegetative cells of the unicellular green alga *Chlamydomonas* are haploid. Under certain conditions, two cells of opposite mating type act as gametes and fuse to form a zygote. The zygote then undergoes immediate meiosis to produce four haploid cells, two of each mating type. The haploid cells divide further by ordinary mitosis, giving rise to clones of haploid cells. The two types of gametes in *Chlamydomonas* can be distinguished by their unequal size or by the fact that one mating type is motile while the other is not (usually the smaller gamete is motile).

Alternation of generations occurs in many species of organisms. For instance, in the brown alga *Ectocarpus*, meiosis occurs in enlarged terminal cells of the diploid plant, and *zoospores* are produced. The haploid zoospores develop into plants which resemble the diploid plant in appearance but which have cells containing a haploid number of chromosomes. Motile gametes with a haploid number of chromosomes are formed by the haploid plant. Gametes of opposite mating types then undergo syngamy and develop into a diploid plant in the next generation.

Unlike the isomorphic alternation of generations in *Ectocarpus*, ferns show a heteromorphic alternation of generations. The familiar fern body is diploid, and it produces haploid spores by meiosis. The spores develop into small, flat green plant bodies composed of haploid cells, which in turn give rise to gametes. When two gametes of opposite mating types fuse, a diploid zygote is formed which develops into a diploid vegetative fern plant body. In the haploid body forms, as in bacteria, direct phenotypic expression of all genes is possible, and the phenomena of dominance and recessiveness usually are not encountered.

The basic plan of meiosis is the same in all organisms with a sexual phase (Fig. 10-21). The nucleus divides twice with only one replication of chromosomes. This

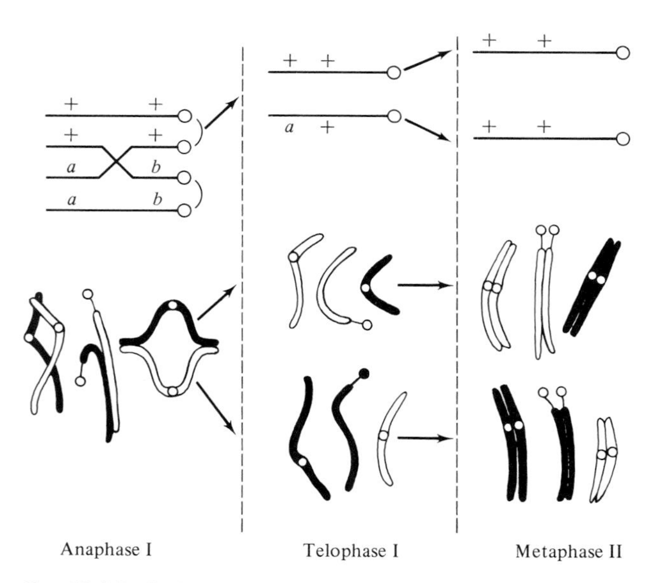

fig. 10-21. A diagram showing the plan of meiosis.

action reduces the number of chromosomes in each resultant nucleus to half the number of chromosomes in the premeiotic nucleus. Meiosis also provides a mechanism for segregating the maternal and paternal sets of chromosome pairs into separate reproductive cells. In the usual case of a diploid premeiotic nucleus, a set of four haploid nuclei is produced. Many of the basic features of mitosis are found in meiosis. It is generally assumed that the striking similarities between the two processes reflect common underlying mechanisms.

The G_2 period in meiosis merges into a very long prophase which may be subdivided into five stages. The first stage, *Leptonema* (Gr., thin thread), resembles the earliest stage of prophase of mitosis except that the cells and nuclei undergoing meiosis are larger in size and the rate of the process is slower than in mitosis of somatic cells. The chromosomes (Fig. 10-22) become very thin and uncoiled, and they develop a larger

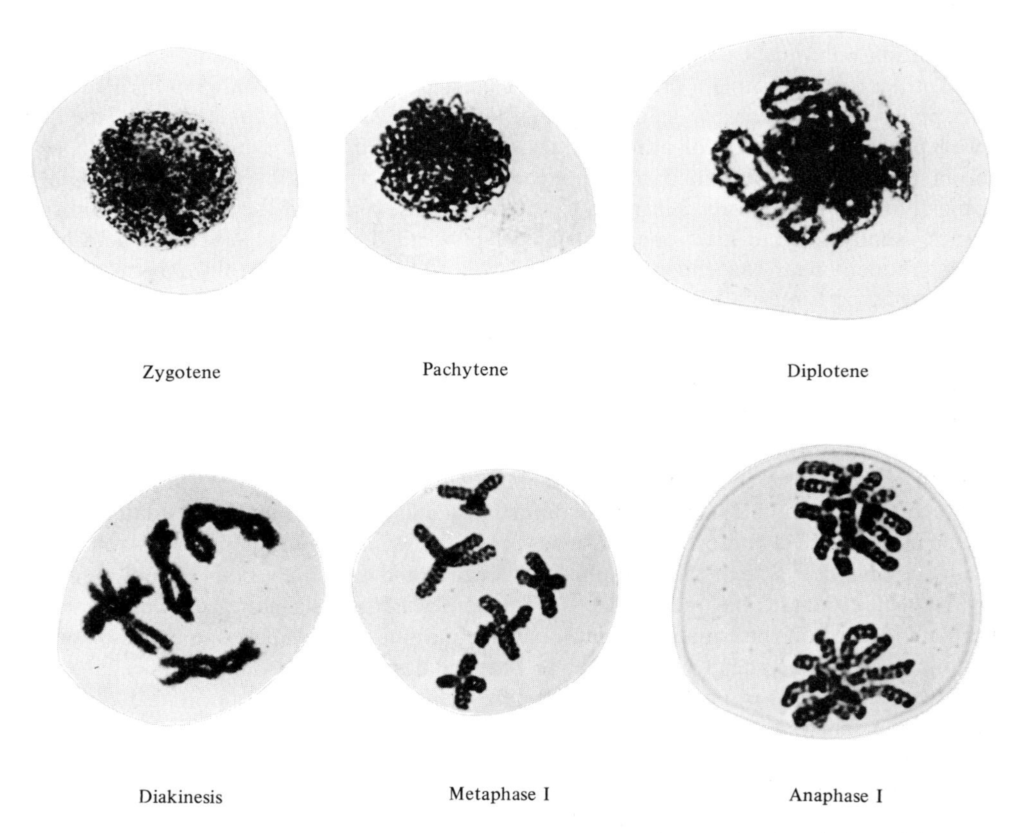

fig. 10-22. Stages of the first meiotic division in *Amphiuma.* See text for description of the various stages. (Courtesy of Dr. A. H. Sparrow.)

series of chromomeres than do mitotic chromosomes. The chromomeres, which are constant in number, size, and position for homologous chromosomes, apparently represent localized areas of increased coiling. The nucleolus frequently becomes attached to a particular chromosome characteristic of the species.

In the second stage, *Zygonema* (yolked thread), the chromosomes become shortened. This stage is characterized by the intimate association of homologous chromosomes.

During this process, called *synapsis*, the pair of homologous chromosomes appears closely in apposition, forming *bivalent* chromosomes. The chromosome pairing tends to begin at certain defined locations along their length, usually at or near the ends, and, once initiated, proceeds to involve the entire length of the chromosome.

The third stage, *Pachynema* (thick thread), is characterized by stable bivalent chromosomes. Although at first glance the cells appear to contain a haploid number of chromosomes, careful observation reveals that the chromosomes are bivalent and are composed of two units. In contrast to mitosis, limited incorporation of DNA precursors takes place during leptonema, zygonema, and pachynema. During pachynema (which occupies a relatively long time), the bivalent chromosomes shorten, thicken, and tend to assume a rodlike form. In species with polytene chromosomes, the pachynema stage is particularly well-suited for the observation of the chromosomal fine structure: banding patterns, morphology, heterochromatin distribution, etc.

The fourth stage, *Diplonema* (double thread), is characterized by the partial separation of the chromosomes into pairs or even four separate chromatids. However, the chromatids continue to be held together at one or more points along their length. Thus, they may resemble a cross if joined at one point, appear as a loop if there are two points of adhesion, or as a series of loops if they are held together at three or more points. The points of adhesion are called *chiasmata.* Chiasmata appear to be modal points corresponding morphologically to genetic crossing over. Longer chromosomes tend to have more chiasmata than short ones, but even the shortest chromosomes usually form at least one chiasma per bivalent. In some species chiasmata are more frequent near the end of the chromosomes. During diplonema chromosomes continue to coil internally and shorten.

The fifth stage, *Diakinesis,* is characterized by the further contraction of the chromosomes (increased tightness of coiling) and the *terminalization* of the chiasmata: the movement of the chiasmata toward the ends of the chromosomes. The chromosomes frequently move to the periphery of the nucleus. The nucleolus becomes detached from the chromosomes with which it has been associated and may disappear.

With the onset of the first meiotic metaphase, the nuclear membrane disappears and a bipolar spindle forms. The chromosomes move to the equatorial plate. Each bivalent meiotic chromosome possesses two functionally undivided centromeres which lie on either side of the metaphase plate, oriented in the long axis of the spindle. By way of contrast, the metaphase chromosomes in mitosis have one centromere per pair located on the equatorial plate. During anaphase in meiosis, one chromosome from every bivalent goes to each pole, so that the number of chromosomes is halved. The two chromatids of each chromosome are held together at the undivided centromere but otherwise are completely divided after the chromosomes separate. The doubling of the centromeres characteristic of mitosis does not take place in the first meiotic anaphase. Thus, at the end of the first meiotic division, each daughter cell has a haploid number of chromosomes, but because the chromosomes are duplicated, it has the DNA content expected in a diploid cell.

During the first telophase, a new nuclear membrane forms and the cells undergo a period of reorganization. The chromosomes uncoil somewhat and nucleoli may form. Although interphase occurs in some species, the second division may follow directly, at times even without a division of the cytoplasm. Interphase, if it is present, is brief, and the coiling of the chromosomes persists. No increase in DNA takes place between the first and second meiotic divisions; the occurrence of an interphase between the two divisions suggests that additional RNA and protein synthesis may be required to carry meiosis through to completion.

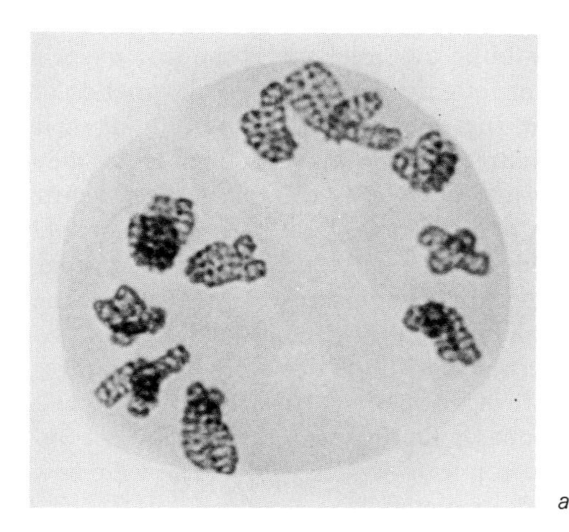

a

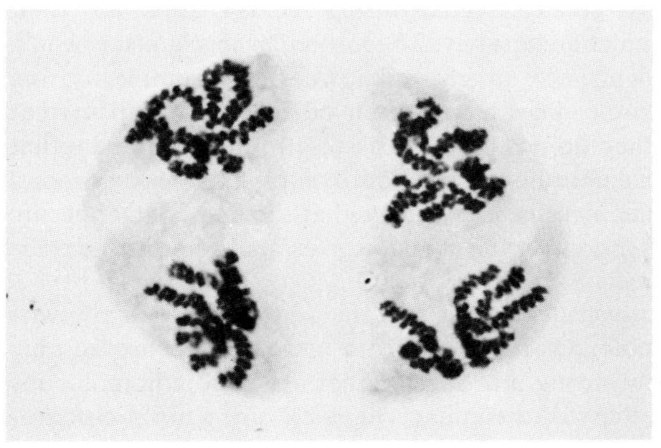

b

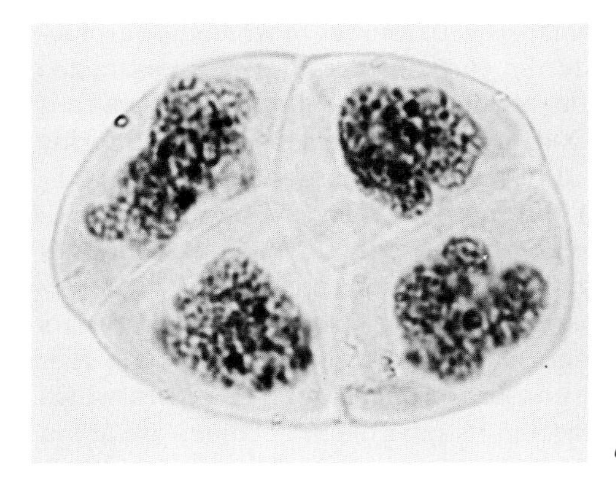

c

fig. 10-23. Photomicrographs of the second meiotic division in a cell of *Trilium.* (*a*) Prophase II showing widely separated chromatids held together only at their centromeres; (*b*) metaphase II showing tightly coiled chromosomes and the very lightly stained centromeres; and (*c*) telophase II showing the invagination of cell walls to form four separate microspores.

The second meiotic division is more like a mitotic division than is the first meiotic division. During the prophase of the second meiotic division, the two chromatids of each chromosome seem to repel each other so that they remain joined only at their common centromere (Fig. 10-23). The chromatids shorten and the nucleoli, if they were formed during the previous telophase, disappear. During metaphase, the nuclear membranes disappear and a spindle forms. The chromosomes move into the equatorial plate of the spindle. As noted above, sometimes the first and second meiotic divisions merge; in this case, the first meiotic spindle appears to split into two spindles and the second meiotic division begins without a telophase, interphase, and second prophase.

The anaphase of the second meiotic division starts with the doubling of the centromeres of each chromosome. The chromatids then move apart toward the poles, and look like the chromosomes in a mitotic anaphase. During telophase of the second meiotic division, nuclei are formed and the cytoplasm divides to produce four new cells, each containing a haploid number of chromosomes.

During mitosis, and to an even greater degree during meiosis, cells and their organelles follow a very complicated choreography. The molecular mechanisms which are responsible for these movements are largely unknown. For example, during synapsis pairs of homologous chromosomes attract each other and line up so that the gene sites correspond. While they do not fuse, the association is to intimate that they frequently appear to be a single chromosome. Before synapsis, the chromosomes may be several microns apart. Some investigators believe that the first contact occurs purely by chance. In any event, after contact the chromosomes associate by a zipper-like phenomenon in both directions.

The specificity of the pairing is illustrated by the fact that chromosomes may twist about so as to bring together homologous regions when a piece of one chromosome is inverted. The force is sufficiently strong and specific that even short homologous regions on chromosomes that are otherwise dissimilar will pair. Pairing of the chromosomes may begin at any point. If a third homologous chromosome is present it remains unpaired during synapsis of the other two. Synapsis will occur even when the chromosomes are stretched out, although ordinarily the chromosomes are in a contracted state. The repulsive electrostatic force of the highly charged phosphate residues is overcome, possibly by the basic proteins. Yet, at a later stage of meiosis (during diplonema) the attractive forces disappear and the chromosomes separate.

The fact that chromomeres are contracted chromosomes has been shown by microdissection studies. Contraction represents a region of dense DNA; coiling of chromosomes is a different phenomenon which may or may not be accompanied by contraction. When a chromosome is subjected to stretching, the chromomere disappears and the thickness of the chromosome becomes uniform throughout its length. It is curious that chromomeres are so constant in location and size. The forces which cause localized contraction of the chromosome and its subsequent uncoiling are not at all understood. Presumably these phenomena occur as the result of the various kinds of intermolecular forces described in Chapter 3. It is relatively easy to see how two complementary strands of DNA are held together. It should be remembered, however, that the chromosome is composed of many double-stranded DNA molecules and contains, in addition, the basic histone proteins. How molecular complementarity occurs in chromosomes is unknown.

The phenomenon of *crossing over* is the exchange of homologous segments by adjoining chromatids during the course of meiosis. This process results in an uncoupling of genetic characters which normally appear on a single chromosome, that is to say, the uncoupling of linked genetic traits. Thus, crossing over provides a temendous multiplication of possibilities for recombination of genetic traits. It is generally agreed that each chiasma in a meiotic division represents one instance of crossing over. Cytological studies show that crossing over occurs when the chromatids are in tetrad form. Studies with tritiated thymidine indicate that crossing over is less frequent between sister chromatids than between nonidentical chromatids.

Crossovers are not completely random events. Rather, the phenomenon takes place with remarkable precision. It occurs after the replication of DNA and almost always represents an exactly reciprocal exchange of material between two non-sister chromatids. The portions of the chromatids which are interchanged correspond exactly. If two or more crossovers occur at widely spaced points on a chromosome, they appear to be independent of each other in location, frequency of occurrence, or combination of chromatids. If a crossover takes place at a point between two chromatids, however, it reduces the probability of a second crossover occurring near it between the same two chromatids. This phenomenon is called *positive interference*. On the other hand, there is an increase in probability for the occurrence of extremely closely spaced crossovers, a phenomenon known as *negative interference*.

Interference may be regarded as a property of the mechanism that breaks the chromatids to effect crossovers. When multiple crossovers occur in a single bivalent, the frequency of two-, three-, and four-chromatid crossovers begins to approach randomness. Meselson and Weigle[50] have shown that recombination of genes in viruses involves the breakage and reunion of the DNA strands. Breakage and reunion

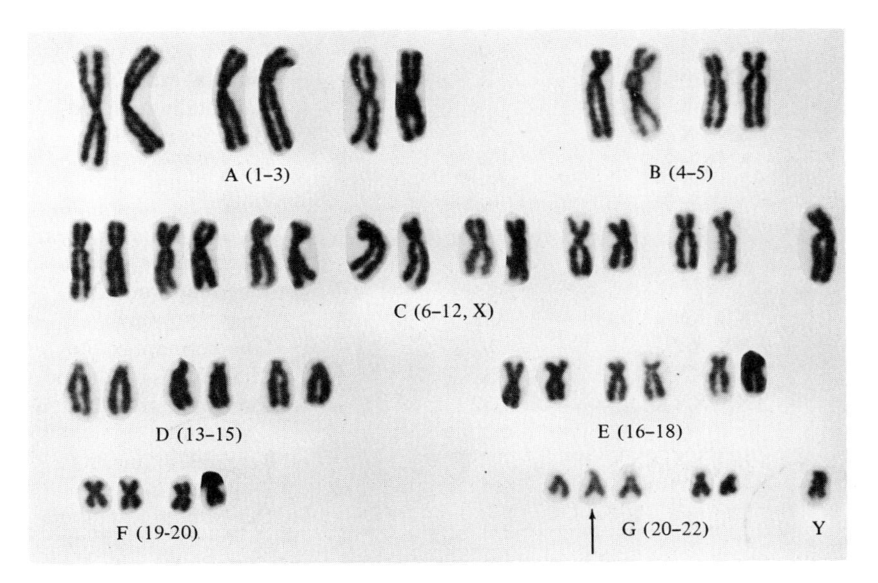

fig. 10-24. A chromosome karyotype from a patient with Down's syndrome (mongoloid idiocy) showing trisomy of chromosome 21. Down's syndrome is characterized by mental retardation, an abnormal folding of the eyelids, short stature, stubby hands and feet, a lack of normal folds in the palms, and frequently the presence of congenital malformations, particularly of the heart. (Courtesy of Dr. David Yi-Yung Hsia. From D. Y. Hsia. *Human Developmental Genetics*. Chicago: Year Book Medical Publishers, 1968. Copyright © 1968, Year Book Medical Publishers; reprinted by permission.)

[50] Meselson, M., and Weigle, J. J. *Proc. Natl. Acad. Sci.*, *47*, 857 (1961).

fig. 10-25. Some sex chromosome variants in human beings. (Adapted from Miller, Orlando J. The sex chromosome anomalies, *Am. J. Obstet. Gynecol., 90,* 1078–1139 [1964].)

CHROMOSOME NUMBER	SEX CHROMOSOME CONSTITUTION	NUMBER OF SEX CHROMATIN BODIES (BARR)	FERTILITY	REMARKS
		Male Habitus		
46	XY	0	+	Normal male
47	XYY	0	+(−)	Male, possible tendency toward criminal behavior
47	XXY	1	−	Klinefelter's syndrome[a]
48	XXXY	2	−	Resembles Klinefelter's syndrome
48	XXYY	1	−	Resembles Klinefelter's syndrome
49	XXXXY	3	−	Severely retarded
49	XXXYY	2	−	Resembles Klinefelter's syndrome
		Female Habitus		
46	XX	1	+	Normal female
45	XO	0	−	Turner's syndrome[b]
47	XXX	2	±	Triple-X syndrome; mentally retarded
48	XXXX	3	?	Mentally retarded
49	XXXXX	4	?	Mentally retarded
		Mosaics		
45/46	XO/XY	0	−	Male or female appearance; male pseudohermaphrodite
45/46	XO/XX	0/1	−	Turner's syndrome
46	XX/XY	0/1	−	True hermaphrodite
46/47	XX/XXY	1	−	Klinefelter's syndrome
46/47	XX/XXX	1/2	−	Some are true hermaphrodites
45/46/47	XO/XX/XXX	0/1/2	−	Resembles Turner's syndrome

[a] Klinefelter's syndrome is characterized by elevated gonadotropins, small, firm testes with Leydig cell failure resulting in low fertility and gynecomastia. There is also some mental deficiency in many cases.

[b] Turner's syndrome is characterized by a short stature, delayed or absent sexual development, incomplete gonads and infertility, webbing of the neck and fingers, pigmented nevi, and other abnormalities.

probably also occurs in crossing over of chromatids during meiosis, but the process must have a much higher order of complexity. Several theories have attempted to account for chromatid breakage in terms of localized strain or tension in the bivalent;

after the strain is relieved, recombination follows. A number of theoretical models of crossing over have been suggested, but none is entirely satisfactory.[51]

Nonreciprocal crossovers rarely occur. They represent instances in which the normal mechanism of genetic recombination operates improperly. A related phenomenon is the imperfect separation or *nondisjunction* of the chromatids at the crossover points. The combination of imperfect crossing over and nondisjunction may result in *duplication,* the addition of an extra segment in tandem, in reverse tandem, or as a displaced piece, to a chromosome. *Inversions* are structural aberrations of genes in which a portion of a chromosome has become rearranged in reverse order as a consequence of abnormal breakage. There are two general types of inversion which depend upon whether or not the centromere is included. If the inversion is confined to a single arm of a chromosome, it is termed *paracentric*; a *paricentric* inversion, on the other hand, includes the centromere and usually results in a visible alteration of chromosome appearance.

The individuals that result from such abnormalities in meiosis have provided the grist for a multitude of genetic studies. In humans, for example, Down's syndrome (Mongoloid idiocy) is generally characterized by trisomy of chromosome 21; consequently the chromosome complement is 47 instead of the normal 46 (Fig. 10-24). Many variants involving the sex chromosomes have been studied (Fig. 10-25).

extranuclear DNA

It has long been appreciated from genetic studies that some properties of mitochondria and chloroplasts can be inherited by a mechanism which does not involve the chromosomes or the nucleus.[52] Although mitochondria and chloroplasts are distributed to both daughter cells, they divide independently of nuclear division or cell division, often during interphase. The observation of Feulgen-staining material within mitochondria and chloroplasts gave rise to the belief that these organelles might contain DNA.[53] The presence of DNA in these organelles was also reported by the studies of Nass and Nass,[54] who demonstrated the presence of heavy metal–staining filaments, which were removed by prior treatment with DNAse, in electron micrographs.

Final proof of the presence of DNA in chloroplasts and mitochondria came from its actual isolation from the washed, isolated organelles.[55] Mitochondrial DNA is resistant to enzymatic attack from DNAse until the mitochondrial membrane is lysed. After treatment of mitochondria with digitonin, DNA is hydrolyzed by DNAse. Extranuclear DNA comprises from 1 to 3 percent of the total cellular DNA. The DNA isolated from chloroplasts and mitochondria has a buoyant density in cesium chloride gradients of 1.701; this is in contrast to nuclear DNA, which has a buoyant density

---

[51] Uhl, C. H. *Genetics*, *51*, 191 (1965); Whitehouse, H. L. K. *Sci. Progr.*, *53*, 285 (1965).
[52] Ephrussi, B. *Nucleo-Cytoplasmic Relations in Microorganisms*. Fair Lawn, N.J.: Oxford University Press, 1963; Wilkie, D. *The Cytoplasm in Heredity*. London: Methuen, 1964.
[53] Chevremont, M., and Chevremont-Comhaire, S. *Compt. Rend. Soc. Biol.*, *151*, 1621 (1957); Ris, H., and Plaut, W. *J. Cell Biol.*, *13*, 383 (1962).
[54] Nass, M. M. K., and Nass, S. *J. Cell Biol.*, *19*, 593 (1963).
[55] Chun, E. H. L., Vaughan, M. H., Jr., and Rich, A. *J. Mol. Biol.*, *7*, 130 (1963); Sager, R., and Ishida, M. R. *Proc. Natl. Acad. Sci.*, *50*, 725 (1963); Luck, D. J. L., and Reich, E. *Proc. Natl. Acad. Sci.*, *52*, 931 (1964); Rabinowitz, M., Sinclair, J. H., DeSalle, L., Haselkorn, R., and Swift, H. *Proc. Natl. Acad. Sci.*, *53*, 1126 (1965).

of 1.712. Like bacterial DNA, the DNA in mitochondria is circular in form.[56] The base composition of mitochondrial DNA differs from that of nuclear DNA (Fig. 10-26). Mitochondrial DNA has a molecular weight in the neighborhood of 7–10

fig. 10-26. Differences in composition of yeast nuclear DNA (N-DNA) and yeast mitochondrial DNA (Mt-DNA). (From Tewari, K., Votch, W., Mahler, H. R., and Mackler, B. *J. Mol. Biol., 20,* 463 [1966]. Copyright Academic Press; reprinted by permission.)

SPECIES	METHOD USED	MOLE (PERCENT) A+T	G+C	A	T	G	C
N-DNA	From T_m(84°C)	64	36				
	From ρ (1.693)	64	39				
	From A_{260}/A_{260} at pH 3.0 (1.59)	66	34				
	From paper electrophoresis of nucleotides	65.9	34.1	31.2	34.7	15.6	18.5
Mt-DNA	From T_m (75°C)	86	14				
	From ρ (1.679)	81	19				
	From A_{260}/A_{260} (1.71)	75	25				
	From paper electrophoresis	78.8	21.3	41.3	37.5	11.3	10.0

$\times 10^6$. Thus, mitochondrial DNA has the capacity to code for approximately 25 to 45 polypeptides with an average molecular weight of 20,000. Significant differences in the annealing properties of mitochondrial and nuclear DNA have been found. Heat-denatured or alkaline-denatured DNA from mitochondria renatures under conditions in which nuclear DNA fails to renature.

Mitochondria contain a DNA polymerase, and studies using tritiated thymidine have demonstrated conclusively the replication of mitochondrial DNA. The replication of mitochondrial DNA, like that of nuclear DNA, appears to be semiconservative.[57] The replication of mitochondrial DNA occurs independently of the replication of nuclear DNA, often during different phases of the cell cycle. In addition, chloroplasts and mitochondria contain a DNA-dependent RNA polymerase. These organelles also contain RNA, much of which is in the form of ribosomes.[58] Transfer-RNA also appears to be present.[59]

It is well known that isolated mitochondria are able to incorporate radioactive amino acids into TCA-precipitable material.[60] Unlike ordinary cellular protein synthesis on polyribosomes, protein synthesis in mitochondria does not require the addition of ATP, presumably because there is an ATP generating system already

[56] Van Bruggen, E. F. J., Borst, P., Ruttenberg, G. J. C. M., Gruber, M., and Kroon, A. M. *Biochim. Biophys. Acta, 119,* 437 (1966); Sinclair, J. H., and Stevens, B. J. *Proc. Natl. Acad. Sci., 56,* 508 (1966); Nass, M. M. K. *Proc. Natl. Acad. Sci., 56,* 1215 (1966).
[57] Reich, E., and Luck, D. J. L. *Proc. Natl. Acad. Sci., 55,* 1600 (1966).
[58] Watson, M. L., and Aldridge, W. G. *J. Histochem. Cytochem., 12,* 96 (1964); Andre, J., and Marinozzi, V. *J. Microsc., 4,* 615 (1965); Rendi, R. *Exptl. Cell Res., 17,* 585 (1959); Alaev, N. R. *Biokhimiya, 29,* 413 (1964).
[59] Wintersberger, E., and Tuppy, H. *Biochem. Z., 341,* 399 (1965).
[60] Roodyn, D. B., Reis, P. J., and Work, T. S. *Biochem. J., 80,* 9 (1961); Buchanan, J., and Tapley, D. F. *Endocrinology, 79,* 81 (1966).

present. Inhibitors of oxidative phosphorylation, such as cyanide, 2,4-dinitrophenol, or anaerobiosis, also inhibit amino acid incorporation in mitochondria. Actinomycin D, which prevents the formation of messenger-RNA by inhibiting the transcription of DNA, and acroflavine, which combines with polynucleotides and thus renders them functionally ineffective, both block mitochondrial protein synthesis.[61]

Protein synthesis in mitochondria is also blocked by puromycin and chloramphenicol. The sensitivity of mitochondrial protein synthesis to chloramphenicol is particularly noteworthy because, although protein synthesis in bacteria is inhibited by it, mammalian ribosomal systems are rather resistant to its action. Much of the labeled amino acids are incorporated into mitochondrial membrane structural proteins during mitochondrial protein synthesis.[62]

Mutations in which purely mitochondrial functions are affected have been reported,[63] and the genetic traits transmitted by mitochondrial DNA are altered by ultraviolet light, *x*-rays, and DNA-binding dyes.[64]

Centrosomes (basal bodies, kinetosomes) also replicate independently of nuclear division. On cytological grounds (dye complexes, etc.) it has been presumed that these organelles also contain DNA. However, DNA has not yet been isolated from them.

evolution of eukaryotic cells[65]

The distinction between eukaryotic and prokaryotic cells, as manifested by numerous fundamental physiological differences between these cell types, is a divergence of singular importance in living systems. Let us summarize some conjectures concerning the origin of the autonomously dividing intracellular organelles as well as the evolution of mitosis.

A great deal of circumstantial evidence can be mustered to support the theory brought forward by numerous biologists during the past six decades that mitochondria, chloroplasts, and centrioles (basal bodies or kinetosomes) originated as free-living prokaryotic cells which became incorporated into large amoeboid cells as a result of parasitism. An endosymbiotic relationship then developed. These intracellular organelles are about the same size as bacteria; they contain a circular double-stranded loop of DNA similar to that of bacteria, and the lipids of mitochondrial membranes resemble those of bacterial membranes more closely than those of the cell membrane of eukaryotic cells. Like mitochondria, many bacteria carry on cytochrome-catalyzed respiration; bacteria, on the other hand, carry on a host of other metabolic processes. It seems highly likely that the redundancy intrinsic in symbiotic relations would be eliminated after a period of association; the symbiont would tend to lose those metabolic functions carried on by the host.

---

[61] Wintersberger, E. *Biochem. Z.*, *341*, 409 (1965).
[62] Roodyn, D. B., Suttie, J. W., and Work, T. S. *Biochem. J.*, *83*, 29 (1962); *85*, 177 (1962).
[63] Luck, D. J. L., and Reich, E. *Proc. Natl. Acad. Sci.*, *52*, 931 (1964); Mahler, H. R., Mackler, B., Grandchamp, S., and Slonimski, P. P. *Biochemistry*, *3*, 668 (1964); Mounolou, J. C., Jakob, H., and Slonimski, P. P. *Biochem. Biophys. Res. Commun.*, *24*, 218 (1966); Tewari, K., Vötch, W., Mahler, H. R., and Mackler, B. *J. Mol. Biol.*, *20*, 453 (1966); Clark-Walker, G., and Linnane, A. W. *J. Cell Biol.*, *34*, 1 (1967).
[64] Lyman, H., Epstein, H. T., and Schiff, J. A. *Biochim. Biophys. Acta*, *50*, 301 (1961); Gibor, A., and Granick, S. *J. Cell Biol.*, *15*, 599 (1962).
[65] This section is based largely on the cogent presentation of Sagan, L. *J. Theoret. Biol.*, *14*, 225 (1967), which contains a list of pertinent references in the literature. It should be noted that others have presented similar theories.

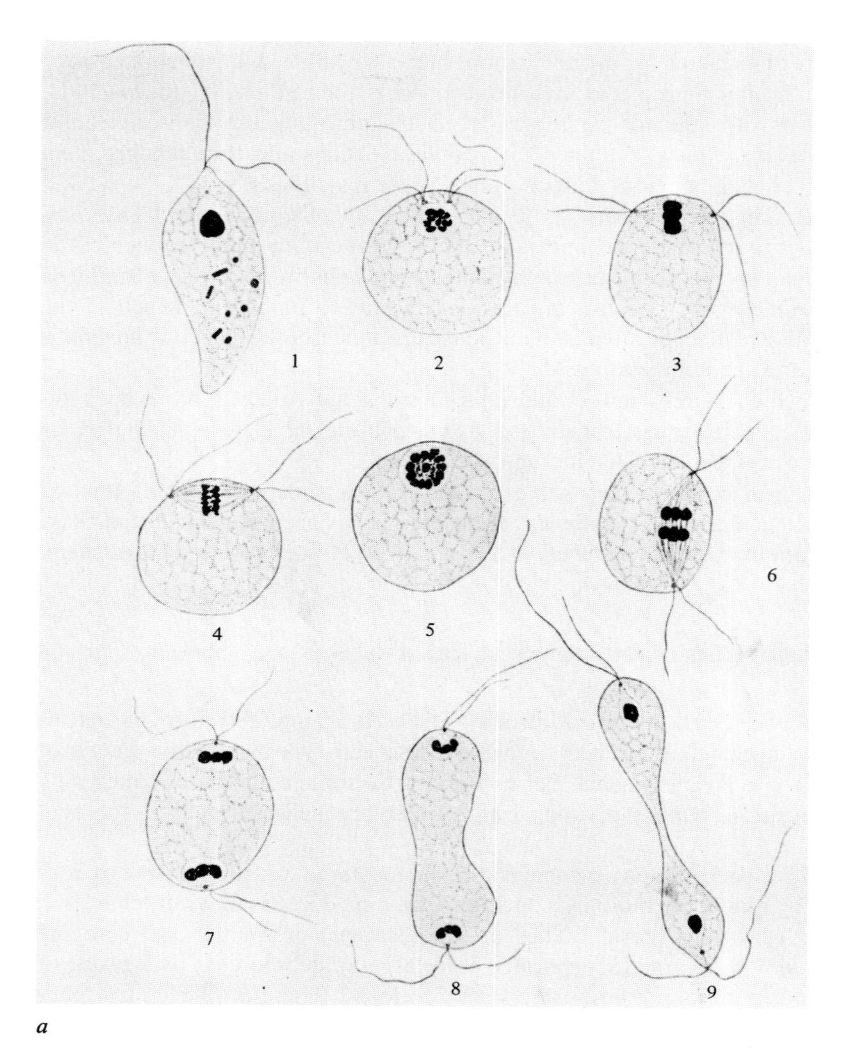

a

fig. 10-27. Examples of cell division in present-day protists associated with division of basal bodies to which flagella are attached. (*a*) Cell division in *Heteromita uncinata*; basal bodies and flagella divide and form poles of the mitotic spindle. (*b*) Cell division in *Cryptobia helices*; basal bodies and flagella divide and appear to pull nuclear elements apart to form two daughter nuclei, but a mitotic spindle is absent. (From Wenyon, C. M. *Protozoology*. Baltimore: Williams & Wilkins, 1926, vol. 1, pp. 118 and 639; © 1926, The Williams & Wilkins Co., Baltimore, Md. 21202, USA.)

One can speculate about the forces which favored the development of cytochrome-catalyzed oxidative phosphorylation in prokaryotic cells and the establishment of a parasitic endosymbiosis in eukaryotic cells. Prokaryotic cells developed in the primitive earth about 3×10^9 years ago when there was a reducing type of atmosphere. Under the conditions prevailing in a reducing atmosphere, many compounds of biological importance, including nucleic acids, can be formed (Chapter 1). The photodissociation of water vapor in the atmosphere may have resulted in the production of sufficient molecular oxygen to be a hazard for the reduced nucleic acids of primitive self-replicating systems. Genes coding for the enzymes which lead to the synthesis of

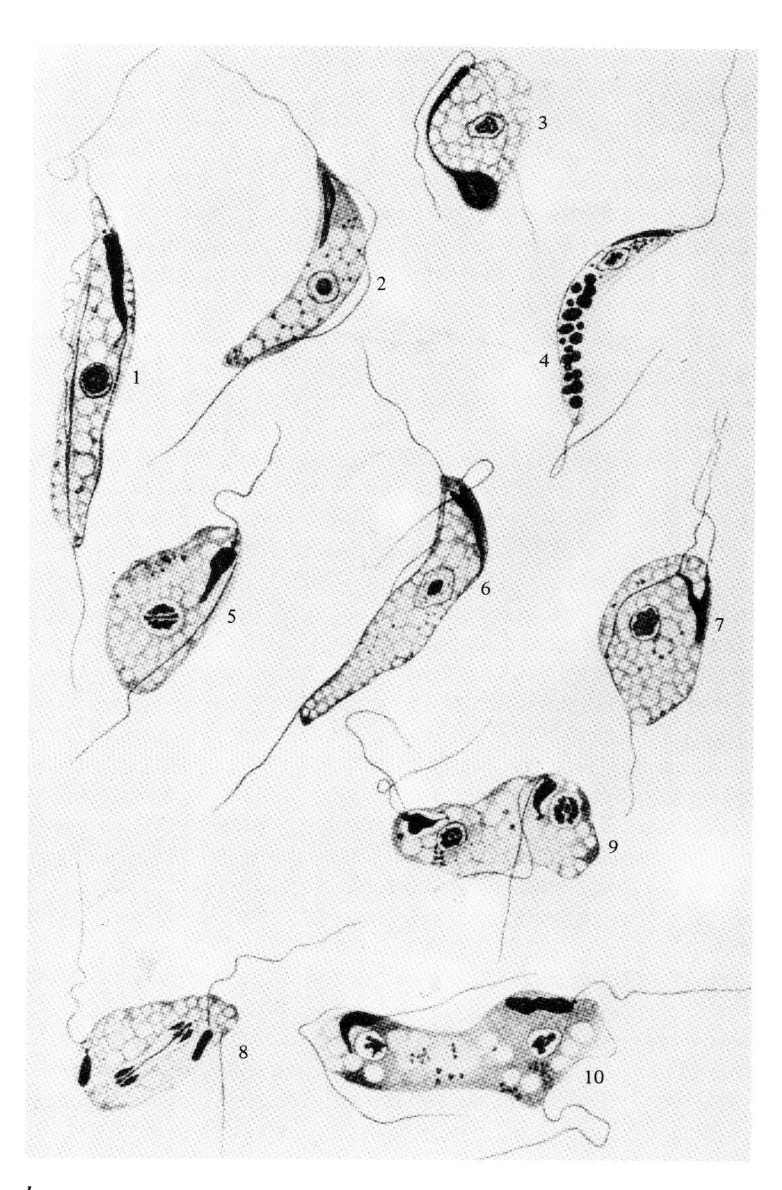

b

porphyrins (coenzymes of peroxidase, catalase, and the cytochromes) evolved which protected nucleic acids and other metabolic systems from oxidation. Eventually organisms evolved mechanisms for producing ATP by utilizing radiant energy from the sun absorbed by chlorophyll-like prophyrin pigments.

Initially, atmospheric hydrogen or hydrogen derived from H_2S was used for the reduction of CO_2 for the biosynthesis of glucose. Eventually, however, a population of cells evolved which utilized water as the source of hydrogen atoms in photosynthesis (Chapter 5). The success of these organisms, which incidentally released oxygen as a byproduct of photosynthesis, led to a change from a reducing atmosphere to an oxidizing atmosphere. All living forms had to adapt to an atmosphere containing oxygen if their survival was not to be restricted to localized anaerobic environments.

Geological evidence indicates that oxygen was present in the atmosphere 2.7×10^9 years ago and became quite abundant 1.2×10^9 years ago.

Associated with the development of an oxidizing atmosphere was the formation of an ozone layer in the upper atmosphere. This layer effectively filtered most of the ultraviolet light. Thus, the major energy source for abiogenic synthesis was removed, and any organic matter so produced would have been rapidly oxidized. At this time, all terrestrial life became dependent upon photosynthesis. Heterotrophic organisms which were unable to carry on photosynthesis relied upon organic matter produced by photosynthetic or chemosynthetic cells. An obvious selective advantage would accrue to large heterotrophic cells which could ingest smaller prokaryotes by phagocytosis. Endosymbiosis by such a heterotrophic anaerobe (following the ingestion of the promitochondrion) may have resulted in the evolution of the first aerobic amitotic amoeboid organisms.

Owing to the fact that almost all eukaryotic cells contain mitochondria, they are characteristically aerobic. Incomplete mitosis is common in various protists; mitosis probably occurred later in evolution. In general, the amount of cellular DNA increases with the complexity of the organism. It is presumed that the increased amounts of DNA code for additional gene sites which are required for expression of the larger number of characteristics needed by the cells of a complex organism. Thus it is plausible that the increase in DNA came about as the result of nondivisional synapsis or reduplication of chromatin material which coded for additional gene loci.

Wilson pointed out that a fundamental dualism or separation exists in the processes constituting mitosis; the replication of the chromatic element involves one series of processes, while their separation into the daughter nuclei by the mitotic apparatus introduces a second group of processes. The centrioles appear to occupy a key position in the latter group of processes, and their structural similarity to the basal bodies of cilia has been pointed out above (that is, they both possess the nine-plus-two unit filament complex). It may be conjectured that the separation of chromatic material by mitosis came about after the parasitic endosymbiosis of a flagellated prokaryote by an amoeboid host.

Prior to the evolution of mitosis, cells may have utilized reduplication of cistrons or genomes and multinuclearity or polyploidy to ensure the distribution of DNA to the daughter cells. Many lower eukaryotic cells (which by definition contain nuclei surrounded by a membrane and, in addition, mitochondria) have incomplete mitosis; they lack centrioles, and they fail to form an equatorial plate and spindle. In these cells the chromatic granules tend to wander toward the daughter nuclei. These species probably do not represent degenerate forms, but rather they appear to be the descendants which branched off the main line of evolutionary development. Sexuality in the meiotic sense does not exist in these organisms.

It seems likely that an ancient amoeboid cell acquired a motile flagellar prokaryote, perhaps a spirochetelike organism, containing a nine-plus-two axial filament complex. Such amoeboid cells would have developed an immense selective advantage as a result of motility. The nine-plus-two unit structure may have evolved to form centrioles and was utilized as the motile apparatus for mitosis. Perhaps initially the reduplication of the basal body and its DNA provided a means of ensuring the inheritance of the motile flagellar apparatus. Gradually the separation came to involve the nuclear material of the host cell. Forms of eukaryotic cells, certain amoeboid flagellates, are known where the basal body serves a dual function of generating flagella and serving as an extranuclear division center. The flagella and mitotic spindle are attached to the same structure (Fig. 10-27). In other cases when the nine-plus-two unit basal body divides, one of the daughter structures gives rise to the flagella while the other functions as a centriole in mitosis. The flagella eventually were lost and the function of the centrioles was restricted to mitosis. Other intermediate forms also are known.

gene expression

While the mechanisms which determine whether or not a gene will be expressed by transcription and translation are poorly understood in eukaryotic cells, it is worthwhile outlining experimental approaches which are being used to investigate this problem. It has long been known that the bands of the giant polytene chromosomes of the fruit fly vary in different types of cells and undergo changes during the development of the insect. In some instances the modifications of band width or appearance are slight, but at times a single band becomes expanded locally, forming a *puff* or *Balbiani ring* (Fig. 10-28). The puff is thought to represent a localized uncoiling of the DNA; in a giant polytene chromosome, the uncoiling involves numerous homologous segments and produces a very complex structure. The equivalent state in an ordinary chromosome might well pass unnoticed. The puffs characteristically stain lightly with chromatin stain.

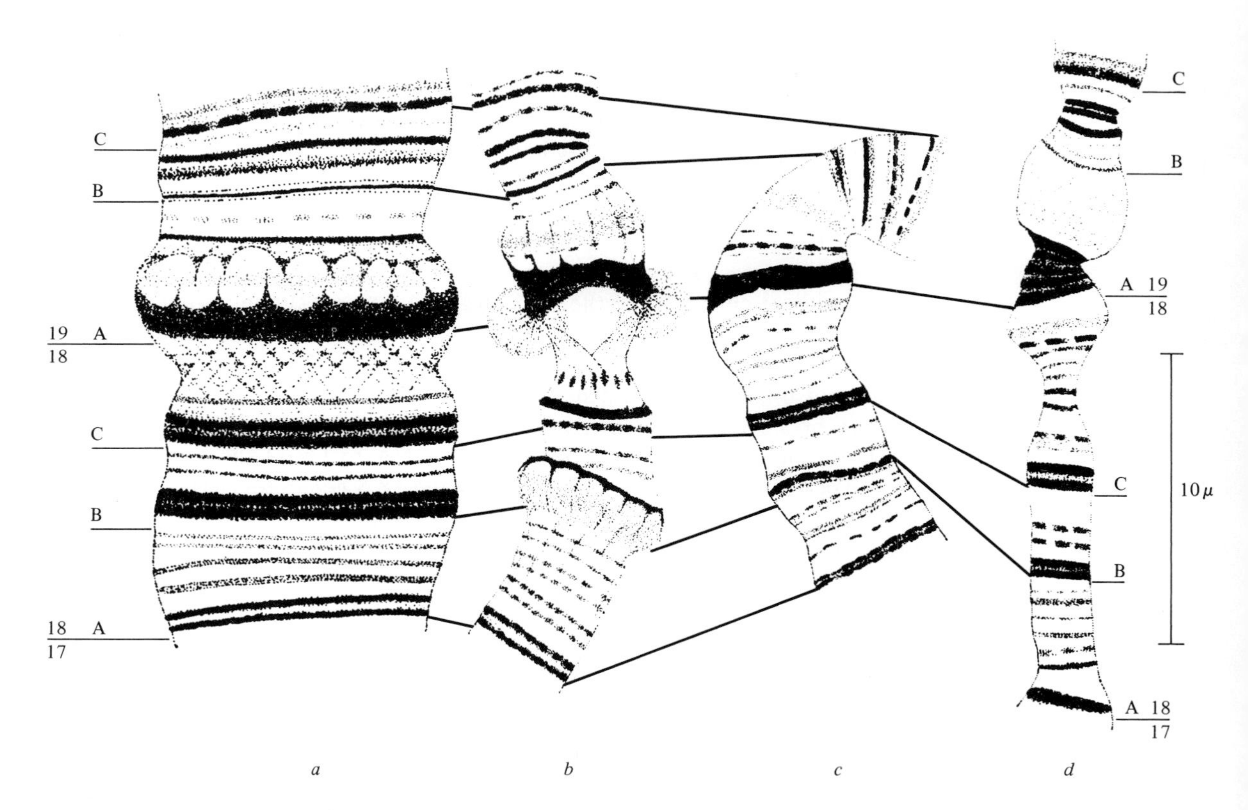

fig. 10-28. A drawing of homologous regions of a polytene chromosome from different tissues of *Chironomus tentans* showing Balbiani rings and the variation in appearance: (*a*) salivary gland, (*b*) Malpighian tubule, (*c*) rectum, and (*d*) midgut. (From Beermann, W. Chromomeren konstanz und spezifische Modifikation der Chromosomerenstruktur in der Entwicklung und Organidifferenzierung von *Chironomus tentans. Chromosoma, 5,* 139–198. Berlin-Göttingen-Heidelberg: Springer [1952].)

Beermann[66] proposed that the puffs represented activated loci of genetic activity. Studies utilizing tritiated uridine, a pyrimidine base which is incorporated into RNA but not into DNA, disclosed that RNA synthesis is greater in the region of puffs than elsewhere. Presumably the puffs are regions where active synthesis of messenger-RNA takes place. The amount of RNA synthesized appears to be proportional to the size of the puffs. Various puffs in the salivary gland chromosomes produce RNA of different base compositions.

The extensive studies of Beermann and his associates have shown that certain puffs can be correlated with phenotypic traits; that is, the appearance of a given puff corresponds to the expression of a phenotypic trait. Furthermore, the molting hormone, *ecdysone*, has been used to induce reproducible changes in the pattern of Balbiani rings. In some cases the size of the induced rings is greater when more hormone is injected.

Another system which has been used to study gene expression involves the DNA which codes for ribosomal-RNA. The r-DNA is located at a specific chromosomal site, the *nucleolar organizer*, which appears in most animal cells as a secondary constriction on one or more metaphase chromosomes. In most diploid cells both nucleolar organizers on the pair of homologous chromosomes are functional, and most cells contain two visible nucleoli. Homozygous mutants of *Xenopus laevis* which lack nucleoli do not synthesize r-RNA but can synthesize other classes of RNA.[67] The heterozygotes of this mutant have half as much r-DNA as the wild type. As outlined in Chapter 6, r-DNA gives rise to a very large 45 *S* species of RNA from which, in turn, the 28 *S* and 18 *S* r-RNA originate.

The 18 *S* and 28 *S* species of r-RNA have different base compositions; the G + C content of 28 *S* r-RNA is greater than that of 18 *S* r-RNA. Hybridization experiments using purified r-RNA and DNA indicate that the 28 *S* and 18 *S* r-RNA arise from different gene sites.[68] It is estimated that in *X. laevis* the r-DNA sites are reduplicated approximately 800 times. It is possible to visualize three arrangements of the gene sites: (1) independent clustering of the 28 *S* and 18 *S* genes, (2) alternating sequences of 28 *S* and 18 *S* r-DNA, or (3) a mixture of gene clustering and alternating sequences. Yankofsky and Spiegelman demonstrated that hybrids formed from DNA and r-RNA have a somewhat higher buoyant density in CsCl gradients than hybrids of m-RNA and DNA. Hybridization experiments showed that prior combination with 18 *S* RNA affects the density of both 28 *S* and 18 *S* DNA to about the same extent.[69] From these experiments, it appears that the 28 *S* and 18 *S* gene sites are not independently clustered.

Recently, it has become clear that loops of DNA (for example in lampbrush chromosomes) may actually leave the chromosomes and move into the nucleoplasm. This appears particularly true for the DNA of the nucleolar organizer, which becomes detached and operates to make more and more nucleoli. This phenomenon operates to amplify specific DNA genes, as needed for development and differentiation of cells,

[66] Beermann, W., in Rudnick, D., ed. *Development Cytology*. New York: Ronald Press, 1959, pp. 83 ff.; Pavan, C. *Brookhaven Symp. Biol.*, *18*, 222 (1965).
[67] Elsdale, T. R., Fischberg, M., and Smith, S. *Exptl. Cell Res.*, *14*, 642 (1958); Fischberg, M., and Wallace, H., in Mitchell, J. S., ed. *The Cell Nucleus*. London: Butterworth, 1960, p. 30; Brown, D. D., and Gurdon, J., *Proc. Natl. Acad. Sci.*, *51*, 139 (1964); *J. Mol. Biol.*, *19*, 399 (1966); Hay, E. D., and Gurdon, J. *J. Cell Sci.*, *2*, 151 (1967).
[68] Yankofsky, S. A., and Spiegelman, S. *Proc. Natl. Acad. Sci.*, *48*, 1466 (1962); *49*, 538 (1963); Ritossa, F. M., and Spiegelman, S. *Proc. Natl. Acad. Sci.*, *53*, 737 (1965).
[69] Brown, D. D., in Monroy, A., and Moscona, A. A., eds. *Current Topics in Development Biology*. New York: Academic Press, 1967, vol. 2, p. 48.

by increasing the capacity for transcription and RNA synthesis. Loop formation appears to be prevalent in oöcytes; for example, the synthesis of r-RNA in the *X. laevis* oöcyte is extremely intense.[70]

While the anucleolate mutant of *X. laevis* lacks the structural genes for 28 *S* and 18 *S* RNA, a hybrid can be formed between the third species of r-RNA, 5 *S* RNA, and the DNA of the mutant. The mutant, however, does not synthesize 5 *S* r-RNA; the lack of 28 *S* and 18 *S* r-RNA appears to repress the synthesis of 5 *S* r-RNA. These mutants provide a system for studying the mechanism of this repression of transcription.

The mature oöcyte is quiescent metabolically and synthesizes practically no RNA. Within seconds of fertilization, however, glycolysis is activated, and the rate of oxygen consumption and protein synthesis increases markedly.[71] In many animals, normal or nearly normal development can be obtained by artificial activation of the egg. This phenomenon is called *parthenogenesis.* Although the yield from parthenogenesis generally is very low, it was once thought that studying such methods would yield answers to questions about normal fertilization. After many years of research, however, it is now believed that the parthenogenetic agents neither imitate the sperm nor replace its effective component. One common method of stimulation is to increase the osmotic pressure of the surrounding water by adding KCl. A pin prick may also cause development to begin.

The rate at which amino acids are incorporated into proteins is greatly increased after fertilization.[72] Hultin concluded from cross-experiments using high-speed super-

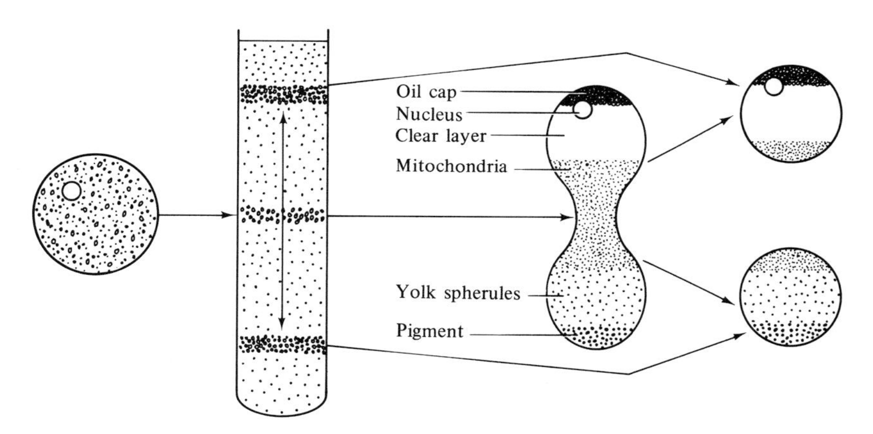

fig. 10-29. Method of production of large quantities of nonnucleate fragments of unfertilized eggs of sea urchins and other animals by centrifugation on layers of sucrose–sea-water solutions of increasing density. For many species of echinoderms the following mixtures of isosmotic (1.1 M) sucrose and sea water are suitable for each of the four layers starting from the bottom: 3 : 1, 3 : 2, 2 : 2, and 0 : 1. The eggs are introduced with the 2 : 2 layer; centrifugation is at 12,000 × *g* for 10 to 15 min. The eggs break into a nucleated fragment which forms a sediment and a nonnucleated fragment which floats. (From Tyler, A., and Tyler, B. S., in Boolootian, R. A., ed. *Physiology of Echinodermata.* New York: Wiley, 1966, p. 683.)

---

[70] Beirnstiel, M. L., Wallace, H., Sirlin, J. L., and Fischberg, M. *Natl. Cancer Inst. Monograph, 23,* 431 (1966).
[71] Epel, D., in Deering, R. A., and Trask, M., eds. *The Molecular Aspects of Biological Development.* Washington: N.A.S.A. Contract Report CR-673, 1967.
[72] Hultin, T. *Exptl. Cell Res., 1,* 599 (1950); *3,* 494 (1952); Hoberman, H. D., Metz, C. B., and Graff, J. *J. Gen. Physiol., 35,* 639 (1952).

natant fractions and ribosomes from fertilized and unfertilized egg homogenates that the inactivity of the ribosomes is responsible for the lack of protein synthesis in unfertilized eggs.[73] The high-speed supernatant fractions from unfertilized eggs and those from early embyros are able to support protein synthesis *in vitro* equally well.[74]

Unfertilized eggs contain an abundant supply of ribosomes which almost uniformly are found singly. After fertilization, increasing amounts of ribosomal aggregates (polyribosomes) can be found in sucrose gradients.[75] It has been shown that amino acid incorporation in fertilized eggs (like in other tissues) occurs in association with the polyribosomes.

Nonnucleate fragments of sea urchin eggs can be prepared by centrifuging at 12,000 × g for 15 min in a gradient of sea water to 1.1 M sucrose (Fig. 10.29). Experiments with such nonnuncleated fragments showed a lack of protein synthesis.[76] On the other hand, after parthenogenetic activation, these nonnucleated egg fragments carried on protein synthesis at a rate equal to that of fertilized ova (Fig. 10-30).

fig. 10-30. Influence of polyuricylic acid on incorporation of L-phenylalanine-^{14}C into protein with homogenates and sonicates of eggs and embryos of *Lytechinus pictus.*[a] (From Tyler, A. *Am. Zool., 3,* 119 [1963].)

PREPARATION	COUNTS PER MINUTE, MINUS t_0		
	WITHOUT POLYURIDYLIC ACID	WITH POLYURIDYLIC ACID	INCREASE
Homogenates of:			
Unfertilized eggs	53, 56 avg 55 ($t_0 = 50$)	987, 916 avg 952	897
Blastulae (just hatching)	274, 261 avg 268 ($t_0 = 73$)	903, 891 avg 897	629
Sonicates of:			
Unfertilized eggs	34, 40 avg 37 ($t_0 = 79$)	849, 888 avg 869	832
Blastulae (just hatching)	123, 124 avg 124 ($t_0 = 67$)	1049, 1014 avg 1032	908

[a] Incubation mixture = 0.225 ml homogenate or sonicate (derived from 1.5 × 10^5 eggs in 0.01 M Tris, 0.01 M MgAc, 0.275 ml of reaction mixture (0.8 ml M/8 PEP; 0.1 ml of 0.0038 M L-phenylalanine-^{14}C at 9.8 c/mole; 0.1 ml of 0.1 M ATP, with or without polyuridylic acid at 0.08 M calculated as uridylic acid).

Similar experiments have been performed with frogs' eggs.[77] The increase in protein synthesis can be inhibited by puromycin or cycloheximide.[78] Actinomycin (which inhibits the formation of m-RNA by transcription of DNA) does not inhibit the fertilization of sea urchin eggs, their subsequent development, or the increase in

[73] Hultin, T. *Exptl. Cell Res., 25,* 405 (1961).
[74] Stavy, L., and Gross, P. R. *Proc. Natl. Acad. Sci., 57,* 735 (1967).
[75] Monroy, A., and Tyler, A. *Arch. Biochem. Biophys., 103,* 431 (1963); Stafford, D. W., Sofer, W. H., and Iverson, R. M. *Proc. Natl. Acad. Sci., 52,* 313 (1964); Spirin, A. S., and Nemer, M. *Science, 150,* 214 (1965).
[76] Brachet, J., Ficq, A., and Tencer, R. *Exptl. Cell Res., 32,* 168 (1963); Denny, P. C., and Tyler, A. *Biochem. Biophys. Res. Commun., 14,* 245 (1964).
[77] Smith, L. D., and Ecker, R. E. *Science, 150,* 777 (1965).
[78] Hultin, T. *Experentia, 17,* 410 (1961); Karnofsky, D., and Simmel, E. B. *Progr. Exptl. Tumor Res., 3,* 254 (1963).

protein synthesis.[79] The pattern of soluble protein synthesized, as determined by electrophoretic studies, appears to be the same in fertilized sea urchin eggs, in non-nucleate fragments, and in sea urchin eggs in the presence of actinomycin.[80]

It has been concluded from experiments such as those described above that oöcytes contain masked messenger-RNA which is uncovered at the time of fertilization. This hypothesis has received additional support from the ability of unfertilized-egg RNA to form hybrids with DNA[81] and from studies in which the RNA has been labeled with radioactive uridine. In such studies, it was found that approximately 10 to 15 percent of the RNA sediments heterogeneously and can be regarded as m-RNA. About 1.5 percent of the labeled RNA hybridizes with homologous DNA.[82]

The m-RNA in unfertilized eggs sediments in large aggregates with r-RNA and appears to be resistant to degradation by RNAse.[83] The RNAse-resistant aggregates of RNA can be rendered sensitive to hydrolysis by RNAse after treatment with very dilute trypsin. The m-RNA in the unfertilized egg appears to be protected by a polypeptide material.[84] An attractive hypothesis of the mechanism of activation of protein synthesis upon fertilization is that the changes in the ionic composition of cells which are known to occur upon fertilization may activate a proteolytic enzyme. This enzyme in turn removes a protecting polypeptide around RNA aggregates by limited proteolysis.

A similar situation obtains in the erythropoietic system. It has been shown by several investigators[85] that RNA synthesis stops at an early stage in the development of the red blood cells—at the stage when the erythroblast is transformed into a normoblast. The synthesis of hemoglobin, however, does not commence until a much later stage of development. Presumably the m-RNA required for hemoglobin synthesis must be present in the developing red blood cell and must be activated at a later time. The phenomenon of masked m-RNA confuses the experiments aimed at elucidating the mechanisms controlling gene expression.

In addition to the burst of protein synthesis which utilizes masked m-RNA synthesized during the oögenesis which follows fertilization or parthenogenetic stimulation, there is also a significant synthesis of heavy RNA (m-RNA) immediately after fertilization.[86] A very large percentage of the new RNA synthesized during early embryonic development resembles DNA in its base composition. In addition, a large amount of labeled nucleotides is incorporated into the terminal CpCpA sequences of 4 *S* t-RNA after fertilization. New synthesis of r-RNA or 4 *S* RNA cannot be detected before the blastula stage. Because actinomycin prevents the transcription of new RNA, its use after fertilization results in an arrest of embryonic development.

---

[79] Gross, P. R., and Cousineau, G. H. *Exptl. Cell Res.*, *33*, 368 (1964).
[80] Spiegel, M., Ozaki, H., and Tyler, A. *Biochem. Biophys. Res. Commun.*, *21*, 135 (1965); Tyler, A. *Biol. Bull.*, *130*, 450 (1966); Terman, S. A., and Gross, P. R. *Biochem. Biophys. Res. Commun.*, *21*, 595 (1965).
[81] Whiteley, A. H., McCarthy, B. J., and Whiteley, H. R. *Proc. Natl. Acad. Sci.*, *55*, 519 (1966); Glisin, V. R., Glisin, M. V., and Doty, P. *Proc. Natl. Acad. Sci.*, *56*, 285 (1966).
[82] Gross, P. R., Malkin, L. I., and Hubbard, M. *J. Mol. Biol.*, *13*, 463 (1965); Slater, D. W., and Spiegelman, S. *Proc. Natl. Acad. Sci.*, *56*, 164 (1966).
[83] Kaulenas, M. S., and Fairbairn, D. *Develop. Biol.*, *14*, 481 (1966).
[84] Monroy, A., Maggio, R., and Rinaldi, A. M. *Proc. Natl. Acad. Sci.*, *54*, 107 (1965); Mano, Y. *Biochem. Biophys. Res. Commun.*, *25*, 216 (1966).
[85] Marks, P. A., Rifkind, R. A., and Danon, D. *Proc. Natl. Acad. Sci.*, *50*, 336 (1963); Borsook, H. *Ann. N.Y. Acad. Sci.*, *119*, 523 (1964).
[86] Gross, P. R., Malkin, L. I., and Moyer, W. A. *Proc. Natl. Acad. Sci.*, *51*, 407 (1964); Comb, D. G., Katz, S., Branda, R., and Pinzino, C. J. *J. Mol. Biol.*, *14*, 195 (1965); Mintz, B. *J. Exptl. Zool.*, *157*, 85 (1964).

The sea urchin embryo treated with actinomycin develops to the blastula stage, synthesizing protein coded by the maternal m-RNA. Because it lacks new m-RNA, however, its development is arrested at this stage. The development of a gastrula requires turning on new gene sites for the transcription of a new kind of m-RNA. The gene sites which code for ribosomal RNA do not become active in transcription until after gastrulation has begun. A similar sequence of events has been found in the amphibian embryo.[87] The unfertilized egg appears to contain adequate machinery for protein synthesis including ribosomes, but the instructional messenger for development depends upon transcription initiated by fertilization. Thus, the embryo provides a good system for investigating the mechanisms involved in gene repression and depression.

Because all cells have the same complement of DNA, they should be plenipotential. That is, any type of differentiated cells should have all possible capacities for other specializations. The clearest evidence of the plenipotentiality of differentiated cells is the production of hormones by tumors of tissues that normally do not produce hormones.[88] The most common of these are tumors of the lung which sometimes produce the anterior pituitary hormone ACTH, occasionally in sufficient quantity to produce Cushing's syndrome (the disease state of hyperadrenalism due to greatly excessive production of ACTH). Tumors of lung and other nonglandular tissues such as fibrosarcomas (connective tissue), liver tumors, gastrointenstinal tumors, etc., have been known to produce a variety of hormones including ACTH, thyrotropin, gonadotropin, erythropoietin, serotonin, insulin, melanocyte-stimulating hormone, parathormone, estrogens, and vasopressin. It is clear that the normal repressing mechanism that prevents hormone synthesis is lifted in the tumor.

control of cell division and organ size

After dividing, cells grow until they reach a size characteristic for that type of cell; then growth stops. At this point the cell may remain quiescent for a variable period of time or it may begin another cell-division sequence. Although epidermal cells and some gastrointestinal epithelial cells are arrested in the G_2 phase, most interphase cells which are not committed to division are in the G_1 phase. The normal tendency of cells is to divide. Cells that enter the S phase and begin to replicate their DNA appear to be committed to a cycle of cell division. The decision of a cell to divide is made during interphase. The failure to divide appears to be a block or

---

[87] Brown, D. D., and Littna, E. *J. Mol. Biol.*, *20*, 81 (1966).

[88] August, J. T., and Hiatt, H. H. *New Engl. J. Med.*, *258*, 17 (1958); Goldman, K. P. *Brit. J. Diseases Chest*, *55*, 162 (1961); Meador, C. K., Liddle, G. W., Island, D. P., Nicholson, W. E., Lucas, C. P., Nuckton, J. G., and Leutscher, J. A. *J. Clin. Endocrinol. Metab.*, *22*, 693 (1962); Nichols, J., Warren, J. C., and Mantz, F. A. *J. Am. Med. Assoc.*, *182*, 713 (1962); Liddle, G. W., Island, D. P., Ney, R. L., Nicholson, W. E., and Schimuzur, N. *Arch. Internal Med.*, *111*, 471 (1963); Engel, F. L., and Kahana, L. *Am. J. Med.*, *34*, 726 (1963); Pfohl, R. A., and Doe, R. P. *Ann. Int. Med.*, *58*, 993, (1963); Macks, L. J., Rosenbaum, D. L., and Russfield, A. B. *Ann. Internal Med.*, *58*, 143 (1963); Amatruda, T. T., Jr., Mulrow, P. J., Gallagher, J. C., and Sawyer, W. H. *New Engl. J. Med.*, *269*, 544 (1963); Odell, W. D., Bates, R. W. Rivlin, R. S., Lipsett, M. B., and Hertz, R. *J. Clin. Endocrinol. Metab.*, *23*, 658 (1963); Hung, W., Blizzard, R. M., Migeon, C. J., Camacho, A. M., and Nyhan, W. L. *J. Pediat.*, *63*, 895 (1963); Peart, W. S., Porter, K. A., Robertson, J. I. S., Sandler, M., and Baldock, E. *Lancet*, *I*, 239 (1963); Hallwright, G. P., North, K. A. K., and Reid, J. D. *J. Clin. Endocrinol. Metab.*, *24*, 496 (1964); Tashjian, A. H., Jr., Levine, L., and Munson, P. L. *J. Exptl. Med.*, *119*, 467 (1964); Law, D. H., Liddle, G. W., Scott, H. W., Jr., and Tauber, S. D. *New Engl. J. Med.*, *273*, 292 (1965); Fusco, F. D., and Rosen, S. W. *New Engl. J. Med.*, *275*, 507 (1966); Faiman, C., Colwell, J. A., Ryan, R. J., Hershman, J. M., and Shields, T. W. *New Engl. J. Med.*, *277*, 1395 (1967).

inhibition of the normal division process so that the cell remains in the G_1 phase. In some cases, cell division can be stimulated; for example, lymphocytes can be stimulated to divide by phytohemagglutinin, and the cells of target organs can be stimulated by hormones.

Since a cell that has begun to replicate its DNA has committed itself to divide, the control of cell division appears to involve the initiation of DNA biosynthesis. One limiting factor that prevents initiation may be the intracellular concentration of deoxyribonucleotides. High concentrations of deoxyribonucleotides are found in rapidly proliferating cells.[89] The cellular content of DNA polymerase, thymidine kinase, and thymidylate synthetase is also proportional to the mitotic rate.[90] The rise in amounts of these enzymes in liver following partial hepatectomy can be inhibited by the administration of actinomycin. It should be noted, however, that the activity of these enzymes in regenerating liver reaches a maximum *after* the rate of DNA synthesis has begun to decline.[91]

There are a number of pieces of evidence that indicate that DNA biosynthesis is preceded by the synthesis of specific RNA and protein.[92] The inhibition of RNA synthesis a few hours before DNA synthesis is scheduled to commence inhibits subsequent DNA synthesis. There appears to be a period toward the end of the G_1 phase (about 2 hours before the onset of DNA replication) during which cells are particularly sensitive to inhibition of division by actinomycin.[93] Very small doses of actinomycin which are ineffective during other times of the cell cycle will prevent late G_1 cells from beginning DNA synthesis. Late G_1 cells treated with puromycin or cycloheximide are subject to a delay in the onset of DNA synthesis.[94] After DNA synthesis has begun, cells appear to become relatively insensitive to the inhibitory effects of puromycin.[95] The particular proteins which are required for DNA synthesis, however, remain unidentified.

Another actinomycin-sensitive and puromycin-sensitive period has been found in the late S or early G_2 phase of mammalian cells.[96] The inhibition produced during this period suggests that proteins (currently unidentified) which are necessary for mitosis are synthesized during the G_2 phase. Cells exposed to the amino acid analog *p*-fluorophenylalanine during G_2 show a prolongation of the time of mitosis. This suggests that the proteins synthesized in the presence of the analog are defective.[97] Colchicine and the periwinkle alkaloids which stop mitosis in metaphase appear to act during the G_2 period.

The size of cells in a given organ is approximately the same in both small and large animals. Thus, the parenchymal cells of the rat and of the elephant liver are approximately the same size, even though the overall size of the organ is very different. Also,

---

[89] Rotherham, J., and Schneider, W. C. *J. Biol. Chem.*, *232*, 853 (1958); Schneider, W. C. *J. Natl. Cancer Inst.*, *18*, 569, 579 (1957).
[90] O'Brien, J. S. *Cancer Res.*, *22*, 267 (1962); Davidson, J. N., in 15th Symp. on Fundamental Cancer Research, Anderson Hosp. and Tumor Inst. *Molecular Basis of Neoplasia.* Austin, Texas: University of Texas Press, 1962, p. 420.
[91] Bollum, F. J., and Potter, V. R. *Cancer Res.*, *19*, 561 (1959); Hiatt, H. H., and Bojarski, T. B. *Biochem. Biophys. Res. Commun.*, *2*, 35 (1960).
[92] Powell, W. F. *Biochim. Biophys. Acta*, *55*, 969, 979 (1962); Stone, G. E., and Prescott, D. M. *J. Cell Biol.*, *21*, 275 (1964).
[93] Baserga, R., Estensen, R. D., Petersen, R. O., and Layde, J. P. *Proc. Natl. Acad. Sci.*, *54*, 745, 1141 (1965); *J. Cellular Comp. Physiol.*, *68*, 177 (1966).
[94] Terasima, T., and Yasukawa, M. *Exptl. Cell Res.*, *44*, 669 (1966).
[95] Mueller, G. C., Kajiwara, K., Stubblefield, E., and Rueckert, R. R. *Cancer Res.*, *22*, 1084 (1962).
[96] Kishimoto, S., and Lieberman, I. *Exptl. Cell Res.*, *36*, 92 (1964); Tobey, R. A., Petersen, D. F., Anderson, E. C., and Puck, T. T. *Biophys. J.*, *6*, 567 (1966).
[97] Biesele, J. J., and Jacquez, J. A. *Ann. N.Y. Acad. Sci.*, *58*, 1276 (1954); Sisken, J. E., and Wilkes, E. *J. Cell Biol*, *34*, 97 (1967).

it is well known that many organs will respond to certain changes in the environment by becoming larger or smaller. In almost all cases, the positive or negative growth response can be shown to follow a change in functional load—in the case of enlargement of the organ, a load which cannot be handled by increased activity of the organ. Thus, high protein intake results in an enlargement of the kidney, and the salt glands of marine birds change size *pari passu* with the amount of salt ingested. After its partial ablation, an organ responds by growing back to a size which will duplicate, as far as possible, its initial functional capacity.

In rats and mice, the two main lobes of the liver (the median and left lateral) can easily be excised; such surgery removes approximately 68 percent of the liver mass. After a lag of approximately 24 hours following partial hepatectomy, there ensues a period of rapid growth, and within a week the liver has grown to 90 percent of its original mass. Liver regeneration also follows the necrosis produced by toxic agents such as carbon tetrachloride. After the removal of one kidney, the contralateral kidney may double its mass and excretory function.

It is known that regeneration and compensatory growth occur to a greater extent in young than in old animals, that growth is more rapid when the diet is high in protein, and that growth will not occur in the absence of an intact pituitary gland. Thyroid and adrenal cortical hormones increase the rate of regeneration. Regeneration and compensatory growth may result from either or both of two processes: *hypertrophy* and *hyperplasia*. Hypertrophy refers to the increase in size of the cells of an organ, while hyperplasia refers to the increase in the number of cells as a result of mitosis. The enlargement of muscle as a result of exercise is due to hypertrophy and not to the creation of new muscle cells. On the other hand, hyperplasia is the major process responsible for liver regeneration. In the compensatory growth of the contralateral kidney following nephrectomy, the glomeruli enlarge but the tubules grow by hyperplasia.

Within 12 to 24 hours after partial hepatectomy, the concentrations of deoxyribonucleotides are increased severalfold as the result of *de novo* synthesis from small molecules.[98] The enzymes responsible for catalyzing some of these synthetic steps, including deoxycytidylate deaminase, thymidylate synthetase, and thymidine kinase, are increased from several to 25 times their normal concentration.[99] Most of these enzymes are characterized by marked instability in the absence of their substrates; the activity of these enzymes in normal liver can be increased by the continuous infusion of thymidine deoxyribose.[100] The increase of these enzymes in regenerating liver, however, does not represent only decreased destruction because the increase in enzyme levels can be inhibited by *x*-irradiation or by the administration of actinomycin. Thus, although stabilization of the enzyme activity by substrates may be a factor in regenerating liver, the synthesis of new enzyme molecules appears to be more important in increasing the enzyme activity. The levels of DNA polymerase in regenerating liver also are increased, and they remain elevated for a long period of time.[101] In addition, the levels of *o*-nitrophenol-pyrophorylase and RNA polymerase are increased severalfold within 12 hours after partial hepatectomy.[102]

---

[98] Bucher, N. L. R. *Intern. Rev. Cytol.*, *15*, 245 (1963).

[99] Fausto, N., and van Lancker, J. L. *J. Biol. Chem.*, *240*, 1247 (1965); Maley, G. F., Lorenson, M. G., and Maley, F. *Biochem. Biophys. Res. Commun.*, *18*, 364 (1965).

[100] Adelstein, S. J., and Kohn, H. I. *Biochim. Biophys. Acta*, *138*, 163 (1967).

[101] Giudice, G., and Novelli, G. D. *Biochem. Biophys. Res. Commun.*, *12*, 383 (1963).

[102] Bresnick, E. *J. Biol. Chem.*, *240*, 2550 (1965); Tsukada, K., and Lieberman, I. *J. Biol. Chem.*, *239*, 2952 (1964); Ro, T. S., and Busch, H. *Biochim. Biophys. Acta*, *134*, 184 (1967).

The stability of certain types of m-RNA appears to be increased in rapidly growing tissues. For example, the half-life of the m-RNA for thymidine kinase is 7.5 hours; in normal liver it is only 3.0 hours for this type of m-RNA.[103] Similarly, after a 12-hour lag after unilateral nephrectomy, there is an increase in the synthesis of the enzymes concerned with RNA and DNA synthesis; and after 36 hours, cell division begins in the contralateral kidney. Early inhibition of protein and RNA synthesis prevents DNA synthesis and cell division, but administration of inhibitors later has markedly less effect. During the first 12 hours r-RNA is formed; during the second 12 hours rapidly labeled nuclear RNA with a short half-life is formed; and during the last phase RNA synthesis stabilizes at a steady high level. The content of polyribosomes in regenerating liver is increased.

Morphological changes accompany these changes in enzyme levels and polynucleotide synthesis in regenerating liver. Immediately after hepatectomy, an infiltration of lipid and loss of glycogen can be observed. After a few hours the membrane of the well-developed rough endoplasmic reticulum disappears from the hepatocytes while rosettes of ribosomes (polyribosomes), free in the cytoplasm, appear in increasing numbers. After 9 to 12 hours membranes of smooth endoplasmic reticulum, enclosing dilated cisternae (Fig. 10-31), begin to form. Numerous mitochondria are found closely associated with the re-forming membranes. Mitosis begins about 24 hours after hepatectomy. After 24 to 48 hours ribosomes begin to be associated with the membrane system, and after 4 days the liver cells have a normal appearance.

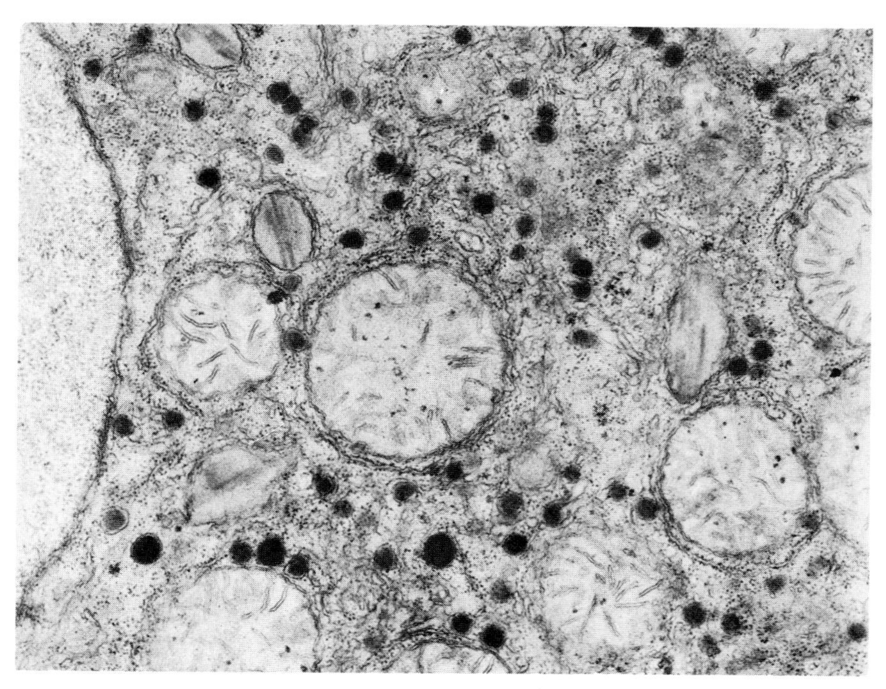

fig. 10-31. An electron micrograph of regenerating rat liver showing the reformation of smooth endoplasmic reticulum enclosing dilated cisternae. Numerous mitochondria are found in the neighborhood of the re-forming membrane system. (Courtesy of Dr. Nancy L. Trotter.)

[103] Roth, J. S. *Life Science*, *3*, 1145 (1964); Bresnick, E., Williams, S. S., and Mosse, H. *Cancer Res.*, *27*, 469 (1967); Webb, T. E., Blobel, G., and Potter, V. R. *Cancer Res.*, *26*, 253 (1966).

The nature of the stimulus which results in hyperplasia of regenerating liver is unknown. Ligation of the portal vein branches to the main lobes of the liver appears to be equivalent to resection in terms of the hyperplasia which ensues.[104] Temporary ligation of these blood vessels for 2 minutes results in only transitory changes, but ligation for 10 minutes results in considerable hyperplasia. A great deal of effort has been directed in search of humoral factors which might control regeneration. Experiments with parabiosis failed to give incontrovertible evidence of a humoral factor.[105] On the other hand, subcutaneous autoimplants of liver tissue, completely free from the portal circulation, exhibit increased DNA synthesis and mitosis after partial resection of the remaining liver.[106] It may be that cell division is controlled by a balance between stimulatory and inhibitory factors. Even though a humoral factor has not yet been unequivocably demonstrated in liver, it seems highly probable that this mechanism is involved in the control of organ size.

In the case of pig epidermis, a low-molecular-weight basic glycoprotein has been isolated which appears to inhibit mitosis of the stem cells in the basal layers.[107] Bullough[108] has applied the generic term *chalones* to such regulatory antimitotic substances. Some circumstantial evidence indicates that chalones are tissue-specific but are not entirely species-specific. Of course, it is attractive to suppose that one factor in malignant transformation of cells is the inhibition of chalone production.

It should be noted parenthetically that when tumor invades the liver or kidney and damages the major portion of functioning cell mass, it does not cause regeneration or compensatory growth. Working out the mechanisms which control cell division and organ size is one of the most important contemporary problems in cell biology.

aging [109]

Aging may be defined as changes which occur as the organism grows older (particularly in the post-reproductive period) which result in a decreased ability on the part of the individual organism to survive. Aging is a deteriorative process; it results in increased vulnerability, as the individual organism grows older, to death from accidental causes of random incidence. No death is wholly natural. All deaths are in some degree accidental.

Strehler has proposed four criteria for an aging process: (1) *universality*; the phenomenon should occur in all older members of the species. This criteria eliminates hereditary defects and diseases which are dependent upon a specific environment. (2) *Progressiveness*; The onset of an aging process should be a gradual and cumulative

[104] Weinbren, K., and Tarsh, E. *Brit. J. Exptl. Pathol.*, *45*, 475 (1964); Lieberman, I., and Short, J. *Am. J. Physiol.*, *208*, 896 (1965).
[105] Fisher, B., Fisher, E. R., and Saffer, E. *Cancer Res.*, *23*, 914 (1963); Kim, S., and Cohen, P. P. *Arch. Biochem. Biophys.*, *109*, 421 (1965); Heimann, R., Pechet, G. S., Tank, R., and MacDonald, R. A. *Exptl. Molec. Pathol.*, *2*, 442 (1963).
[106] Leong, G. F., Grisham, J. W., Hole, B. V., and Albright, M. L. *Cancer Res.*, *24*, 1496 (1964); Virolinen, M. *Exptl. Cell Res.*, *33*, 588 (1964).
[107] Setälä, K. *Acta Radiol.*, suppl. 237, 1 (1965).
[108] Bullough, W. S. *The Evolution of Differentiation*. New York: Academic Press, 1967.
[109] Lansing, A. I. *J. Gerontol.*, *2*, 228 (1947); Brien, P. *Biol. Revs.*, *28*, 308 (1953); Jones, H. B. *Advan. Biol. Med. Phys.*, *4*, 281 (1956); Verzar, F. *Gerontologia*, *1*, 363 (1957); Failla, G. *Ann. N.Y. Acad. Sci.*, *71*, 1124 (1958); Maynard Smith, J., *Nature*, *184*, 956 (1959); Szilard, L. *Nature*, *184*, 956 (1959); *Proc. Natl. Acad. Sci.*, *45*, 30 (1959); Strehler, B. L. *Quart. Rev. Biol.*, *34*, 117, (1959); Strehler, B. L., and Mildvan, A. S. *Science*, *132*, 14 (1960); von Hahn, H. P., and Verzar, F. *Gerontologia*, *7*, 105 (1963); Comfort, A. *Ageing, The Biology of Senescence*. New York: Holt, Rinehart & Winston, 1964.

occurrence. Events of sudden occurrence such as the occlusion of a coronary artery, a a cerebrovascular accident, or the initiation of a tumor are not in themselves part of the aging process even though predisposing factors may very well be. (3) *Intrinsicality*; This criterion is designed to eliminate age-correlated changes which are due to causes extrinsic to the organism. (4) *Deleteriousness*; Aging changes result in a decline in the functional capacity of the organism which is reflected in an increased mortality rate.

Gompertz noted that the mortality rate of a number of populations increases as a log function of age:

$$R_m = R_0 e^{\alpha t} + A$$

where α is a rate constant and A is an additive constant to correct for age-independent causes of death. Similar relations are obtained for cause-specific mortality rates; for example, death rate due to cerebral vascular accidents adheres to a Gompertz function with a slope parallel to that for the total mortality. Survival curves do not prove senescence; similar curves are obtained by critical predation. If a limited, circumscribed population of fish were heavily fished using a net with a large mesh, this type of curve would be obtained. There is a saying, with some basis in fact, that carp don't grow old.

Some functional changes indicative of aging processes in man are:

1. Progressive increase in skin wrinkles, roughness, pigmented areas, warts, moles, etc. accompanied by change in texture, color, and distribution of hair.
2. Degeneration of tissues which support teeth; progressive wearing of teeth
3. Progressive achlorhydria
4. Progressive increase in intestinal diverticula
5. Progressive decrease in pulmonary and vascular elasticity
6. Deposition of cholesterol and fibrosis of arteries
7. Diminution of hearing actuity, particularly at high frequencies
8. Progressive loss of visual accommodation
9. Progressive loss of muscle mass as evidenced, for example, by decreased total body potassium
10. Changes in endocrine gland secretion

Loss of function increases linearly with increasing age.

Mammals are made up of three types of tissue components: (1) cells which multiply throughout life (such as white blood cells and epithelial cells); (2) cells incapable of division, renewal, and replacement (such as neurons), and (3) extracellular material (such as collagen and elastin). The grand theories of aging have focused attention on (1) changes—epigenetic, mutational, infective, immunological—in the functions of multiplying cells; (2) a loss of, or irreparable injury to, nonmultiplying cells; and (3) primary, irreversible changes in the extracellular materials which result in the decline in vigor that constitutes senescence.

The theories of aging can be divided into two groups:

1. *Aging due to structural instability of cells.* Cellular structures of potential importance in aging processes are not those which are readily destroyed or which "turn over," but are generally those which have a lifetime comparable to that of the organism. Cellular components may be destroyed because of thermal instability or by free radicals which arise from oxygen and ionizing radiation. In connection with the latter process, peroxidase-destroying enzymes such as catalase and antioxidants such as vitamin E may be important in the long-term survival of somatic cells. One such factor is intracellular DNA.

2. *Genetic instability as a source of aging.* This theory can be tested by determining whether conditions which result in increased mutagenesis also increase senescence. At present there is no direct means for measuring mutations in somatic, nondividing cells. There definitely is not a 1-to-1 ratio between increase in mutagenesis and acceleration of senescence. It has been found, however, that the amount of histone irreversibly bound to DNA in bovine thymus glands increases with age. Tissue-cultured cells also show senescence, dying out after a number of divisions. DNA repair mechanisms may compensate for genetically determined senescence.

The Szilard theory assumes that the primary event responsible for the aging process is a destructive "hit" which renders a chromosome functionally inactive. It is assumed that "aging hits" are random events and that the probability that a chromosome of a somatic cell suffers such a "hit" per unit time remains constant throughout life. It is also assumed that the rate of "hits" is characteristic of the species and does not vary appreciably from individual to individual. A somatic cell "dies" or becomes functionally inactive when two homologous chromosomes are "hit," or when a chromosome homologous to one containing genetically defective sites is "hit." As an organism grows older, the number of surviving cells diminishes at a continually accelerating rate, until a critical level is reached when it becomes very likely that the individual will die. According to Szilard's view, the main reason some adults live shorter lives than others is that they have inherited more genetic faults. Some individuals will die, however, because they incur a greater-than-average number of "hits" because of environmental conditions or a failure of reparative mechanisms. If the number of critical faults is 2, the cell fraction surviving at death is $\frac{1}{4}$ and if n is 4, the cell fraction surviving at death is $\frac{1}{12}$. Szilard concludes $2 < n < 4$. This theory predicts the concordance of age of death of identical twins and the reduction in life span of the progeny of irradiated mice. Maynard-Smith objected that Szilard's theory predicts that an inbred strain should sometimes survive better than a hybrid animal whereas this has rarely if ever been observed.

Burnet has proposed a theory of senescence which holds that the critical somatic mutations are those which result in a loss of the ability to suppress antibody formation to homologous proteins. As the individual ages, there is an increase in auto-immune reactions. These reactions might well be of precisely the polymorphic, diffuse, and variable type which characterizes the infirmities of aging. A "hit" in this sense does not incapacitate a cell but instead causes it and its progeny to commence activity deleterious to the individual.

Cross-linking of macromolecules such as collagen and DNA may also be the direct result of environmental factors including radiation. Changes in the physical properties of collagen may have far-reaching consequences in cellular metabolism and function. Rats fed restricted diets possess collagen with physical properties similar to that obtained from much younger animals chronologically fed ad libitum. Irradiated animals also had more youthful tails.

Understanding the mechanisms of aging at the cellular level is one of the important but difficult problems facing cell physiologists.

references

Alston, R. E. *Cellular Continuity and Development.* Chicago: Scott, Foresman, 1967.

Bonner, J., and Ts'o, P. O. P., eds. *The Nucleohistones.* San Francisco: Holden-Day, 1964.

Cole, A. Chromosome structure, in Cole, A., ed. *Theoretical and Experimental Biophysics.* New York: Marcel Dekker, 1967, vol. 1, p. 305 ff.

Hayes, W. *The Genetics of Bacteria and Their Viruses.* New York: Wiley, 1964.

Ingram, V. M. *The Biosynthesis of Macromolecules.* New York: W. A. Benjamin, 1965.

Levine, L., ed. *The Cell in Mitosis.* New York: Academic Press, 1963.

Locke, M., ed. *Control Mechanisms in Developmental Processes.* 26th Symp., The Society for Developmental Biology. New York: Academic Press, 1967.

Mazia, D. Mitosis and the physiology of cell division, in Brachet, J., and Mirsky, A. E., eds. *The Cell.* New York: Academic Press, 1961, vol. 3, p. 77 ff.

Medoff, G., and Swartz, M. N. DNA—structure and enzymatic synthesis. *New Engl. J. Med., 276*, 728, 788 (1967).

Moses, M. J. The nucleus and chromosomes: a cytological perspective, in Bourne, G. H., ed. *Cytology and Cell Physiology*, 3rd ed. New York: Academic Press, 1964, p. 423 ff.

Rhoades, M. M. Meiosis, in Brachet, J., and Mirsky, A. E., eds. *The Cell.* New York: Academic Press, 1961, vol. 3, p. 1 ff.

Srb, A. M., Owen, R. D., and Edgar, R. S. *General Genetics*, 2nd ed. San Francisco: Freeman, 1965.

Stahl, F. W. *The Mechanics of Inheritance.* Englewood Cliffs, N.J.: Prentice-Hall, 1964.

Stern, C. *Principles of Human Genetics*, 2nd ed. San Francisco: Freeman, 1960.

Strehler, B. L. *Time, Cells, and Aging.* New York: Academic Press, 1962.

Teir, H., and Rytömaa, T., eds. *Control of Cellular Growth in Adult Organisms.* New York: Academic Press, 1967.

Waddington, C. H. *The Strategy of the Genes.* London: G. Allen, 1957.

Watson, J. D. *Molecular Biology of the Gene.* New York: W. A. Benjamin, 1965.

White, M. J. D. *The Chromosomes*, 5th ed. London: Methuen, 1961.

Whitehouse, H. L. K. *Towards an Understanding of the Mechanism of Heredity.* New York: St. Martin's Press, 1965.

Wilson, E. B. *The Cell in Development and Heredity*, 3rd ed. New York: Macmillan, 1925.

Young, W. J., Merz, T., and Swanson, C. P. *Cytogenetics.* Englewood Cliffs, N.J.: Prentice-Hall, 1967.

index

a

b

d

e

f

g

h

l

m

O

P

S

w

x

y

z

Designed by Rita Naughton
Set in Times New Roman and Univers
Composed by Santype, Ltd.
Printed by The Murray Printing Co.
Bound by American Book-Stratford Press, Inc.
HARPER & ROW, PUBLISHERS, INC.

69 70 71 7 6 5 4 3 2 1